The Dance of Number

Dance Moves
Mastering Algebra and Mathematical Reasoning

Volume 2

By James D. Nickel

Nickel, James D.
The Dance of Number: Dance Moves, Volume 2
Text /James D. Nickel—1st Edition
Index

Published in the United States by Sound Mind Press, Wenatchee, Washington
www.biblicalchristianworldview.net/donCurriculum.html
First printing by CreateSpace: 2018

Printed in the United States of America
Cover design by James D. Nickel.
Image source: iStockPhoto

Content summary:
1. Algebra. 2. Geometry. 3. Trigonometry. 4. Mathematical Reasoning. 5. Theology–Trinitarian.

ISBN: 978-0-9991054-7-4 (paperback)

v.1.1 printing, August 2018
v.1.2 printing, September 2018

CONTENTS

PART 2: DANCE MOVES, VOLUME 2
ALGEBRA AND MATHEMATICAL REASONING

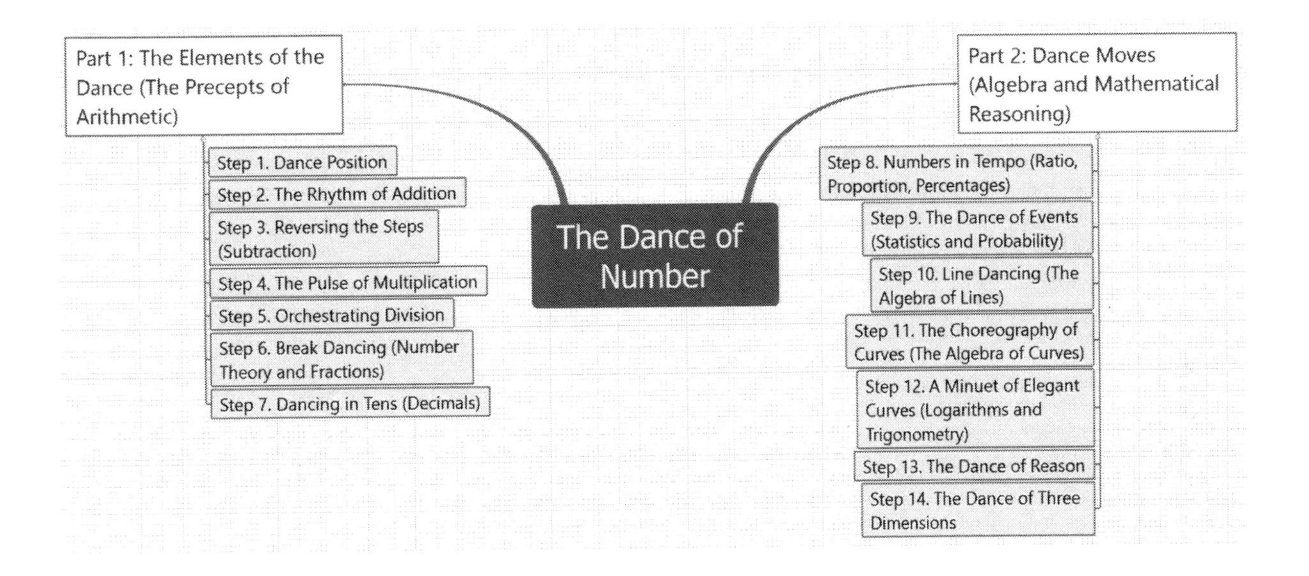

> Whoever despises the high wisdom of mathematics nourishes himself on delusion ...
>
> Leonardo da Vinci (1452-1519).

STEP 12. A MINUET OF ELEGANT CURVES

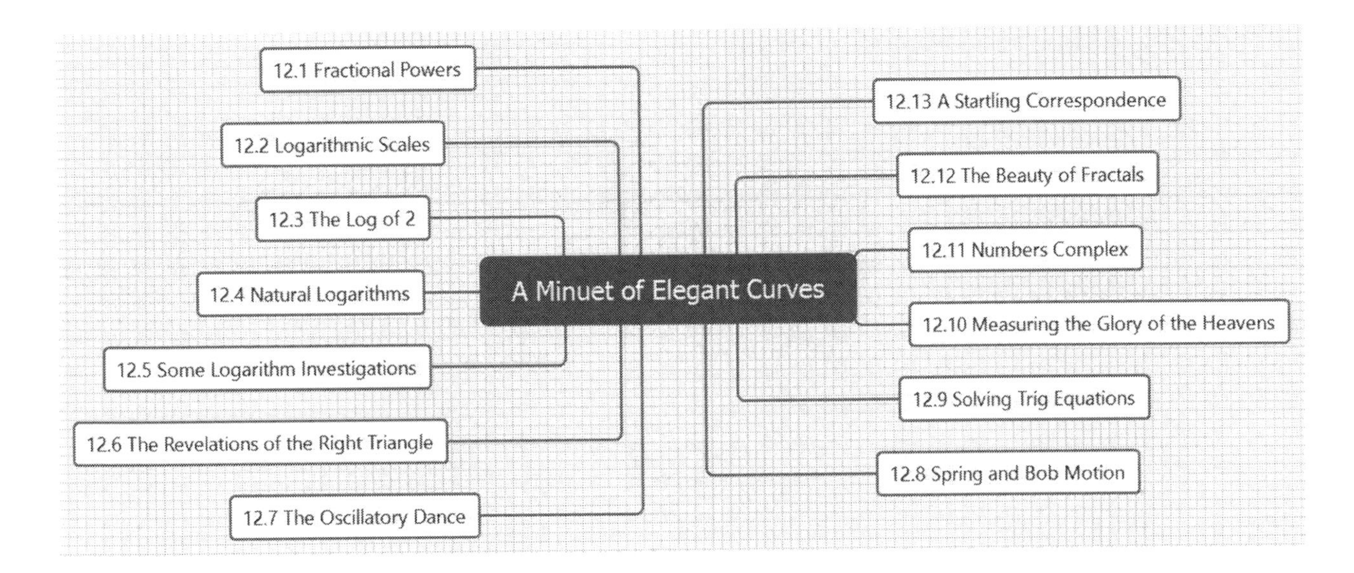

> The number systems employed in mathematics can be divided into five principal states, going from the simplest to the most complicated. They are: (1) the system consisting of the positive integers only; (2) the next higher stage, comprising the positive and negative integers and zero; (3) the rational numbers, which include fractions as well as integers; (4) the real numbers, which include the irrational numbers, such as π; (5) the complex numbers, which introduce the "imaginary" number square root of -1.
>
> Philip J. Davis, "Number," *Scientific American*, 211, (September, 1964), 51-59.

12.1 Fractional Powers

In Lesson 4.2, we considered a rope wrapped around a series of posts that multiplies our strength by ten times when the rope makes one complete turn (Figure 1). This arrangement generates our base 10 or decimal system.

Terms & Concepts Introduced
1. Centripetal acceleration
2. Fractional exponent
3. Logarithm

Table 1		
Post	Power Factor	Exponential Notation
P1	10	10^1
P2	100	10^2
P3	1000	10^3
P4	10,000	10^4
P5	100,000	10^5

We get the same result by wrapping a rope multiple times around one post (Figure 2). The number of posts, or rope turns, is the **logarithm** of the power of 10.[1] The mathematical symbol of logarithm in base 10 is log.[2]

P1 P2

Figure 1.

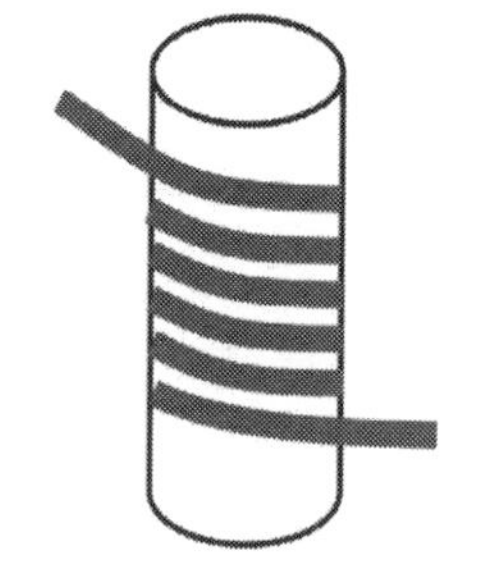

Figure 2.

Table 2		
Exponential Notation	Post or Turn(s)	Logarithmic Notation
10^1	1	$\log 10^1 = 1$
10^2	2	$\log 10^2 = 2$
10^3	3	$\log 10^3 = 3$
10^4	4	$\log 10^4 = 4$
10^5	5	$\log 10^5 = 5$

As we see from Table 2, logs are the number of turns. Better yet, logs are exponents.

Logs are exponents.

$$\log 10^x = x$$

In general:

$\log 10^x = x$

Instead of whole turns, what about partial turns? By partial turns, we mean fractional turns like half of a turn, third of a turn, etc. This means that the exponent is a fraction. Investigate Table 3.

---

[1] *Logarithm* comes from two Greek words, *logos* and *arithmos*, together meaning "the word concerning arithmetic." See Lesson 4.4. A logarithm of a number is the exponent to which 10 must be raised to obtain the number.

[2] Sometimes you will see the symbol "log x" instead of "$\log_{10}x$" to indicate base 10. By mathematical convention "log x" means "logarithm of x in base 10."

Table 3		
Fractional Turn	**Exponential Notation**	**Logarithmic Notation**
Half of a turn	$10^{1/2}$	$\log 10^{1/2} = 1/2$
A third of a turn	$10^{1/3}$	$\log 10^{1/3} = 1/3$
A fourth of a turn	$10^{1/4}$	$\log 10^{1/4} = 1/4$
A fifth of a turn	$10^{1/5}$	$\log 10^{1/5} = 1/5$
A sixth of a turn	$10^{1/6}$	$\log 10^{1/6} = 1/6$

FRACTIONAL POWERS NOTATION

Note the **fractional exponents** in the exponential notation. We can write square and cube roots as fractional exponents. By the Babylonian algorithm for square roots and cube roots, we calculate that $\sqrt{10} \approx 3.16$ and $\sqrt[3]{10} \approx 2.15$. Note the equivalence of the symbolic notation:

$\sqrt{10} \approx 3.16 \Leftrightarrow 10^{1/2} \approx 3.16$

Note also: $\sqrt{10} \approx -3.16 \Leftrightarrow 10^{1/2} \approx -3.16$ since $-(3.16)^2 \approx 10$. Therefore: $\sqrt{10} = 10^{1/2} \approx 3.16$ or -3.16

$\sqrt[3]{10} \approx 2.15 \Leftrightarrow 10^{1/3} \approx 2.15$

Note also: $\sqrt[3]{10} \neq -2.15 \Leftrightarrow 10^{1/3} \neq -2.15$ since $-(2.15)^3 \approx -10$.

Observing that $10 = 10^1$, we write:

$\sqrt{10^1} \Leftrightarrow 10^{1/2}$

$\sqrt[3]{10^1} \Leftrightarrow 10^{1/3}$

> In general:
>
> $\sqrt[n]{b^e} \Leftrightarrow b^{e/n}$

Let's compare arithmetic with the radical sign and fractional exponents. First, we explore square roots where the radicand is positive:

$$\left(\sqrt{10}\right)^2 = \sqrt{10}\sqrt{10} = \sqrt{10 \cdot 10} = \sqrt{100} = 10$$

We get the same result with fractional exponents:

$$\left(10^{1/2}\right)^2 = \left(10^{1/2}\right)\left(10^{1/2}\right) = 10^{1/2+1/2} = 10^1 = 10$$

Or, by applying the Power of Powers Law directly:

$$\left(10^{1/2}\right)^2 = 10^{(1/2)(2)} = 10^1 = 10$$

Now for cube roots:

$$\left(\sqrt[3]{10}\right)^3 = \sqrt[3]{10}\sqrt[3]{10}\sqrt[3]{10} = \sqrt[3]{10 \cdot 10 \cdot 10} = \sqrt[3]{100} = 10$$

Again, we get the same result with fractional exponents:

$$\left(10^{1/3}\right)^3 = \left(10^{1/3}\right)\left(10^{1/3}\right)\left(10^{1/3}\right) = 10^{1/3+1/3+1/3} = 10^1 = 10$$

Or, by applying the Power of Powers Law directly:

$$\left(10^{1/3}\right)^3 = 10^{(1/3)(3)} = 10^1 = 10$$

In general, where $x > 0$:

$$\left(\sqrt{x}\right)^2 = \sqrt{x}\sqrt{x} = \sqrt{xx} = \sqrt{x^2} = x$$

$$\left(x^{1/2}\right)^2 = \left(x^{1/2}\right)\left(x^{1/2}\right) = x^{1/2+1/2} = x^1 = x$$

$$\left(x^{1/2}\right)^2 = x^{(1/2)(2)} = x^1 = x$$

$$\left(\sqrt[3]{x}\right)^3 = \left(\sqrt[3]{x}\right)\left(\sqrt[3]{x}\right)\left(\sqrt[3]{x}\right) = \sqrt[3]{xxx} = \sqrt[3]{x^3} = x$$

$$\left(x^{1/3}\right)^3 = \left(x^{1/3}\right)\left(x^{1/3}\right)\left(x^{1/3}\right) = x^{1/3+1/3+1/3} = x^1 = x$$

$$\left(x^{1/3}\right)^3 = x^{(1/3)(3)} = x^1 = x$$

FRACTIONAL POWERS OF POSITIVE NUMBERS

Example 1. What is $25^{3/2}$?

First, since $3/2 = 1.5$, we know $25^{3/2}$ is between 25^1 and 25^2, or 25 and 625.

By the Power of Powers Law, we know that $25^{3/2} = \left(25^{1/2}\right)^3$.

Since $25^{1/2} = \sqrt{25} = 5$ then:

$$\left(25^{1/2}\right)^3 = 5^3 = 125$$

Therefore, $25^{3/2} = 125$. Finding the $3/2$ power of a number is equivalent to finding the cube of the square root.

Example 2. What is $8^{2/3}$?

Since $2/3 \approx 0.6$, we know $8^{2/3}$ is between 8^0 and 8^1, or 1 and 8.

By the Power of a Power Law, $8^{2/3} = \left(8^2\right)^{1/3}$.

Since $8^2 = 64$, then:

$$64^{1/3} = 4$$

We found the cube root of the square of 8.

Or, by the Power of a Power Law, $8^{2/3} = \left(8^{1/3}\right)^2$.

Since $8^{1/3} = 2$:

$$\left(8^{1/3}\right)^2 = 2^2 = 4$$

By this reasoning, we found the square of the cube root of 8.

Both methods are true, based upon the Power of a Power Law, and our knowledge of square and cube roots will help us determine which way is easier.

> In general, if we let $a, b \in \mathbb{Z}$, $b \neq 0$, $x \in \mathbb{R}$ and $x \neq 0$, then:
>
> $x^{a/b} = \left(x^{1/b}\right)^a = (x^a)^{1/b}$

Fractional exponents can be negative. The negative exponent means you must use this relationship:

$$b^{-a} = \frac{1}{b^a}$$

Example 3. What is $64^{-2/3}$?

First, we know this:

$$64^{-\frac{2}{3}} = \frac{1}{64^{\frac{2}{3}}}$$

By $x^{a/b} = \left(x^{1/b}\right)^a$, we write:

$$\frac{1}{64^{\frac{2}{3}}} = \frac{1}{\left(64^{\frac{1}{3}}\right)^2} = \frac{1}{4^2} = \frac{1}{16}$$

Therefore:

$$64^{-\frac{2}{3}} = \frac{1}{16}$$

Example 4. What is $4096^{1/2} \cdot 4096^{1/3}$?

We invoke two Power Laws:

$b^m b^n = b^{m+n}$ and $(b^m)^n = b^{mn}$

$$4096^{1/2} \cdot 4096^{1/3} = 4096^{1/3+1/2} = 4096^{5/6} = \left(4096^{1/6}\right)^5 = 4^5 = 1024$$

Note also: $4096^{1/2} = \sqrt{4096}$ and $4096^{1/3} = \sqrt[3]{4096} \Rightarrow \sqrt{4096}\sqrt[3]{4096} = 64 \cdot 16 =$ $(60 + 4)(20 - 4) = 1200 + 80 - 240 - 16 = 1024$

The Power of a Quotient Law that states, in general, where $b \neq 0$:

$$\left(\frac{a}{b}\right)^m = \frac{a^m}{b^m}$$

This law states that we can either divide a by b and then find the mth power of the quotient, or we can divide m^{th} power of a by the mth power of b.

Example 5. What is $\left(\frac{9}{4}\right)^2$?

$$\left(\frac{9}{4}\right)^2 = 2.25^2 = 5.0625 \text{ or } \left(\frac{9}{4}\right)^2 = \frac{9^2}{4^2} = \frac{81}{16} = 5.0625$$

EVEN AND ODD POWERS, EVEN AND ODD ROOTS

Let's first explore what happens when we find an even power of a negative number. Let's consider $(-3)^2$. We get:

$(-3)^2 = (-3)(-3) = 9$

Therefore:

$-\sqrt{9} = -3$ or $-9^{1/2} = -3$

Remember (Lesson 5.15 and Lesson 11.6), to evaluate $-9^{1/2}$, you must perform two operations in this order:

1. Exponentiation
2. Multiplication

> In general, $x^2 = c$ and $c > 0 \Leftrightarrow x = \sqrt{c}$ or $x = -\sqrt{c}$

Note also that since $(3)(3) = 9$, then:

$\sqrt{9} = 3$ or $9^{1/2} = 3$

As we have already noted (Lesson 11.3), there are two square roots of every positive number, positive or negative.

Now, let's consider $(-3)^3$. We get:

$(-3)^3 = (-3)(-3)(-3) = -27$

Therefore:

$\sqrt[3]{-27} = -3$ or $-27^{1/3} = -3$

With the fractional exponent without the parentheses, we extract the third root of 27 first and then multiply by -1. Our answer: -3.

Note: $3^3 = 27 \Leftrightarrow \sqrt[3]{27} = 3$

There is only one cube root of a positive number and only one cube root of a negative number. There is a one-to-one equivalence.

Let's consider $(-3)^4$. We get:

$(-3)^4 = (-3)(-3)(-3)(-3) = 81$

Therefore:

$-\sqrt[4]{81} = -3$ or $-81^{1/4} = -3$

Note also that since $3 \cdot 3 \cdot 3 \cdot 3 = 81$, then:

$\sqrt[4]{81} = 3$ or $81^{1/4} = 3$

There are two fourth roots of every positive number, positive or negative.

Now, let's consider $(-3)^5$. We get:

$(-3)^5 = (-3)(-3)(-3)(-3)(-3) = -243$

Therefore:

$\sqrt[5]{-243} = -3$ or $-243^{1/5} = -3$

Note: $3^5 = 243 \Leftrightarrow \sqrt[5]{243} = 3$

There is only one fifth root of a positive number and only one fifth root of a negative number.

Do you see the dance between odd and even powers, odd and even roots?

Table 4: Powers	
The *even* power of a positive number is always a	positive number
The *even* power of a negative number is always a	positive number
The *odd* power of positive number is always a	positive number
The *odd* power of negative number is always a	negative number

Table 5: Roots	
The *even* positive root of a positive number is always a	positive number
The *even* negative root of a positive number is always a	negative number
The *odd* root of positive number is always a	positive number
The *odd* root of negative number is always a	negative number

Note: We cannot extract the positive or negative even root of a negative number in the real number world. In Lesson 12.11, we will explore this how this observation opens the window to a whole new set of numbers.

The graphs of even and odd powers and even and odd roots reveal, in a perichoretic manner, the relationships in Table 3 and Table 4. Study the signs of the arguments and images of each function carefully.

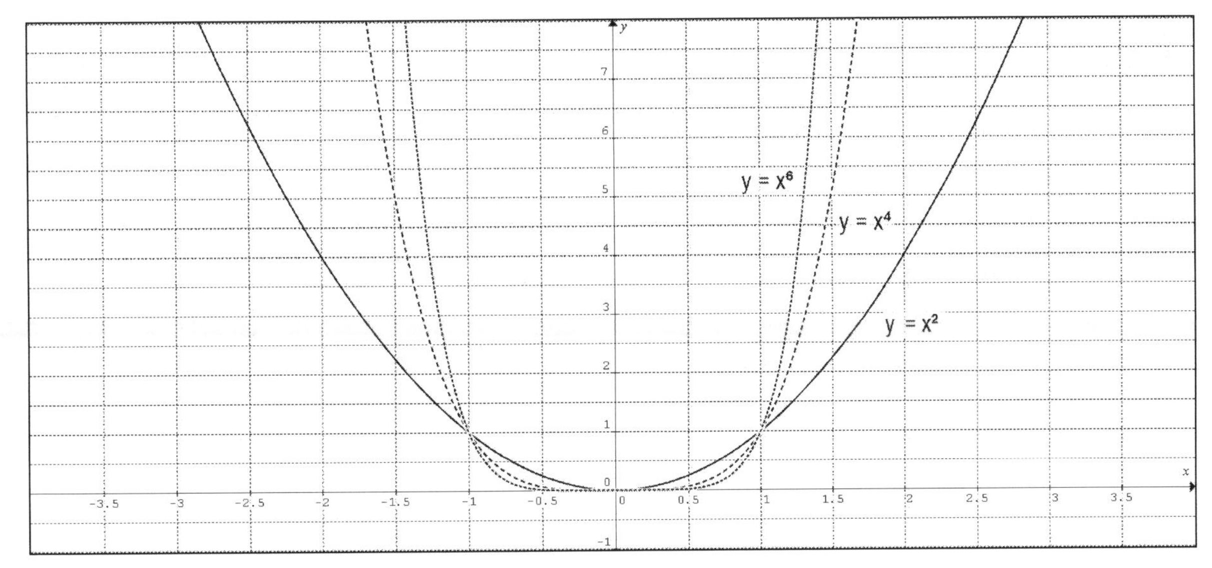

Figure 3: Even Powers. (Even functions, many-to-one.)

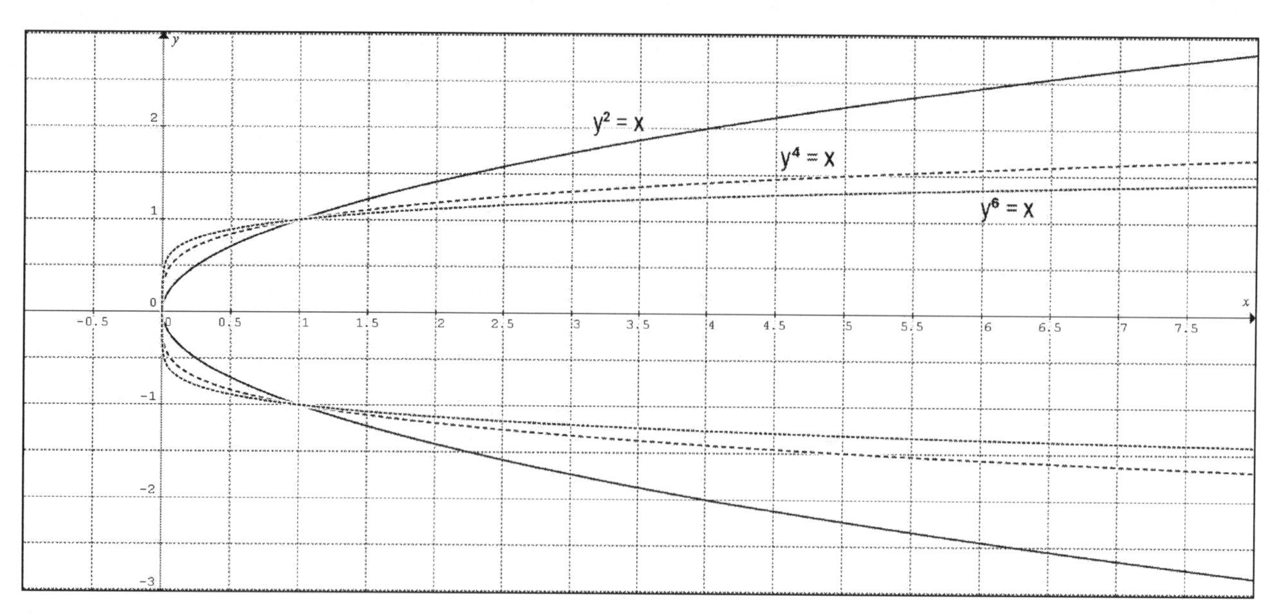

Figure 4. Even Roots. (Double-valued relations, one-to-many mapping.) Note: $y^2 = x \Leftrightarrow y = \sqrt{x}$ or $y = -\sqrt{x} \Leftrightarrow y = x^{1/2}$ or $y = -x^{1/2}$, $y^4 = x \Leftrightarrow y = \sqrt[4]{x}$ or $y = -\sqrt[4]{x} \Leftrightarrow y = x^{1/4}$ or $y = -x^{1/4}$, and $y^6 = x \Leftrightarrow y = \sqrt[6]{x}$ or $y = -\sqrt[6]{x} \Leftrightarrow y = x^{1/6}$ or $y = -x^{1/6}$

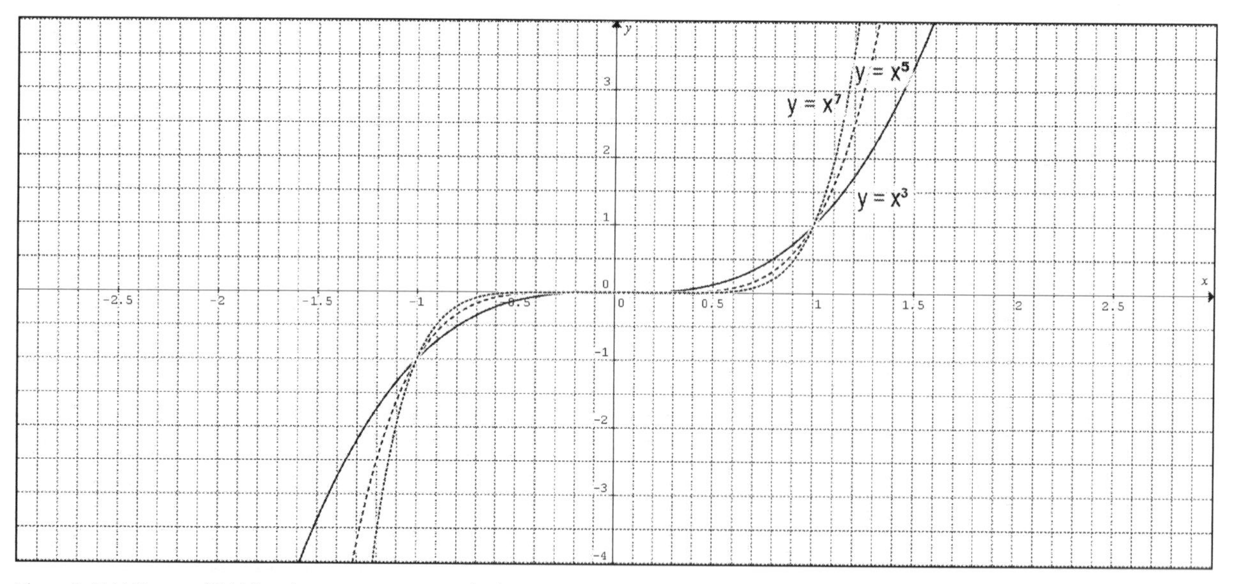

Figure 5. Odd Powers. (Odd functions, one-to-one mapping.)

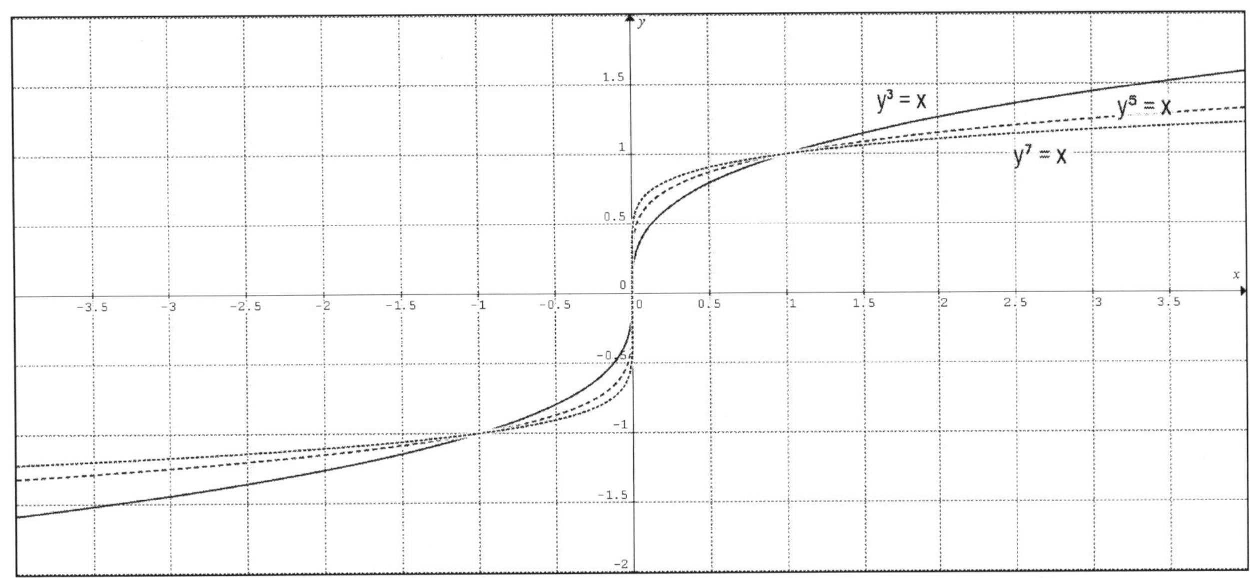

Figure 6. Odd Roots. (Odd functions, one-to-one mapping.) Note: $y^3 = x \Leftrightarrow y = \sqrt[3]{x} \Leftrightarrow y = x^{1/3}$, $y^5 = x \Leftrightarrow y = \sqrt[5]{x} \Leftrightarrow y = x^{1/5}$, and $y^7 = x \Leftrightarrow y = \sqrt[7]{x} \Leftrightarrow y = x^{1/7}$

FRACTIONAL POWERS OF NEGATIVE NUMBERS

Let's now walk through some examples of finding a fractional power of a negative number.

Example 6. What is $(-27)^{-\frac{4}{3}}$?

First, we remove the negative exponent:

$$(-27)^{-\frac{4}{3}} = \frac{1}{(-27)^{\frac{4}{3}}}$$

We can apply our conclusions above. We know that since (-3)(-3)(-3) = -27, then $(-27)^{\frac{1}{3}} = -3$. We get:

$$(-27)^{-\frac{4}{3}} = \frac{1}{(-27)^{\frac{4}{3}}} = \frac{1}{\left[(-27)^{\frac{1}{3}}\right]^4} = \frac{1}{(-3)^4} = \frac{1}{81}$$

Note that the correct use of parentheses is critical in these calculate. Note carefully:

$$(-27)^{-\frac{4}{3}} \neq -27^{-\frac{4}{3}}$$

Why? We calculate $-27^{-4/3}$ as follows:

$$-27^{-\frac{4}{3}} = -\frac{1}{(27)^{\frac{4}{3}}} = -\frac{1}{\left[(27)^{\frac{1}{3}}\right]^4} = -\frac{1}{(3)^4} = -\frac{1}{81}$$

Therefore:

$$(-27)^{-\frac{4}{3}} = \frac{1}{81} \text{ and } -27^{-\frac{4}{3}} = -\frac{1}{81}$$

Let's try a few more examples:

Example 7. What is $(-8)^{-\frac{5}{3}}$?

$$(-8)^{-\frac{5}{3}} = \frac{1}{(-8)^{\frac{5}{3}}} = \frac{1}{\left[(-8)^{\frac{1}{3}}\right]^5} = \frac{1}{(-2)^5} = \frac{1}{-32} = -\frac{1}{32}$$

In general (Lesson 6.7), $\frac{-a}{b} = -\frac{a}{b}$ because a negative divided by a positive is a negative, and $\frac{a}{-b} = -\frac{a}{b}$ because a positive divided by a negative is a negative. The conventional way of writing a negative fraction is always in this form:

$$-\frac{a}{b}$$

Example 8. What is $\left(\frac{4}{9}\right)^{-\frac{3}{2}}$?

$$\left(\frac{4}{9}\right)^{-\frac{3}{2}} = \frac{1}{\left(\frac{4}{9}\right)^{\frac{3}{2}}} = \frac{1}{\left[\left(\frac{4}{9}\right)^{\frac{1}{2}}\right]^3} = \frac{1}{\left(\frac{4^{\frac{1}{2}}}{9^{\frac{1}{2}}}\right)^3} = \frac{1}{\left(\frac{2}{3}\right)^3} = \frac{1}{\frac{2^3}{3^3}} = \frac{1}{\frac{8}{27}} = \frac{27}{8} = 3\frac{3}{8}$$

P IN PEMDAS

The P in PEMDAS stands for parentheses. Up to this point in our studies, we have seen how both the horizontal fraction bar (Lesson 11.1) and the extended square root symbol (Lesson 11.6) function as parentheses and we need to use parentheses if we are evaluating a numerical expression with a calculator.

$\frac{8+16}{3}$ changes to:
(8 +16)/3

$\sqrt{15+2^2}$ changes to:
SQRT(15 + 2^2)

To find the answer to a power with fractional exponents on the calculator, we make this change:

$2^{4/3}$ changes to:
2^(4/3)

QUESTION

If one turn around a post multiplies our strength by a factor of 10, then what fraction of a turn doubles our strength? In other words, what is log 2?

By the Babylonian algorithm, we know:

$10^{1/2} \approx 3.16$

Extending this algorithm, we know:

$10^{1/3} \approx 2.15$

Therefore, we know log 2 must be close to 1/3, in fact, a little less than 1/3. In our next lesson, we will explore how to find this answer.

Table 6: Properties of Radicals (Fractional Powers)	
Property	**Example**
$\sqrt[n]{ab} = \sqrt[n]{a}\sqrt[n]{b}$ $(ab)^{\frac{1}{n}} = a^{\frac{1}{n}}b^{\frac{1}{n}}$	$\sqrt[3]{96} = \sqrt[3]{8}\sqrt[3]{12} = 2\sqrt[3]{12}$ $96^{\frac{1}{3}} = 8^{\frac{1}{3}} \cdot 12^{\frac{1}{3}} = 2 \cdot 12^{\frac{1}{3}}$
$\sqrt[n]{\frac{a}{b}} = \frac{\sqrt[n]{a}}{\sqrt[n]{b}}$ $\left(\frac{a}{b}\right)^{\frac{1}{n}} = \frac{a^{\frac{1}{n}}}{b^{\frac{1}{n}}}$	$\sqrt{\frac{121}{16}} = \frac{\sqrt{121}}{\sqrt{16}} = \frac{11}{4}$ $\left(\frac{121}{16}\right)^{\frac{1}{2}} = \frac{121^{\frac{1}{2}}}{16^{\frac{1}{2}}} = \frac{11}{4}$
$\sqrt[m]{\sqrt[n]{a}} = \sqrt[mn]{a}$ $\left(a^{\frac{1}{n}}\right)^{\frac{1}{m}} = a^{\frac{1}{nm}}$	$\sqrt[3]{\sqrt{4096}} = \sqrt[6]{4096} = 4$ $\left(4096^{\frac{1}{2}}\right)^{\frac{1}{3}} = 4096^{\frac{1}{6}} = 4$
$\sqrt[n]{a^m} = \left(\sqrt[n]{a}\right)^m$ $(a^m)^{\frac{1}{n}} = \left(a^{\frac{1}{n}}\right)^m = a^{\frac{m}{n}}$	$\sqrt[4]{81^3} = \left(\sqrt[4]{81}\right)^3 = 3^3 = 27$ $(81^3)^{\frac{1}{4}} = \left(81^{\frac{1}{4}}\right)^3 = 3^3 = 27$
$\left(\sqrt[n]{a}\right)^n = \sqrt[n]{a^n} = a$ if $a > 0$ $\left(a^{\frac{1}{n}}\right)^n = (a^n)^{\frac{1}{n}} = a$ if $a > 0$	$\left(\sqrt[5]{13}\right)^5 = \sqrt[5]{13^5} = 13$ $\left(13^{\frac{1}{5}}\right)^5 = (13^5)^{\frac{1}{5}} = 13$

EXERCISES

Define the following terms:

1. Logarithm
2. Fractional exponent
3. Centripetal acceleration (See homework exercise below.)
4. Explain why logs are exponents.

Demonstrate, with an example:

5. The fourth root of a number is the square root of the square root of that number.
6. The sixth root of a number is the cube root of the square root of that number.
7. The eighth root of a number is the square root of the square root of the square root of that number.
8. The ninth root of a number is the cube root of the cube root of that number.

True or False (Assume a, $b > 0$. If False, explain why.):

9. $\sqrt[n]{a+b} = \sqrt[n]{a} + \sqrt[n]{b}$
10. $\sqrt[n]{ab} = \sqrt[n]{a}\sqrt[n]{b}$
11. $\sqrt[n]{a-b} = \sqrt[n]{a} - \sqrt[n]{b}$
12. $\sqrt[n]{\frac{a}{b}} = \frac{\sqrt[n]{a}}{\sqrt[n]{b}}$

Simplify the following expressions:

13. 10^{-3}
14. $\left(\frac{3}{4}\right)^{-2}$
15. $25^{3/2}$
16. $64^{-3/2}$
17. $(2^{-2} \div 2^{3})^{-2}$
18. $(2^{4} \times 2^{-5})^{4}$
19. $(2^{-4})^{-3}$
20. $27^{2/3}$
21. $(-27)^{2/3}$
22. $-27^{-2/3}$
23. $(-27)^{-2/3}$
24. $64^{3/2}$
25. $(-2)^{5}$
26. $\left(2\frac{1}{2}\right)^{3}$ (Hint: $2\frac{1}{2} = \frac{5}{2}$)
27. $\left(-2\frac{1}{2}\right)^{3}$
28. $\left(-2\frac{1}{2}\right)^{-3}$
29. $\left(6\frac{1}{4}\right)^{\frac{1}{2}}$
30. $\left(6\frac{1}{4}\right)^{-\frac{1}{2}}$

Figure 7. The Royal Tweed Bridge in Berwick, Northumberland, England. The engineers designed the long arch on the left according to the parabola $f(x) = 1 - \frac{2x^2}{37}$ (Domain: $-4.3 \le x \le 4.3$). Graph this function and compare it with the picture. Source: Wikimedia Commons.

31. $\left(3\frac{3}{8}\right)^{\frac{2}{3}}$

32. $\left(3\frac{3}{8}\right)^{-\frac{2}{3}}$

33. $\left(-3\frac{3}{8}\right)^{-\frac{2}{3}}$

34. $\left(-3\frac{3}{8}\right)^{-\frac{1}{3}}$

In the following exercises, we are going to determine the gravitational acceleration that the Sun gives to the Earth (Figure 8). This type of acceleration is **centripetal acceleration.**[3]

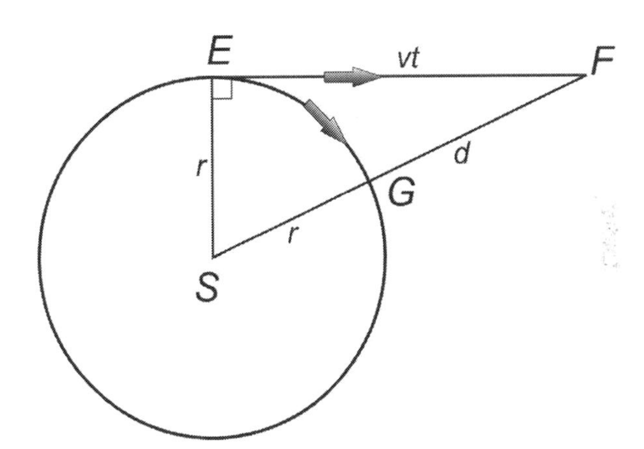

Figure 8. The pull of the Sun's gravity on the Earth.

35. We assume that the path of the Earth E around the Sun is circular. If there were no gravitational force, the Earth would move with a constant velocity v in t seconds following a straight path indicated by $\overline{EF}$.[4] Why is EF represented by vt in the figure?
36. During that time t, the Sun pulls the Earth in a distance $FG = d$. Since ΔFES is a right triangle, use the Pythagorean Theorem to state an equation containing the variables r, d, and vt.
37. Simplifying as much as possible, solve the equation derived in Question 36 for v^2t^2.
38. We assume that the Earth falls distance d with constant acceleration a.[5] In the seventeenth century, Galileo Galilei determined that the distance d that any object falls under constant acceleration is $d = \frac{1}{2}at^2$. Multiply both sides of this equation by 2.
39. Perform the arithmetic operations on the equation you wrote in Question 37 to isolate the expression $2d$.
40. Substitute $2d$ in the equation you derived in Question 39 with the equation you derived in Question 38.
41. Solve the equation you derived in Question 40 for v^2.
42. We allow t to become very small, i.e., $t \to 0$. $t \to 0 \Rightarrow d \to$?
43. Given your result in Question 42, solve the equation you derived in Question 41 for a. This result gives you the acceleration that the Sun imparts to the Earth at each point E on the Earth's path around the Sun. This acceleration is centripetal because it causes the Earth to move toward the center of its path; i.e., the Sun. Retain this result for a derivation in Lesson 12.8.

---

[3] Centripetal, in Latin, means "seeking the center." Centripetal acceleration of a point around the circle is the force that attracts that point to the center of the circle.

[4] Newton's first law of motion states that an object either remains at rest or continues to move at a constant velocity in a straight line unless acted upon by a force.

[5] The pull of the gravity of the Earth on any object near the surface of the Earth also undergoes constant acceleration.

12.2 Logarithmic Scales

Terms & Concepts Introduced
1. Division Law of Logs
2. Index of the Slide Rule
3. Linear scales
4. Logarithmic scales
5. Logical Equivalency between Exponentiation and Logarithms
6. Multiplication Law of Logs
7. Slide Rule

At the end of the last lesson, we came to this conclusion:

$\log 2 \approx {}^{1}/_{3} = 0.\overline{3}$

The exact value of log 2, rounded to three decimal places is:

$\log 2 \approx 0.301$

This value of log 2 means that about 3/10 of a turn of a piece of rope around a post is required to multiply our strength by 2. Note the logical equivalency between logarithms and power of 10:

$\log 2 \approx 0.301 \Leftrightarrow 10^{0.301} \approx 2$

Logs are exponents.

About 12/25 ≈ 0.477 of a turn of a piece of rope around a post is required to multiply our strength by 3. Again, note the logical equivalency:

$\log 3 \approx 0477 \Leftrightarrow 10^{0.477} \approx 3$

In general, for $x, b \in \mathbb{R}, x > 0$:

$\log b = x \Leftrightarrow 10^{x} = b$

$\log b = x \Leftrightarrow 10^{x} = b$

Multiplication Law of Logs

What will happen if we wind the rope 0.301 of a turn on one post and then 0.477 of a turn on the next post? These two turns are equivalent to 0.778 of a turn on one post. If 0.301 of a turn multiplies our strength by 2 and 0.477 of a turn multiplies our strength by 3, 0.778, the sum of 0.301 and 0.477, multiplies our strength by a factor of 6.

Note:

$\log 6 \approx 0.778 \Leftrightarrow 10^{0.778} \approx 6$

In other words, we find log (3 · 2) by adding the log 3 to the log of 2, or:

$\log 6 = \log (3 \cdot 2) = \log 3 + \log 2$

In general, for $a, b \in \mathbb{R}, a, b > 0$:

$\log ab = \log a + \log b$

$\log ab = \log a + \log b$

Multiplying the log of a product is the same as adding the log of the two factors.

In general, for $a, b \in \mathbb{R}$:

$10^{a}10^{b} = 10^{a+b}$

Do you see a similarity, a perichoretic interpenetration, between this law and the Product Law of Exponents? Why? Exponentiation and logarithms are inverses of each other.[1] Follow along with this

[1] One of the interesting twists of history is that logarithms were developed before exponents were in use. The original idea for turning multiplication into addition came from a trigonometric identity known to John Napier: (cos θ)(cos ω) =

mathematical reasoning of the proof of the Multiplication Law of Logs, a proof that interpenetrates with the Product Law of Exponents:

We know:

1. $\log 10^x = x$ (Lesson 12.1)
2. $\log b = x \Leftrightarrow 10^x = b$
3. $10^a 10^b = 10^{a+b}$

Step 1. Let $a = 10^c \Leftrightarrow \log a = c$

Step 2. Let $b = 10^d \Leftrightarrow \log b = d$

Step 3. $10^c 10^d = 10^{c+d} = ab$

Or:

Step 4. $10^{c+d} = ab$

Step 5. Using the Balance Beam Principle, we invoke the log of both sides of the equation in Step 4:

$\log(10^{c+d}) = \log ab$

Step 6. $\log(10^{c+d}) = c + d$

Step 7. From Step 1, Step 2, Step 5, and Step 6, we conclude: $\log ab = \log a +$ lob b

QED

DIVISION LAW OF LOGS

If we take the log of a quotient, what happens?

$\log {}^6/_2 = \log 3 = \log 6 - \log 2$ because $\log 3 \approx 0.477$ and $\log 6 - \log 2 \approx 0.778 - 0.301 = 0.477$

In general, for $a, b \in \mathbb{R}$, $a, b > 0$:

$\log {}^a/_b = \log a - \log b$

$\log {}^a/_b = \log a - \log b$

Dividing the log of a quotient is the same as subtracting the log of the divided and divisor.

In general, for $a, b \in \mathbb{R}$:

$$\frac{10^a}{10^b} = 10^{a-b}$$

Do you again see a perichoretic interpenetration between this law and the Quotient Law of Exponents?

Again, follow along with this proof of the Division Law of Logs, a proof that interpenetrates with the Quotient Law of Exponents:

We know:

1. $\log 10^x = x$
2. $\log b = x \Leftrightarrow 10^x = b$
3. $\dfrac{10^a}{10^b} = 10^{a-b}$

Step 1. Let $a = 10^c \Leftrightarrow \log a = c$

Step 2. Let $b = 10^d \Leftrightarrow \log b = d$

Step 3. $\dfrac{10^c}{10^d} = 10^{c-d} = \dfrac{a}{b}$

${}^1/_2[\cos(\theta - \omega) + \cos(\theta + \omega)]$. In Lesson 12.6, we will learn what "cos" means. In the homework exercises of Lesson 13.6, we will show why this identity is true.

Or:

Step 4. $10^{c-d} = \frac{a}{b}$

Step 5. Using the Balance Beam Principle, we invoke the log of both sides of the equation in Step 4:

$$\log\left(10^{c-d}\right) = \log\frac{a}{b}$$

Step 6. $\log\left(10^{c-d}\right) = c - d$

Step 7. From Step 1, Step 2, Step 5, and Step 6, we conclude: $\log {}^{a}/_{b} = \log a - \log b$

QED

To summarize this section, note the beautiful symmetric inverse relationship between exponentiation and logarithms as revealed in the graph in Figure 1 and Table 1.

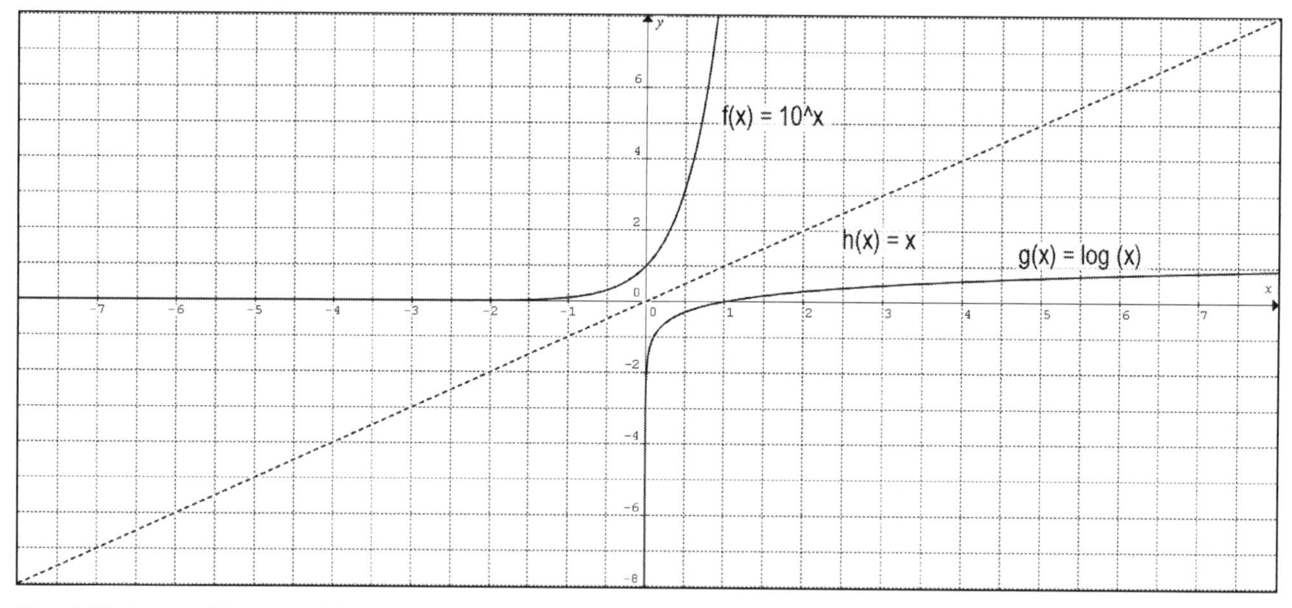

Figure 1. The inverses of the exponential and logarithmic functions ($\log b = x \Leftrightarrow 10^x = b$) are a reflection through the line $y = x$.

Table 1: Symmetric Properties of Exponential Compared to Logarithmic Functions

	Exponential	**Logarithmic**
Form	$y = f(x) = b^x, b > 0, b \neq 1$	$y = f(x) = \log_b x, b > 1$
Domain	All real numbers: $(-\infty, \infty)$	All positive real numbers: $(0, \infty)$
Range	All positive real numbers: $(0, \infty)$	All real numbers: $(-\infty, \infty)$
y-intercept	1	None
Zeroes	None	1
Horizontal asymptote	*x-axis*	None
Vertical asymptote	None	*y*-axis
Mapping	One-to-one	One-to-one
Inverse Mapping	One-to-one (Logarithmic)	One-to-one (Exponential)

LINEAR SCALES

We can use two number lines to demonstrate addition and subtraction. These number lines are analog **linear scales**.

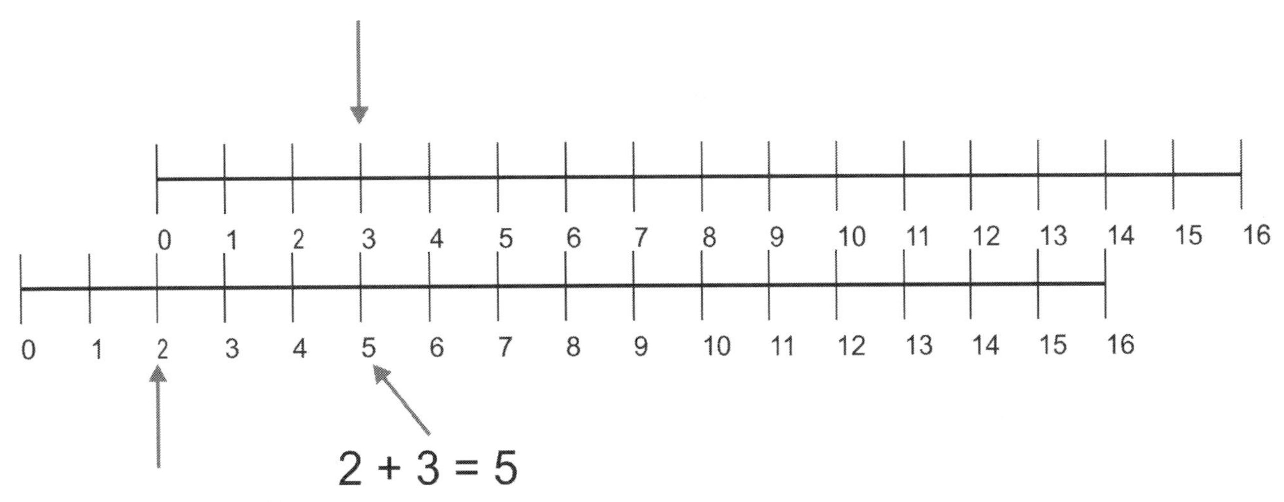

Figure 2. Linear Scales for Addition.

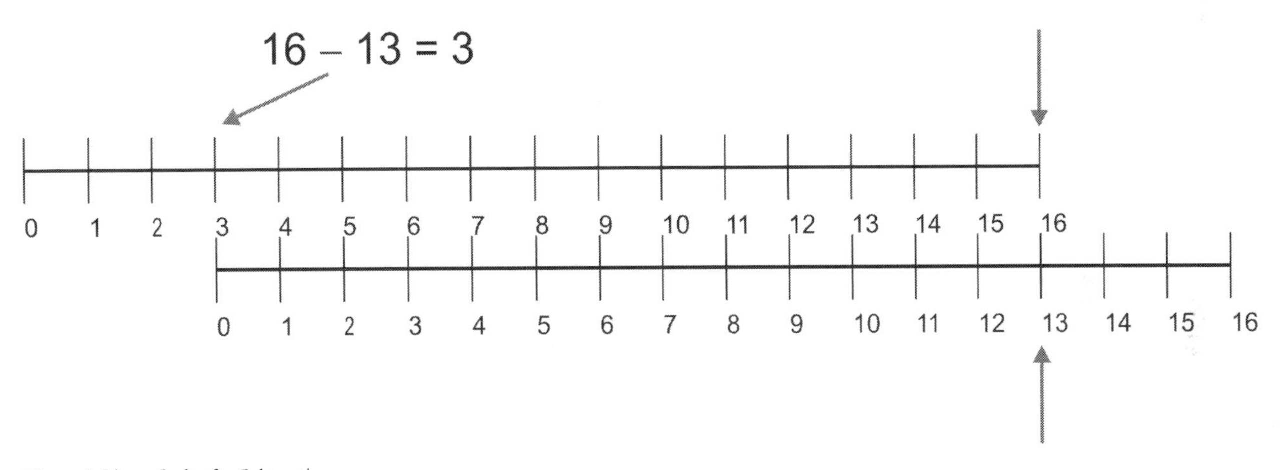

Figure 3. Linear Scales for Subtraction.

Experiment with more addition and subtraction problems using either inch or centimeter rulers. You must place one of the rulers upside-down and reverse the numbers; i.e., on an inch scale, label 12 as 0, 11 as 1, 10 as 2, 9 as 3, 8 as 4, and 7 as 5. When 6 is upside-down, it looks like 9, so place a label on 6 so that it looks like 6. Continue labeling 5 as 7, 4 as 8, etc.

LOGARITHMIC SCALES

The following number lines are **logarithmic scales**, also analog in nature, and we use them, besides other functions, to multiply or divide:

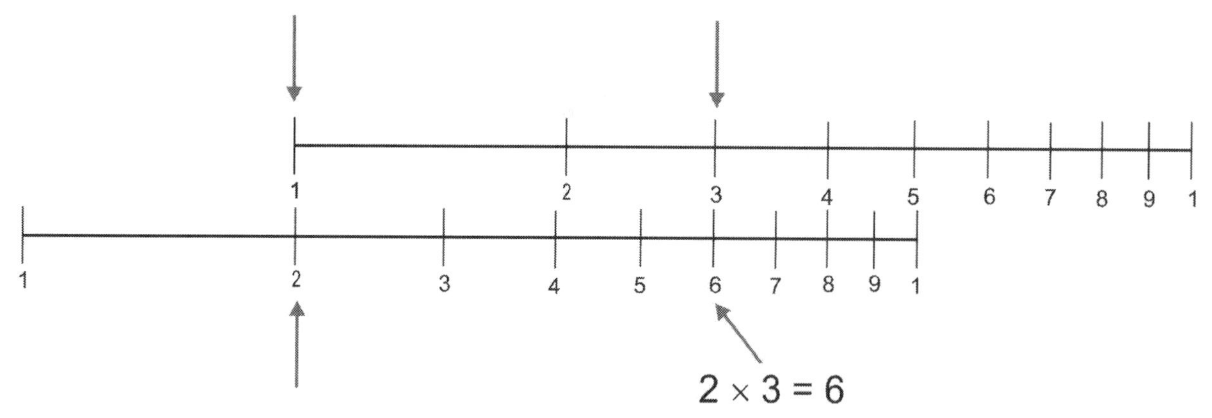

Figure 4. Logarithmic Scales for Multiplication.

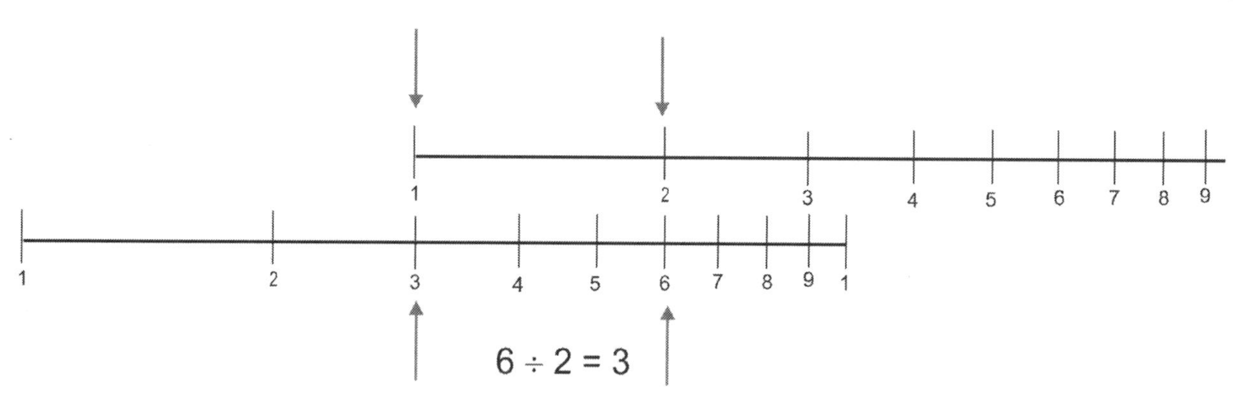

Figure 5. Logarithmic Scales for Division.

Unlike linear scales, the tick marks between numbers in logarithmic scales are unequal. Note also that logarithmic scales begin with 1 and end with 1. Logarithmic scales are constructed using logs of the numbers between 1 and 10, representing rope strength from a multiplicative factor of 1 to 10. The value of log x, column three in Table 2, are approximations rounded to the nearest thousandths.

Table 2		
x	**$10^{\log x}$**	**log x**
1	10^{0}	0.000
2	$10^{0.301}$	0.301
3	$10^{0.477}$	0.477
4	$10^{0.602}$	0.602
5	$10^{0.700}$	0.700
6	$10^{0.778}$	0.778
7	$10^{0.845}$	0.845

Table 2

x	$10^{\log x}$	log x
8	$10^{0.903}$	0.903
9	$10^{0.954}$	0.954
10	10^{1}	1.000

In your notebook and with this table, calculate (1) $2 \cdot 4$, (2) $3 \cdot 3$, (3) $8 \div 4$, and (4) $9 \div 3$ by either adding or subtracting logs.

Answers:

1. $2 \cdot 4$

   $\log (2 \cdot 4) = \log 2 + \log 4 \approx 0.301 + 0.602 = 0.903 = \log 8$

   Since $\log 8 = 0.903 \Leftrightarrow 10^{0.903} = 8$, then $2 \cdot 4 = 8$

2. $3 \cdot 3$

   $\log (3 \cdot 3) = \log 3 + \log 3 \approx 0.477 + 0.477 = 0.954 = \log 9$

   Since $\log 9 = 0.954 \Leftrightarrow 10^{0.954} = 9$, then $3 \cdot 3 = 9$

3. $8 \div 4$

   $\log (8 \div 4) = \log 8 - \log 4 \approx 0.903 - 0.602 = 0.301 = \log 2$

   Since $\log 2 = 0.301 \Leftrightarrow 10^{0.301} = 2$, then $8 \div 4 = 2$

4. $9 \div 3$

   $\log (9 \div 3) = \log 9 - \log 3 \approx 0.954 + 0.477 = 0.477 = \log 3$

   Since $\log 3 = 0.477 \Leftrightarrow 10^{0.477} = 3$, then $9 \div 3 = 3$

Table 3 gives us the information for the construction of logarithmic scales, i.e., the reason for the uneven spaces between units.

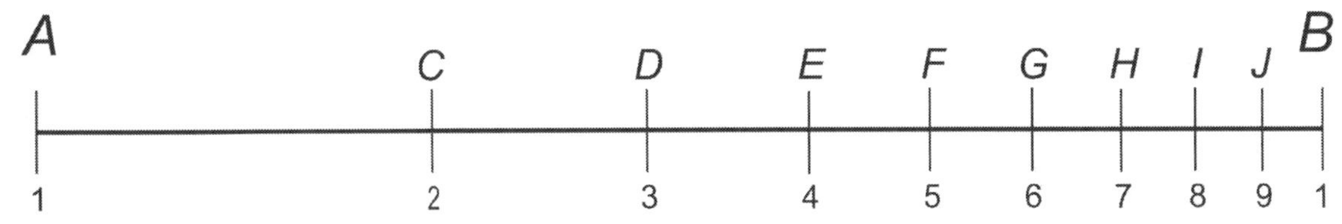

Figure 6. Logarithmic Scales.

Table 3

Distance	Point:Number	Percentage of AB
A	A: 1	0% of AB
AC	C: 2	30.1% of AB
AD	D: 3	47.7% of AB
AE	E: 4	60.2% of AB
AF	F: 5	70% of AB
AG	G: 6	77.8% of AB
AH	H: 7	84.5% of AB
AI	I: 8	90.3% of AB

Table 3		
Distance	**Point:Number**	**Percentage of *AB***
AJ	*J*: 9	95.4% of *AB*
AB	*B*: 10	100% of *AB*

Point *B* is labeled 1 even though it is 10. Why? The scale can be interpreted to represent numbers between:

Table 4	
Minimum	**Maximum**
1	10
10	100
100	10000
1000	10,000
0.1	1
0.01	0.1
etc.	etc.

With the advent of the electronic calculator, we can calculate square roots, cube roots, and logarithms (note the LOG key) by pushing buttons. Before the invention of these mechanical devices, students, like me, used **slide rules** to calculate square roots and cube roots.[2] These slides rules were designed to make use of logarithmic scales.

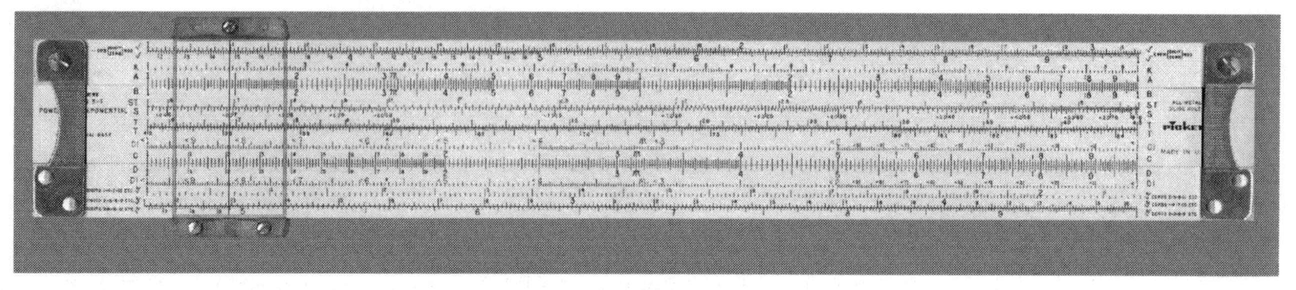

Figure 7. Slide Rule. Source: James D. Nickel. This is the slide rule I used for math classes in university.

In Figure 7, note the logarithmic scale labeled with the letter C (the D scale is a duplicate of the C scale). Second, note the moveable vertical hairline mechanism.[3]

The name of this mechanical device comes from middle part, a section that we can slide either left or right. The two numbers labeled 1 on the C and D scales are the **index** of these scales. The tick marks between the numbers 1 and 2, 2 and 3, 3 and 4, etc. are also logarithmic, a percentage of the total distance *d* between the left index and the right index. For example, since log 2.1 = 0.3222, the tick mark that represents 2.1 (or 21, 210, 0.21, etc.) is 32.22% of *d*. Since log 2.2 = 0.3424, the tick mark that represents 2.2 (or 22, 220, 0.22, etc.) is 34.24% of *d*.

[2] The British mathematician William Oughtred (1575-1660) invented the slide rule in the 1620s.

[3] Isaac Newton originally suggested this hairline mechanism in 1675. It was first called a runner because you could "run" back and forth on the rule. The runner become a constructed reality one hundred years later.

To multiply 2 by 3 (or 2 by 30, 20 by 3, 20 by 30, 200 by 300, 0.2 by 0.3, etc.), slide the left index of the C scale to the left until it lands on 2 on the D scale. Move the hairline to 3 on the C scale and read you answer on the D scale (Figure 8). With logs, we are adding log 2 to log 3 to get log 6. Using log laws:

$\log 2 + \log 3 = \log(2 \cdot 3) \Leftrightarrow 0.301 + 0.477 = 0.778$

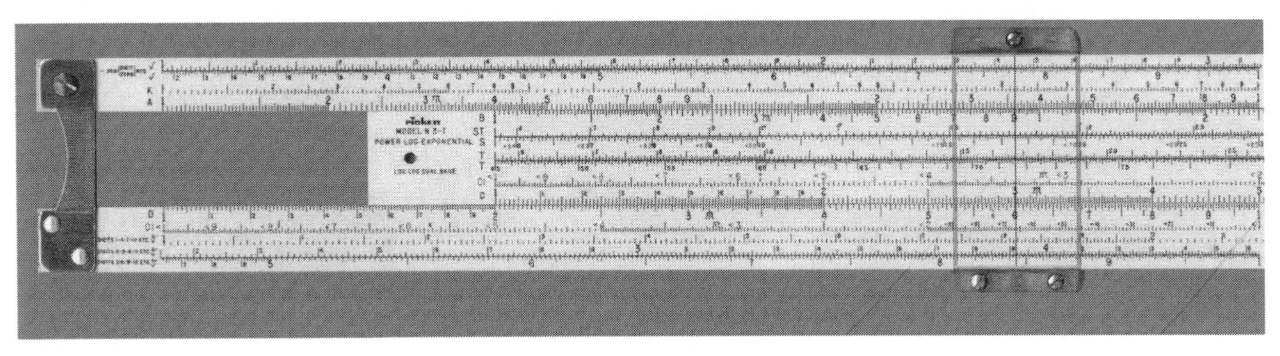

Figure 8. 2 × 3 = 6. Source: James D. Nickel.

To multiply 3 by 4 (or 3 by 40, 30 by 4, 30 by 40, 300 by 400, 0.003 by 0.04, etc.), slide the right index of the C scale to the right until it lands on 3 on the D scale. Move the hairline to 4 on the C scale and read you answer on the D scale (Figure 9). Do you see the product 12? With logs, we are adding log 3 to log 4 to get log 12. Using log laws:

$\log 3 + \log 4 = \log(3 \cdot 4) \Leftrightarrow 0.477 + 0.602 = 1.079$

Figure 9. 3 × 4 = 12. Source: James D. Nickel.

Based upon the type of multiplication problem, we slide the middle section left or right. The one skill I developed from using this slide rule was number sense. I had to estimate the answer in my mind, especially when dealing with decimals, before I began manipulating the scales.

To divide 8 by 4 (or 8 by 40, 80 by 4, 80 by 40, 800 by 400, 0.08 by 0.4, etc.), slide the hairline over the dividend on the D scale. Slide the divisor on the C scale over the dividend and read the quotient on the D scale under the left index of the C scale (Figure 10). With logs, we are subtracting log 4 from log 8 to get log 2. Using log laws:

$\log 8 - \log 4 = \log {}^{8}/_{4} \Leftrightarrow 0.903 - 0.602 = 0.301$

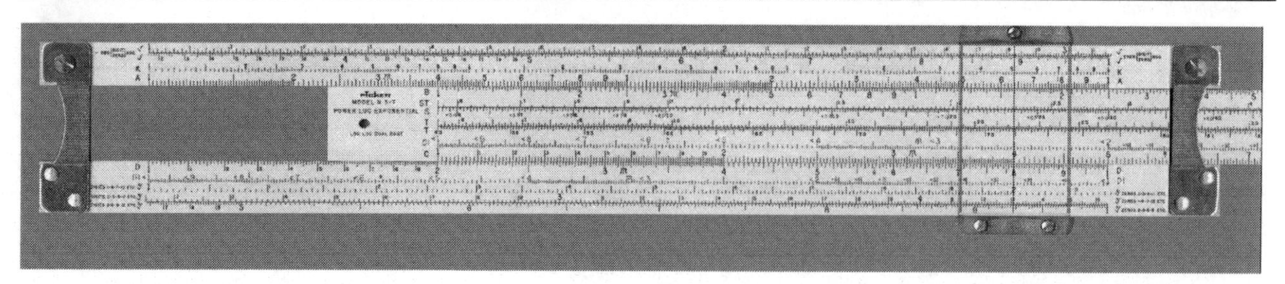

Figure 10. $8 \div 4 = 2$. Source: James D. Nickel.

EXERCISES

Define the following terms:

1. Multiplication Law of Logs
2. Division Law of Logs
3. (a) Linear scale and (b) an example of a linear scale
4. Logarithmic scale
5. Slide Rule
6. Index of Slide Rule

> The miraculous powers of modern calculation are due to three inventions: the Arabic Notation, Decimal Fractions, and Logarithms.
> Florian Cajori, *A History of Mathematics* (1893).

Answer the following questions:

7. State how you would solve $10^x = k$ for x.
8. In symbols, what is the logical equivalency between logarithms and exponentiation?
9. Explain what the equation "$\log n = x$" means. (Remember to use base 10 in your explanation.)
10. How is the logarithmic scale on the slide rule constructed? Explain in detail.
11. Multiplication is replaced by what arithmetic operation when using logarithms?
12. Division is replaced by what arithmetic operation when using logarithms?
13. Explain the reasoning that justifies Step 7 in the proof of (a) the Multiplication Law of Logs and (b) the Division Law of Logs.

Solve the following equations for x.

14. $\log 10{,}000 = x$
15. $\log 1000 = x$
16. $\log 1{,}000{,}000 = x$
17. $\log 10^{30} = x$
18. $\log 10^n = x$
19. $\log 0.001 = x$

Transform the following equations into logarithmic notation.

20. $10{,}000 = 10^4$
21. $1000 = 10^3$
22. $50 = 10^x$
23. $n = 10^x$

Field Projects:

24. If you have access to a carpenter shop or carpentry tools, construct two duplicate log scales. Ask for help from a parent, relative, or friend who has carpentry skills.
25. Try to obtain a slide rule, either an older friend/relative, or an antique store. You can also find used slide rules for sale online. There are also slide rule software applications for personal computers and smart phones. Access websites that explain how to use a slide rule and experiment.

12.3 The Log of 2

Concept Introduced
1. Radix method of computing logarithms

Very little attention is paid today to the work of some 17th century mathematicians, especially Henry Briggs (1561-1630). An English Puritan and professor of geometry at Gresham College[1] in London, Briggs tediously calculated the logs of numbers by hand so that scientists of his day could multiply and divide large numbers, numbers that were prevalent in astronomical work.[2] Today, we have calculators and computers that do this work and we tend to go mindlessly about our business, blind to the mathematical heritage and reasoning behind these machines.

As we saw in Lesson 12.1, $\log 2 \approx 0.301 \Leftrightarrow 10^{0.301} \approx 2$. Let's see how Briggs determined 0.301 by using powers of 10 and the Babylonian algorithm. Briggs needed to solve the equation $10^x = 2$. By definition:

$$10^x = 2 \Leftrightarrow x = \log 2$$

How is x determined?

Briggs computed logarithms by calculating, using the Babylonian algorithm, successive square roots of 10:

- $10^{\frac{1}{2}} = \sqrt{10}$
- $10^{\frac{1}{4}} = \left(10^{\frac{1}{2}}\right)^{\frac{1}{2}} = \sqrt{\sqrt{10}}$
- $10^{\frac{1}{8}} = \left(\left(10^{\frac{1}{2}}\right)^{\frac{1}{2}}\right)^{\frac{1}{2}} = \sqrt{\sqrt{\sqrt{10}}}$
- $10^{\frac{1}{16}} = \left(\left(\left(10^{\frac{1}{2}}\right)^{\frac{1}{2}}\right)^{\frac{1}{2}}\right)^{\frac{1}{2}} = \sqrt{\sqrt{\sqrt{\sqrt{10}}}}$
- $10^{\frac{1}{32}} = \left(\left(\left(\left(10^{\frac{1}{2}}\right)^{\frac{1}{2}}\right)^{\frac{1}{2}}\right)^{\frac{1}{2}}\right)^{\frac{1}{2}} = \sqrt{\sqrt{\sqrt{\sqrt{\sqrt{10}}}}}$
- etc.

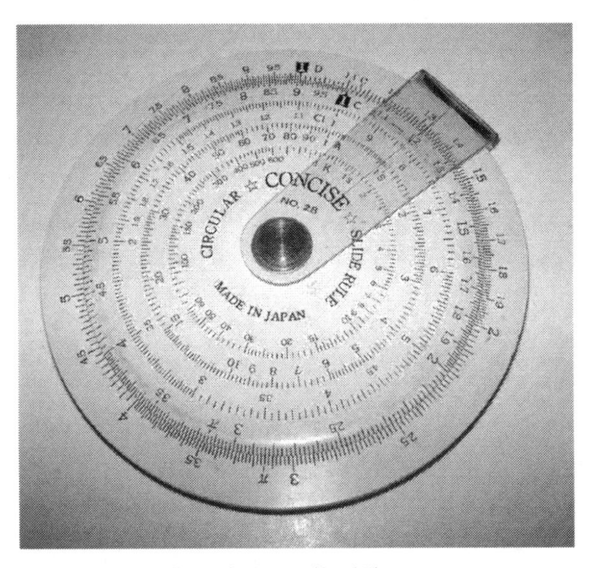

Figure 1. Circular Slide Rule. Source: iStockPhoto.

[1] In the 17th century, Gresham College was England's scientific center for navigation, geometry, astronomy, and surveying.
[2] The French mathematician Pierre-Simon de Laplace (1749-1827) once asserted that logarithms "by shortening the labors doubled the life of the astronomer."

We have already calculated $\sqrt{10}$ using the Babylonian algorithm. We are going to use our spreadsheet program to help us find the rest. (Sorry, Mr. Briggs. But imagine him doing this work by hand!) To the ten-millionths pace, $\sqrt{10} \approx 3.162277$.

We use the same algorithm to find:

$$\sqrt{3.16227} = 10^{\frac{1}{4}} = \left(10^{\frac{1}{2}}\right)^{\frac{1}{2}} = \sqrt{\sqrt{10}}$$

With a starting estimate of 2, the Babylonian algorithm gives us 1.7782794.

Table 1 gives us ten successive square roots of 10, each calculated to the nearest ten-millionths. Confirm each entry with your spreadsheet program.

Table 1

Exponent: k	10^k
1	10.0000000
$^1/_2$	3.1622777
$^1/_4$	1.7782794
$^1/_8$	1.3335214
$^1/_{16}$	1.1547820
$^1/_{32}$	1.0746078
$^1/_{64}$	1.0366329
$^1/_{128}$	1.0181517
$^1/_{256}$	1.0090350
$^1/_{512}$	1.0045073
$^1/_{1024}$	1.0022511

To get the precision he desired, Briggs computed 54 successive square roots of 10. Doing those computations by hand takes significant mental prowess.

What can we conclude from these calculations?

$10^{\frac{1}{2}} \approx 3.1622777 \Leftrightarrow \log 3.1622777 = 0.5$ (This answer is very accurate.)

$10^{\frac{1}{4}} \approx 1.7782794 \Leftrightarrow \log 1.7782794 = 0.25$

WHAT IS LOG 17.78?

We also can find log 17.78 by this reasoning:

$\log 17.78 = x \Leftrightarrow 10^x = 17.78$

We know:

$$\log 1.7782794 = 0.25 \Leftrightarrow 10^{0.25} = 1.7782794$$
$$\log 10 = 1 \Leftrightarrow 10^1 = 10$$

Multiplying $10^{0.25}$ by 10^1, we get:

$10^{0.25} \cdot 10^1 = 10^{1.25} = 1.7782794 \cdot 10 \approx 17.78$

Therefore:

$10^{1.25} \approx 17.78 \Leftrightarrow \log 17.78 \approx 1.25$

WHAT IS $10^{3/4}$?

Can we use this table to find $10^{\frac{3}{4}}$? First, we note:

$$10^{\frac{3}{4}} = 10^{\left(\frac{1}{2}+\frac{1}{4}\right)} = 10^{\frac{1}{2}} \cdot 10^{\frac{1}{4}}$$

We know, therefore, that $10^{\frac{1}{2}}$ and $10^{\frac{1}{4}}$ are factors of $10^{\frac{3}{4}}$.

Second, since we want to find $10^{\frac{3}{4}}$, we let $10^{\left(\frac{1}{2}+\frac{1}{4}\right)} = x$ and note:

$$10^{\left(\frac{1}{2}+\frac{1}{4}\right)} = x \Leftrightarrow \log x = \left(\frac{1}{2}+\frac{1}{4}\right) = \frac{3}{4}$$

Next, we invoke the Multiplication Law of Logs; i.e., $\log ab = \log a + \log b$. Since $\log 3.162277 = 0.5$ and $\log 1.7782794 = 0.25$, then:

$$\log(3.162277 \cdot 1.7782794) = 0.5 + 0.25 = 0.75 = \frac{3}{4}$$

Therefore, $\log(3.1622777 \cdot 1.7782794) = \frac{3}{4} \Leftrightarrow 10^{\frac{3}{4}} = 3.1622777 \cdot 1.7782794 = 5.6234133$. Our conclusion:

$10^{\frac{3}{4}} \approx 5.6234133$ (eight significant digits)

To summarize, we used Table 1 to find a fractional power of 10, $10^{\frac{3}{4}} \approx 5.6234133$, and, by doing so, added another entry into the Table, between row one and row two (See Table 2.) and discovered a new logarithm:

$$\log 5.6234133 = \frac{3}{4} = 0.75$$

Table 2	
Exponent: k	**10^k**
1	10.0000000
$^3/_4$	**5.6234133**
$^1/_2$	3.1622777
⋮	⋮

LET'S THINK

Based on this example, if we can get enough numbers in column one of Table 1 to make up almost any number, then, by multiplying the proper numbers in column two, we can compute 10^x for any x.

If we keep extending the table; i.e., find 10^k when $k = 1/2048, 1/4096, 1/8192$, etc., we should note that 10^k for a very small k generates a number slightly greater than 1. We get 1 plus a minuscule amount. Let's denote this value as the Greek letter delta, i.e., Δ.

In other words, as the entries in column one get closer and closer to zero, the entries in column two get closer and closer to 1. We are thinking in limits. As $k \to 0$, $10^k \to 1$ (Figure 2). Or, using limit notation:

$\lim_{k \to 0} 10^k = 1$ (This limit makes sense since $10^0 = 1$.)

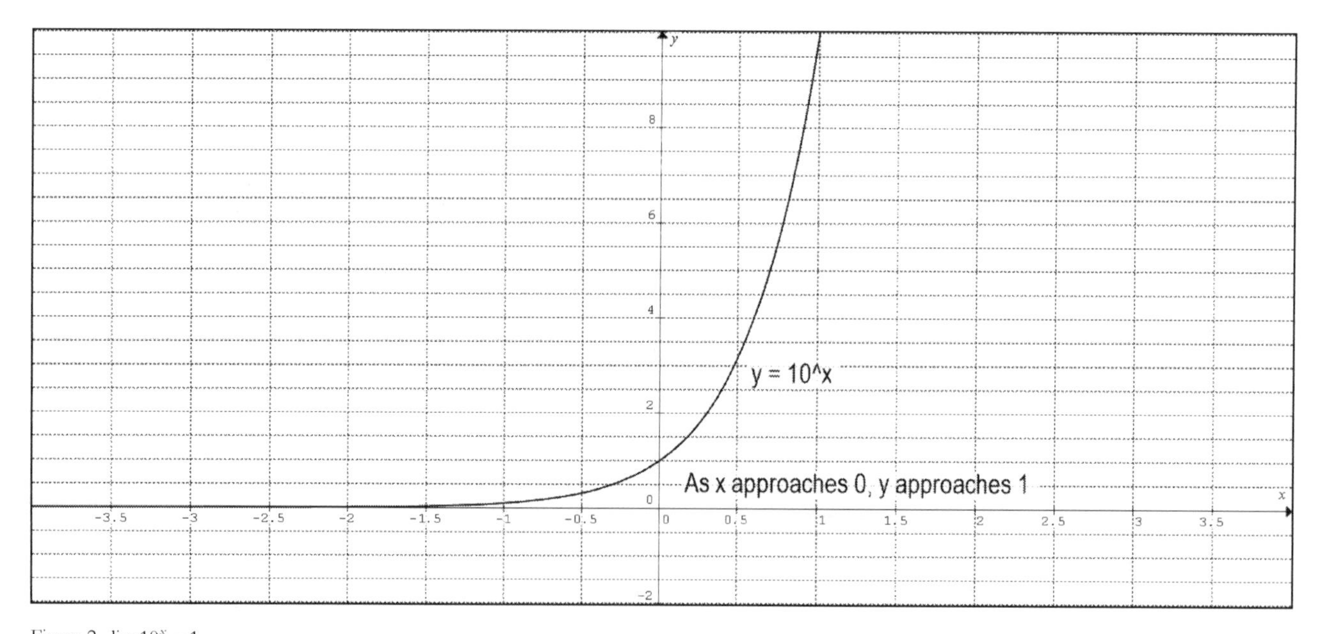

Figure 2. $\lim_{x \to 0} 10^x = 1$

Take some time to study Table 1 and see if you can discover another pattern. It looks like, as k gets very small, that each decimal part in column two is very close to half the preceding decimal number part. For example, if we round, we note:

- $\dfrac{10^{\frac{1}{64}}}{2} \approx \dfrac{0.036}{2} = 0.018 \approx 10^{\frac{1}{128}}$
- $\dfrac{10^{\frac{1}{128}}}{2} \approx \dfrac{0.018}{2} = 0.009 \approx 10^{\frac{1}{256}}$
- $\dfrac{10^{\frac{1}{256}}}{2} \approx \dfrac{0.0090}{2} = 0.0045 \approx 10^{\frac{1}{512}}$
- $\dfrac{10^{\frac{1}{512}}}{2} \approx \dfrac{0.00450}{2} = 0.00225 \approx 10^{\frac{1}{1024}}$

The next entry, $10^{\frac{1}{2048}}$, should be:

$$10^{\frac{1}{2048}} \approx 1 + \frac{0.0022511}{2} = 1.00112555$$

We learn from this type of thinking that instead of using the Babylonian algorithm to calculate these square roots, we can estimate them. Furthermore, we can guess the ultimate threshold, the final limit of these roots. In other words, if we compute $\Delta/1024$ and let Δ get very, very small ($\Delta \to 0$), what is the answer? It will be a number very close to 0.0022511Δ, but not exactly. We can get a better value by introducing a correction factor.

Since Briggs computed 54 successive square roots, he looked for a shorter way. First, he subtracted 1 from 10^k to get the fractional part. Next, he divided the result by k; i.e., he calculated:

$$\frac{10^k - 1}{k}$$

Let's do that now and add four columns to Table 1, column two, $1024k$, column four, $\Delta\left(10^k\right)$, column five, $\dfrac{10^k - 1}{k}$ and column six, $\Delta\left(\dfrac{10^k - 1}{k}\right)$. We now have the six-column depicted in Table 3.

Table 3					
Exponent: k = log 10^k	$1024k$	10^k	$\Delta(10^k)$ (4 places, decimal part only)	$\frac{10^k - 1}{k}$	$\Delta\left(\frac{10^k - 1}{k}\right)$ (4 places, decimal part only)
$2^0 = 1$	1024	10.0000000		9.0000	
$2^{-1} = 1/2$	512	3.1622777		4.3246	
$2^{-2} = 1/4$	256	1.7782794		3.1131	
$2^{-3} = 1/8$	128	1.3335214		2.6682	
$2^{-4} = 1/16$	64	1.1547820	1787	2.4765	1917
$2^{-5} = 1/32$	32	1.0746078	802	2.3874	891
$2^{-6} = 1/64$	16	1.0366329	380	2.3445	429
$2^{-7} = 1/128$	8	1.0181517	184	2.3234	211
$2^{-8} = 1/256$	4	1.0090350	91	2.3130	104
$2^{-9} = 1/512$	2	1.0045073	45	2.3077	53
$2^{-10} = 1/1024$	1	1.0022511	23	2.3051	26
				$\downarrow$	26
$\Delta/1024$ (as $\Delta \to 0$)	Δ	$1 + 0.002248585\Delta$ (correct limiting value)	$\leftarrow$	2.3025 (correct limiting value is 2.302585)	

With this calculation adjustment, Briggs discovered that he could calculate logarithms just as precise as before, but by taking only 27 successive square roots.

Note that the differences in column six are very close to the differences in column four, especially as k gets lesser. The division by 2 pattern with the decimal part difference also holds. What is the limiting value of column five? As k gets lesser, the differences in column six become 13, 7, 3, 2, and 1 and since 13 + 7 + 3 + 2 + 1 = 26, we subtract 0.0026 from 2.3051 to get 2.3025 as our approximate limiting value, to four decimal places. The more precise limiting value[3] of $\frac{10^k - 1}{k}$ as $k \to 0$ is $2.302585 \approx 2.3026$ (Figure 3).

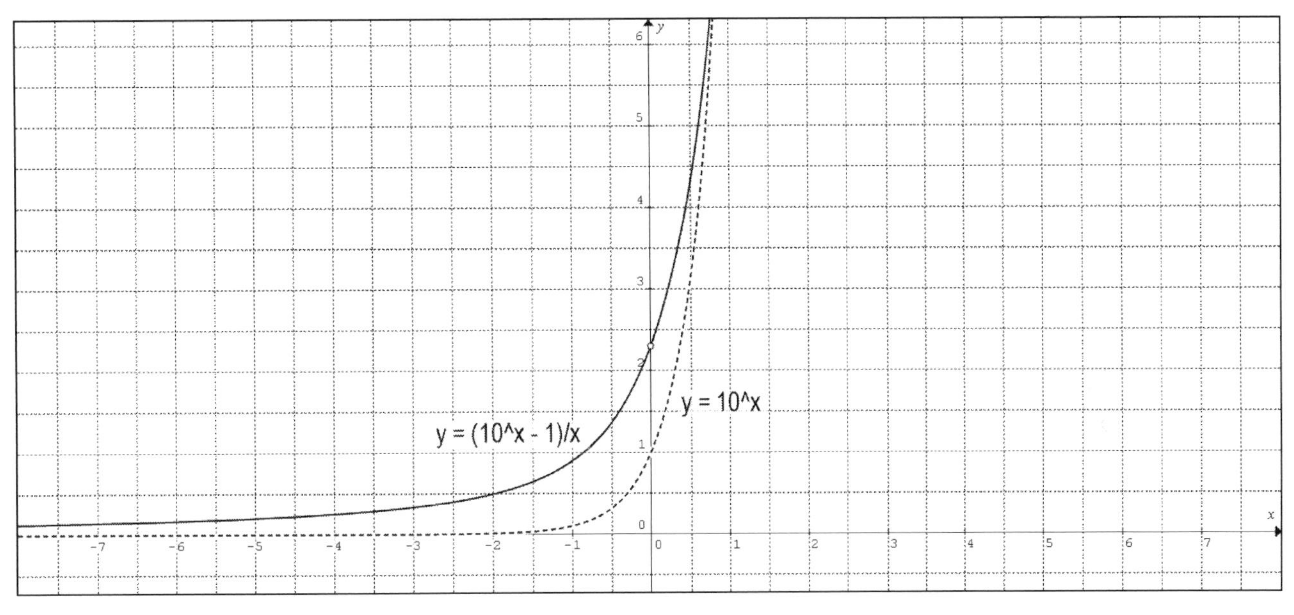

Figure 3. $\lim_{x\to 0}\frac{10^x - 1}{x} = 2.302585$ [Note the open circle on the graph at (0, 2.302585). This circle means that there is no image for the function when the argument is zero. Why?]

Using the limit notation:

$$\lim_{k\to 0}\left(\frac{10^k - 1}{k}\right) \approx 2.302585$$

Since the actual difference is 0.000002515, we subtract 0.000002515 from the decimal part of 1.0022511 in column three, and we get:

$$0.0022511 - 0.000002515 = 0.002248585$$

Therefore, our limiting value for our third column, 10^k, is $1 + 0.002248585\Delta$. Using limit notation:

$$\lim_{\Delta\to 0}\left(10^{\Delta/1024}\right) \approx 1 + 0.002248585\Delta$$

[3] We must transcend arithmetic to find this value and Calculus methods do the job.

Now, if we let $\Delta = 1/1{,}000{,}000$, a value very close to 0, then:

$$10^{\frac{\frac{1}{1{,}000{,}000}}{1024}} = 10^{\frac{1}{1{,}024{,}000{,}000}} = 1 + 0.002248585\left(\frac{1}{1{,}000{,}000}\right) \approx 1.000000002$$

(This is a value very close to 1.)

We get the same answer using the formula $1 + 2.302585\left(\Delta/_{1024}\right)$ because:

$$\frac{2.302585}{1024} \approx 0.0022486 \text{ or } 0.002248585 \text{ rounded to the nearest ten-millionth}$$

In other words, the value of 10^k (column three) will approximately equal $1 + 2.302585k$.

To summarize using limit notation and setting $k = \Delta/1024$:

$$\frac{2.302585}{1024} \approx 0.002248585 \Rightarrow \lim_{\Delta \to 0}\left(10^{\Delta/_{1024}}\right) \approx 1 + \left(\lim_{k \to 0}\left(\frac{10^k - 1}{k}\right)\right)\Delta/_{1024}$$

Or:

$$\lim_{\Delta \to 0} 10^{\Delta/_{1024}} \approx 1 + 2.302585\left(\Delta/_{1024}\right)$$

To reduce calculation effort, Briggs found that he could rewrite $\lim_{\Delta \to 0}\left(10^{\Delta/_{1024}}\right)$ (column three) using a factor, $\lim_{k \to 0}\left(\frac{10^k - 1}{k}\right) \approx 2.302585$, derived in column six. This observation will lead us to an unexpected and, indeed, surprising result, the explication of which we will explore in Lesson 12.5 under the section entitled "The Briggs way to find the base of the natural logarithms."

WHAT IS LOG 2?

Based on this analysis, we have all we need to calculate log 2. We are going to follow the reasoning and calculation method used by Briggs over three centuries ago (1620), the **radix method of computing logarithms**. Our task is to compute the logarithm of 2, or to find x in the equation $\log 2 = x$. Or, we find x such that $10^x = 2$ since $\log 2 = x \Leftrightarrow 10^x = 2$. Can we estimate first? We know that $\log 1.7782794 = {}^1/_4 = 0.25$ and $\log 3.1622777 = {}^1/_2 = 0.5$. Therefore:

$0.25 < \log 2 < 0.5$

Or:

${}^1/_4 < \log 2 < {}^1/_2$

We now have a window, i.e., boundary conditions, with which to work.

ITERATION #1

We know that log 2 will not be a clean fraction, a rational number; it is irrational.[4] We must invoke a series of iterations to get a pretty close estimate of this irrational number. Since $\log 1.7782794 = 0.25 \Leftrightarrow$

[4] In Lesson 13.9, we will prove that log 2 is irrational.

$10^{\frac{1}{4}} = 1.7782794$, we know that $10^{\frac{1}{4}}$, being less than 2, will be a factor of 2; i.e., $2 \approx 10^{\frac{1}{4}} \approx 1.7782794$.

We proceed to factor $10^{\frac{1}{4}}$ from 2 by dividing: (Remember: $10^x = 2$)

$$\frac{10^x}{10^{\frac{1}{4}}} = 10^{x-\frac{1}{4}} = \frac{2}{1.7782794} \approx 1.124683$$

We have taken a quarter ($^1/_4 = 0.25$) away from the logarithm; i.e., we have subtracted $^1/_4$ from the exponent of 10^x. The quotient of the division $\frac{10^x}{10^{\frac{1}{4}}} \approx 1.124683$ is now the number whose logarithm we need to find.

ITERATION #2

We look to the table to find the next number that is less than 1.124683 and it is $1.0746078 = 10^{\frac{1}{32}}$. We conclude that 1.0746078 is another factor of 2, the second factor; i.e., $2 \approx 10^{\frac{1}{4}} \cdot 10^{\frac{1}{32}} \approx$ (1.7782794)(1.0746078). We proceed to factor this number, $10^{\frac{1}{32}}$, from 1.124682 as follows:

$$\frac{10^{x-\frac{1}{4}}}{10^{\frac{1}{32}}} = 10^{x-\frac{1}{4}-\frac{1}{32}} = 10^{x-\left(\frac{1}{4}+\frac{1}{32}\right)} = \frac{1.124682}{1.0746078} \approx 1.046598$$

We have taken $^1/_{32} = 0.03125$ away from the logarithm; i.e., we have subtracted $^1/_{32}$ from the exponent of $10^{x-\frac{1}{4}}$. The quotient of the division $\frac{10^{x-\frac{1}{4}}}{10^{\frac{1}{32}}} \approx 1.046598$ is now the number whose logarithm we need to find.

ITERATION #3

We again look to the table to find the next number that is less than 1.046598 and it is 1.0366329 = $10^{\frac{1}{64}}$. We conclude that 1.0366329 is the third factor of 2; i.e., $2 \approx 10^{\frac{1}{4}} \cdot 10^{\frac{1}{32}} \cdot 10^{\frac{1}{64}} \approx$ (1.7782794)(1.0746078)(1.0366329).

As before, we factor this number, $10^{\frac{1}{64}}$, from 1.046598 as follows:

$$\frac{10^{x-\left(\frac{1}{4}+\frac{1}{32}\right)}}{10^{\frac{1}{64}}} = 10^{x-\frac{1}{4}-\frac{1}{32}-\frac{1}{64}} = 10^{x-\left(\frac{1}{4}+\frac{1}{32}+\frac{1}{64}\right)} = \frac{1.046598}{1.0366329} = 1.009613$$

We have taken $^1/_{64} = 0.015625$ away from the logarithm; i.e., we have subtracted $^1/_{64}$ from the exponent of $10^{x-\left(\frac{1}{4}+\frac{1}{32}\right)}$. We are getting closer. The quotient of the division $\frac{10^{x-\left(\frac{1}{4}+\frac{1}{32}\right)}}{10^{\frac{1}{64}}} \approx 1.009613$ is now the number whose logarithm we need to find.

ITERATION #4

We again look to the table to find the next number that is less than 1.009613 and it is $1.0090350 = 10^{\frac{1}{256}}$. We conclude that 1.0090350 is the fourth factor of 2; i.e., $2 \approx 10^{\frac{1}{4}} \cdot 10^{\frac{1}{32}} \cdot 10^{\frac{1}{64}} \cdot 10^{\frac{1}{256}} \approx$ (1.7782794)(1.0746078)(1.0366329)(1.0090350). We factor this number, $10^{\frac{1}{256}}$, from 1.009613 as follows:

$$\frac{10^{x-\left(\frac{1}{4}+\frac{1}{32}+\frac{1}{64}\right)}}{10^{\frac{1}{256}}} = 10^{x-\frac{1}{4}-\frac{1}{32}-\frac{1}{64}-\frac{1}{256}} = 10^{x-\left(\frac{1}{4}+\frac{1}{32}+\frac{1}{64}+\frac{1}{256}\right)} = \frac{1.009613}{1.0090350} = 1.000573$$

We have taken $^1/_{256} = 0.00390625$ away from the logarithm; i.e., we have subtracted $^1/_{256}$ from the exponent of $10^{x-\left(\frac{1}{4}+\frac{1}{32}+\frac{1}{64}\right)}$. The quotient of the division $\frac{10^{x-\left(\frac{1}{4}+\frac{1}{32}+\frac{1}{64}\right)}}{10^{\frac{1}{256}}} \approx 1.000573$ is now the number whose logarithm we need to find.

ITERATION #5

We look to the table to find the next number that is less than 1.000573, but this number is beyond the calculated limits of our table, i.e., $10^{\frac{1}{1024}} = 1.0022511$. To calculate this factor as a power of 10, we make use our formula $\lim_{\Delta\to 0} 10^{\Delta/1024} \approx 1 + 2.302585\left(\Delta/_{1024}\right)$. We know that $1.000573 = 1 + 2.302585\left(\Delta/_{1024}\right)$. Solving for Δ, we get:

$$1.000573 = 1 + 2.302585\left(\Delta/_{1024}\right) \Leftrightarrow 1.000573 - 1 = 2.302585\left(\Delta/_{1024}\right) \Leftrightarrow$$

$$(0.000573)(1024) = 2.302585\Delta \Leftrightarrow \Delta = \frac{(0.000573)(1024)}{2.302585} \approx 0.255$$

We now have our final power, $10^{\frac{0.255}{1024}}$, and last factor, 1.000573. We conclude:

$2 \approx (1.7782794)(1.0746078)(1.0366329)(1.0090350)(1.000573)$

Since $1.7782794 = 10^{\frac{1}{4}}$, $1.0746078 = 10^{\frac{1}{32}}$, $1.0366329 = 10^{\frac{1}{64}}$, $1.0090350 = 10^{\frac{1}{256}}$, and $1.000573 = 10^{\frac{0.255}{1024}}$, we also conclude:

$$2 \approx 10^{\frac{1}{4}} \cdot 10^{\frac{1}{32}} \cdot 10^{\frac{1}{64}} \cdot 10^{\frac{1}{256}} \cdot 10^{\frac{0.255}{1024}}$$

To find x, we add back the exponents that we subtracted in the five iterations. Therefore, we can estimate $10^x = 2$ as:

$$10^x = \left(10^{\frac{1}{4}}\right)\left(10^{\frac{1}{32}}\right)\left(10^{\frac{1}{64}}\right)\left(10^{\frac{1}{256}}\right)\left(10^{\frac{0.255}{1024}}\right) = 10^{\frac{1}{4}+\frac{1}{32}+\frac{1}{64}+\frac{1}{256}+\frac{0.255}{1024}} = 10^{0.30103} \approx 2$$

Therefore, $\log 2 \approx 0.30103$ since $10^{0.30103} \approx 2 \Leftrightarrow \log 2 \approx 0.30103$, a value accurate to five decimal places.

QED

> Calculators and computers make things faster and easier and we appreciate that. Sometimes, though, as in the case of the Briggs calculations, the use of calculators bypasses an immense amount of mathematical learning.
>
> James D. Nickel

In review, we have solved the equation $10^x = 2$ for x and, as a result, calculated log 2. In the radix method developed by Briggs, all we used was the Babylonian algorithm for finding square roots to generate Table 1, the fractional powers of 10 of the form of the form $10^{\frac{1}{2^n}}$ for $n = 1$ to 10, i.e., dividing a given exponent by 2 to get the next exponent. Then, we started with an estimate for log 2 by finding the closest power of 10 in the table that is less than 2 ($1.7782794 = 10^{\frac{1}{4}}$). We know $10^{\frac{1}{4}}$ is a factor of 10^x, or 1.7782794 is a factor of 2. To find the other factor we divide 2 by 1.7782794 (or $\frac{10^x}{10^{\frac{1}{4}}}$). With this new factor, we return to Table 1 to find the closest power of 10 that is less than it. We continue this process until we run out of powers; i.e., get a factor k that is less than $10^{\frac{1}{1024}}$, or $k < 1.0022511$. To estimate the last factor, $10^{\frac{\Delta}{1024}}$, we solve this equation for Δ:

$$k = 1 + 2.302585\left(\Delta/1024\right)$$

In general, if we want to find $\log x$ by the radix method, we set:

$$y = \log x \Leftrightarrow 10^y = x$$

We calculate y as follows:

$$y = \frac{b_1}{2^1} + \frac{b_2}{2^2} + \frac{b_3}{2^3} + \frac{b_4}{2^4} + \ldots \text{ where:}$$

$$x = 10^y = 10^{\frac{b_1}{2^1}+\frac{b_2}{2^2}+\frac{b_3}{2^3}+\frac{b_4}{2^4}+\ldots} = 10^{\frac{b_1}{2^1}}10^{\frac{b_2}{2^2}}10^{\frac{b_3}{2^3}}10^{\frac{b_4}{2^4}}\ldots = \left(10^{\frac{1}{2^1}}\right)^{b_1}\left(10^{\frac{1}{2^2}}\right)^{b_2}\left(10^{\frac{1}{2^3}}\right)^{b_3}\left(10^{\frac{1}{2^4}}\right)^{b_4}\ldots$$

Note: b_1, b_2, b_3, b_4, … are either 0 or 1, depending upon the outworking of the radix algorithm.

We can now add a new row to the original table.

Table 4	
Exponent: *k*	**10^k**
1.00000	10.0000000
0.75000	5.6234133
0.50000	3.1622777
0.30103	**2.0000000**
0.25000	1.7782794
⋮	⋮

Doing calculations this way, Mr. Briggs spent many, many years working with pencil and paper to generate the logarithmic tables, first published in 1624 as *Arithmetica logarithmica.* These tables used to grace the appendices in science and math textbooks. Engineers also incorporated them into the construction of the analog slide rule. Mr. Briggs was reported to have said, "I computed successively 54 square roots of 10."[5] If the above calculations tired you as they did me, then hats off to Mr. Briggs! He calculated 27 successive square roots of 10 and used the Δ formula to calculate the other 27. He also computed his answers to 16 decimal places, rounding off to 14 in his published tables. He calculated the log of numbers from 1 to 20,000 and from 90,000 to 1000,000.[6] Today, logarithmic tables are computed using expansions of series.[7]

HENRICI
BRIGGII
CANON
LOGARITHMORUM
PRO NUMERIS
SERIE NATURALI
CRESCENTIBUS
AB I. AD 20000.

VIENNÆ AUSTRIÆ.

TYPIS JOANNIS THOMÆ TRATTNER, CÆS. REG. MAJ. AULÆ BIBLIOPOLÆ, ET UNIVERSIT. TYPOGRAPHI.

Figure 4. Title page of log tables, from 1 to 20,000, by Henry Briggs. Source: Public Domain.

EXERCISES

Answer the following questions:

1. What is the radix method of computing the logarithm of a number?
2. Why is there no image for the function $y = f(x) = \dfrac{10^x - 1}{x}$ when $x = 0$?
3. Explain why $10^{\frac{b_1}{2^1}+\frac{b_2}{2^2}+\frac{b_3}{2^3}+\frac{b_4}{2^4}+\dots} = 10^{\frac{b_1}{2^1}}10^{\frac{b_2}{2^2}}10^{\frac{b_3}{2^3}}10^{\frac{b_4}{2^4}}\dots$

---

[5] Richard Feynman (1918-1988), *The Feynman Lectures on Physics: Commemorative Issue* (Reading: Addison-Wesley, [1963] 1989), I:22-6. The reasoning in this lesson is an extension of the mathematical exegesis of Feynman, who was following the thinking of Briggs.

[6] The gap between 20,000 and 90,000 was filled with the help of the Dutch bookseller and publisher Adriaen Vlacq (1600-1666). Between 1924 and 1949, 20-place tables were constructed in England to celebrate the tercentenary (300th anniversary) of John Napier's discovery.

[7] A series is the sum of a patterned sequence of numbers. See Step 13 for more explanation.

4. Explain why $10^{\frac{b_1}{2^1}}10^{\frac{b_2}{2^2}}10^{\frac{b_3}{2^3}}10^{\frac{b_4}{2^4}}\ldots = \left(10^{\frac{1}{2^1}}\right)^{b_1}\left(10^{\frac{1}{2^2}}\right)^{b_2}\left(10^{\frac{1}{2^3}}\right)^{b_3}\left(10^{\frac{1}{2^4}}\right)^{b_4}\ldots$

Use Table 1 to calculate the following powers. Use spreadsheet software to do the calculations for your intermediate iteration work setting the number format to seven decimal places.

5. $10^{3/8}$
6. $10^{5/8}$
7. $10^{7/8}$
8. $10^{5/16}$
9. $10^{3/32}$

Use Table 1 to calculate the following logs. Round your answer to the nearest hundredth.

10. log 107
11. log 3162
12. log 1333

Use the radix method and Table 1 to calculate the following logs to five decimal places. Use spreadsheet software to do the calculations for your intermediate iteration work setting the number format to seven decimal places. Round your solution to Δ to three decimal places.

13. log 3
14. log 4

Imagine doing all this calculation work with pencil and paper!

Field Project:

15. Research and write a short essay on the life of Henry Briggs.

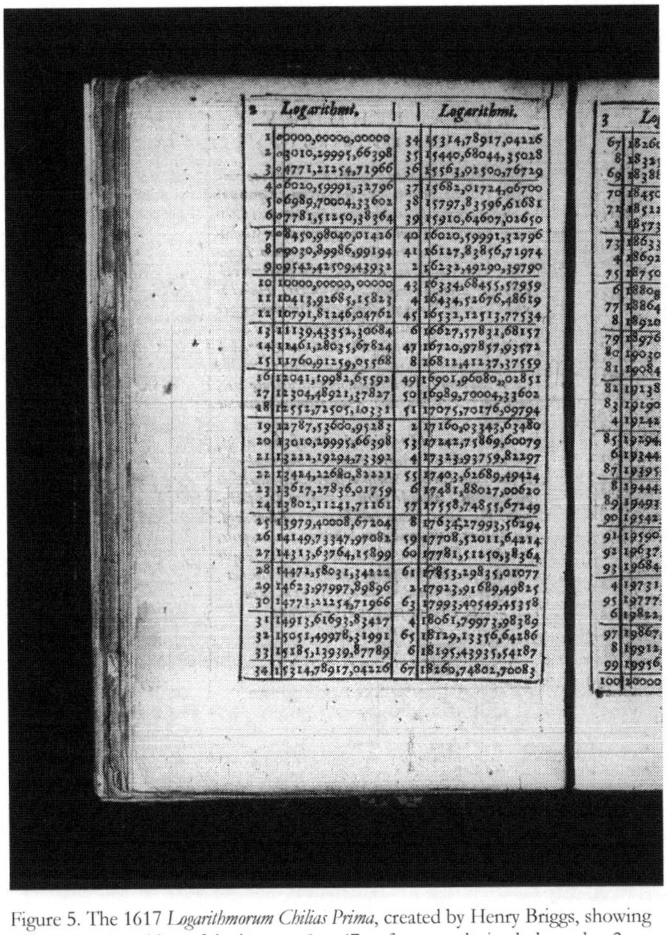

Figure 5. The 1617 *Logarithmorum Chilias Prima*, created by Henry Briggs, showing the base-10 logarithm of the integers 0 to 67 to fourteen decimal places. log 2 = 0.30102999566398. Source: Public Domain.

12.4 Natural Logarithms

Terms, Symbols & Concepts Introduced
1. Σ
2. Common logarithms
3. Index of summation
4. Log of a Power Law
5. Log of Reciprocal Law
6. log-log plane
7. Natural logarithms
8. Normal curve
9. Sigma notation
10. Standard deviation

Before the advent of the electronic calculator in the late 1960s, people had to work out all arithmetical operations by hand. By the early 17th century, advances had been made both in astronomy and in exploring the world through sea voyages. Both these advances necessitated arithmetical calculations using large numbers. The Scottish mathematician John Napier (1550-1617) noted these difficulties.

Napier removed these difficulties by developing a system of arithmetic, as we noted in Lesson 12.1, that replaced multiplication by addition and division by subtraction.[1] He connected logs to exponents by establishing the equivalency that logs are exponents, or:

$\log 10^a = a$ for all $a \in \mathbb{R}$[2]

Logs are exponents.

> Seeing there is nothing that is so troublesome to mathematical practice, nor that doth more molest and hinder calculators, than the multiplication, divisions, square and cubical extractions of great numbers.... I began therefore to consider in my mind by what certain and ready art I might remove those hindrances.
>
> John Napier, *Mirifici logarithmorum canonis descriptio* (1614). Cited in George A. Gibson, "Napier and the Invention of Logarithms." In *Handbook of the Napier Tercentenary Celebration, or Modern Instruments and Methods of Calculations*, E. M. Horsburgh, ed. (Los Angeles: Tomash Publishers, ([1914] 1982), p. 9.

Inverse Property of Logarithms

This equation represents the inverse property of logarithms, i.e., the logarithm undoes raising 10 to a power, leaving the exponent a as the result.

We can proof this equation by first stating that $\log 10^a$ is equal to some number. We are not sure that number is a. We let that number be c and write:

$\log 10^a = c$

Since $\log b = x \Leftrightarrow 10^x = b$, then:

$\log 10^a = c \Leftrightarrow 10^c = 10^a \Leftrightarrow c = a.$

Figure 1. Jobst Bürgi, co-discoverer of logarithms. Source: Public Domain.

[1] The Swiss instrument maker Jobst Bürgi (1552-1632) conceived of logarithms independently of Napier and published his results in 1620, three years after Napier died and six years after Napier published *Mirifici logarithmorum canonis descriptio.*

[2] Again, this notation means that a can be any real number, positive, negative, or zero.

Therefore:

$\log 10^a = a$
QED

We could also prove $\log 10^a = a$ by starting with $\log b = x \Leftrightarrow 10^x = b$ and substitute b with 10^a. We get:

$\log 10^a = x \Leftrightarrow 10^x = 10^a \Leftrightarrow x = a \Rightarrow \log 10^a = a$
QED

By similar reasoning, we can prove that $10^{\log a} = a$ for $a > 0$.[3] This equation means that raising 10 to the power of a logarithm undoes the logarithm, leaving a as a result.

Let's start by stating that $10^{\log a}$ is equal to some number. We are not sure that number is a. We let that number be c and write:

$10^{\log a} = c$

Since $\log b = x \Leftrightarrow 10^x = b$, then:

$10^{\log a} = c \Leftrightarrow \log c = \log a \Leftrightarrow c = a.$

Therefore:

$10^{\log a} = a$
QED

We could also prove $10^{\log a} = a$ for $a > 0$ by starting with $10^x = b \Leftrightarrow \log b = x$ and substitute x with $\log a$. We get:

$10^{\log a} = b \Leftrightarrow \log b = \log a \Leftrightarrow b = a \Rightarrow 10^{\log a} = a$
QED

LOG LAWS AND EXPONENTIAL LAWS

We can base log laws on the exponential laws by interpenetrating them in perichoretic fashion.

$b^m b^n = b^{m+n}$ interpenetrates the Multiplication Law of Logs: $\log ab = \log a + \log b$

$\frac{b^m}{b^n} = b^{m-n}$ interpenetrates the Division Law of Logs: $\log \frac{a}{b} = \log a - \log b$

Let's investigate two more log laws, the log of a power and the log of a reciprocal.

LOG OF A POWER LAW

We know that $\log 1000 = 3$ since $10^3 = 1000$. Since $\log 10 = 1$ and $1000 = 10^3$, then:

$\log 1000 = \log 10^3 = 3(\log 10) = 3 \cdot 1 = 3$

[3] We must restrict a since $\log a$ is not valid for non-positive arguments.

From this observation, we can infer a general Log of a Power. For $a, b \in \mathbb{R}$, $a, b > 0$:

$\log a^b = b \log a$

$\log a^b = b \log a$

This relationship is a very useful property, as we shall see in Lesson 12.5.

To prove the Log of a Power Law, we start with the exponential law, the Power of a Power Law:

$(10^c)^b = 10^{cb}$

Taking the log of both sides, we get:

$\log (10^c)^b = \log 10^{cb}$

Since $\log 10^a = a$ for all a and cb is a real number, then:

$\log 10^{cb} = cb$

Therefore, by substitution:

$\log (10^c)^b = cb$

Since $c = \log 10^c$, then, by substitution:

$\log (10^c)^b = cb = \log 10^c (b)$

By the Commutative Law of Multiplication, we write:

$\log (10^c)^b = b \log 10^c$

If we let $10^c = a$, we can substitute and conclude our proof:

$\log a^b = b \log a$

QED

Therefore, the Power of a Power Law interpenetrates with the Log of a Power Law. Go through this proof several times to make sure you understand what is happening.

LOG OF A RECIPROCAL LAW

Since the reciprocal of a is $^1/_a$, what is $\log {^1/_a}$? Since $^1/_a = a^{-1}$ (Lesson 11.15), then by the Log of a Power and remembering that $-1x = x$, we engage the following logic.

For $a \in \mathbb{R}$, $a > 0$:

$\log {^1/_a} = \log a^{-1} = -1(\log a) = -\log a$, or:

$\log {^1/_a} = -\log a$

$\log a^{-1} = -\log a$

QED

We can also proof this law using the Division Law of Logs:

$\log {^1/_a} = \log 1 - \log a = 0 - \log a = -\log a$

QED

LOGARITHMS AND OUR WORLD

We use logarithms to find the number of payments on a loan or the time to reach an investment goal. We also use logarithms to model many creational processes. Here are some examples:

- The loudness of sound is the logarithm of the actual sound intensity, and dB (decibels) are a logarithmic scale.
- The brightness of light is the logarithm of the light energy.
- We measure star magnitudes on a logarithmic scale.
- Logarithms are used to measure the pH or acidity of a chemical solution.[4]
- Logarithms are used to measure earthquake intensity on the Richter scale.
- Logarithms are used in the analysis of radioactive decay.
- Logarithms are related to the frequency of notes on the musical scale.

THE BASE OF THE NATURAL LOGARITHMS

The equation $\log 10^a = a$ can be restated for any base.[5] We can use the notation $\log_b x$ to mean log of x to base b where $b \in \mathbb{R}$, $b > 0$ and $b \neq 1$. Therefore, $\log_{10} 10^a = a$ or, in general:

$$\log_b b^a = a$$

Napier, along with Briggs, began working with decimal logs, or logs to the base 10, known as **common logarithms**. It is standard procedure to write the base of a common log without a subscript. We write:

$\log x$ instead of $\log_{10} x$

Since the notation $\log x$ is the accepted convention, scientific calculators with the LOG key calculate decimal or common logs.

Inspect Table 1.

Table 1		
x	Power of 10	log x
0.00001	10^{-4}	-4
0.0001	10^{-3}	-3
0.001	10^{-2}	-2
0.1	10^{-1}	-1
1	10^{0}	0
10	10^{1}	1
100	10^{2}	2
1000	10^{3}	3
10,000	10^{4}	4
100,000	10^{5}	5
1,000,000	10^{6}	6
10,000,000	10^{7}	7
100,000,000	10^{8}	8

[4] The pH is the negative logarithm of the concentration of free hydrogen ions. pH = -log (hydrogen ion concentration) = -log [H+].

[5] As we shall shortly see, we are not limited to decimal logs, or logs to the base 10. We can use other bases. We will discover in Lesson 12.5 that all the properties of logs are true no matter what the value of the base.

Table 1		
x	Power of 10	log x
1,000,000,000	10^9	9
10,000,000,000	10^{10}	10
100,000,000,000	10^{11}	11
1,000,000,000,000	10^{12}	12

It is easy to compute logs of powers of 10, but what about the other numbers, log 2, log 3, log 4, log 11, log 15, log 20, log 50, etc. There are huge gaps, i.e., fractional powers of 10, that need to be calculated and both Briggs and Napier calculated these gaps by hand, taking many years to complete. It is from these tables that we can state that log 2 = 0.301, etc.

Napier began to play with other bases to see if he could close these gaps. Table 2 shows some logs to the base 2 where Figure 2 is a continuous graph of this table.

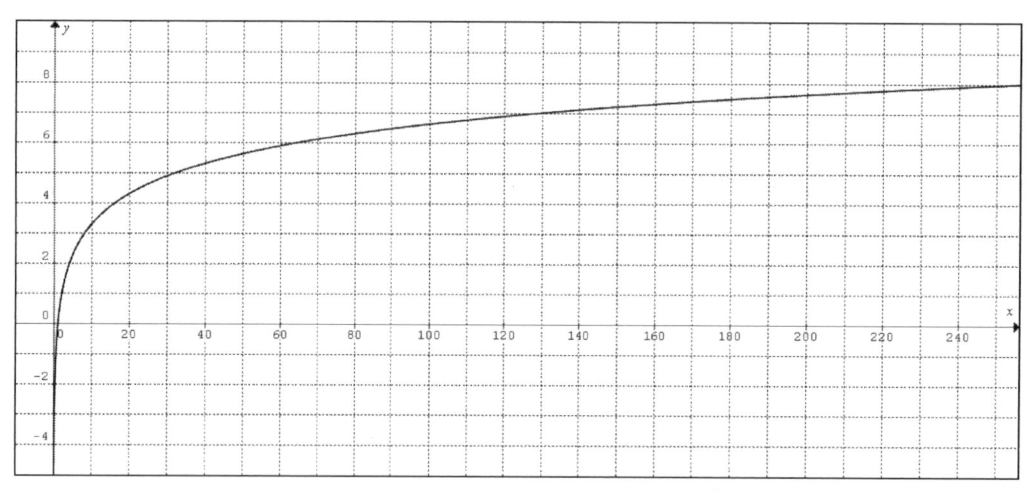

Figure 2. $y = \log_2 x$ (Note: On the graph pictured, for the domain of $0 < x \leq 256$, the range is $-\infty \leq y \leq 8$.)

> Mathematics is the abstract key which turns the lock of the physical universe.
>
> John Polkinghorne, *One World: The Interaction of Science and Theology* (1986), p. 46.

Table 2		
x	Power of 2	$\log_2 x$
0.0625	2^{-4}	-4
0.125	2^{-3}	-3
0.25	2^{-2}	-2
0.5	2^{-1}	-1
1	2^{0}	0
2	2^{1}	1
4	2^{2}	2
8	2^{3}	3
16	2^{4}	4
32	2^{5}	5
64	2^{6}	6
128	2^{7}	7
256	2^{8}	8
512	2^{9}	9
1024	2^{10}	10
2048	2^{11}	11
4096	2^{12}	12

Note that we get more condensed values of x in base 2. Therefore, this base is better than base 10 logs, but base 2 logs have a serious limitation. What happens if we want to multiply 3 by 22? What is the $\log_2 3$? What is the $\log_2 22$?

From the table, we note that the $\log_2 3$ must be between 1 and 2, and the $\log_2 22$ must be between 4 and 5. To find the $\log_2 3$, we must determine x such that $2^x = 3$, an equation that we do not yet know how to solve. We know for certain that x will not be a positive integer; it may be a mixed number or its decimal equivalent or an irrational number as revealed by the graph in Figure 3.

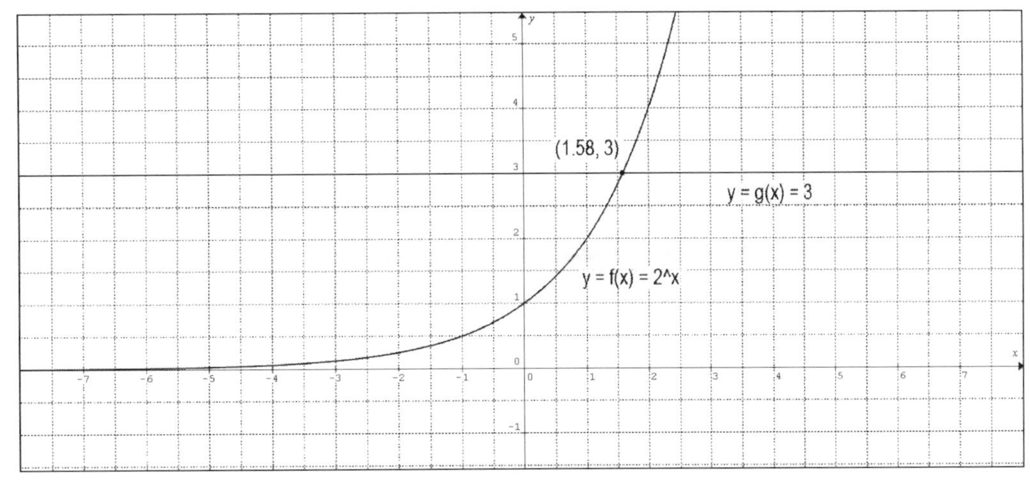

Figure 3. The graphical solution to $2^x = 3$.

Let's see how we would calculate 2^x when $x = 1.5$; i.e., $2^{1.5}$. Since $1.5 = 3/2$, we need to calculate $2^{3/2}$:

$$\left(2^{3/2}\right)^2 = 2^{3/2 \cdot 2} = 2^{6/2} = 2^3 = 8$$

$$\left(2^{3/2}\right)^2 = 8 \Rightarrow 2^{3/2} = \sqrt{8} \approx 2.8$$

We haven't quite got $\log_2 3$, but we are getting close. Our graph shows us that $\log_2 3 \approx 1.58$.[6] We can show that the solution to $2^x = 3$ is an irrational number and that we can approximate x to any desired precision using fractional powers. This process is the pathway that Napier took in constructing his precision logarithm tables.

THE PROBLEM WITH GAPS

We reassert that 10 is not a very good base of logarithms because of the significant gaps. Base 2 is a better base, but it still has many gaps. We can try 1 as the base, but that does no good since all powers of 1 are 1; i.e., $1^x = 1$. It is not good to try a base less than 1 because a fraction less than 1 raised to a power gets lesser and lesser. Therefore, let's try a number between 1 and 2 as a base. Let's start with 1.1 as a base.

Pascal's Triangle with its delineation of powers of 1.1 simplifies our calculations at this point:

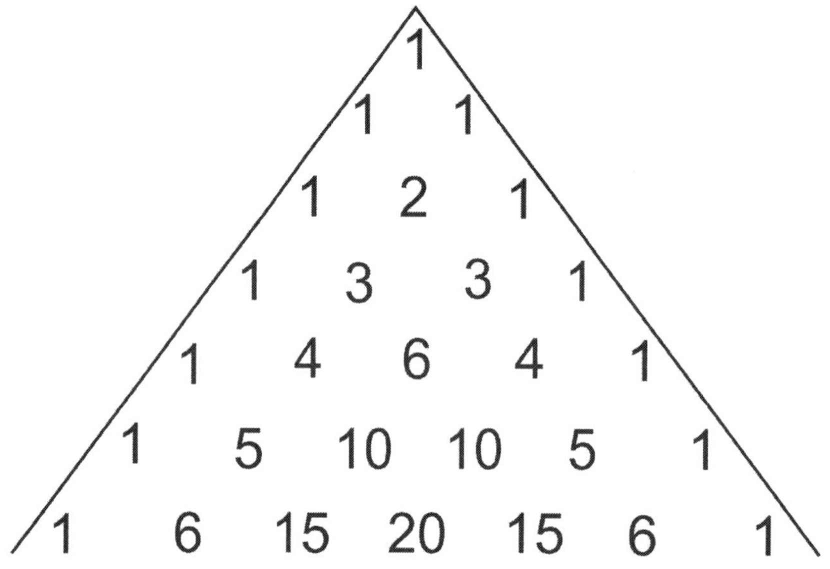

Figure 4. Pascal's Triangle.

[6] Note: $2^{1.58} \approx 2.9897$

We generate Table 3.

Table 3	
n	1.1^n
0	1
1	1.1
2	1.21
3	1.331
4	1.4641
5	1.61051
6	1.771561
7	1.948717
8	2.14358881

Note that these numbers grow slowly and that there are many numbers between 1 and 2. The calculation of those troublesome gaps is eased somewhat by this base. Do you think that a lesser number would be an even better choice? Let's try 1.001 as a base (Table 4).

Table 4	
n	1.001^n
0	1
1	1.001
2	1.002001
3	1.0030003001
4	1.004006004001
5	1.005010010005001
6	1.006015020015006001
7	1.007021035035021007001
8	1.008028056070056028008001

In this case, we separate the terms in Pascal's Triangle by pairs of zeroes. Note how the numbers in the triangle fit neatly into the decimal expansion. At first, we may wonder if we will ever reach 2. Eventually, we will, yet very slowly.

Mathematicians have proved that the powers of any number greater than 1, even slightly greater than 1, will converge to infinity. The closer the number is to 1, the slower the rate of growth. Although this table of powers of 1.001 contains an excellent density of numbers, the drawback is its slow rate of growth. Very large exponents are needed to produce small numbers. For example, $1.001^{1000} \approx 2.716923932$. So, if the exponents were 1000 times as big, we could make the table more proportionate. With this in mind, let's consider 1.001^{1000} as a base. We are going to raise this base to a fractional power and make use of the Product Law of Exponents:

$$\left(1.001^{1000}\right)^{\frac{1}{1000}} = 1.001^{1000 \cdot \frac{1}{1000}} = 1.001^{\frac{1000}{1000}} = 1.001^1$$

$$\left(1.001^{1000}\right)^{\frac{2}{1000}} = 1.001^{1000 \cdot \frac{2}{1000}} = 1.001^{\frac{2000}{1000}} = 1.001^{2}$$

$$\left(1.001^{1000}\right)^{\frac{3}{1000}} = 1.001^{1000 \cdot \frac{3}{1000}} = 1.001^{\frac{3000}{1000}} = 1.001^{3}$$

etc.

Note that we are successively raising 1.001^{1000} to a fractional power in incremental steps of 1/1000; i.e., 1/1000, 2/1000, 3/1000, etc. Converting these fractions to decimals, we get Table 5.

Table 5		
$^{1}/_{1000}$	=	0.001
$^{2}/_{1000}$	=	0.002
$^{3}/_{1000}$	=	0.003
$^{4}/_{1000}$	=	0.004
etc.		

We now generate Table 6.

Table 6		
$(1.001^{1000})^{0}$	1.001^{0}	1
$(1.001^{1000})^{0.001}$	1.001^{1}	1.001
$(1.001^{1000})^{0.002}$	1.001^{2}	1.002001
$(1.001^{1000})^{0.003}$	1.001^{3}	1.0030003001
$(1.001^{1000})^{0.004}$	1.001^{4}	1.004006004001
$(1.001^{1000})^{0.005}$	1.001^{5}	1.005010010005001
$(1.001^{1000})^{0.006}$	1.001^{6}	1.006015020015006001
$(1.001^{1000})^{0.007}$	1.001^{7}	1.007021035035021007001
$(1.001^{1000})^{0.008}$	1.001^{8}	1.008028056070056028008001

The exponents and the corresponding results do not grow disproportionately. The density is unimpaired. Therefore, the base of 1.001^{1000} is an excellent choice. Can we improve on this choice? Yes. Consider the base of $1.0001^{10{,}000}$, but why stop there? What about the base of $1.00001^{100{,}000}$? We could continue *ad infinitum* with this type of thinking until we converge to the natural or best number. What is this number?

THE GAP PROBLEM LEADS TO AN UNEXPECTED WONDER

Let's see what happens if we do this (Table 7).

Table 7	
1.001^{1000}	2.716923932
$1.0001^{10,000}$	2.718145927
$1.00001^{100,000}$	2.718268237
$1.000001^{1,000,000}$	2.718280469
$1.0000001^{10,000,000}$	2.718281693
$1.00000001^{100,000,000}$	2.718281815
⋮	⋮
e	2.718281828

It is by this analysis that we discover e as a *natural* base for logarithm work. The base of **natural logarithms** is, therefore, e. We write:

$\ln x$ instead of $\log_e x$

Using the notation $\ln x$ is accepted convention, so all scientific calculators with the LN key calculate natural logs.

We have already encountered e (Lesson 8.15) in our study of compound interest at a rate of 100%.

Given $A = \left(1 + \frac{1}{n}\right)^n$, we generate Table 8.

Table 8		
n	$1+{}^1/_n$	A
1	2	2
2	1.5	2.25
3	1.333...	2.37037
4	1.25	2.44141
5	1.2	2.48832
10	1.1	2.59374
50	1.02	2.69159
100	1.01	2.70481
1000	1.001	2.71692
10,0000	1.0001	2.71815
100,000	1.00001	2.71827
1,000,000	1.000001	2.71828
10,000,000	1.0000001	2.71828

The results in this table are almost too incredible to comprehend. It is another wonder of Mathematics. The number e, along with its irrational friend π, also appears in the probability theory of normal distributions,[7] i.e., the **normal curve** or bell curve, a symmetrical curve derived from a complex function:

$$f(x,\mu,\sigma)=\frac{1}{\sigma\sqrt{2\pi}}e^{-\frac{(x-\mu)^2}{2\sigma^2}}$$

With one variable, i.e., removing the variables μ and σ, we simplify the function:

$$f(x)=\frac{1}{\sqrt{2\pi}}e^{-\frac{x^2}{2}}$$

The graph of this function (Figure 5) helps us find the area under this beautifully symmetric curve, a graph studied when you take a comprehensive course in Statistics/Probability.

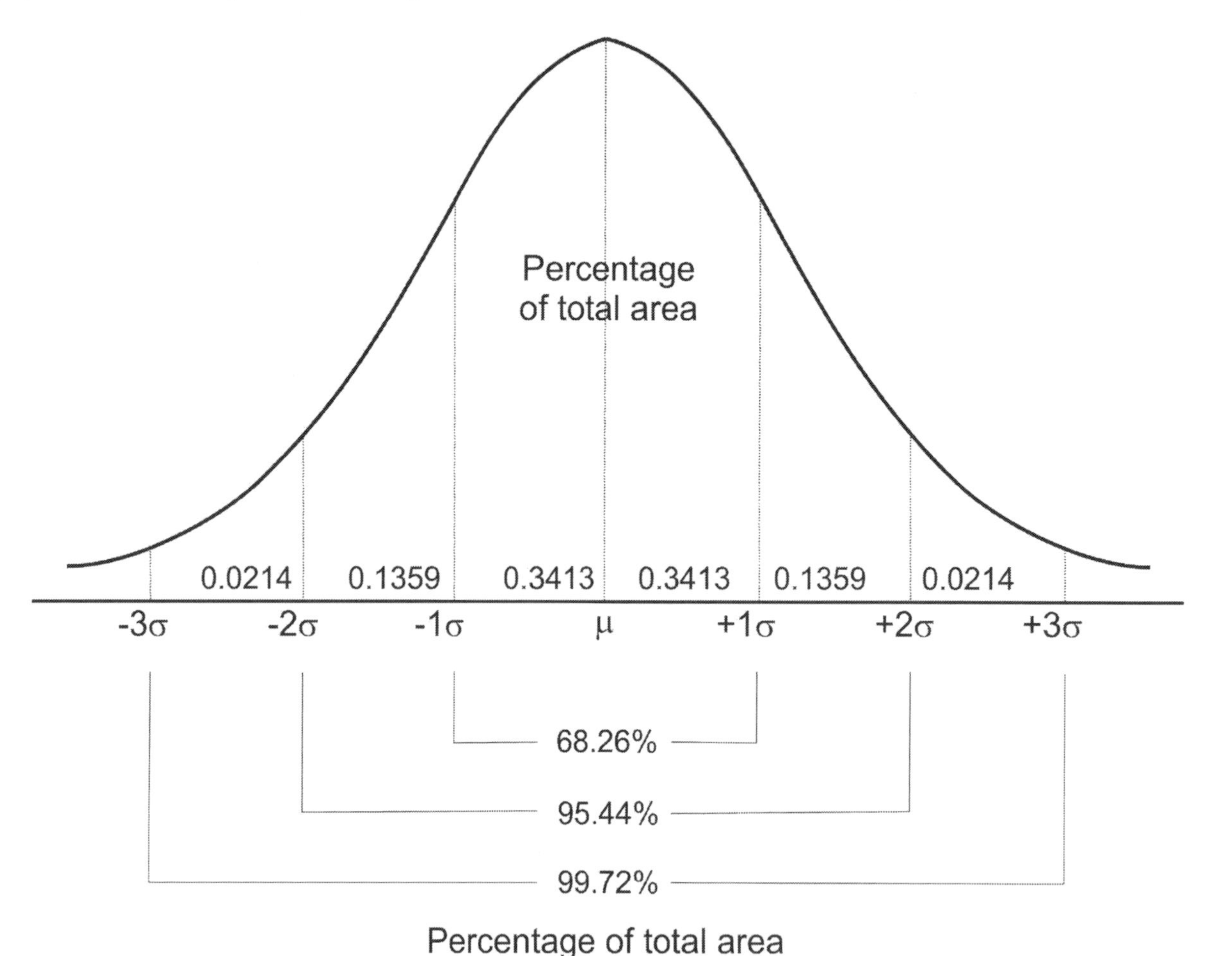

Figure 5. The Bell or Normal Curve. μ is the mean of a distribution of values and σ (Greek lower-case *sigma*) represents the **standard deviation** of the individual values from the mean. The probability that an individual value will deviate from the mean by $\pm\sigma$ is 68.26%. Note how area under the curve interpenetrates the probability of an event.

[7] A normal distribution is the distribution of many numbers, taken at random, that form a symmetrical bell-shaped graph. In 1733, the French mathematician Abraham de Moivre (1667-1754) first published detail about this type of curve.

> The beauty of mathematics only shows itself to more patient followers.
>
> Maryam Mirzakhani (1977-2017), first woman and first Iranian honored with the Fields Medal (2014).

The marvelous connection between the base of the natural logarithms, the calculation of compound interest at 100%, and a host of other interconnections in the world of Mathematics and science is too amazing to be just a coincidence. Like π, the number *e* interpenetrates a multiplicity of branches of Mathematics.[8] Is it not one of the astounding particular details in the rationality of the invisible and visible realms of creation that is grounded in the rationality of the perichoretic God of Scripture, the Triune God, Father, Son, and Spirit, the Creator and Sustainer of all things?

MIRIFICI
Logarithmorum
Canonis deſcriptio,
Ejuſque uſus, in utraque *Trigonometria; ut etiam in* omni Logiſtica Mathematica, *Ampliſsimi, Faciliimi, & expeditiſſimi explicatio.*
Authore ac Inventore, IOANNE NEPERO, Barone Merchiſtonii, *&c. Scoto.*
EDINBURGI, Ex officina ANDREÆ HART *Bibliopolæ*, CIↃ. DC. XIV.

Figure 6. Cover of John Napier's *Mirifici logarithmorum canonis descriptio* (1614). Source: Public Domain.

EXERCISES

Define the following terms:

1. Log of a Power Law
2. Log of Reciprocal Law
3. Common logarithms

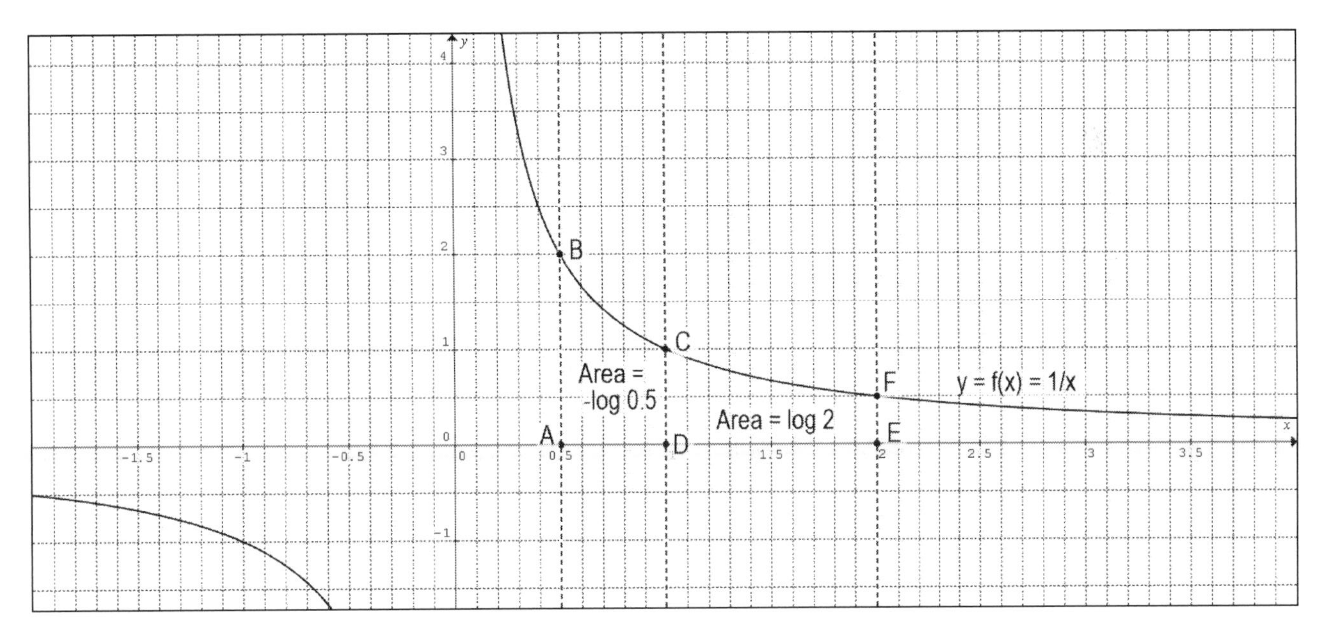

Figure 7. Interpenetration of Inverse Proportions (Hyperbola) and Logarithms: The area under the curve from *B* to *C*, i.e., the section *ABCD*, is -log 0.5 ≈ 0.3010 and the area under the curve from *C* to *F*; i.e., section *CDEF*, is log 2 = 0.3010.

[8] For a fascinating study of this number, see Eli Maor, *e: The Story of a Number* (Princeton: Princeton University Press, 1994).

4. Natural logarithms
5. Normal curve
6. Standard deviation
7. Sigma notation (See homework exercise below.)
8. Index of summation (See homework exercise below.)
9. log-log plane (See homework exercise below.)

Evaluate, if possible, using the inverse property of logarithms:

10. $\log 10^{8.9}$
11. $\log 10^{2x+5}$ when $x = -3$
12. $10^{\log 4.2}$
13. $10^{\log -8.3}$
14. $10^{\log (x+1)}$ when $x > -1$

- Biologists use the function $P(t) = P_0e^{kt}$ to describe population growth.
- Physicists use the function $V = Ae^{-t/RC}$ to describe voltage across the resistor in a circuit.

Solve the following equations for x where $\log_2 x$ means the log to the base 2 of x.

15. $\log_2 1024 = x$
16. $\log_2 32 = x$
17. $\log_2 4096 = x$
18. $\log_2 2^{15} = x$
19. $\log_2 2^n = x$
20. $\log_2 0.125 = x$

Transform the following equations into logarithmic notation in base 2.

21. $16 = 2^4$
22. $8 = 2^3$
23. $100 = 2^x$
24. $n = 2^x$

Answer the following questions:

25. Why is (a) $\log 1 = 0$? (b) $\log_2 1 = 0$? (c) $\ln 1 = 0$?
26. True or False. Logs are powers.
27. Using log laws, show why $-\log {}^1/_2 = \log 2$ (Refer to Figure 7).
28. Show that $\log \sqrt[n]{a} = \dfrac{\log a}{n}$.
29. Explain the reasoning behind this proof:

$$\log x^n = \log\left(\overbrace{x \cdot x \cdot \ldots \cdot x}^{n \text{ times}}\right) = \overbrace{\log x + \log x + \ldots + \log x}^{n \text{ times}} = n \log x$$

Simplify the log of the following expressions using log laws:

30. $\log ab^2$
31. $\log a^3bc$
32. $\log \dfrac{a^2}{c}$
33. $\log \dfrac{b}{\sqrt[3]{d}}$

34. $\log \dfrac{ab^3}{c\sqrt[3]{d}}$

We calculate the standard deviation σ of a set of numbers by performing the following steps:
(1) Compute the mean μ of the set of numbers.
(2) Find the difference between each number in the set and the mean.
(3) Square these differences.
(4) Compute the mean of these squares.
(5) Compute the square root of this mean.t

35. Compute the standard deviation to the nearest hundredth of this set of numbers (representing the scores for a 12-point quiz): 9, 2, 5, 4, 12, 7, 8, 11, 9, 3, 7, 4, 12, 5, 4, 10, 9, 6, 9, 4.

$\sum_{i=1}^{n} x_i$ means sum a list of *n* numbers from first ($i = 1$ or x_1) to last ($i = n$ or x_n) where Σ is the Greek capital letter *sigma*. Therefore, $x_1 + x_2 + x_3 + \ldots + x_n = \sum_{i=1}^{n} x_i$. (Read "summation, *i* from 1 to *n*, of *x* sub *i*.") When mathematicians use Σ they refer to it as **sigma notation**.[9] The letter *i* is the **index of summation**, a placeholder subscript. In our example, *i* takes the values sequentially from 1 to *n*. We can use any letter as the index of summation as long as it is not used elsewhere in the notation. Describe the meaning of the following symbols:

36. $\sum_{k=1}^{3} k$

37. $\sum_{k=1}^{4} \dfrac{1}{k}$

38. $\sum_{j=0}^{4} \left(1 + j^2\right)$

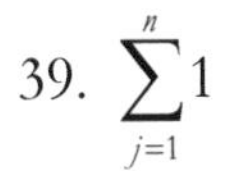

39. $\sum_{j=1}^{n} 1$

40. $\sigma = \sqrt{\dfrac{\sum_{i=1}^{n} (x_i - \mu)^2}{n}}$

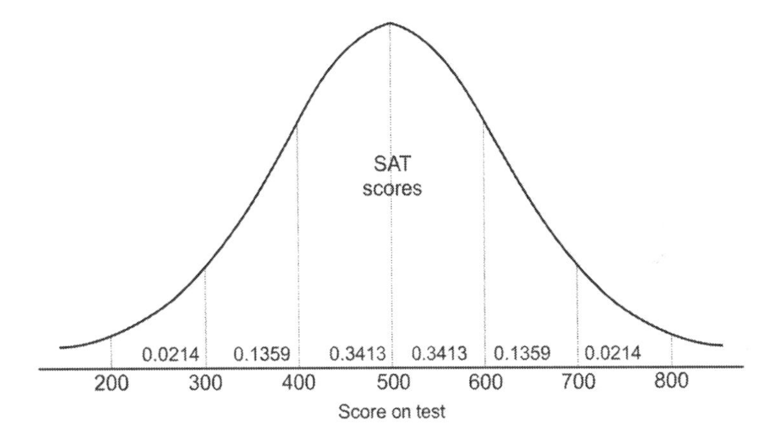

Figure 8.

In the United States, most college-bound students take the Standard Aptitude Test (SAT), an exam designed to reflect a normal distribution. Use Figure 8 to answer the following questions:
41. What is μ?
42. What is σ?
43. What percentage of students score between 500 and 600 points?
44. What percentage of students score between 600 and 800 points?
45. What percentage of students score more than 800 points?

---

[9] It was the Swiss mathematician Leonhard Euler (1707-1783) who introduced sigma notation to the mathematical world.

For the following questions, assume you have a fair coin.

46. If you toss one coin five times, what is the exact probability as a percentage that you will get no heads, one head, two heads, three heads, four heads, and five heads? (Hint: Use the Combination formula from Lesson 9.4 or Pascal's Triangle. In Microsoft Excel, using the COMBIN (a, b) formula to help you. Remember that the sum of these six events must be 100%).
47. If you toss one coin ten times, what is the probability as a percentage to the nearest thousandths that you will get 0 heads, one head, two heads, three heads, four heads, five heads, six heads, seven heads, eight heads, nine heads, and ten heads?
48. If you toss one coin 1000 times, what will the distribution of the probabilities of getting 0 to 1000 heads approximate? (Hint: Recall the Law of Large Numbers from Lesson 9.7.)

Using Microsoft Excel, approximate e by evaluating $\left(1+\frac{1}{x}\right)^x$ to seven decimal places for the following values of x:

49. $x = 90$
50. $x = 500$
51. $x = 25{,}000$
52. $x = 60{,}000$
53. $x = 75{,}000$
54. $x = 79{,}000$
55. How accurate an approximate for e do you obtain if you use $x = 10{,}000$?

Scientists measure the brightness of celestial objects on a scale of magnitudes that measure the energy output of the object observed. In this scale, named the Pogson scale in honor of the English astronomer N. R. Pogson (1829-1891), a difference of five magnitudes corresponds to a ratio of 100:1 in energy. For any two objects having magnitudes m_1 and m_2, the corresponding ratio of their intensity of brightness $\frac{I_1}{I_2}$ is given by:

$$|m_2 - m_1| = 2.5\log\left(\frac{I_1}{I_2}\right)$$

Table 9: Light Ratios for Selected Magnitude Differences

$m_2 - m_1$	$\frac{I_1}{I_2}$
0	1
0.5	1.6
1	2.5
2	6.3
5	100
10	10,000

56. Show that a ratio of $\frac{I_1}{I_2} = 100$ gives a magnitude difference, $|m_2 - m_1|$, of 5.

57. Show that a ratio of $\frac{l_1}{l_2} = 10{,}000$ gives a magnitude difference of 10.

58. Given: $10^{0.4} \approx 2.5$, find the ratio $\frac{l_1}{l_2}$ if $|m_2 - m_1| = 1$. Round to the nearest tenth.

Scientists set the magnitude scale for stars so that the brightest stars in the night sky have an average magnitude of about +1.0. The magnitudes increase numerically in a positive direction with decreasing brightness (e.g., a star with magnitude 2 is greater in brightness than a star with magnitude 3). For the following exercises, you may use a scientific calculator to find the answer recognizing that $\log a = b \Leftrightarrow 10^b = a$.

Table 10: Apparent Visual Magnitudes For Selected Celestial Objects	
Object	**Apparent Magnitude**
Sun	-26.5
Full Moon	-12.5
Venus (brightest planet)	-4
Sirius (brightest star)	-1.5
Big Dipper stars	+2.0
Cassiopeia stars	+3.0
Pleiades stars	+4.0
Uranus	+6.0
Neptune	+9.0
Pluto	+15.0

59. If a star's magnitude is 7 and another star's magnitude is 5, how many times brighter is the star of magnitude 5 than the star of magnitude 7? Round to the nearest tenth.
60. If a star's magnitude is 8 and another star's magnitude is 2, how many times brighter is the star of magnitude 5 than the star of magnitude 7? Round to the nearest unit.
61. How many times brighter is Uranus than Neptune? Round to the nearest unit.
62. How many times brighter is the full Moon than Venus? Round to the nearest unit.
63. How many times brighter is Sirius than the Big Dipper stars? Round to the nearest unit.
64. How many times brighter is the Sun than Sirius? Write your answer in Scientific Notation rounding the mantissa to the nearest hundred.

Table 11: Limiting Magnitudes for Various Instruments	
Instrument	**Faintest Detectable Magnitude**
Human eye (city)	+ 3.0
Human eye (open country)	+6.5

Table 11: Limiting Magnitudes for Various Instruments	
Instrument	Faintest Detectable Magnitude
Binoculars	+10.0
10-cm (4-inch) telescope	+12.0
1-meter (40-inch) telescope	+17.0
Largest reflectors	+24.5
Hubble Space Telescope	+30.0

65. How many times greater is the light receiving capacity of the binoculars compared with the human eye in the city? Round to the nearest unit.
66. How many times greater is the light receiving capacity of a 10-cm telescope compared with the human eye in the open country? Round to the nearest unit.
67. How many times greater is the light receiving capacity of the Hubble Space Telescope compared with the human eye in the city? Write your answer in Scientific Notation rounding the mantissa to the nearest hundred.

Johannes Kepler's Third Law of Planetary Motion (Lesson 8.6) states if D is the distance of the semi-major axis of a planet from the Sun, and T is the length of its year, then for all the planets $T^2/D^3 = c$ (a fixed number).

68. Solve this equation for T^2.
69. We learned that, in our Solar System, $c = 1$. Solve the equation you derived in Question 68 for T, positive solution only.
70. Write the equation you derived in Question 69 using function notation $y = f(x)$ by substituting x for D and y for T.

Our planetary data from Lesson 8.6 is:

Table 12		
Planet	x = D	y = T
Pluto	39.51	247.70
Neptune	30.07	165.00
Uranus	19.19	84.00
Saturn	9.54	29.46
Jupiter	5.20	11.86
Mars	1.52	1.88
Earth	1.00	1.00
Venus	0.72	0.62
Mercury	0.39	0.24

Answer the following questions:

71. Using the Cartesian coordinate plane, plot the nine coordinates, in general (x, y), of the third law function and graph the function.

72. This uniform scale is awkward because the data is extreme. We can use logarithmic laws to restate the function by taking the common log of both sides of the function you derived in Question 70. (Note: Remove the $f(x)$ symbol, just use y.)
73. Let $Y = \log y$ and $X = \log x$. Substitute Y for $\log y$ and X for $\log x$ for the function you derived in Question 72.
74. Complete the following table, rounding each value to the nearest hundredth:

Table 13

Planet	x = D	X = log x	y = T	Y = log y
Pluto	39.51		247.70	
Neptune	30.07		165.00	
Uranus	19.19		84.00	
Saturn	9.54		29.46	
Jupiter	5.20		11.86	
Mars	1.52		1.88	
Earth	1.00		1.00	
Venus	0.72		0.62	
Mercury	0.39		0.24	

75. (a) Using the Cartesian coordinate plane, plot the nine coordinates, in general (X, Y), of the third law function.
(b) What do you notice about the result?
(c) There seems to be a planet missing in this graph. Can you find out what is in this location in space? (Hint: Refer to any astronomy textbook that covers our Solar System.)

Our planetary analysis has shown us that we can convert the Cartesian coordinate plane into a **log-log plane**. Scientists us the log-log coordinate system to understand relationships in the data that cannot be seen if the data in question is plotted on the Cartesian coordinate plane.

Some Wonders of e

$$\ln 2 = 1 - \frac{1}{2} + \frac{1}{3} - \frac{1}{4} + \frac{1}{5} - \frac{1}{6} + \frac{1}{7} - \ldots$$

$$e = 1 + \frac{1}{1!} + \frac{1}{2!} + \frac{1}{3!} + \frac{1}{4!} + \frac{1}{5!} + \frac{1}{6!} + \ldots$$

$$e = \frac{1}{1!} + \frac{2}{2!} + \frac{3}{3!} + \frac{4}{4!} + \frac{5}{5!} + \frac{6}{6!} + \ldots$$

$$e = 1 + \frac{3}{2!} + \frac{5}{4!} + \frac{7}{6!} + \frac{9}{8!} + \frac{11}{10!} + \ldots$$

$$e = 2\left(\frac{1}{1!} + \frac{2}{3!} + \frac{3}{5!} + \frac{4}{7!} + \frac{5}{9!} + \ldots\right)$$

$$\frac{1}{e} = e^{-1} = \frac{2}{3!} + \frac{4}{5!} + \frac{6}{7!} + \frac{8}{9!} + \frac{10}{11!} + \ldots$$

$$e^x = 1 + \frac{x}{1!} + \frac{x^2}{2!} + \frac{x^3}{3!} + \frac{x^4}{4!} + \ldots$$

$$\frac{1}{e^x} = e^{-x} = 1 - \frac{x}{1!} + \frac{x^2}{2!} - \frac{x^3}{3!} + \frac{x^4}{4!} - \ldots$$

$$2 = \frac{e^{\frac{1}{1}} \cdot e^{\frac{1}{3}} \cdot e^{\frac{1}{5}} \cdot e^{\frac{1}{7}} \cdot e^{\frac{1}{9}} \cdot e^{\frac{1}{11}} \cdot \ldots}{e^{\frac{1}{2}} \cdot e^{\frac{1}{4}} \cdot e^{\frac{1}{6}} \cdot e^{\frac{1}{8}} \cdot e^{\frac{1}{10}} \cdot e^{\frac{1}{12}} \cdot \ldots}$$

12.5 Some Logarithm Investigations

Terms & Concepts Introduced
1. Prime Number Theorem
2. Characteristic of a log
3. Mantissa of a log

In this lesson, as a conclusion of our study of logarithmic operations, we will explore six regions of interest:

1. How to go from one base to another, following the method of Briggs.
2. The dance between common and natural logarithms.
3. Prime numbers and their relationship to logarithms.
4. How log tables were used to calculate before the invention of calculators and personal computers.
5. Solving equations using logarithms.
6. More logarithmic scales on the slide rule.

The Briggs Way to Find the Base of the Natural Logs

Changing Bases

In Lesson 12.4, we saw how e, the base of the natural logarithms, is derived from the compound interest formula where the rate is 100%. We can discover that same number by invoking the reasoning of Henry Briggs using Table 3 of Lesson 12.3.

Let's say that we can determine the logarithms for a given base b; i.e., we can solve the equation $b^x = c$ for any c or we can compute $\log_b c = x$ for all positive values of c.

Let's say that we want to calculate the logarithm of c to another base, and we let n be that base. We need to solve $n^y = c$ or compute $\log_n c = y$. Note, because of the different base, $y \neq x$. Since $y \neq x$, then y must be a factor of x.[1] We let that factor be t. Therefore:

$$ty = x$$

We can solve this equation for t or y:

$$ty = x \Leftrightarrow t = \frac{x}{y}$$

$$ty = x \Leftrightarrow y = \frac{x}{t}$$

We now let $n = b^t$. Since we know n and b, we can find t. We know that $t = \log_b n$ because:

$$n = b^t \Leftrightarrow \log_b n = t$$

We note that $b^{ty} = (b^t)^y$. Since $n = b^t$, then:

$$(b^t)^y = n^y = c$$

Therefore, $\log_b c = ty$ and, since $y = \frac{x}{t}$, then $\log_n c = \frac{x}{t}$. We have two equations representing the log of c in two difference bases:

$$\log_b c = ty$$

$$\log_n c = y = \frac{x}{t}$$

[1] This factor is not necessarily an integer.

Or:

$\log_b c = x$ (Given)

$\log_n c = \dfrac{x}{t}$

Therefore:

$$\log_n c = \frac{\log_b c}{t} = \left(\frac{1}{t}\right)\log_b c$$

> Therefore, any logarithmic table, in base b, is equivalent to any other logarithmic table, in base n, if we multiply each logarithm in base b by a constant.

What is the constant $\dfrac{1}{t}$? What is t? $t = \log_b n$. Why?

We want to prove $\log_n c = \dfrac{\log_b c}{\log_b n}$ where $c, b, n \in \mathbb{R}$, $b, n \neq 1$. Follow along:

Let $y = \log_n c$

Therefore:

$y = \log_n c \Leftrightarrow n^y = c$

We take $\log_b$ of both sides:

$n^y = c \Leftrightarrow \log_b n^y = \log_b c$

Invoking the Log of a Power Law:

$\log_b n^y = \log_b c \Leftrightarrow y(\log_b n) = \log_b c$

Since $y = \log_n c$, we substitute:

$y(\log_b n) = \log_b c \Leftrightarrow (\log_n c)(\log_b n) = \log_b c$

Solving for $\log_n c$:

$$(\log_n c)(\log_b n) = \log_b c \Leftrightarrow \log_n c = \frac{\log_b c}{\log_b n}$$

QED

Therefore, $t = \log_b n$. If we choose any base, we can translate the logarithms calculated in that base to another base. The meaning of this translation, as we have already stated, is that all logarithm functions, whatever the base, are similar to each other. Therefore, the dance of all the log laws apply to logs of any base.

Let's find another way to convert from a common logarithm to a logarithm in any other base. We start with these two log inverse equations proved in Lesson 12.4:

$\log 10^x = x$ for all x
$10^{\log x} = x$ for $x > 0$

Next, we choose another base b. We have this equivalency:

$x = b^y \Leftrightarrow \log_b x = y$

Since $b = 10^{\log b}$, then, by substitution:

$x = b^y \Leftrightarrow x = (10^{\log b})^y \Leftrightarrow x = 10^{(\log b)(y)} \Leftrightarrow x = 10^{y \log b}$

Taking the log of both sides and using $\log 10^x = x$ for all x, we get:

$x = 10^{y \log b} \Leftrightarrow \log x = \log (10^{y \log b}) \Leftrightarrow \log x = y \log b$

Since $\log_b x = y$, then, by substitution:

$\log x = (\log_b x)(\log b) \Leftrightarrow \log_b x = \dfrac{\log x}{\log b}$

QED

Note that this conclusion is another way of writing $\log_n c = \dfrac{\log_b c}{\log_b n}$ where $b = 10$.

Given $\log_b x = \dfrac{\log x}{\log b}$, if we let $b = 2$ and we want to calculate $\log_2 8$, all we need to do is divide log 8 by log 2.[2] We write:

$$\log_2 8 = \frac{\log 8}{\log 2} \approx \frac{0.90309}{0.30103} = 3$$

We confirm our work by noting:

$\log_2 8 = x \Leftrightarrow 2^x = 8 \Leftrightarrow x = 3$

FINDING THE BASE OF THE NATURAL LOGARITHMS

Recall (Lesson 12.3) that:

$$\lim_{\Delta \to 0} 10^{\Delta/1024} \approx 1 + 2.302585\left(\Delta/1024\right)$$

Therefore, for small exponents k (or, as $k \to 0$), we can easily calculate 10^k since:

$10^k = 1 + 2.302585k$

Let's state this relationship in another way. We know that $k = \Delta/1024$. Therefore, by substitution:

$10^k = 1 + 2.302585\left(\Delta/1024\right)$

If we let $n = 2.302585\left(\Delta/1024\right)$, then:

$2.302585\left(\Delta/1024\right) = 2.302585k$ and $2.302585k = n$

Solving $2.302585k = n$ for k, we get:

[2] Go ahead and compute log 8 and log 2 using a scientific calculator. First, press the LOG key. Second, press 8 or 2. Finally, press the ENTER or = key.

$$2.302585k = n \Leftrightarrow k = \frac{n}{2.302585}$$

We conclude, by substitution:

$$10^{\frac{n}{2.302585}} = 1 + n$$

To summarize, we reasoned:

$$10^k = 1 + 2.302585k \Leftrightarrow 10^{\frac{n}{2.302585}} = 1 + n \text{ where } n = 2.302585\left(\Delta/_{1024}\right)$$

We know that logarithms to any other base are multiples of logarithms to the base 10:

$\log_n c = \dfrac{\log_{10} c}{\log_{10} n}$ where the multiplicative factor is $\dfrac{1}{\log_{10} n}$ (Note: We use $\log_{10}$ to emphasize base 10.)

We chose base 10 because we use a base 10 decimal system and, for this reason, Briggs starting with this base. Is there a way in which we can change the scale of our logarithms using a multiplicative factor to a naturally mathematical one, one not base 10, a natural base?

Since $10^{\frac{n}{2.302585}} = 1 + n$, we can proceed to multiply all the logarithms to the base 10 by 2.302585. Our answers will correspond to another base, our mathematically natural base. Why? We let e be this base. We note:

$$10^{\frac{n}{2.302585}} = 1 + n \Leftrightarrow \log(1+n) = \frac{n}{2.302585}$$

Multiplying both sides of this equation by 2.302585, we get:

$$\log(1+n) = \frac{n}{2.302585} \Leftrightarrow (2.302585)\log(1 + n) = n$$

We let (2.302585)log = ln, our natural definition where $\log_e = \ln$. Therefore:

$(2.302585)\log(1 + n) = \ln(1 + n)$

Since $(2.302585)\log(1 + n)$, then:

$\ln(1 + n) = n \Leftrightarrow e^n = 1 + n$ as $n \to 0$

Note that this expression, $e^n = 1 + n$ as $n \to 0$, is very clean and efficient. *It is a mathematically natural.* Compare it with the somewhat cumbersome $10^{\frac{n}{2.302585}} = 1 + n$ for base 10 logs.

What is the value of e that generates this efficiency? We know that $e^n = 1 + n$ and $10^{\frac{n}{2.302585}} = 1 + n$. Therefore, by substitution:

$$e^n = 10^{\frac{n}{2.302585}}$$

Letting $n = 1$, we get:

$$e^1 = e = 10^{\frac{1}{2.302585}}$$

Since $\frac{1}{2.302585} \approx 0.434294$, then:

$$10^{\frac{1}{2.302585}} \approx 10^{0.434294}$$

Since $\lim_{k \to 0}\left(\frac{10^k - 1}{k}\right) \approx 2.302585$, then the exponent of 10, approximately 0.434294, is an irrational number. We now invoke Table 3 of Lesson 12.3 to approximate this number. We must solve this equation for e:

$$10^{0.434294} = e$$

We can cut our work short by finding x such that $0.434294 = \frac{x}{1024}$:

$$0.434294 = \frac{x}{1024} \Leftrightarrow x \approx 444.717$$

Now, we can partition 444.717 as follows (This step is equivalent to our iteration steps in 12.3.):

444.717 = 256 + 128 + 32 + 16 + 8 + 4 + 0.717

Or, invoking the Associative Law of Addition:

444.717 = 4 + 8 + 16 + 32 + 128 + 256 + 0.717

Therefore, e, as an exponent of a sum of powers of 10, will be the product of six numbers. We can estimate e, rounded to five decimal places, as:

$$e = 10^{\frac{1}{4}} \cdot 10^{\frac{1}{8}} \cdot 10^{\frac{1}{16}} \cdot 10^{\frac{1}{32}} \cdot 10^{\frac{1}{128}} \cdot 10^{\frac{1}{256}} \cdot 10^{\frac{0.717}{1024}}$$

We retrieve the decimal equivalents from Table 1 of Lesson 12.3. Also, you may use a calculator to compute this product of seven factors. By doing so, we get this equivalency:

$e = (1.7782794)(1.3335214)(1.0746078)(1.0366329)(1.0181517)(1.0090350)(1.0016136) \approx 2.71828$

The actual value of e, to ten decimal places, is 2.7182818284. Our derivation of e in Lesson 12.4 and our derivation in this lesson are as different as apples are from oranges. They both yield the same value; both interpenetrate in a perichoretic dance. Such is one of the many natural wonders of this fascinating number e, the base of the natural logarithms.

THE DANCE BETWEEN THE COMMON AND THE NATURAL

We can convert from log to ln for any x by doing this calculation:

ln x = 2.302585(log x)

We observe: $\ln x = 2.302585(\log x) \Leftrightarrow \log x = \frac{\ln x}{2.302585} = 0.434294(\ln x)$

Therefore, we can convert from ln to log for any x by doing this calculation:

log x = 0.434294(ln x)

This is the dance between common logs and natural logs.

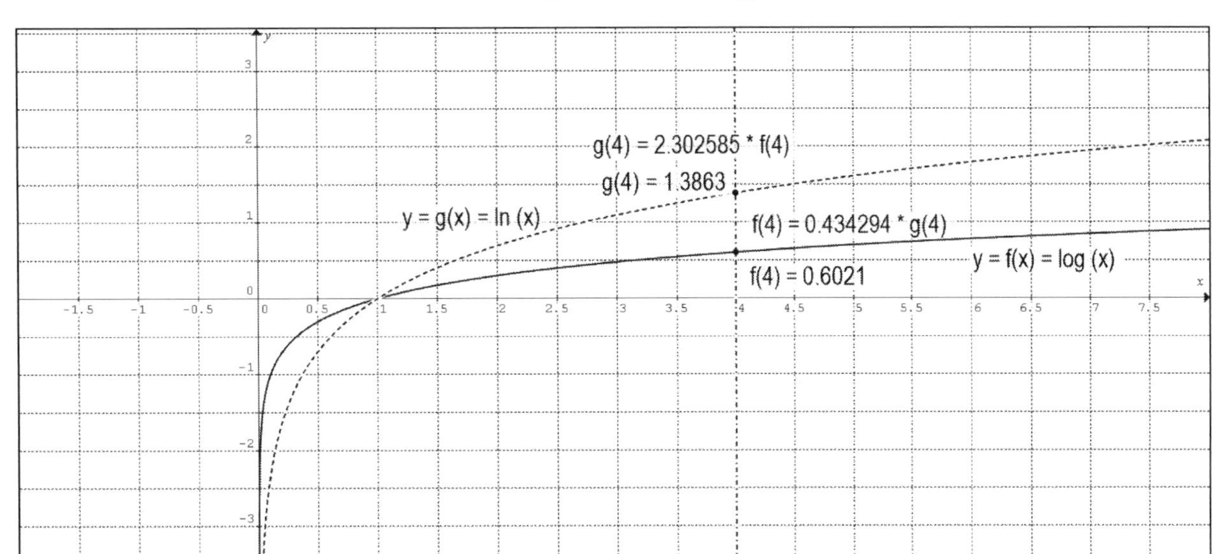

Figure 1. The dance between ln x and log x for common arguments.

We can also use $\log_n c = \frac{\log_b c}{\log_b n}$ to find these multiplicative factors. To convert from ln x to log x, we set $b = e$ and $n = 10$. Making these substitutions, noting that we can write $\log_{10} c$ as $\log c$ and $\log_e c$ as $\ln c$, we get:

$$\log c = \frac{\ln c}{\ln 10}$$

We assume we know all the natural logarithms. Therefore, we know ln 10 and, in fact, ln 10 = 2.302585. (Confirm this with your scientific calculator.) Substituting, we get:

$$\log c = \frac{\ln c}{2.302585} = \frac{1}{2.302585} \ln c = 0.434294(\ln c)$$

To convert from log x to ln x, we set $b = 10$ and $n = e$. Making these substitutions, we get:

$$\ln c = \frac{\log c}{\log e}$$

We assume we know all the common logarithms. Therefore, we know log e, and, in fact, log e = 0.434294. (Confirm this with your scientific calculator.[3]) Substituting, we get:

$$\ln c = \frac{\log c}{0.434294} = \frac{1}{0.434294} \log c = 2.302585(\log c)$$

[3] First, press the LOG key. Second, to enter e, press the e^x key and enter 1 for the exponent. Finally, press the ENTER or = key. Some scientific calculators have a separate e key.

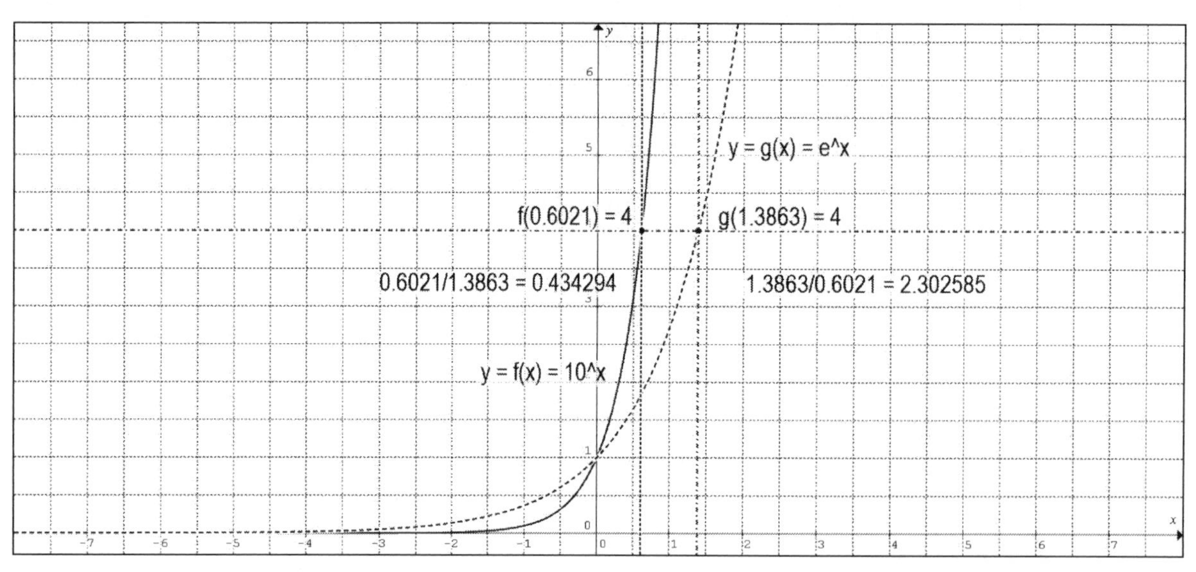

Figure 2. The dance between e^x and 10^x for common images.

PRIME NUMBERS REVISITED

In Lesson 6.1, we considered the density of prime numbers between 2 and powers of 10 as revealed in Table 1.

Table 1	
n	Number of Primes Between 2 and n
10^2	25
10^3	168
10^4	1229
10^5	9593
10^6	78,499
10^7	664,579
10^8	5,761,455
10^9	50,847,534
10^{10}	455,052,512
10^{11}	4,118,054,813
10^{12}	37,607,912,081
10^{13}	346,065,536,839
10^{14}	3,204,941,750,802
10^{15}	29,844,570,422,669

There is a marvelous pattern revealed if we consider natural logarithms. We can find it in Table 2.

Table 2				
n	P (Number of Primes)	$\frac{n}{\ln n}$	D (Difference)	Percent Error
10^2	25	21	4	16.00
10^3	168	144	24	14.29
10^4	1229	1085	144	11.72
10^5	9593	8685	908	9.47
10^6	78,499	72,382	6117	7.79
10^7	664,579	620,420	44,159	6.64
10^8	5,761,455	5,428,680	332,775	5.78
10^9	50,847,534	48,254,945	2,592,589	5.10
10^{10}	455,052,512	434,294,945	20,758,019	4.56
10^{11}	4,118,054,813	3,948,131,889	169,922,924	4.13
10^{12}	37,607,912,081	36,191,208,672	1,416,703,346	3.77
10^{13}	346,065,536,839	334,072,662,679	11,992,874,160	3.47
10^{14}	3,204,941,750,802	3,102,103,502,550	102,838,248,252	3.21
10^{15}	29,844,570,422,669	28,952,965,081,228	891,605,341,441	2.99

> ... the prime number theorem, the most important truth about the natural numbers discovered in modern times.
>
> Constance Reid, *From Zero to Infinity* ([1955, 1960, 1964, 1992] 2006), p. 157.

We focus on the last column. We calculate it by dividing D, column four, by P, column two. As n gets greater, the percent error gets lesser. As n approaches infinity, as $n \to \infty$, the percent error gets closer and closer to zero. Carl Friedrich Gauss (1777-1855) noted this relationship in 1792, when only 15 years old, and assumed that there was a pattern that could be proved. He stated the **Prime Number Theorem** as a conjecture: The number of primes less than n is approximately equal to n divided by the natural logarithm of n, or:

$$P \approx \frac{n}{\ln n}$$

Using limit notation, we write:

$$\lim_{n \to \infty} P = \frac{n}{\ln n}$$

The proof of this conjecture had to wait until 1896 when two mathematicians, the Frenchman Joacques Salomon Hadamard (1865-1963) and the Belgian C. J. de la Vallée-Poussin (1866-1962), independently proved it.

> That the average behavior of the prime number distribution can be described by the logarithmic function is a very remarkable discovery, for it is surprising that two mathematical concepts which seem so unrelated should be in fact so intimately connected.
>
> Richard Courant and Herbert Robbins, *What is Mathematics?* ([1941] 1996), p. 30.

Let's review the four laws of logs:

1. $\log ab = \log a + \log b$
2. $\log a/b = \log a - \log b$
3. $\log a^b = b \log a$
4. $\log a^{-1} = -\log a$

In review and by convention:

$\log_{10} x$ is normally written, by convention, as $\log x$.
$\log_e x$ is normally written, by convention, as $\ln x$.

Scientific calculators have two logarithm keys:

1. LOG (common logs)
2. LN (natural logs)

USING LOG TABLES BC (BEFORE CALCULATORS)

As mentioned in the last lesson, Tables of Logarithms, originating with John Napier, used to grace the back pages of every science and mathematics textbook. On the next page, let's look a section of a common log table and discover how to use it.[4] Now, with electronic calculators, we just punch a key.

[4] From Lipman Bers with Frank Karal, *Calculus* (New York: Holt, Rinehart and Winston, [1969] 1976).

728 TABLES

Table 6 Mantissas of common logarithms of numbers 100–999

N	0	1	2	3	4	5	6	7	8	9
10	0000	0043	0086	0128	0170	0212	0253	0294	0334	0374
11	0414	0453	0492	0531	0569	0607	0645	0682	0719	0755
12	0792	0828	0864	0899	0934	0969	1004	1038	1072	1106
13	1139	1173	1206	1239	1271	1303	1335	1367	1399	1430
14	1461	1492	1523	1553	1584	1614	1644	1673	1703	1732
15	1761	1790	1818	1847	1875	1903	1931	1959	1987	2014
16	2041	2068	2095	2122	2148	2175	2201	2227	2253	2279
17	2304	2330	2355	2380	2405	2430	2455	2480	2504	2529
18	2553	2577	2601	2625	2648	2672	2695	2718	2742	2765
19	2788	2810	2833	2856	2878	2900	2923	2945	2967	2989
20	3010	3032	3054	3075	3096	3118	3139	3160	3181	3201
21	3222	3243	3263	3284	3304	3324	3345	3365	3385	3404
22	3424	3444	3464	3483	3502	3522	3541	3560	3579	3598
23	3617	3636	3655	3674	3692	3711	3729	3747	3766	3784
24	3802	3820	3838	3856	3874	3892	3909	3927	3945	3962
25	3979	3997	4014	4031	4048	4065	4082	4099	4116	4133
26	4150	4166	4183	4200	4216	4232	4249	4265	4281	4298
27	4314	4330	4346	4362	4378	4393	4409	4425	4440	4456
28	4472	4487	4502	4518	4533	4548	4564	4579	4594	4609
29	4624	4639	4654	4669	4683	4698	4713	4728	4742	4757
30	4771	4786	4800	4814	4829	4843	4857	4871	4886	4900
31	4914	4928	4942	4955	4969	4983	4997	5011	5024	5038
32	5051	5065	5079	5092	5105	5119	5132	5145	5159	5172
33	5185	5198	5211	5224	5237	5250	5263	5276	5289	5302
34	5315	5328	5340	5353	5366	5378	5391	5403	5416	5428
35	5441	5453	5465	5478	5490	5502	5514	5527	5539	5551
36	5563	5575	5587	5599	5611	5623	5635	5647	5658	5670
37	5682	5694	5705	5717	5729	5740	5752	5763	5775	5786
38	5798	5809	5821	5832	5843	5855	5866	5877	5888	5899
39	5911	5922	5933	5944	5955	5966	5977	5988	5999	6010
40	6021	6031	6042	6053	6064	6075	6085	6096	6107	6117
41	6128	6138	6149	6160	6170	6180	6191	6201	6212	6222
42	6232	6243	6253	6263	6274	6284	6294	6304	6314	6325
43	6335	6345	6355	6365	6375	6385	6395	6405	6415	6425
44	6435	6444	6454	6464	6474	6484	6493	6503	6513	6522
45	6532	6542	6551	6561	6571	6580	6590	6599	6609	6618
46	6628	6637	6646	6656	6665	6675	6684	6693	6702	6712
47	6721	6730	6739	6749	6758	6767	6776	6785	6794	6803
48	6812	6821	6830	6839	6848	6857	6866	6875	6884	6893
49	6902	6911	6920	6928	6937	6946	6955	6964	6972	6981
50	6990	6998	7007	7016	7024	7033	7042	7050	7059	7067
51	7076	7084	7093	7101	7110	7118	7126	7135	7143	7152
52	7160	7168	7177	7185	7193	7202	7210	7218	7226	7235
53	7243	7251	7259	7267	7275	7284	7292	7300	7308	7316
54	7324	7332	7340	7348	7356	7364	7372	7380	7388	7396

Figure 3.

Table 6 (continued) Mantissas of common logarithms of numbers 100–999

N	0	1	2	3	4	5	6	7	8	9
55	7404	7412	7419	7427	7435	7443	7451	7459	7466	7474
56	7482	7490	7497	7505	7513	7520	7528	7536	7543	7551
57	7559	7566	7574	7582	7589	7597	7604	7612	7619	7627
58	7634	7642	7649	7657	7664	7672	7679	7686	7694	7701
59	7709	7716	7723	7731	7738	7745	7752	7760	7767	7774
60	7782	7789	7796	7803	7810	7818	7825	7832	7839	7846
61	7853	7860	7868	7875	7882	7889	7896	7903	7910	7917
62	7924	7931	7938	7945	7952	7959	7966	7973	7980	7987
63	7993	8000	8007	8014	8021	8028	8035	8041	8048	8055
64	8062	8069	8075	8082	8089	8096	8102	8109	8116	8122
65	8129	8136	8142	8149	8156	8162	8169	8176	8182	8189
66	8195	8202	8209	8215	8222	8228	8235	8241	8248	8254
67	8261	8267	8274	8280	8287	8293	8299	8306	8312	8319
68	8325	8331	8338	8344	8351	8357	8363	8370	8376	8382
69	8388	8395	8401	8407	8414	8420	8426	8432	8439	8445
70	8451	8457	8463	8470	8476	8482	8488	8494	8500	8506
71	8513	8519	8525	8531	8537	8543	8549	8555	8561	8567
72	8573	8579	8585	8591	8597	8603	8609	8615	8621	8627
73	8633	8639	8645	8651	8657	8663	8669	8675	8681	8686
74	8692	8698	8704	8710	8716	8722	8727	8733	8739	8745
75	8751	8756	8762	8768	8774	8779	8785	8791	8797	8802
76	8808	8814	8820	8825	8831	8837	8842	8848	8854	8859
77	8865	8871	8876	8882	8887	8893	8899	8904	8910	8915
78	8921	8927	8932	8938	8943	8949	8954	8960	8965	8971
79	8976	8982	8987	8993	8998	9004	9009	9015	9020	9025
80	9031	9036	9042	9047	9053	9058	9063	9069	9074	9079
81	9085	9090	9096	9101	9106	9112	9117	9122	9128	9133
82	9138	9143	9149	9154	9159	9165	9170	9175	9180	9186
83	9191	9196	9201	9206	9212	9217	9222	9227	9232	9238
84	9243	9248	9253	9258	9263	9269	9274	9279	9284	9289
85	9294	9299	9304	9309	9315	9320	9325	9330	9335	9340
86	9345	9350	9355	9360	9365	9370	9375	9380	9385	9390
87	9395	9400	9405	9410	9415	9420	9425	9430	9435	9440
88	9445	9450	9455	9460	9465	9469	9474	9479	9484	9489
89	9494	9499	9504	9509	9513	9518	9523	9528	9533	9538
90	9542	9547	9552	9557	9562	9566	9571	9576	9581	9586
91	9590	9595	9600	9605	9609	9614	9619	9624	9628	9633
92	9638	9643	9647	9652	9657	9661	9666	9671	9675	9680
93	9685	9689	9694	9699	9703	9708	9713	9717	9722	9727
94	9731	9736	9741	9745	9750	9754	9759	9763	9768	9773
95	9777	9782	9786	9791	9795	9800	9805	9809	9814	9818
96	9823	9827	9832	9836	9841	9845	9850	9854	9859	9863
97	9868	9872	9877	9881	9886	9890	9894	9899	9903	9908
98	9912	9917	9921	9926	9930	9934	9939	9943	9948	9952
99	9956	9961	9965	9969	9974	9978	9983	9987	9991	9996

Figure 4.

We want to find the log of a number, or log N. In the table, N could represent a variety of numbers, resembling the slide rule. There are three digits that make up N, two digits in the first column and the one digit in the first row. Let's look at the cell containing the number 1761 (Figure 3), the intersection of the coordinates, so to speak, 15 and 0. These three digits, 1, 5, and 0, comprise the foundational number 1.50 where:

$$\log 1.50 = 0.1761$$

We place the decimal point in this manner. We can use the log of the foundational number to find the log of 15.0 or log 150:

$$\log 15.0 = 1.1761$$
$$\log 150 = 2.1761$$

Let's look at the three numbers written in Scientific Notation and the computation of their logs (We make use of the Multiplication Law of Logs and Log of a Power Law.):

$$1.50 = 1.50 \times 10^0$$
$$\log 1.50 = \log (1.50 \times 10^0) = \log 1.50 + \log 10^0 = 0.1761 + 0 = 0.1761$$
$$15.0 = 1.50 \times 10^1$$
$$\log 15.0 = \log (1.50 \times 10^1) = \log 1.50 + \log 10^1 = 0.1761 + 1 = 1.1761$$
$$150 = 1.50 \times 10^2$$
$$\log 150 = \log (1.50 \times 10^2) = \log 1.50 + \log 10^2 = 0.1761 + 2 = 2.1761$$

In general, we can write any number in Scientific Notation; i.e., $z = m10^c$, where m is the mantissa and c is the characteristic. To find the log of any number z, we write in symbols:

$$\log z = \log m10^c = \log m + \log 10^c = \log m + c = c.\log m$$

If we write z in Scientific Notation, the characteristic c will always be the **characteristic of the log**, the number before the decimal point. The decimal part of the log is the **mantissa of the log**. It is the log of the mantissa m.

> The log of any number written in Scientific Notation is the sum of its characteristic and the log of its mantissa.

Log Tables are usually titled like this: "Four-Place Mantissas for Common Logarithms" or, for better accuracy, "Five-Place Mantissas for Common Logarithms." The four- or five-digit numbers comprising the cells in these tables are always decimals, $0.n_1n_2n_3n_4$ or $0.n_1n_2n_3n_4n_5$.

Logarithms are the other inverse of exponentiation. If we know the log of number that is in the form $c.\log m$, then $m10^c$ is the inverse of $c.\log m$.

We reveal this inverse relationship by this equivalency:

$$\log a = b \Leftrightarrow 10^b = a$$

If we write a in Scientific Notation ($m10^c$), we have this equivalency:

$$\log m10^c = c.\log m \Leftrightarrow 10^{c.\log m} = m10^c$$

Let's see how this works with an example of how scientists computed numbers before the invention of electronic calculators. We want to calculate 12^{35} using logs. 12^{35} means 12 is a factor thirty-five times. To multiply by 12, we add log 12 to the log of the number being multiplied. If we multiply by 12 thirty-five times, we will add log 12 thirty-five times. To start, we let $x = 12^{35}$ and then take the log of both sides. We get:

$x = 12^{35} \Leftrightarrow \log x = \log 12^{35} \Leftrightarrow \log x = 35(\log 12)$
(Note: 35(log 12) is the addition of log 12 thirty-five times.)

Since log 12 = 1.07918 (Note the Five-Place Mantissa. It is 1.0792 in Figure 3 of the Four-Place Mantissa Table.), we get:

$\log x = 35(\log 12) \Leftrightarrow \log x = 35(1.07918) \Leftrightarrow \log x = 37.77134$

We want to solve for x. We must find the inverse log of 37.77134; i.e., we want to find the log of some number that is equal to 37.77134. We recall that:

$\log m10^c = c.\log m \Leftrightarrow 10^{c.\log m} = m10^c$

Since $\log x = 37.77134$, then $x = m10^c$. Replacing x with $m10^c$, we write this equivalency:

$\log m10^c = 37.77134 \Leftrightarrow 10^{37.77134} = m10^c$

To write x in Scientific Notation, we know that 37 will be the characteristic. Therefore:

$x = m10^{37}$

What is m? It will be the inverse of log m, or, since $\log m = b \Leftrightarrow 10^b = m$, then:

$\log 5.90663 = 0.77134 \Leftrightarrow 10^{0.77134} = 5.90663$
(Note: In Figure 4 of the Four-Place Mantissa Table, 0.7713 (rounded) is about half-way between 5.90 and 5.91.)

> The inverse is going from the mantissa in the table to the number it represents, going from the log of a number back to that number.

Since $m = 5.91$ (rounded), then:

$x = 5.91 \times 10^{37}$

Talk about work and lots of careful thinking! If we punch this key sequence in our calculators, we get our answer without much thinking:

1. 12
2. ^
3. 35
4. ENTER/=

We get (rounded): 5.91×10^{37}

Here is how we use a scientific calculator to solve $x = 12^{35}$ using logs.

Step 1. $x = 12^{35} \Leftrightarrow \log x = \log 12^{35}$

Step 2. $\log x = \log 12^{35} \Leftrightarrow \log x = 35(\log 12)$

Step 3. $\log x = 37.77134361$ (Carry the decimal places if your calculator display allows for it.)
In general $\log x = c.\log m$. In this example, $c = 37$ and $\log m = 0.77134361$. We want our answer in Scientific Notation, so we know that the characteristic c of this notation will be 37. We know that $x = m10^{37}$. Therefore:

Step 4. $\log x = 37.77134361 \Leftrightarrow x = m10^{37}$
We know that the mantissa m in Scientific Notation will be the inverse log of 0.77134361 or:

$m = 10^{0.77134361} \approx 5.91$. Scientific calculators will show this inverse as a function above the LOG key. Its label is "10^x". To invoke this function, there will be a key labeled "2nd" or "2ndf", meaning second function. Push the second function key, push the LOG key, enter 0.77134361, and then push the ENTER/= key. You will get a result and we can round it to 5.91. Therefore:

Step 5. $\log m = 0.77134361 \Leftrightarrow m = 10^{0.77134361} \approx 5.91 \Rightarrow x = 5.91 \times 10^{37}$

SOLVING EQUATIONS USING LOGS

Although we no longer use logs to calculate powers or products or quotients, they are the strategy to help us solve equations in a certain form. With powers, we have two possibilities for the location of the unknown x either as the base or the exponent:

Equation 1. $x^a = b$

To solve Equation 1, we extract the ath root of both sides. When the base is unknown, we invoke extraction of roots as the solution strategy.

Equation 2. $a^x = b$

To solve Equation 2, we take the logarithm of both sides. When the exponent is unknown, we invoke logs as the solution strategy.

Let's solve $10^x = 3$. Since x is the exponent, we can solve this equation by either taking the common log of both sides or the natural log of both sides.

Case 1. We take the common log of both sides:

$10^x = 3 \Leftrightarrow \log 10^x = \log 3$

Since $\log 10^x = x(\log 10) = x$ (See footnote[5]), we have this equivalency:

$\log 10^x = \log 3 \Leftrightarrow x = \log 3$

How nice! Since $\log 3 = 0.477$ (three decimal places), then:

$x = \log 3 \Leftrightarrow x = 0.477$

Case 2. We could also take the natural log of both sides. We write:

$$\ln 10^x = \ln 3 \Leftrightarrow x(\ln 10) = \ln 3 \Leftrightarrow x = \frac{\ln 3}{\ln 10}$$

We surrender to the scientific calculator to find these natural logs. Since $\ln 3 = 1.0986$ (rounded) and $\ln 10 = 2.3026$ (rounded), then:

$$x = \frac{1.0986}{2.3026} \approx 0.477$$

Since we are solving $10^x = 3$ where 10 is the base of a power, it is sound reasoning to invoke common logs in the solution. As we can see from our work, invoking common logs minimizes the arithmetic.

[5] $x(\log 10)$ means x times log 10 where log 10 is a number (equal to 1 in this case). As we have been doing, we can write $x(\log 10)$ as $x \log 10$ just as we can write $x(y)$ as xy.

We can graph the solution (Figure 5) to confirm the perichoretic relationship between Algebra and Geometry:

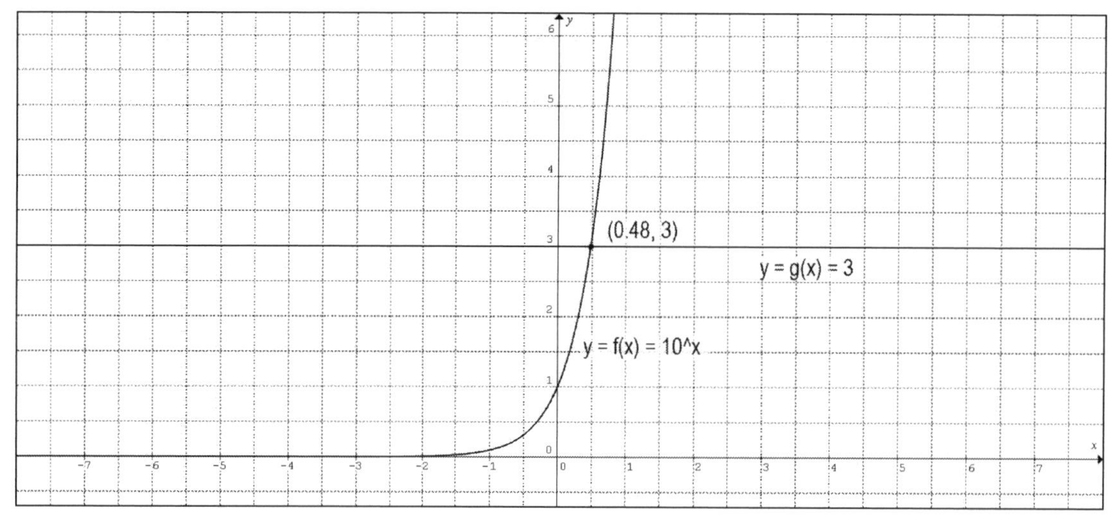

Figure 5. The graphical solution to $10^x = 3$.

When the base is unknown, extraction of roots is the solution method. For example, we want to solve $x^3 = 3$ for x. The solution strategy is the extract the cube root from both sides:

$x^3 = 3 \Leftrightarrow x = 3^{\frac{1}{3}} \approx 1.442$ and graphing (Figure 6) confirms our solution:

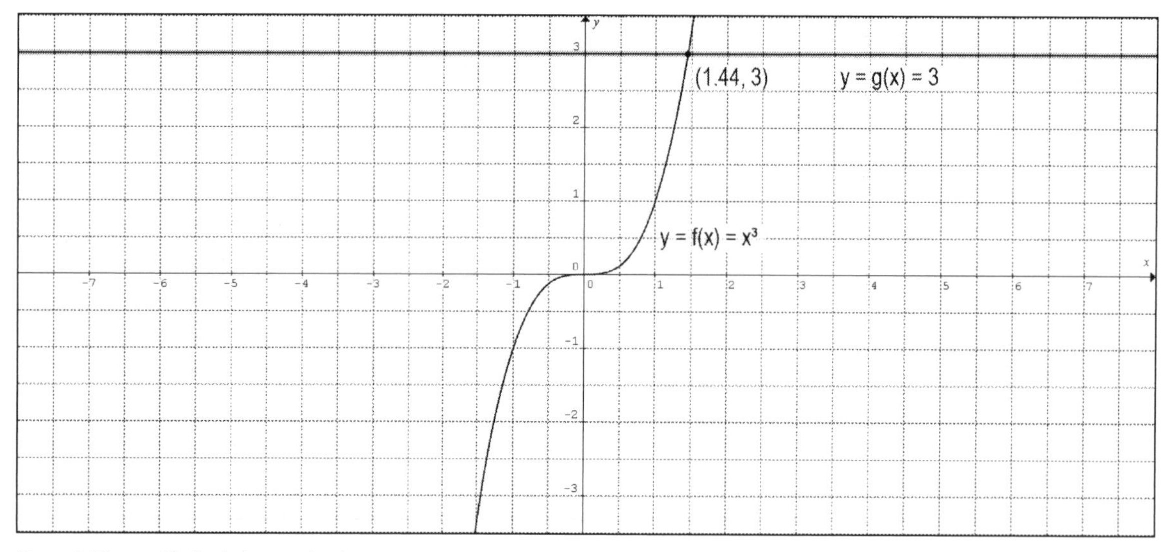

Figure 6. The graphical solution to $x^3 = 3$.

We can now complete our graphic (Figure 7) that we started in Lesson 2.3.

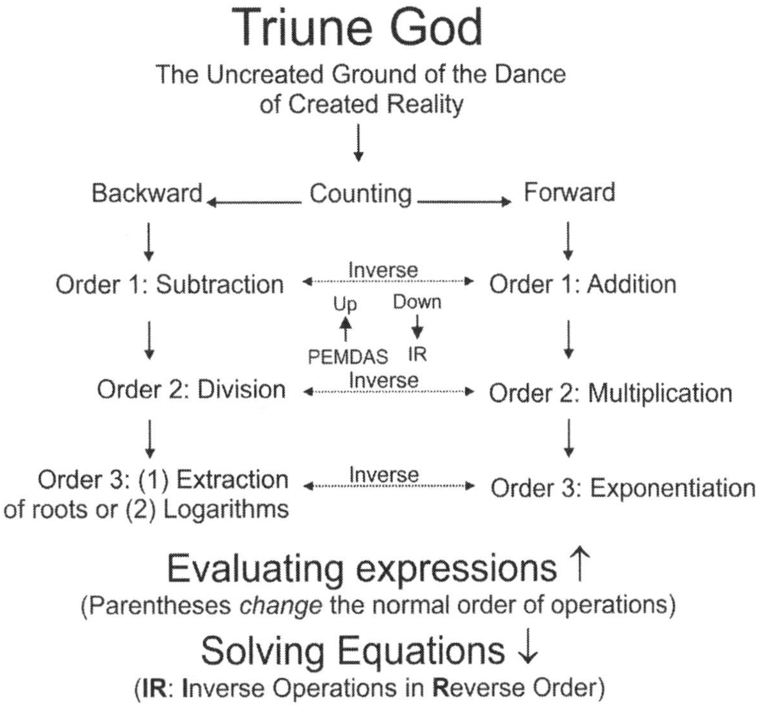

Triune God

The Uncreated Ground of the Dance
of Created Reality

↓

Backward ← Counting → Forward

↓ ↓

Order 1: Subtraction ←Inverse→ Order 1: Addition

Up ↑ PEMDAS Down ↓ IR

↓ ↓

Order 2: Division ←Inverse→ Order 2: Multiplication

↓ ↓

Order 3: (1) Extraction of roots or (2) Logarithms ←Inverse→ Order 3: Exponentiation

Evaluating expressions ↑
(Parentheses *change* the normal order of operations)

Solving Equations ↓
(**IR**: **I**nverse Operations in **R**everse Order)

Figure 7.

THE SLIDE RULE REVISITED

Note the A and B scales in Figure 8.

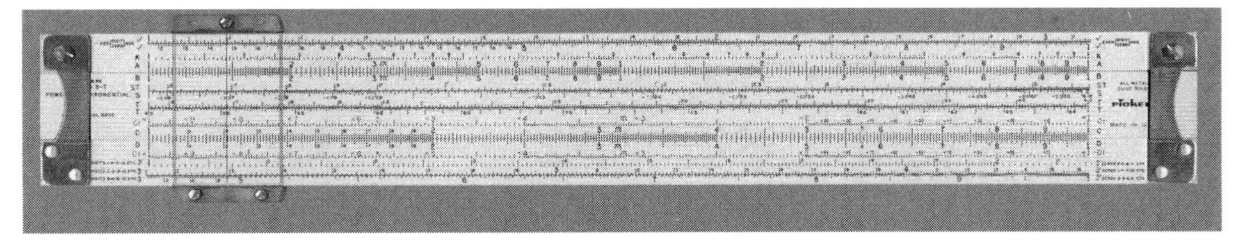

Figure 8. Slide Rule. Source: James D. Nickel.

When compared to the C and D scales, the A and B scales are reduced to half and printed twice. Why? They represent the square and square root functions. Our log law confirms this:

$$\log x^{\frac{1}{2}} = \frac{1}{2}\log x$$

Note the K scale in Figure 8. When compared to the C and D scales, the K scale is reduced to one-third and printed three times. They represent the cube and cube root functions:

$$\log x^{\frac{1}{3}} = \frac{1}{3}\log x$$

Remember our dance patterns in square roots and cube roots, the dance of pairs of 2 and pairs of 3 in Lesson 11.10?

Table 3

x	$\sqrt{x}$	$\sqrt[3]{x}$		x	$\sqrt{x}$	$\sqrt[3]{x}$
8	≈ 2.828	= 2		5	≈ 2.236	≈ 1.710
80	≈ 8.944	≈ 4.308		50	≈ 7.071	≈ 3.684
800	≈ 28.28	≈ 9.283		500	≈ 22.36	≈ 7.937
8000	≈ 89.44	= 20		5000	≈ 70.71	≈ 17.10
80,000	≈ 282.8	≈ 43.08		50,000	≈ 223.6	≈ 36.84
800,000	≈ 8944	≈ 92.83		500,000	≈ 707.1	≈ 79.37
8,000,000	≈ 2828	200		5,000,000	≈ 2236	≈ 171.0
80,000,000	≈ 8944	≈ 430.8		50,000,000	≈ 7071	≈ 368.4
800,000,000	≈ 28,280	≈ 9283		500,000,000	≈ 22360	≈ 793.7

Inspect the two $\sqrt{\ }$ scales above the K scale in Figure 9.

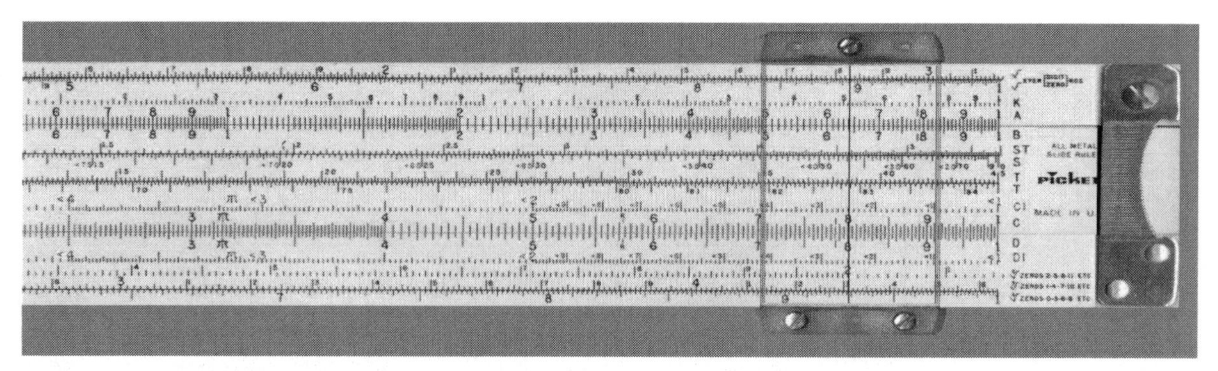

Figure 9. Source: James D. Nickel.

Do you see $\sqrt{8} \approx 2.83$ and $\sqrt{80} \approx 8.94$? They also could represent $\sqrt{800} \approx 28.3$ and $\sqrt{8000} \approx 89.4$. Continuing, they could represent $\sqrt{80{,}000} \approx 283$ and $\sqrt{800{,}000} \approx 894$.

Inspect the three $\sqrt[3]{}$ scales on the bottom of the slide rule in Figure 10.

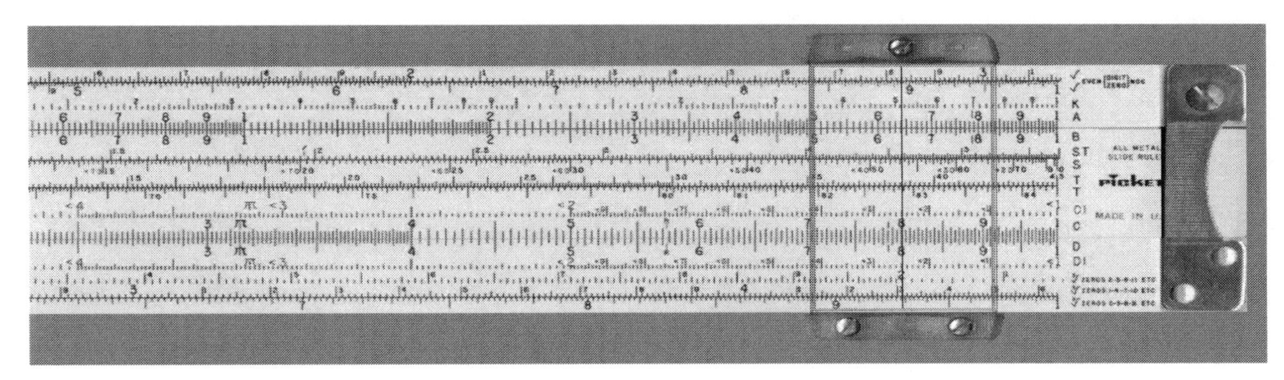

Figure 10. Source: James D. Nickel.

Do you see $\sqrt[3]{8} = 2$, $\sqrt[3]{80} \approx 4.31$, and $\sqrt[3]{800} \approx 9.28$? They also could represent $\sqrt[3]{8000} = 20$, $\sqrt[3]{80{,}000} \approx 43.1$, and $\sqrt[3]{800{,}000} \approx 92.8$. Continuing, they could represent $\sqrt[3]{8{,}000{,}000} = 200$, $\sqrt[3]{80{,}000{,}000} \approx 431$, and $\sqrt[3]{800{,}000{,}000} \approx 928$.

Using slide rules required of a student a mastery knowledge of patterns revealed in our lessons that explored the nature of square roots and cube roots.

EXERCISES

1. Prove $\log_n c = \dfrac{\log_b c}{\log_b n}$ where $c, b, n \in \mathbb{R}$, $b, n \neq 1$ without referring to the text. (Hint: Reread and study the proof in the text, rewrite the proof in your notebook, and then write the proof without any assistance.)

Answer the following questions:

2. Write $\log_n c = \dfrac{\log_b c}{\log_b n}$ when $b = 10$ and $n = 3$. (Hint: Use common log notation; i.e., the notation "$\log_{10}x$" can be written as "$\log x$".)
3. Write $\log_n c = \dfrac{\log_b c}{\log_b n}$ when $b = e$ and $n = 2$. (Hint: Use natural log notation; i.e., the notation "$\log_e x$" can be written as "$\ln x$.")
4. What is the value, to six decimal places, of $\dfrac{\ln x}{\log x}$ for all $x > 0$?
5. What is the value, to six decimal places, of $\dfrac{\log x}{\ln x}$ for all $x > 0$?
6. (a) Write the Prime Number Theorem in limit notation.
   (b) Explain what the notation means.
7. Explain the relationship between the characteristic of a number z in Scientific Notation to the characteristic of the log of that number written in the form $c.\log m$.
8. Explain the relationship between the mantissa of a number z in Scientific Notation to the mantissa of the log of that number written in the form $c.\log m$.
9. What is the method for solving $x^2 = 16$ for x?
10. What is the method for solving $2^x = 16$ for x?

11. What is the log of the square root of a positive number?
12. What is the log of the cube root of a positive number?
13. (a) Using a scientific calculator, solve $3^x = 81$ for x using natural and common logs as your method. (b) What do you notice about your solution using either method? (c) Explain your answer to (b).
14. Write the following six equations as three pairs such that the two equations in each pair have the same meaning:
    (a) $y = 10^x$
    (b) $x = \dfrac{y}{6}$
    (c) $y = x^3$
    (d) $y = 6x$
    (e) $x = \log y$
    (f) $x = y^{\frac{1}{3}}$
15. Match each exponential law in column one with its corresponding logarithm law in column two:

(a) $b^{m+n} = b^m b^n$	(f) $\log_b \dfrac{x}{y} = \log_b x - \log_b y$
(b) $b^{m-n} = \dfrac{b^m}{b^n}$	(g) $\log_b \left(x^y\right) = y \log_b x$
(c) $b^0 = 1$	(h) $\log_b \dfrac{1}{x} = -\log_b x$
(d) $b^{-n} = \dfrac{1}{b^n}$	(i) $\log_b 1 = 0$
(e) $\left(b^m\right)^n = b^{mn}$	(j) $\log_b xy = \log_b x + \log_b y$

If $f(x) = e^x$, explain, without graphing, the nature of following graphs when compared to $f(x)$:
16. $g(x) = e^{-x}$
17. $g(x) = -e^x$
18. $g(x) = \dfrac{1}{3}e^x$
19. $g(x) = e^{2x}$
20. $g(x) = 3e^x$
21. $g(x) = e^{-0.5x}$

If $f(x) = \ln x$, explain, without graphing, the nature of following graphs when compared to $f(x)$:
22. $g(x) = -\ln x$
23. $g(x) = \ln -x$ (Hint: Think carefully about this.)
24. $g(x) = \dfrac{1}{2}\ln x$
25. $g(x) = \ln 0.5x$
26. $g(x) = \ln 2x$
27. $g(x) = -0.2 \ln x$

Using natural logs, a scientific calculator, and the change of base formula, find x:

28. $\log_2 16 = x$
29. $\log_3 243 = x$
30. $\log_4 64 = x$
31. $\log_5 3125 = x$

Using natural logs, the change of base formula, and graphing software, graph:

32. $f(x) = \log_2 x$
33. $f(x) = \log_3 x$
34. $f(x) = \log_4 x$
35. $f(x) = \log_5 x$
36. Graph the functions in the previous four questions along with the functions $f(x) = \log x$ and $f(x) = \ln x$ together.

Use logarithmic methods, common logs, and your scientific calculator to solve the following equations for x, rounding to the nearest hundredth: (Check your answers using your calculator.)

37. $2^x = 24$
38. $3^x = 5$
39. $12^x = 2$
40. $6(3^x) = 54$
41. $5(2^x) = 100$
42. $12(2^x) = 144$
43. $x = (4.027)^{25}$ (Write in Scientific Notation.)
44. $\log x = 1.7302$
45. $x = \sqrt[5]{68.23}$
46. $x = \log_2 3$
47. $x^{0.34} = 2$
48. $\log (x^2) - 8.9 = -5.7$ (Homework, Lesson 11.6)

Answer the following questions using common logarithms and your scientific calculator:

49. Suppose that one of your great uncles deposited \$100 for you in a bank fifty years ago at 3% interest, compounded yearly.
    (a) What is the account worth now?
    (b) What would the account be worth if it was deposited at the same interest rate one hundred and fifty years ago?

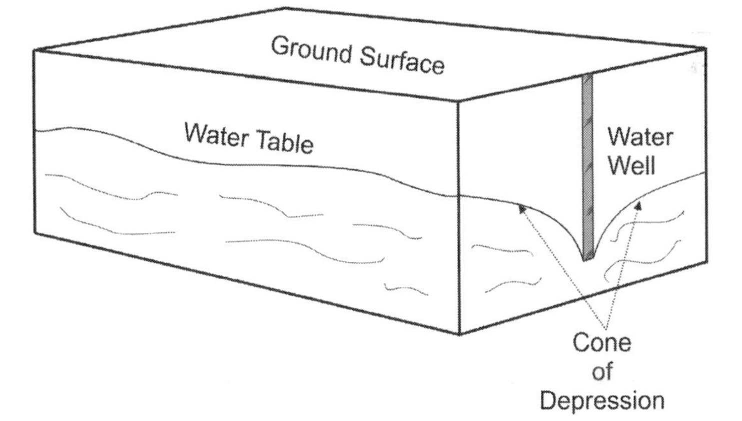

Figure 11. In Hydrogeology, the cone of depression is a function of the natural logarithm.

50. Suppose that you leave \$1000 on deposit at 5% interest compounded yearly. When will the account be worth \$10,000? Round to the nearest tenth of a year.
51. From the compound interest formula, determine how long, to the nearest tenth of a year, it will take for an initial investment to double at the following constant rates of interest:
    (a) 1%
    (b) 5%

(c) 10%

52. (a) Derive a general formula to determine how long it will take for an initial investment to double at a constant interest rate of r% using common logarithms.
(b) Do the same with natural logarithms.
53. (a) Derive a general formula to determine how long it will take for an initial investment to triple at a constant interest rate of r% using common logarithms.
(b) Do the same with natural logarithms.
54. How many years, rounded to the nearest tenth, are necessary for an initial investment of $20,000 to double if 6% interest is paid and interest is compounded quarterly? (Hint: Review Lesson 8.16.)
55. In finance, there is a Rule of 72, a formula for determine how many years it will take for an investment to double. The formula is $72 = rn$ where r = rate of growth, or return, and n = number of years to double. Develop a spreadsheet using the formula you derived in Question 52 and the Rule of 72 to complete the table at the right, rounding all answers to the nearest tenth.

r	n	Rule of 72
3%		
4%		
5%		
6%		
7%		
8%		
9%		
10%		
11%		
12%		
15%		
20%		
30%		

The pitch of a musical note depends upon its frequency, the number of vibrations per second (Lesson 9.8). It is the quality of a sound governed by the rate of vibrations producing it. In an even-tempered scale, the A note above middle C has a frequency of 440 Hz. Doubling this frequency generates a note an octave higher or 880 Hz. The A note an octave below 440 Hz has a frequency of 220 Hz. For any note of frequency f_1, we can generate this table:

Note	Frequency
	f_1
1 octave higher	$2f_1$
2 octaves higher	2^2f_1
3 octaves higher	2^3f_1
n octaves higher	2^nf_1

If f_1 and f_2 are the frequencies of any two notes ($f_1 \geq f_2$), the number of octaves between them is n where:

$$f_2 = 2^n f_1 \Leftrightarrow 2^n = \frac{f_1}{f_2}$$

To solve for n, we can take $\log_2$ of both sides. We write:

$$2^n = \frac{f_1}{f_2} \Leftrightarrow \log_2 2^n = \log_2 \frac{f_1}{f_2} \Leftrightarrow n = \log_2 \frac{f_1}{f_2}$$

Using a scientific calculator and common logarithms, answer these questions:

56. How many octaves, rounded to the nearest tenth, above 440 Hz is 20,000 Hz (20 kHz), the highest pitch humans can hear?
57. How many octaves, rounded to the nearest tenth, above 440 Hz is 45,000 Hz (45 kHz), the highest pitch dogs can hear?

58. How many octaves, rounded to the nearest tenth, are there between the highest pitch dogs can hear and the highest pitch humans can hear?

There are twelve notes on a piano in an octave. Starting from A (440 Hz), we have these notes in order:

A, A♯, B, C, C♯, D, D♯, E, F, F♯, G, and G♯

The interval between two adjacent keys on a piano is defined to be 100 cents, a unit of measurement in pitch.

59. How many cents in an octave?
60. State the formula for the number of cents c between two notes with frequencies f_1 and f_2.
61. Use the formula you derived in Question 60 to find the frequency of Middle C on the piano rounded to the nearest thousandths. (Use a scientific calculator and logarithms.)

Radioactive substances decay over a time period by emitting particles from some of its atoms, thus changing those atoms to another substance and making the weight of the unchanged material decrease with time. If w_u = weight of the unchanged material, w_o = original weight, and t = time, we have this equation:

$w_u = w_o b^{-t}$ where $b > 1$

Using a scientific calculator and common logarithms, answer this question:

62. The half-life of a substance is the time it takes for half the substance to decay.[6] The half-life of this substance is 3.5 days. What fraction of the original amount, as a percentage rounded to the nearest hundredth, remains after (a) 1 day, (b) 3 days, (c) 8 days, (d) 10 days (e) 20 days (f) 30 days? (Hint: Solve for b first leaving any numbers in your answer to nine decimal places.)

Assumptions one must consider when investigating radioactive decay and calculating results using logarithms.

1. The isotope (one of two or more atoms with the same atomic number but with different numbers of neutrons) under consideration has decayed, i.e., turned into its stable product, at a constant rate. Many physical parameters, parameters that could change over time, could imply that this rate is *not* constant.
2. You must guess what the original amount of the isotope was.
3. The constant decay rate follows a pattern that can be modeled using exponential functions.

[6] Carbon-14, an isotope of the element Carbon, is radioactive, and used by scientists to date old objects containing carbon remnants. The half-life of the radioactive decay of Carbon-14 is 5600 years. After eight half-lives, only 1/256 (Note: $2^8 = 256$) of the original radioactive carbon remains, an amount much too small to reliably measure. Because of this limitation and given the assumptions in the text box on this page, Carbon-14 dating works in theory for objects up to 40,000 years in age. Why? $39{,}200 = 5600 \cdot 7$ and $44{,}800 = 5600 \cdot 8$.

12.6 The Revelations of the Right Triangle

Terms, Symbols & Concepts Introduced
1. $\cong$
2. *Almagest*
3. Central angle
4. Chord
5. Circular functions
6. Corollary
7. Cosecant
8. Cosine
9. Cotangent
10. Directed angle
11. Initial side of an angle
12. Radian measure
13. Rationalizing the denominator
14. Secant
15. Sine
16. Tangent
17. Terminal side of an angle
18. Trigonometric functions
19. Unit circle

When we studied linear equations (Step 10), we made frequent use of the Pythagorean Theorem. We calculated the slope of a linear equation as the ratio of the Δy to the Δx in a right triangle. We also derived a formula for calculating the distance between any two points in the Cartesian coordinate plane by constructing a right triangle and calculating its hypotenuse. Let's investigate the circle and discover how this theorem forms a bridge to a new mathematical branch of mathematical study and a correspondingly beautiful curve.

The Unit Circle

The circle in Figure 1 is a **unit circle** because its radius is 1 and its origin is the coordinates (0, 0). By the Pythagorean Theorem, the equation of this circle is:

$$x^2 + y^2 = 1$$

We let $P(x, y)$ be a point in Quadrant I on the circumference of this circle. We let the Greek letter *theta*, θ, represent a positive angle, a **directed angle** measured counterclockwise, between the positive x-axis (the three o'clock position), or $\overline{OA}$, the **initial side**, and the hypotenuse $\overline{OP}$, the **terminal side**.[1] We can now identify a new group of very important functions, **circular functions**. Another name for these functions is **trigonometric**[2] **functions**. The Greek astronomer Hipparchus (ca. 180-125 BC), who lived in Rhodes and Alexandria, first systematized the relationships in a right triangle to solve astronomical problems.

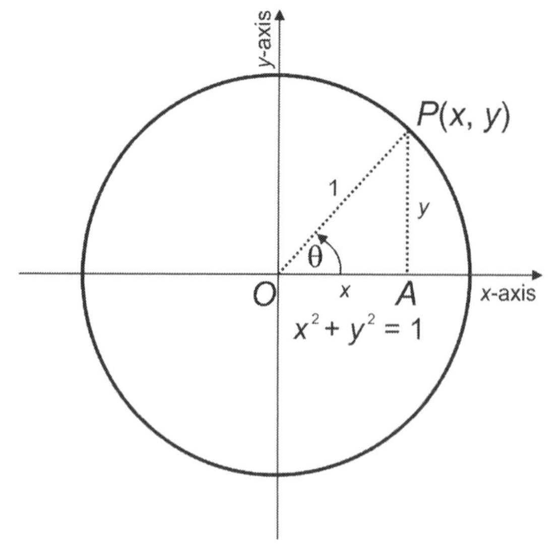

Figure 1. The Pythagorean Theorem in the unit circle.

Similar Right Triangles

Builders and land surveyors in ancient Egypt noticed and made use of a pattern between two similar triangles. The two right triangles in Figure 2 are similar (Lesson 8.1). We note this symbolically by writing $\Delta ABC \sim \Delta DEF$. In we situate these triangles in the Cartesian coordinate plane, we see that the two line segments, $\overline{AB}$ and $\overline{DE}$, have the same slope (Lesson 10.6).

[1] Negative angles are measured clockwise from the initial side to the terminal side of an angle.
[2] Trigonometry is Greek for "triangle measurement." The Greeks did not use this term to name their study of right angle triangles. The German mathematician Bartholomaeus Pitiscus (1561-1613) first used this term in 1596.

In ΔABC, the slope is:

$$\frac{\Delta y}{\Delta x} = \frac{y_2 - y_1}{x_2 - x_1} = \frac{4-2}{2-1} = 2$$

In ΔDEF, the slope is:

$$\frac{\Delta y}{\Delta x} = \frac{y_2 - y_1}{x_2 - x_1} = \frac{6-2}{3-1} = \frac{4}{2} = 2$$

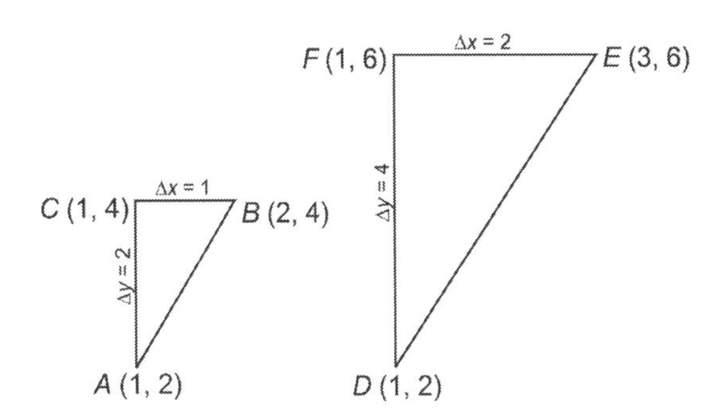

Figure 2. Similar triangles.

In Lesson 8.1, we learned that the corresponding angles of two similar triangles are always equal. In Figure 2:

$m\angle A = m\angle D$, $m\angle B = m\angle E$, and $m\angle C = m\angle F$ (the two right angles)

We also learned that the corresponding sides of two similar triangles are proportional; i.e., they have the same ratio. In Figure 2:

$$\frac{AC}{DF} = \frac{BC}{EF} = \frac{AB}{DE} = \frac{1}{2}$$

As a **corollary**,[3] the ratio of adjacent sides in ΔABC will be equal to the corresponding ratio of adjacent sides in ΔDEF. In Figure 2:

$$\frac{AC}{BC} = \frac{2}{1} = 2 \text{ and } \frac{DF}{EF} = \frac{4}{2} = 2$$

What we need to note is that this equivalence of ratios, $\frac{AC}{BC} = \frac{DF}{EF}$, will remain true for *every* right triangle sharing an acute angle equal to $m\angle A$. This unity in diversity interpenetration is the *key* to understanding the nature of trigonometry because mathematicians ground the elements of trigonometry in these ratios.

THE METHOD OF HIPPARCHUS

The ancient Babylonians knew these trigonometric ratios in the context of the unit circle. Hipparchus borrowed from this source in the construction of his tables of ratios. He began with the circle and its circumference of 360° (Figure 4). Next, he divided the diameter $\overline{AC}$ of the circle into 120 equal parts. Finally, he divided each part of the circumference and diameter into 60 parts, minutes, and each of these into 60 parts, seconds, by using the Babylonian sexagesimal fractions.

Figure 3. Hipparchus, from "The School of Athens," by Raphael. Source: Public Domain.

Therefore, for a given $\overset{\frown}{AB}$ in degrees (Lesson 5.1), Hipparchus gave the number of units in the corresponding **chord**[4]

---

[3] Corollary means "consequence." The word is from the Latin *corollarium* meaning "money paid for a garland or wreath." Corolla is a diminutive of *corona* meaning "wreath or crown." In mathematics, a corollary is a theorem that follows from, and is often appended to, one already proved.

[4] A *chord*, meaning "agreement," is a line segment that joins the ends of an arc.

$\overline{AB}$ using the symbol crd θ to represent the length of the chord of a **central angle**[5] whose measure is θ.

The number of units in the chord $\overline{AB}$ corresponding to the number of degrees in $\overset{\frown}{AB}$ is equivalent to a well-known trigonometric ratio. In Figure 4, this ratio is $\frac{AM}{OA}$. It is the ratio of the length of the side opposite θ to the length of the hypotenuse, the side opposite the right angle.

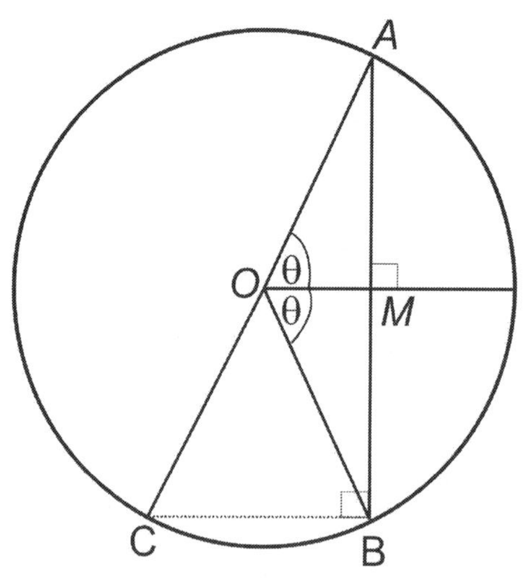

Figure 4. The method of Hipparchus.

Since Hipparchus worked with the diameter $\overline{AC}$ instead of the radius $\overline{OA}$, the ratio he worked with was $\frac{AB}{AC}$, a ratio proportional to $\frac{AM}{OA}$. Why? Since ΔAMO and ΔABC are both right triangles, $\Delta AMO \sim \Delta ABC$.

The measure of the central angle of the $\overset{\frown}{AB}$ is 2θ. A theorem that we can prove in the geometry of circles is that the measure of this central angle 2θ is equal to $m\overset{\frown}{AB}$. Hipparchus, aware of this theorem, set the chord length AB equal to crd 2θ; i.e., AB = crd 2θ. Since AC = 120 units, Hipparchus derived this equation:

$$\frac{AB}{AC} = \frac{\text{crd } 2\theta}{120} = \frac{AM}{OA}$$

Based upon the work of Hipparchus, the Roman astronomer Claudius Ptolemy (ca. 85-ca. 165), who lived in Egypt, calculated a table of chords, in 15-minute intervals, from 0° to 90°. These tables, the first formal western presentation of trigonometry,[6] are printed in his famous work entitled *Almagest*.[7]

Figure 5. Claudius Ptolemy. Source: Public Domain.

THE JOURNEY TO SINE

We now know this trigonometric ratio $\frac{AM}{OA}$ as the **sine** ratio. How we got that word has a fascinating history. We start our voyage in India. The Hindu mathematician and astronomer Aryabhata the Elder (476-ca. 550) named this ratio *ardha-jya*, meaning "half-chord," AM in the Figure 4. *Ardha-jya* was later abbreviated to *jya*, a word that also means "bow string." Since $\overset{\frown}{AB}$ resembles a

[5] A *central angle* of a circle is an angle whose vertex is the center of that circle.
[6] Before Hipparchus, Hindu mathematicians had developed tables of chords in their astronomical work.
[7] *Almagest* is Arabic for "the greatest." This work was originally entitled *Syntaxis mathematica*, meaning "mathematical collection," in which Ptolemy also enshrined the geocentric view of the structure of our Solar System. Arab scientists renamed this work after translating it ca. 827.

bow, a flexible arc which shoots aerodynamic projectiles, i.e., arrows, this connection makes sense.

Next, we travel to the lands of Islam. Arab translators turned *jya* phonetically into *jiba*, a word without meaning in Arabic. According to the Arabic practice of omitting the vowels in writing, a convention similar to Hebrew language, *jiba* turned into *jb*.

Our journey now ends in Western Europe. European Arabic-to-Latin translators, having no knowledge of the Sanskrit (ancient Indic) origin, assumed *jb* to be an abbreviation of *jaib*, Arabic for "cove," "bay," "bulge," or "bosom." Using *jaib* also makes sense because $\widehat{AB}$ looks like a curve or a bulge. When Gerard of Cremona (ca. 1114-1187) translated Ptolemy's *Almagest* in the 12th century, he translated *jaib* into the Latin equivalent *sinus*, meaning "curve," from which we derive the English sine.

THE OTHER TRIG RATIO NAMES

The mathematicians of the Western Europe named the trigonometric ratios by interpreting the lengths of line segments related to the central angle of the unit circle, an angle representing one of the acute angles of a right triangle. Let's see how they did it. Walk slowly through this explanation so that you understand and visually note each inference by referring to Figure 6.

As we have seen in our discussion of the unit circle, we can rotate the radius of the unit circle, $OP = 1$, in a counterclockwise direction. Let's assume the initial position of the radius as $\overline{OA}$. We then rotate the radius segment to $\overline{OP}$, its terminal position. As we do so, the radius segment will generate an angle equal to θ.

The tangents to the circle at points A and B meet the extension of the radius $\overline{OP}$ at E and F respectively. The line segments, $\overline{PC}$, perpendicular to $\overline{OA}$, and $\overline{PD}$, perpendicular to $\overline{OB}$, form three similar right triangles, ΔOCP, ΔOAE, and ΔOBF. Note also the other right triangles in the figure, ΔHOG, ΔODP, ΔHDP, ΔPCG, and ΔOPG.

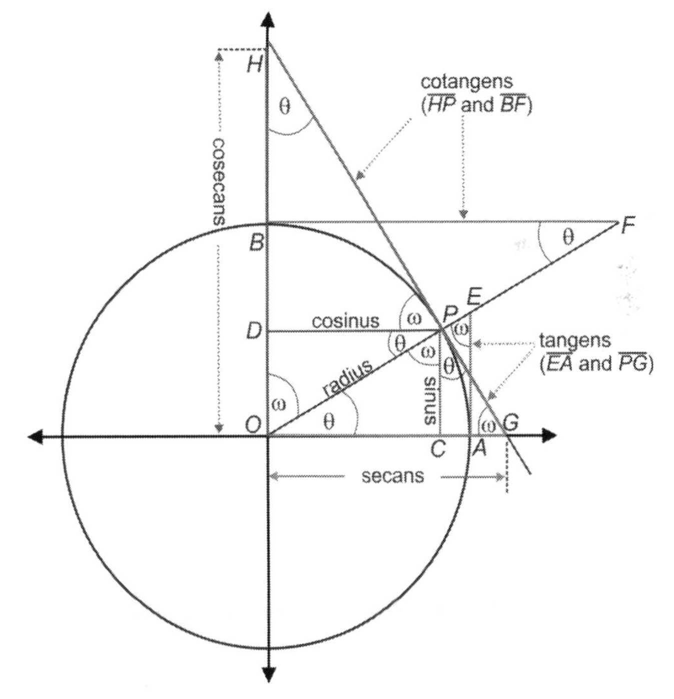

Figure 6. The six trig ratios.

Based upon similarity relationships between right triangles, note equal angles, labeled θ and ω, the Greek letter *omega*.

(Note: $OA = OB = OP = 1$ since all radii of a circle are equal.)

Consider the line segment $\overline{HG}$ tangent to the circle at P. It can be divided into two segments, $\overline{PG}$ and $\overline{PH}$ such that:

- $PG = AE$
- $PH = BF$

Why? $\Delta OAE \cong \Delta OPG$, where $\cong$ is the symbol for congruence, and $\Delta HPO \cong \Delta FBO$. When two triangles are congruent, having the same shape and size, their corresponding parts, sides and angles, are equal.

To prove this congruence, we invoke some geometric congruence[8] theorems, propositions that state the minimum requirement for the congruency of two triangles. One theorem states that two triangles are congruent if two angles and their included side of one triangle is equal to the corresponding two angles and their included side of the second triangle.[9]

Note carefully, when comparing ΔOAE with ΔOPG:

1. $m\angle OEA = m\angle OGP = \omega$ (angle)
2. OA (radius) $= OP$ (radius) $= 1$ (included side)
3. $m\angle EOA = m\angle GOP = \theta$ (angle)

Note also, when comparing ΔHPO with ΔFBO:

1. $m\angle OHP = m\angle OFB = \theta$ (angle)
2. PO (radius) $= BO$ (radius) $= 1$ (included side)
3. $m\angle HOP = m\angle FOB = \omega$ (angle)

From these definitions and observations, we can develop the following ratios and equalities:

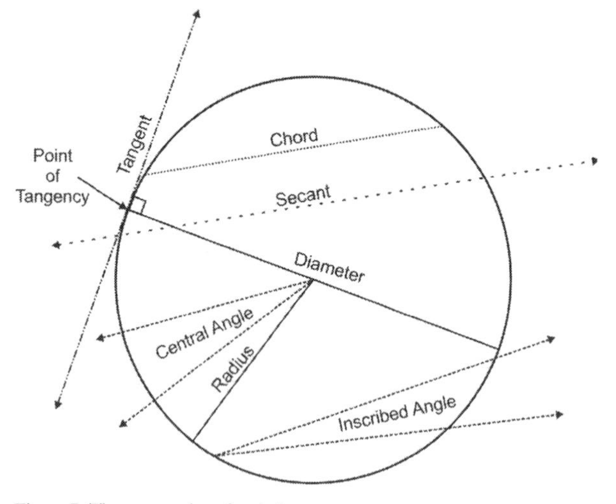

Figure 7. The geography of a circle.

- radius $= OA = OB = OP = 1$
- **sinus** $\theta = \dfrac{PC}{OP} = PC = OD$
- **cosinus** $\theta = \dfrac{OC}{OP} = OC = PD$
- **tangens** $\theta = \dfrac{AE}{OA} = AE = PG = \dfrac{PC}{OC}$
- **cotangus** $\theta = \dfrac{BF}{OB} = BF = PH = \dfrac{OC}{PC}$
- **secans** $\theta = \dfrac{OE}{OA} = OE = OG = \dfrac{OP}{OC}$
- **cosecans** $\theta = \dfrac{OF}{OB} = OF = OH = \dfrac{OP}{PC}$

[8] According to Lesson 4.2, congruent figures are the same size and shape.

[9] In brief, this theorem is the ASA (angle-included side-angle) Congruence theorem, Book I, Proposition 26 (first part) of Euclid's *Elements*. Other congruence theorems involving three components of a triangle are, as acronyms, SSS, SAS, and AAS (the second part of Book I, Proposition 26). See the relevant homework exercise in Lesson 12.12.

In 1583, Thomas Fincke (1561-1656) introduced names to two ratios that had been known by other names:

- Tangent (Latin: *tangere*) means "to touch."
- Secant (Latin: *secare*) means "to cut."

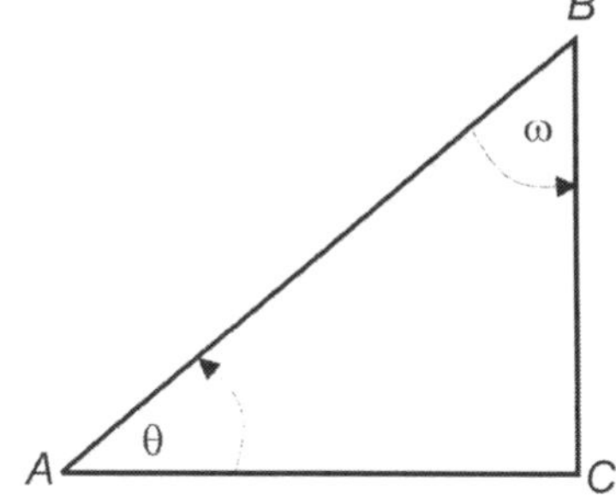

Figure 8. Right ΔABC.

The English mathematician and astronomer Edmund Gunter (1581-1626) first suggested cosine, cotangent, and co-secant in 1620, replacing *sinus complementi* and *tangens complementi*: the *sinus* and *tangens* of the complimentary angles.

Today, we abbreviate sine as **sin**, cosine as **cos**, tangent as **tan**, cotangent as **cot**, secant as **sec**, and cosecant as **csc**. In Figure 8, we note all six ratios,[10] related to the three sides of the right ΔABC, where θ is an acute angle.

We summarize the names and their associated ratios as follows:[11] (See if you can make sense of these ratios given the above discussion.)

1. $\sin\theta = \dfrac{BC}{AB}$ (side **o**pposite θ over the **h**ypotenuse)

   MEMORY AID: *soh* (sine, opposite, hypotenuse)

   a. $\cos\theta = \dfrac{AC}{AB}$ (side **a**djacent θ over the **h**ypotenuse)

      MEMORY AID: *cah* (cosine, adjacent, hypotenuse)

      i. $\tan\theta = \dfrac{BC}{AC}$ (side **o**pposite θ over the side **a**djacent θ)

         MEMORY AID: *toa* (tangent, opposite, adjacent)

      ii. $\cot\theta = \dfrac{AC}{BC}$ (side adjacent θ over the side opposite θ)

   b. $\sec\theta = \dfrac{AB}{AC}$ (hypotenuse over the side adjacent θ)

2. $\csc\theta = \dfrac{AB}{BC}$ (hypotenuse over the side opposite θ)

RECIPROCAL RELATIONSHIPS

Scientific calculators have specific keys for the sin, cos, and tan ratios. Also, note the dance of these reciprocal relationships, or reciprocal identities, based on Figure 8:

1. $\sin\theta = \dfrac{BC}{AB}$ and $\csc\theta = \dfrac{AB}{BC} \Rightarrow (\sin\theta)(\csc\theta) = \dfrac{\overset{1}{\cancel{BC}}}{\underset{1}{\cancel{AB}}}\cdot\dfrac{\overset{1}{\cancel{AB}}}{\underset{1}{\cancel{BC}}} = 1$

---

[10] 3! = 6, the Fundamental Counting Principle from Step 9.

[11] We engage the Hebrew literary structure known as chiasm so we can note the reciprocal connection between sine and cosecant, cosine and secant, and tangent and cotangent.

Therefore:

$$\sin\theta = \frac{1}{\csc\theta} \text{ and } \csc\theta = \frac{1}{\sin\theta}$$

2. $\cos\theta = \dfrac{AC}{AB}$ and $\sec\theta = \dfrac{AB}{AC} \Rightarrow (\cos\theta)(\sec\theta) = \dfrac{\cancel{AC}}{\cancel{AB}} \cdot \dfrac{\cancel{AB}}{\cancel{AC}} = 1$

Therefore:

$$\cos\theta = \frac{1}{\sec\theta} \text{ and } \sec\theta = \frac{1}{\cos\theta}$$

3. $\tan\theta = \dfrac{BC}{AC}$ and $\cot\theta = \dfrac{AC}{BC} \Rightarrow (\tan\theta)(\cot\theta) = \dfrac{\cancel{BC}}{\cancel{AC}} \cdot \dfrac{\cancel{AC}}{\cancel{BC}} = 1$

Therefore:

$$\tan\theta = \frac{1}{\cot\theta} \text{ and } \cot\theta = \frac{1}{\tan\theta}$$

Also, note:

1. $\sin\theta = \dfrac{BC}{AB}$ and $\cos\theta = \dfrac{AC}{AB} \Rightarrow \dfrac{\sin\theta}{\cos\theta} =$

$$\frac{\frac{BC}{AB}}{\frac{AC}{AB}} = \frac{BC}{AB} \div \frac{AC}{AB} = \frac{BC}{\cancel{AB}} \cdot \frac{\cancel{AB}}{AC} = \frac{BC}{AC} = \tan\theta$$

Therefore:

$$\frac{\sin\theta}{\cos\theta} = \tan\theta$$

2. $\sin\theta = \dfrac{BC}{AB}$ and $\cos\theta = \dfrac{AC}{AB} \Rightarrow \dfrac{\cos\theta}{\sin\theta} =$

$$\frac{\frac{AC}{AB}}{\frac{BC}{AB}} = \frac{AC}{AB} \div \frac{BC}{AB} = \frac{AC}{\cancel{AB}} \cdot \frac{\cancel{AB}}{BC} = \frac{AC}{BC} = \cot\theta$$

Therefore:

$$\frac{\cos\theta}{\sin\theta} = \cot\theta$$

COMPLEMENTARY ANGLES

Since $\theta + \omega = 90°$ (the measure of a right angle), we call ω the complementary[12] angle of θ. Remember from Lesson 8.7, two angles are complimentary if their sum is 90°. The *co-* prefix in

[12] Complement comes from the Latin meaning "to fill out" or "to complete."

cosinus, cosecant, and cotangent carry the complementary angle concept in their etymology. We write this equivalency:

$\theta + \omega = 90° \Leftrightarrow \omega = 90° - \theta$

Based on Figure 8, we discover this complementary dance, or trig complementary identities:

1. $\sin\theta = \dfrac{BC}{AB} = \cos\omega = \cos(90° - \theta)$ and $\cos\theta = \dfrac{AC}{AB} = \sin\omega = \sin(90° - \theta)$

   Therefore:

$\sin\theta = \cos(90° - \theta)$ and $\cos\theta = \sin(90° - \theta)$

2. $\sec\theta = \dfrac{AB}{AC} = \csc\omega = \csc(90° - \theta)$ and $\csc\theta = \dfrac{AB}{BC} = \sec\omega = \sec(90° - \theta)$

   Therefore:

$\sec\theta = \csc(90° - \theta)$ and $\csc\theta = \sec(90° - \theta)$

3. $\tan\theta = \dfrac{BC}{AC} = \cot\omega = \cot(90° - \theta)$ and $\cot\theta = \dfrac{AC}{BC} = \tan\omega = \tan(90° - \theta)$

   Therefore:

$\tan\theta = \cot(90° - \theta)$ and $\cot\theta = \tan(90° - \theta)$

QUADRANT I BEHAVIOR

Let's investigate the nature of these ratios as θ varies in measurement from 0° to 90° (Figure 9); i.e., θ is acute. First, we set the circle as a unit circle, i.e., hypotenuse = 1.

Since $\sin\theta = \dfrac{\text{side opposite } \theta}{\text{hypotenuse}}$, then:

- $\sin\theta = \dfrac{BC}{1} = BC$
- $\cos\theta = \dfrac{AC}{1} = AC$
- $\tan\theta = \dfrac{BC}{AC} = DE$

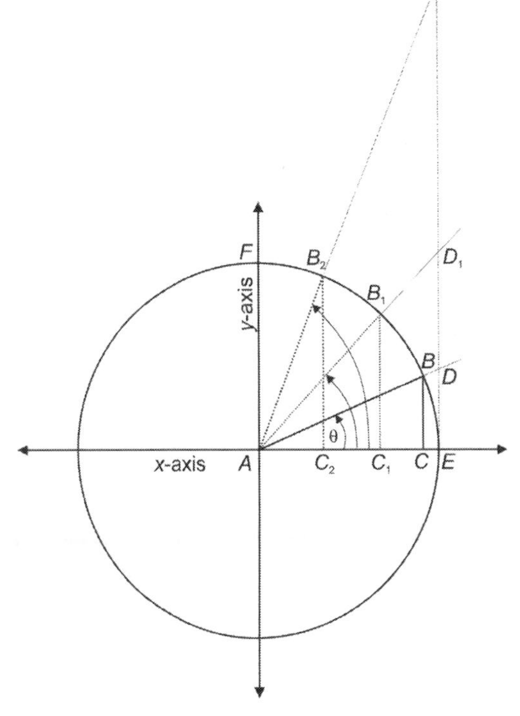

Figure 9. The behavior of the sine, cosine, and tangent ratios.

As θ gets lesser, *BC* gets lesser and *AC* gets greater; it approaches *AE*. If θ = 0, then:

- $\sin\theta = 0$ since $BC = 0$
- $\cos\theta = 1$ since $AC = 1$
- $\tan\theta = \dfrac{BC}{AC} = DE = 0$

As θ gets greater, *BC* gets greater and *AC* gets lesser. Note: $B_2C_2 > B_1C_1 > BC$ and $A_2C_2 < A_1C_1 < AC$. Also, note: $D_2E > D_1E > DE$. As θ gets greater, tan θ gets very, very great in the positive direction.

If $\theta = 90°$, then:

- $\sin \theta = 1$ since $FA = 1$
- $\cos \theta = 0$ since C becomes A.
- $\tan \theta = \dfrac{BC}{AC}$ is undefined (Lesson 5.15) since we cannot divide by 0.

  If $\theta = 89.9°$:

  $$\frac{BC}{AC} = 572.96$$

  If $\theta = 89.99999999°$:

  $$\frac{BC}{AC} = 5{,}729{,}577{,}951$$

  We also note:

  As $\sin \theta \to 1$, $\cos \theta \to 0 \Rightarrow \tan \theta$ gets greater and greater because $\tan\theta = \dfrac{BC}{AC} = \dfrac{\sin\theta}{\cos\theta}$.

We now know the behavior of three trigonometric functions as θ varies in measurement from 0° to 90° (Table 1).

Table 1

θ	sin θ	cos θ	tan θ
0°	0	1	0
As θ goes from 0° to 90°	goes from 0 to 1	goes from 1 to 0	goes from 0 to very large
90°	1	0	Undefined

SPECIAL ANGLES

What happens to some of the degree measures between 0° to 90°? Let's consider at the equilateral ΔABD with each side of length 2 (Figure 10). This type of triangle is also equiangular; i.e., each angle equals 60°.

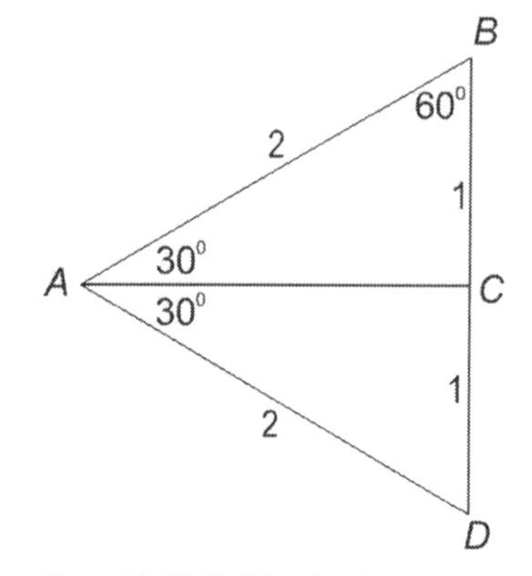

Figure 10. 30-60 right triangle.

Construct an angle bisector[13] AC of $\angle BAD$. Therefore:

$$m\angle BAC = m\angle DAC = 30°$$

Since $AB = AD = BD = 2$, then $CB = CD = 1$ because the angle bisector of $\angle BAD$ is also the perpendicular bisector[14] of $\overline{BD}$.

What is AC? By the Pythagorean Theorem:

$$AD^2 = AC^2 + CD^2 \Leftrightarrow AC^2 = AD^2 - CD^2$$

Therefore, we calculate AC as follows:

---

[13] Remember, an angle bisector divides a given angle in half (Lesson 5.3).

[14] Remember, the perpendicular bisector is a line divides a given line segment in half intersecting it at a 90° angle (Lesson 5.2).

$AC = \sqrt{AD^2 - CD^2} = \sqrt{4-1} = \sqrt{3}$

Knowing these lengths, we can determine the trigonometric ratios for 30° and 60°:

- $\sin 30° = \frac{1}{2}$
- $\cos 30° = \frac{\sqrt{3}}{2} \approx 0.866$
- $\tan 30° = \frac{1}{\sqrt{3}} = \frac{\sqrt{3}}{3} \approx 0.577$ (See footnote[15])
- $\sin 60° = \frac{\sqrt{3}}{2} \approx 0.866$
- $\cos 60° = \frac{1}{2}$
- $\tan 60° = \sqrt{3} \approx 1.732$ (Memory aid: George Washington, the first President of the United States, was born in 1732.)

Now, let's consider 45° (Figure 11). First, draw two line segments $\overline{AB}$ and $\overline{DB}$ perpendicular to each other, i.e., $m\angle ABD = 90°$. Second, draw an angle bisector $\overline{BC}$ of $\angle ABD$ with length of 1 unit. Construct a line segment $\overline{AD}$ perpendicular to $\overline{BC}$ of 2 units in length so that $\overline{BC}$ is the perpendicular bisector of $\overline{AD}$. ΔBCD is now a right triangle with legs $DC = BC = 1$. Knowing these lengths, DB, the length of the hypotenuse of ΔBCD, is:

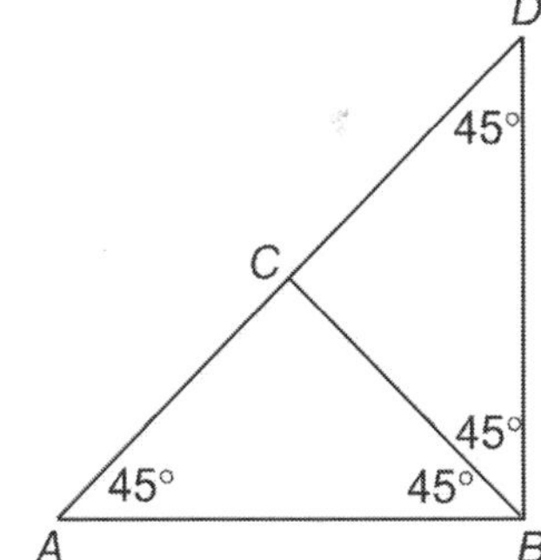

Figure 11. 45-45 right triangle.

$DB = \sqrt{DC^2 - BC^2} = \sqrt{1+1} = \sqrt{2}$

We, therefore, know:

- $\sin 45° = \cos 45° = \frac{1}{\sqrt{2}} = \frac{\sqrt{2}}{2} \approx 0.707$ (after rationalizing the denominator[16])
- $\tan 45° = 1$

Table 2 includes these results. Do you see the beautiful symmetry dancing between sin θ and cos θ? (Hint: Think complements.)

---

[15] It is a mathematical convention to not leave a root in the denominator of a fraction; i.e., $\sqrt{3}$ in $\frac{1}{\sqrt{3}}$. In this case, we **rationalize the denominator** by multiplying the numerator and denominator by $\sqrt{3}$. Therefore, $\frac{1}{\sqrt{3}} = \frac{\sqrt{3}}{\sqrt{3}\cdot\sqrt{3}} = \frac{\sqrt{3}}{3}$. The reason for doing this rationalization is that, in pre-calculator days, it was easier to generate a decimal estimate by dividing by a rational number 3 than by an irrational number $\sqrt{3}$.

[16] $\frac{1}{\sqrt{2}} = \frac{\sqrt{2}}{\sqrt{2}\cdot\sqrt{2}} = \frac{\sqrt{2}}{2}$

Table 2

θ (°)	θ (rad)	sin θ	cos θ	tan θ
0°	0	0	1	0
30°	$\frac{\pi}{6}$	$\frac{1}{2} = 0.5$	$\frac{\sqrt{3}}{2} \approx 0.866$	$\frac{\sqrt{3}}{3} \approx 0.577$
45°	$\frac{\pi}{4}$	$\frac{\sqrt{2}}{2} \approx 0.707$	$\frac{\sqrt{2}}{2} \approx 0.707$	1
60°	$\frac{\pi}{3}$	$\frac{\sqrt{3}}{2} \approx 0.866$	$\frac{1}{2} = 0.5$	$\sqrt{3} \approx 1.732$
90°	$\frac{\pi}{2}$	1	0	Undefined

PYTHAGOREAN RELATIONSHIPS

In the unit circle (Figure 1 at the beginning of this lesson), we know, by the Pythagorean Theorem:

$x^2 + y^2 = 1 \Leftrightarrow y^2 + x^2 = 1$

Since sin θ = y and cos θ = x, we substitute:

$(\sin\theta)^2 + (\cos\theta)^2 = 1$

When we square a trigonometric ratio, it is mathematical convention to write $(\sin\theta)^2$ and $(\cos\theta)^2$ in a different form. We write:

$\sin^2\theta$ instead of $(\sin\theta)^2$
$\cos^2\theta$ instead of $(\cos\theta)^2$

Therefore, $(\sin\theta)^2 + (\cos\theta)^2 = 1$ is written this way, the fundamental Pythagorean identity in trigonometry:

$$\boxed{\sin^2\theta + \cos^2\theta = 1}$$

Dividing both sides by $\cos^2\theta$, we get:

$$\frac{\sin^2\theta}{\cos^2\theta} + 1 = \frac{1}{\cos^2\theta} \Leftrightarrow$$

$$\boxed{\tan\theta + 1 = \sec^2\theta}$$

Why?

Dividing both sides of $\sin^2\theta + \cos^2\theta = 1$ by $\sin^2\theta$, we get:

$$1 + \frac{\cos^2\theta}{\sin^2\theta} = \frac{1}{\sin^2\theta} \Leftrightarrow$$

$$\boxed{1 + \cot\theta = \csc^2\theta}$$

Why?

RADIANS

Note the second column in Table 2 where the abbreviation *rad* stands for **radians**. Radians is the preferred way to denote angle measure in trigonometry. In Figure 12, We can write $m\overset{\frown}{BC}$ in degrees or radians, a word associated with radius. James Thomson (1822-1892), brother of the renowned physicist William Thomson, as known as Lord Kelvin (1824-1907), first used radians in 1871. Radian measure is the measure the length of the arc in a curve like a circle. It is the standard angular measure in the International System of Units (SI).

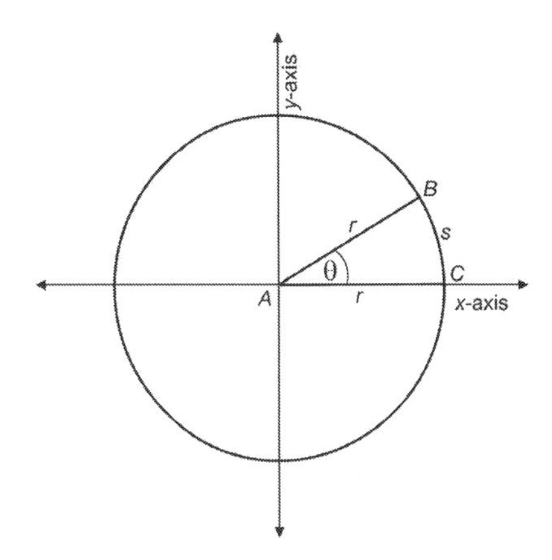

Figure 12. Radians.

In general, the radian measure of θ in Figure 12 is determined by dividing the arc length, $s = m\overset{\frown}{BC}$, by r, the radius of the circle.

We write:

$$\theta = \frac{s}{r}$$

Because the units of measure for s and r are configured to be the same (e.g., inches, centimeters, etc.), this ratio is unitless; it is just a real number. When we, therefore, measure angles in radians, we state a number; we do not append a unit to it.

When $r = s$, one radian is the angle, measured at the center of a circle, that subtends[17] an arc length of one radius along the circle's circumference. Since the circumference C of a circle measures 2π radii ($C = 2\pi r$ where r = radius) and since each of these radii corresponds to a central angle of 1 radian, we have this relationship in the unit circle:

Conversion facts:
$360° = 2\pi \Leftrightarrow 180° = \pi$
$1° \approx 0.01745$ radians
1 radian $\approx 57.2958°$

$360° = 2\pi$ (≈ 6.28) Remember this!

Therefore:

- $180° = \pi$ (≈ 3.14)
- $90° = \frac{\pi}{2}$ (≈ 1.57) since $\frac{180°}{2} = 90°$ and $\pi \div 2 = \frac{\pi}{2}$
- $60° = \frac{\pi}{3}$ (≈ 1.05) since $\frac{180°}{3} = 60°$ and $\pi \div 3 = \frac{\pi}{3}$
- $45° = \frac{\pi}{4}$ (≈ 0.785) since $\frac{90°}{2} = 45°$ and $\frac{\pi}{2} \div 2 = \frac{\pi}{4}$
- $30° = \frac{\pi}{6}$ (≈ 0.524) since $\frac{60°}{2} = 30°$ and $\frac{\pi}{3} \div 2 = \frac{\pi}{6}$

Also:

- $360° = 2\pi \Leftrightarrow 1° = \frac{2\pi}{360°} = \frac{\pi}{180°} \approx 0.01745$ radians

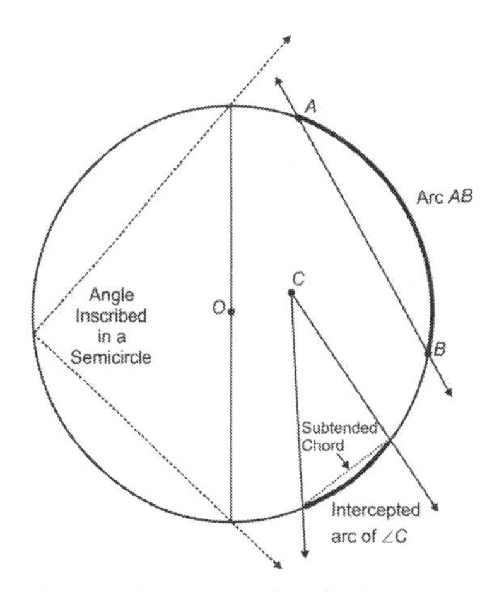

Figure 13. More geography of a circle.

[17] Subtend, from Latin, means "under stretch." In geometry, it means "to extend underneath." See Lesson 7.11.

- $360° = 2\pi \Leftrightarrow 1 \text{ radian} = \frac{360°}{2\pi} = \frac{180°}{\pi} \approx 57.2958°$

As a proportion, where *r* is in radians and *d* is in degrees:

$$\frac{d}{180} = \frac{r}{\pi}$$

To convert *d* degrees to *r* radians:

$$\frac{d}{180} = \frac{r}{\pi} \Leftrightarrow r = \frac{\pi d}{180}$$

To convert *r* radians to *d* degrees:

$$\frac{d}{180} = \frac{r}{\pi} \Leftrightarrow d = \frac{180r}{\pi}$$

Memorize this!

$$\frac{d}{180} = \frac{r}{\pi}$$

where *d* is in degrees and *r* is in radians.

In higher branches of Mathematics, namely Calculus, radian measure simplifies many formulas, and that is why mathematicians use it.

Older mathematics textbooks had trig tables in addition to log tables in the back of the book. With the advent of the scientific calculator,[18] we no longer need these tables. You can enter any degree or radian on the keys of these calculators and then punch the sin, cos, or tan key to get the corresponding approximate ratio in decimal form.

> During the first half of the 14th century an important school of astronomy grew up also at Oxford, in particular at Merton College. One of the results of the work there was the development of trigonometry ... John Maudith (1310) and Richard of Wallingford (c. 1292-1335) are the initiators of Western trigonometry.... An important improvement in technique adopted by these writers was to use the Hindu-Arabic practice, already found in the tables of al-Zarqali and other astronomical tables in wide circulation, of basing plane trigonometry on sines instead of chords, as had been done in the old Greco-Roman tradition dating from Hipparchus.
>
> Alistair C. Crombie, *The History of Science from Augustine to Galileo*, ([1959, 1970, 1979] 1995), I:110.

EXERCISES

Define the following words, phrases, or symbol:

1. Unit circle
2. Directed angle
3. Initial side of an angle
4. Terminal side of an angle
5. Circular (trigonometric) functions
6. Corollary
7. Chord

[18] These calculators have both degree and radian modes. Make sure you set these modes correctly.

8. Central angle (in a circle)
9. *Almagest*
10. Sine
11. ≅
12. Cosine
13. Tangent
14. Cotangent
15. Secant
16. Cosecant
17. Rationalizing the denominator
18. Radian measure

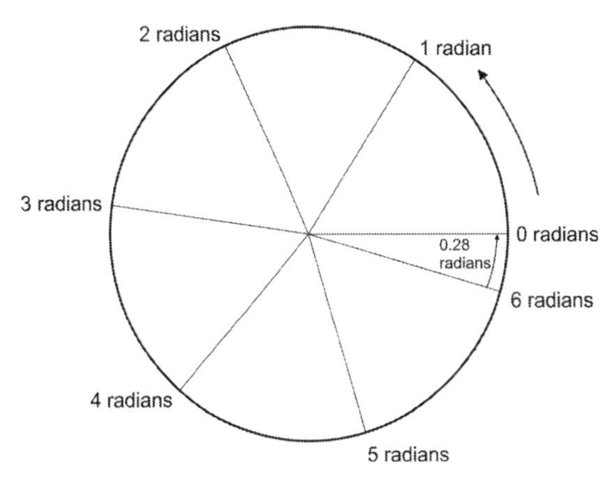

Figure 14. Radians around a circle.

Answer the following questions:

19. Lay two quarters on a flat surface so that their edges are in contact. Hold one still and roll the other one around it so that it starts and ends at the same place. How many rotations does the moving quarter make?
20. If one circular gear has 80 teeth and a second circular gear has 40 teeth, how many revolutions will the lesser gear make while rotating around the circumference of the greater gear, starting and ending at the same place?
21. If one circle has a circumference of 13 in and a second circle has a circumference of 2.6 in, how many revolutions will the lesser circle make while rotating around the circumference of the greater circle, starting and ending at the same place?
22. If one circle has a circumference of r in and a second circle has a circumference of k in ($r > k$), how many revolutions will the lesser circle make while rotating around the circumference of the greater circle, starting and ending at the same place?
23. True or False. When a directed angle is measured counterclockwise, it is designated as a negative angle.

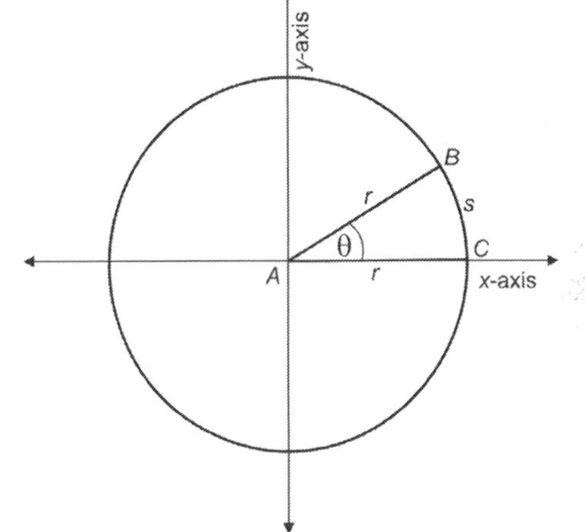

Figure 15.

24. In Figure 15, $m\overset{\frown}{BC} = s$, $AC = AB = r$.
    (a) State the measure of θ in radians regarding r and s.
    (b) If $s = r$, state the measure of θ in radians.
25. Prove that, in general, $\tan\theta = \dfrac{\sin\theta}{\cos\theta}$.

26. Prove that, in general, $\cot\theta = \dfrac{\cos\theta}{\sin\theta}$.

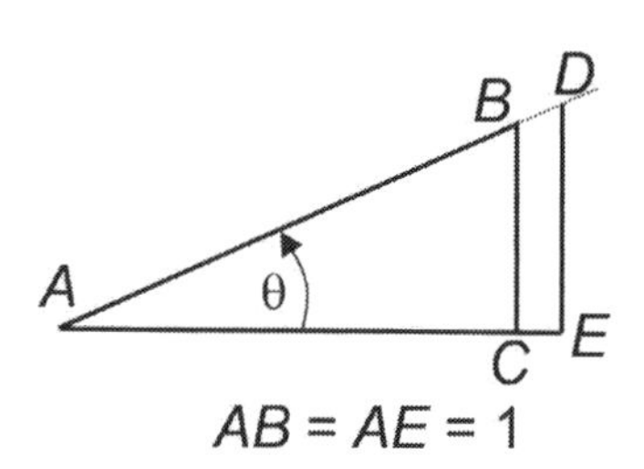

Figure 16.

27. Why is $\dfrac{\sin^2\theta}{\cos^2\theta} + 1 = \dfrac{1}{\cos^2\theta} \Leftrightarrow \tan^2\theta + 1 = \sec^2\theta$?

28. Why is $1 + \dfrac{\cos^2\theta}{\sin^2\theta} = \dfrac{1}{\sin^2\theta} \Leftrightarrow 1 + \cot^2\theta = \csc^2\theta$?

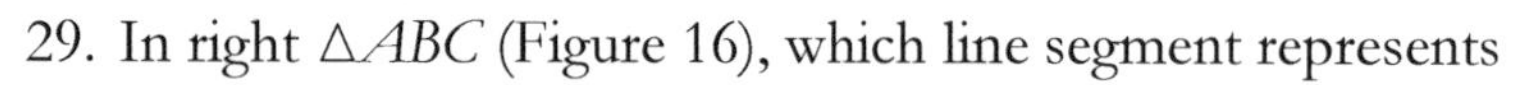

29. In right $\triangle ABC$ (Figure 16), which line segment represents (a) $\sin\theta$, (b) $\cos\theta$, and (c) $\tan\theta$?

30. Explain this notation: $\lim\limits_{\theta \to \pi/2} \tan\theta = \infty$

31. What is the meaning of the prefix "co" in cotangent, cosine, and cosecant?

32. What was the initial reason for invoking the method of rationalizing the denominator?

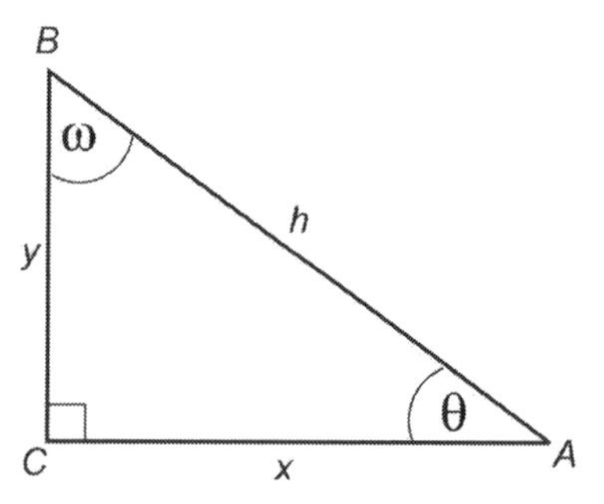

Figure 17.

Given the right $\triangle ABC$ (Figure 17) where $y = BC$, $h = AB$, and $x = AC$:

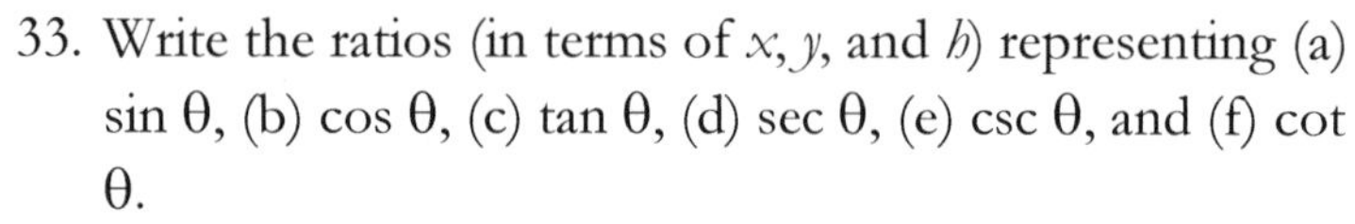

33. Write the ratios (in terms of x, y, and h) representing (a) $\sin\theta$, (b) $\cos\theta$, (c) $\tan\theta$, (d) $\sec\theta$, (e) $\csc\theta$, and (f) $\cot\theta$.

From these definitions show that the following identities are true:

34. $\tan\theta = \dfrac{\sin\theta}{\cos\theta}$

35. $\cot\theta = \dfrac{\cos\theta}{\sin\theta}$

36. $\sec\theta = \dfrac{1}{\cos\theta}$

37. $\csc\theta = \dfrac{1}{\sin\theta}$

From the same definitions, prove the following reciprocal identities:

38. $\tan\theta = \dfrac{1}{\cot\theta}$

39. $\sec\theta = \dfrac{1}{\cos\theta}$

40. $\csc\theta = \dfrac{1}{\sin\theta}$

If two angles θ and ω are complementary, then $\theta + \omega = 90°$:

41. Write a formula for θ in terms of ω.

42. Write a formula for ω in terms of θ.

Use Figure 17, to prove the following identities:

43. $\sin\theta = \cos(90° - \theta)$

44. $\cos\theta = \sin(90° - \theta)$
45. $\tan\theta = \cot(90° - \theta)$
46. $\cot\theta = \tan(90° - \theta)$

If two angles θ and ω are complementary, then show: (Hint: Make use of Figure 17.)
47. $\sin\theta = \cos\omega$
48. $\cos\theta = \sin\omega$
49. $\tan\theta = \cot\omega$
50. $\cot\theta = \tan\omega$
51. $\sec\theta = \csc\omega$
52. $\csc\theta = \sec\omega$

If $360° = 2\pi$ radians:
53. One degree equals how many radians (leave your answer in π)?
54. One radian equals how many degrees (leave your answer in π)?

Using the proportion $\frac{d}{180} = \frac{r}{\pi}$, convert the following from degrees to radians (leave your answer in π):
55. 15°
56. 30°
57. 45°
58. 60°
59. 90°
60. 120°
61. 160°
62. 240°
63. 260°
64. 320°

Using the proportion $\frac{d}{180} = \frac{r}{\pi}$, convert the following from radians to degrees:

65. $\frac{\pi}{2}$
66. $\frac{\pi}{3}$

67. $\frac{\pi}{4}$

68. $\frac{\pi}{5}$

69. $\frac{\pi}{6}$

70. $\frac{3\pi}{2}$

71. $\frac{5\pi}{6}$

72. $\frac{7\pi}{8}$

73. 3π

74. $\frac{7\pi}{2}$

75. $\frac{8\pi}{3}$

76. $\frac{9\pi}{5}$

> We turned aside, not indeed to the uplands of the Delectable Mountains, but into a strange corridor of things like anagrams and acrostics called Sines, Cosines and Tangents ... I have never met these creatures since. With my third and successful examination they passed away like the phantasmagoria of a fevered dream. I am assured that they are most helpful in engineering, astronomy and things like that. It is very important to build bridges and canals and to comprehend all the stresses and potentialities of matter, to say nothing of counting all the stars and even universes and measuring how far off they are, and foretelling eclipses, the arrival of comets and such like. I am very glad there are quite a number of people born with a gift and a liking for all of this; like great chess-players who play sixteen games at once blindfold and die quite soon of epilepsy. Serve them right! I hope the Mathematicians, however, are well rewarded. I promise never to backleg their profession nor take the bread out of their mouths.
>
> Winston Churchill, "Examinations," *My Early Life: 1874-1904* ([1930, 1958] 1996), p. 26.

Answer these questions:

77. In Figure 18, find $\frac{AB}{BC}$ as a fraction in lowest terms. (Hint: To start, let $AD = 1$.)

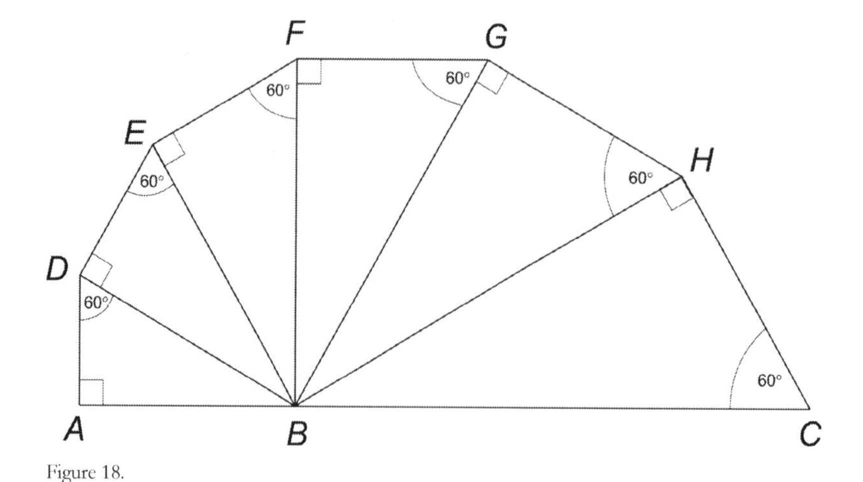

Figure 18.

78. Complete the following conversion table (leave answers in π or as rational numbers where necessary). Remember, 1 mil is $\frac{1}{6400}$ of a circle, and 1 grad is $\frac{1}{400}$ of a circle.

	TO:			
FROM:	**Degrees**	**Radians**	**Grads**	**Mils**
1 Degree is:	--------------			
1 Radian is:		--------------		
1 Grad is:			--------------	
1 Mil is:				--------------

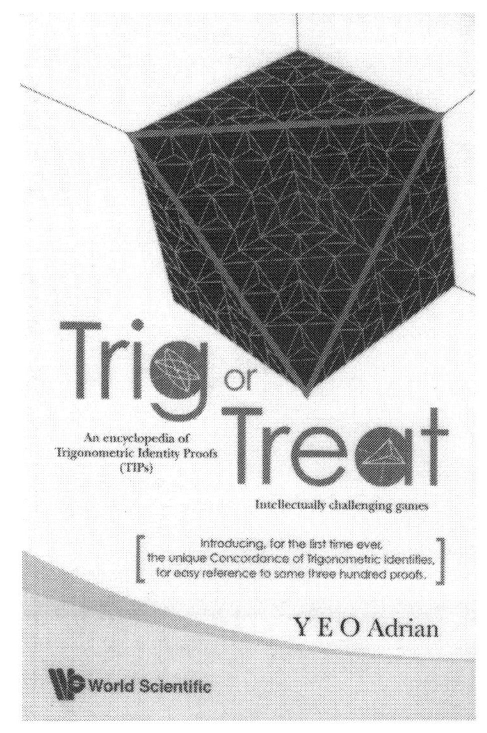

Figure 19.

12.7 The Oscillatory Dance

Terms, Symbols & Concepts Introduced
1. Algebraic function
2. ASTC
3. Coterminal angles
4. Law of Sines
5. Period
6. Periodic function
7. Power series
8. Transcendental function

How do the trigonometric ratios behave between 90° to 360°? For Quadrant I (from 0° to 90°), all ratios are positive as we measure θ counterclockwise from the positive x-axis or the three-o'clock position.

Quadrant II Behavior (from 90° to 180°)

Let's consider a typical angle $\angle EAB_3$, in Quadrant II. This angle is an obtuse angle, and the slope of line segment $\overline{B_3A}$ is negative. Why? The coordinates of A are (0, 0), and the coordinates of B_3 are, in general, $(-x, y)$. The slope, the tangent ratio, is:

$$\frac{\Delta y}{\Delta x} = \frac{y}{-x} = -\frac{y}{x}$$

We determine the trigonometric ratios for any obtuse angle in Quadrant II by applying our definitions to $\angle B_3AC_3$ in right ΔB_3AC_3. Remember, the radius of this unit circle is 1. If we let $\theta = \angle B_3AC_3$, we get:

- $\sin\theta = y = B_3C_3$
- $\cos\theta = -x = AC_3$
- $\tan\theta = -\dfrac{y}{x} = D_3E$

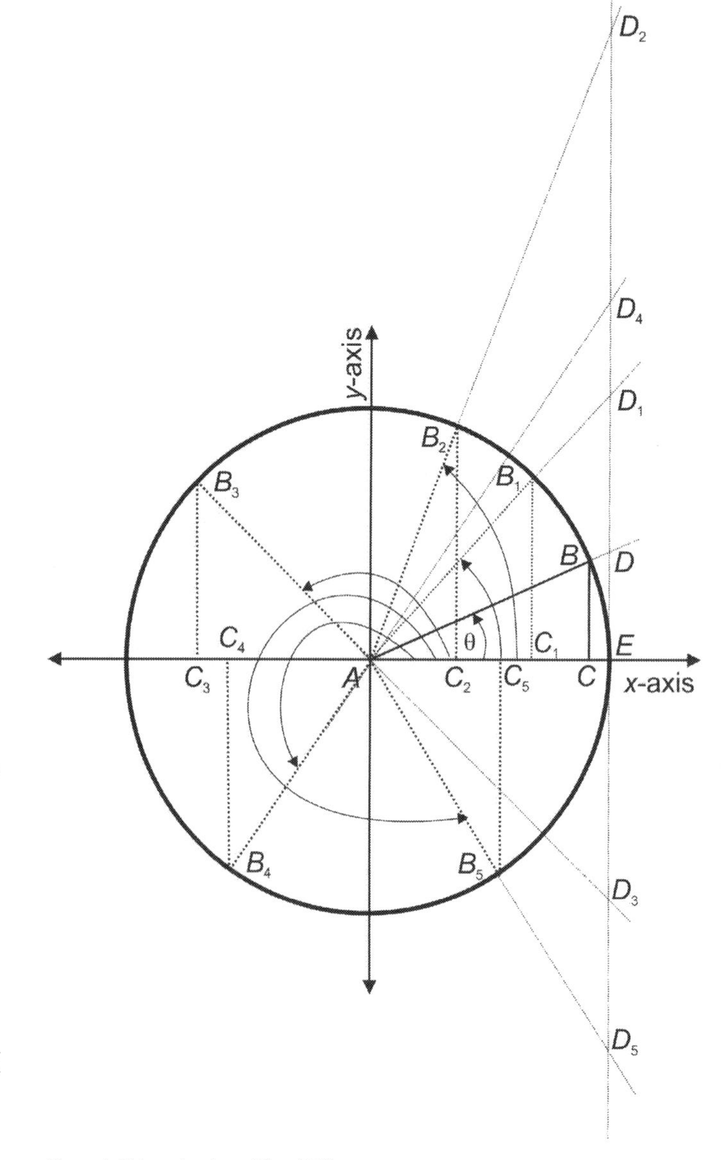

Figure 1. Trig ratios from 0° to 360°.

Quadrant III Behavior (from 180° to 270°)

Let's consider a typical angle, $\angle EAB_4$, in Quadrant III. This angle is also an obtuse angle, and the slope of line segment $\overline{B_4A}$ is positive because the coordinates of A are (0, 0), and the coordinates of B_4 are, in general, $(-x, -y)$. The slope, the tangent ratio is:

$$\frac{\Delta y}{\Delta x} = \frac{-y}{-x} = \frac{y}{x}$$

We determine the trigonometric ratios for any obtuse angle in Quadrant III by applying our definitions to $\angle B_4AC_4$ in right ΔB_4AC_4. If we let $\theta = \angle B_4AC_4$, we get:

- $\sin\theta = -y = B_4C_4$

- $\cos\theta = -x = AC_4$
- $\tan\theta = \dfrac{-y}{-x} = \dfrac{y}{x} = D_4E$

QUADRANT IV BEHAVIOR (FROM 270° TO 360°)

Finally, let's consider a typical angle, $\angle EAB_5$, in Quadrant IV. This angle is also an obtuse angle, and the slope of line segment $\overline{B_5A}$ is negative because the coordinates of A are (0, 0), and the coordinates of B_5 are, in general, $(x, -y)$. The slope, the tangent ratio, is:

$$\frac{\Delta y}{\Delta x} = \frac{-y}{x} = -\frac{y}{x}$$

We determine the trigonometric ratios for any obtuse angle in Quadrant IV by applying our definitions to $\angle B_5AC_5$ in right ΔB_5AC_5. If we let $\theta = \angle B_5AC_5$, we get:

- $\sin\theta = -y = B_5C_5$
- $\cos\theta = x = AC_5$
- $\tan\theta = -\dfrac{y}{x} = D_5E$

From this analysis, we can complete Table 1, trigonometric ratios for select angles between 0° to 360°.

Table 1

θ (°)	θ (rad)	sin θ	cos θ	tan θ
0°	0	0	1	0
30°	$\frac{\pi}{6}$	$\frac{1}{2} = 0.5$	$\frac{\sqrt{3}}{2} = 0.866$	$\frac{\sqrt{3}}{3} = 0.577$
45°	$\frac{\pi}{4}$	$\frac{\sqrt{2}}{2} = 0.707$	$\frac{\sqrt{2}}{2} = 0.707$	1
60°	$\frac{\pi}{3}$	$\frac{\sqrt{3}}{2} = 0.866$	$\frac{1}{2} = 0.5$	$\sqrt{3} = 1.732$
90°	$\frac{\pi}{2}$	1	0	Undefined
120°	$\frac{2\pi}{3}$	$\frac{\sqrt{3}}{2} = 0.866$	$-\frac{1}{2} = -0.5$	$-\sqrt{3} = -1.732$
135°	$\frac{3\pi}{4}$	$\frac{\sqrt{2}}{2} = 0.707$	$\frac{\sqrt{2}}{2} = -0.707$	-1
150°	$\frac{5\pi}{6}$	$\frac{1}{2} = 0.5$	$-\frac{\sqrt{3}}{2} = -0.866$	$-\frac{\sqrt{3}}{3} = -0.577$
180°	π	0	-1	0
210°	$\frac{7\pi}{6}$	$-\frac{1}{2} = -0.5$	$-\frac{\sqrt{3}}{2} = -0.866$	$\frac{\sqrt{3}}{3} = 0.577$

Table 1

θ (°)	θ (rad)	sin θ	cos θ	tan θ
225°	$\frac{5\pi}{4}$	$-\frac{\sqrt{2}}{2} = -0.707$	$-\frac{\sqrt{2}}{2} = -0.707$	1
240°	$\frac{4\pi}{3}$	$-\frac{\sqrt{3}}{2} = -0.866$	$-\frac{1}{2} = -0.5$	$\sqrt{3} = 1.732$
270°	$\frac{3\pi}{2}$	-1	0	Undefined
300°	$\frac{5\pi}{3}$	$-\frac{\sqrt{3}}{2} = -0.866$	$\frac{1}{2} = 0.5$	$-\sqrt{3} = -1.732$
315°	$\frac{7\pi}{4}$	$-\frac{\sqrt{2}}{2} = -0.707$	$\frac{\sqrt{2}}{2} = 0.707$	-1
330°	$\frac{11\pi}{6}$	$-\frac{1}{2} = -0.5$	$\frac{\sqrt{3}}{2} = 0.866$	$-\frac{\sqrt{3}}{3} = -0.577$
360°	2π	0	1	0

Table 2 summarizes the behavior of these three trigonometric ratios.

Table 2

Range of θ	Trig Ratios		
Degrees and Radians	sin θ	cos θ	tan θ
0° → 90° $0 \to \frac{\pi}{2}$	0 → 1	1→ 0	0 → +∞
90° → 180° $\frac{\pi}{2} \to \pi$	1 → 0	0 → -1	-∞ → 0
180° → 270° $\pi \to \frac{3\pi}{2}$	0 → -1	-1 → 0	0 → +∞
270° → 360° $\frac{3\pi}{2} \to 2\pi$	-1 → 0	0 → 1	-∞ → 0

THE TANGENT RATIO

First, note the use of +∞ and -∞ in the tan θ column. From 0° to 90° (0 to π/2), the tangent ratio increases to a very large number until, at 90°, we encounter division by zero. At 90°, the ratio is technically undefined, symbolized by +∞. The positive sign tells us that the tangent ratio is getting greater in the positive direction as θ gets closer and closer to 90° as Figure 1 reveals.

From 90° to 180° ($\pi/2$ to π), the tangent ratio increases from a very large negative number until, at 180°, the ratio is zero. At 180°, the ratio is technically undefined, symbolized this time by $-\infty$. The negative sign tells us that the tangent ratio, as θ gets closer and closer to 180°, is going from very large in the negative direction until it reaches zero at 180°. Inspecting Figure 1 will confirm what is happening.

From 180° to 270° (π to $3\pi/2$), the tangent ratio increases to a very large number until, at 270°, we encounter division by zero. At 270°, the ratio is, again, undefined, symbolized by $+\infty$. The positive sign tells us that the tangent ratio is getting greater in the positive direction as θ gets closer and closer to 270° as Figure 1 reveals.

From 270° to 360° ($3\pi/2$ to 2π), the tangent ratio increases from a very large negative number until, at 360°, the ratio is zero. At 270°, the ratio is technically undefined, symbolized again by $-\infty$. The negative sign tells us that the tangent ratio, as θ gets closer and closer to 360°, is going from very large in the negative direction until it reaches zero at 360°. Inspecting Figure 1 will again confirm what is happening.

SIGN CHANGES

We also note that as θ increases through the four quadrants from 0° to 360°, the trigonometric ratios remain the same except for sign changes. Figure 2 and Figure 3 encapsulate the sign of these ratios as θ moves counterclockwise through the four quadrants. In Quadrant I, **a**ll three trig ratios are positive, only the **s**ine ratio is positive in Quadrant II, only the **t**angent ratio is positive in Quadrant III, and only the **c**osine ratio is positive in Quadrant IV. The acronym **ASTC** summarizes these findings.

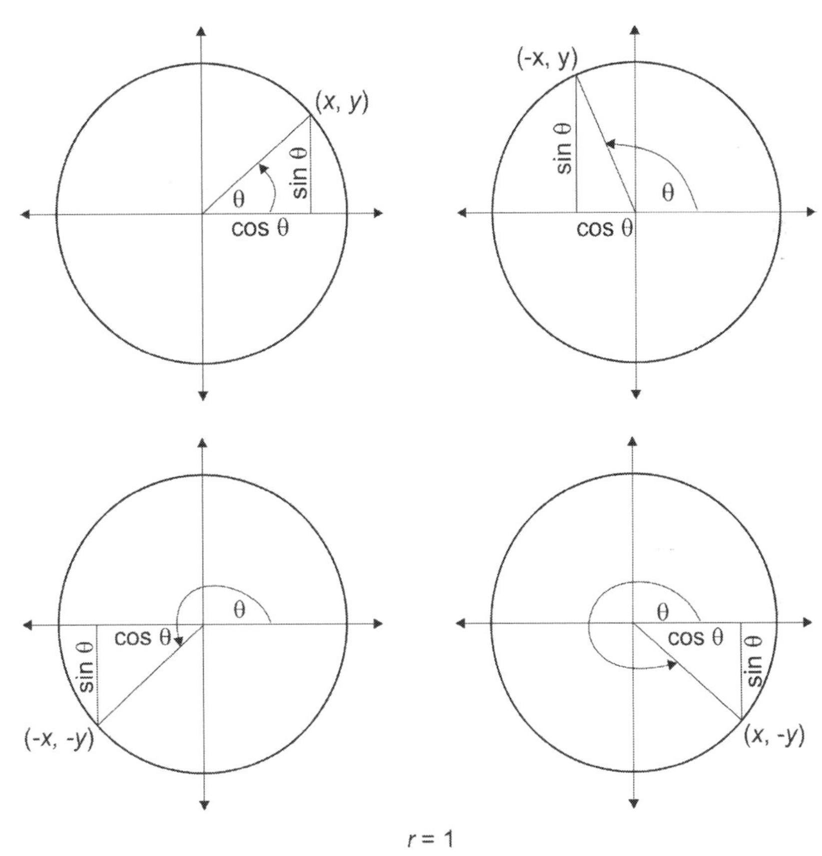

Figure 2. Sign changes for points on the unit circle as θ moves counterclockwise through the four quadrants.

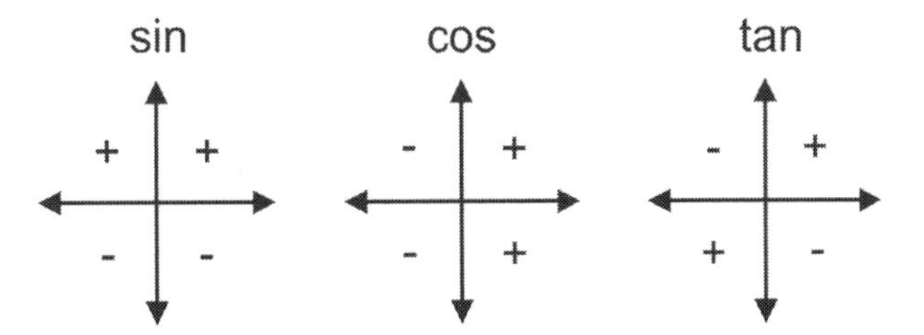

Figure 3. Sign changes for three trig ratios as θ, starting from the positive x-axis, moves counterclockwise through the four quadrants.

GRAPHING SIN θ, COS θ, AND TAN θ

The best way to visualize the dance of these ratios is to graph them. The results are elegant curves that are many-to-one functions. Note the x-axis is now the θ-axis since the independent variable represents radians.

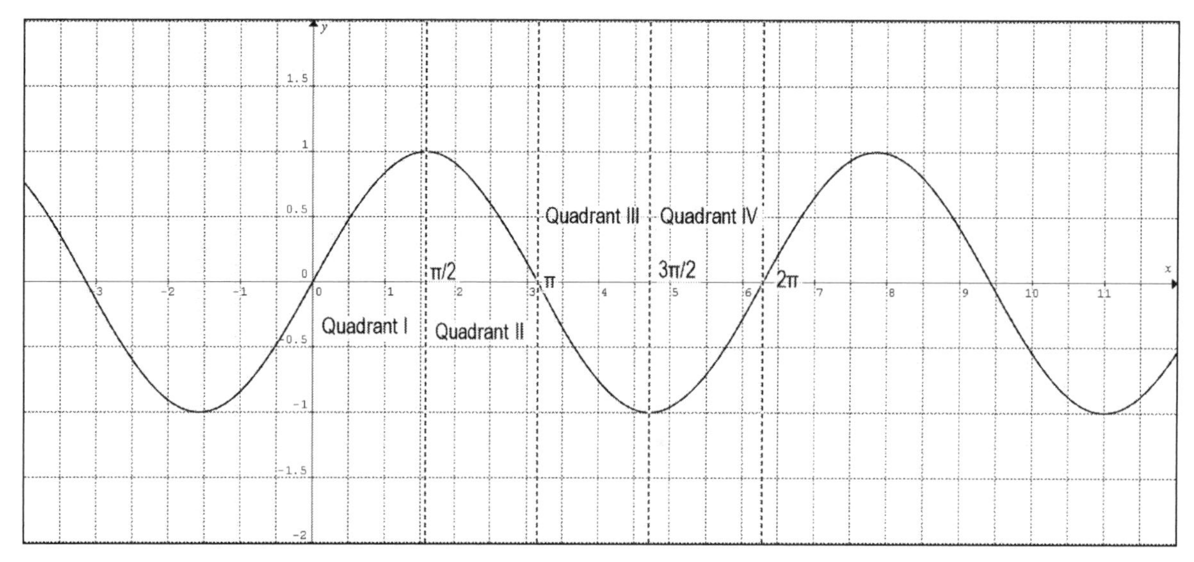

Figure 4. $y = f(\theta) = \sin \theta$

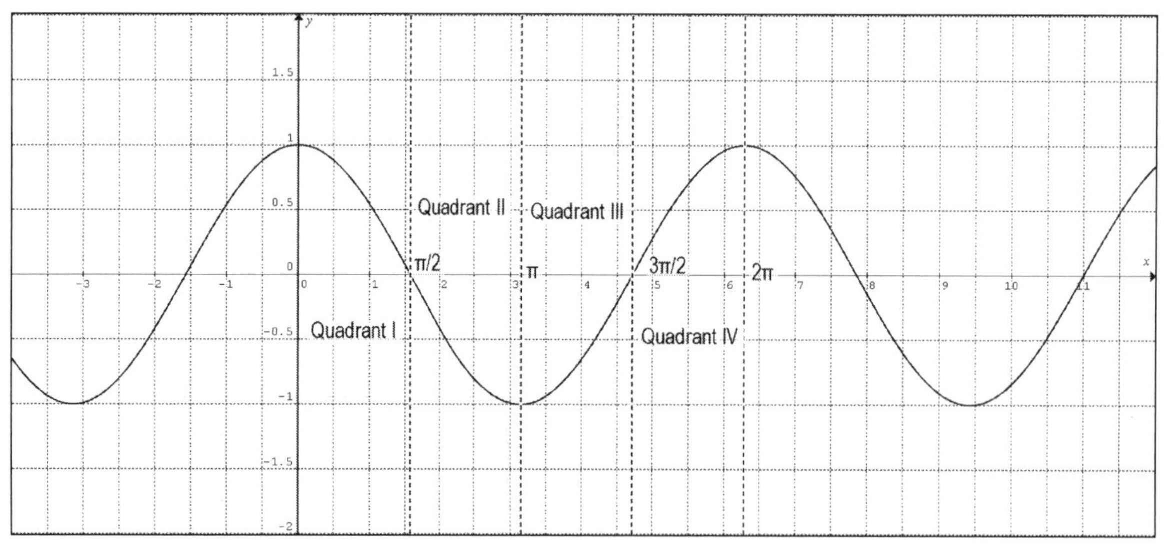

Figure 5. $y = f(\theta) = \cos \theta$

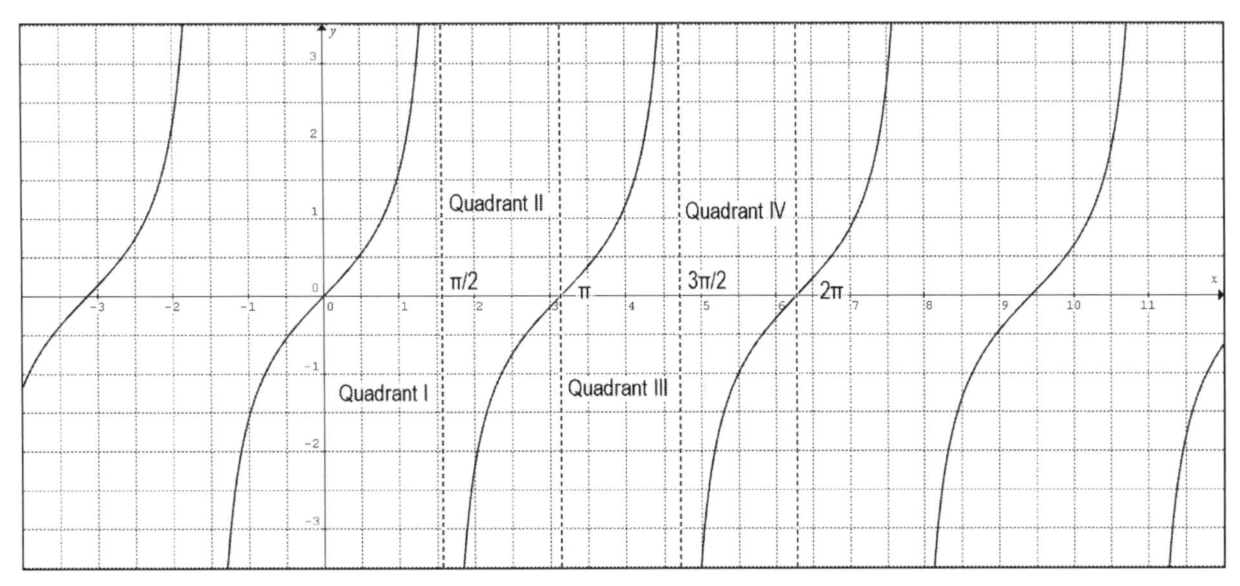

Figure 6. $y = f(\theta) = \tan\theta$

Spend some time comparing Tables 1 and 2 with the data in Figures 1, 2, and 3 along with the graphs of Figures 4, 5, and 6. Note how the dance of the graphs coinhere with the changing of signs and the values of the ratios. In Figure 6, we also see the interplay of +∞ and -∞ at division by zero. Using limit notation:

$$\lim_{\theta \to \left(\frac{\pi}{2}\right)^-} \tan\theta = +\infty \text{ and } \lim_{\theta \to \left(\frac{\pi}{2}\right)^+} \tan\theta = -\infty$$

$$\lim_{\theta \to \left(\frac{3\pi}{2}\right)^-} \tan\theta = +\infty \text{ and } \lim_{\theta \to \left(\frac{3\pi}{2}\right)^+} \tan\theta = -\infty$$

What do these limit symbols mean?

$\lim_{\theta \to \left(\frac{\pi}{2}\right)^-}$ means as θ approaches π/2 from the *left* of the line θ = π/2.

$\lim_{\theta \to \left(\frac{\pi}{2}\right)^+}$ means as θ approaches π/2 from the *right* of the line θ = π/2.

$\lim_{\theta \to \left(\frac{3\pi}{2}\right)^-}$ means as θ approaches 3π/2 from the *left* of the line θ = 3π/2.

$\lim_{\theta \to \left(\frac{3\pi}{2}\right)^+}$ means as θ approaches 3π/2 from the *right* of the line θ = 3π/2.

The lines, θ = π/2 and θ = 3π/2 are vertical asymptotes (Lesson 10.8) on the tangent graph (Figure 6).

PERIODIC BEHAVIOR

The graph the equations y = sin θ, y = cos θ, and y = tan θ reveal the cyclical or periodic pattern of these functions. Note that for angles greater than 360° (2π), the ratio sequence starts over; i.e., sin 390° = sin (360° + 30°) = sin 30°.

A function $f(x)$ is **periodic** with **period** p ($p \in \mathbb{R}$ and $p \neq 0$) if:

$f(x + p) = f(x)$ for all x.

For the sine and cosine functions, $p = 360°$, or $p = 2\pi$. For the tangent function, $p = 180°$, or $p = \pi$.

The microphone can change the human voice and musical sounds into electrical current. If we connect this microphone to a special instrument, an oscilloscope, we will see a graph that will display periodic behavior. These graphs will not be as simple as the ones we have seen so far. Their complexity arises from the addition and/or subtraction of basic trig functions strung together. See Lesson 12.8 for an example of the addition of a series of sine functions that produce, or report on, Middle C played on a piano.

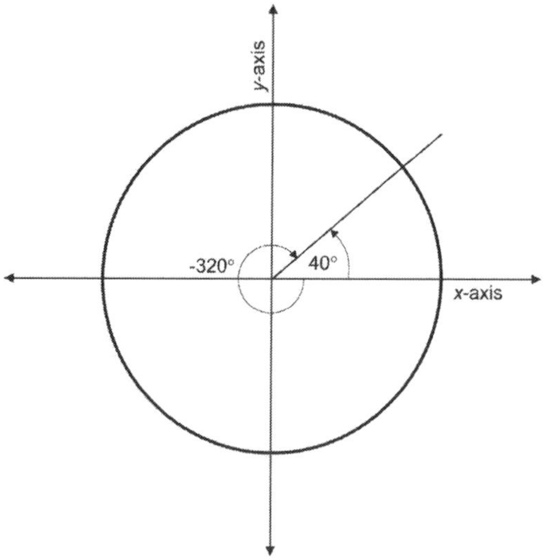

Figure 7. 40° = -320° (40° – 360° = -320°)

COTERMINAL ANGLES

Coterminal angles are angles that result from adding or subtracting multiples of 360° (2π) to or from a given angle (Figure 7). For example, one coterminal angle of 45° is 405° (45° + 360°). Another is -315° (45 – 360°).[1]

If $n \in \mathbb{Z}$, we define coterminal angles of θ as:

$\theta \pm 2\pi n$ or $\theta \pm 360n°$

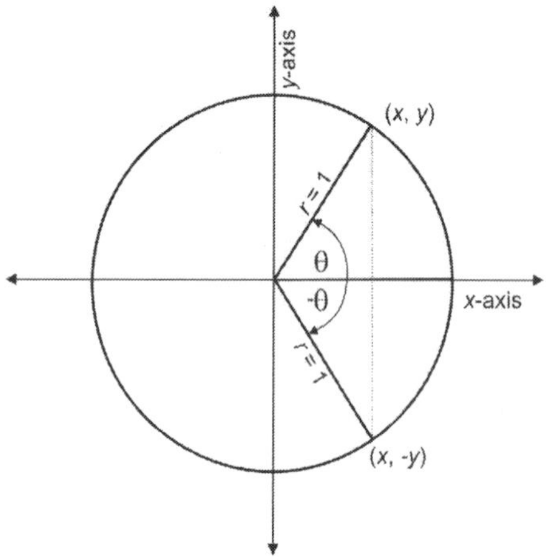

Figure 8. Opposite angles.

OPPOSITE IDENTITIES

We measure angles in a clockwise direction as negative angles. Figure 8 reveals these opposite identities.
(Note: $-\theta = 360° - \theta$, or $-\theta = 2\pi - \theta$)

- $\sin \theta = y$ and $\sin(-\theta) = -y \Rightarrow$

  $\boxed{\sin(-\theta) = -\sin \theta}$

- $\cos \theta = x$ and $\cos(-\theta) = x \Rightarrow$

  $\boxed{\cos(-\theta) = \cos \theta}$

- $\tan \theta = \dfrac{y}{x}$ and $\tan(-\theta) = \dfrac{-y}{x} = -\dfrac{y}{x} \Rightarrow$

  $\boxed{\tan(-\theta) = -\tan \theta}$

[1] Recall that the standard for measuring positive angles is that the initial side of the angle is the three o'clock position on the coordinate grid and terminal side is determined by rotating the initial side in a counterclockwise direction of θ degrees, or θ radians.

EVEN/ODD FUNCTIONS

The cosine function and its reciprocal, the secant function, are even functions (Lesson 11.13) because:

$\cos(-\theta) = \cos\theta$
$\sec(-\theta) = \sec\theta$

The sine function and its reciprocal, the cosecant function, are odd functions. Also, the tangent function and its reciprocal, the cotangent function, are odd functions. Why?

$\sin(-\theta) = -\sin\theta$
$\csc(-\theta) = -\csc\theta$
$\tan(-\theta) = -\tan\theta$
$\cot(-\theta) = -\cot\theta$

TRANSCENDENTAL FUNCTIONS

A function $y = f(x)$ is an **algebraic function** if, given an argument, the image can be computed by performing a finite number of additions, subtractions, multiplications, and divisions. Also, given an image, the argument can be solved by generating a finite number of equivalent equations. Linear equations, quadratic equations, and cubic equations are algebraic in nature.

A function that is not algebraic is **transcendental**. The most important transcendental functions are logarithmic functions, exponential functions, and trigonometric functions. These functions involve evaluation and solutions methods that are not algebraic; i.e., they rely on pre-calculated tables now programmed into scientific calculators.

> ... the primary importance of trigonometry lies ... in the mathematical description of vibrations, rotations, and periodic phenomena of all kinds, including light, sound, alternating currents, and the orbits of the planets around the sun. What matters most in the subject is not making computations about triangles, but grasping the trigonometric functions as indispensable tools in science, engineering and higher mathematics.
>
> George F. Simmons, *Precalculus Mathematics in a Nutshell* ([1987] 1997), p. 93.

ALGEBRAIC APPROXIMATION OF TRIG FUNCTIONS

Figure 9. Brook Taylor (1685-1731). Source: Public Domain.

Mathematicians use a variety of methods to calculate trig ratios. For example, without going into any derivation (it requires methods of Calculus), we can approximate both sine and cosine functions using **power series**. A power series in x, where subscripted a represents constants, is defined as an infinite sum:

$$a_0 + a_1x + a_2x^2 + a_3x^3 + \dots$$

Thanks to the work of the English mathematician Brook Taylor[2] (1685-1731), if x is measured in radians, we can approximate both $\sin x$ and $\cos x$ by an infinite power series:

$$\sin x = x - \frac{x^3}{3!} + \frac{x^5}{5!} - \frac{x^7}{7!} + \dots$$

$$\cos x = 1 - \frac{x^2}{2!} + \frac{x^4}{4!} - \frac{x^6}{6!} + \dots$$

Let's see how the sine power series works. In Figure 10, we graph $y = \sin x$ and $y = x - \frac{x^3}{3!}$ together.

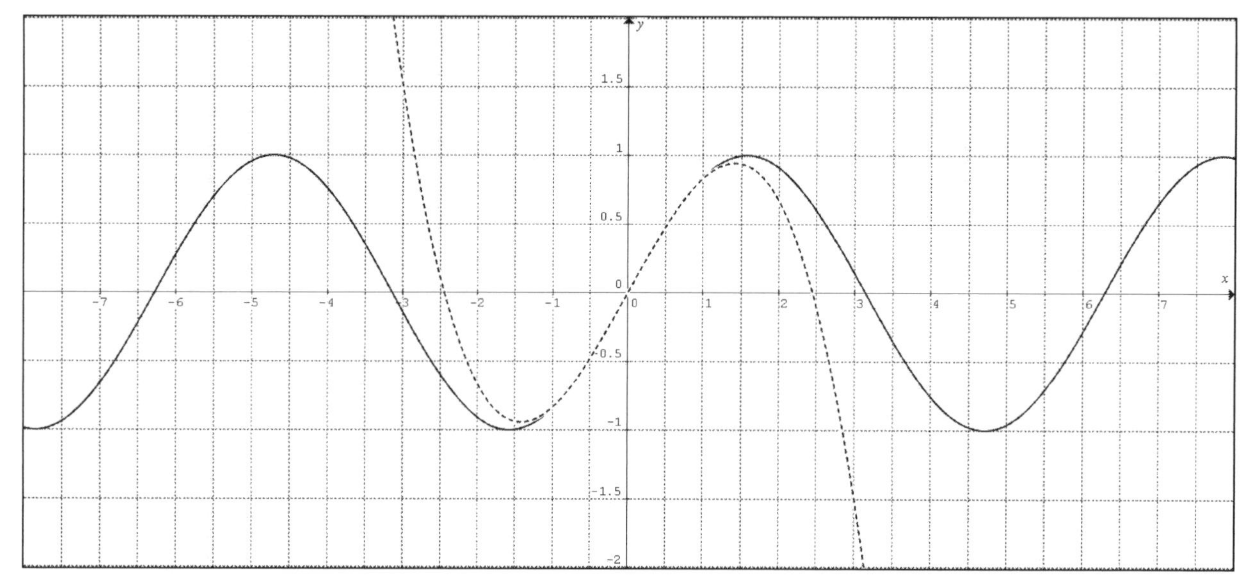

Figure 10.

[2] In the 18th and 19th centuries, it was much easier to apply the methods of Calculus to powers series than to trigonometric functions.

Now, let's graph $y = \sin x$ and $y = x - \dfrac{x^3}{3!} + \dfrac{x^5}{5!}$ together (Figure 11).

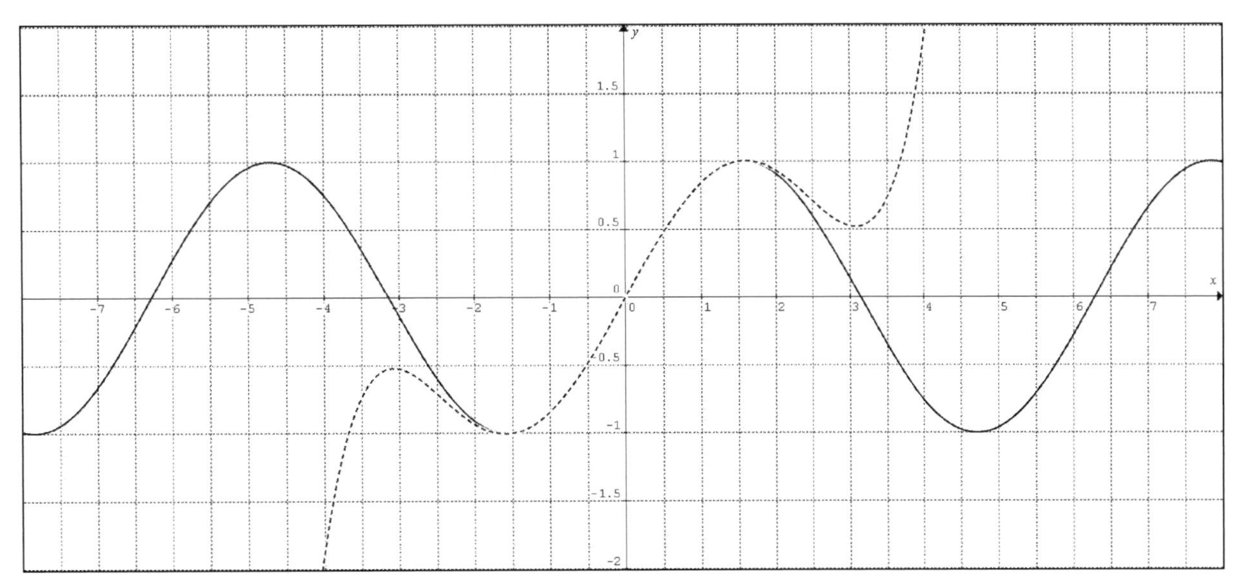

Figure 11.

In Figure 12, we graph $y = \sin x$ and $y = x - \dfrac{x^3}{3!} + \dfrac{x^5}{5!} - \dfrac{x^7}{7!}$ together.

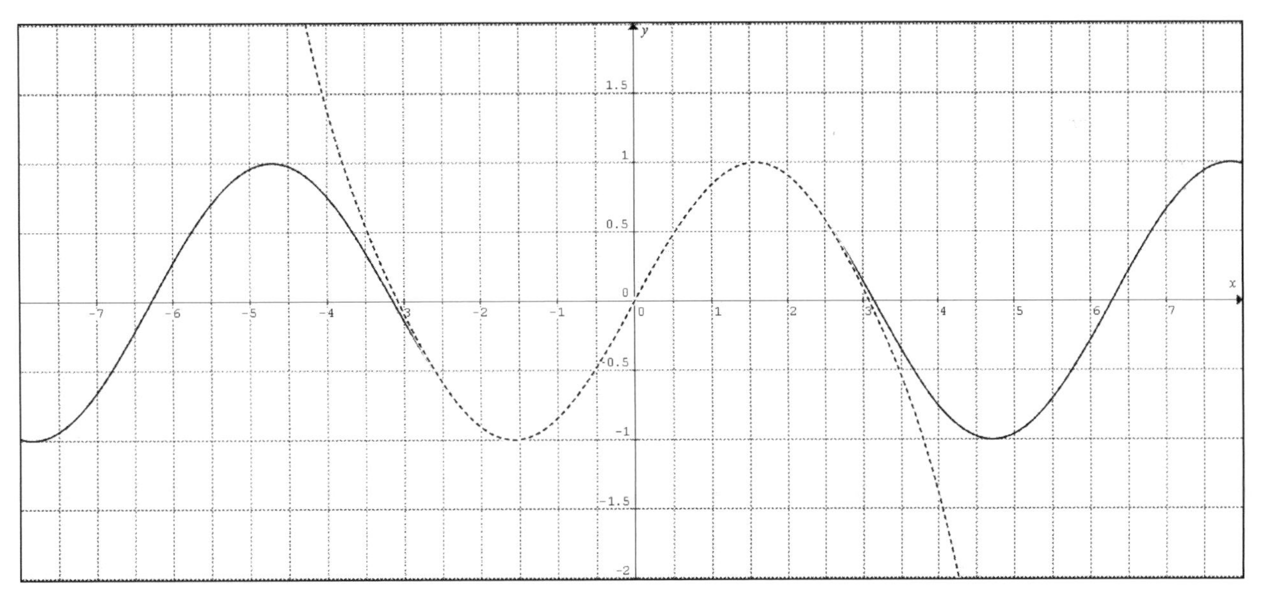

Figure 12.

In Figure 13, we graph $y = \sin x$ and $y = x - \frac{x^3}{3!} + \frac{x^5}{5!} - \frac{x^7}{7!} + \frac{x^9}{9!}$ together.

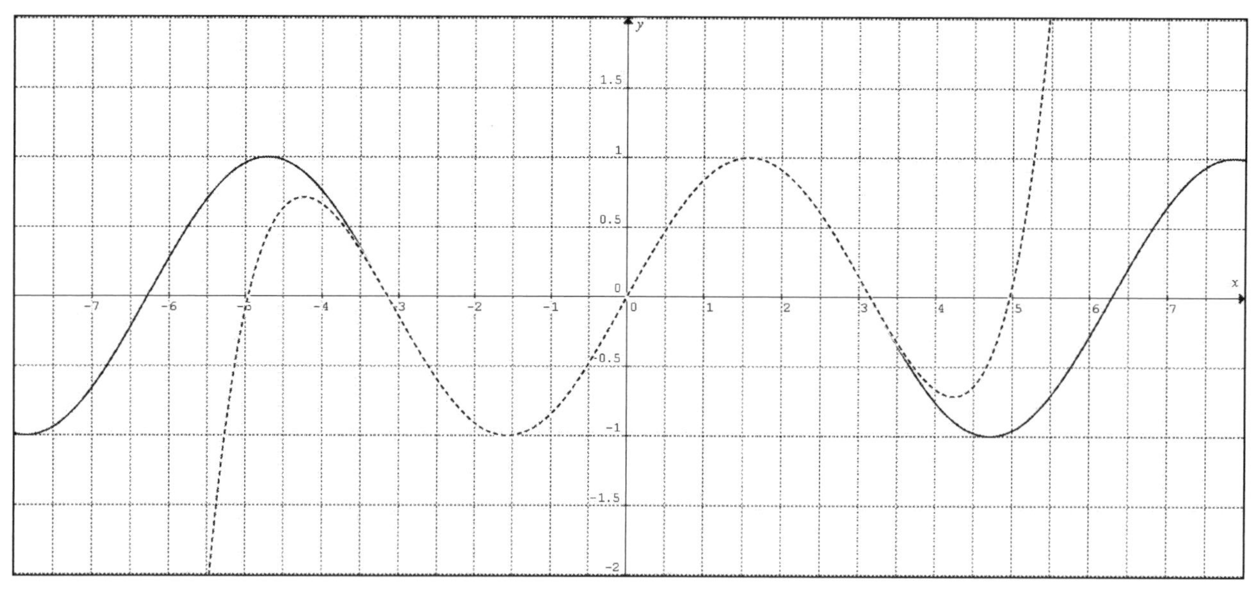

Figure 13.

In Figure 14, we graph $y = \sin x$ and $y = x - \frac{x^3}{3!} + \frac{x^5}{5!} - \frac{x^7}{7!} + \frac{x^9}{9!} - \frac{x^{11}}{11!}$ together.

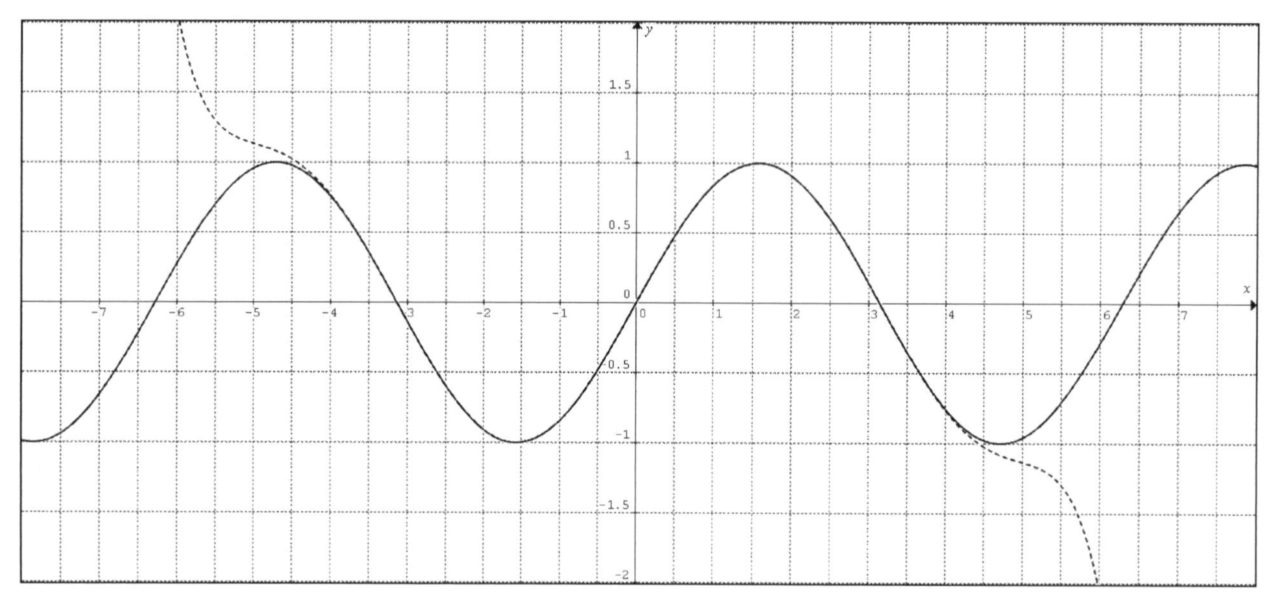

Figure 14.

As we continue this process to infinity, i.e., at the limit, the infinite power series developed by Taylor fits the sine curve.

Table 3: Trig Ratios in Quadrant I					
DEG	**SIN**	**COS**	**TAN**	**COT**	**DEG**
0	0.0000	1.0000	0.0000	$+\infty$	**90**
1	0.0175	0.9999	0.0175	57.2900	**89**
2	0.0349	0.9994	0.0349	28.6363	**88**
3	0.0523	0.9986	0.0524	19.0811	**87**
4	0.0698	0.9976	0.0699	14.3007	**86**
5	0.0872	0.9962	0.0875	11.4301	**85**
6	0.1045	0.9945	0.1051	9.5144	**84**
7	0.1219	0.9926	0.1228	8.1443	**83**
8	0.1392	0.9903	0.1405	7.1154	**82**
9	0.1564	0.9877	0.1584	6.3138	**81**
10	0.1737	0.9848	0.1763	5.6713	**80**
11	0.1908	0.9816	0.1944	5.1446	**79**
12	0.2079	0.9782	0.2126	4.7046	**78**
13	0.2250	0.9744	0.2309	4.3315	**77**
14	0.2419	0.9703	0.2493	4.0108	**76**
15	0.2588	0.9659	0.2680	3.7321	**75**
16	0.2736	0.9613	0.2868	3.4874	**74**
17	0.2924	0.9563	0.3057	3.2709	**73**
18	0.3090	0.9511	0.3249	3.0777	**72**
19	0.3256	0.9455	0.3443	2.9042	**71**
20	0.3420	0.9397	0.3640	2.7475	**70**
21	0.3584	0.9336	0.3839	2.6051	**69**
22	0.3746	0.9272	0.4040	2.4751	**68**
23	0.3907	0.9205	0.4245	2.3559	**67**
24	0.4067	0.9136	0.4452	2.2460	**66**
25	0.4226	0.9063	0.4663	2.1445	**65**
26	0.4384	0.8988	0.4877	2.0503	**64**
27	0.4540	0.8910	0.5095	1.9626	**63**
28	0.4695	0.8830	0.5317	1.8807	**62**
29	0.4848	0.8746	0.5543	1.8040	**61**
30	0.5000	0.8660	0.5774	1.7321	**60**
31	0.5150	0.8572	0.6009	1.6643	**59**
32	0.5299	0.8481	0.6249	1.6003	**58**
33	0.5446	0.8387	0.6494	1.5400	**57**
34	0.5592	0.8290	0.6745	1.4826	**56**
35	0.5736	0.8192	0.7002	1.4281	**55**
36	0.5878	0.8090	0.7265	1.3764	**54**
37	0.6018	0.7986	0.7536	1.3270	**53**
38	0.6157	0.7880	0.7813	1.2800	**52**
39	0.6293	0.7772	0.8098	1.2349	**51**
40	0.6428	0.7660	0.8391	1.1919	**50**
41	0.6561	0.7547	0.8693	1.1504	**49**
42	0.6691	0.7431	0.9004	1.1106	**48**
43	0.6820	0.7314	0.9325	1.0723	**47**
44	0.6947	0.7193	0.9657	1.0355	**46**
45	0.7071	0.7071	1.0000	1.0000	**45**
	COS	**SIN**	**COT**	**TAN**	**DEG**

EXERCISES

Define the following terms/symbols:

1. ASTC
2. Periodic function
3. Period
4. Coterminal angles
5. Algebraic function
6. Transcendental function
7. Power series
8. Law of Sines (See homework exercise below.)

Answer the following questions based on Table 3:

9. What is (a) cos 36° (b) sin 64° (c) tan 36°, and (d) cot 64°?
10. What is (a) cos -64° (b) sin -36° (c) tan -64°, and (d) cot -36°?
11. What is the positive acute angle, in degrees, (a) whose sine is 0.8572, (b) whose cosine is 0.6820, (c) whose tangent is 1.5400, and (d) whose cotangent is 0.4040?
12. What is the negative acute angle, in degrees, (a) whose sine is -0.9455, (b) whose cosine is 0.3907, (c) whose tangent is -3.2709, and (d) whose cotangent is -0.7813?

If $n \in \mathbb{Z}$, we define coterminal angles of θ as $\theta \pm 2\pi n$ or $\theta \pm 360n°$. State a positive and a negative coterminal angle of the following angles when $n = 1$:

13. 23°
14. 122.5°
15. $\frac{3\pi}{2}$
16. $\frac{5\pi}{4}$

Write the following negative angles as equivalent positive angles between 0° and 360°.

17. -45°
18. -125°
19. -240°
20. -722°

Write the following negative angles as equivalent positive angles between 0 and 2π:

21. $-\frac{2\pi}{3}$
22. $-\frac{\pi}{2}$
23. $-\frac{3\pi}{4}$
24. $-\frac{13\pi}{6}$

Explain the following notation:

25. $\lim\limits_{\theta \to \left(\frac{\pi}{2}\right)^-} \tan\theta = +\infty$

26. $\lim\limits_{\theta \to \left(\frac{3\pi}{2}\right)^-} \tan\theta = +\infty$

27. $\lim\limits_{\theta \to \left(\frac{\pi}{2}\right)^+} \tan\theta = -\infty$

28. $\lim\limits_{\theta \to \left(\frac{3\pi}{2}\right)^+} \tan\theta = -\infty$

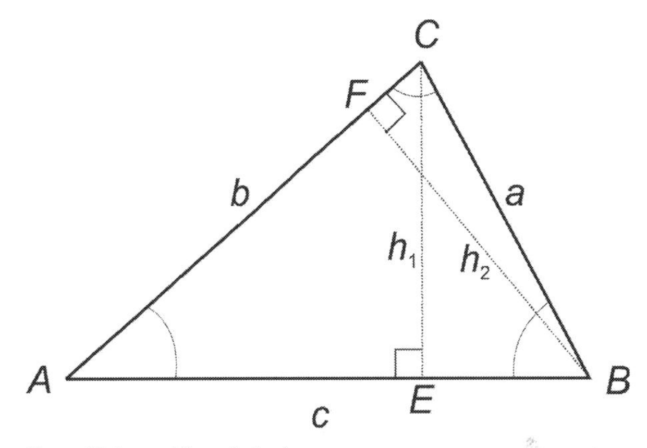

Figure 15. Law of Sines derivation.

Although the dance of trigonometry begins with a right triangle in a unit circle, we can use its methods to find engaging relationships in any triangle. Use ΔABC with sides a, b, and c (Figure 15) to answer the following questions:

29. Note that the height (altitude) of ΔABC is h_1. Using a, b, and h_1, write and equation for:
    (a) sin A
    (b) sin B
30. Solve both equations you derived in Question 29 for h_1.
31. From the equations you derived in Question 30, write a proportion relating sin A, a, sin B, and b.
32. Note that another height (altitude) of ΔABC is h_2. Using a, c, and h_2, write and equation for:
    (a) sin A
    (b) sin C
33. Solve both equations you derived in Question 32 for h_2.
34. From the equations you derived in Question 33, write a proportion relating sin A, a, sin C, and c.
35. From Question 31 and 34, write a multiple proportion relating sin A, a, sin B, b sin C, and c. Your result is the **Law of Sines**.
36. Derive a general formula for the area of ΔABC if you know the value of b, c, and m$\angle A$. (Hint: Use the altitude h_1 and note the two right triangles formed by it. Also, sin A will be a term in the formula.)

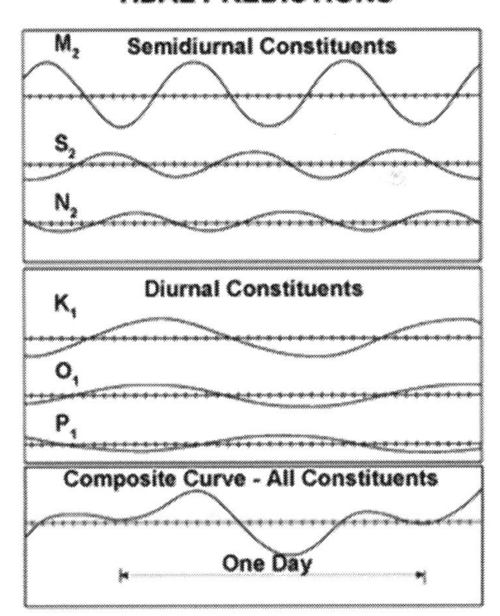

Figure 16. Trigonometric motion and tides. Source: Public Domain.

12.8 Spring and Bob Motion

Terms & Concepts Introduced
1. Amplitude
2. Crest
3. Displacement
4. Hooke's Law of springs
5. Parametric equations
6. Projection
7. Radius vector
8. Trough
9. Wave height
10. Wavelength

In the periodic function $y = f(x) = \sin x$, the maximum value of the images is 1, and this value is the **amplitude**[1] of the function.

In the same function, the period is 2π because the images repeat on successive intervals compared to what happens to these images in the interval from 0 to 2π. We name this interval so because it comes from a physical situation in which x represents time. The variable x can also represent distance per cycle. In this case, the interval 2π is the **wavelength** of the periodic function, signified by the Greek letter *lambda*, λ.[2] Wavelength is the distance from the top of one **crest**, the maximum image, of a wave to the top of the next crest. The **trough** of a periodic function is its minimum image. The **wave height** is the vertical distance from the crest to the trough. The amplitude is one-half the wave height.

That we can substitute angles with time makes trigonometric functions fruitful as they interpenetrate physical phenomena, as we shall shortly see.

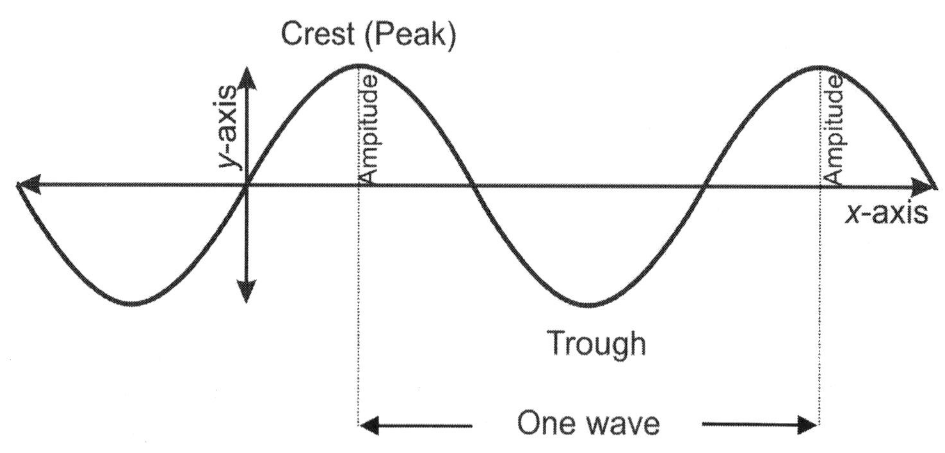

Figure 1.

Variations on the Theme

The great usefulness of the sine functions, along with her sisters, cosine, tangent, cotangent, secant, and cosecant, is that there an infinite number of variations on their main themes.

For example, one variation of $y = f(x) = \sin x$ is:

$y = g(x) = 2 \sin x$

Here we are multiplying the image of $f(x)$ by 2. Based on our previous study of composition functions (Lesson 11.13), the graph expands vertically, or it stretches away from the x-axis by a factor of 2 (Figure 2).

---

[1] Amplitude, from the Latin, means "large" or "abundant." As distance, the amplitude is always positive.

[2] Note: $\lambda = \dfrac{\text{distance/second}}{\text{cycles/second}} = \dfrac{\text{distance}}{\text{second}} \div \dfrac{\text{cycles}}{\text{second}} = \dfrac{\text{distance}}{\cancel{\text{second}}_{1}} \cdot \dfrac{\cancel{\text{second}}^{1}}{\text{cycles}} = \text{distance/cycle}$

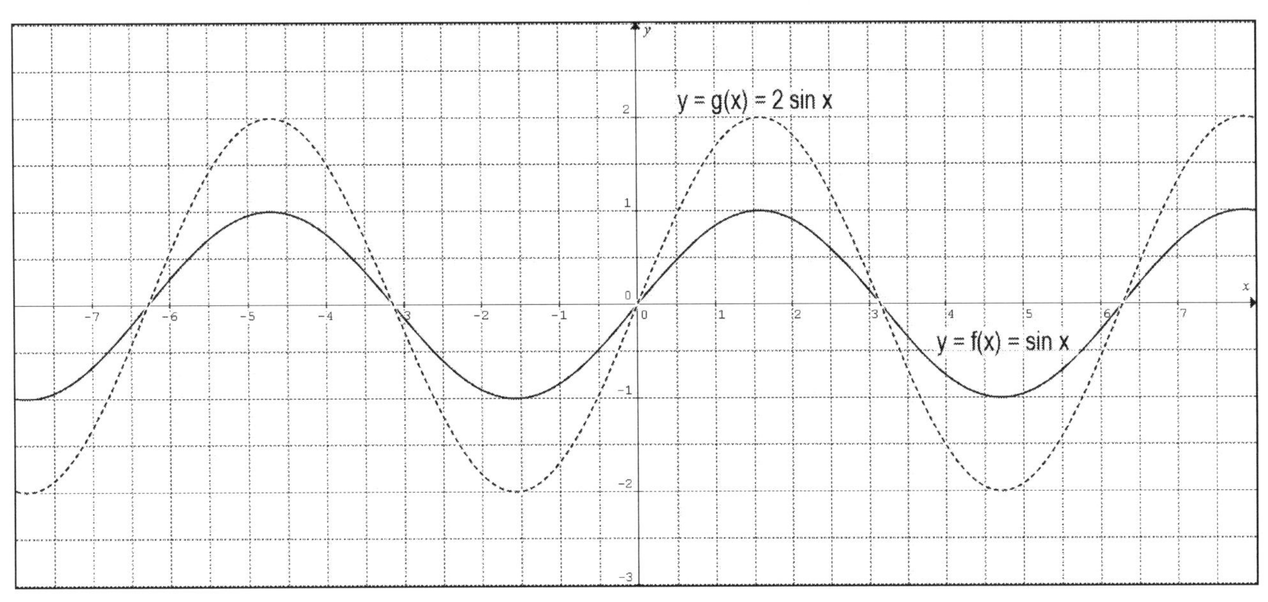

Figure 2. $y = f(x) = \sin x$ and $y = g(x) = 2 \sin x$

The period of $g(x)$ remains 2π, but the amplitude is 2. In general, one variation on the theme would be:

$y = g(x) = a \sin x$
Amplitude: a
Period: 2π

Another variation would be:

$y = h(x) = \sin 2x$

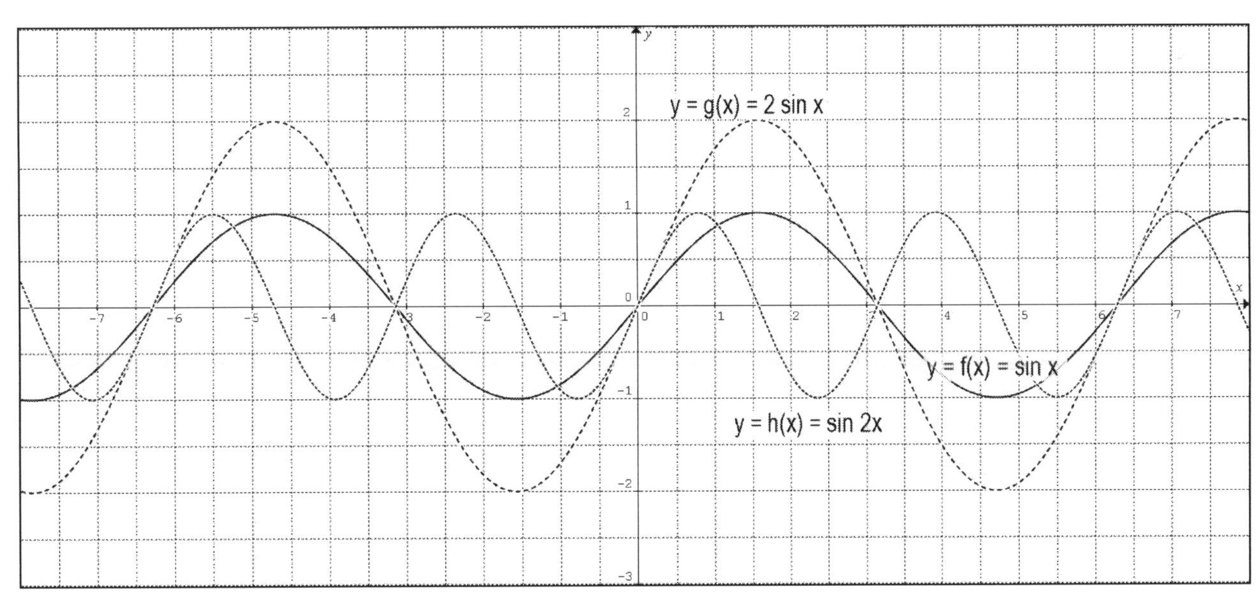

Figure 3. $y = f(x) = \sin x$, $y = g(x) = 2 \sin x$, and $y = g(x) = \sin 2x$

Here we are multiplying the argument of $f(x)$ by 2 meaning the graph of $h(x)$ is compressed horizontally, or it shrinks toward from the y-axis by a factor of 2 (Figure 3).

The amplitude of $h(x)$ remains the same as the amplitude of $f(x)$, i.e., 1, but the period is now π instead of 2π. It is worth noting that we can calculate this period by dividing the period of the base function $f(x)$ by the coefficient of x. In general, this variation on the theme would be:

$y = h(x) = \sin bx$

Amplitude: 1

Period: $\dfrac{2\pi}{b}$

Another variation on the theme is to combine $g(x)$ and $h(x)$ to create $i(x)$:

$y = i(x) = a \sin bx$

Amplitude: a

Period: $\dfrac{2\pi}{b}$

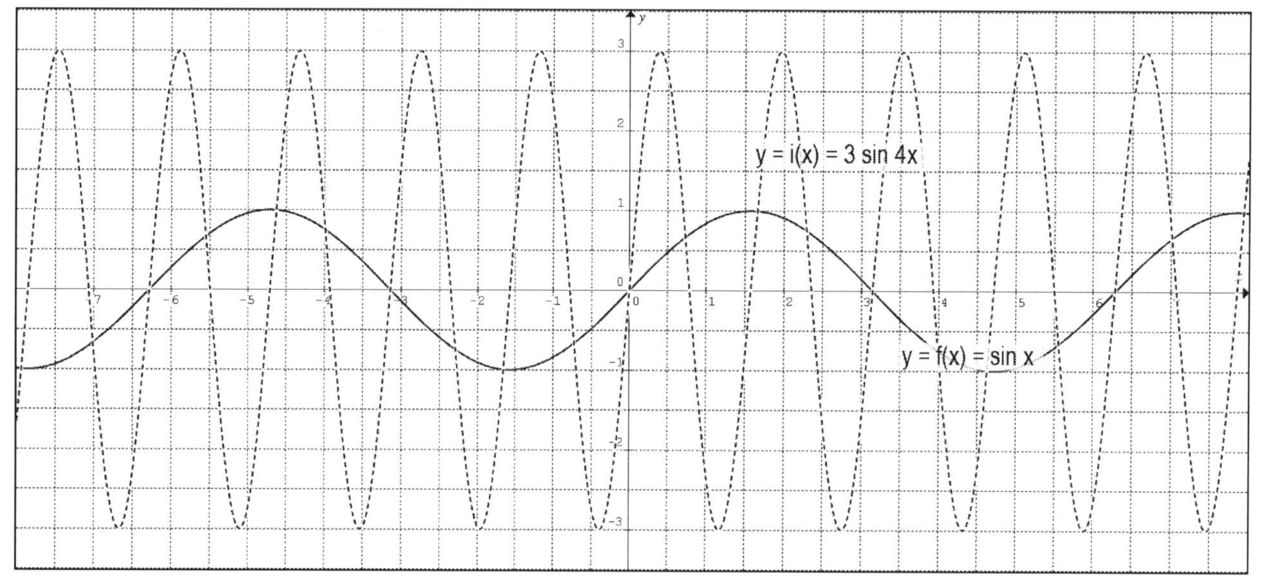

Figure 4. $y = f(x) = \sin x$ and $y = i(x) = 3 \sin 4x$

In Figure 4, what is happening to $i(x)$ when compared to $f(x)$? $i(x)$ is compressed horizontally, or it shrinks toward from the y-axis by a factor of 4 while, at the same time, $i(x)$ expands vertically, or it stretches away from the x-axis by a factor of 3. The amplitude of $i(x)$ is 3 and its period is $\dfrac{2\pi}{4} = \dfrac{\pi}{2}$.

What happens to $f(x)$ if $g(x) = \sin (x + \dfrac{\pi}{2})$? We know that $g(x)$ is shifted left $\dfrac{\pi}{2}$ units (Figure 5). In Physics, the result is a phase shift left by $\dfrac{\pi}{2}$ units and $g(x) = \cos x$.

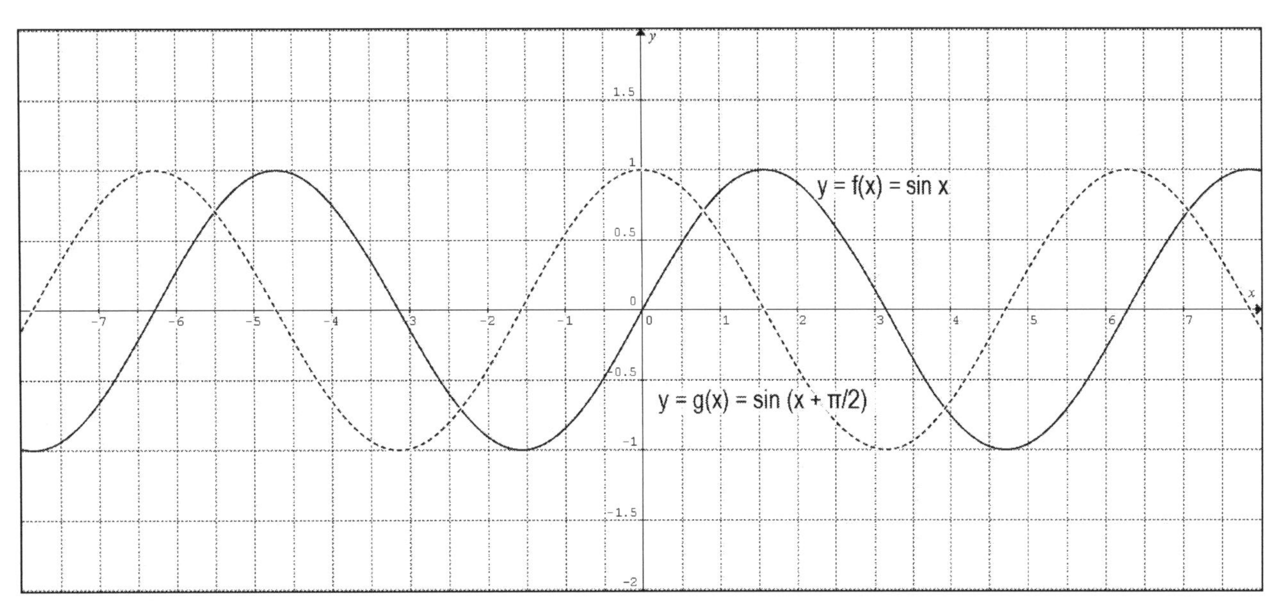

Figure 5. $y = f(x) = \sin x$ and $y = g(x) = \sin (x + \frac{\pi}{2})$

By our analysis, we acquire this phase-shift identity:

$$\sin (x + \frac{\pi}{2}) = \cos x$$

ROBERT HOOKE

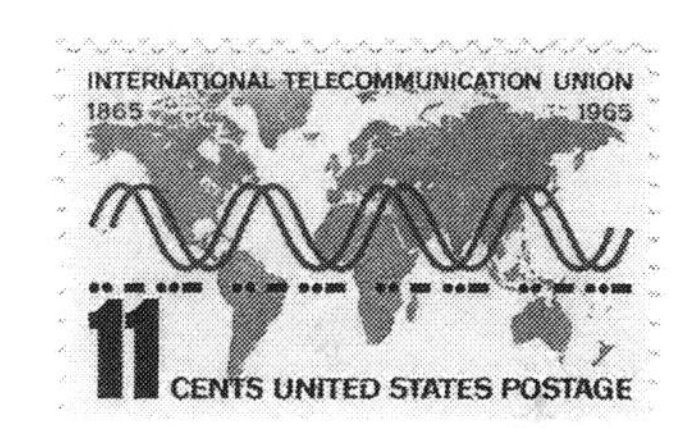

Figure 6. Source: United States Postal Service

In the 17th century scientists needed to find a way to measure small periods of time accurately so ships traveling the seas could determine their longitude.[3] Their success in this search led to a better understand of other aspects of the physical world, especially light and sound.

The motion of a pendulum and the motion of a bob, or weight, on a spring caught the eye of English physicist Robert Hooke (1635-1703), professor of Mathematics at Gresham College in England and a contemporary of Newton.[4]

THE MOTION OF A BOB ON A SPRING

If we attach a weight to a spring (Figure 7), the pull of gravity stretches the spring until it settles in a position of rest, its equilibrium, *d* units below.[5] We generate motion of the bob on the spring by pulling

[3] Determining longitude and latitude gave a ship captain certainty of location, especially near shores. Ships sinking will all hands and all goods was an all too common occurrence in this century.

[4] Isaac Newton's famous phrase, "standing on the shoulders of giants," came from a letter that he wrote to the hunch-backed Hooke as an insult. Newton and Hooke clashed several times during their lifetime over issues of the ownership of scientific discovery. Bernard Silvester of Chartres (ca. 1150) first used the Latin phrase *nanos gigantum humeris insidentes* reflecting his respect for earlier learned authorities. He wrote, "We are like dwarfs standing on the shoulders of giants, so that we can see more things than them, and can see further, not because our vision is sharper or our stature higher, but because we can raise ourselves up thanks to their giant stature." Cited in Alistair C. Crombie, *The History of Science from Augustine to Galileo* (Mineola: Dover Publications, [1959, 1970, 1979] 1995), 1:46.

[5] Equilibrium is where the tension in the spring offsets the force of gravity.

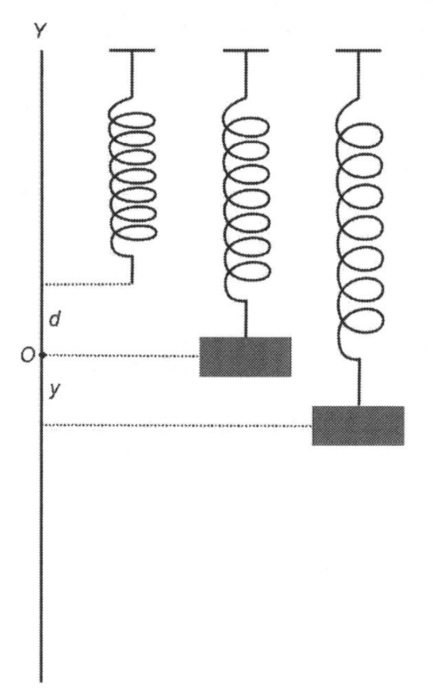

Figure 7. Spring and bob motion.

it down y units and then releasing it. Technically, y is the **displacement**, the difference between the position of a body at a given time and that occupied at first, from the equilibrium position.

After releasing the bob, it moves upward through the equilibrium position and continues to some highest position and then moves downward. It is the nature of this up and down motion that Hooke investigated.

For his analysis, Hooke disregarded the effects of air resistance and the energy lost in the expansion and contraction of the spring. We introduce the Y-axis parallel to the spring and set the equilibrium position, point O, to $y = 0$. The displacement below O is negative, and the displacement above O is positive; e.g., at $y = -0.75$, the bob is 0.75 units below the equilibrium position. What, then, is the formula that relates the displacement of the bob with the time it is in motion?

In Figure 8, we can follow the up and down motion of the bob. Starting from the equilibrium O, we pull the bob down to Q_1 and let go. It moves up through Q_2, Q_3, O, Q_4, Q_5, and reaches its maximum at Q_6. In displacement, it moves from negative to zero to positive. Then, it reverses direction and moves down through Q_7, Q_8, O, Q_9, and reaches its minimum at Q_1, its starting point. In displacement, it moves from positive to zero to negative. If we neglect air resistance and loss of energy in the spring, the process repeats, *ad infinitum*.

The displacement changes, a repetitive cycle from negative to zero to positive and from positive to zero to negative, mean that a trig function interpenetrates the situation; i.e., a trig function is embedded in the movement of the bob on the spring.

Figure 8 only shows vertical motion. Since the bob goes through this motion in time, let's add the time factor to our analysis, the x-axis in Figure 9. We let a unit circle represent the diameter of the minimum to maximum displacement, $Q_2 Q_5$, and start to graph the displacement once the bob returns to equilibrium O. Then, after a period of time, the bob is at Q_1 where Q_1 is the **projection**[6] of P_1 on the

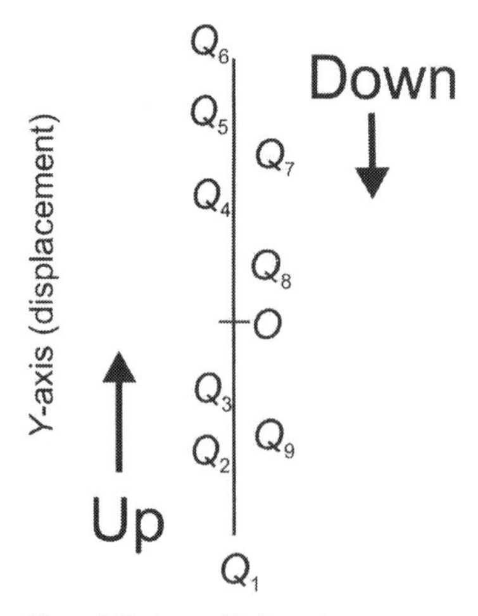

Figure 8. Spring and bob motion.

[6] Technically (refer to Figure 9), the projection of P_1 on the Y-axis is the point Q_1 such that Q_1 is the intersection of $\overline{Q_1 P_1}$ that passes through P_1 and is perpendicular to the Y-axis. Think of light rays projecting an image on a screen.

vertical line, the Y-axis. We have similar projections of Q_2 with P_2, Q_3 with P_3, Q_4 with P_4, Q_5 with P_5, and Q_6 with P_6.

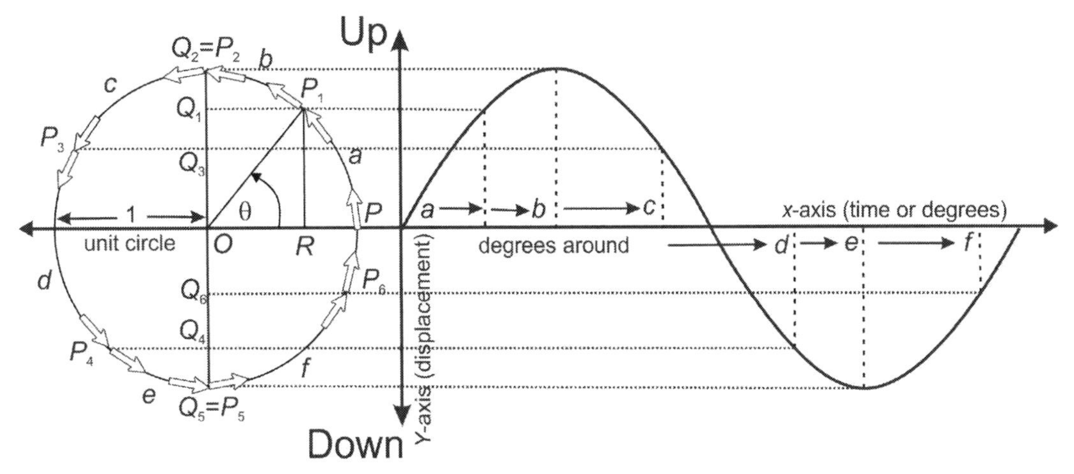

Figure 9. Spring and bob motion modeled by $Y = \sin x$.

As the bob moves from O to Q_1, a point on the circle follows an arc, a radian measure of $a = \theta$ from P to P_1. At $\theta = 0$, R and P are the same point, and $\sin \theta = 0$. As θ increases, PR is $\sin \theta$ and the graph to the right of the Y-axis is the sine curve. In Figure 9, we see specific arc lengths, a through f, along with the portions of the sine curve associated with each arc length.

SEEKING A GENERAL DESCRIPTION

The maximum image, the maximum displacement, in $y = \sin x$ is 1, the amplitude. We could pull farther down on the string to increase this amplitude. Any amplitude within the constraints of the spring is possible. If we let D stand for this amplitude, we must adjust our base function. Since we are multiplying the image of the base function by a constant D, we write:

$$y = D \sin x$$

The x-axis represents θ, an angle in radians. Although θ could be in degrees, in this situation a radian measure of 1.57 units is easier to work with than 90 units ($\frac{\pi}{2} = 90°$). Since the motion of the bob on a spring occurs in time, it would be convenient to associate time, not angles, with the x-axis. Suppose that in one second P revolves around the circle f times.[7] For each revolution, θ increases by 2π radians. Therefore, the size of the angle that describes the amount of the revolution of P in one second is $2\pi f$. If P revolves for t seconds and makes f revolutions per second, it will make ft revolutions in t seconds. The angle generated by these ft revolutions will be $2\pi ft$ meaning that the value of θ in t seconds will be $2\pi ft$. We adjust our function with a scale change to the argument which is now represented, not by the angle θ, but by t representing time:

$$y = D \sin 2\pi ft$$

[7] f stands for **frequency**, the number of occurrences of an event within a given period. In periodic motion, the event is the period.

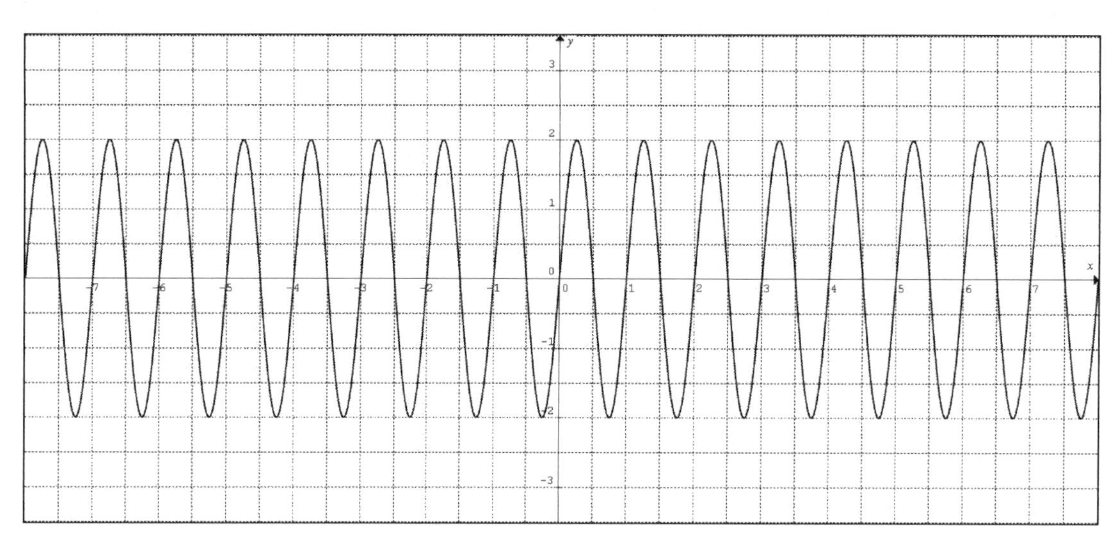

Figure 10. Spring and bob motion modeled by $y = 2 \sin 2\pi t$ (The x-axis represents time.)

If $f = 1$ and $D = 2$ (Figure 10), P makes one revolution per second. We observe that the revolution of P per second also represents the number of oscillations per second of Q. We have:

$$y = 2 \sin 2\pi t$$

From the graph, we clearly see that the period is 1 second.
If $f = 2$, P makes two revolutions per second. We have:

$$y = 2 \sin 2\pi(2t) = 2 \sin 4\pi t$$

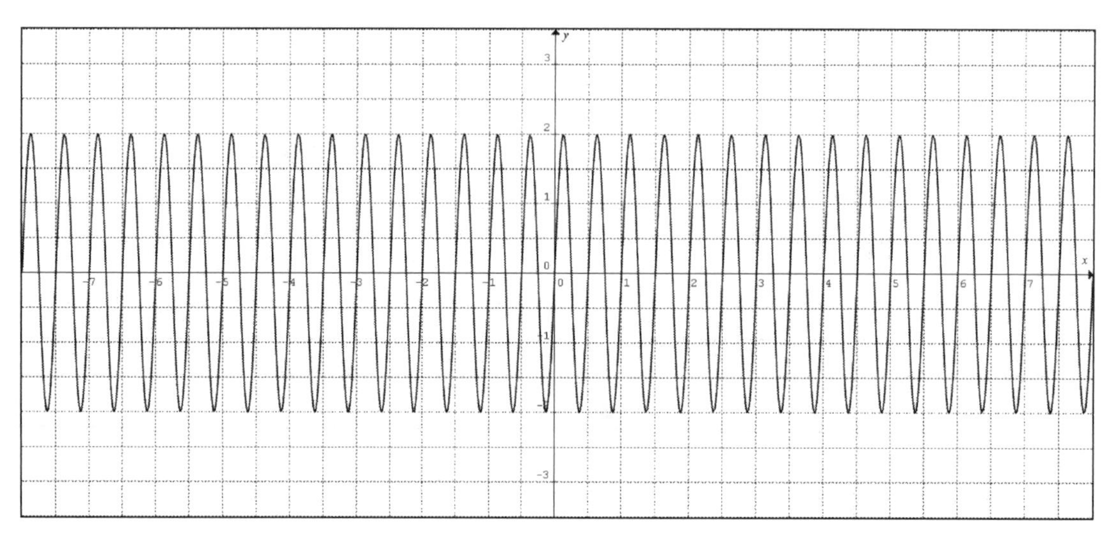

Figure 11. Spring and bob motion modeled by $y = 2 \sin 4\pi t$ (The x-axis represents time.)

In Figure 11, we see that the period is 0.5 or ½ second. So, what is the relationship between the frequency f and the period T?

$$T = \frac{1}{f} \Leftrightarrow f = \frac{1}{T}$$

If $f = 3$, then $T = \frac{1}{3}$ and if $T = \frac{1}{4}$, then $f = 4$. Frequency is the reciprocal of the period and the period is the reciprocal of the frequency.

That the motion of P around a circle correlates to the oscillation of Q, the motion of a bob on a spring, is a beautiful perichoretic dance. The theoretical, the motion of P around a circle, coinheres with the empirical, the motion of a bob on a spring.[8]

ANALYSIS OF ACCELERATION

What is the acceleration of Q? What is its rate of change per second every second? We have understood the motion of Q as the motion of P as it travels around a unit circle at constant velocity v. If an object moves in a circular path, it will be subject to centripetal acceleration (Lesson 12.1). In a circle, we have determined that this acceleration is $\frac{v^2}{r}$ where r is the radius. In our situation, since $r = 1$, the acceleration directed toward the center of the circle is v^2, represented by the arrow vector in Figure 12.[9]

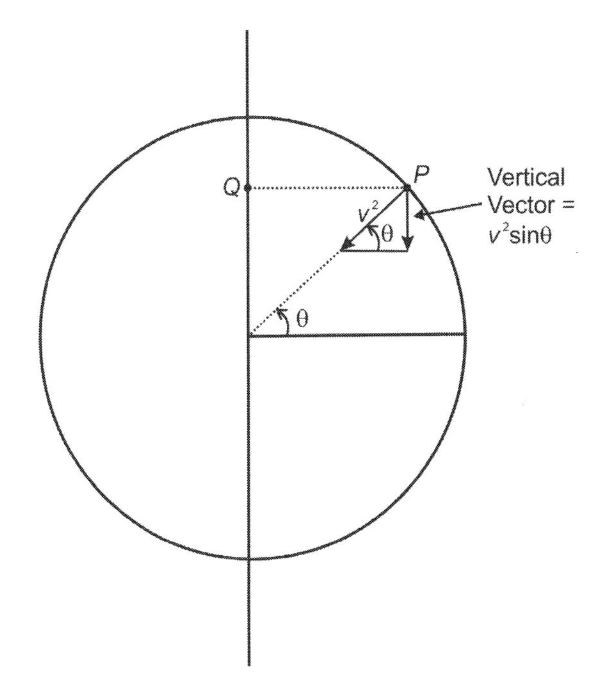

Figure 12.

We are not interested in the motion of P. We are concerned with the motion of Q, a motion that moves in the same way as the vertical motion of P. Thanks to the work of Galileo Galilei (1564-1642), we can parse motion into its vertical and horizontal components and understand each motion independently of the other. We want to find the vertical acceleration of P which will be, because P coinheres in Q, the vertical acceleration of Q. The vertical component of the acceleration is the perpendicular vector dropped from P. We create a right triangle, note θ, and conclude that the magnitude of this vertical vector is $v^2 \sin\theta$. Why?

We let y be the vertical component. By the definition of the sine ratio, we get:

$$\sin\theta = \frac{y}{v^2} \Leftrightarrow y = v^2 \sin\theta$$

If we let a be the vertical component of the acceleration, then:

$$a = v^2 \sin\theta$$

From Figure 9, $\sin\theta = y$. Substituting, we get:

$$a = v^2 y$$

---

[8] Thanks to the indefatigable work of James Clerk Maxwell and Albert Einstein, it wasn't until the late 19th/early 20th century that scientists finally understood that the theoretical interpenetrates the empirical and the empirical interpenetrates the theoretical. For those aware of philosophical matters, this viewpoint overturned the philosophy of the German thinker Immanuel Kant (1724-1804), a way of thinking driven by both the successes of Newtonian mechanics and Newton's separation of absolute mathematical time and space from relative mathematical time and space. This dualism ultimately divides the theoretical from the empirical, and this is exactly what ancient Greeks philosophers did when they separated form from matter.

[9] In physics, vectors are signified by arrows to show direction. The length of the arrow represents the magnitude.

When y is positive, we know that the acceleration due to gravity pulls the object downward. We must, therefore, write:

$$a = -v^2y$$

Since the moving point P makes f revolutions per second, P covers f circumferences per second. The velocity v of P is, therefore:

$$v = 2\pi f \Rightarrow v^2 = 4\pi^2 f^2$$

To find the acceleration of the vertical motion of P, or the acceleration the vertical motion of Q on the Y-axis, we substitute:

$$a = -v^2y \text{ and } v^2 = 4\pi^2 f^2 \Rightarrow a = -4\pi^2 f^2 y$$

The motion of Q as described by $y = \sin 2\pi ft$ is subject to an acceleration of:

$$a = -4\pi^2 f^2 y$$

Make sure you study the logic of this section to understand both the physical and mathematical processes.

HOOKE'S LAW

Is the motion of a bob on a spring in real coherence with the sine function; i.e., is its motion sinusoidal? The motion up may be faster than the motion down in the same period. Historically, it took some insight from Robert Hooke to answer "yes" to this question.

Figure 13. Floor tile to honor Robert Hooke in Westminster Abbey, London. Source: Rita Greer, Wikimedia Commons.

Hooke developed a simple law governing a stretched string. When we stretch, or compress a spring, it seeks to return to its normal length after we release it; i.e., when a spring is stretched or compressed, it exerts a force. **Hooke's Law** states that the force is a constant multiplied by the amount of compression or extension. In symbols, if L is the increase or decrease in length of the spring, F is the force exerted by the spring, and c is the stiffness constant of the spring, Hooke's Law is:

$$F = cL$$

> Ut tension, sic vis.
> (As the extension, so the force.)
> Robert Hooke (1635-1703).

This law states that if c is very large, i.e., the spring is very stiff, the spring exerts considerable force even if L is small. The mathematics, indeed, coinheres with our experience of springs.

Review Figure 7. We suppose that a bob of mass m is attached to the spring. After we do this, the force of gravity pulls the spring down a distance d to is equilibrium. This rest position is reached when the force of gravity acting on the bob offsets the upward force exerted by the spring. According to Newton's second law of motion, the force of gravity is $32m$.[10] According to Hooke's law, the upward force exerted by the spring pulled downward a distance d is cd. Since these two forces offset each other, we have this equation:

[10] Isaac Newton's second law states that $F = ma$. When a force is applied to a mass, the force is equal to the mass times its acceleration. The acceleration of the Earth's gravity on any object of mass m near the surface of the Earth is 32 feet per second every second. In the metric system, it is 9.8 meters per second every second.

$32m = cd$

At equilibrium, we pull the spring down a distance y. Since y, being a vector, is negative, the total extension of the spring is:

$d + (-y) = d - y$

Note how the Algebraic Definition of Subtraction coinheres in a physical situation. The force that the spring exerts in an upward direction is now, by Hooke's Law:

$c(d - y) = cd - cy$

The weight of the bob exerts a downward force, so the net upward force is:

$cd - cy - 32m$

What is the net upward force? Since $32m = cd$, the net upward force is:

$-cy$

We know that this force, based on Newton's second law $F = ma$, will be equal to ma, or:

$ma = -cy$

Solving this equation for a, we get:

$$ma = -cy \Leftrightarrow a = \frac{-cy}{m} \Leftrightarrow a = -\frac{c}{m}y$$

We have already established another result for a:

$a = -4\pi^2 f^2 y$

Comparing these two equations, we note that acceleration is a constant multiplied by the displacement y. The constant is $-\frac{c}{m}$ in $a = -\frac{c}{m}y$, and the constant is $-4\pi^2 f^2 y$ in $a = -4\pi^2 f^2 y$.

The acceleration given by $a = -4\pi^2 f^2 y$ represents the motion of Q given by:

$y = \sin 2\pi ft$

We conclude that the acceleration $a = -\frac{c}{m}y$ is precisely the same form as $a = -4\pi^2 f^2 y$, except for the way we express the constant. Since acceleration determines motion, the motion of the bob must be truly sinusoidal, represented by:

$y = \sin 2\pi ft$

What is the algebraic representation of f?
From our analysis, we know this:

$$\frac{c}{m} = 4\pi^2 f^2$$

Solving for f, we get:

$$\frac{c}{m} = 4\pi^2 f^2 \Leftrightarrow f^2 = \frac{c}{4\pi^2 m} \Rightarrow f = \sqrt{\frac{c}{4\pi^2 m}} = \frac{1}{2\pi}\sqrt{\frac{c}{m}}$$ (Note: We are only concerned with positive f.)

Knowing $f = \frac{1}{2\pi}\sqrt{\frac{c}{m}}$, we can write the sinusoidal function like this:

$$y = \sin 2\pi\left(\frac{1}{2\pi}\sqrt{\frac{c}{m}}\right)t \Leftrightarrow y = \sin\sqrt{\frac{c}{m}}t$$

Since the initial displacement influences motion, we must add D to the formula:

$$y = D\sin\sqrt{\frac{c}{m}}t$$

What is the period T? Since $T = \frac{1}{f}$ and $f = \frac{1}{2\pi}\sqrt{\frac{c}{m}}$, we write:

$$T = \frac{1}{\frac{1}{2\pi}\sqrt{\frac{c}{m}}} \Leftrightarrow T = \frac{2\pi}{\sqrt{\frac{c}{m}}} \Leftrightarrow T = \frac{2\pi\sqrt{\frac{c}{m}}}{\sqrt{\frac{c}{m}}\sqrt{\frac{c}{m}}} \Leftrightarrow T = \frac{2\pi\sqrt{\frac{c}{m}}}{\frac{c}{m}} \Leftrightarrow T = 2\pi\left(\frac{m}{k}\right)\sqrt{\frac{c}{m}} \Leftrightarrow$$

$$T = T = \frac{2\pi\left(\frac{m}{c}\right)\sqrt{\frac{c}{m}}\sqrt{\frac{m}{c}}}{\sqrt{\frac{m}{c}}} \Leftrightarrow \frac{2\pi\left(\frac{m}{c}\right)\sqrt{\frac{cm}{mc}}}{\sqrt{\frac{m}{c}}} \Leftrightarrow T = \frac{2\pi\left(\frac{m}{c}\right)}{\sqrt{\frac{m}{c}}} \Leftrightarrow T = \frac{2\pi\left(\frac{m}{c}\right)\sqrt{\frac{m}{c}}}{\sqrt{\frac{m}{c}}\sqrt{\frac{m}{c}}} \Leftrightarrow$$

$$T = \frac{2\pi\left(\frac{m}{c}\right)\sqrt{\frac{m}{c}}}{\frac{m}{c}} \Leftrightarrow T = 2\pi\sqrt{\frac{m}{c}}$$

What is significant about $T = 2\pi\sqrt{\frac{m}{c}}$? Since the variable L is missing, we conclude that the period is independent of the amplitude L of the motion; i.e., whether one pulls the bob down a great distance or a short distance and then releases it, the time for the bob to go through each complete oscillation will be the same. Testing by experiment confirms the conclusion of these algebraic operations. That abstract methods of Mathematics comports with the nature of the motion of a bob on the spring should stun and awe the beholder of such wonders.

LOSS OF ENERGY ADJUSTMENT

If we consider air resistance and loss of energy in the spring as the bob moves, the sine curve will decay by a function involving e:

$y = e^{-kx}\sin x$ where $-k$ is the decay factor dependent, primarily, on the strength of the spring.

Figure 14 represents what happens when $k = 0.009$.

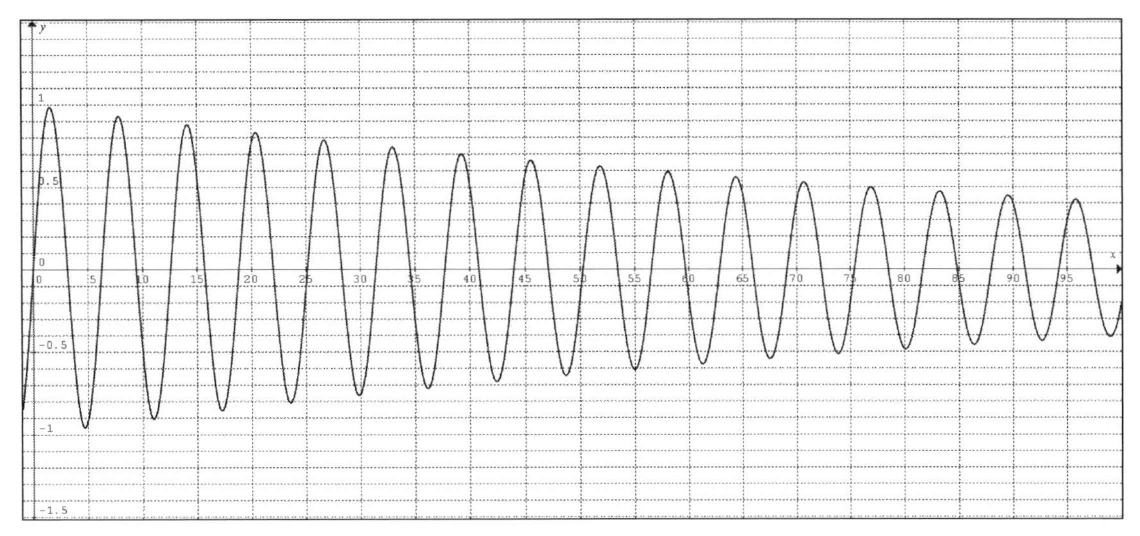

Figure 14. Decaying sine curve.

To offset this decay, we give the bob a little push every time it reaches its lowest position; i.e., we add energy to keep the bob moving. Such an action alters the amplitude, but, because $T = 2\pi\sqrt{\frac{m}{c}}$, *it will not change the period.* By adding a little bit of energy, each successive oscillation of the bob will continue to take the same amount of time. We have, therefore, developed the theory for the construction of an accurate timepiece, a watch! All we need to do is create a gear system that reports the oscillation of the bob as hands on a dial.

Before the invention of wrist watches that tell time by vibrating quartz crystals (ca. late 1960s), these watches were driven by a spring coiled in a spiral that carried a balancing weight that expanded and contracted on a periodic basis. As the spring unwound, the balance weight exerted more force to maintain regularity. A person with such a watch had to rewind it daily to keep accurate time.

Figure 15. Self-winding wrist watch, issued to soldiers in WWI. Source: Wikimedia Commons.

Figure 16. Christiaan Huygens. Source: Public Domain.

The Dutch mathematician Christiaan Huygens (1629-1695) invented the spiral spring regulator in 1675. In 1772, the British carpenter and horologist John Harrison (1693-1776) designed and manufactured the first marine chronometer, the H4, a device that enabled navigators to accurately compute their longitude at sea.[11] This mechanical timepiece facilitated England's mastery over the oceans and thereby led to the creation of the British Empire. It was by the chronometer that Britannia ruled the waves.

Figure 17. Joseph Fourier. Source: Public Domain.

We can describe any wavelike, or regular, motion mathematically in terms of trigonometric functions. Some examples are the path of meandering rivers, ocean tides, the crest and trough of ocean waves, the ebb and flow of alternating electric current, and the majestic rotation of galaxies.

The graphs of sounds that are pleasing to the ear display order and regularity. We write this periodicity as follows:

$$y = D \sin 2\pi ft$$

This equation describes very simple sounds, like those of a tuning fork. For complex sounds, the equation still holds but is expanded in the terms of a summation of a mathematical series, named the Fourier series after its originator, the mathematician and physicist Joseph Fourier (1768-1830). The work of this Frenchman in the analysis of heat[12] provided the foundation for the mathematical study of music, a study that has enabled man in the 20th century to construct electronic gadgets like the musical synthesizer.

Using the Fourier series middle C on the piano can be described mathematically as follows (Figure 20):

$$y = \sin 2(512t) + 0.2 \sin 2(1024t) + 0.25 \sin 2(1536t) + 0.1 \sin 2(2048t) + 0.1 \sin 2(2560t)$$

Every sound that is pleasing to the ear can be described mathematically as the summation of sinusoidal functions. Noise and dissonant music do not display regularity and we cannot them using the above mathematical work.

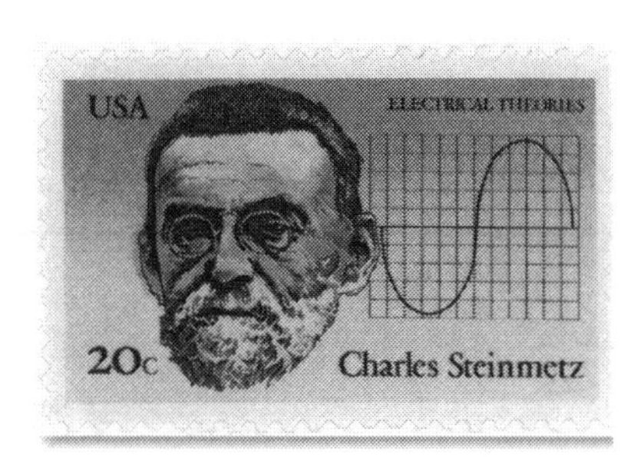

Figure 18. Source: United States Postal Service.

Figure 19. John Harrison. Source: Public Domain.

[11] Harrison won the prize of £20,000 offered by the British government. See Dava Sobel, *Longitude* (New York: Walker and Company, 1995).

[12] Joseph Fourier, *The Analytical Theory of Heat*, trans. Alexander Freeman (Cambridge: Cambridge University Press, 1878).

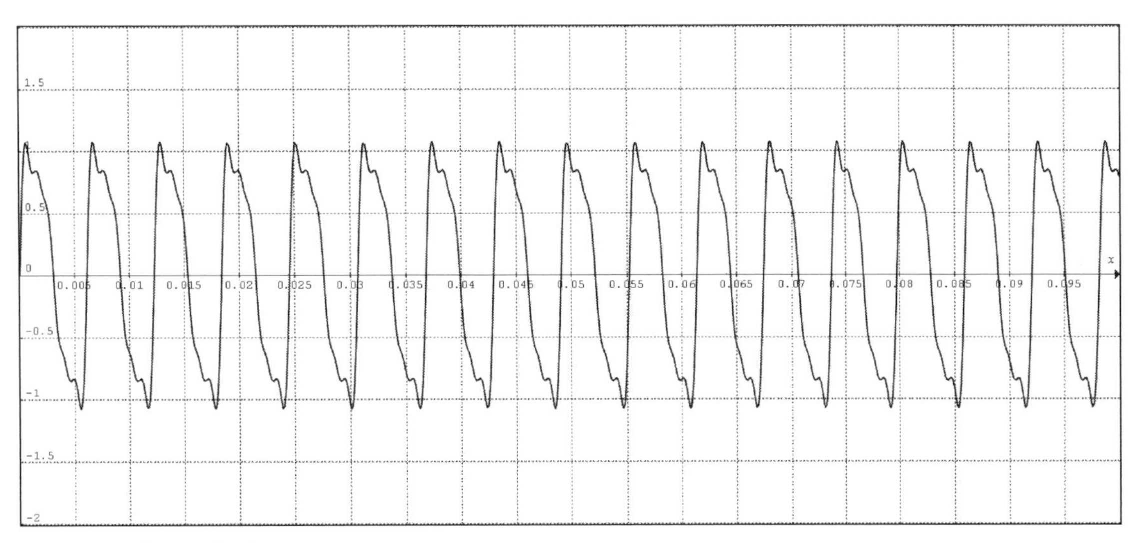

Figure 20. Middle C on the piano.

Note the wondrous order and complexity in music. To fully comprehend it involves a thorough knowledge of trigonometry and the foundation of trigonometry is the simple right triangle. Note also the progression from a simple right triangle to oscillatory motion and the complex order of music. In fact, sinusoidal functions not only describe sound waves, but they also completely describe the distinct, wavelike motion of visible light and in fact, the entire electromagnetic spectrum. What *unity in diversity*! Who is the originator of light and the electromagnetic spectrum? The architect is the God revealed by the light of the cosmos Jesus Christ, the ultimate, eternal, and relational One and the Many

EXERCISES

Define the following terms:

1. Amplitude
2. Wavelength
3. Crest
4. Trough
5. Wave height
6. Displacement
7. Projection of point P on line l when P is not on l
8. Hooke's Law of springs
9. Parametric equations (See homework exercise below.)
10. Radius vector (See homework exercise below.)

> ... the trigonometric functions apply to all wave motions, sound, radio, light, water waves, waves in gases, and many other types of wave motions. The person who understands trigonometric functions and their properties understands in one swoop all the phenomena governed by these functions
>
> Morris Kline, *Mathematics for the Nonmathematician* ([1967] 1985), p. 548.

Answer the following questions:

11. In Figure 12, why is the magnitude of the vertical vector $v^2 \sin \theta$?
12. Why does e^{-x} represent decay?
13. Explain the interplay between the motion of a bob on a spring with the motion of a point around the circumference of a circle.
14. Explain how composition of functions is applicable with trig functions.
15. Describe the relationship between period, frequency, and wavelength. Use the fact the velocity is distance traveled per time in your answer.

Table 1: The Electromagnetic Spectrum
Speed of Light (v) ≈ 300,000 km/s
1 Å (Ångström) = 0.0000000001 m = 0.1 nm

f (Hz)	λ (meters)						
10^{21}	3×10^{-13}		↑ Gamma Rays				
10^{20}	3×10^{-12}	↑ X-rays	Gamma Rays				
10^{19}	3×10^{-11}	X-rays	Gamma Rays				
10^{18}	3×10^{-10}	X-rays	Gamma Rays ↓	↑ Ultraviolet radiation			
10^{17}	3×10^{-9}	X-rays		Ultraviolet radiation			
10^{16}	3×10^{-8}	X-rays ↓		Ultraviolet radiation ↓			
				Visible light	Violet	4000Å	4×10^{-7} m
				Visible light	Indigo	4300Å	
				Visible light	Blue	4800Å	
				Visible light	Green	5300Å	
				Visible light	Yellow	5800Å	
10^{15}	3×10^{-7}			Visible light	Orange	6100Å	
				Visible light	Red	7000Å	7×10^{-7} m
10^{14}	3×10^{-6}		↑ Infrared radiation				
10^{13}	3×10^{-5}		Infrared radiation				↑ Micro-waves
10^{12}	3×10^{-4}		Infrared radiation ↓				Micro-waves
10^{11}	3×10^{-3}				↑ Communication bands: Amateur, police, airplanes, etc.		Micro-waves
10^{10}	3×10^{-2}	↑ Radio waves			Communication bands		Micro-waves
10^{9}	3×10^{-1}	Radio waves			Communication bands		Micro-waves ↓
10^{8}	3×10^{0}	Radio waves	↑ TV	↑ AM/FM radio	Communication bands		
10^{7}	3×10^{1}	Radio waves	TV ↓	AM/FM radio	Communication bands		
10^{6}	3×10^{2}	Radio waves		AM/FM radio	Communication bands		
10^{5}	3×10^{3}	Radio waves		AM/FM radio ↓	Communication bands		
10^{4}	3×10^{4}	Radio waves			Communication bands		
10^{3}	3×10^{5}	Radio waves			Communication bands ↓		
10^{2}	3×10^{6}	Radio waves					
10^{1}	3×10^{7}	Radio waves					
10^{0}	3×10^{8}	Radio waves ↓					

16. The wavelength is $\lambda = \frac{v}{f}$ where v is the velocity of the wave and f is its frequency. More specifically, in terms of units involved, $\lambda = \frac{\text{distance/second}}{\text{cycles/second}}$. Show why this division produces the unit for λ as distance/cycle.
17. A musical note has a frequency of 440 Hz. State its:
    (a) sine wave function in terms of radians and time t.
    (b) period.
18. A guitar string pulled aside 2 mm vibrates at 400 Hz. Write an equation in radians stating its position at time t.
19. A guitar stretched 0.5 cm vibrates at 25 Hz. Write an equation in radians stating its position at time t.
20. Determine the wavelength in meters, rounded to the nearest unit, of a local FM radio station that is 96.3 on the dial. (Hint: 96.3 stands for 96.3 million cycles per second or 96.3 MHz).
21. Determine the wavelength in meters, rounded to the nearest unit, of a local AM radio station that is 560 on the dial. (Hint: 560 stands for 560 thousand cycles per second or 560 kHz).
22. Some microwaves have a frequency of 5×10^{10} Hz. What is the exact corresponding wavelength in millimeters?
23. Some x-rays have a frequency of 10^{18} Hz. What is the exact corresponding wavelength in millimeters?

The patterned shape of a sinusoidal curve pictures periodic nature of the elemental trigonometric function $y = f(x) = \sin x$. Answer the following questions:

24. What is the image, or the displacement, of f at the crest?
25. What is the image or the displacement, of f at the trough?
26. What is the wave height of f?
27. What is the amplitude of f?
28. In radians, what is the wavelength of f?
29. What is the wave height and amplitude of $y = 2 \sin x$?
30. What is the wave height and amplitude of $y = 3 \sin x$?
31. In radians, what is the wavelength of $y = \sin 2x$?
32. In radians, what is the wavelength of $y = \sin 3x$?

State the (a) amplitude, (b) frequency, (c) period, and (d) wavelength revealed in the following functions:

33. $y = f(t) = 2 \sin 3t$
34. $y = f(t) = 5 \sin \frac{t}{6}$
35. $y = f(t) = 8 \sin \frac{t}{9}$
36. $y = f(t) = \frac{1}{2} \sin 12t$

In the following problems, explain why the following equivalencies are true; i.e., account for the operation performed on the equation on the left to generate the equation on the right.

37. $T = \frac{1}{\frac{1}{2\pi}\sqrt{\frac{c}{m}}} \Leftrightarrow T = \frac{2\pi}{\sqrt{\frac{c}{m}}}$

38. $T = \dfrac{2\pi}{\sqrt{\dfrac{c}{m}}} \Leftrightarrow T = \dfrac{2\pi\sqrt{\dfrac{c}{m}}}{\sqrt{\dfrac{c}{m}}\sqrt{\dfrac{c}{m}}}$

39. $T = \dfrac{2\pi\sqrt{\dfrac{c}{m}}}{\sqrt{\dfrac{c}{m}}\sqrt{\dfrac{c}{m}}} \Leftrightarrow T = \dfrac{2\pi\sqrt{\dfrac{c}{m}}}{\dfrac{c}{m}}$

40. $T = \dfrac{2\pi\sqrt{\dfrac{c}{m}}}{\dfrac{c}{m}} \Leftrightarrow T = 2\pi\left(\dfrac{m}{c}\right)\sqrt{\dfrac{c}{m}}$

41. $T = 2\pi\left(\dfrac{m}{c}\right)\sqrt{\dfrac{c}{m}} \Leftrightarrow T = \dfrac{2\pi\left(\dfrac{m}{c}\right)\sqrt{\dfrac{c}{m}}\sqrt{\dfrac{m}{c}}}{\sqrt{\dfrac{m}{c}}}$

42. $T = \dfrac{2\pi\left(\dfrac{m}{c}\right)\sqrt{\dfrac{c}{m}}\sqrt{\dfrac{m}{c}}}{\sqrt{\dfrac{m}{c}}} \Leftrightarrow T = \dfrac{2\pi\left(\dfrac{m}{c}\right)\sqrt{\dfrac{cm}{mc}}}{\sqrt{\dfrac{m}{c}}}$

43. $T = \dfrac{2\pi\left(\dfrac{m}{c}\right)\sqrt{\dfrac{cm}{mc}}}{\sqrt{\dfrac{m}{c}}} \Leftrightarrow T = \dfrac{2\pi\left(\dfrac{m}{c}\right)}{\sqrt{\dfrac{m}{c}}}$

44. $T = \dfrac{2\pi\left(\dfrac{m}{c}\right)}{\sqrt{\dfrac{m}{c}}} \Leftrightarrow T = \dfrac{2\pi\left(\dfrac{m}{c}\right)\sqrt{\dfrac{m}{c}}}{\sqrt{\dfrac{m}{c}}\sqrt{\dfrac{m}{c}}}$

45. $T = \dfrac{2\pi\left(\dfrac{m}{c}\right)\sqrt{\dfrac{m}{c}}}{\sqrt{\dfrac{m}{c}}\sqrt{\dfrac{m}{c}}} \Leftrightarrow T = \dfrac{2\pi\left(\dfrac{m}{c}\right)\sqrt{\dfrac{m}{c}}}{\dfrac{m}{c}}$

46. $T = \dfrac{2\pi\left(\dfrac{m}{c}\right)\sqrt{\dfrac{m}{c}}}{\dfrac{m}{c}} \Leftrightarrow T = 2\pi\sqrt{\dfrac{m}{c}}$

Figure 21. The periodic motion of the pendulum. Source: iStockPhoto.

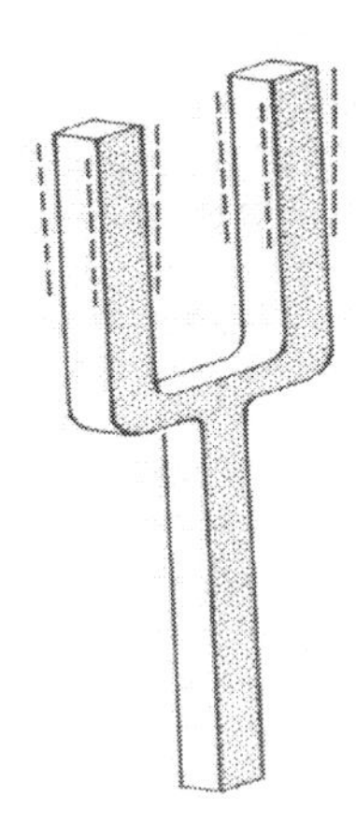

Figure 22. Tuning fork reveals periodic motion.

As we have noted, logarithms are used to measure earthquake intensity on the Richter scale, developed by the American physicist Charles Richter (1900-1985). The Richter scale function is:

$R(a) = \log a$

where a is the amplitude of the earthquake measured in microns (micrometers)

Recall these unit conversions:

$1000\ \mu\text{m} = 1\ \text{mm} \Leftrightarrow 1{,}000{,}000\ \mu\text{m} = 1\ \text{m}$

The amplitude of a seismic wave is the amount the ground moves as the surface wave goes past. We can measure amplitude from a signal recorded on a seismograph.

If the waves of one earthquake have amplitude k times those of another, their Richter scale values differ by $\log k$.

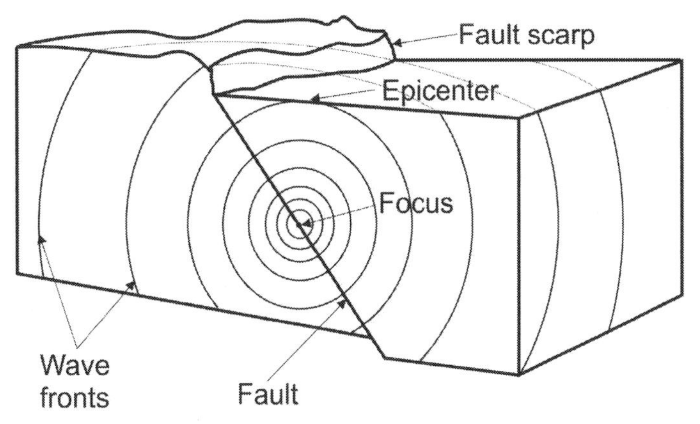

Figure 23. Seismic waves radiate from the focus of an earthquake.

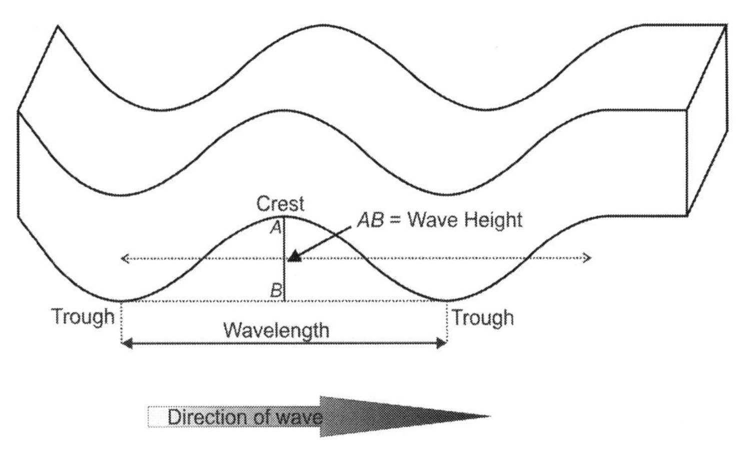

Figure 24. Surface waves (sinusoidal) and wave amplitude.

Because the Richter scale is in common logs, a difference of d on the Richter scale corresponds to one having waves with 10^d times the amplitude of the waves of the other.

The energy yield of an earthquake, which closely correlates to its destructive power, scales with the 3/2 power of the shaking amplitude. In other words, a difference in magnitude of 1.0 is equivalent to a factor of $\left(10^1\right)^{\frac{3}{2}} = 10^{\frac{3}{2}} = 31.6$ in the energy released. A difference in magnitude of 2.0 is equivalent to a factor of $\left(10^2\right)^{\frac{3}{2}} = 10^3 = 1000$ in the energy released. Answer the following questions:

47. A strong earthquake has a Richter value of 6; i.e., $R(a) = 6$, equivalent to an energy yield of 15 kilotons. It causes much destructive force over a wide area. Since $R(a) = \log a$, find a in meters.

48. A weak earthquake has a Richter value of 4; i.e., $R(a) = 4$, equivalent to an energy yield of 15 metric tons. It causes noticeable shaking of indoor items, rattling noises. Since $R(a) = \log a$, find a in millimeters.
49. (a) What is the difference in Richter values between a strong and weak earthquake?
    (b) What is the difference in amplitude between a strong and weak earthquake?
50. On 18 April 1906, an earthquake struck San Francisco, California. Its Richter value has been estimated to be 7.8 (low estimate: 7.7; high estimate: 8.5). It had an energy yield of 7.6 megatons and caused serious damage over large areas killing 3000 people in a population of 410,000. What was the amplitude of this earthquake rounded to the nearest meter?
51. On 17 October 1989, another earthquake struck San Francisco, California. Its Richter value was measured as 6.9, an energy yield of 340 kilotons. 63 people died in a population of 700,000. What was the amplitude of this earthquake rounded to the nearest meter?
52. On 12 January 2010, an earthquake with the Richter value of 7.0 struck Haiti. Between 100,000 and 160,000 people died and caused major damage in its capital, Port-au-Prince (population $\approx$ 900,000), about 16 miles from the epicenter. What was the amplitude of this earthquake in meters?
53. On 15 August 2007, an earthquake with the Richter value of 8.0 struck Peru. (Note: I was in the region of this earthquake, near Lima, one week before it happened.) 519 people died. What was the amplitude of this earthquake in meters?
54. On 27 February 2010, an earthquake with the Richter value of 8.8 struck Chile. It had an energy yield of 240 megatons. 525 people died.
    (a) What was the amplitude of this earthquake in meters?
    (b) How many times greater is the amplitude of this earthquake than the amplitude of the earthquake in Haiti?
55. Determine the amplitude in meters of these earthquakes:
    (a) Chile (1960): 9.5
    (b) Alaska (1964): 9.2
    (c) Japan (2011): 8.9

The Motion of a Projectile Launched by a Cannon.

Suppose that a cannon is inclined at an angle of 35° to the ground (Figure 25). It fires a shell with a velocity of 250 ft/sec. Let's try to analyze the subsequent motion of the shell by considering its horizontal and vertical motions separately, as per the method of Galileo. In Physics, what we are doing is the derivation and algebraic analysis of **parametric equations.**[13] Note the rectangle constructed ($OQRP$). The distance traveled in one second is represented by the **radius vector**[14] $\overrightarrow{OR}$. We represent the horizontal distance traveled in one second by the vector $\overrightarrow{OP}$ and the vertical distance traveled in one second is represented by the vector $\overrightarrow{OQ}$. Let's determine these distances with the help of trigonometry.

56. Write a ratio that represents cos 35°.
57. Write a ratio that represents sin 35°.
58. What is OR if the shell travels one second?

[13] A parametric equation defines a group of quantities as functions of one or more independent variables which are parameters.

[14] A radius vector is a line of variable length drawn from a fixed origin to another point, usually a point on a curve. See Johannes Kepler's Third Law of Planetary motion discussed in Lesson 8.6.

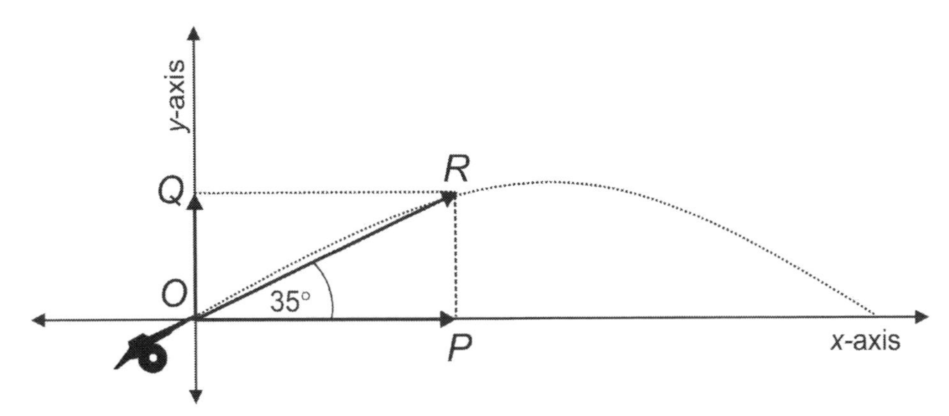

Figure 25.

59. Substitute your answer in Question 58 in Question 56 and solve for OP (round to the nearest unit), the horizontal velocity in ft/s. (Note: In your calculations, round the cosine ratio to the nearest thousandths.)
60. Substitute your answer in Question 58 in Question 57 and solve for RP (round to the nearest unit), the vertical velocity in ft/s. (Note: In your calculations, round the cosine ratio to the nearest thousandths.)
61. Since $OQ = RP$ (Why?), solve Question 60 for OQ, the vertical velocity in ft/sec.
62. Write a parametric equation for x in terms of t; i.e., $x = f(t)$ if no force acts to accelerate or decelerate the horizontal motion.
63. Since the force of gravity pulls the shell downward and at $16t^2$ feet per second, write a parametric equation for y in terms of t; i.e., $y = g(t)$. (Hint: the downward pull, represented in vectors, means a negative amount.)
64. Solve $x = f(t)$ and $y = g(t)$ for $y = f(x)$. Write the coefficients as rational numbers.
65. (a) What Conic Section does $y = f(x)$ represent?
    (b) Graph this function.
66. What is the range of the shell rounded to the nearest tenth of a foot (i.e., how far from the starting point will the projectile strike the ground again)?
67. (a) On its trajectory, use $y = g(t)$ to find the exact maximum height of the shell. (Refer to Lesson 11.14.)
    (b) At what exact time does the shell reach this heigh; i.e., what is the maximum image?
    (c) Use $x = f(t)$ to find exactly how far has the shell travelled horizontally at the time it reaches its maximum height; i.e., find the value of x when the maximum image reached.
    (d) Use $y = f(x)$ from Question 64 to obtain the same answers as (a) and (c).

12.9 Solving Trig Equations

Terms & Concepts Introduced
1. arccos
2. arcsin
3. arctan
4. Law of Cosines
5. Reference angle

We know, given $y = ax$ (one-to-one function), to solve for x, we do this:

$$y = ax \Leftrightarrow x = \frac{y}{a}$$

We then exchange x with y, since they are placeholders, and we get the inverse function, the method of solution; i.e., the rule of the inverse is divide by a:

$$y = \frac{x}{a}$$

Given $y = ax^2$ (many-to-one function), to solve for x, we do this:

$$y = ax^2 \Leftrightarrow x^2 = \frac{y}{a} \Leftrightarrow x = \sqrt{\frac{y}{a}} \text{ or } x = -\sqrt{\frac{y}{a}}$$

The solution is a double-valued relation (one-to-many). It has two parts where each part is a one-to-one function. If the equation is embedded in a physical situation, the context determines if we use both parts or only one part. Both parts are the inverse of the original function. For many-to-one functions, we know, by the vertical line test, that there will be as many parts in the inverse as the maximum number of times the vertical line intersects the graph. For $y = ax^2$, a vertical line intersects that graph in maximally in two places.[1]

For logarithmic functions (one-to-one), the inverse, for common logarithms is:

$$y = \log x \Leftrightarrow x = 10^y$$

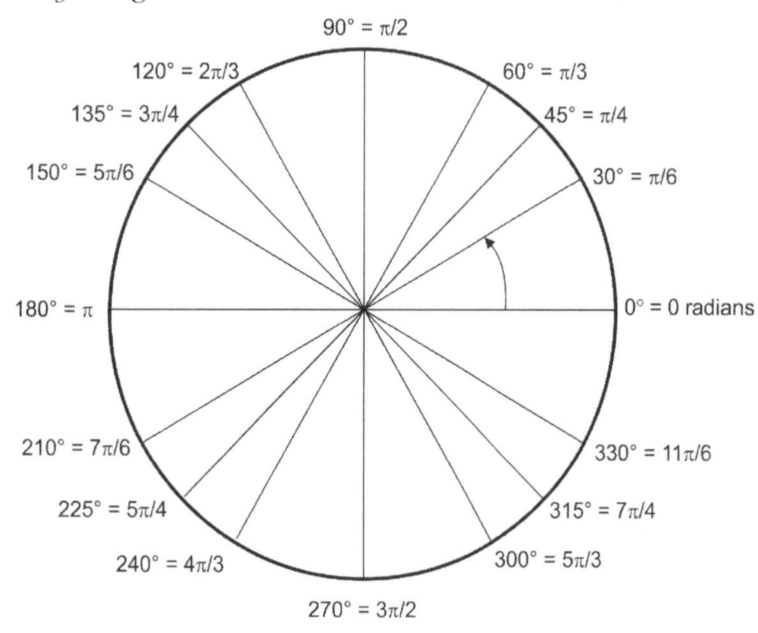

Figure 1. Common angles in the unit circle.

For natural logarithms, the inverse is:

$$y = \ln x \Leftrightarrow x = e^y$$

Since log functions are transcendental, we cannot solve them algebraically. We must invoke log tables or press the *log* or *ln* keys on a scientific calculator to find the solutions. Being one-to-one functions, we do not need to worry about multiple solutions as we do with quadratics. We will get one and only one solution.

Inverse Sine

Given $y = \sin x$ (many-to-one function), to solve for x we cannot use algebraic methods. We must use

[1] Note that the vertical line intersects the minimum, the smiling parabola, or maximum, the frowning parabola, point only once.

trig tables or press the *sin* key on a scientific calculator. The notation that mathematicians use for the inverse is:

$y = \sin x \Leftrightarrow x = \sin^{-1} y$

We read $x = \sin^{-1} y$ as "x is the inverse sine function of y." (Note: $\sin^{-1} y$ does *not* mean the "reciprocal of the sine"; i.e., $\frac{1}{\sin y} = \csc y$.) An alternative notation is:

$y = \sin x \Leftrightarrow x = \arcsin y$

In this notation, **arc** represents the "angle, in radians, whose sine is y."[2] Using arc removes any ambiguity, but, because of efficiency, $\sin^{-1}$ is the standard notation.

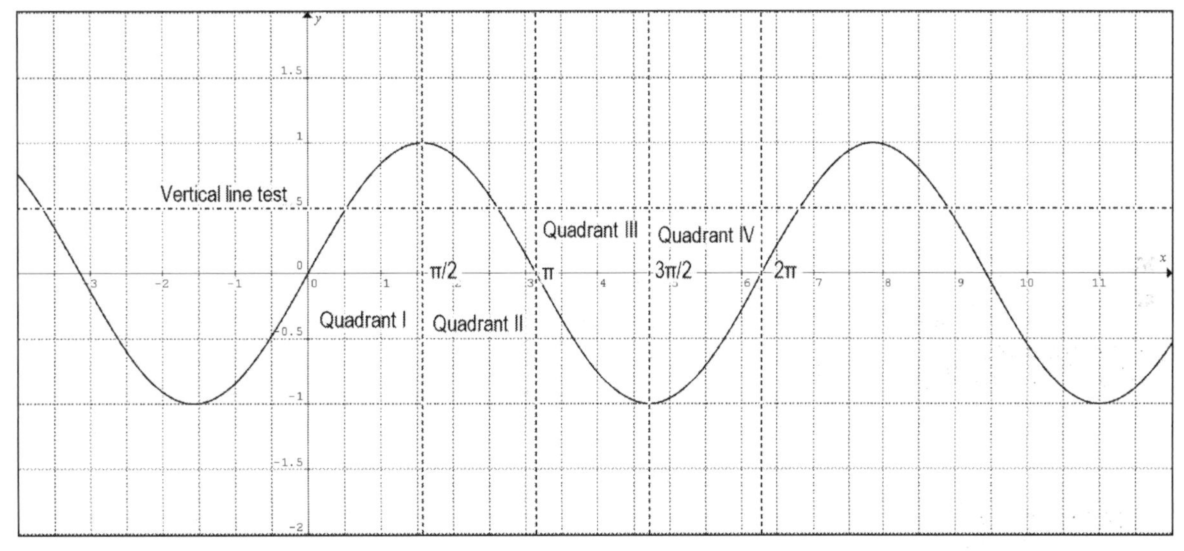

Figure 2. Vertical line test for the sine function (x-axis is in radians).

What does the vertical line test tell us about the sine function? The inverse is not a double-valued relation; it is a multiple-valued relation. In fact, because of the periodic nature of the sine function, there are technically an infinite number of solutions.[3]

We can partition the sine curve into segments that reflect a one-to-one relationship (Figure 2). For example, from the domain $-\frac{\pi}{2}$ to $\frac{\pi}{2}$, the images of $\sin x$ in that range vary increasingly from -1 to 1. We can also limit the domain to range from $\frac{\pi}{2}$ to $\frac{3\pi}{2}$. In this domain, the images of $\sin x$ in that the range vary decreasingly from 1 to -1.

Since the images of $\sin x$ range between -1 and 1, mathematicians establish the domain of $\sin^{-1} x$ to take argument values between -1 and 1, meaning that the images of $\sin^{-1} x$ will be between $-\frac{\pi}{2}$ to $\frac{\pi}{2}$.

We write:

$y = \sin x \Leftrightarrow x = \sin^{-1} y$

---

[2] Arc refers to radian measure on the circumference, an arc, of a circle.

[3] Gladly, the context of the problem will only point to one of those solutions.

Exchanging y with x, the inverse function becomes:

> $y = \sin^{-1} x$ where, if the argument domain is $-1 \le x \le 1 \Rightarrow$ there is a unique image in this range: $-\frac{\pi}{2} \le y \le \frac{\pi}{2}$ or $-90° \le y \le 90°$.

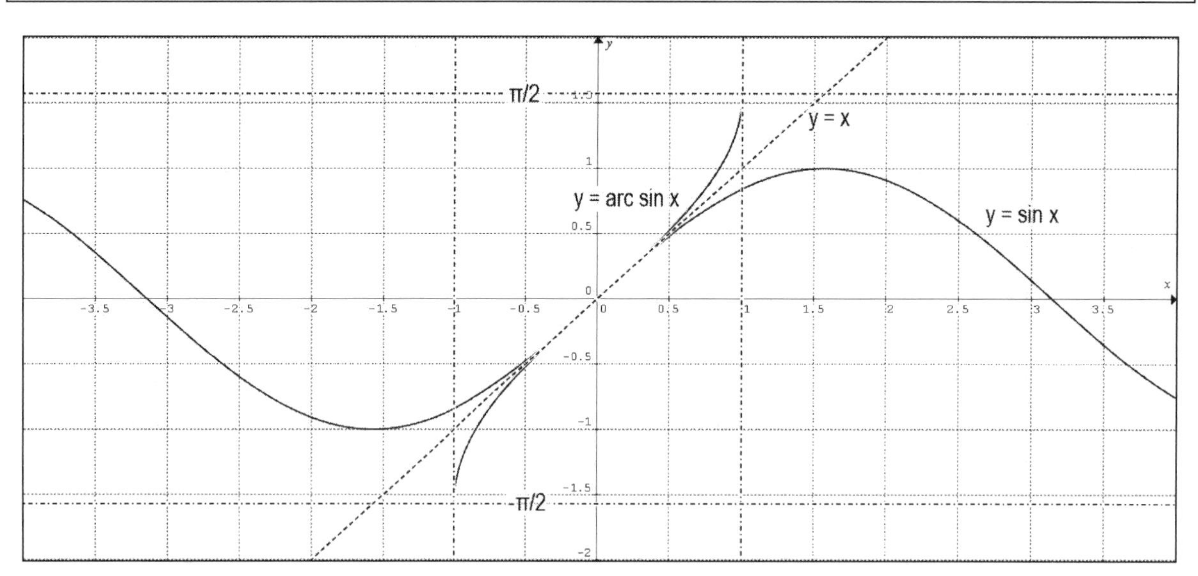

Figure 3. The beautiful reflecton symmetry of sin x and $\sin^{-1} x$.

For example, let's find y if $x = \frac{\sqrt{2}}{2}$. (Refer to Table 2 of Lesson 12.6 to find the angle in radians when $\sin\theta = \frac{\sqrt{2}}{2}$.) We do the following:

$$y = \sin^{-1}\frac{\sqrt{2}}{2} = \frac{\pi}{4} \approx 0.785\ (45°)$$

If $x = -\frac{\sqrt{2}}{2}$ (Use Figure 2 to determine the magnitude and sign.):

$$y = \sin^{-1}\left(-\frac{\sqrt{2}}{2}\right) = -\frac{\pi}{4} \approx -0.785\ (-45°)$$

The range of the inverse function covers positive angles in Quadrant I and negative angles in Quadrant IV. What about the other quadrants?

Table 1

	0	$\frac{\pi}{6}$	$\frac{\pi}{4}$	$\frac{\pi}{3}$	$\frac{\pi}{2}$
sin	0	$\frac{1}{2}$	$\frac{\sqrt{2}}{2}$	$\frac{\sqrt{3}}{2}$	1
cos	1	$\frac{\sqrt{3}}{2}$	$\frac{\sqrt{2}}{2}$	$\frac{1}{2}$	0
tan	0	$\frac{\sqrt{3}}{3}$	1	$\sqrt{3}$	Undefined

REFERENCE ANGLES

In Geometry, angles are never negative. In trigonometry, we can have negative angles. Because the trig ratios unfold from the unit circle, we always start our measurement of positive angle θ sweeping the initial side $\overline{OA}$ on the positive x-axis counterclockwise to the terminal position $\overline{OP}$ to get the angle desired, either in Quadrant I, II, III, or IV (Figure 4). Angles measured clockwise from the positive x-axis are, by definition, negative angles.

Since a right triangle in a unit circle can picture every possible angle, it is preferable to understand angles greater than 90° as acute. The **reference angle**, therefore, is the positive acute angle formed by the terminal side and the x-axis. In Figure 4, all four angles have the same reference angle θ: (Note: τ is the Greek letter *tau*.)

- $\sin \tau = \sin \theta$
- $\sin \omega = -\sin \theta$ (Negative, because ω is in Quadrant III)
- $\sin -\theta = -\sin \theta$ (Note: In our example, $\sin -\frac{\pi}{4} = -\sin \frac{\pi}{4}$ since -0.785 is the opposite of 0.785.)

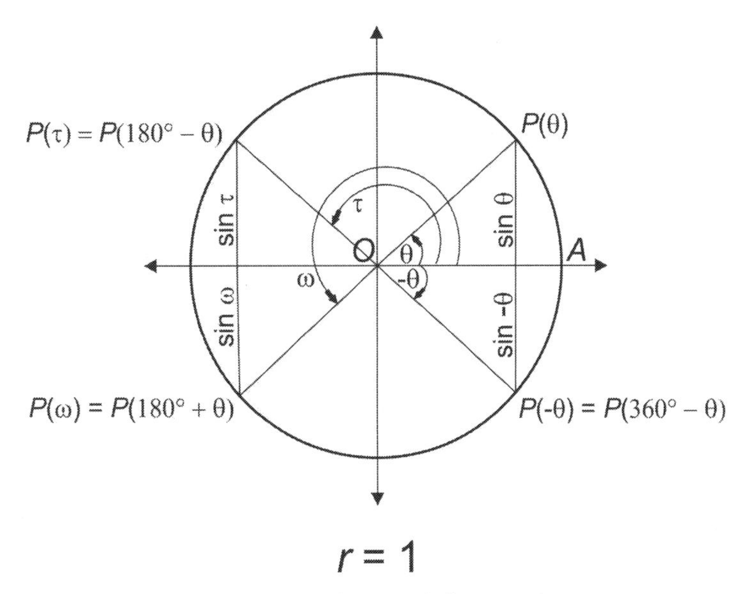

Figure 4. Four angles with the same reference angle θ.

In general, we conclude:

$$\sin -\theta = -\sin \theta$$

Note also that the cosines of all four angles, and, by implication,[4] the tangent of all four angles are the same, expect for signs (ASTC from Lesson 12.7).

We see the following relationships between the angles θ, τ, and ω:

$\tau = 180° - \theta \Leftrightarrow \theta = 180° - \tau$
$\omega = 180° + \theta \Leftrightarrow \theta = \omega - 180°$

In radians:

$\tau = \pi - \theta \Leftrightarrow \theta = \pi - \tau$
$\omega = \pi + \theta \Leftrightarrow \theta = \omega - \pi$

[4] $\tan \theta = \frac{\sin \theta}{\cos \theta}$

We can now generate the following Reference-Angle identities.

REFERENCE-ANGLE IDENTITIES

Since $\tau = 180° - \theta$:

$$\sin(180° - \theta) = \sin\theta \text{ or } \sin(\pi - \theta) = \sin\theta$$

Since τ is in Quadrant II with have this cosine identity:

$$\cos(180° - \theta) = -\cos\theta \text{ or } \cos(\pi - \theta) = -\cos\theta$$

Since $\tan\theta = \dfrac{\sin\theta}{\cos\theta}$, we have this tangent identity:

$$\tan(180° - \theta) = -\tan\theta \text{ or } \tan(\pi - \theta) = -\tan\theta$$

These identities are useful when considering angles in Quadrant II, i.e., between $\dfrac{\pi}{2}$ and π.

For angles in Quadrant III (remember ASTC), the identities are:

$$\sin(\theta + 180°) = -\sin\theta \text{ or } \sin(\theta + \pi) = -\sin\theta$$

$$\cos(\theta + 180°) = -\cos\theta \text{ or } \cos(\theta + \pi) = -\cos\theta$$

$$\tan(\theta + 180°) = \tan\theta \text{ or } \tan(\theta + \pi) = \tan\theta$$

For angles in Quadrant IV, the identities are:

$$\sin(-\theta) = \sin(360° - \theta) = -\sin\theta \text{ or } \sin(-\theta) = \sin(2\pi - \theta) = -\sin\theta$$

$$\cos(-\theta) = \cos(360° - \theta) = \cos\theta \text{ or } \cos(-\theta) = \cos(2\pi - \theta) = \cos\theta$$

$$\tan(-\theta) = \tan(360° - \theta) = -\tan\theta \text{ or } \tan(-\theta) = \tan(2\pi - \theta) = -\tan\theta$$

Table 2 summarizes how to compute reference angles based on Figure 5. As we have noted, the trig ratios of the reference angle will have the same magnitude but will differ in sign based on Quadrant location.

Table 2: Reference Angles

Quadrant	ε = Reference Angle (degrees)
I	$\varepsilon = \theta$
II	$\varepsilon = \theta = 180° - \alpha$
III	$\varepsilon = \theta = \beta - 180°$
IV	$\varepsilon = \theta = 360° - \gamma$

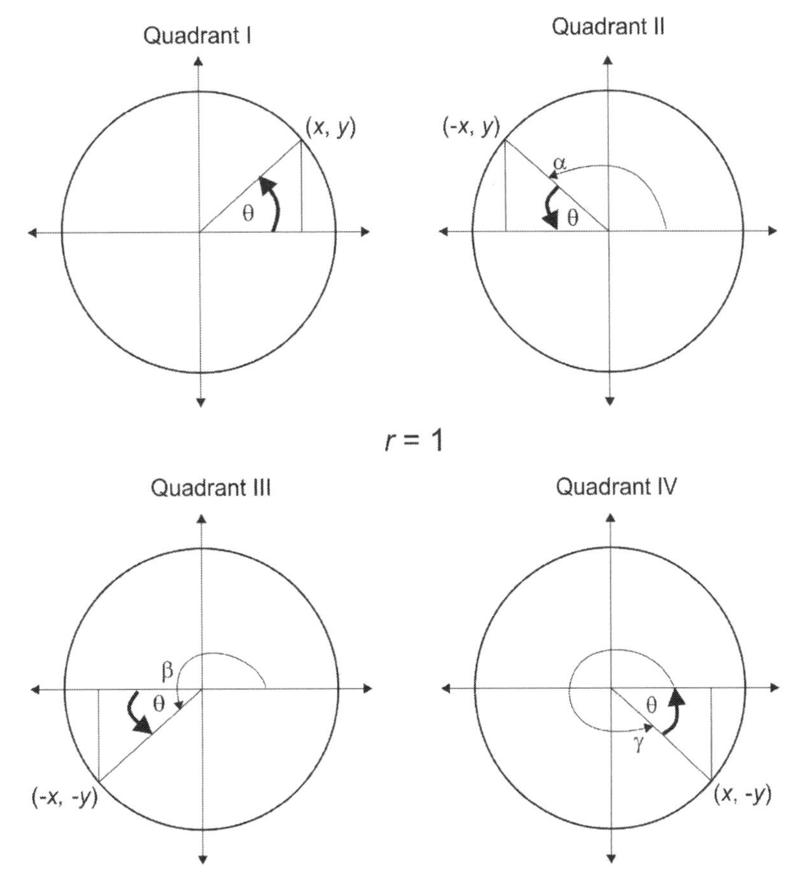

Figure 5. How to compute reference angles in the four quadrants. The right angle of the triangle is always drawn on the x-axis.

Let's shift from the unit circle to the sine curve and review what happens between 0 and 2π (Figure 6):

1. There are two angles ($\frac{\pi}{4} \approx 0.785$ and $\frac{3\pi}{4} \approx 2.356$), one in Quadrant I and the other in Quadrant II that generate the same positive image $\frac{\sqrt{2}}{2} \approx 0.707$.

2. There are two angles ($\frac{5\pi}{4} \approx 3.927$ and $\frac{7\pi}{4} \approx 5.498$), one in Quadrant III and the other in Quadrant IV that generate the same negative image $-\frac{\sqrt{2}}{2} \approx -0.707$.

If we continue the graph in Figure 6 either to the left or the right, we see that there are an infinite number of solutions for $\sin x = \frac{\sqrt{2}}{2} \approx 0.707$ or $\sin x = -\frac{\sqrt{2}}{2} \approx -0.707$.

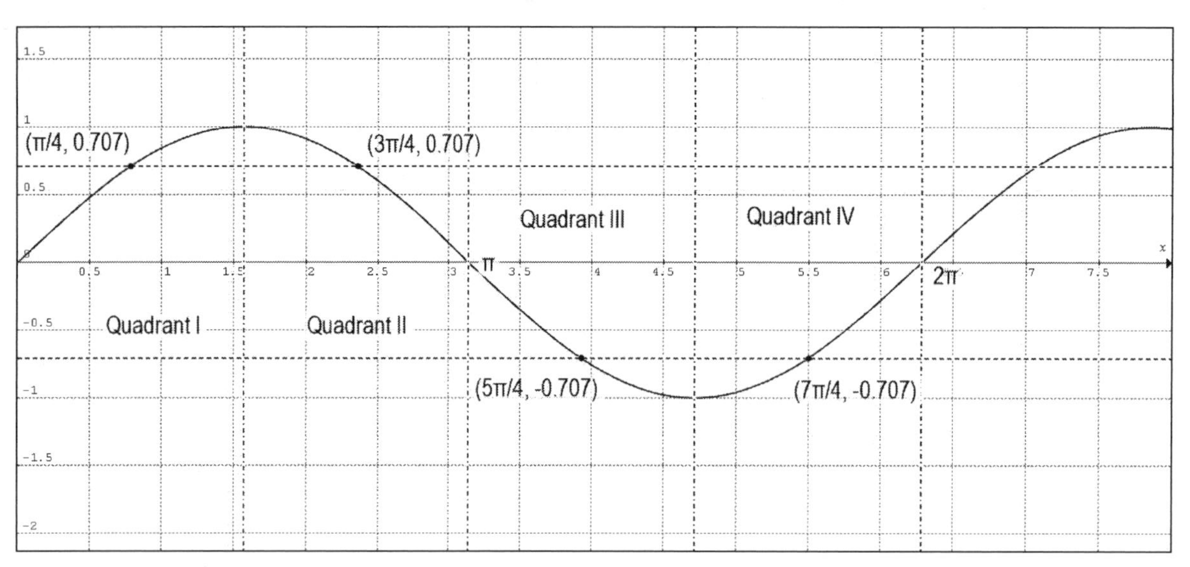

Figure 6. $y = \sin x$ (This relationship is many-to-one mapping.)

Use Figure 6 as a guide for the following analysis.

For the equation, $\sin x = \frac{\sqrt{2}}{2}$, trig tables or your scientific calculator will give only one solution:

$$\sin x = \frac{\sqrt{2}}{2} \Leftrightarrow x = \sin^{-1}\frac{\sqrt{2}}{2} = \frac{\pi}{4} \approx 0.785$$

(Note: See Table 1 where we read the answer by observing that the angle whose sin is $\frac{\sqrt{2}}{2} \approx$ 0.707 is $\frac{\pi}{4}$.)

There is another solution involving an angle in Quadrant II. Since $\pi - \frac{\pi}{4} = \frac{3\pi}{4}$ (a reference-angle identity), then:

$$\sin x = \frac{\sqrt{2}}{2} \Leftrightarrow x = \pi - \sin^{-1}\frac{\sqrt{2}}{2} = \frac{3\pi}{4} \approx 2.356$$

For the equation, $\sin x = -\frac{\sqrt{2}}{2}$, trig tables or your scientific calculator will give only one solution:

$$\sin x = -\frac{\sqrt{2}}{2} \Leftrightarrow x = \sin^{-1}\left(-\frac{\sqrt{2}}{2}\right) = -\frac{\pi}{4}$$

This solution involves an angle in Quadrant IV; i.e., $x = 2\pi + \left(-\frac{\pi}{4}\right) = \frac{7\pi}{4} \approx 5.498$.

Since $\frac{5\pi}{4} = \pi - \left(-\frac{\pi}{4}\right)$ and noting the reference angle identity $\sin(\pi - \theta) = \sin\theta$, we conclude:

$\sin x = -\frac{\sqrt{2}}{2} \Leftrightarrow x = \pi - \sin^{-1} -\frac{\sqrt{2}}{2}$

There is another solution involving an angle in Quadrant III; i.e., $x = \pi - \left(-\frac{\pi}{4}\right) = \frac{5\pi}{4} \approx 3.927$.

How do we summarize our findings? Table 3, where $\frac{\sqrt{2}}{2} \approx 0.707$, covers angles ranging from 0 to 2π, Quadrants I to IV.

Table 3: Sine

Solution Method	Quadrant
1. $\sin x = 0.707 \Leftrightarrow x = \sin^{-1} 0.707 = \frac{\pi}{4}$	I
2. $\sin x = 0.707 \Leftrightarrow x = \pi - \sin^{-1} 0.707 = \pi - \frac{\pi}{4} = \frac{3\pi}{4}$	II
3. $\sin x = -0.707 \Leftrightarrow x = \sin^{-1} -0.707 = -\frac{\pi}{4} = \frac{7\pi}{4}$	IV
4. $\sin x = -0.707 \Leftrightarrow x = \pi - \sin^{-1} -0.707 = \pi - \left(-\frac{\pi}{4}\right) = \frac{5\pi}{4}$	III

In summary, we construct Table 4.

Table 4

Solution Method	Quadrant
1. $\sin x = c \Leftrightarrow x = \sin^{-1} c$	I or IV
2. $\sin x = c \Leftrightarrow x = \pi - \sin^{-1} c$	II or III

All other solutions will involve coterminal angles related to our summary in Table 3. In general, for $n \in +\mathbb{Z}$:

Arcsin solution methods:

Part 1. $\sin x = c \Leftrightarrow x = \sin^{-1}c \pm 2\pi n$

Part 2. $\sin x = c \Leftrightarrow x = \pi - \sin^{-1}c \pm 2\pi n$

Or:

Part 1. $\sin x = c \Leftrightarrow x = \sin^{-1}c \pm 360n°$

Part 2. $\sin x = c \Leftrightarrow x = 180° - \sin^{-1}c \pm 360n°$

With these additions, we have a general method to find all the solutions for the equation $\sin x = c$. The periodic nature of these functions requires this extra detail.

INVERSE COSINE

The notation that mathematicians use for the inverse of the cosine is similar to the inverse of sin:

$y = \cos x \Leftrightarrow x = \cos^{-1} y$

We note (Figure 7) that in the graph if cos x (in radians) the images decrease from 1 to -1 as the arguments increase from 0 to π. In this domain, there is only one image for each argument. Exchanging y with x, the inverse function becomes:

$y = \cos^{-1} x$

For this inverse function, we choose the arguments between -1 and 1. For this interval, the images range from 0 to π.

We conclude:

> $y = \cos^{-1} x$ where, if the argument domain is $-1 \le x \le 1 \Rightarrow$ there is a unique image in this range: $0 \le y \le \pi$ or $0° \le y \le 180°$.

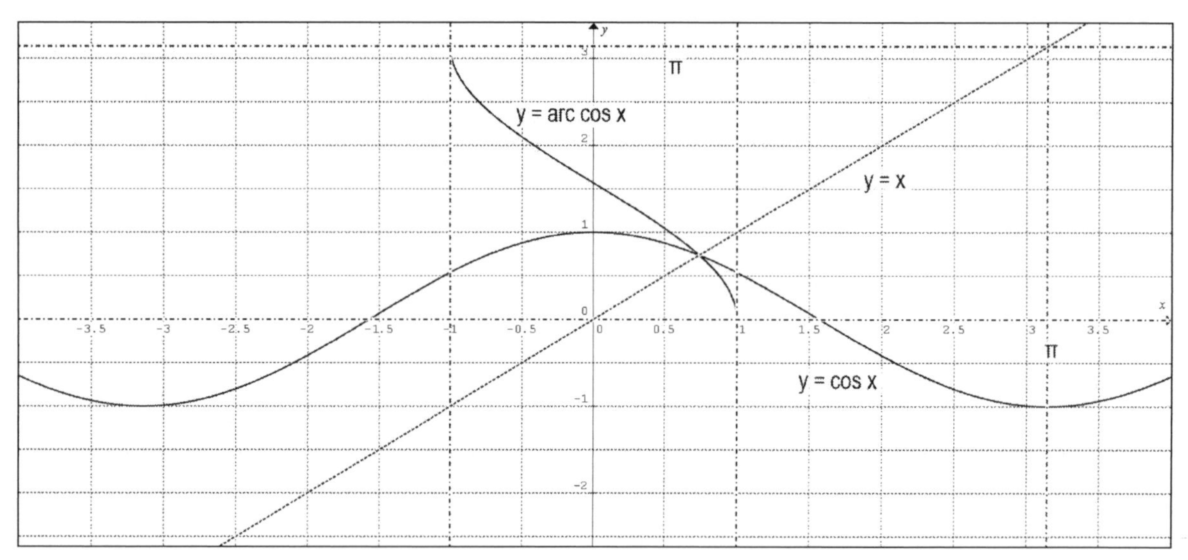

Figure 7. The reflecton symmetry of cos x and $\cos^{-1} x$.

For example, find y if $x = \dfrac{\sqrt{3}}{2} \approx 0.866$:

$$y = \cos^{-1} \frac{\sqrt{3}}{2} = \frac{\pi}{6} \approx 0.524\ (30°)$$

If $x = -\dfrac{\sqrt{3}}{2} \approx -0.866$ (Use Figure 7 to determine the magnitude and sign):

$$y = \cos^{-1} -\frac{\sqrt{3}}{2} = \pi - \frac{\pi}{6} = \frac{5\pi}{6} \approx 2.618\ (150°)$$

Let's shift from the unit circle to the cosine curve and review what happens between 0 and 2π (Figure 7):

1. There are two angles ($\frac{\pi}{6} \approx 0.524$ and $\frac{11\pi}{6} \approx 5.760$), one in Quadrant I and the other in Quadrant IV that generate the same positive image $\frac{\sqrt{3}}{2} \approx 0.866$.

2. There are two angles ($\frac{5\pi}{6} \approx 2.618$ and $\frac{7\pi}{6} \approx 3.665$), one in Quadrant II and the other in Quadrant III that generate the same negative image $-\frac{\sqrt{3}}{2} \approx -0.866$.

If we continue the graph in Figure 8 either to the left or the right, we see that there are an infinite number of solutions for $\cos x = 0.866$ or $\cos x = -0.866$.

For the equation, $\cos x = 0.866$, trig tables or your scientific calculator will give only one solution:

$$\cos x = 0.866 \Leftrightarrow x = \cos^{-1} 0.866 = \frac{\pi}{6} \text{ (Quadrant I)}$$

(Note: See Table 1 where we read the answer from the table by stating that the angle whose cos is $\frac{\sqrt{3}}{2} \approx 0.866$ is $\frac{\pi}{6}$.)

There is another solution:

$$\cos x = 0.866 \Leftrightarrow x = \cos^{-1} 0.866 = -\frac{\pi}{6} \text{ (Quadrant IV)}$$

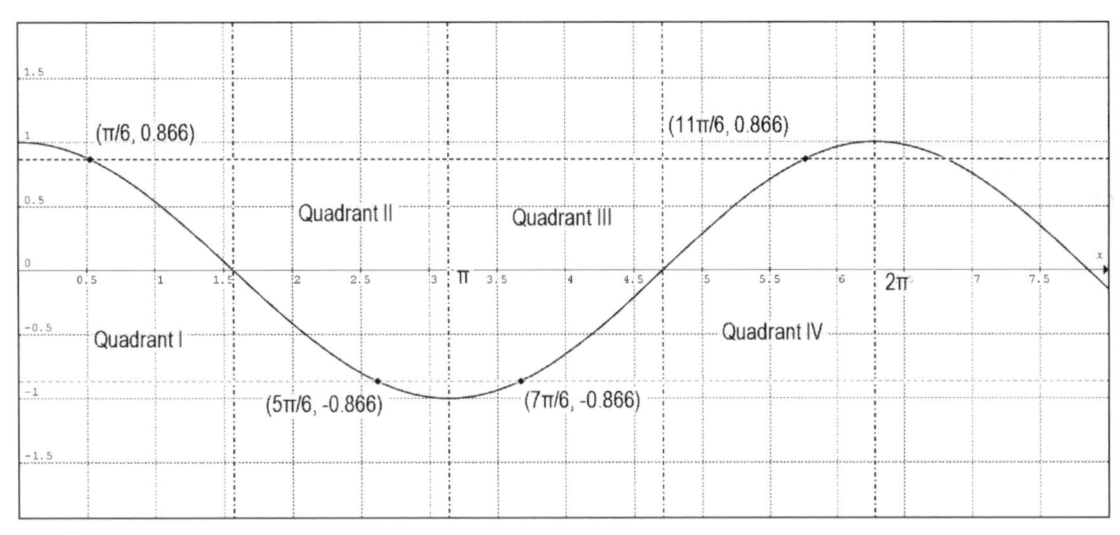

Figure 8. $y = \cos x$ (This relationship is many-to-one mapping.)

Since $-\frac{\pi}{6} = 2\pi - \frac{\pi}{6} = \frac{11\pi}{6}$, coterminal angles will be used in our general solution.

Also, from our reference angle analysis:

$$2\pi - \frac{\pi}{6} = \frac{11\pi}{6}$$

For the equation, $\cos x = -0.866$, trig tables or your scientific calculator will give only one solution:

$\cos x = -0.866 \Leftrightarrow x = \cos^{-1} -0.866 = \frac{5\pi}{6}$ (Quadrant II)

From our reference angle analysis:

$\pi - \frac{\pi}{6} = \frac{5\pi}{6}$

Here is the other solution in Quadrant III:

$\cos x = -0.866 \Leftrightarrow x = \cos^{-1} -0.866 = \frac{7\pi}{6}$

Since $\frac{7\pi}{6} = 2\pi - \frac{5\pi}{6} = \frac{11\pi}{6}$, coterminal angles will be used in our general solution.

We summarize our findings adding 2π in our solution process where needed for angles ranging from 0 to 2π (Table 5).

Table 5: Cosine

Solution Method	Quadrant
1. $\cos x = 0.866 \Leftrightarrow x = \cos^{-1} 0.866 = \frac{\pi}{6}$	I
2. $\cos x = 0.866 \Leftrightarrow x = -\cos^{-1} 0.866 + 2\pi = -\frac{\pi}{6} + 2\pi = \frac{11\pi}{6}$	IV
3. $\cos x = -0.866 \Leftrightarrow x = \cos^{-1} -0.866 = \frac{5\pi}{6}$	II
4. $\cos x = -0.866 \Leftrightarrow x = -\cos^{-1} -0.866 + 2\pi = -\frac{5\pi}{6} + 2\pi = \frac{7\pi}{6}$	III

In summary, we construct Table 6.

Table 6

Solution Method	Quadrant
1. $\cos x = c \Leftrightarrow x = \cos^{-1} c$	I or II
2. $\cos x = c \Leftrightarrow x = -\cos^{-1} c + 2\pi$	III or IV

All other solutions will involve coterminal angles related to our summary in Table 6. In general, for $n \in +\mathbb{Z}$:

Arccos solution methods:

Part 1: $\cos x = c \Leftrightarrow x = \cos^{-1}c \pm 2\pi n$

Part 2: $\cos x = c \Leftrightarrow x = -\cos^{-1}c \pm 2\pi n$

Or:

Part 1: $\cos x = c \Leftrightarrow x = \cos^{-1}c \pm 360n°$

Part 2: $\cos x = c \Leftrightarrow x = -\cos^{-1}c \pm 360n°$

INVERSE TANGENT

The notation that mathematicians use for the inverse of the tangent is:

$y = \tan x \Leftrightarrow x = \tan^{-1} y$

We note (Figure 9) that in the graph if tan x (in radians) the images range from $-\infty$ to ∞ as the arguments range from $-\frac{\pi}{2}$ to $\frac{\pi}{2}$. In this domain, there is only one image for each argument. Exchanging y with x, the inverse function becomes:

$y = \tan^{-1} x$

For the inverse function, we choose the arguments between $-\infty$ and ∞. For this interval, the images range from $-\frac{\pi}{2}$ to $\frac{\pi}{2}$.

We conclude:

> y = $\tan^{-1}$ x where, if the argument domain is $-\infty < x < \infty$ (i.e., it is defined for the range of all real numbers) $\Rightarrow$ there is a unique image in this range: $-\frac{\pi}{2} \leq y \leq \frac{\pi}{2}$ or $-90° \leq y \leq 90°$.

For example, find y if $x = \sqrt{3}$, then:

$y = \tan^{-1} \sqrt{3} = \frac{\pi}{3} \approx 1.047\ (60°)$

If $x = -\sqrt{3}$, then: (Use Figure 9 to determine the magnitude and sign.)

$y = \tan^{-1} -\sqrt{3} = -\frac{\pi}{3} \approx -1.047\ (-60°)$

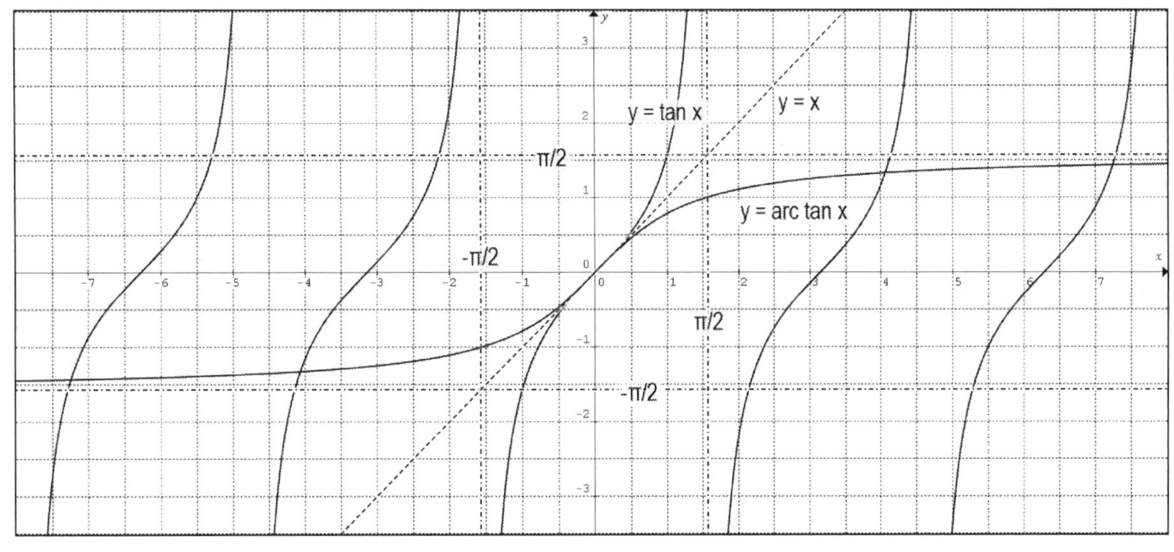

Figure 9. The reflecton symmetry of tan x and $\tan^{-1} x$.

Let's shift from the unit circle to the tangent curve and review what happens between 0 and 2π (Figure 10):

1. There are two angles ($\frac{\pi}{3} \approx 1.407$ and $\frac{4\pi}{3} \approx 4.189$), one in Quadrant I and the other in Quadrant III that generate the same positive image $\sqrt{3} \approx 1.732$.
2. There are two angles ($\frac{2\pi}{3} \approx 2.094$ and $\frac{5\pi}{3} \approx 5.236$), one in Quadrant II and the other in Quadrant IV that generate the same negative image $-\sqrt{3} \approx -1.732$.

If we continue the graph in Figure 10 either to the left or to the right, we see that there are an infinite number of solutions for $\tan x = 1.732$ or $\tan x = -1.732$.

For the equation, $\tan x = 1.732$, trig tables or your scientific calculator will give only one solution:

$$\tan x = 1.732 \Leftrightarrow x = \tan^{-1} 1.732 = \frac{\pi}{3} \text{ (Quadrant I)}$$

(Note: See Table 1 where we read the answer from the table by stating that the angle whose tan is $\sqrt{3} \approx 1.732$ is $\frac{\pi}{3}$.)

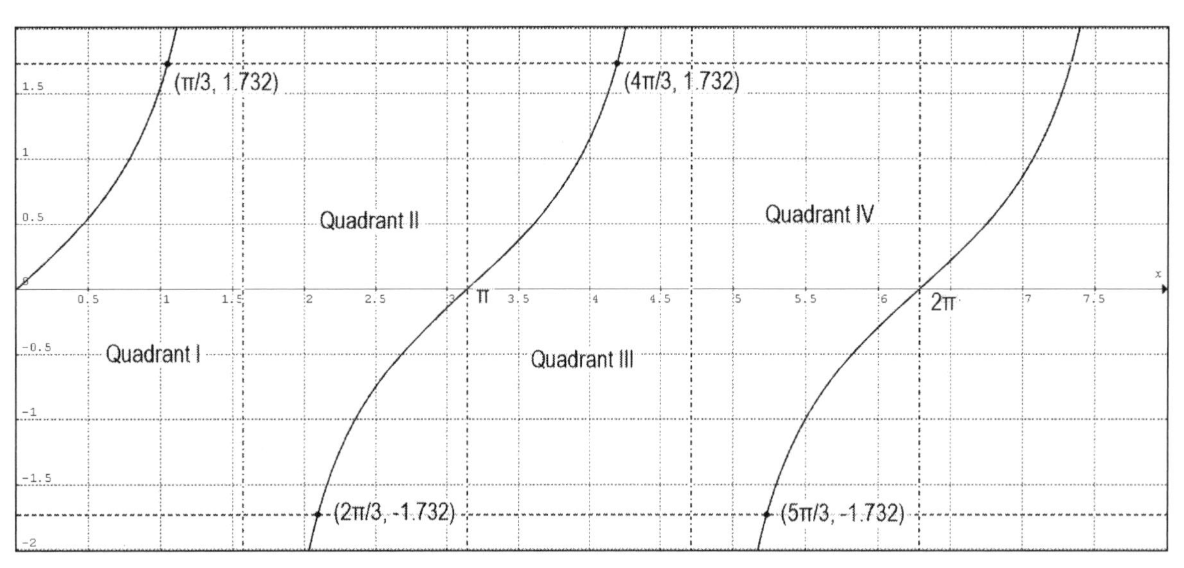

Figure 10. $y = \tan x$ (This relationship is many-to-one mapping.)

Here is the other solution:

$$\tan x = 1.732 \Leftrightarrow x = \tan^{-1} 1.732 = \frac{4\pi}{3} \text{ (Quadrant III)}$$

Since $\frac{\pi}{3} + \pi = \frac{4\pi}{3}$, coterminal angles will be used in our general solution.

Also, from our reference angle analysis:

$$\frac{4\pi}{3} - \pi = \frac{\pi}{3}$$

For the equation, tan x = -1.732, trig tables or your scientific calculator will give only one solution:

$$\tan x = -1.732 \Leftrightarrow x = \tan^{-1} -1.732 = -\frac{\pi}{3} \text{ (Quadrant IV)}$$

From our reference angle analysis:

Since $\frac{5\pi}{3} = 2\pi - \frac{\pi}{3}$, coterminal angles will be used in our general solution.

Therefore:

$$\tan x = -1.732 \Leftrightarrow x = \tan^{-1} -1.732 = \frac{5\pi}{3}$$

Our reference angle analysis also states:

$$\pi - \frac{\pi}{3} = \frac{2\pi}{3}$$

Therefore, the other solution in Quadrant II is:

$$\tan x = -1.732 \Leftrightarrow x = \tan^{-1} -1.732 = \frac{2\pi}{3}$$

We summarize our findings for angles ranging from 0 to 2π (Table 7).

Table 7: Tangent	
Solution Method	**Quadrant**
1. $\tan x = 1.732 \Leftrightarrow x = \tan^{-1} 1.732 = \frac{\pi}{3}$	I
2. $\tan x = 1.732 \Leftrightarrow x = \tan^{-1} 1.732 + \pi = \frac{\pi}{3} + \pi = \frac{4\pi}{3}$	III
3. $\tan x = -1.732 \Leftrightarrow x = \tan^{-1} -1.732 = -\frac{\pi}{3} = \frac{5\pi}{3}$	IV
4. $\tan x = -1.732 \Leftrightarrow x = \tan^{-1} -1.732 + \pi = -\frac{\pi}{3} + \pi = \frac{2\pi}{3}$	II

In summary, we construct Table 8.

Table 8	
Solution Method	**Quadrant**
1. $\tan x = c \Leftrightarrow x = \tan^{-1} c$	I or IV
2. $\tan x = c \Leftrightarrow x = \tan^{-1} c + \pi$	II or III

All other solutions will involve coterminal angles related to our summary in Table 8.

In general, for $n \in +\mathbb{Z}$:

arctan solution method:
$\tan x = c \Leftrightarrow x = \tan^{-1}c \pm \pi n$
Or:
$\tan x = c \Leftrightarrow x = \tan^{-1}c \pm 180n°$

You will need to read the material from Inverse Sine to Inverse Tangent three to four times before you understand it. Make sure that you study the graphs carefully as you read the text.

A LESSON FROM SPACE

When a space capsule returns to Earth from its mission in space, it reenters the Earth's atmosphere at an angle ∞ in radians (Figure 11).

To prevent the capsule from bouncing off the atmosphere and returning to space, it is necessary that:

$$\sin \theta \geq 0.026$$

To prevent it from entering too quickly and burning up in the atmosphere, it is necessary that:

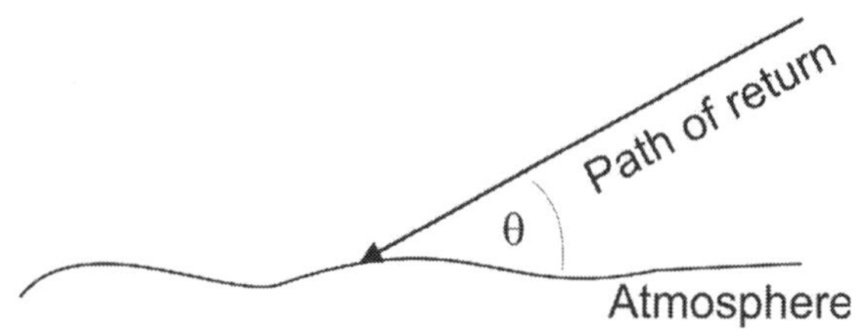

Figure 11. θ is exaggerated.

$$\sin \theta \leq 0.105$$

To prevent it from entering so quickly that the deceleration causes injury to the astronauts, it is necessary that:

$$\sin \theta \leq 0.035$$

Problem 1. How small can θ be?

From the information given, we know $0.026 \leq \sin \theta \leq 0.035$. In your notebook, verify this result with the number line. We must find θ when $\sin \theta = 0.026$ or, using inverses and a scientific calculator:[5]

$$\theta = \sin^{-1} 0.026 \approx 0.026\ (1.49°)$$

The smallest θ can be is 0.026 radians.

Problem 2. How large can θ be?

We must find θ when $\sin \theta = 0.035$ or, using inverses:

$$\theta = \sin^{-1} 0.035 \approx 0.035\ (2.01°)$$

The largest that θ can be is 0.035 radians.

We note, in degrees:

$$0.026 \leq \sin \theta \leq 0.035 \Leftrightarrow 1.49° \leq \theta \leq 2.01°$$

[5] Make sure the mode is in radians. Press the $\sin^{-1}$ key, then enter 0.026. Next, press "ENTER" to find the value of the inverse. You can do the same in the degree mode.

In radians:

$$0.026 \leq \sin\theta \leq 0.035 \Leftrightarrow 0.026 \leq \theta \leq 0.035$$

From these two problems, it is interesting to note that as sin x as x (radians) approaches 0, sin $x = x$. Using limit notation:

$$\lim_{x \to 0} \sin x = x \text{ or } \lim_{x \to 0} \frac{\sin x}{x} = 1$$

EXERCISES

Define the following terms:

1. arcsin
2. Reference angle
3. arccos
4. arctan
5. Law of Cosines (See homework exercise below.)

Your scientific calculator has three trigonometric keys: sin, cos, tan. Each of these has a respective inverse key: $\sin^{-1}$, $\cos^{-1}$, $\tan^{-1}$ standing for, respectively, arc sine, abbreviated arcsin, arc cosine, abbreviated arccos, and arc tangent, abbreviated arctan. To find sin 30°, make sure that the calculator is in DEG (degree) mode (its default), enter 30, and press the sin key. Your answer should be 0.5. Given 0.5, you can determine the inverse, or $\sin^{-1}$ (the angle measure in degrees that generates the answer 0.5), by pressing the SHIFT (2nd) key and then the sin key. Your answer should be 30.

Figure 12. Source: iStockPhoto.

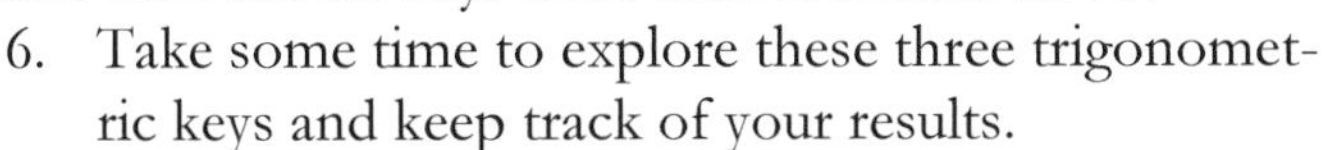

6. Take some time to explore these three trigonometric keys and keep track of your results.
7. Change the mode to RAD for radians and compare your answers based upon your answers to Question 6.
8. Verify the sign changes for sin, cos, and tan for each of the four Quadrants. Use either DEG or RAD mode.
9. With your scientific calculator in RAD mode, explain how you evaluate the trig functions for these Quadrant I angles:

   (a) $\csc \dfrac{\pi}{3}$

   (b) $\sec \dfrac{\pi}{6}$

   (c) $\cot \dfrac{\pi}{4}$

   (Round your answers to the nearest ten-thousandths. Hint: $\sin x = \dfrac{1}{\csc x}$, $\cos x = \dfrac{1}{\sec x}$, and $\tan x = \dfrac{1}{\cot x}$.)
10. Why does tan 90° and tan 270° generate an error?

Find the reference angle for the following angles:

11. (a) 40°, (b) 300°, (c) 129°, (d) 150°, (e) 265°
12. (a) $\frac{2\pi}{3}$, (b) $\frac{9\pi}{4}$, (c) $\frac{9\pi}{8}$, (d) $\frac{11\pi}{6}$, (e) $-\frac{6\pi}{5}$

Set your scientific calculator mode to RAD (radians) and evaluate these expressions. (Round to the nearest ten-thousandths were necessary.)

13. $\sin^{-1} 0$
14. $\sin^{-1} 1$
15. $\sin^{-1} -0.5$
16. $\sin^{-1} -\frac{\sqrt{3}}{2}$
17. $\sin^{-1} [\sin \frac{\pi}{11}]$
18. $\sin^{-1} [\sin \frac{2\pi}{11}]$
19. $\sin^{-1} [\sin \frac{3\pi}{11}]$
20. $\tan^{-1} 0$
21. $\tan^{-1} 1$
22. $\tan^{-1} -1$
23. $\tan^{-1} 0.5$
24. $\tan^{-1} -\frac{\sqrt{3}}{2}$
25. $\tan^{-1} \frac{\sqrt{3}}{2}$
26. $\tan^{-1} \frac{\sqrt{3}}{3}$
27. $\tan^{-1} -\frac{\sqrt{3}}{3}$
28. $\sin [\tan^{-1} -\sqrt{3}\,]$
29. $\sin^{-1} [\sin \frac{4\pi}{11}]$
30. $\sin^{-1} [\sin \frac{5\pi}{11}]$
31. $\sin^{-1} [\sin \frac{6\pi}{11}]$ What is unusual about the answer? Why?
32. $\cos [\sin^{-1} 1]$
33. $\cos [2 \sin^{-1} -1]$

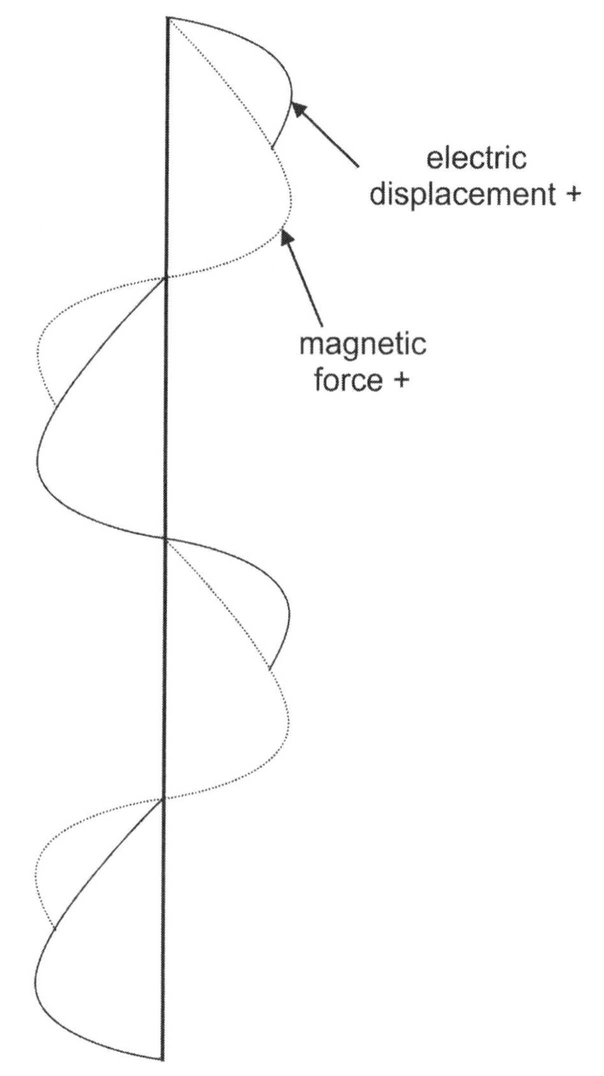

Figure 13. James Clerk Maxwell's illustration of an electromagnetic doubly transverse wave. The energy fluctuations in the electric and magnetic fields and the wave directions are at right angles to each to other.

Are the following equations solvable?

34. $\sin x = -0.5$
35. $\sin x = -1.1$
36. $\tan x = 10^{10}$

37. $\cos x = -0.5$
38. $\cos x = -2$

Solve the following equations for the unknown variable in positive degrees for the given quadrant. If no quadrant is given, the terminate side of the angle will be on either the x-axis or y-axis (Round to the nearest tenth were necessary.)
39. $\sin x = -0.5$ (Quadrant IV)
40. $\sin x = 0.8$ (Quadrant II)
41. $\sin x = -1$
42. $\cos x = \dfrac{\sqrt{2}}{2}$ (Quadrant I)
43. $\cos x = 0.2$ (Quadrant IV)
44. $\cos x = -0.4$ (Quadrant III)
45. $\tan x = 1$ (Quadrant I)
46. $\tan x = -0.3$ (Quadrant II)
47. $\tan x = 0.2$ (Quadrant III)

Solve the following equations for the unknown variable in radians for the given quadrant. (Round to the nearest ten-thousandths were necessary.)
48. $\sin x = -0.6$ (Quadrant III)
49. $\cos x = 0.4$ (Quadrant IV)
50. $\tan x = 3$ (Quadrant III)
51. $\tan x = -5$ (Quadrant II)

Answer this question involving the Law of Sines:

52. Using ΔABC in Figure 14 as a guide, solve $\dfrac{a}{\sin A} = \dfrac{b}{\sin B}$ for:

   (a) A (an angle)
   (b) B (an angle)
   (c) a
   (d) b

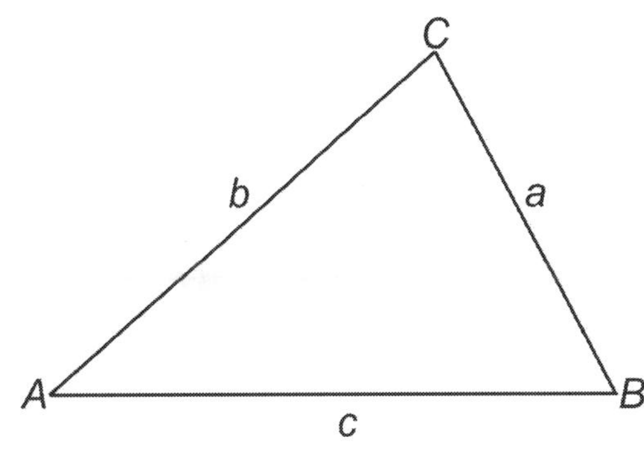

Figure 14.

The **Law of Cosines** (Figure 15) is an important law that interpenetrates many situations in Physics, and it is like the Pythagorean Theorem. It involves one side of a triangle as it relates to the other two sides and the angle between those two sides. In symbols:

$c^2 = a^2 + b^2 - 2ab \cos \theta$ where θ is the angle opposite c.

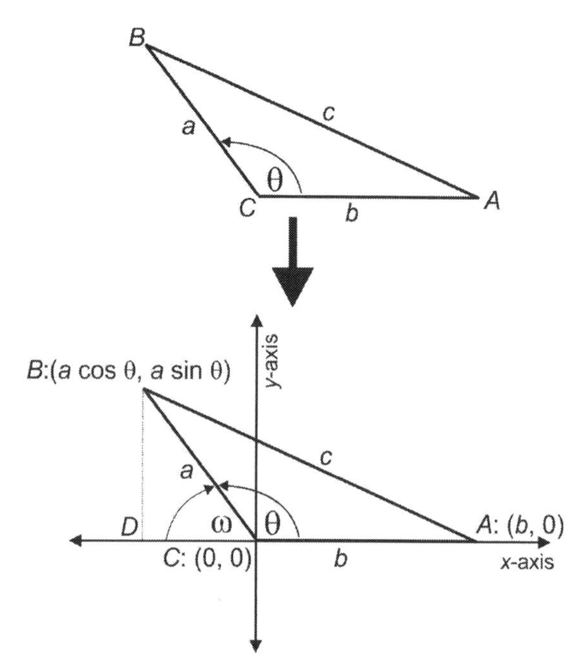

Figure 15. Derivation of the Law of Cosines.

Placing ΔABC in the x-y coordinate plane simplifies the proof. Answer the following questions:

53. Explain why the coordinates of point B are ($a \cos \theta$, $b \cos \theta$). (Hint: Let ($-x$, y) the coordinates of B and consider ΔBDC. You will need to use the Reference-Angle Identities to solve for x and y.)
54. Use the Distance Formula (Lesson 11.9) to find the distance between point A and point B and QED the proof.
55. Explain what the Law of Cosines becomes when $\theta = \frac{\pi}{2}$.
56. Solve the Law of Cosines for c.
57. Solve the Law of Cosines for θ. (Note: The answer to this question will enable to find any included angle of a triangle if you know the lengths of its three sides. You will use this observation in a homework exercise in Lesson 12.13.)
58. Solve the Law of Cosines for a. Simplify your answer as much as possible. (Hint: You must use the Quadratic Formula.)
59. Solve the Law of Cosines for b. Simplify your answer as much as possible.

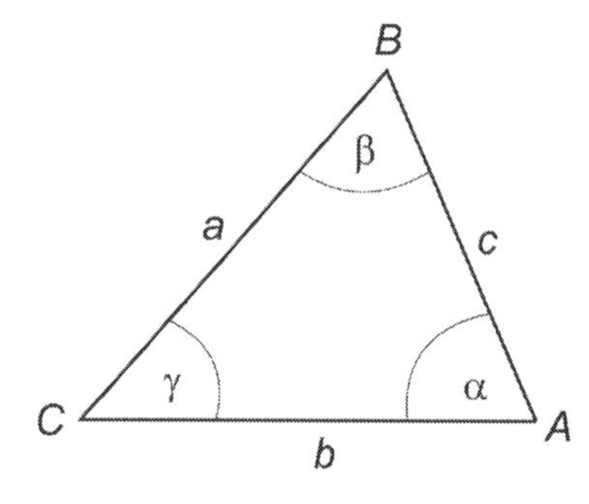

$$a^2 = b^2 + c^2 - 2bc \cos \alpha$$
$$b^2 = c^2 + a^2 - 2ca \cos \beta$$
$$c^2 = a^2 + b^2 - 2ab \cos \gamma$$

Figure 16. Law of Cosines for a general triangle.

12.10 Measuring the Glory of the Heavens

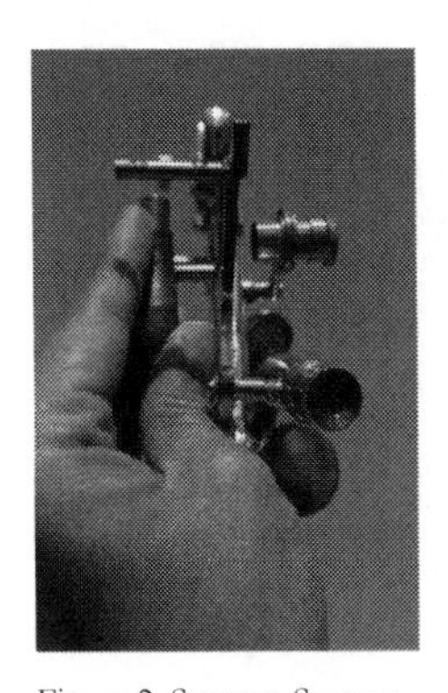

Figure 2. Sextant. Source: iStockPhoto.

Terms & Concepts Introduced
1. Astrolabe
2. Batter
3. Mariner's quadrant
4. Parallax
5. Seked
6. Sextant
7. Triangulation

The ancient Greek astronomers investigated the nature of triangles on the surface of a sphere instead of a plane. They did this because, in their geocentric cosmological system, the Sun and each of the planets orbited the Earth in arcs along a distinct sphere, i.e., a great circle.[1] The combined pattern of these orbits reflected a mathematical harmony and the phrase "music of the spheres" finds its origin in the studies of ancient Greek astronomers, probably from Pythagoras.[2]

Greek derivations can easily translate to triangles in a plane. In this lesson, we will unfold how one, the **triangulation**[3] method, can measure both terrestrial and celestial distances. Let the words of science historian Stanley L. Jaki (1924-2009) put trigonometry into its historical context:

> The science of trigonometry, one of the brilliant inventions of the Greek mind, was in a sense a precursor of telescopes. It brought faraway objects within the compass of measurement and first made it possible for man to penetrate in a quantitative manner the far reaches of space ….[4]

> Creation is a wonderfully wrought hymn to the power and love of the Father. The Father's Word, His Son, brought forth and currently sustains the rational order of the form and matter of the universe as a kind of musical harmony, richly and multifariously toned, guided by the Spirit with an inward rhythm and accord, a joyful dance of giving and receiving, indeed, the symphony of the pleasurable joy of the Triune dance. The intermingling of the melody and cadence of the cosmic elements, of their motion and rest, sing the glory of their Triune Creator. It is this orchestration of all things one with the other which is music in its truest, most perfect, and most glorious form.
>
> Amplification of the summary of the thoughts of Gregory of Nyssa, *In Inscriptiones Psalmorum* (1.3:19-22), by David Bentley Hart, *The Beauty of the Infinite*, p. 275.

---

[1] A great circle is a circle with its center at the center of a sphere. See Lesson 3.2.

[2] The Pythagoreans identified the cosmic order with music. According to early Christian theologians (e.g., Gregory of Nyssa), it was the music, indeed, the dance of the Triune God who is love. See Leo Spitzer, *Classical and Christian Ideas of World Harmony* (Baltimore: Johns Hopkins University Press, 1963), pp. 19-20. According to science historian and theologian Stanley L. Jaki, in *Principles or Patterns and Other Essays* (Wilmington: Intercollegiate Studies Institute, 1995), "… the first unambiguous declarations about the unrestricted rationality of the universe are found not in Greek philosophical writings but in the writings of Saint Athanasius, the great defender of the divinity of the Logos against the Arians" (p. 173). The *logos*, the Son of the Father, is the full revelation of the love that exists in Triune fellowship. The Son, the *logos*, is also the ground of the dance of the unrestricted rationality of the universe. Order, harmony, and rationality are grounded in the Triune God who is love.

[3] Triangulation is a surveying technique in which a region is divided into a series of triangles based upon a known or measurable distance so that distances that cannot be measured can be calculated by means of trigonometric ratios.

[4] Stanley L. Jaki, *The Relevance of Physics* (Edinburgh: Scottish Academic Press, [1966] 1992), p. 189.

Let's first see how we can use trigonometry to find the height of a tree. To do this, we need to construct a device that can measure angles. The ancients constructed such a device, the **astrolabe**.[5] Professional surveyors and navigators now use a **sextant**.[6] Since a sextant is expensive, you may want to contact a local carpenter to see what he uses to measure the slope or grade of a roof.[7]

Figure 1. Astrolabe. Source: James D. Nickel.

You can construct a sextant, a tool similar to a **mariner's quadrant**,[8] what Christopher Columbus probably used on his voyages to the New World. You will need an eight or ten-inch drinking straw, eight to ten inches of string, a heavy nut, bolt, or key, an eight inch by ten inch piece of cardboard, clear tape, a straight pin, and a hole punch.

Figure 3. Claudius Ptolemy using a Quadrant. From *Clavdio Tolomeo Principe de gli Astrologi, et de Geografi*, published by Giordano Ziletti (1564). Source: Public Domain.

Photocopy the protractor in Figure 4. Cut along the dotted line. Punch out the black hole on the base of the protractor. Align the straight edge of the protractor with the ten-inch side of the cardboard and tape it to the cardboard. Push the straight pin through the cardboard at the center of the protractor hole and run the string through the hole. Tie several knots in the end of the string so that it cannot be pulled back through the hole. At the other end of the string, tie the nut, bolt, or key so that it hangs freely as a plumb bob. Finally, tape the drink straw to the same ten-inch side of the cardboard that has the protractor's straight edge.

Go outside and sight a tree through the drinking straw. (Caution: *Do not use this instrument to look directly at the Sun.*) Read the protractor angle where the string hangs to find the altitude (Lesson 8.7), the angular measure above the horizon, of the tree.[9] The precision of this measuring tool one unit of angle.

> The astrolabe was the chief astronomical instrument of both the Arab and the Latin astronomers of the Middle Ages and was known as "the mathematical jewel."
>
> Alistair C. Crombie, *The History of Science from Augustine to Galileo* ([1959, 1970, 1979] 1995), I:104.

[5] Astrolabe means "to take the stars."

[6] A graduated instrument using a 60° arc (one-sixth of a circle). Sextant means "a sixth part."

[7] For example, the Dasco Pro Company makes an inexpensive carpentry tool called an *Angle Finder Plus Level.* Many carpenters now use laser beam technology to measure angles.

[8] A mariner's quadrant, meaning a fourth part of a circle, is like a sextant and predates it. It has a graduated arc of 90°, or a quarter of a circle.

[9] You will need a friend to read the scale as you hold the aimed protractor still.

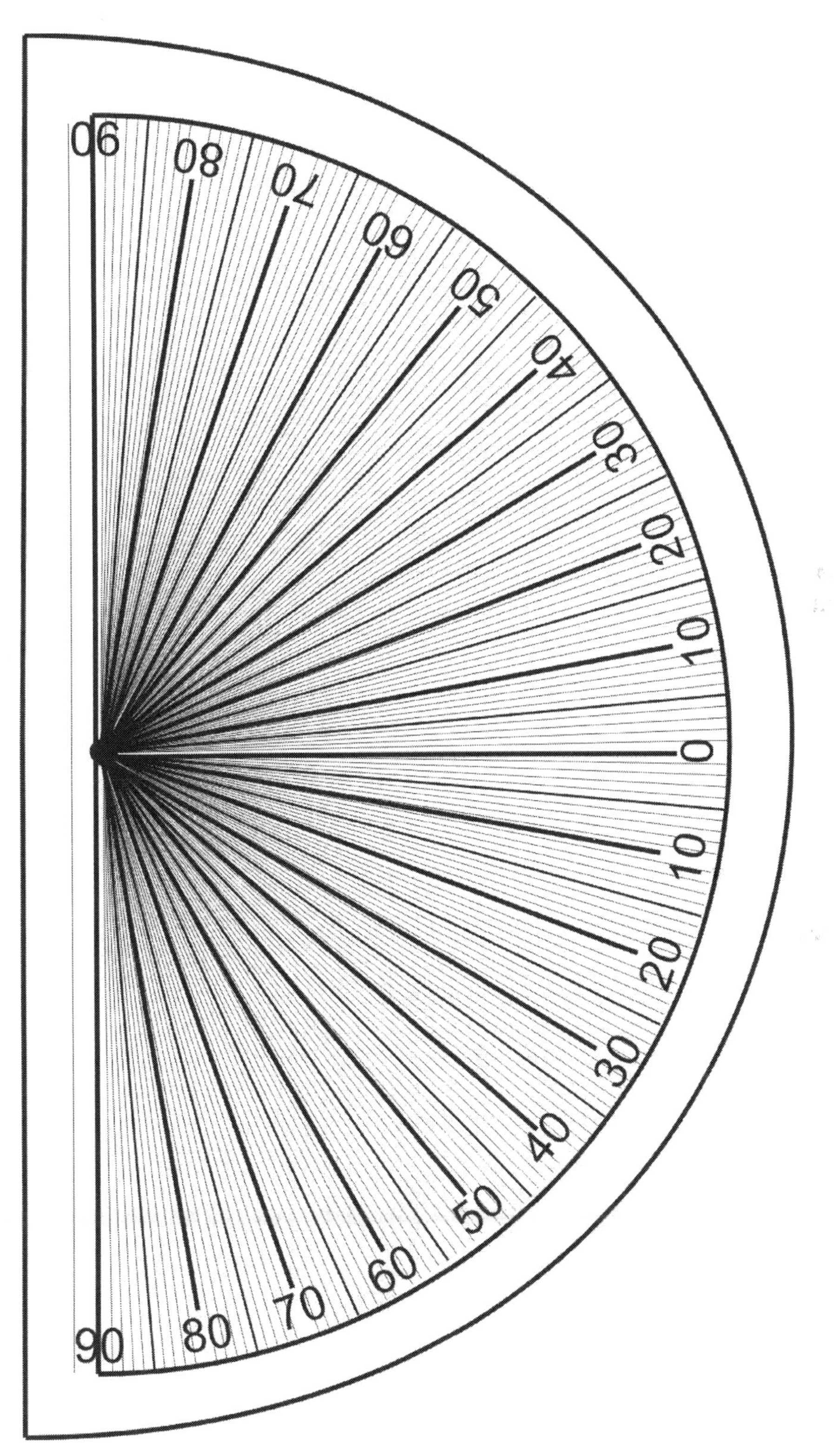

Figure 4. Protractor.

THE EGYPTIANS AND THE BEGINNINGS OF TRIGONOMETRY

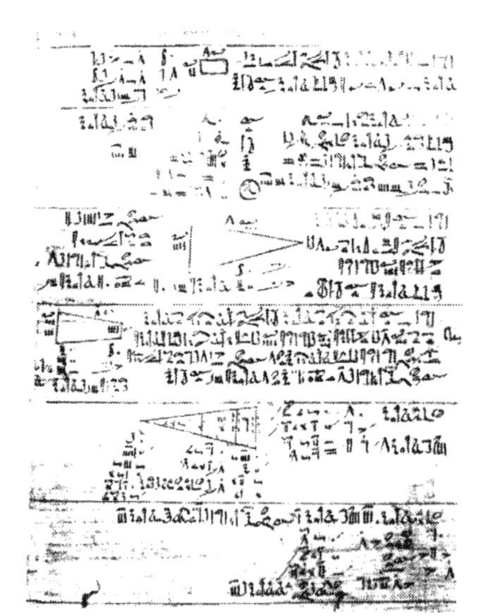

Figure 5. A portion of the Rhind Papyrus. Source: Public Domain.

In 1858, the Scottish lawyer and antiquarian Alexander Henry Rhind (1833-1863) purchased a collection of 84 ancient Egyptian mathematical problems composed by a man named Ahmes the scribe, now named The Rhind Papyrus.[10] This paper, entitled *Direction for Attaining a Knowledge of all Secret Things*, was made from a papyrus plant and has been dated ca. 1650 BC.

A section of these problems are pyramid-oriented[11] and use the word **seked.** Egyptian pyramids had a square base, and Ahmes posed the following problem:

Figure 6. The Great Pyramid. Source: iStockPhoto.

The height of a pyramid is 250 cubits, and its base is 360 cubits, what is its seked?

Ahmes then gives the solution and by it, we discover that the seked thus calculated is the measure of θ in Figure 7. Technically, the seked is, using modern trigonometry, the cotangent of the angle between the base of the pyramid and one of its faces.

In Figure 7, we note right ΔABS where AB is the height and BS is half the length of the base. Ahmes used this right triangle because the first thing he did in his solution is calculate half of the base:

½ of 360 = 180

Since the tangent ratio in this triangle is $\frac{AB}{BS}$, the *co*mplementary ratio, or *co*tangent, is the reciprocal, or $\frac{BS}{AB}$. In the right ΔABS, we write:

$$\tan \theta = \frac{AB}{BS}$$

$$\cot \theta = \frac{BS}{AB}$$

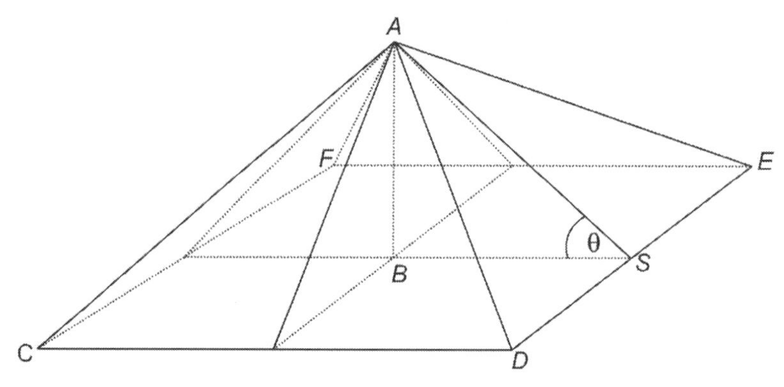

Figure 7. The seked.

Recall that two angles are complementary if their sum is 90°. Therefore, in a right triangle, its two acute triangles are always complementary:

$\tan \theta = \cot (90° - \theta)$, where $90° - \theta = m\angle BAS$

[10] The source for much of the information in this section is the book by Eli Maor, *Trigonometric Delights* (Princeton: Princeton University Press, 1998), pp. 3-9. See also Glen Van Brummelen, *The Mathematics of the Heavens and the Earth: The Early History of Trigonometry* (Princeton: Princeton University Press, 2009), pp. 10-11.

[11] The Egyptians built some of their pyramids to represent astronomical relationships.

$\cot\theta = \tan(90° - \theta)$

In a roundabout way, Ahmes calculated the cotangent ratio of BS to AB or:

$$\frac{BS}{AB} = \frac{180}{250} = \frac{18}{25}$$

Since Egyptians only used unit fractions, i.e., fractions whose numerator is 1 (Lesson 6.6), Ahmes wrote 18/25 as:

$$\frac{18}{25} = \frac{1}{2} + \frac{1}{5} + \frac{1}{50}$$

Next, Ahmes multiplied his answer by 7. Why? Ancient Egyptians builders measured horizontal distances in palms[12] and vertical distances in cubits (Lesson 6.14).[13] For these ancient architects:

28 digits = 1 cubit and 4 digits = 1 palm $\Rightarrow$ 1 cubit = 7 palms

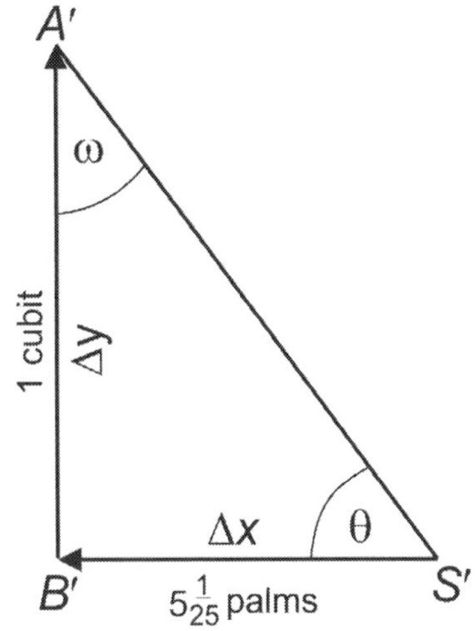

Converting cubits to palms, we write:

$$\frac{18}{25}\cancel{\text{cubits}} \cdot \frac{7\text{ palms}}{\cancel{\text{cubit}}} = \frac{126}{25}\text{palms} = 5\frac{1}{25}\text{ palms}$$

To these builders, $5\frac{1}{25}$ represented a ratio, not a number. For the right triangle, it represented what modern builders call a **batter**,[14] a Δx-to-Δy (horizontal-to-vertical) slope.[15]

The builders of the Egyptian pyramids used the Δx-to-Δy ratio to ensure a constant slope for each face of the pyramid. In Ahmes' example, the builders would have used the $\dfrac{5\,{}^{1}\!/_{25}\text{ palms}}{1\text{ cubit}}$ ratio. This ratio means that for every $5\frac{1}{25}$ palms of horizontal distance, they made sure that the equivalent vertical distance was one cubit (Figure 8). By this method, these builders guaranteed that the right triangle $A'B'S'$ would be similar to the right triangle ABS (or, in symbols, $\Delta A'B'S' \sim \Delta ABS$), and thereby each face of the pyramid would maintain the same seked.

Figure 8.

In summary, the concept of angle measurement, as we know it today, does not appear in Egyptian writings. They were not dealing with quantitative trigonometry; they were only dealing with Δx-to-Δy ratios. In this sense, though, their work foreshadowed trigonometry; it was a prototype of a more sophisticated trigonometry to come.

What is θ?

---

[12] Think of the palm of the hand and note that the hand was also a unit of Egyptian measure (Lesson 6.14).

[13] Ahmes disregarded this distinction when, in his problem, he gave the measurement of the base of the pyramid, a horizontal distance, in cubits.

[14] Technically, a batter is the slope, as of the outer face of a wall, that recedes from bottom to top; i.e., it is the gradual backward slope in a wall or similar structure.

[15] The cotangent ratio is a Δx-to-Δy slope while the tangent ratio is a Δy-to-Δx slope, reflecting the reciprocal relationship between tangent and cotangent.

$\cot\theta = \dfrac{18}{25} = 0.72 \Leftrightarrow \theta = \cot^{-1}(0.72)$

Most scientific calculators do not have a function to find the inverse cotangent so we will use the complement of the cotangent, the tangent. We set $\omega = 90° - \theta$. Therefore:

$\omega = \tan^{-1}(0.72) \Leftrightarrow \omega = 35.75°$
(This measure is the complement of the angle we are after.)

Since $\omega = 90° - \theta$, then $\theta = 90° - \omega$. Therefore:

$\theta = 90° - 35.75° = 54.25°$

This measurement corresponds closely to the actual face-to-base angles of the pyramids of Egypt. So, Ahmes the scribe knew of what he wrote.

FINDING THE HEIGHT OF A TREE

Let's use trigonometry to demonstrate how we can, starting from the principles of finding the height of a tree, find the distance from the Earth to a star.

Knowing your height (Figure 9), BD, the altitude of the tree θ, and the distance, AB, from you to the tree, we can find the height of the tree, $DC = CB + BD$, using the tangent ratio.

By definition:

$\tan\theta = \dfrac{CB}{AB}$

Solving for CB, we get:

$\tan\theta = \dfrac{CB}{AB} \Leftrightarrow CB = AB(\tan\theta)$

Therefore: $DC = CB + BD$ or $DC = AB(\tan\theta) + BD$

QED

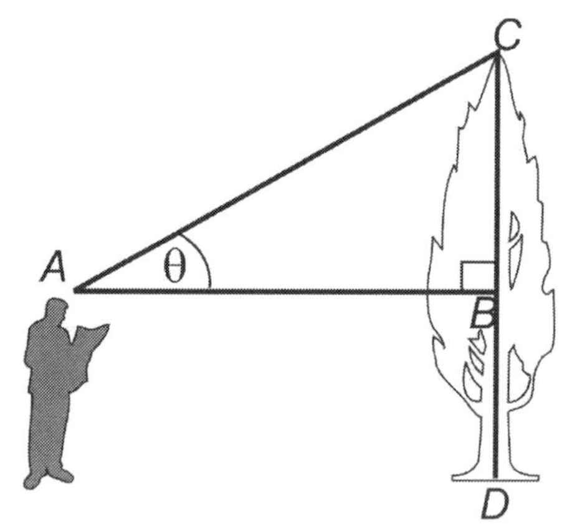

Figure 9. Finding the height of a tree.

FINDING THE HEIGHT OF A MOUNTAIN

What about measuring the height of a mountain? Since a mountain is not straight like a tree, we must try another approach. Knowing your height (Figure 10), CE, we take two altitude measurements, θ and ω, between two measurable points A and B. Let's derive the formula for calculating the height $DE = DC + CE$ of the mountain.

By definition:

$$\tan\theta = \frac{DC}{AB+BC}$$

Solving for DC, we get:

$$\tan\theta = \frac{DC}{AB+BC} \Leftrightarrow DC = (AB + BC)\tan\theta$$

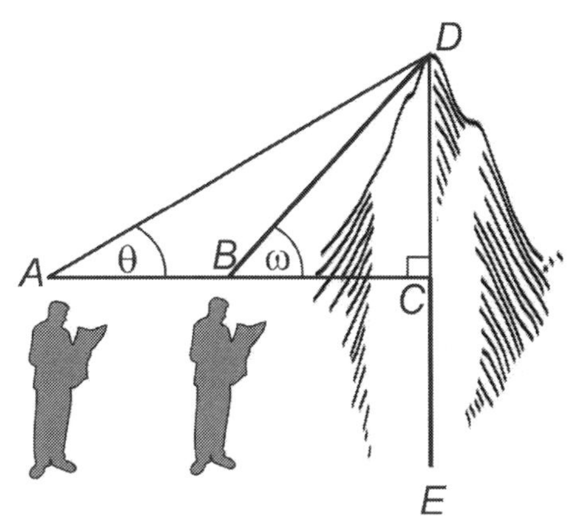

Figure 10. Finding the height of a mountain.

By definition:

$$\tan\omega = \frac{DC}{BC}$$

Solving for DC, we get:

$$\tan\omega = \frac{DC}{BC} \Leftrightarrow DC = (BC)\tan\omega$$

Solving for BC, we get:

$$DC = (BC)\tan\omega \Leftrightarrow BC = \frac{DC}{\tan\omega}$$

Substituting BC into the equation $DC = (AB + BC)\tan\theta$, we get:

$$BC = \frac{DC}{\tan\omega} \text{ and } DC = (AB + BC)\tan\theta \Rightarrow DC = \left(AB + \frac{DC}{\tan\omega}\right)\tan\theta$$

Applying the Distributive Law, we get:

$$DC = \left(AB + \frac{DC}{\tan\omega}\right)\tan\theta \Leftrightarrow DC = AB\cdot\tan\theta + DC\left(\frac{\tan\theta}{\tan\omega}\right)$$

We want to solve for DC. Follow along:

$$DC = AB\cdot\tan\theta + DC\left(\frac{\tan\theta}{\tan\omega}\right) \Leftrightarrow DC - DC\left(\frac{\tan\theta}{\tan\omega}\right) = (AB)\tan\theta \Leftrightarrow$$

$$DC\left(1 - \frac{\tan\theta}{\tan\omega}\right) = (AB)\tan\theta \Leftrightarrow DC = \frac{(AB)\tan\theta}{1 - \frac{\tan\theta}{\tan\omega}} \Leftrightarrow DC = \frac{(AB)\tan\theta}{\frac{\tan\omega - \tan\theta}{\tan\omega}} \Leftrightarrow$$

$$DC = \frac{(AB)(\tan\theta)(\tan\omega)}{\tan\omega - \tan\theta}$$

QED

We note that with a mountain, it is okay to drop CE since the ratio of your height to the height of the mountain is minuscule.

FINDING THE RADIUS OF THE EARTH

Once we know the height of a mountain, we can calculate the radius of the Earth (Figure 11). By definition:

$\sin\theta = \dfrac{r}{r+h}$ (We will prove that ΔABC is a right triangle under these conditions in Lesson 13.9.)

We want to solve for r. Follow along:

$$\sin\theta = \frac{r}{r+h} \Leftrightarrow (r+h)\sin\theta = r \Leftrightarrow$$

$$r(\sin\theta) + h(\sin\theta) = r \Leftrightarrow$$

$$r - r(\sin\theta) = h(\sin\theta) \Leftrightarrow r(1-\sin\theta) = h(\sin\theta) \Leftrightarrow$$

$$r = \frac{h(\sin\theta)}{1-\sin\theta}$$

If h (height of a mountain) = 3 miles and $\theta = 87°46'$ (modern value), then $r = 3947$ miles. If you found the algebraic operations too difficult, you should remember that the method described is an alternative to tunneling down to the center of the Earth and then measuring the radius by applying a yard or meter stick from the center all the way to the surface.

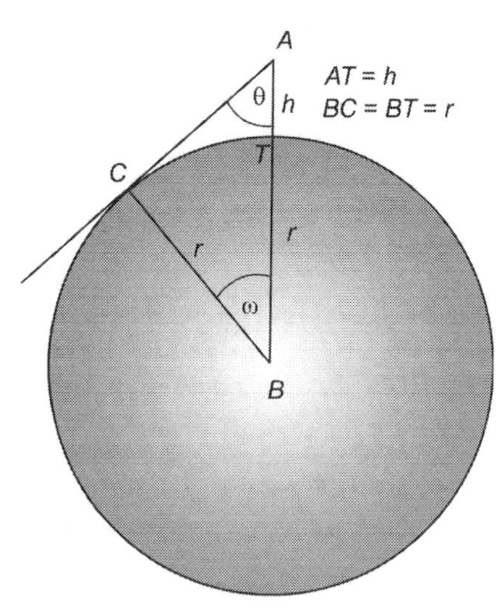

Figure 11. Finding the radius of the Earth.

FINDING THE DISTANCE BETWEEN ANY TWO POINTS ON THE EARTH

Now that we know the radius of the Earth, we can measure the distance between any two points at the same latitude on the surface of the Earth (Figure 12). We need to find the radian measure of $\overparen{AB}$, or $\text{m}\overparen{AB}$.

Since $\Delta AOO'$ is a right triangle, then:

$$\theta + \omega = \frac{\pi}{2} \Leftrightarrow \theta = \frac{\pi}{2} - \omega$$

(Note: $\theta = \text{m}\angle EOA$ is the latitude of A.)

Since $\overline{EO} \parallel \overline{AO'}$, $\theta = \text{m}\angle OAO'$ because alternate interior angles are equal when a transversal cuts two parallel lines (Lesson 8.7).

Note also, by definition:

$$\cos\theta = \frac{O'A}{r} \Leftrightarrow O'A = r\cos\theta$$

(Note: r is the radius of the Earth.)

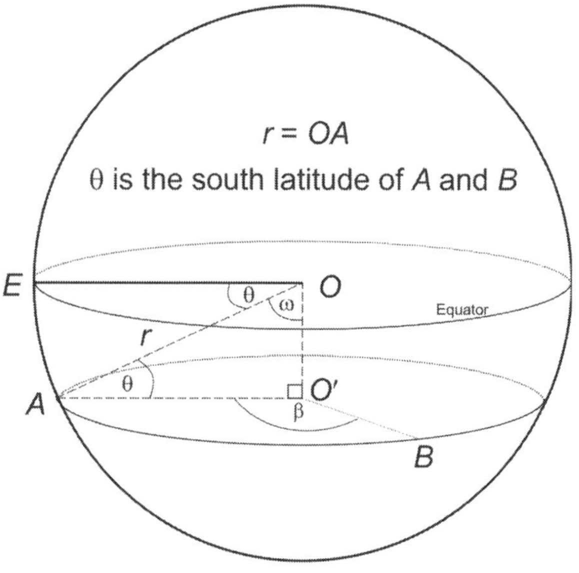

Let β = difference in longitude from A to B (in degrees). Therefore, β is to 360° as $\text{m}\overparen{AB}$ is to $2\pi(O'A)$. We can generate this proportion and solve for $\text{m}\overparen{AB}$:

Figure 12. Finding the distance between two points at the same latitude.

$$\frac{\beta}{360°} = \frac{\text{m}\overparen{AB}}{2\pi(O'A)} \Leftrightarrow \text{m}\overparen{AB} = \frac{\beta[2\pi(O'A)]}{360°} \Leftrightarrow \text{m}\overparen{AB} = \frac{\beta[\pi(O'A)]}{180°}$$

Since $O'A = r\cos\theta$, we substitute:

$$m\overset{\frown}{AB} = \frac{\beta\left[\pi(O'A)\right]}{180°} \Leftrightarrow m\overset{\frown}{AB} = \left(\frac{\beta\pi}{180°}\right) r\cos\theta \Leftrightarrow m\overset{\frown}{AB} = \frac{\beta r\pi\cos\theta}{180°}$$

QED

All we need to know is the radius of the Earth, the latitude of A, which is the latitude of B, and the longitude difference between A and B.

FINDING THE RADIUS OF THE MOON

Finally, knowing the radius of the Earth, we can determine the distance from the Earth to the Moon and the radius of the Moon.

Let P and Q be two points on the equator (Figure 13). Assume the Moon is directly overhead at P. Regard the Moon as a point M.[16] Assume the Moon is visible from Q; i.e., $\overline{QM}$ is tangent to the Earth at Q. QE = radius of the Earth. θ = difference in longitude from P to Q. The modern value is $89°4' = \theta$.

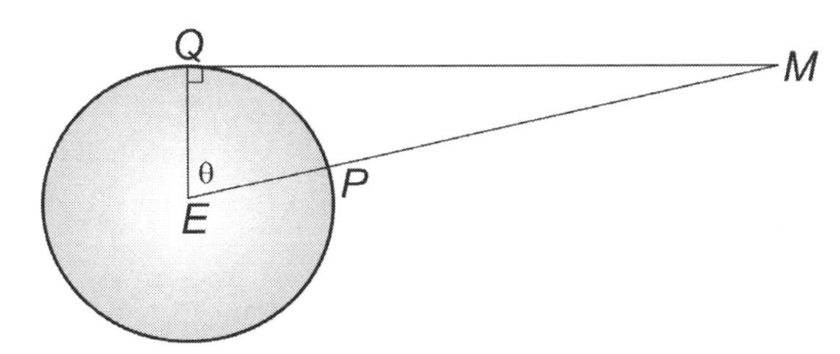

Figure 13. Finding the distance from the Earth to the Moon.

By definition:

$\cos\theta = \frac{QE}{EM}$ (Again, we will prove that ΔMEQ is a right triangle under these conditions in Lesson 13.9.)

Solving for EM, we get:

$$\cos\theta = \frac{QE}{EM} \Leftrightarrow EM(\cos\theta) = QE \Leftrightarrow$$

$$EM = \frac{QE}{\cos\theta}$$

Since $QE = 3947$, $EM = \frac{3947}{\cos\left(89 + \frac{4}{60}°\right)} \approx 242{,}310$

> Galileo computed by simple trigonometrical methods the height of those "enormous peaks (of the Moon)," obtaining a value of about four miles. He could not dream that in 1964, four hundred years after his birth, man would be able, by using Laser beams, to measure directly the height of those peaks and fully confirm his result.
>
> Stanley L. Jaki, *The Relevance of Physics* ([1966] 1992), p. 197.

Since $PM = EM - EP$, then PM (the distance from the Earth to the Moon) is:

$242{,}310 - 3947 = 238{,}363$ miles

[16] Regarding massive astronomical objects as points is a common practice in discipline of Classical Physics, or Newtonian mechanics. The phrase often used is "point-mass."

At E (Figure 14), measure the angle θ between $\overline{EM}$ and $\overline{ER}$. The modern value is $15'$; i.e., 15 minutes. Therefore, $\theta = 15'$. Since 1 degree $(1°) = 60$ minutes $(60')$, then $1' = \frac{1}{60}°$. Therefore:

$$15' = \frac{15°}{60} = \frac{1}{4}° = 0.25°$$

Let $EM = PM$ (the distance from the Earth to the Moon).

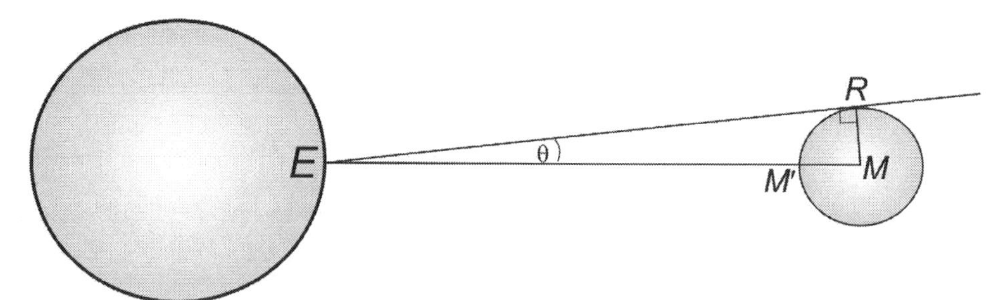

Figure 14. Finding the radius of the Moon.

Since ΔEMR is a right triangle, by definition:

$$\sin\theta = \frac{MR}{EM} \Leftrightarrow MR = (EM)\sin\theta$$

Therefore, MR (the radius of the Moon) is:

$238{,}363(\sin 15') = 238{,}363(\sin 0.25°) \approx 1040$ miles

FINDING THE DISTANCE FROM THE EARTH TO A STAR

Let's now try to calculate the distance from the Earth to a star. Given heliocentric cosmology, i.e., the Earth orbits the Sun, a nearby star would exhibit a **parallax**,[17] apparent angular shift, on the more distant background stars if observed from two different positions of the Earth's orbit. The telescopes and instrumentation of 16th and 17th centuries could not measure a star's parallax. In the 19th century, accurate instruments appeared and, with the principles of trigonometry, scientists could determine a star's parallax (Figure 15).

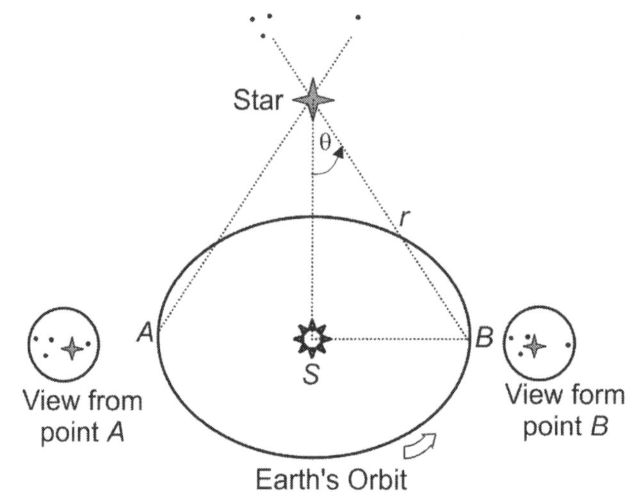

Figure 15. Parallax.

Given 1 degree $(1°) = 60$ minutes $(60')$ and 1 minute $(1') = 60$ seconds $(60'')$, then $1° = 3600''$ or $1'' = \frac{1}{3600}°$. Recall (Lesson 7.11) that a parsec (pc) is the distance to a celestial object that exhibits a **par**allax, θ, of one **sec**ond $(1'')$ when viewed from the Earth at a right angle to the Sun. We have also established (Lesson 7.11) that one astronomical

[17] Parallax, from the Greek *parallaxis*, means to "change alongside" or "exchange."

unit (AU) is the average distance from the Earth to the Sun (1 AU = 92,955,808 miles or 9.2955808×10^7 miles).

Using trigonometry and a scientific calculator, we can calculate the distance, in miles, of one parsec (pc). We let $r = 1$ pc and $\theta = \sin 1''$. By definition:

$$\sin 1'' = \frac{SB}{r} \Leftrightarrow r(\sin 1'') = SB \Leftrightarrow r = \frac{SB}{\sin 1''}$$

Since $\sin 1'' = \sin\left(\frac{1}{3600}°\right)$ and $SB = 9.2955808 \times 10^7$, then:

$$r = \frac{9.2955808 \times 10^7}{4.848136811 \times 10^{-6}} \approx 1.9173512 \times 10^{13} \text{ miles}$$

To the nearest AU, 1.9173512×10^{13} miles is approximately:

$$\frac{1.9173512 \times 10^{13} \cancel{\text{miles}}}{9.2955808 \times 10^7 \cancel{\text{miles}} / \text{AU}} \approx 206{,}265 \text{ AU}$$

Since light travels at approximately 186,000 miles per second, how many miles does light travels in one year? We can approximate:

$$\text{Speed of light in miles per year} = \frac{1.86 \times 10^5 \text{ miles}}{\cancel{\text{sec}}} \cdot \frac{3.15576 \times 10^7 \cancel{\text{sec}}}{\text{year}} \approx 5.87 \times 10^{12} \text{ miles per light-year}$$

What is the distance of one pc in light-years?

$$\frac{1.9173512 \times 10^{13} \cancel{\text{miles}} / \text{pc}}{5.87 \times 10^{12} \cancel{\text{miles}} / \text{light-year}} \approx 3.27 \text{ light-years per pc}$$

In 1838, the Prussian astronomer Friedrich Wilhelm Bessel (1784-1846), who also developed a class of mathematical functions named after him, measured the parallax, θ, of the star 61 Cygni to be 0.29″ ($\theta = 0.29''$).

Remember, 1 pc = 206,265 AU = 1″ measured parallax. If a star's parallax is greater than 1″, then the star is less than 1 pc away. If a star's parallax is less than 1″ (as with 61 Cygni), then the star is greater than 1 pc away. We have, therefore, indications of an inverse proportion (Lesson 8.8).

Figure 16. Friedrich Wilhelm Bessel. Source: Public Domain.

We can now calculate d, 61 Cygni's distance from the Earth. Follow along: We let $d = r$ in Figure 15. By definition:

$$\sin\theta = \frac{SB}{d} \Leftrightarrow d(\sin\theta) = SB \Leftrightarrow d = \frac{SB}{\sin\theta}$$

Since $\theta = 0.29''$ and $SB = 1$ AU, then:

$$d = \frac{1 \text{ AU}}{\sin(0.29'')} \approx 711{,}258 \text{ AU}$$

Converting AU to light-years, we get:

$$d = (711{,}258\ \cancel{AU})\left(\frac{\cancel{pc}}{206{,}265\ \cancel{AU}}\right)\left(\frac{3.2665\text{ light-years}}{\cancel{pc}}\right) \approx 11.264\text{ light-years}^{18}$$

This determination of parallax is considered by many astronomers to be proof that heliocentricism is the cosmology of our Solar System.

By the above demonstrations, I hope that you realize the quantitative power of trigonometry. With a few measuring tools, you can chart the heavens. And, who should we ponder upon as we consider the heights of the heavens?

> When I consider Your heavens, the work of Your fingers, the moon and the stars, which You have ordained; What is man that You take thought of him, and the son of man that You care for him? Yet You have made him a little lower than God, and You crown him with glory and majesty! You make him to rule over the works of Your hands; You have put all things under his feet, all sheep and oxen, and also the beasts of the field, the birds of the heavens and the fish of the sea, whatever passes through the paths of the seas. O Lord, our Lord, how majestic is Your name in all the earth! (Psalm 8:3-9).

> God's gracious action in creation belongs from the first to that delight, pleasure, and regard that the Trinity enjoys from eternity, as an outward and unnecessary expression of that love; and thus creation must be received before all else as gift and as beauty.
>
> David Bentley Hart, *The Beauty of the Infinite* (2003), p. 249.

EXERCISES

Define the following words:

1. Triangulation
2. Astrolabe
3. Mariner's quadrant
4. Sextant
5. Seked
6. Batter
7. Parallax

Answer the following questions:

8. Show that $\frac{1}{2}+\frac{1}{5}+\frac{1}{50}=\frac{18}{25}$.
9. Use logarithms and a scientific calculator to compute $d = (711{,}258\ \cancel{AU})\left(\frac{\cancel{pc}}{206{,}265\ \cancel{AU}}\right)\left(\frac{3.2665\text{ light-years}}{\cancel{pc}}\right)$ rounded to the nearest thousandths. (Hint: When taking logs of numbers, keep as many decimal places as your calculator allows.)

---

[18] Do you see how calculating with logarithms saved the day in the era before calculators/computers?

Use trigonometric functions and your scientific calculator to solve the following questions.[19] Where needed, draw a diagram to represent the situation. Then, name your answer by setting what you want to find equal to a variable. Write an equation or equations involving that variable. Finally, solve for that variable by entering the entirety of the numeric expression into your calculator; do not do the calculator work in parts.

10. Solve for ω in degrees, rounded to the nearest hundredth, where $\cot \omega = 0.25$.
11. Find the height of a tree from your eye if the altitude of the tree is 50° and your distance from that tree is 100 ft. Round to the nearest foot.
12. Use the formula derived in the text for finding the height of a mountain if $AB = 500$ feet, $\theta = 60°$, and $\omega = 65°$. Round to the nearest foot.
13. Find the distance in miles of the arc length between two points on the Earth with the same latitude of 39.5° where one location has longitude of 190° and the other location 130°. Let the radius of the Earth be 3947 miles and use the formula derived in the text. Round to the nearest mile.
14. Compute $r = \dfrac{h(\sin\theta)}{1-\sin\theta}$ when $h = 3$ miles and $\theta = 87°46'$.

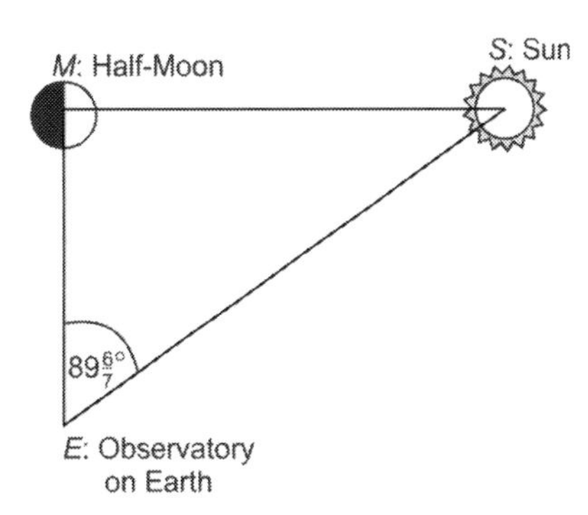

Figure 17. The figure is not drawn to scale.

15. Ancient Hindu astronomers could determine a unit ratio comparing the distance from the Earth to the Moon to the distance from the Earth to the Sun. Use Figure 17 to determine that ratio. (Assume ΔMSE is a right triangle and round the consequent of the ratio to the nearest unit.)
16. As viewed from the top of a cliff 326 feet above the level of the water, the angle of depression of a boat is 24°. How far out from the cliff is the boat to the nearest tenth of a foot?
17. The Washington Monument is Washington, DC, is 555 feet high. If a boy five feet tall stands 100 ft from the monument and looks at the top of it, how much, to the nearest tenth of a degree, is his line of sight elevated above the horizontal and how, to the nearest tenth of a foot, far is his eye from the top of the monument?
18. At a certain time of day, the elevation of the Sun above the horizon is 50° and at that time a tree casts a shadow 80 feet long on level ground. How high is the tree to the nearest tenth of a foot?

[19] For some of the homework ideas in this section, credit goes to James Edgar Thompson (1892-1982), *Trigonometry for the Practical Worker* [1931, 1946, 1962] 1982.

19. The width of a river is determined by Mr. Washington, a surveyor. First, at a point five feet from one bank, he sights the transit telescope on a stone B directly opposite on the other bank. Second, he turns the telescope through $\angle BAC$ such that $m\angle BAC = 90°$ with $\overline{AC}$. Third, he then measures $AC = 100$ feet. Fourth, he sets the transit is set up at C and sights the telescope on the original point A. Finally, he turns the transit through $\angle ACB$ to sight again the stone at B. The angle found is $73°42'$. What is the width of the river to the nearest tenth of a foot?
20. In World War I, an observer in a stationary captive balloon at a known height above a level plain in the rear of a front line trench, sights on the trench and finds its angle of depression to be 35°. He then sights on an enemy machine gun beyond the trench and finds its angle of depression to be 20°. If the height of the balloon is 2000 feet, how far is the gun from the trench to the nearest tenth of a foot?
21. To determine the height of one of the great redwood trees of California, a surveyor lays off a distance of 300 feet from its foot and at the end of the line sets up a transit. He levels the telescope and then sights on the top of the tree. If the angle of elevation is $65°12'$, and the telescope is five feet above the level ground, find the height of the tree to the nearest tenth of a foot.

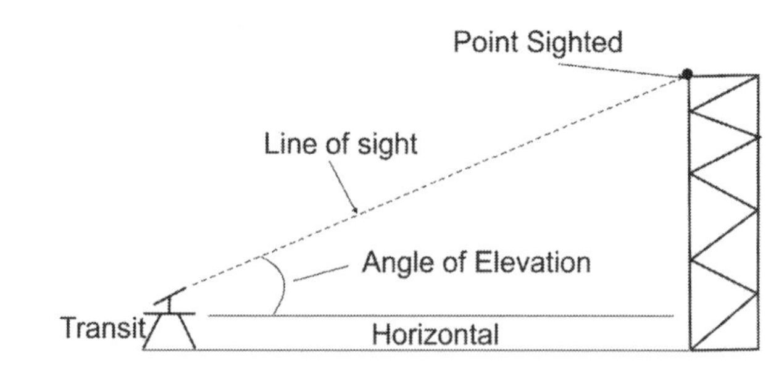

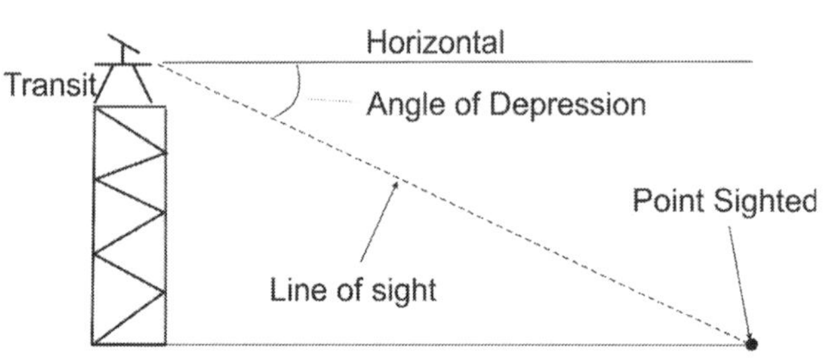

Figure 18. Angle of elevation and angle of depression.

22. A tree 90 feet high casts a shadow 117 feet long. Find the angle of elevation of the Sun to the nearest tenth of a degree.
23. From a tower, 94 feet high situated on the bank of a river, the angle of depression of the opposite bank is $25°13'$. Find the width of the river to the nearest tenth of a foot.
24. From a balloon directly above a certain building, the angle of depression of a river eight miles away is $10°14'$. Find the height of the balloon above the level of the river rounded to the nearest tenth of a mile.
25. From a tower 58 feet high, the angles of depression of two objects situated in the same horizontal line with the base of the tower and on the same side are $30°13.25'$ and $45°46.25'$ respectively. Find the distance between the two objects to the nearest tenth of a foot.
26. From the top of a hill, the angles of depression of two successive milestones on a straight level road leading to the hill are 15° and 5°. Find the height of the hill to the nearest tenth of a mile.
27. If the Sun is at a 30° angle off the horizon at 5 PM, how far from your west fence, a fence that is two meters tall, should you start your cactus garden for it to get the full Sun until then? Round your answer to the nearest tenth of a meter.
28. You have the happy chore of erecting a television antenna, a chore that in today's digital world is no longer necessary. You decide that the guy wires should be at a 35° angle on your roof and you will need 3 of them. How much guy wire, rounded to the nearest tenth of a meter do you need if your antenna is 4 meters high? Rounded to the nearest tenth of a meter, how far away from the antenna base should you put the root supports?

29. A ladder 40 feet long may be so placed that it will just reach a window sill 33 feet above the street level on one side of a street. By turning it over without moving its foot, it will just reach a window sill 21 feet up the other side. Find its inclination above the street in each position, rounded to the nearest tenth of a degree, and find the width of the street, rounded to the nearest tenth of a foot.

30. You are looking over a piece of property that's bounded by two farm roads that intersect at right angles and a state highway that cuts across at a 20° angle (Figure 19). The previous owner just put a fence around the land and tells you it took 750 meters of fence to do so. What is the area of the land rounded to the nearest tenth of a square meter?

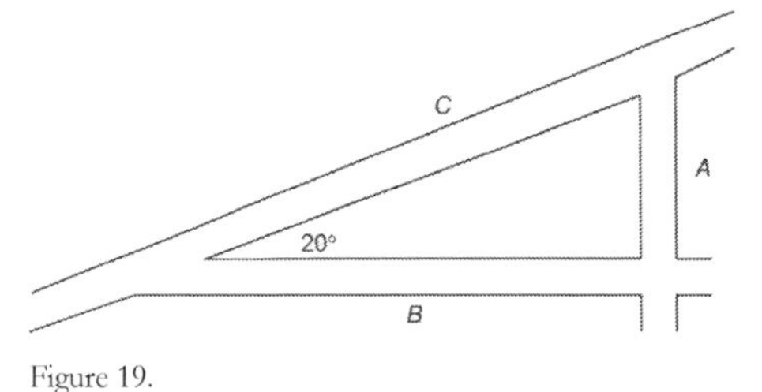

Figure 19.

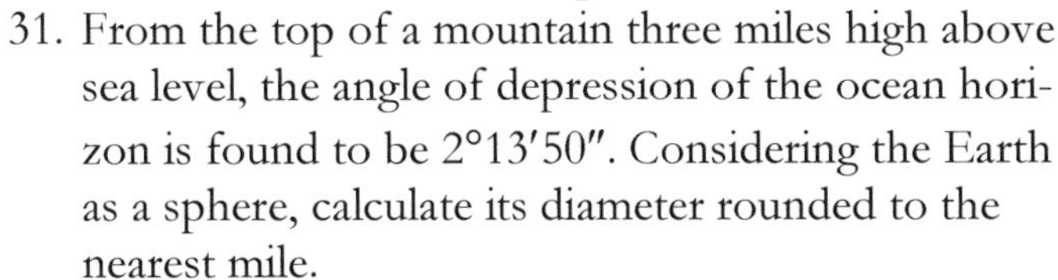
31. From the top of a mountain three miles high above sea level, the angle of depression of the ocean horizon is found to be 2°13′50″. Considering the Earth as a sphere, calculate its diameter rounded to the nearest mile.

32. Rounded to the nearest mile, determine how many miles in 1° of latitude. Let the radius r of the Earth, assumed to be a sphere, be 3947 miles and use your scientific calculator's value of π.

Figure 20.

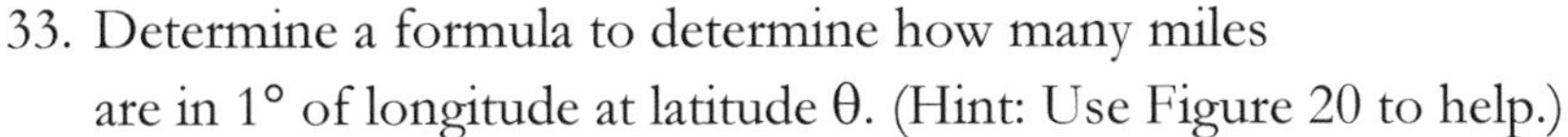
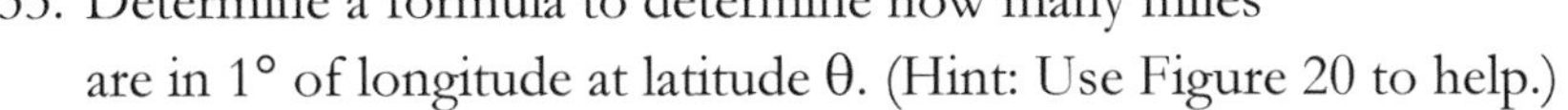
33. Determine a formula to determine how many miles are in 1° of longitude at latitude θ. (Hint: Use Figure 20 to help.)

34. Rounded to the nearest mile, determine how many miles are in 1° of longitude at latitude (a) 32°N, (b) 0°, and (c) 90°N. Again, let the radius r of the Earth be 3947 miles and use your scientific calculator's value of π.

35. The equatorial parallax of the Sun is 8.8″. Using the diameter of the Earth as found in Question 31, find the distance from the Earth, its point mass, to the point mass of the Sun (rounded to the nearest mile). (Hint: In Figure 21, the equatorial parallax is $\angle APB$.)

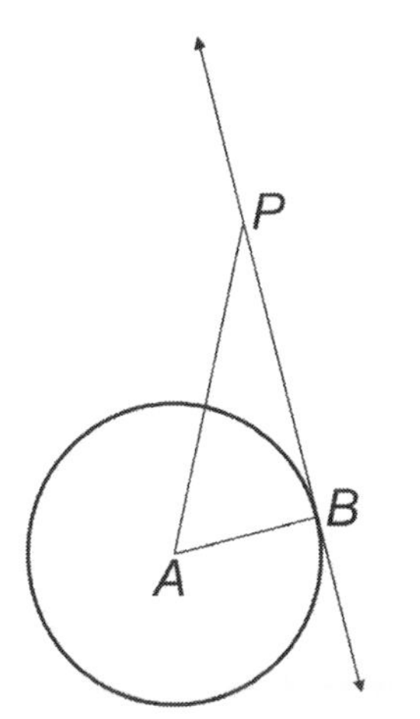

Figure 21. *A* is the center of the Earth; its point mass. *P* is the point mass of the Sun.

36. From a point on the Earth the Sun is sighted with a transit (Figure 22), first on one edge and then on the other, and the angle between the lines of is 32′4″. Using the Earth-Sun distance found in Question 35,

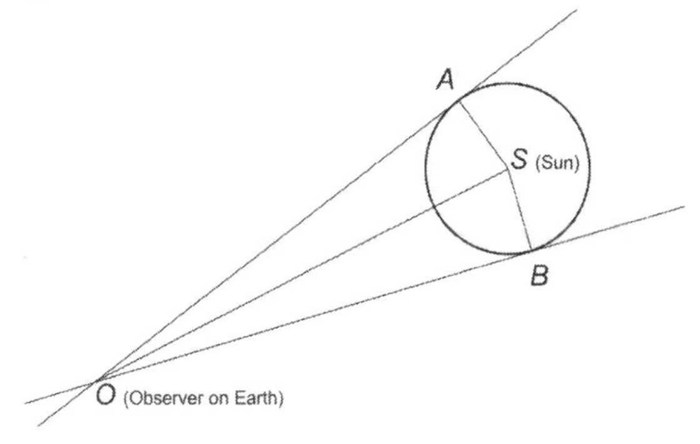

Figure 22.

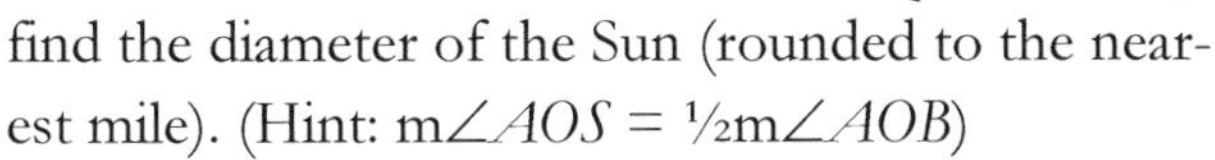
find the diameter of the Sun (rounded to the nearest mile). (Hint: $m\angle AOS = \frac{1}{2}m\angle AOB$)

37. The line from a fixed star is perpendicular to the line joining two opposite positions of the Earth in its path, and the annual parallax of the star is 1.826″ (Figure 23). Using the Earth-Sun distance found in Question 35, find the distance of the star from the Earth. Write your answer in Scientific Notation with three significant figures.
38. Field Project: Using your Protractor Sextant, a measuring rule, and your scientific calculator, calculate the heights of several tall objects (e.g., a tree in your backyard, a radio tower, a building) and the distance of 1° longitude, to the nearest mile, at your latitude.

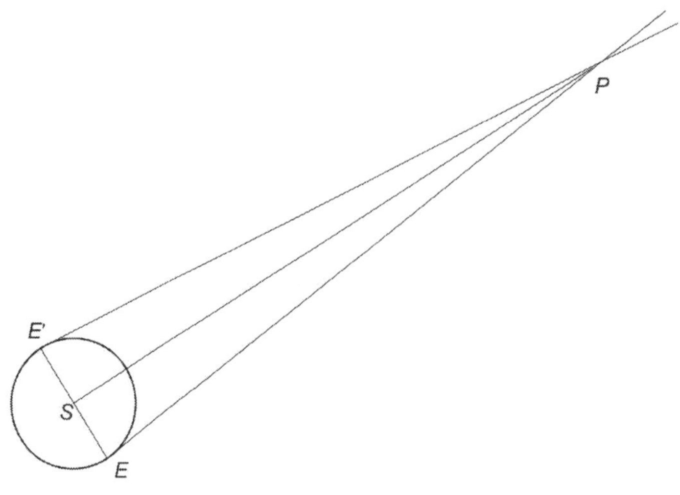

Figure 23.

> I believe that ... a theology of nature may be sustained only with a recovery of the full Christian framework of knowledge, for it is through the incarnation of the Word of God among us in Jesus Christ that the ultimate secret of the whole created order is disclosed: in the comprehensive purpose of God's love for the universe. This implies that all the laws of nature, and all patterns of order in the universe, are finally and satisfyingly intelligible only as they are ontologically linked to the love of God, the supreme power of order.
>
> Thomas F. Torrance, *The Christian Frame of Mind* (1989), p. 83.

> The Hindu mathematicians ... had developed a system of numerals in which the value of a digit was shown by its position. They knew the use of zero, they could extract square and cube roots, they understood fractions, problems of interest, the summation of arithmetical and geometrical series, the solution of determinate and indeterminate equations of the first and second degrees, permutations and combinations and other operations of simple arithmetic and algebra. They also developed trigonometrical technique for expressing the motions of the heavenly bodies and introduced trigonometrical tables of sines.
>
> Alistair C. Crombie, *The History of Science from Augustine to Galileo*, ([1959, 1970, 1979] 1995), I:65.

12.11 Numbers Complex

Terms, Symbols & Concepts Introduced
1. $\mathbb{C}$
2. Complex analysis
3. Complex conjugate
4. Complex number plane
5. Complex numbers
6. Degree of a polynomial
7. Fundamental Theorem of Algebra
8. Imaginary numbers
9. Lateral unit
10. Monomial
11. Parallelogram Law
12. Polynomial
13. Pure imaginary number

Let's reconsider the answer to the question we explored in Lesson 11.6, "What is the square root of a negative number?" Let's start by asking, "What is the square root of -1?" Written in symbols, what is $\sqrt{-1}$?

By our definition of square roots, we must find a number that is equal to -1 when multiplied by itself. These two numbers can either be both positive or both negative. If they are both positive, (1)(1), then our product is 1, a positive number. If they are both negative, (-1)(-1), our product is, again, 1, a positive number. No real number will work.

But, alas, we can extend our concept of number to include $\sqrt{-1}$. We note that it was not until early in the 19th century that mathematicians authorized the square root of negative numbers as valid numbers into the corpus of Mathematics.

Leonhard Euler (1707-1783) provided a shorthand notation for $\sqrt{-1}$ by letting $i = \sqrt{-1}$ where i stands for **imaginary number**[1] as named by René Descartes (1596-1650) in 1637. Carl Friedrich Gauss (1777-1855) originally did not like the word imaginary and thought it to be an ill-adapted name. He preferred the term **lateral unit**.[2]

Mathematicians define the square root of any negative number as an imaginary number, and these square roots are part of an extension of the set of real numbers. Mathematicians name this extension complex numbers, denoted by the symbol $\mathbb{C}$.

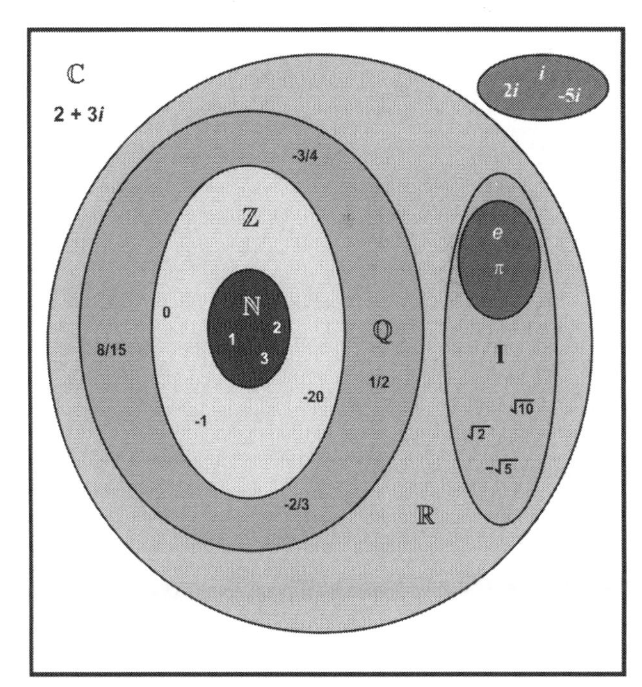

Figure 1. Venn Diagram of Number Systems: Natural to Complex.

Complex Numbers

Numbers of the form $a + bi$ are **complex numbers**,[3] where $a, b \in \mathbb{R}$. There are, therefore, two components to every complex number:

1. a is the real part.
2. bi is the imaginary part.

If $a = 0$, then the complex number is a **pure imaginary number**, or:

$a + bi$ and $a = 0 \Rightarrow bi$ (a pure imaginary number)

---

[1] Imaginary numbers were called sophisticated or subtle before then. See Paul J. Nahin, *An Imaginary Tale: The Story of* $\sqrt{-1}$ (Princeton: Princeton University Press, 1998).

[2] *Lateral* means "on the side."

[3] Rafael Bombelli (1526-1572) introduced the complex number concept in his treatise *L'Algebra* in 1572 in the context of the solution of cubic equations, equations like $x^3 - 7x^2 + 17x - 15 = 0$.

If $b = 0$, then the complex number is a real number, or:

$a + bi$ and $b = 0 \Rightarrow a \in \mathbb{R}$

Every real number is a complex number, or $\mathbb{R} \subset \mathbb{C}$. The Venn Diagram (Figure 1) depicts all the sets of numbers we have studied so far: (1) Natural numbers, (2) Integers, (3) Rational numbers, (4) Irrational numbers, (5) Real numbers, and (6) Complex numbers.

Note how these sets interrelate:

$\mathbb{Q} \cap \mathrm{I} = \varnothing$

$\mathbb{R} = \mathbb{Q} \cup \mathrm{I}$

$\mathbb{N} \subset \mathbb{Z} \subset \mathbb{Q} \subset \mathbb{R} \subset \mathbb{C}$

Figure 2. Source: iStockPhoto.

Like Matryoshka or Russian nesting dolls (Figure 2), the complex number system envelops the imaginary numbers and the real numbers, the real numbers envelope the irrational numbers and the rational numbers, the rational numbers envelop the integers, and the integers envelop the natural numbers.

SOLUTIONS TO EQUATIONS AND NUMBER SYSTEMS

Let's solve a few simple equations for x. Note that the algebraic methods require an extension of number systems as each solution unfolds:[4]

Equation 1. $x + 3 = 8$

$x + 3 = 8 \Leftrightarrow x = 5$

$5 \in \mathbb{N}$

(Note: $\mathbb{N} \subset \mathbb{Z} \subset \mathbb{Q} \subset \mathbb{R} \subset \mathbb{C}$)

Equation 2. $x + 8 = 3$

$x + 8 = 3 \Leftrightarrow x = -5$

$-5 \in \mathbb{Z}$

(Note: $\mathbb{Z} \subset \mathbb{Q} \subset \mathbb{R} \subset \mathbb{C}$)

Equation 3. $3x = 2$

$3x = 2 \Leftrightarrow x = \frac{2}{3}$

$\frac{2}{3} \in \mathbb{Q}$

(Note: $\mathbb{Q} \subset \mathbb{R} \subset \mathbb{C}$)

Equation 4. $x^2 = 2$

$x^2 = 2 \Leftrightarrow x = \sqrt{2}$ or $x = -\sqrt{2}$

---

[4] For a rigorous discussion of number systems, the way mathematicians explore and justify these ideas, see Friedrich Waismann, *Introduction to Mathematical Thinking: The Formation of Concepts in Modern Mathematics* (Mineola: Dover Publications, [1951, 1959, 1966] 2003).

$\sqrt{2}, -\sqrt{2} \in \mathbb{R}$

(Note: $\mathbb{R} \subset \mathbb{C}$)

Equation 5. $x^2 + 4 = 0$

$x^2 + 4 = 0 \Leftrightarrow x^2 = -4 \Leftrightarrow x = \sqrt{-4}$ or $x = -\sqrt{-4}$

$\sqrt{-4}, -\sqrt{-4} \in \mathbb{C}$

How do we solve Equation 5? Let's start with $x^2 + 1 = 0$:

$x^2 + 1 = 0 \Leftrightarrow x^2 = -1$

$i = x \Rightarrow i^2 = -1$

The Building Block of Complex Numbers:
$i^2 = -1$

Let's now return to Equation 5. We have this:

$x^2 = -4 \Leftrightarrow x^2 = (4)(-1)$ since $-1x = x$ for all $x \in \mathbb{R}$

$i^2 = -1 \Rightarrow x^2 = 4i^2$

Extracting the square root of both sides, we get:

$x^2 = 4i^2 \Leftrightarrow x = 2i$ or $-2i$

(Note: It is mathematical convention to write i after rational numbers, but before irrational numbers.[5])

We observe:

$i = x \Rightarrow i^2 = -1 \Rightarrow i = \sqrt{-1}$

It seems like an arbitrary decision to invent a number i such that $i^2 = -1$. But the mathematical derivations that result from this decision are consistent and, as scientists soon found out, true to the rational nature of the workings of the physical world.

Why not invent a number j such that $j = x/0$; i.e., why don't we allow for division by zero, in the same way that we allow for the square root of a negative number? The reason why mathematicians do not permit division by zero is that, by doing so, we get crazy results, like 1 = 2. Allowing for division by zero does not comport with the rational nature of reality; i.e., we can build a bridge that will collapse if we accept division by zero.

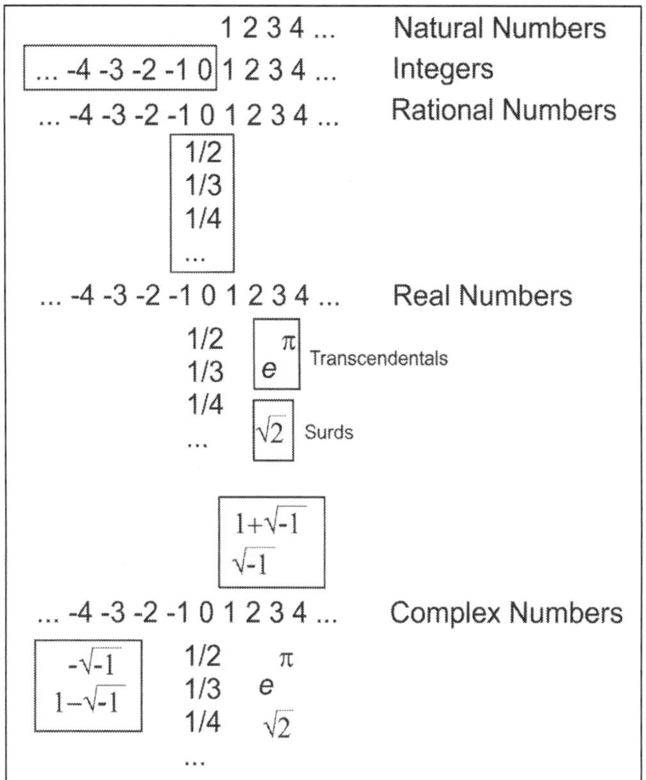

1 2 3 4 ... Natural Numbers

... -4 -3 -2 -1 0 1 2 3 4 ... Integers

... -4 -3 -2 -1 0 1 2 3 4 ... Rational Numbers
1/2
1/3
1/4
...

... -4 -3 -2 -1 0 1 2 3 4 ... Real Numbers
1/2 π
1/3 e Transcendentals
1/4 √2 Surds
...

1+√-1
√-1

... -4 -3 -2 -1 0 1 2 3 4 ... Complex Numbers
-√-1
1–√-1
1/2 π
1/3 e
1/4 √2
...

Figure 3. Natural numbers to Complex numbers.

[5] For example, to simplify $\sqrt{-45}$, we write: $\sqrt{-45} = \sqrt{-1}\sqrt{45} = \sqrt{-1}(3\sqrt{5}) = i3\sqrt{5} = 3i\sqrt{5}$

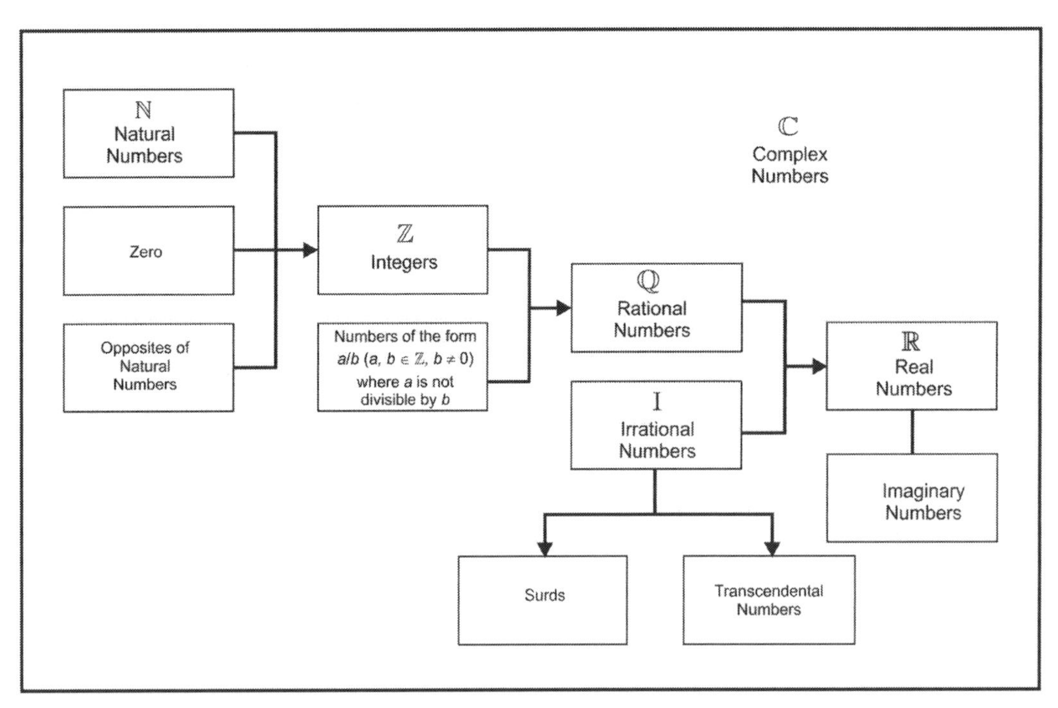

Figure 4. From Natural numbers to Complex numbers.

COMPLEX NUMBER PLANE

Mathematicians use the number line to picture, or represent, the set of real numbers, or the real number continuum. How could we represent a complex number, consisting of a real number and an imaginary number? It was Gauss who fully developed a way to do this using the **complex number plane**.[6]

The plane is two dimensional just like the Cartesian coordinate plane. The x-axis is the real number axis, and the y-axis is the imaginary number axis. We plot any real number a with the coordinates $(a, 0)$ and we plot any imaginary number bi with the coordinates $(0, b)$. We plot any complex number $a + bi$ with the coordinates (a, b).

Since we can visualize real numbers on a one-dimensional number line, positive or negative numbers are numbers, respectively, to the right or

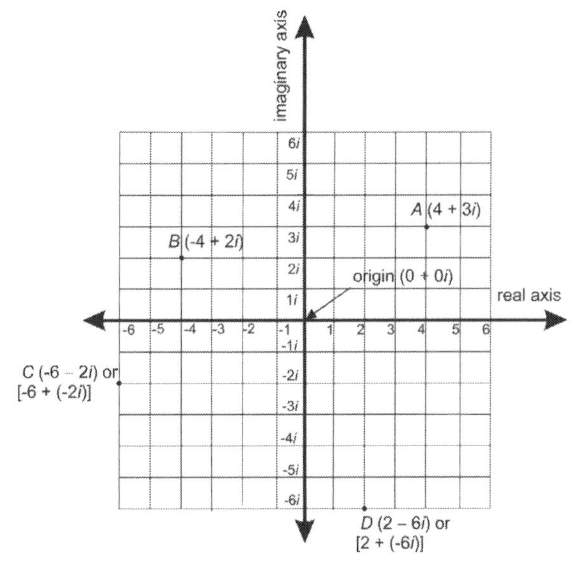

Figure 5. The Complex Number Plane.

[6] The English mathematician John Wallis (1616-1703) first conceived of the elementary idea of a complex number plane in 1685. Two other men share the honors of representing complex numbers geometrically. In 1797, the Norwegian cartographer Caspar Wessel (1745-1818) read a paper before the Danish Academy of Sciences entitled "On the Analytic Representation of Direction." (Note: Direction implies vectors and, consequently, the physics of motion.) In 1806, the French bookkeeper Jean Robert Argand (1768-1822) published a paper anonymously in which he pictured complex numbers in a two-dimensional plane.

left of the origin. Since we visualize complex numbers on a two-dimensional plane, i.e., there are two components, we cannot define a complex number as positive or negative.

ARITHMETIC OPERATIONS

We can add, subtract, multiply, divide, exponentiate, and extract roots of complex numbers. Let's investigate some of these operations.

To add or subtract two complex numbers, we add or subtract the real number component and the imaginary number component separately.

Some examples:

Example 1. $(3 + 4i) + (-7 + 2i) =$
$3 - 7 + 4i + 2i =$
$-4 + i(4 + 2) =$
$-4 + i6 =$
$-4 + 6i$

Example 2. $(3 + 4i) - (-7 + 2i) =$
$3 + 7 + 4i - 2i =$
$10 + i(4 - 2) =$
$10 + i2 =$
$10 + 2i$

Or, since $a - b = a + (-b)$:
$(3 + 4i) - (-7 + 2i) =$
$(3 + 4i) + (7 - 2i) =$
$3 + 7 + 4i - 2i =$
$10 + i(4 - 2) =$
$10 + i2 =$
$10 + 2i$

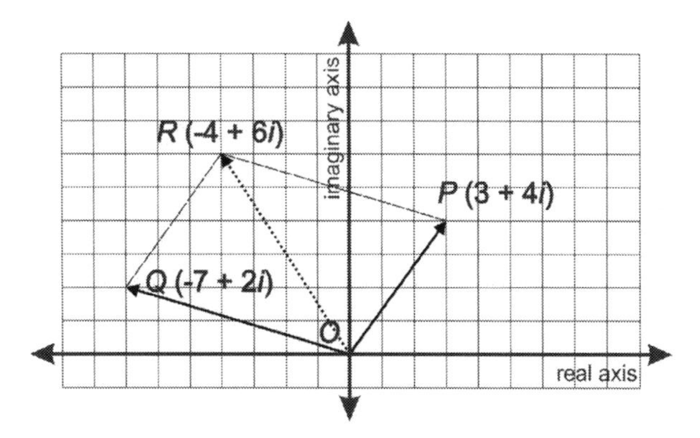

Figure 6. Complex Number or Vector Addition: $(3 + 4i) + (-7 + 2i)$

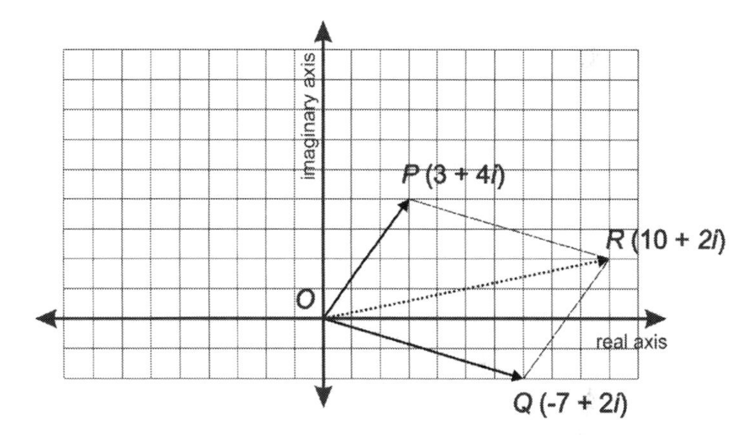

Figure 7. Complex Number or Vector Subtraction: $(3 + 4i) - (-7 + 2i) = 3 + 4i) + (7 - 2i)$

In general:

$(a + bi) + (c + di) = (a + c) + (b + d)i$
$(a + bi) - (c + di) = (a - c) + (b - d)i$

We graphically portray these operations on the complex number plane in Figures 6 and 7.

The components of addition, the two addends, and the sum, unfold a parallelogram, one of the famous diagrams designed by Isaac Newton (1643-1727). He used it to picture the addition of vectors to illustrate his **Parallelogram Law**, a law that represents the fundamental laws of mechanics for the addition of forces and velocities. That the addition of complex numbers should interpenetrate a law derived by Newton, decades before the invention of complex numbers, should, indeed, be a surprise.

According to Alfred North Whitehead (1861-1947):

> One of the most fascinating characteristics of mathematics is the surprising way in which the ideas and results of different parts of the subject dovetail into each other.[7]

He goes on to reflect on what I have been calling the perichoretic nature of the interplay between the abstract and the concrete:

---

[7] Alfred North Whitehead, *An Introduction to Mathematics* (New York: Oxford University Press, [1911, 1948] 1958), p. 71.

During the discussions of this and the previous chapter [imaginary numbers and the general properties of number – JN] we have been guided merely by the most abstract of pure mathematical considerations; and yet at the end of them we have been led back to the most fundamental of all the laws of nature, laws which have to be in the mind of every engineer as he designs an engine and of every naval architect as he calculates the stability of a ship. It is no paradox to say that in our most theoretical moods we may be nearest to our most practical applications.[8]

Let's see what happens with multiplication (Figures 8 and 9):

Example 3. $(3 + 4i)(7 - 2i)$

Since $a - b = a + (-b)$, we can rewrite this problem:
$(3 + 4i)[7 + (-2i)]$

We must sum four products:

1. $3 \cdot 7 = 21$
2. $4i \cdot 7 = 28i$
3. $-2i \cdot 3 = -6i$
4. $4i \cdot -2i = -8i^2 = 8$ since $i^2 = -1$

The product is:
$21 + 28i + (-6i) + 8 = 29 + 22i$

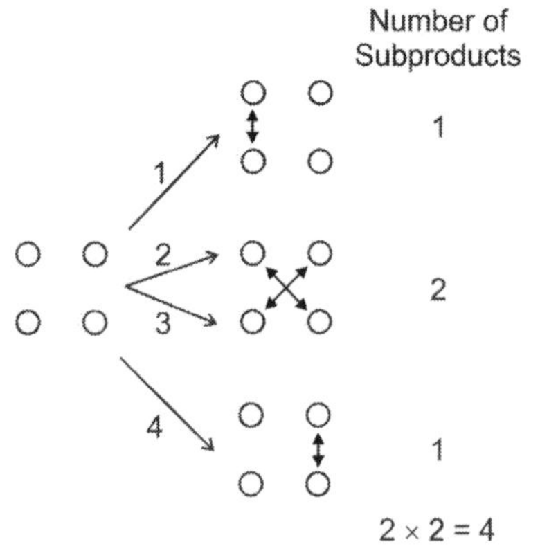

Figure 8. Two-Digit by Two-Digit Paradigm.

In general:

$$(a + bi)(c + di) = ac + bdi^2 + bci + adi$$
$$i^2 = -1 \Rightarrow ac + bdi^2 + bci + adi = (ac - bd) + (ad + bc)i$$

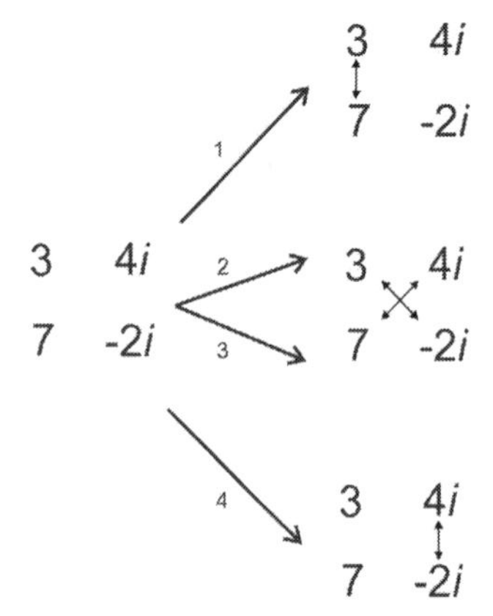

Figure 9. Complex Number Multiplication.

Let's try multiplying the number 1 by i and then multiply the product by i recursively. We get:

1. $1i = i$
2. $ii = i^2 = -1$
3. $-1i = -i$
4. $-ii = -i^2 = 1$

After four iterations of the recursive algorithm, we return to our starting point. On the complex number plane, we the result is Figure 10.

[8] Whitehead, *Ibid.*

Multiplying any number by i rotates that number counterclockwise around the origin by 90° = π/2 radians. Because rotating i counterclockwise by 90° produces -1, this turning is a graphical picture of why $ii = i^2 = -1$. Connecting the four points generates either a circle or a square.

What about powers of i?

$i^0 = 1$
$i^1 = \sqrt{-1} = i$
$i^2 = ii = -1$
$i^3 = i^2 i = -i$
$i^4 = i^3 i = i^2 i^2 = 1 \; -i$
$i^5 = i^4 i = \sqrt{-1} = i$
$i^6 = i^5 i = -1$

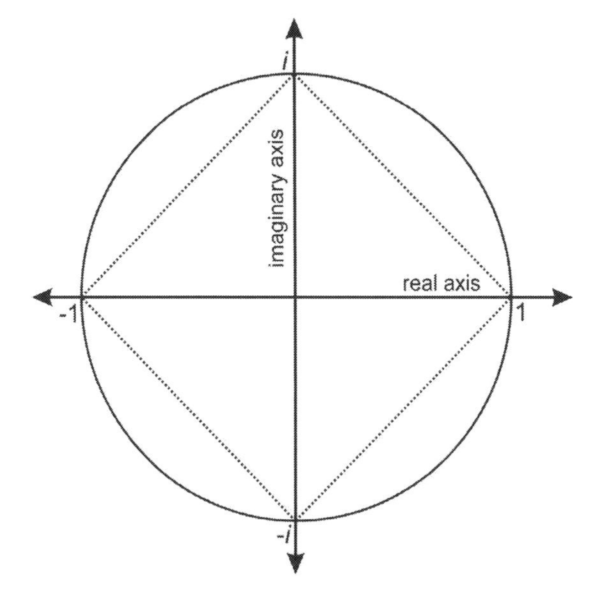

Figure 10. Multiplication by i and rotational dynamics.

Note that the values repeat every fourth power, reflecting Figure 10, revealing that a square/circle is embedded in the graphical representation of the powers of i.

Let's see what $(-5i)^2$ and $(5i)^2$ equal:

$(-5i)^2 = (-5i)(-5i) = 25i^2 = 25(-1) = -25$
$(5i)^2 = (5i)(5i) = 25i^2 = 25(-1) = -25$

The **complex conjugate**[9] of bi is $-bi$. The complex conjugate of $a + bi$ is $a - bi$. If we multiply a complex number by its conjugate, we get:

$(a + bi)(a - bi) = a^2 - b^2i^2 = a^2 - b^2(-1) = a^2 + b^2$ (We note that the imaginary part disappears.)
$(bi)(-bi) = (b)(-b)i^2 = (b)(-b)(-1) = (b)(b) = b^2$ (Again, the imaginary part disappears.)

We use complex conjugates to facilitate division. For example, we want to divide $2 + 3i$ by $1 - 6i$. We write:

$$\frac{2+3i}{1-6i}$$

To evaluate, we multiply the numerator and denominator by the complex conjugate of the denominator. We write:

$$\frac{2+3i}{1-6i} = \left(\frac{2+3i}{1-6i}\right)\left(\frac{1+6i}{1+6i}\right) = \frac{(2+3i)(1+6i)}{(1-6i)(1+6i)}$$

Next, we multiply the complex numbers in both numerator and denominator. We write:

$$\frac{(2+3i)(1+6i)}{(1-6i)(1+6i)} = \frac{2+3i+12i+18i^2}{1-36i^2}$$

Since $i^2 = -1$, we write:

[9] Conjugate, in Latin, means to "yoke together."

$$\frac{2+3i+12i+18i^2}{1-36i^2}=\frac{2+3i+12i-18}{1+36}=\frac{-16+15i}{37}=-\frac{16}{37}+\frac{15i}{37}$$ (in the form $a + bi$)

THE FUNDAMENTAL THEOREM OF ALGEBRA

In 1799, at the age of 22, Carl Friedrich Gauss showed, by a proof that is beautiful, elegant, but not at all intuitive, that with this extension of $\mathbb{R}$ to $\mathbb{C}$, we can solve every algebraic equation. Technically, this proof, the **Fundamental Theorem of Algebra**, states that a **polynomial**[10] of degree n has exactly n complex solutions or roots. $\mathbb{C}$ is sufficient for the solution of every polynomial equation; i.e., $\mathbb{C}$ encapsulates everything needed to solve any equation written algebraically, i.e., an equation written in terms of a finite number of algebraic symbols.

FRACTALS AND EMBODIED MATHEMATICS

We have only scratched the surface of the wonderful world of complex numbers. Complex numbers are fascinating because of their many revelations, especially in science and engineering. These numbers are used in the theory of alternating current in electricity, and in conjunction with recursive algorithms, are used to generate, with computers, beautiful geometric art known as fractals (Lesson 12.12).

Finally, the study of functions of a complex variable is known as **complex analysis**. Its conclusions have practical use in the manifold applications of Mathematics as well as in other branches of Mathematics. So, much study of this beautiful dance of number awaits you in the future.

EXERCISES

Define the following.

1. Imaginary number i
2. Lateral unit
3. Pure imaginary number
4. Complex numbers
5. $\mathbb{C}$
6. Complex number plane
7. Parallelogram Law
8. Complex conjugate
9. Fundamental Theorem of Algebra
10. Polynomial
11. Degree of a polynomial
12. Monomial
13. Complex analysis

Some amazing revelations of Complex Numbers embedded in the nature and analysis of:

- Electrical engineering (AC: alternating current)
- Laser physics
- Quantum mechanics
- Electromagnetic wave theory

Rewrite the following in terms of i following mathematical convention:

14. $\sqrt{-16}$
15. $\sqrt{-17}$
16. $\sqrt{-18}$
17. $\sqrt{-24}/4$

---

[10] A general polynomial equation of **degree** n is of the form $y = p(x) = a_nx^n + a_{n-1}x^{n-1} + \ldots + a_2x^2 + a_1x + a_0$ where n is a non-negative integer and a_n is the coefficient of x^n, a_{n-1} is the coefficient of x^{n-1}, etc., down to a_0, which is the coefficient of x^0 (or 1). A **monomial** is a single term of a polynomial that is in the form ax^n where n is a non-negative integer. Refer to Lesson 14.3.

Determine the value of each of the following imaginary powers: (Hint. See if you can develop a pattern to help you find the answers.)
18. i^8
19. i^{15}
20. i^{33}
21. i^{126}
22. $(3i^9)(5i^6)$
23. i^{999}
24. $i + i^2 + i^3 + i^4 + \ldots + i^{100}$

Answer the following questions:
25. What is the complex conjugate of $6i$?
26. What is the complex conjugate of $-i$?
27. What is the complex conjugate of $2 + 3i$?
28. What is the complex conjugate of $2 - 3i$?

True or False.
29. $i^0 = 1$
30. $\sqrt{-83} = -\sqrt{83}$
31. All real numbers are complex numbers.
32. All complex numbers are real numbers.
33. Multiplying any complex number z by i rotates that number by $\pi/2$ radians clockwise about the origin.
34. $3x^2$ is a monomial.
35. $4x^{-1}$ is a monomial.
36. 2 is a monomial.
37. $3x^{2/3}$ is a monomial.
38. $-6x$ is a monomial.

Plot the following complex numbers in one Complex Number Plane:
39. $A = 3 + 2i$
40. $B = -2 + 3i$
41. $C = -3i$
42. $D = 6$
43. $E = -3 - 4i$
44. $F = 4 + i$

Simplify so that your answers are in the form $a + bi$:
45. $6 - i + 18 + 7i$
46. $(6 - i)(18 + 7i)$
47. $(4 + 5i)/i$
48. $i/(4 + 5i)$
49. $(6 - i)/(18 + 7i)$
50. $(18 + 7i)/(6 - i)$
51. $(3 + i)(12 - 3i)/(2 - 3i)$
52. $(a + bi)/(c + di)$

Exactly solve these equations for the unknown variable:
53. $x^2 + 9x + 1 = 0$
54. $x(x - 9) = -25$

55. $x^2 - 6x + 9 = 0$
56. $4x^2 + 1 = x$
57. $3x(2x - 1) = -1$

Using the Law of Sines to find the height of a mountain. Answer the following questions based upon Figure 11 with the aid of your scientific calculator. We want to find x. We can use the sine ratio (ΔADC) to find x since $\sin 15° = \dfrac{x}{y}$. We need to find y using

Figure 11.

ΔABD. We know $\angle DAB$ and AB.

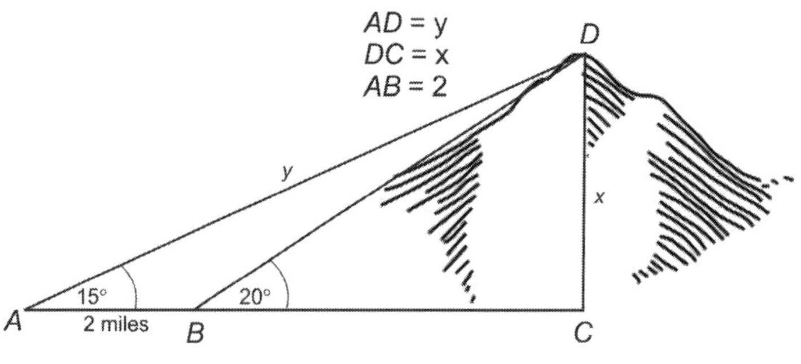

58. What is $m\angle DBA$?
59. Use the Law of Sines in ΔABD to find and expression for y.
60. Use the sine ratio for ΔADC to find x, rounded to the nearest hundredth of a mile.
61. Substitute $m\angle DAB$ with α, $m\angle DBA$ with β and AB with z. Derive a general formula to solve for x.

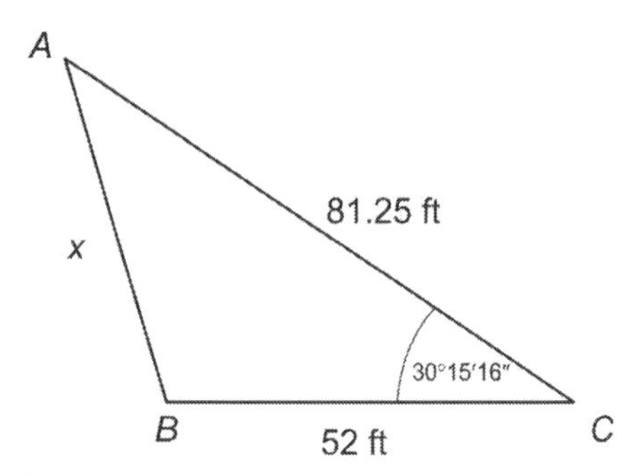

Figure 12.

Use the Law of Cosines and a scientific calculator to find x.

62. Find x in Figure 12, rounded to the nearest unit.
63. Find x in Figure 13, rounded to the nearest hundredth of a degree.

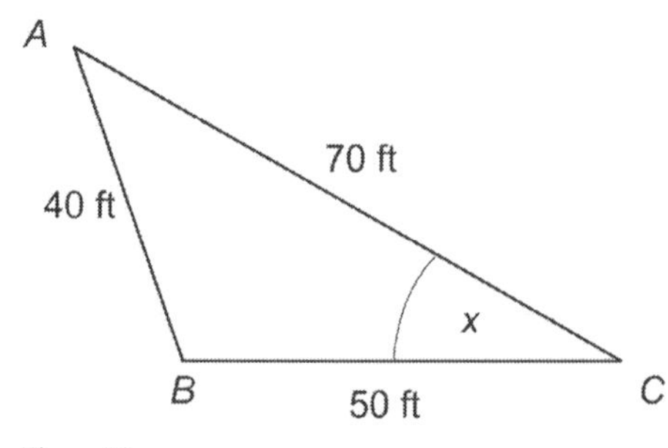

Figure 13.

Answer the following questions:

64. What is wrong with the following mathematical reasoning?

Given: $a = b,\ a,\ b \neq 0$

Step 1. $a = b \Leftrightarrow a^2 = ab$

Step 2. $a^2 = ab \Leftrightarrow a^2 - b^2 = ab - b^2$

Step 3. $a^2 - b^2 = ab - b^2 \Leftrightarrow (a + b)(a - b) = b(a - b)$

Step 4. $a + b)(a - b) = b(a - b) \Leftrightarrow$

$$\frac{(a+b)(a-b)}{(a-b)} = \frac{b(a-b)}{(a-b)}$$

Step 5. $$\frac{(a+b)\overset{1}{\cancel{(a-b)}}}{\underset{1}{\cancel{(a-b)}}} = \frac{b\overset{1}{\cancel{(a-b)}}}{\underset{1}{\cancel{(a-b)}}} \Leftrightarrow a+b=b$$

65. Carefully explain the flaw in this mathematical reasoning:

$$-1 = \left(\sqrt{-1}\right)^2 = \left(\sqrt{-1}\right)\left(\sqrt{-1}\right) = \sqrt{(-1)(-1)} = \sqrt{1} = 1 \Rightarrow -1 = 1$$

(Hint: Start by solving $x^2 = -1$ for x using the Quadratic Formula.)

Figure 14. Fractal Geometry and the Barnsley fern.
Source: Wikimedia Commons.

Figure 15. Fractal Geometry. Source: James D. Nickel.

12.12 THE BEAUTY OF FRACTALS

Terms & Concepts Introduced
1. Absolute value/modulus of a complex number
2. Argument/amplitude of a complex number
3. Fractal geometry
4. Julia set
5. Mandelbrot set
6. Polar coordinate plane
7. Polar/trigonometric form of a complex number
8. SAS Triangle Area Formula

Early in the 20th century, the French mathematician Gaston Maurice Julia (1893-1978), after losing his nose fighting in World War I, devised an iterative mathematical formula, using the arithmetic of complex numbers, for what is now termed the Julia Set.[1]

Before we visualize these wonders, let's simplify Julia's iteration formula. Given a complex number of the form $a + bi$, we square it. Then, we square the result. We continue this process *ad infinitum*. What happens when we picture this iteration on the complex number plane?

SQUARING A COMPLEX NUMBER

Let's start with an example. Consider the complex number $2 + 3i$. Squaring this number, we get:

$(2 + 3i)^2 = -5 + 12i$

Let's plot these points (Figure 1) and draw some conclusions. Next, let's draw a line segment from the origin to each complex number (Figure 2).

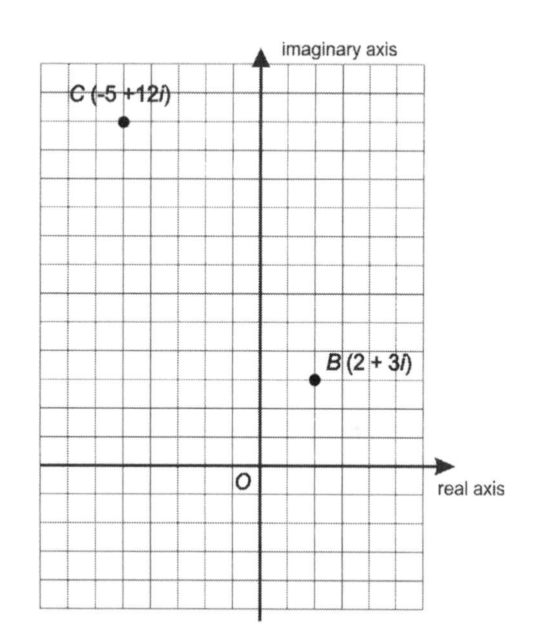

Figure 1. $(2 + 3i)^2 = 5 + 12i$

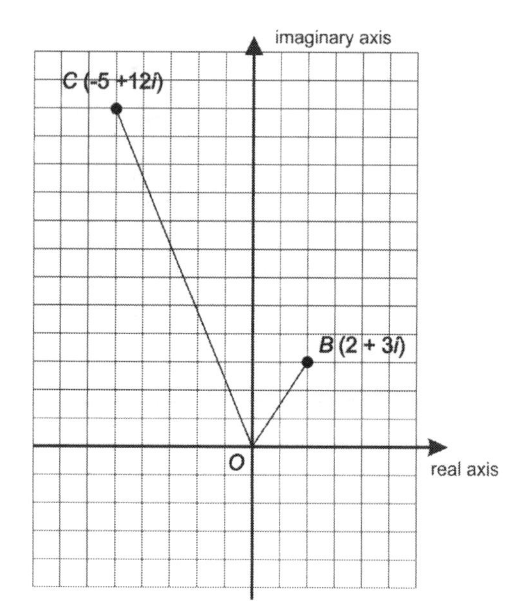

Figure 2. $(2 + 3i)^2 = 5 + 12i$

[1] For an understanding of the fractalness of complex numbers, I am indebted to Edward Burger and Michael Starbird, *The Heart of Mathematics: An Invitation to Effective Thinking* (Emeryville: Key Curriculum Press, 2000), pp. 457-480.

Let's now make use of trigonometry to quantify what we are seeing. We first create another two-dimensional coordinate system, consisting of concentric circles instead of square grids, the **Polar coordinate plane** (Figure 4).

In Figure 3, the phase angle θ, a Physics term, that $\overline{OP}$ makes with the positive real axis is the **argument**[2] or **amplitude**[3] of the complex number $a + bi$. The length $r = OP$ is the **absolute value** or **modulus**[4] of $a + bi$. With these definitions in mind, we can convert a complex number into a vector, i.e., direction θ and magnitude r (Lesson 3.2).

By the Pythagorean Theorem:

$$r = \sqrt{a^2+b^2}$$

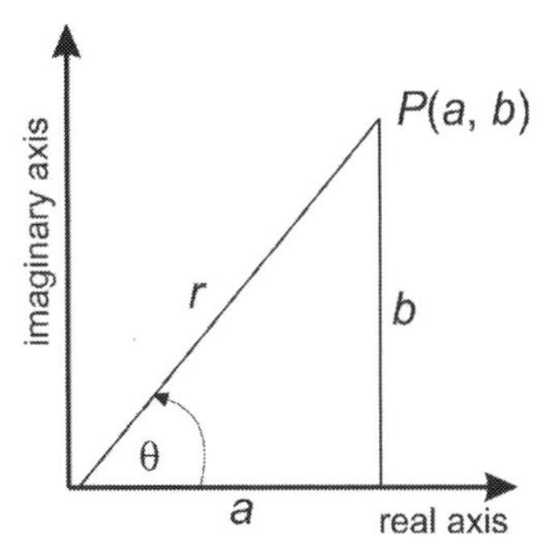

Figure 3.

It was the German mathematician Carl Friedrich Gauss (1777-1855) who introduced the vector concept to the complex number plane. Since we can consider $a + bi$ as a vector, $|a + bi|$ is the magnitude of the vector defined as follows:

$$r = |a + bi| = \sqrt{a^2+b^2}$$

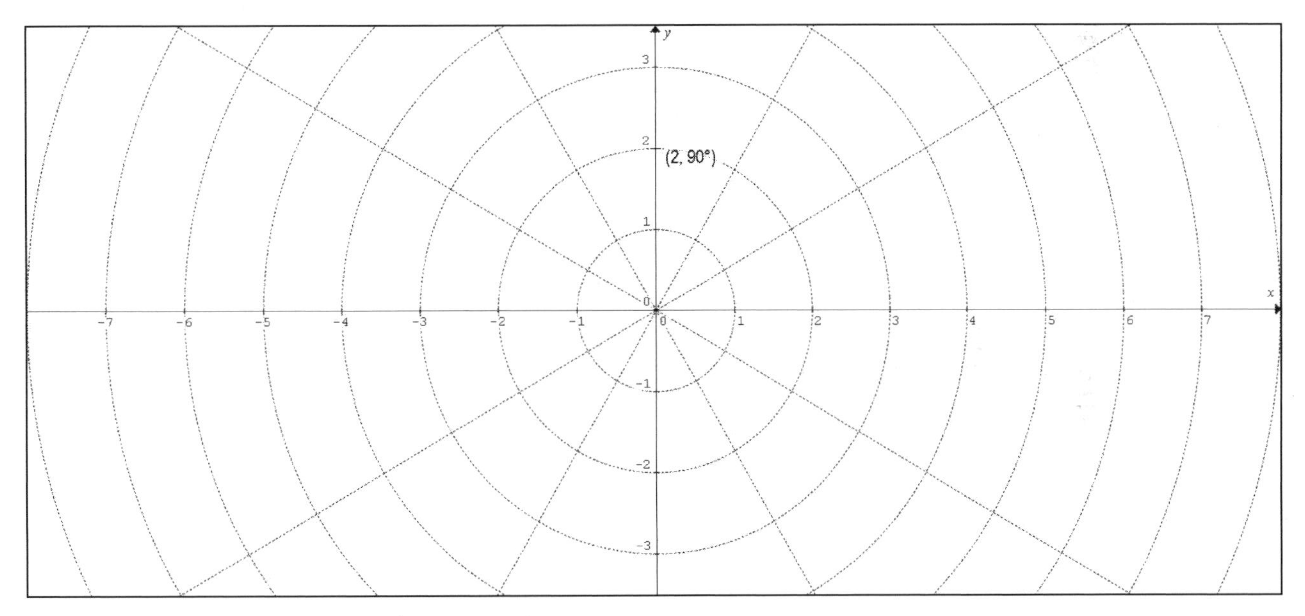

Figure 4. Polar coordinate system whereby (r, θ) can be plotted.

We can note four more useful relationships from Figure 3:

1. $\cos\theta = \dfrac{a}{r} \Leftrightarrow a = r\cos\theta$

2. $\sin\theta = \dfrac{b}{r} \Leftrightarrow b = r\sin\theta$

---

[2] Argument is Latin meaning "make clear."

[3] Remember, amplitude is Latin meaning "large."

[4] Modulus is Latin meaning "measure."

3. $\tan\theta = \dfrac{b}{a} \Leftrightarrow \theta = \tan^{-1}\left(\dfrac{b}{a}\right)$

If $a = 0$, we cannot use $\theta = \tan^{-1}\left(\dfrac{b}{a}\right)$ since we have division by zero. To find θ, we note the following two cases:[5]

Case 1. If $a = 0$ and $b > 0$, $\theta = 90°$ or $\dfrac{\pi}{2}$

Case 2. If $a = 0$ and $b < 0$, $\theta = -90° = 270°$ or $-\dfrac{\pi}{2} = \dfrac{3\pi}{2}$

If $b = 0$, we have two cases:

Case 1. If $a > 0$, then $\theta = 0°$ or 0

Case 2. If $a < 0$, then $\theta = 180°$ or π

4. $r = \sqrt{a^2 + b^2}$

From these equations, we conclude:

$a + bi = r\cos\theta + ir\sin\theta = r(\cos\theta + i\sin\theta)$

Mathematicians commonly abbreviate the expression $r(\cos\theta + i\sin\theta)$ to:

r cis θ

where c represents cos, s represents sin, and i represents $\sqrt{-1}$.

The symbols "r cis θ" is the **polar** or **trigonometric form** of a complex number.

We can, therefore, plot (Figure 4) any point in the Polar coordinate plane using vector representation, i.e., the coordinates (r, θ). We represent this point by its distance r from the origin and θ, the angle of inclination, measured counterclockwise from 0°, a measurement equivalent to the positive x-axis in the Cartesian coordinate plane, or the positive real number axis in the Complex number plane.

Let's now calculate r and θ for the complex number $2 + 3i$ (Figure 5). We get:

$$r = \sqrt{2^2 + 3^2} = \sqrt{4 + 9} = \sqrt{13}$$

$$\theta = \tan^{-1}\left(\frac{3}{2}\right) = \tan^{-1}(1.5) = 56.31°$$

Next, let's determine r_1 and θ_1 for the complex number $(2 + 3i)^2 = -5 + 12i$.

$$r_1 = \sqrt{(-5)^2 + 12^2} = \sqrt{25 + 144} = \sqrt{169} = 13$$

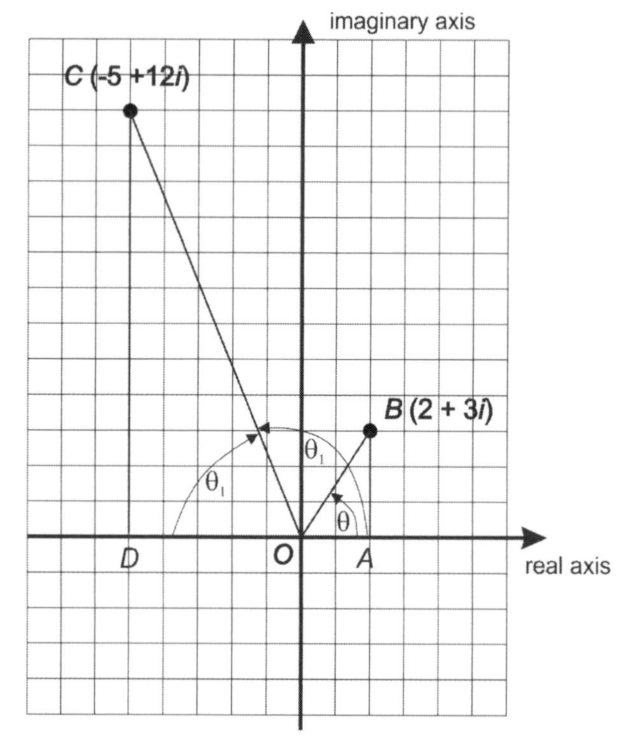

Figure 5. $(2 + 3i)^2 = 5 + 12i$

[5] These cases make sense since, if $a = 0$ and $b \neq 0$, b will be plotted on the imaginary axis.

$$\theta_1 = \tan^{-1}\left(-\frac{12}{5}\right) = \tan^{-1}(-2.4) = -67.38°$$

What can we conclude? First, $r_1 = r^2$ since $13 = \left(\sqrt{13}\right)^2$. In other words, the magnitude r of the vector is squared.

What about θ and θ_1?

For $2 + 3i$, $\theta = m\angle BOA$. For $5 + 12i$, $\theta_1 = m\angle COD$. From our knowledge of trigonometry, $\theta = \tan^{-1}\left(\frac{b}{a}\right)$ will always be negative if the point or ordered pair lies in the second quadrant.

Let's now consider the value of θ_1, a measurement that moves clockwise to $\overline{OC}$ starting at the positive real number axis. We are seeking $m\angle AOC$. We know that the degree measure from the positive real axis to the positive imaginary axis is 90°. From the positive imaginary axis to $\overline{OC}$ is 90° – 67.38° = 22.62°. Therefore, $m\angle AOC = 90° + 22.62° = 112.62°$.

Compare θ_1 with θ. Since $m\angle BOA = 56.31°$ and $m\angle AOC = 112.62°$, $\theta_1 = 2\theta$. θ, when measured counterclockwise from the real axis, doubles. Squaring a complex number interpenetrates multiplication of θ by 2. Quite amazing, isn't it?

Let's summarize our conclusions. When we square a complex number $a + bi$, then:

1. The magnitude r is squared.
2. θ is doubled.

THE ITERATION OF SQUARING

Now, let's return to Julia sets and understand what is meant by the term. Applying the simplified iterative schemed of squaring the complex number each time to the initial complex number $2 + 3i$, we generate Table 1.

Table 1

$(2 + 3i)^2$	=	$-5 + 12i$
$(-5 + 12i)^2$	=	$-119 - 120i$
$(-119 - 120i)^2$	=	$-239 + 28{,}560i$
$(-239 + 28{,}560i)^2$	=	$-815{,}616{,}479 - 13{,}651{,}680i$
$(-815{,}616{,}479 - 13{,}651{,}680i)^2$	=	$665{,}043{,}872{,}449{,}535{,}041 + 22{,}269{,}070{,}348{,}069{,}440i$

The components a and b of these successive complex numbers are getting greater and greater, either in the negative or positive direction. If we plot them, the points are galloping far, far away from the origin.

Next, let's try a different complex number, $0.3 + 0.6i$ (Table 2).

Table 2

$(0.3 + 0.6i)^2$	=	$-0.27 + 0.36i$
$(-0.27 + 0.36i)^2$	=	$-0.0567 - 0.1944i$
$(-0.0567 - 0.1944i)^2$	=	$-0.03457647 + 0.02204496i$
$(-0.03457647 + 0.02204496i)^2$	=	$0.0007095520163 - 0.001524473796i$
$(0.0007095520163 - 0.001524473796i)^2$	=	$-0.000001820556291 - 0.000002163386912i$

In contrast, the components a and b these successive complex numbers are getting closer and closer to zero, either from the negative or positive direction. If we plot them, the points are squeezing closer and closer toward the origin.

Let's do one more (Table 3), the iterative scheme for the initial complex number $0.6 + 0.8i$.

Table 3		
$(0.6 + 0.8i)^2$	=	$-0.28 + 0.96i$
$(-0.28 + 0.96i)^2$	=	$-0.8432 - 0.5376i$
$(-0.8432 - 0.5376i)^2$	=	$0.4219724 + 0.90660864i$
$(0.4219724 + 0.90660864i)^2$	=	$-0.6438784522 + 0.7651277924i$
$(-0.6438784522 + 0.7651277924i)^2$	=	$-0.1708410775 - 0.9852985975i$

What is happening in this case? If we plot the points, they all lie on the circumference of a circle of radius = 1. Can we explain why? Our starting point is $0.6 + 0.8i$ (Figure 6). In this case, $a = 0.6$ and $b = 0.8$ and we calculate r as follows:

$$r = \sqrt{(0.6)^2 + (0.8)^2} = \sqrt{0.36 + 0.64} = \sqrt{1} = 1$$

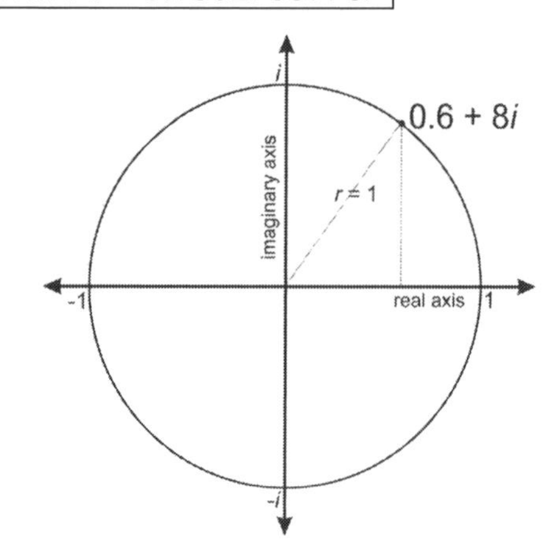

Figure 6. Starting point: $0.6 + 0.8i$

Therefore, when we square the complex number $0.6 + 0.8i$, r will be $1^2 = 1$; i.e., for successive squares of $0.6 + 0.8i$, r will always be 1 because we are squaring 1 with each iteration.

Let's note the patterns with our three starting points, $2 + 3i$, $0.3 + 0.6i$, and $0.6 + 0.8i$.

First, if a starting point is outside the circle centered at the origin with radius 1 (e.g., $2 + 3i$), the iteration values gallop off to infinity.

Second, if a starting point is inside the circle centered at the origin with radius 1 (e.g., $0.3 + 0.6i$), the iteration values squeeze toward the origin.

Third, if a starting point is on the circle centered at the origin with radius 1 (e.g., $0.6 + 0.8i$), the iteration values, when plotted, remain on that circle.

RUDIMENTARY JULIA SET

The circle, therefore, acts as a boundary separating all the starting points that lie outside it from all the starting points that lie inside it. This circle, the interface between these two sets of numbers, is the rudimentary Julia Set. We picture the Julia Set by filling in the circle. In Figure 7, the dark shaded circle represents the set of starting points whose iterations do not gallop off to infinity while everything shaded outside of this circle represents the set of starting points whose iterations gallop off to infinity.

Figure 7. Rudimentary Julia Set. Source: James D. Nickel.

The circle in the complex number plane is the first and basic Julia Set. Now, we are ready to make things interesting and astonishingly beautiful. To do so, we add one extra ingredient to our iterative process. We start with a complex number $a + bi$ that acts like a seed. This number always remains fixed. For example, we let $a + bi = -1 + 0i$.

We then choose any complex number from among an infinite number of possibilities. Let's choose $0 + 0i$. We square $0 + 0i$, add $-1 + 0i$ to it. Then, we take that answer, square it, and add -1 + 0*i* to it. We continue this iterative process *ad infinitum*. Table 4 shows our results.

Table 4		
$(0 + 0i)^2 + (-1 + 0i)$	=	$-1 + 0i$
$(-1 + 0i)^2 + (-1 + 0i)$	=	$0 + 0i$
$(0 + 0i)^2 + (-1 + 0i)$	=	$-1 + 0i$
$(-1 + 0i)^2 + (-1 + 0i)$	=	$0 + 0i$
⋮	=	⋮

Let's choose another complex number: 2 + 3*i*. We get Table 5.

Table 5		
$(2 + 3i)^2 + (-1 + 0i)$	=	$-6 + 12i$
$(-6 + 12i)^2 + (-1 + 0i)$	=	$-109 - 144i$
$(-109 - 144i)^2 + (-1 + 0i)$	=	$-8856 + 31,392i$
$(-8856 + 31,392i)^2 + (-1 + 0i)$	=	$-907,028,929 - 556,015,104i$
⋮	=	⋮

MAKING JULIA BEAUTIFUL

This adding (-1 + 0i) each time, generates a Julia set just as before. Some starting points will iteratively gallop off to infinity. Other starting points will not join this infinity race. If we think of all points in the complex number plane as valid starting points, some will iteratively race to infinity and others will not. The interface, the boundary, between these two sets of complex numbers is the **Julia Set**. The Julia Set for the seed complex number -1 + 0*i* is Figure 8, where appropriate software performed the computations.[6]

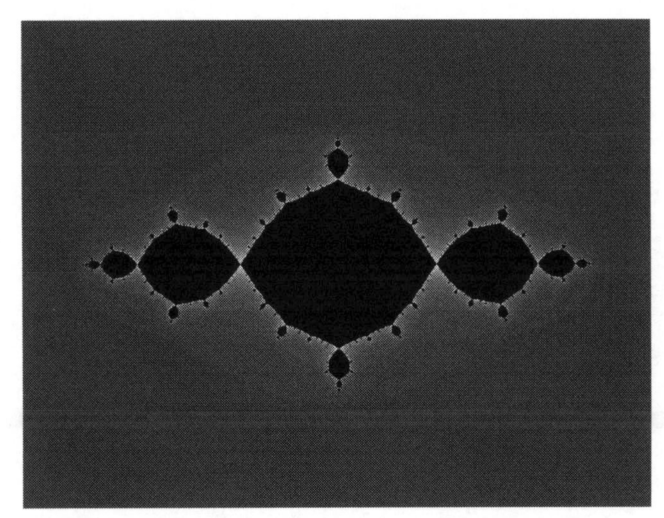

Figure 8. Julia Set where seed is -1 + 0*i*. Source: James D. Nickel.

All the complex number points in the dark region do not gallop off to infinity. Those in the gray region do. The gray region that is darker indicates that the iterative process gallop faster. The shade of

[6] I am using extended edition Ultra Fractal v6.01 to generate these fractal images. You can order this software from www.ultrafractal.com and experiment to your heart's content.

gray represents the pace of the race to infinity.[7] Pause to gaze at this exquisite beauty. Words cannot express it adequately. The wonder of Julia sets is that they infinitely self-replicate; you can zoom in at any point and recognize the same geometric patterns as the original. Figure 9 is one example of a zoom where we set our aim at the small top bubble.

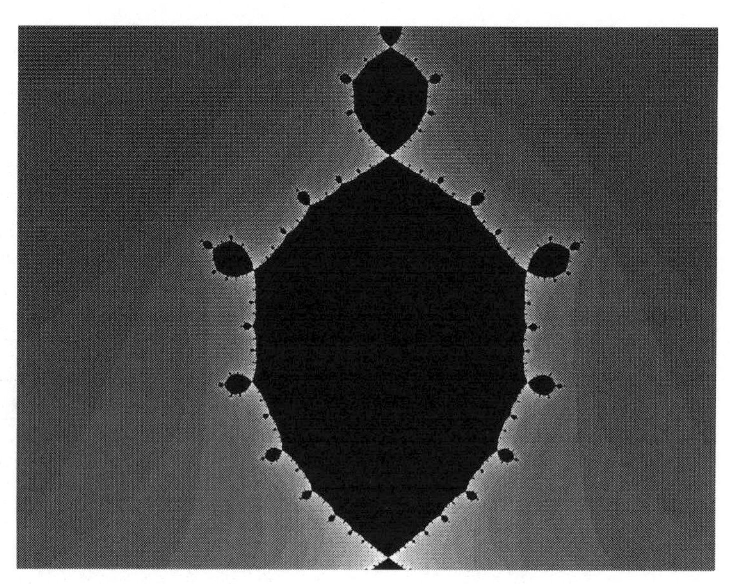

Figure 9. Julia Set where seed is $-1 + 0i$ with zoom feature. Source: James D. Nickel.

The next set of images will reveal the complex, intricate, and beautiful wonders of Julia sets. In Figure 10, the Julia seed is $0.35 + 0.05i$.

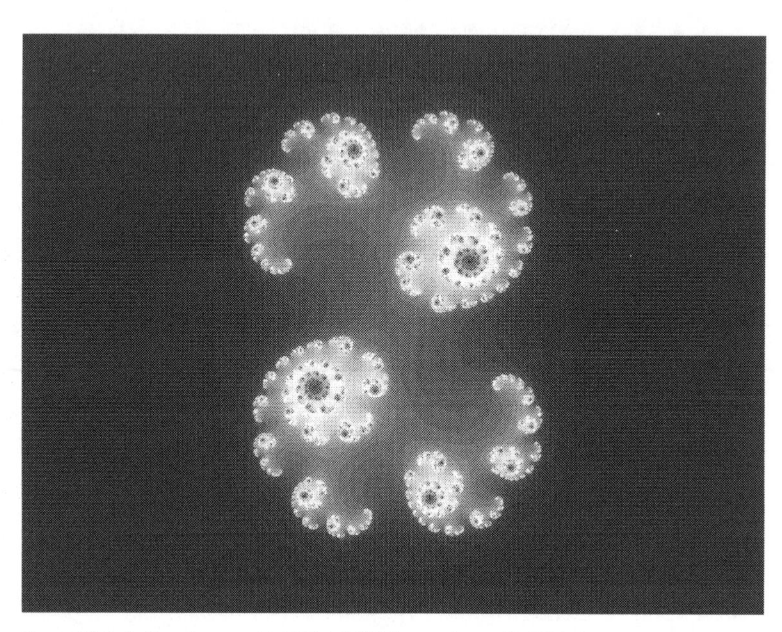

Figure 10. Julia Set where seed is $0.35 + 0.05i$. Source: James D. Nickel.

[7] In color, the Julia sets abound with nearly infinite hues of manifold shades.

In Figure 11, the Julia seed is -0.15 + 0.75*i*.

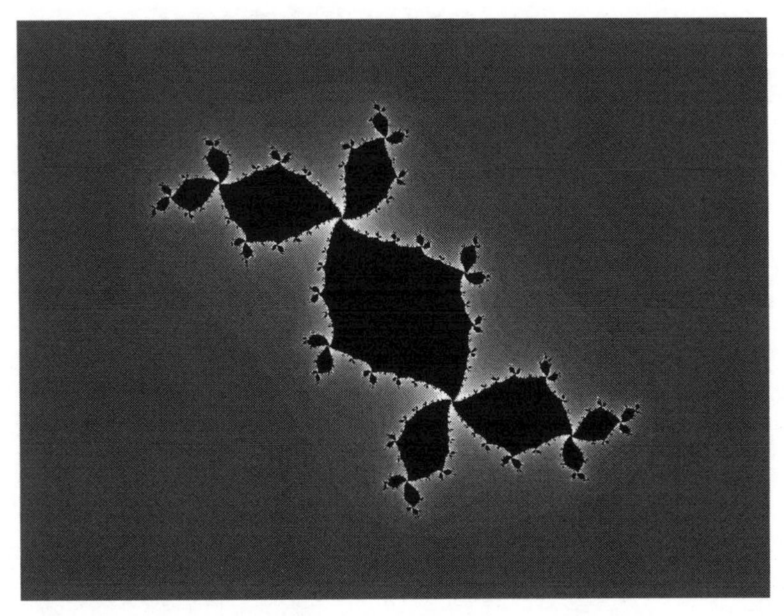

Figure 11. Julia Set where the seed is -0.15 + 0.75*i*. Source: James D. Nickel.

In Figure 12, the Julia seed is -0.194 + 0.65*i*.

Figure 12. Julia Set where the seed is -0.194 + 0.65*i*. Source: James D. Nickel.

In Figure 13, the Julia seed is -0.27334 + 0.00742*i*.

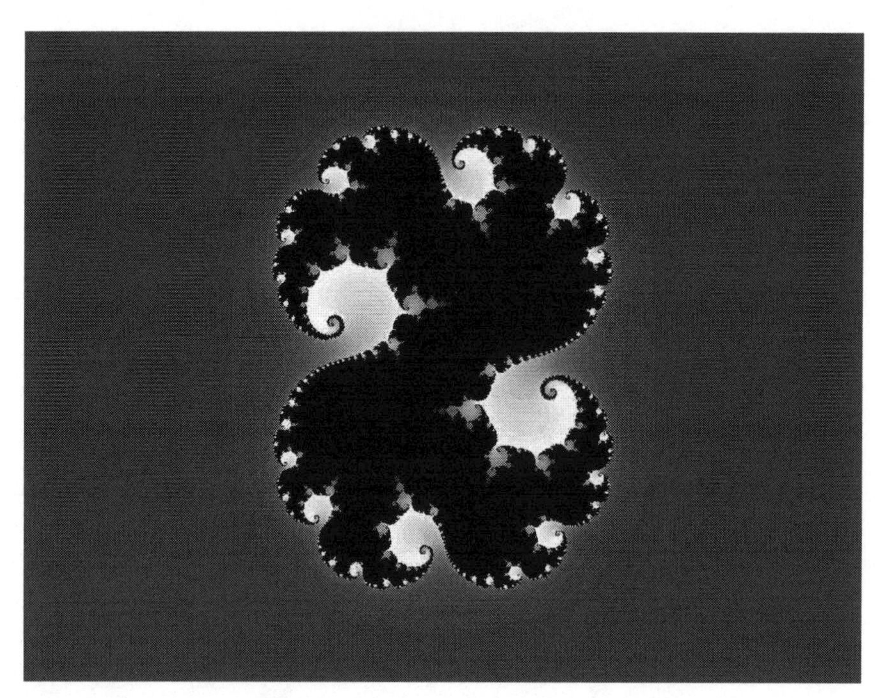

Figure 13. Julia Set where the seed is 0.27334 + 0.00742*i*. Source: James D. Nickel.

In Figure 14, the Julia seed is -0.475.

Figure 14. Julia Set where the seed is -0.475 + 0*i*. Source: James D. Nickel.

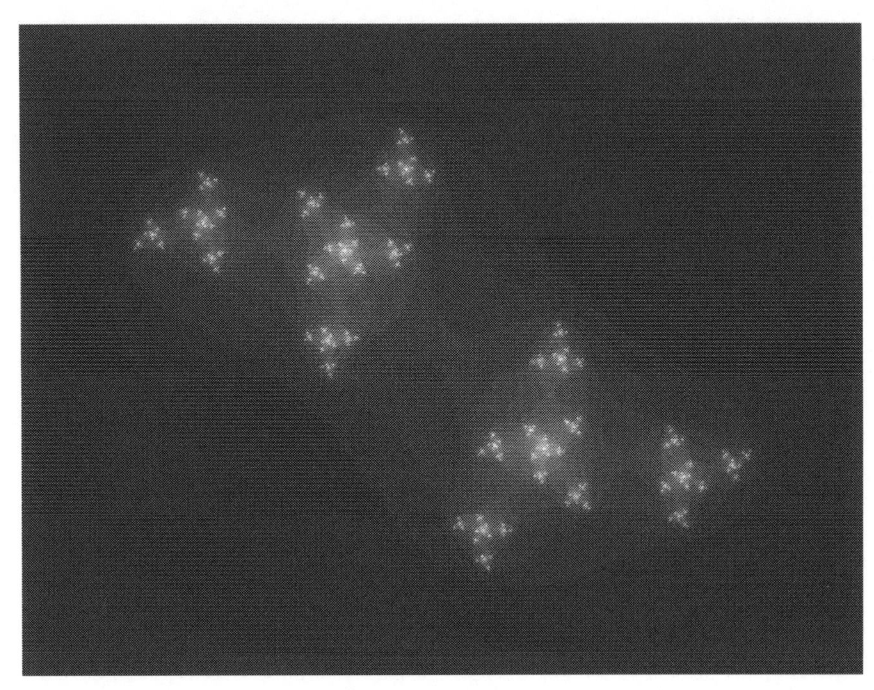

Figure 15. Julia Set where the seed is -0.475 + 0.88*i*. Source: James D. Nickel.

Since there are an infinite number of complex numbers, there are an infinite number of Julia sets. These intricate and infinitely replicated designs have no end. Mathematics and dazzling and spectacular beauty indeed coinhere. Pause to consider that you could immerse yourself in this immensity of beauty forever.[8]

THE MANDELBROT SET

We introduce Dr. Julia to Dr. Mandelbrot. Benoît B. Mandelbrot (1924-2010), a Jewish-American mathematician, is known as the father of **fractal geometry**.[9] Mandelbrot resurrected Julia's work to new heights by standing back from these infinite sets and looking at the big picture. He looked at all the $a + bi$ Julia sets together. The set of all Julia sets is the **Mandelbrot set**. If you can grasp the idea, the Mandelbrot Set is a mathematical object that captures all the information about the infinite number of Julia sets. For each point in the complex number plane, we can draw a unique $a + bi$ Julia Set. The filled in Julia Set will either be one piece or more than one piece. Figure 15 is an example of a Julia Set that is more than one piece.

If the filled in $a + bi$ Julia Set is connected, we denote that the point $a + bi$ as a member of the Mandelbrot set. Therefore, the Mandelbrot set (Figure 16) is the set of all complex numbers $a + bi$ exhibiting the property that the filled in $a + bi$ Julia set is just one piece.

---

[8] That these sets were discovered before computer imagery could picture them is also astounding.

[9] A fractal is a geometric pattern that is repeated at every scale and, therefore, cannot be represented by traditional geometric methods.

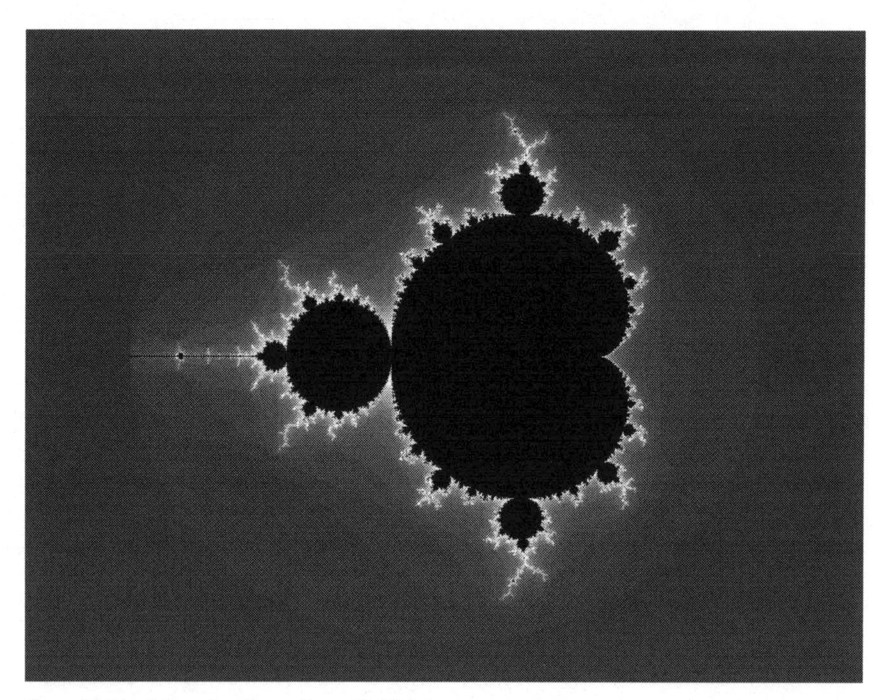

Figure 16. Mandelbrot Set. Source: James D. Nickel.

For each point in or near the Mandelbrot Set (dark shade), we can associate a filled-in Julia Set that is in one piece. If the point is outside the Mandelbrot Set (shades of gray), the related filled-in Julia Set is made of multiple pieces. We can also zoom into different regions of the Mandelbrot Set to marvel at its infinitely detailed and intricate beauty (Figure 17). We can repeat this zoom process *ad infinitum*.

Figure 17. Mandelbrot Set, magnified top portion. Source: James D. Nickel.

In 1980, Loren Carpenter (1947-), a computer graphics researcher for the airplane manufacturer Boeing, developed a fractal algorithm called Reyes rendering that the Pixar animation studio eventually used for all their films. The infinite algorithms that generate these images capture the subtle design of mountains, landscapes, oceans, clouds, trees, shrubs, animals, people, movement, indeed, every aspect of created reality. Isn't it stunning that the ingenuity of man can nearly duplicate, in animation form, the ingenuity of the Triune Creator? Are we able, through fractal geometry, to touch the infinite wisdom of God the Father Almighty, who, through the Word of His Son, is the maker of heaven and earth?

Have you enjoyed this trip into the world of Julia and Mandelbrot set? After this excursion, you should appreciate the reality that the rationality of number is indeed beautiful, not just in the logic of its many and elegant proofs, but in the infinite array of its sometimes fascinating and enthralling geometry. Praise to the Triune God for the visual delight of this breathtaking splendor.

> The universe disclosed to us by science appears to be the most beautiful and glorious material thing imaginable, endowed with an internal mysterious order reminiscent of fractals, an eerie by-product of the mathematics of complexity.
>
> Giuseppe Del Re, *The Cosmic Dance* (2000), p. 19.

EXERCISES

Define the following terms:

1. Polar coordinate plane
2. Argument/amplitude of a complex number
3. Absolute value/modulus of a complex number
4. Polar/trigonometric form of a complex number
5. Julia set
6. Fractal geometry
7. Mandelbrot set

True or False.

8. When we square a complex number $a + bi$, the magnitude r is squared, but θ remains the same.

Set your scientific calculator to the DEG mode and use it to (a) determine the polar coordinates (r, θ) and (b) the polar form $r(\cos\theta + i\sin\theta)$ for each of the following complex numbers: (Keep all numbers positive and, where necessary, round to the nearest tenth.)

9. 2
10. i
11. $3 + 4i$
12. $6 - i$
13. $-2i - 5i$
14. $(1 - i)^2$
15. $(4 + 3i)^2$

In the following questions, show that the magnitude r is squared and θ is doubled when squaring a complex number:

16. $(1 - i)^2$
17. $(4 + 3i)^2$

An inclined plane offsets, or slows down, the force of gravity. We find inclined planes on highways and railroad tracks. Galileo Galilei (1564-1642) used inclined planes in his scientific work because he did not have an accurate timing mechanism to measure the vertical fall of objects. By rolling objects down an inclined plane, he could measure the slower motion and then make conjectures about a true vertical fall of the objects.[10] In his analysis, he ignored friction. Let's follow his thinking in the following exercises. In Figure 18, the plane makes an angle θ with the horizontal. An object of mass m is placed on the plane and the force of gravity, F, acts on this mass pulling straight down.[11] The plane interferes with this straight down motion. Galileo had to figure out to what extent gravity acted on the object as it slid down the plane.

18. Describe the motion of the object when $\theta = 0°$.
19. Describe the motion of the object when $\theta = 90°$.

We see that the weight of the object, W, the downward pull or force F of gravity on the object, is offset by a multiplicative factor involving θ. As we have already noted (Lesson 12.8), $W = 32m$.

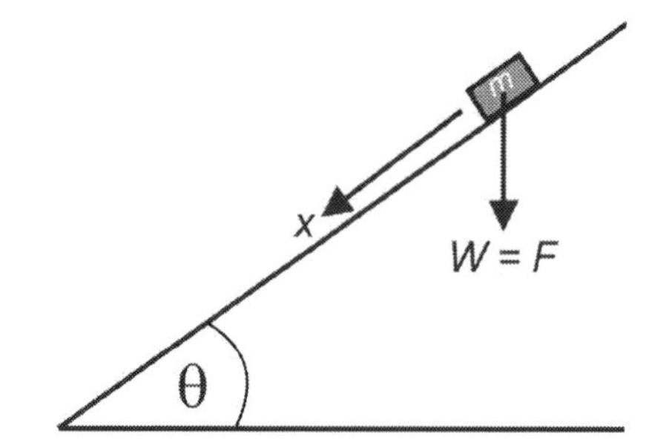

Figure 18.

20. What is the value of this factor when $\theta = 0°$? (Hint: No motion implies no force.)
21. What is the value of this factor when $\theta = 90°$?
22. Is there a trig ratio that represents this factor when $\theta = 0°$ and $\theta = 90°$? If yes, what is the name of the ratio?
23. State a conjecture for x, the downward force along the plane in terms of W, a trig ratio, and θ.

We can confirm this conjecture by experiment (Figure 19). We can place an object of mass m on an inclined plane and connect the object by a rope passed over a pulley at the top to another freely hanging object of weight w. Suppose w, to which the full force of gravity applies, is chosen to balance the force tending to move the weight W down the inclined plane; i.e., the object of mass m does not move.

24. Write an expression for w in terms of W, a trig ratio, and θ. (Hint: Let W represent the hypotenuse of the right triangle, and w represent the force w of the counterbalancing weight, the side opposite θ.)

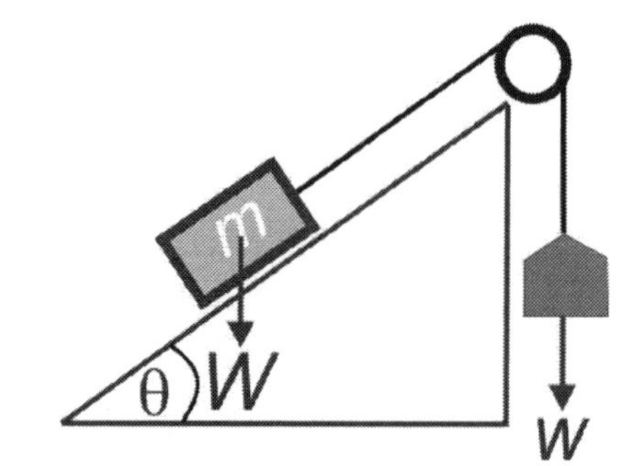

Figure 19.

What is the acceleration of the object sliding down the inclined plane? In other words, if an object of mass m is sliding down the plane under a force described in your answer to Questions 23 and 24, what is the acceleration of the object?

25. Isaac Newton's second law of motion states that force is mass m multiplied by acceleration a. Write an equation that states your answer to Questions 23 and 24 in terms of ma by substituting w with ma.
26. Solve the equation you stated in Question 25 for a (units will be ft/s^2) substituting $W = 32m$, representing the force of gravity pulling down the object of mass m.
27. Based on your answer to Question 26, find the acceleration of the object when (a) $\theta = 0°$, (b) $\theta = 10°$, (c) $\theta = 30°$, (d) $\theta = 45°$, (e) $\theta = 60°$, (f) $\theta = 75°$, (g) $\theta = 80°$, (h) $\theta = 85°$, and (i) $\theta = 90°$. The units will be ft/s^2. Round to the nearest tenth.

What is the velocity of the object sliding down the inclined plane? Answer this question:

28. (a) Since velocity is acceleration multiplied by time t, write a formula representing the velocity of the object of mass m as it slides down the plane.

[10] See Lesson 13.15 and Lesson 13.18 for further mathematical exposition of free-fall motion.
[11] Remember, this force F is equal to the weight W of the object of mass m.

(b) Explain why the unit of velocity is ft/s.

What is the distance traveled of the object sliding down the inclined plane? Answer this question:

29. (a) The distance the object travels down the plane is $\frac{1}{2}at^2$, a formula discovered by Galileo, write a formula representing the distance d of the object of mass m as it slides down the plane.
    (b) Explain why the unit of distance is ft.

Answer the following questions using Figure 20:

30. (a) Solve the formula you derived in Question 29 for t if you know h, the height of the object of mass m.
    (b) Explain why the unit of time is seconds.
    (c) Explain the meaning of the formula.
31. (a) Write a formula for velocity in terms of h.
    (b) Explain its meaning.

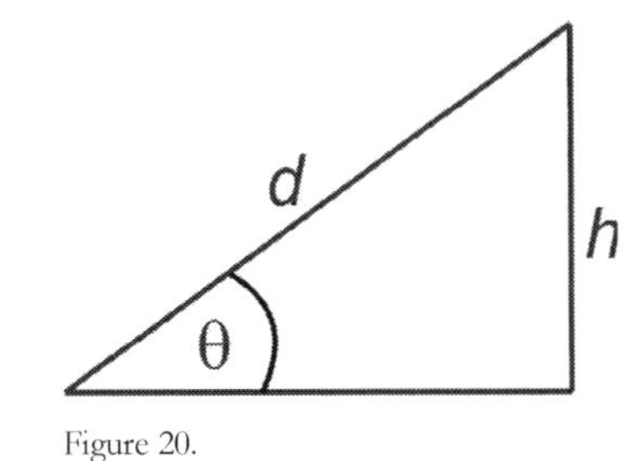

Figure 20.

Answer the following questions based on your conclusions about motion on an inclined plane.

32. (a) How far, to the nearest tenth of a foot, will an object slide down a plane with angle of inclination of 40° in 2 seconds?
    (b) How far would the same object in free fall travel in 2 seconds? (c) What is the difference, rounded to the nearest foot?
33. Suppose a tractor and a motorcycle slide down the same hill of height h with angle of inclination θ. Which vehicle will reach the bottom of the hill sooner?
34. What is the force, to the nearest tenth of a pound, that pushes an eighteen-wheel truck weighing 80,000 pounds down a hill inclined at 15° to the horizontal?
35. You want to push a box up a ramp from ground level to the back of a truck. What force must you push on the box if it weighs 150 pounds, the ramp is 20 feet long, and the height of the back of the truck is five feet?
36. Since work is force multiplied by distance (Lesson 8.3):
    (a) How much work is done using the ramp in Question 35?
    (b) How much work is done lifting the box five feet without the ramp in Question 35?
    (c) Explain your results.
37. What is the velocity, in ft/s, of an object that slides down an inclined plane from a point 25 feet above the ground where the angle of inclination of the plane is 20°?

The Law of Sines and the Law of Cosines enable you to solve triangles that are not right triangles. The following exercises will help you to explore and articulate the conditions that need to exist in a triangle so that you can use these laws, *conditions that uniquely describe a triangle* and, thereby, conditions that establish congruency between triangles. Explain why which law, or both, works and why (Figure 21).

38. The SSS case
39. The SAS case
40. The ASA case
41. The AAS case
42. The ASS case

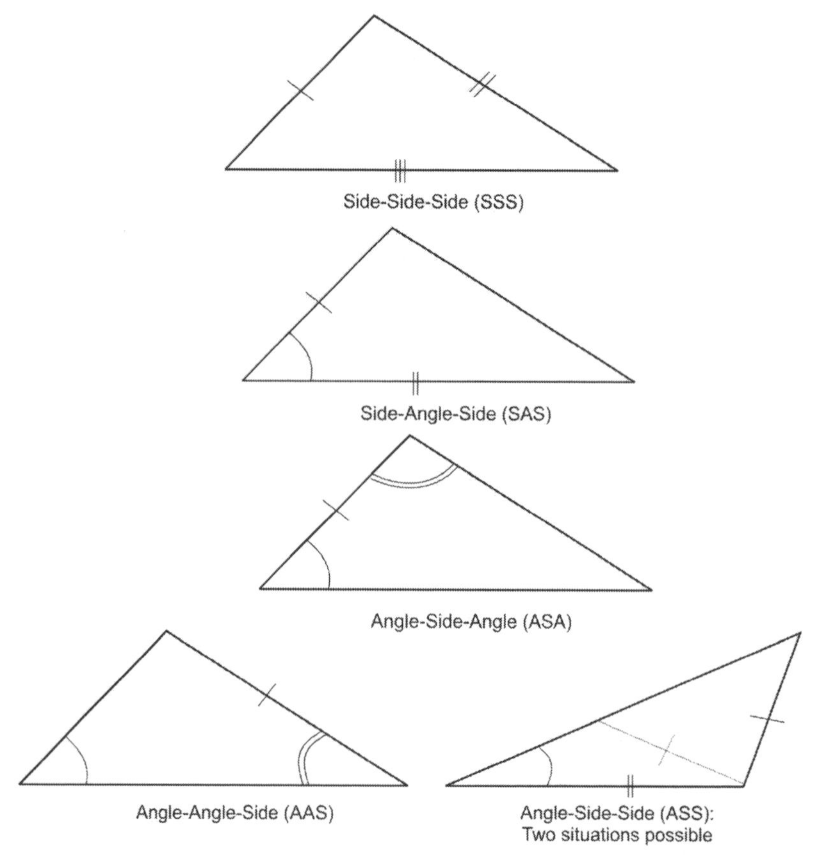

Figure 21.

There is a way to find the **area of any triangle** if we know the **SAS case**, a, b, and θ. There are two cases to consider, when θ is acute and when θ is obtuse. Let $\alpha(\Delta ABC)$ represent the area of ΔABC. Answer the following questions:

43. Inspect Figure 22 carefully and derive a formula for $\alpha(\Delta ABC)$ involving the sine ratio, i.e., $\sin\theta$, a, and b. (Note: We are redoing the proof in Lesson 12.7, Question 36.)
44. Inspect Figure 23 carefully and derive the same formula for $\alpha(\Delta ABC)$ involving the sine ratio, i.e., $\sin\theta$, a, and b. [Hint: Recall from Lesson 12.9 that $\sin(180° - \theta) = \sin\theta$.]

> Only if figures are uniquely determined can they be proved congruent.
>
> J. L. Heilbron, *Geometry Civilized: History, Culture, and Technique* ([1998] 2000), p. 55.

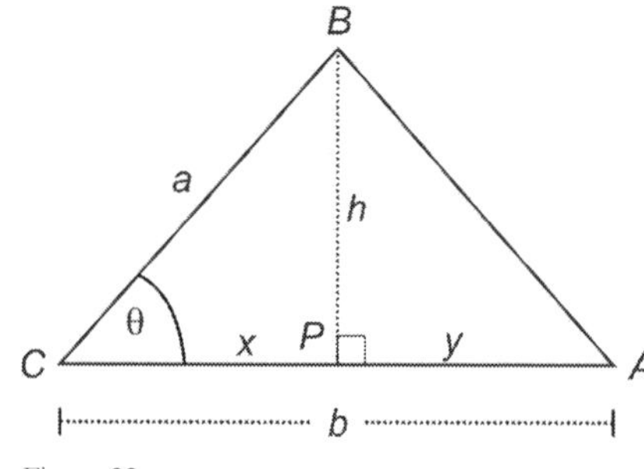

Figure 22.

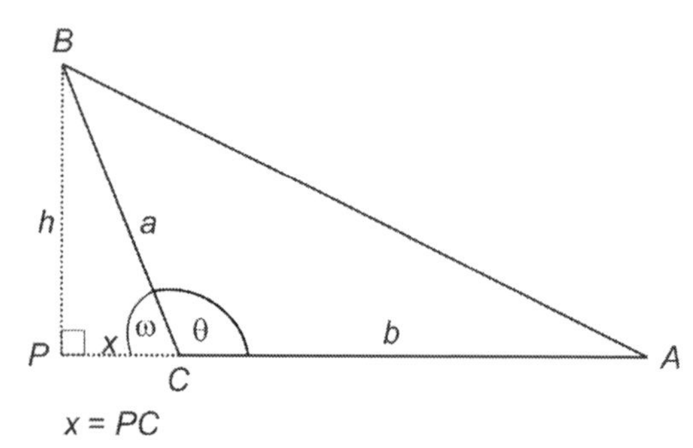

Figure 23.

The Koch snowflake is a fractal and the Swedish mathematician Niels Fabian Helge von Koch (1870-1924) first described its construction in 1904.

45. Let the area of the equilateral triangle in Figure 24 be one unit of area. What is the length of each side?

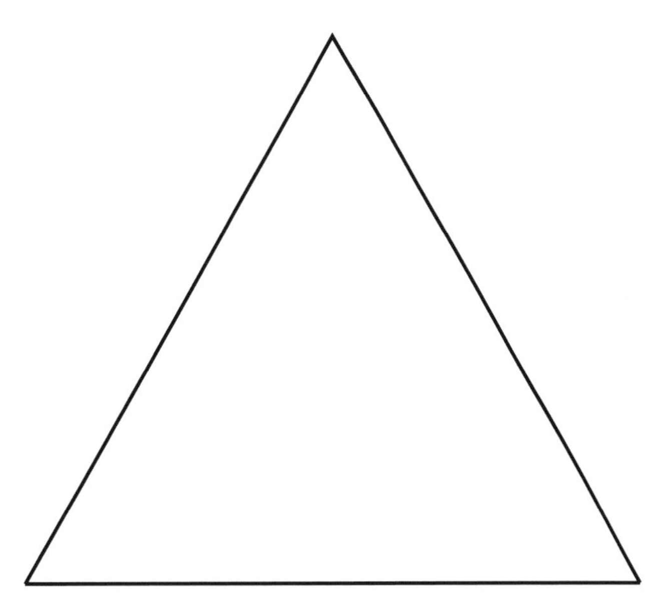

Figure 24.

46. We starting with an equilateral triangle. Each successive triangle is made by dividing each side into three equal parts and then adding a triangular piece on each of the center pieces of the side (Figure 25). Next, we can deduce the area of the figure. Write this area as $1 + x$ where $x =$ the additional area added. Hint: the denominator of x, it will be a fraction, is 9.

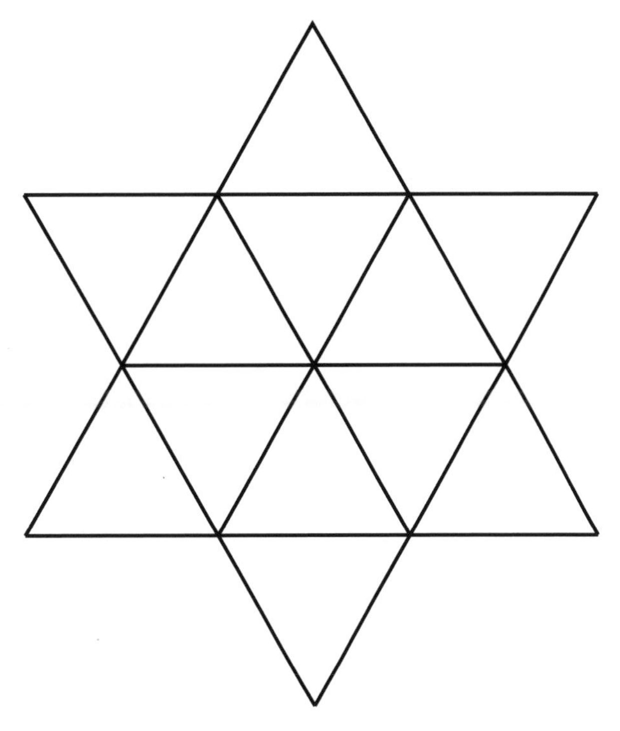

Figure 25.

47. Iterate this process a second time (Figure 26). Determine the total number of sides of this figure. What is the length of each side? What is the area of the figure? Write this area as $1 + x + y$ where y = the additional area added. Hint: the denominator of y, it will be a fraction, is 81.

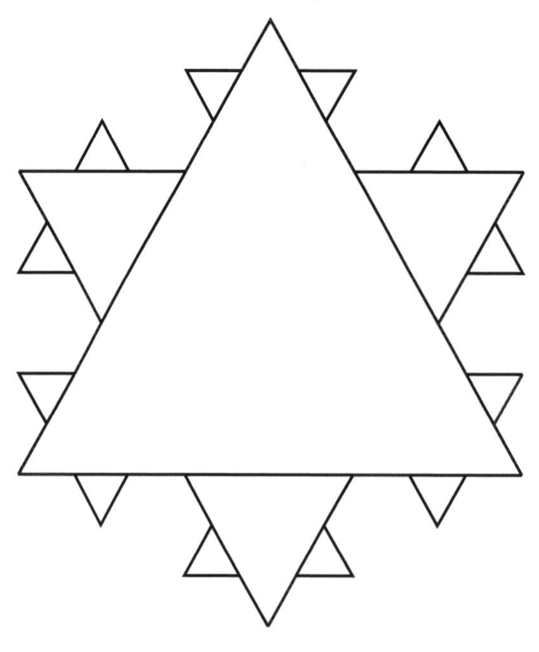

Figure 26.

48. Iterate this process a third time (Figure 27). Determine the total number of sides of this figure. What is the length of each side? We can deduce the area of the figure. Write this area as $1 + x + y + z$ where z = the additional area added. (Hint: the denominator of z, it will be a fraction, is 729.)

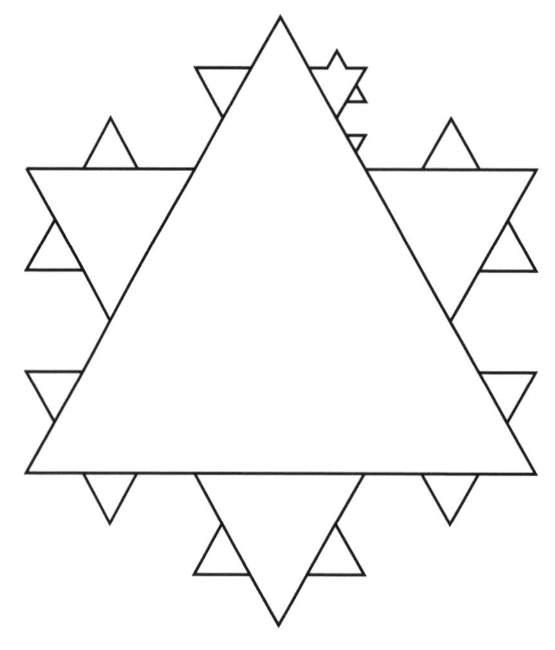

Figure 27.

49. From Question 48, analyze your sum (a sum of four terms), note the pattern, and write a simplified expression for the area of the Koch snowflake (Figure 28) for an infinite number of iterations. In part of your simplification, you should seek to get an expression that looks like this:

$\frac{a^1}{b^1}+\frac{a^2}{b^2}+\frac{a^3}{b^3}+\ldots$ where a and b are distinct positive integers

We will learn how to find this sum in Step 13.

Figure 28.

50. Let the perimeter of the starting equilateral triangle be one unit of length. Write a simplified expression similar to the one you derived in Question 49 for the perimeter of the Koch snowflake for an infinite number of iterations.
51. Field Projects: (a) If you have access to any Fractal software, learn how to use it. (b) Do some internet research to see if you can find and report on a study that connects the Fibonacci numbers with the Mandelbrot set.

Figure 29. A spiral generated by Fractal Geometry. Source: James D. Nickel.

12.13 A Startling Correspondence

Terms & Concepts Introduced
1. Bearing
2. Euler Identity
3. Exponential form of a complex number

Operations with complex numbers launch us into fascinating realms. Taking a journey through this dominion is like investigating the visual wonders of Carlsbad Caverns. Concluding this set of lessons, let's crawl along with Richard Feynman (1918-1988) as he inches through a small opening in this vast cave and excavates a fascinating treasure unearthed by computing complex powers of complex numbers.[1]

Complex Powers of Real Numbers

Instead of first trying to compute complex powers of complex numbers, let's compute complex powers of real numbers. We shall consider 10^{a+bi}. By the Product of Powers Law:

$$10^{a+bi} = 10^a 10^{bi}$$

We already know how to compute 10^a for any $a \in \mathbb{R}$. We also know how to multiply something by something else. So, all we need to do is figure out how to compute 10^{bi}. Since we are raising a real number to an imaginary power, we can reasonably conclude that our answer will be a complex number. We let this answer be $x + yi$. We get:

$$10^{bi} = x + yi$$

If this is true, we can write an equation that is true for its respective conjugates. Recall that the conjugate of bi is $-bi$ and the conjugate of $x + yi$ is $x - yi$. We get:

$$10^{-bi} = x - yi$$

Now, we multiply 10^{bi} by 10^{-bi}. We get:

$$(10^{bi})(10^{-bi}) = 10^0 = 1$$
$$(x + yi)(x - yi) = x^2 + y^2$$

Figure 1. Source: United States Postal Service.

Therefore:

$$1 = x^2 + y^2$$

Does this equation remind you of the equation of a unit circle centered at the origin? It should (Lesson 12.6).

We ask, "How do we compute 10 to an imaginary exponent?" "How do we compute 10^{bi} for a particular value of b?" Feynman guides us along narrow walls of this cave by supposing that if we can compute it for any b, then we can compute it for everything else, b^2, $2b$, $3b$, $\sqrt{b}$, etc. Using a result from our work with logarithms (Lesson 12.3), we know:

$$10^k = 1 + 2.302585k \text{ as } k \to 0 \text{ when } k \in \mathbb{R}$$

Feynman takes a leap of intuition and says, in effect, "Let's assume this equation works for $k \in \mathbb{C}$ and see what happens." If $k \in \mathbb{C}$, then $k = bi$. We write:

---

[1] Richard Feynman, *The Feynman Lectures on Physics: Commemorative Issue*, 1:22-8 to 1:22-10.

$10^{bi} = 1 + 2.302585(bi)$ as $b \to 0$

Since b is small ($b \to 0$), we let b be a small part of 1024.

With this preliminary work behind us, we can compute all the imaginary powers of 10; i.e., we can compute x and y. Let's start with by letting $b = 1/1024$. We write:

$10^{i/1024} = 1.00000 + 2.302585i\left(1/1024\right)$

Or:

$10^{i/1024} = 1.00000 + 0.00224862i$

In our calculations we will limit our precision to six significant figures in the decimal part. If we multiply $10^{i/1024}$ by $10^{i/1024}$, we get:

$10^{i/1024} \cdot 10^{i/1024} = 10^{i/1024 + i/1024} = 10^{i/512}$

What is $10^{i/512}$? We multiply $1.00000 + 0.00224862i$ by $1.00000 + 0.00224862i$. We get:

$10^{i/512} = (1.00000 + 0.00224862i)(1.00000 + 0.00224862i) = 1.00000 + 0.00449724i - 0.000005056$
$= 1.00000 + 0.00450i$

Note: $1.00000 - 0.000005056 \approx 1.00000$

Rounding $0.00449724i$ to five decimal places, we conclude:

$10^{i/512} = 1.00000 + 0.00450i$

We continue this squaring process, $\left(10^{i/512}\right)^2 = 10^{i/256}$, and generate Table 1.

Table 1 Successive Squares of $10^{bi} = 10^{i/1024} = 1.00000 + 0.00224862i$		
Exponent: bi	**$1024b$**	**$10^{bi} = x + yi$**
$i/1024$	1	$1.00000 + 0.00225i$
$i/512$	2	$1.00000 + 0.00450i$
$i/256$	4	$0.99996 + 0.00900i$
$i/128$	8	$0.99984 + 0.01800i$
$i/64$	16	$0.99936 + 0.03599i$
$i/32$	32	$0.99742 + 0.07193i$
$i/16$	64	$0.98967 + 0.14349i$
$i/8$	128	$0.95885 + 0.28402i$
$i/4$	256	$0.83872 + 0.54467i$

Table 1 Successive Squares of $10^{bi} = 10^{i/1024} = 1.00000 + 0.00224862i$		
Exponent: bi	$1024b$	$10^{bi} = x + yi$
$i/2$	512	0.40679 + 0.91365i
$i/1 = i$	1024	-0.66928 + 0.74332*i*

As we inspect the table, we see that the third column is a representation of $x + yi$. Notice that x starts as positive and then moves to negative. What significance is this? We shall see in a moment. Note also that for each x-value and y-value in the third column, $x^2 + y^2 \approx 1$. If we did not invoke rounding or if we carried our precision to more decimal places, we would discover that, indeed, $x^2 + y^2 = 1$. We see that Feynman's intuitive leap is paying off.

For what number b is the real number part of 10^{bi} equal to 0, or $x = 0$? The y-term would have to be i because $0 + 1^2 = 1$. We would, therefore, have:

$$10^{bi} = i \Leftrightarrow bi = \log i$$

Just as we calculated $\log 2$ using Table 3 of Lesson 12.3, we can calculate $\log i$ using Table 1. Without going into the detail,[2] $\log i = 0.68219i \Leftrightarrow 10^{0.68219i} = i$.

In Table 1, we squared the exponents each time. What happens if we let the exponents increase arithmetically? When we do this, we will get a closer look at what is happening with the negative signs. Table 2 represents what happens to $10^{i/8}$ as we increase the exponents arithmetically.

Table 2 Successive Powers of $10^{i/8}$	
m = exponent $\cdot 8i$	$10^{im/8}$
0	1.00000 + 0.00000*i*
1	0.95885 + 0.28402*i*
2	0.83872 + 0.54465*i*
3	0.64944 + 0.76042*i*
4	0.40672 + 0.91356*i*
5	0.13050 + 0.99146*i*
6	-0.15647 + 0.98770*i*
7	-0.43055 + 0.90260*i*
8	-0.66917 + 0.74315*i*
9	-0.85268 + 0.52249*i*
10	-0.96596 + 0.25880*i*
11	-0.99969 – 0.02620*i*
12	-0.95104 – 0.30905*i*
14	-0.62928 – 0.77717*i*
16	-0.10447 – 0.99453*i*

[2] You can verify that $\log i = 0.68226i$ using a scientific graphing calculator produced by Texas Instruments. Make sure the calculator is in complex number mode by pressing the MODE key and select $a + bi$. Press log and then press the 2nd function key i. You should get $\log(i) = 0.6821881769i$.

Table 2 Successive Powers of $10^{i/8}$	
m = exponent · $8i$	$10^{im/8}$
18	$0.45454 - 0.89098i$
20	$0.86648 - 0.49967i$
22	$0.99884 + 0.05287i$
24	$0.80890 + 0.58836i$

OBSERVATIONS AND A REMARKABLE CONCLUSION

> The nature of complex numbers reveals a deep relationship between trigonometric functions and the exponential and logarithmic functions.

How do we calculate these answers?

When $m = 0$:

$$10^{i(0)/8} = 10^0 = 1$$

When $m = 1$:

$$10^{i(1)/8} = 10^{i/8} = 0.95885 + 0.28402i$$

These answers are the values we calculated in Table 1.

When $m = 2$:

$$10^{i(2)/8} = 10^{i/4} = 0.83872 + 0.54465i$$

Again, these values we calculated in Table 1.

When $m = 3$:

$$10^{i(3)/8} = 10^{3i/8}$$

We know that $10^{i/4} \cdot 10^{i/8} = 10^{3i/8}$. Therefore:

$$10^{3i/8} = (0.95882 + 0.28402i)(0.83867 + 0.54465i) = 0.64944 + 0.76042i$$

The rest of the table can be filled out using the Product of Powers Law and values from Table 1.

What do we notice? What is happening to the values of x and y?

We see that x starts from 1, decreases, passes through 0, and continues to -1. Then, x starts increasing again, passes through 0, and marches to 1. With y, y starts from 0, increases to 1, then decreases, passes through 0, continues to -1, and then increases and passes through 0.

Since we know something about trigonometry, we should, therefore, be stunned by this revelation (Lesson 12.7). This behavior is the oscillatory dance of the sine function and cosine function (Figure 2).[3]

Why does 10^{bi} oscillate in such a manner? We know that $10^{0.68219i} = i$. Then:

$$\left(10^{0.68219i}\right)^2 = 10^{1.36438i} = i^2 = -1$$

[3] The interrelation of complex numbers with oscillatory motion is one of the reasons why complex numbers are embedded in the theories of electrical engineering and the study of electromagnetic waves.

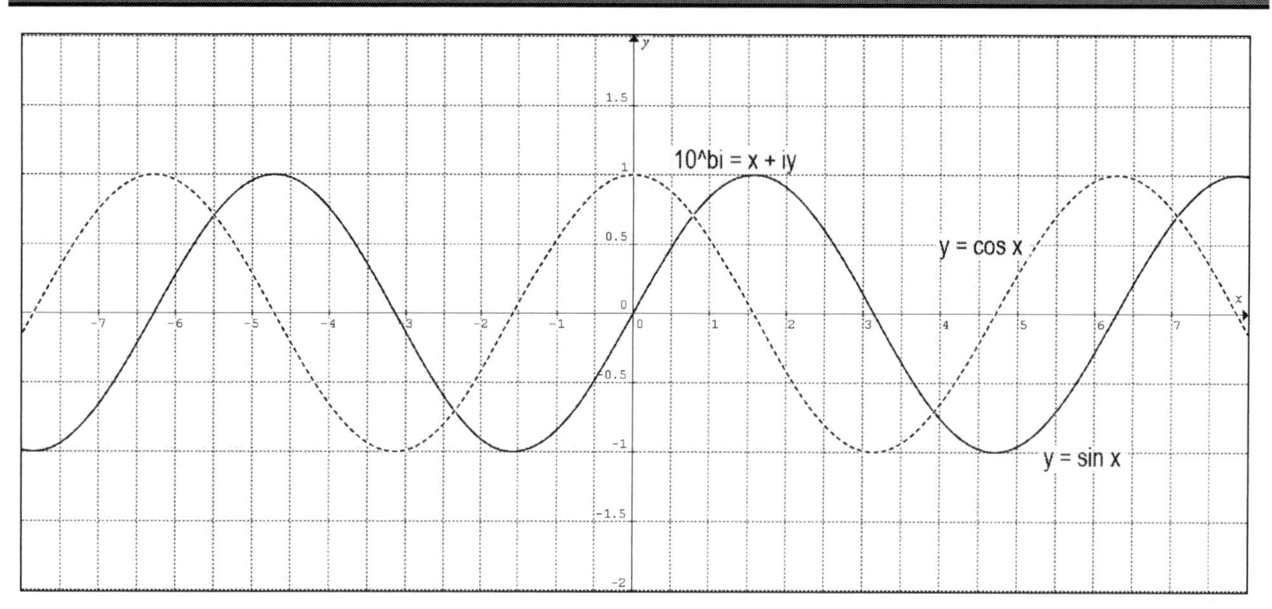

Figure 2. Sine and Cosine functions.

Next, we note:

$\left(10^{0.68219i}\right)^4 = 10^{2.72876i} = (i^2)^2 = i^4 = 1$

We can also show:

$\left(10^{0.68219i}\right)^6 = 10^{4.09314i} = (i^2)^3 = i^6 = -1$

$\left(10^{0.68219i}\right)^8 = 10^{5.45752i} = (i^2)^4 = i^8 = 1$

This analysis should confirm the periodic behavior of these powers.

Feynman's next step is a leap into mathematical glory. Instead of using base 10, he translates these values into the natural base, base $e \approx 2.7182818284$. We started with 10^{bi}. As before, we let $t = 2.302585b$ (Note: $t \in \mathbb{R}$) and write:

$10^{bi} = e^{ti}$

By substitution, we write:

$10^{bi} = x + yi$ and $10^{bi} = e^{ti} \Rightarrow e^{ti} = x + yi$

Since x behaves like the cosine of t (since $t \in \mathbb{R}$) and y behaves like the sine of t (since $t \in \mathbb{R}$), we can write:

$e^{ti} = x + yi = \cos t + \sin ti$

Since $x^2 + y^2 = 1$, then:

$\cos^2 t + \sin^2 t = 1$

The establishment of this identity, usually derived by using the Pythagorean Theorem and right triangles (Lesson 12.6), is, indeed, a marvelous correspondence.

We also know that as $t \to 0$:

$$e^{ti} = 1 + ti$$

We can state this equation because, as $t \to 0$, $\cos t = 1$ and $\sin t = 0$. If $t =$ degrees or radians, then, by use of right triangles and the unit circle, we can also establish:

$$\cos 0 = 1, \text{ and } \sin 0 = 0$$

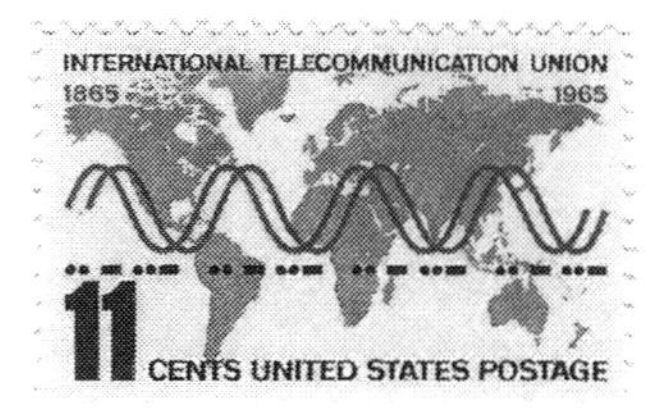

Figure 3. Source: United States Postal Service.

Therefore, as Feynman takes careful note, "all of the various properties of these remarkable functions, which come from taking imaginary powers, are the same as the sine and cosine of trigonometry."[4]

What about the periodicity? Do trigonometric functions and imaginary powers cohere cyclically? To find out, we must determine x when:

$$e^x = i \Leftrightarrow \ln i = x$$

We note that the successive powers of i (i, i^2, i^3, etc.) form the x-axis of Figure 2. What happens to x and y in $e^{ti} = x + yi$? The value of x will give us the period from 0 to i. We know that $\log i = 0.68219i$. Multiplying by the scale factor, 2.302585, we get:

$$\ln i = 2.302585(\log i) = 2.3026(0.68219i) = 1.5708i$$

On the horizontal axis, when it measures $1.5708i$, then, on the vertical axis, the graph will be equal to 1 for y, or $\sin t$, and 0 for x, or $\cos t$.

Lo and behold, in radians, $\pi/2 \approx 1.5708$. We, therefore, know that:

$$\sin \frac{\pi}{2} = 1$$

$$\cos \frac{\pi}{2} = 0$$

For the period from 0 to i^2, we must determine x when:

$$e^x = i^2 \Leftrightarrow \ln i^2 = x$$

By the Log of a Power Law (Lesson 12.4), we know that:

$$\ln i^2 = 2 \ln i$$

We note: $2 \ln i = 2(1.5708i) = 3.1416$. Look familiar? $\pi \approx 3.1416$. Note also:

$$\sin \pi = 0$$

$$\cos \pi = -1$$

Again, these values are a perfect match in the graph in Figure 2. The wonders of correspondence are multiplying!

By only using algebraic operations, i.e., no triangles, no unit circles, we arrived at natural logarithms, i.e., the values that are *natural* to geometry and trigonometry. Therefore, we can substitute t by θ, designating either radians or degrees, and write what Feynman pronounces as "our jewel." Indeed, this jewel is stunning and exquisite:

$$e^{\theta i} = \cos \theta + \sin \theta i$$

---

[4] Richard Feynman, 1:22-9.

If θ is in radians and we let $\theta = \pi$, $\sin \pi = 0$, and $\cos \pi = -1$.

Substituting, we get *the* most famous, *the* most wondrous, *the* most mysterious equation in all Mathematics, the **Euler Identity**:

$e^{\theta i} = \cos\theta + \sin\theta i$, $\theta = \pi$, $\sin \pi = 0$, and $\cos \pi = -1 \Rightarrow e^{\pi i} = -1 \Leftrightarrow e^{i\pi} = -1 \Leftrightarrow e^{i\pi} + 1 = 0$

$$e^{i\pi} + 1 = 0$$

Leonhard Euler (1707-1783), Swiss mathematician par excellence, derived the same equation $e^{\theta i} = \cos\theta + \sin\theta i$ and $e^{i\pi} + 1 = 0$ from a different mathematical starting point, $e = \lim_{n\to\infty}\left(1+\frac{1}{n}\right)^n$. (See Lesson 8.16 and a homework exercise in this lesson.)

> There is a famous formula – perhaps the most compact and famous of all formulas – developed by Euler from a discovery of De Moivre: $e^{i\pi} + 1 = 0$ .... It appeals equally to the mystic, the scientist, the philosopher, the mathematician.
>
> Edward Kasner & James R. Newman, *Mathematics and the Imagination* (1940), p. 103.

THE UNIFICATION OF ALGEBRA AND GEOMETRY

Feynman concludes his exposition by connecting Geometry to Algebra by representing a given complex number $x + yi$ in a plane (Figure 4). As we have noted (Lesson 12.12), the distance from the origin to the point that represents $x + yi$ is r, the modulus, or magnitude, of $x + yi$. The phase angle, the argument or amplitude, of $x + yi$, is θ.

By the Pythagorean Theorem:

$r^2 = x^2 + y^2 \Rightarrow r = \sqrt{x^2+y^2}$

By trigonometry:

$\tan\theta = \frac{y}{x}$

$\cos\theta = \frac{x}{r} \Leftrightarrow x = r\cos\theta$

$\cos\theta = \frac{y}{r} \Leftrightarrow y = r\sin\theta$

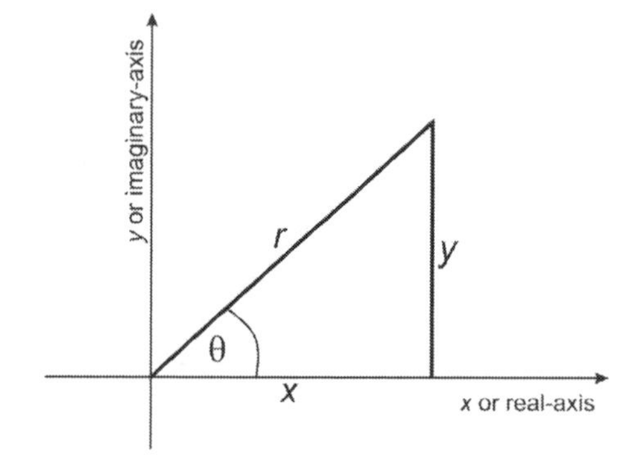

Figure 4. The Exponential form of a complex number $x + yi$ is $re^{\theta i}$.

Since $e^{\theta i} = x + yi$, then, by substitution:

$x + yi = r\cos\theta + r\sin\theta i \Leftrightarrow x + yi = r(\cos\theta + \sin\theta i)$

Since $e^{\theta i} = \cos\theta + \sin\theta i$, then, by substitution:

$x + yi = re^{\theta i}$, the **exponential form of a complex number** (Figure 4).

This equation, $x + yi = re^{\theta i}$, is, according to Feynman, "the unification of algebra and geometry."[5]

[5] Richard Feynman, I:22-10.

In conclusion, we started this curriculum with the notions of counting, the existence of natural numbers, positive integers, and zero. These ideas and the method of counting are grounded in the dance of the Triune God. In other words, the Triune God of Scripture is the *Alpha* of mathematical reasoning.

$$x + yi = re^{\theta i}$$

From counting, we unfolded the basic arithmetic operations, their inverses, and their operations and order. Using algebraic equations and the process of generalization, we methodically extended our concept of number systems:

> [There is a] two-way relation ... between geometry and algebra, where the translation of algebraic equations into geometrical form and of geometrical theorems into algebraic form reveals and clarifies what each really implies.
> Thomas F. Torrance, *Theological Science* ([1969] 1978), p. 250.

1. Adding 0 and the opposites of $\mathbb{N}$ to $\mathbb{N}$, we get $\mathbb{Z}$.
2. Then, we traveled from $\mathbb{Z}$ to the fractional world of $\mathbb{Q}$.
3. Our next stop was the irrational numbers leading us to $\mathbb{R}$.
4. In this Step, we reached our destination: $\mathbb{C}$.

Then, we developed useful mathematical objects like tables of logarithms, powers, and trigonometric functions and discovered the remarkable connection that the sine function and cosine function are what the imaginary powers of real numbers are. We unearthed this striking correlation, this *Omega* of our thinking, without Alpha there cannot be Omega, by reasoning from the construction of a table that just extracted ten successive square roots of 10! (Lesson 12.3). Such are the astonishing gems that mathematical reasoning can unearth.

> The Triune God of Scripture is the Alpha and Omega of mathematical thinking.

EXERCISES

Define the following terms:

1. Exponential form of a complex number $a + bi$.
2. Euler Identity
3. Bearing (See homework exercise below.)

Write the following complex numbers in exponential form: (State θ in radians rounded to the nearest thousandths, if necessary. If π is involved, use it in your answer. State r in simple radical form, if necessary.)

4. i
5. $-i$
6. -1
7. 1
8. $3 + 2i$
9. $6 - \sqrt{3}i$
10. $-2 - 5i$

> In his next chapter of *Lectures on Physics*, entitled "Resonance," Richard Feynman uses this "jewel" of an equation, $e^{\theta i} = \cos \theta + \sin \theta i$, to explain and make sense of the physics of harmonic motion, forced oscillation and damping, electrical resonance, and resonance in the physical creation. Stunning, indeed!

An Euler Magic Square (1770)

68^2	29^2	41^2	37^2
17^2	31^2	79^2	32^2
59^2	28^2	23^2	61^2
11^2	77^2	8^2	49^2

Convert the following numbers in exponential form, where θ is in radians, to complex numbers in the form $a + bi$: (Hint: Use $a + bi = r\cos\theta + r\sin\theta i$ and round a and b, if necessary, to the nearest thousandths.)

11. $5e^{\pi/3 i}$
12. $2e^{2\pi/3 i}$
13. $15e^{3\pi/4 i}$
14. $0.6e^{\pi/4 i}$

Answer the following questions:

15. Show why $(x + yi)(x - yi) = x^2 + y^2$.
16. Solve $1 = x^2 + y^2$ for:
    (a) x.
    (b) y.
17. Show that $10^{i/1024} \cdot 10^{i/1024} = 10^{i/512}$.

Euler's inexplicable identity $e^{i\pi} + 1 = 0$ involves i, π, and e, three amazing numbers.[6] Early in the history of the study of logarithms, e was defined as follows:

$$e = \lim_{n\to\infty}\left(1 + \frac{1}{n}\right)^n$$

Euler used this definition to develop a power series for e.[7] He first recognized that he could apply Pascal's Triangle, i.e., the Binomial Theorem, to this definition.

He began with the combination formula for deriving the terms of a binomial expansion:

$${}_nC_j = \frac{n!}{(n-j)!\,j!}$$

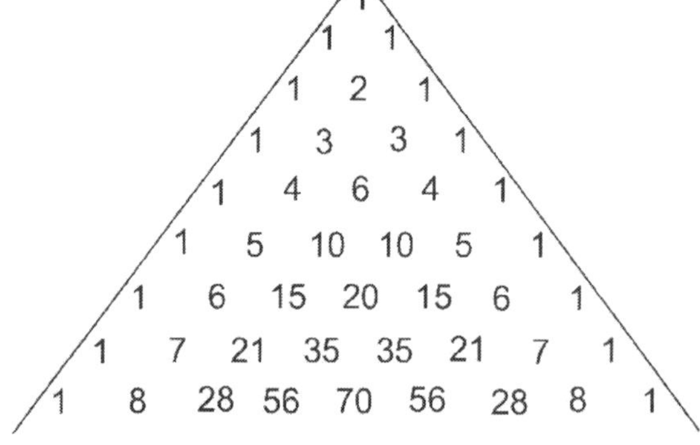

Figure 5. Pascal's Triangle.

Let's follow Euler's thinking by answering the following questions:

18. State how this formula explains each number, the binomial coefficients, in the 6th row of Pascal's Triangle.
19. Rewrite $n! = n \cdot (n - 1) \cdot \ldots \cdot 3 \cdot 2 \cdot 1$ by reversing the factors.
20. Rewrite $(n - j)! = (n - j) \cdot (n - j - 1) \cdot \ldots \cdot 3 \cdot 2 \cdot 1$ by reversing the factors.

---

[6] As we have noted, $i = \sqrt{-1}$, along with e and π, are transcendental numbers. Technically, a transcendental number is a real or complex number that is *not* algebraic; i.e., not a solution of a non-zero polynomial equation having rational number coefficients (Lesson 11.4). We can access an algebraic number using fundamental algebraic operations in the solution process, i.e., using the Balance Beam Principle to add, subtract, multiply, divide, exponentiate, or extract roots. Other numbers, like e and π, are complicated enough that they *transcend* these algebraic operations in the solution process; therefore, mathematicians call these numbers transcendental. Recall that $e \approx 2.71828$ and $\pi \approx 3.14159$.

[7] A power series (in one variable) is an infinite series of the form $\sum_{n=0}^{\infty} a_n(x-c)^n = a_0 + a_1(x-c) + a_2(x-c)^2 + a_3(x-c)^3 + \ldots$

(Note the symbol-saving use of the summation symbol Σ.)

21. From Questions 18 and 20, restate the combination formula ${}_nC_j = \dfrac{n!}{(n-j)!\,j!}$ replacing $n!$ and $(n-j)!$.
22. In your answer to Question 21 all the factors from 1 to $(n-j)$ in the numerator cancel with those in the denominator. What expression is left in the numerator? (Hint: Your answer should start with $n-j+1$ as the first factor.)
23. Rewrite your answer to Question 22 by reversing the factors. (Hint: Your answer should start with n as the first factor.)
24. Rewrite the combination formula based on your answer to Question 23.
25. Apply the formula in Question 24 to calculate the 6th row of Pascal's Triangle. (Hint: recall that $0! = 1$.)

With this work, Euler applied the Binomial Theorem to $\left(1+\dfrac{1}{n}\right)^n$ as follows:

$$\left(1+\frac{1}{n}\right)^n = 1+n\cdot\frac{1}{n}+\frac{n\cdot(n-1)}{2!}\cdot\left(\frac{1}{n}\right)^2+\frac{n\cdot(n-1)(n-2)}{3!}\cdot\left(\frac{1}{n}\right)^3+\ldots+\left(\frac{1}{n}\right)^n$$

If we expand the third term we get:

$$\frac{n\cdot(n-1)}{2!}\cdot\left(\frac{1}{n}\right)^2=\frac{n\cdot(n-1)}{2!}\frac{1}{n^2}=\frac{n-1}{2!n}$$

We can rewrite $\dfrac{n-1}{n}$ as follows (Note: $\dfrac{9}{10}=1-\dfrac{1}{10}$):

$$\frac{n-1}{n}=\frac{n}{n}-\frac{1}{n}=1-\frac{1}{n}$$

Therefore, we get:

$$\frac{n\cdot(n-1)}{2!}\cdot\left(\frac{1}{n}\right)^2=\frac{\left(1-\frac{1}{n}\right)}{2!}$$

With these algebraic manipulations in mind, we get:

$$\left(1+\frac{1}{n}\right)^n=1+1+\frac{\left(1-\frac{1}{n}\right)}{2!}+\frac{\left(1-\frac{1}{n}\right)\left(1-\frac{2}{n}\right)}{3!}+\frac{\left(1-\frac{1}{n}\right)\left(1-\frac{2}{n}\right)\left(1-\frac{3}{n}\right)}{4!}+\ldots+\frac{1}{n^n}$$

Since we are looking for the limit of $\left(1+\dfrac{1}{n}\right)^n$ as $n\to\infty$, we let n increase without bound. Our expansion will have more and more terms. At the same time, the expression within each pair of parentheses in the numerator will tend to 1.

26. Why?

27. From this observation of limits, Euler produced a beautiful equation for e involving the sum of fractional terms with 1 in the numerator of each term in and factorials in the denominators of each term, starting from 0! and increasing by 1. Write this equation, i.e., $e = \lim_{n\to\infty}\left(1+\frac{1}{n}\right)^n = ?$
28. Euler then substituted $\frac{1}{n}$ with $\frac{x}{n}$. Make this substitution and write an equation for e^x, making sure to change $\frac{1}{0!}$, the first term, to 1; i.e., $e^x = \lim_{n\to\infty}\left(1+\frac{x}{n}\right)^n = ?$
29. Euler continued to experiment with the power series for e^x. He decided to see what happened to this series if he substituted x with the *imaginary* expression ix where, of course, $i = \sqrt{-1}$. This substitution took some nerve on Euler's part since e^x had always represented a real number. Now Euler was going to see what would happen to the expression e^{ix}. Write the equation for e^{ix}.

> Sometimes my pencil is smarter than I.
> Leonhard Euler (1707-1783).

30. Knowing the properties of i, $i^2 = -1$, $i^3 = -i$, and $i^4 = 1$, etc., write a new equation for e^{ix} making these substitutions.
31. Now Euler changed the order of the terms collecting all the real terms separately from the imaginary terms. Factoring out i from the imaginary terms, write a new equation for e^{ix}.
32. In Euler's time, the power series of $\sin x$ and $\cos x$ (x in radians) was well known.[8] Write the power series for $\sin x$ and $\cos x$.
33. Given these definitions, Euler made a grand substitution. Make that substitution and write a new equation for e^{ix}.
34. Show that $e^{i\pi} + 1 = 0$ based on your equation in Question 33.

Using a scientific calculator, answer these questions using the Law of Sines, the Law of Cosines, the SAS Triangle Area Formula, or any combination these laws:

35. (a) Sketch ΔABC where $m\angle A = 30°$, $m\angle B = 75°$, and $c = 12$. Note: The vertices A, B, and C are opposite the sides a, b, and c.)
    (b) Find the exact area of this triangle and (c) BC rounded to the nearest tenth.
36. (a) Sketch ΔABC where its three sides are $a = 8$, $b = 11$, and $c = 16$. (Note: The vertices A, B, and C are opposite the sides a, b, and c.)
    (b) Find the area of this triangle rounded to the nearest tenth of a square unit.
37. The area of ΔABC is 40 square units. Find the two possible angles, rounded to the nearest tenth, between two of its sides a and b where $a = 14$ and $b = 7$. (Hint: Refer to Lesson 12.9, the discussion of inverse sine.)

[8] As we have noted (Lesson 12.7), these are known as the Taylor series named in honor of the English mathematician Brook Taylor (1685-1731).

We measure a **bearing** both east and west from north and south, divided into four quadrants. A bearing has been traditionally defined in land surveying terms as a fixed number line which gives the smallest acute angle away from N or S and toward W or E. For example, in Figure 6, the bearing is N 30° W with a magnitude of 2, a vector. In Figure 7, the bearing is S 38° W with a magnitude of 3.

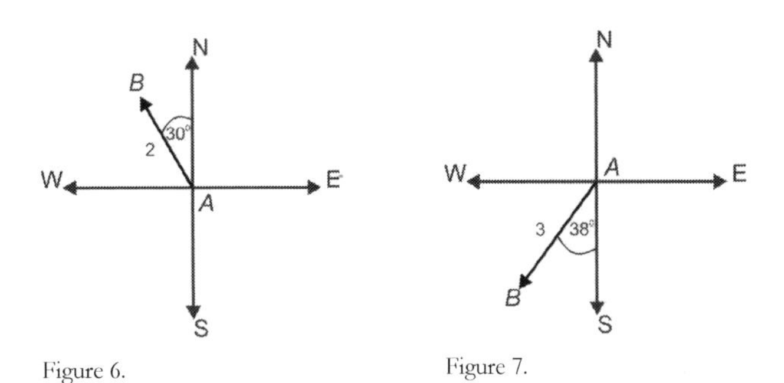

Figure 6. Figure 7.

Answer these questions by making use of either the Law of Cosines or the Law of Sines where applicable:

38. You want to find the measure across a river from point A on your side and point B on the other side of the river. You pick another point C on your side of the river and measure AC, $\angle BCA = \theta$, and $\angle BAC = \omega$. How do you find AB? (Hint: Draw a picture, label points, do not assume that any angle is 90°, and reason to your answer.)
39. A boat travels 2 miles with a bearing N 33° E. At the 2-mile point, it changes its bearing to N 75° E and travels an additional 3 miles (Figure 8). At the 3-mile point, what is its bearing, rounded to the nearest tenth, and distance, rounded to the nearest hundredth, from its starting point? (Hint: you will need investigate the figure carefully and then reason to the multiple steps you need to take to find the solution.)

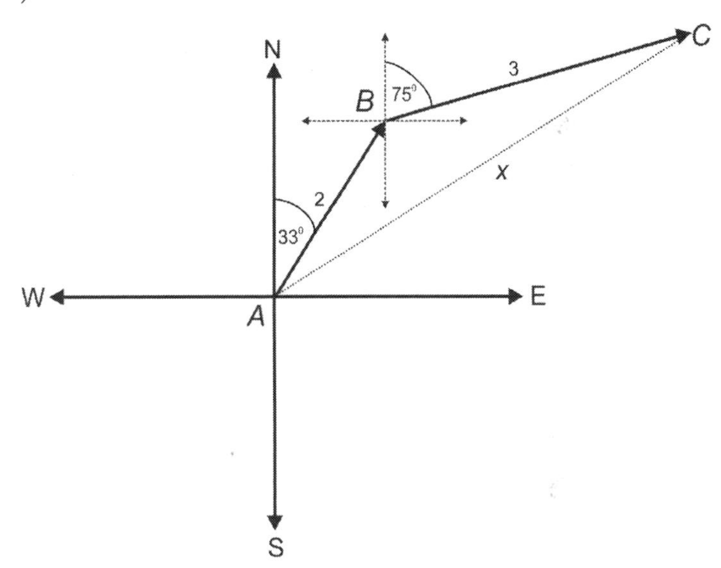

Figure 8.

40. Bill lives 4 miles northeast of John. When Bill spots a tornado at N 65° W, John sees it at N 15° W. At that instant, how far, to the nearest hundredth, is the tornado from John? (Hint: Draw a picture, label points and reason to the steps you need to take to find the solution.)
41. A Navy pilot, Lieutenant Jack Styles, flies from his base 35 miles S 75° E and then 30 miles S 40° E.
    (a) How far, rounded to the nearest tenth, from the base is Lt. Styles.
    (b) Which bearing, rounded to the nearest tenth, should he take to get him directly back to base?
42. A ship sails the ocean in 1824. It left New York with a cargo of goods. Its total weight is 250 tons. It is bound for the port of Liverpool, England. Two cabin boys are on deck, there are 25 passengers aboard with a crew of 15, the wind is blowing at a bearing N 45° E, and the clock points to 3:45 PM. It is June. How old is the captain?

In number we have to do with the rationality of the creation in its impersonal, determinate, and immanent form. Hence in our scientific investigation of the physical world we do not reckon that we have made significant contact with the nature of things or grasped them in the depth of their reality unless we can bring our knowledge of them to a clear, consistent and enlightening mathematical representation. At the same time we are aware that our mathematical equations are meaningful only in so far as they bear upon non-mathematical objective reality independent of them. Hence the physicist is concerned with mathematical formalisations not just as consistent sets of abstract symbols or axioms but with the connection between them and the actual realities he is investigating, i.e., with the openness of mathematical structures to ontological structures in the real world beyond them. Through mathematics he is able to use a notation that carries his reasoning beyond what he is capable of without it, but it requires to be applied to reality. That is to say, without interpretation of its extra-mathematical, empirical reference, mathematical formalization can tell us nothing about the universe.

Thomas F. Torrance, *Christian Theology and Scientific Culture* (1981), p. 110.

STEP 13. THE DANCE OF REASON

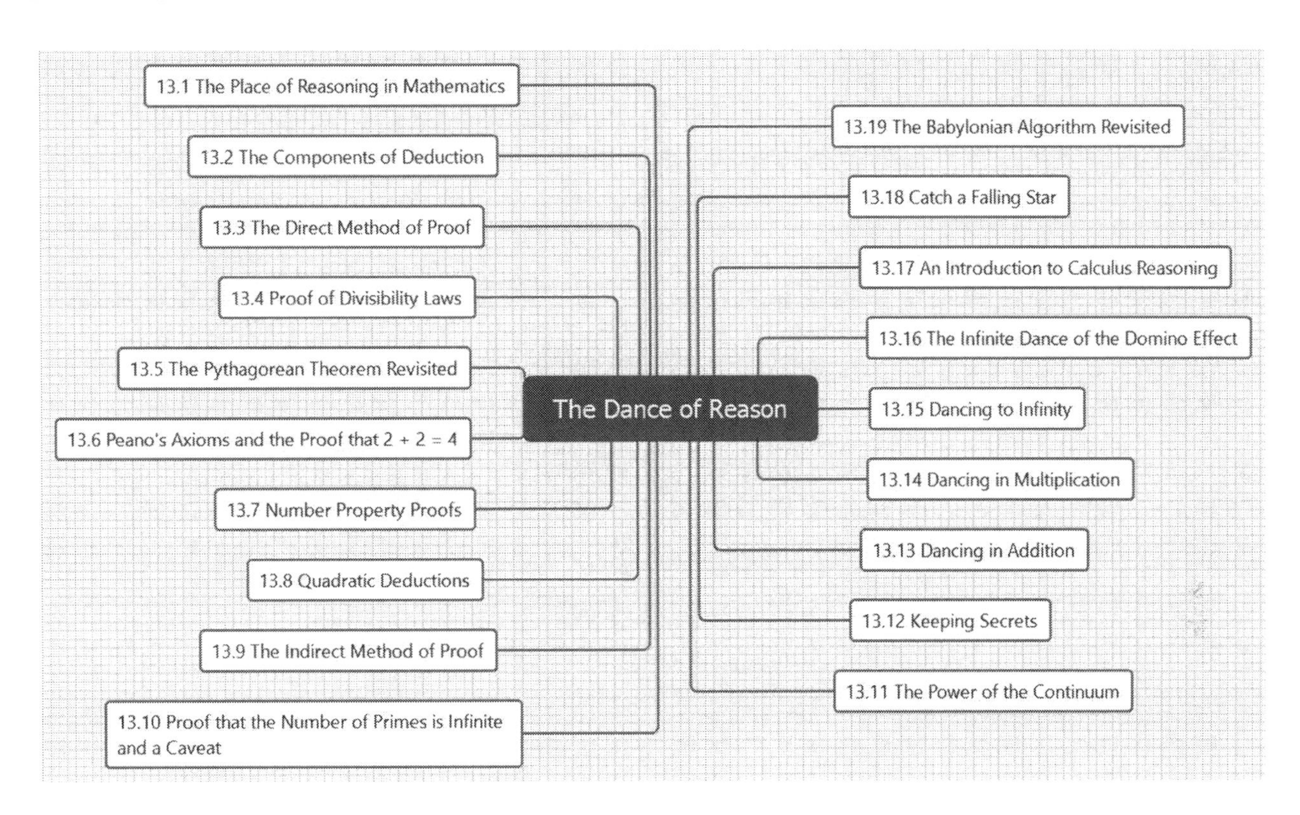

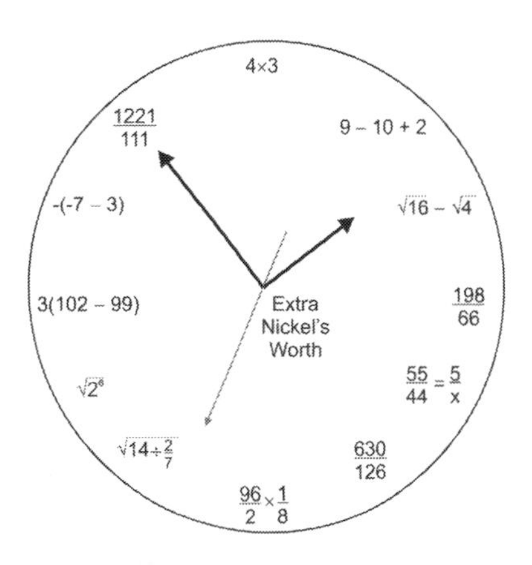

> Mathematics as an expression of the human mind reflects the active will, the contemplative reason, and the desire for aesthetic perfection. Its basic elements are logic and intuition, analysis and construction, generality and individuality.
>
> Richard Courant and Herbert Robbins, *What is Mathematics? An Elementary Approach to Ideas and Methods* ([1941], 1996), from the introductory essay "What is Mathematics."

13.1 The Place of Reasoning in Mathematics

Terms & Concepts Introduced
1. Deductive thinking
2. Field Laws

We have focused Part 1 of this curriculum series on explaining and practicing streamline ways of doing arithmetic, i.e., doing the operations of addition, subtraction, multiplication, and division on sets of numbers, integers and rational numbers. In Part 2, we have explored algebraic operations and have also introduced arithmetic operations involving irrational numbers and complex numbers.

Recap

> Perhaps the most unfortunate fact about mathematics is that it requires us to reason, whereas most human beings are not convinced that reasoning is worth while.
>
> Morris Kline, *Mathematics and the Physical World* ([1959] 1981), p. 1.

Regarding the operations of arithmetic, besides the four basic operations mentioned in the previous paragraph, we have also explored the operations of exponentiation, extraction of roots, and the operation of logarithms, a method of calculation invented by John Napier in the 17th century to make multiplication and division easier. Regarding their inverses, these operations dance together in pairs.

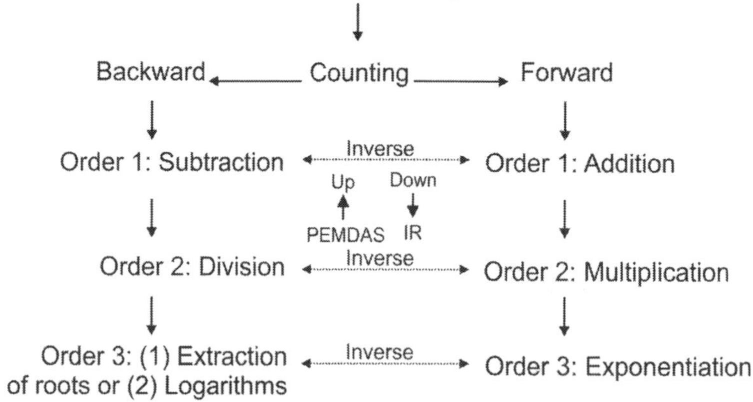

Figure 1.

Table 1	
Operation	**Inverse**
Addition	Subtraction
Multiplication	Division
Exponentiation	Extraction of roots
Exponentiation	Logarithms

Note the two inverses of exponentiation.

1. Extraction of roots:

   If b is an even positive integer:[1]

   $$a^b = c \Leftrightarrow a = \sqrt[b]{c} \text{ or } a = -\sqrt[b]{c}$$

   Using fractional exponents:

   $$a^b = c \Leftrightarrow a = c^{1/b} \text{ or } a = -c^{1/b}$$

   If b is a positive odd integer:[2]

   $$a^b = c \Leftrightarrow a = \sqrt[b]{c}$$

   Using fractional exponents:

   $$a^b = c \Leftrightarrow a = c^{1/b}$$

2. Taking logarithms:

   $$a^b = c \Leftrightarrow b = \log_a c$$

> ... mathematics is *not* just another language. Mathematics is a language plus reasoning; it is like language plus logic. Mathematics is a tool for reasoning.
>
> Richard Feynman, *The Character of Physical Law* ([1965] 1967), p. 40.

These two inverses are necessary because if we know that the bth power of a is c, or $a^b = c$, we can undo exponentiation to find either the base a via extraction of roots or the exponent b via taking logarithms.

We also learned, in a fundamental way, the use of inverses and the Balance Beam Principle to solve certain kinds of equations.

For example, if $x^a = b$, where a and b are parameters, we solve for the unknown x by extracting the ath root of both sides:

$$x^a = b \Leftrightarrow x = b^{1/a}$$

If $a^x = b$, where a and b are parameters, we solve for the unknown x by taking the log to the base a of both sides, noting that logs are exponents; i.e., $\log_a a^x = x$:

$$a^x = b \Leftrightarrow x = \log_a b$$

LAWS OF ALGEBRA

Let's summarize the basic laws of Algebra, denoted as **Field Laws**.[3] Mastering this toolkit, these eleven laws, brings context and understanding to our work with the language of Mathematics. We state each law, first in symbols, and then using word, or rhetoric:

1. Closure Law of Addition: $a, b \in \mathbb{R}, a + b \in \mathbb{R}$

   Adding any two real numbers always generates a real number.

2. Closure Law of Multiplication: $a, b \in \mathbb{R}, ab \in \mathbb{R}$

   Multiplying any two real numbers always generates a real number.

3. Commutative Law of Addition: $a, b \in \mathbb{R}, a + b = b + a$

   Order doesn't matter when we add two numbers. The sum will not change.

---

[1] If b is an even positive integer, we have a many-to-one function.

[2] If b is an odd positive integer, we have a one-to-one function.

[3] A structure of objects related to number or space is a *field* if these eleven laws are true for that structure.

4. Commutative Law of Multiplication: $a, b \in \mathbb{R}, ab = ba$

   Order doesn't matter when we multiply two numbers. The product will not change.

5. Associative Law of Addition: $a, b, c \in \mathbb{R}, a + (b + c) = (a + b) + c$

   We can group any number of addends in pairs without changing the sum of the addends.

6. Associative Law of Multiplication: $a, b, c \in \mathbb{R}, a(bc) = (ab)c$

   We can group any number of factors in pairs without changing the product of the factors.

7. Distributive Law of Multiplication over Addition/Subtraction: a, b, and $c \in \mathbb{R}, a(b + c) = ab + ac$

   We can distribute a factor multiplied by the sum of two addends to the sum of that factor multiplied by the first addend and that factor multiplied by the second addend.
   For subtraction, we write: $a(b - c) = ab - ac$

   We can also multiply by $\frac{1}{a}$, the basis of the Division algorithm (Step 5):

   $$\frac{1}{a}(b+c) = \frac{b}{a} + \frac{c}{a} = \frac{b+c}{a}$$

   $$\frac{1}{a}(b-c) = \frac{b}{a} - \frac{c}{a} = \frac{b-c}{a}$$

8. Identity Element for Addition: $a \in \mathbb{R}, 0 + a = a$

   The sum of zero and any number is that number.

9. Identity Element for Multiplication: $a \in \mathbb{R}, 1a = a$

   The product of one and any number is that number.

> It is impossible to understand algebra if you have not mastered arithmetic: it is impossible to understand calculus if you have not mastered algebra. If you attempt the impossible, without realizing what you are doing, your morale will suffer.
>
> Walter Warwick Sawyer, *Mathematician's Delight* (1944), p. 44.

10. Additive Inverse Law: $a \in \mathbb{R}, a + (-a) = 0$

    The sum of any number and its opposite is the additive identity.

    $a + x = b \Leftrightarrow x = b - a$ (We invoke the inverse operation as the solution strategy.)

    $b = 0 \Rightarrow a + x = 0 \Leftrightarrow x = -a$

11. Multiplicative Inverse Law: $a \in \mathbb{R}, a \neq 0, a\left(\frac{1}{a}\right) = \frac{a}{a} = 1$

    The product of any number and its reciprocal is the multiplicative identity.

    $ax = b \Leftrightarrow x = \frac{b}{a}$ (We invoke the inverse operation as the solution strategy.)

    $b = 1 \Rightarrow ax = 1 \Leftrightarrow x = \frac{1}{a}$

The study of Algebra is primarily the study of operations and order involving the use of inverses to solve a wide variety of equations. Mastery of arithmetic is foundational for the study of Mathematics and its unique language, Algebra is where we learn that Mathematics is not just about the calculation of sums, differences, products, and quotients. The language of Mathematics is not necessary numbers like

2, 3, or 8765. Mathematics, as a language is about justifying ideas related to number and space, interrelated concepts that dance in the tandem of close and careful reasoning. As theoretical biologist Luke Heaton says, "… what matters in mathematics is how we can work from one statement to another …."[4]

Mathematicians talk in symbols that reveal general laws, principles, or identities, e.g., $a(b + c) = ab + ac$. The study of Algebra is a study of a language, the language of mathematical symbols and how we use them, not only to solve equations but to justify rationally coherent ideas that may have nothing to do with numbers.

> Two extremes: to exclude reason, to admit reason only.
>
> Blaise Pascal, *Pensées*, #253.

Scattered throughout the volumes of *The Dance of Number*, we have encountered many examples of how mathematics use close and careful reasoning, i.e., **deductive thinking**, to justify, or prove, a wide variety of ideas, named propositions or theorems by mathematicians. Here is a list of some of these propositions that we have explored, although we have not proved all of them:

1. A reference to Mathematical Induction as a way to prove propositions about natural numbers (Lesson 4.11).
2. A provisional proof of why finger multiplication works (Lesson 4.14).
3. Why Russian peasant multiplication works (Lesson 5.1).
4. The rule for divisibility by 9 (Lesson 5.4, not proved).
5. The rule for divisibility by 7 (Lesson 5.8, not proved).
6. The proof of the area formula for a parallelogram (Lesson 5.8).
7. The rule for divisibility by 11 (Lesson 5.9, not proved).
8. The Fundamental Theorem of Arithmetic (Lesson 6.1, not proved).
9. The use of QED in proofs (Lesson 6.1).
10. A provisional proof that the number of primes is infinite (Lesson 6.1).
11. The Extreme/Mean Law (Lesson 6.7, not proved).
12. The proof that $0.\overline{9} = 1$ (Lesson 7.8).
13. The proof of the area formula for a triangle and a circle (Lesson 8.5).
14. The proof that the sum of the interior angles of a triangle equals 180° (Lesson 8.7).
15. The proof that the rational numbers are countable (Lesson 9.6)
16. A demonstration to show why $\frac{1}{2}+\frac{1}{4}+\frac{1}{8}+\frac{1}{16}+\ldots=1$ (Lesson 11.2).
17. The proof that a triangle inscribed in a semicircle is a right triangle (Lesson 11.3).
18. Several proofs of the Pythagorean Theorem (Lesson 11.3).
19. The Babylonian Algorithm for calculating square roots and cube roots (Lessons 11.7 and 11.10, not proved).
20. Proof of the formula for finding the distance between any two points in the Cartesian coordinate plane (Lesson 11.9).
21. Proof of the Quadratic Formula (Lesson 11.12).
22. Proof of Logarithm Laws (Lesson 12.2 and 12.4).
23. Proof of the Law of Changing Logarithmic Bases (Lesson 12.5).
24. Proofs of a variety of Trigonometric Identities (Lesson 12.6, Lesson 12.7, Lesson 12.8, and Lesson 12.9).
25. Proof of the Law of Sines (Lesson 12.7).
26. Proof of the Law of Cosines (Lesson 12.9).

[4] Luke Heaton, *A Brief History of Mathematical Thought: Key Concepts and Where They Came From* (London: Constable & Robinson, 2015), p. 297.

27. Proof of the Euler identity $e^{i\pi} + 1 = 0$ (Lesson 12.13).

We will explore in this Step, and in Step 14, many more examples, both in the lessons and in the homework exercises, of mathematical proof revealing why the propositions of number and space are justified by using close and careful reasoning, i.e., deductive logic. In our next lesson, we will begin our journey by reviewing some principles of this kind of logic.

EXERCISES

1. Define deductive thinking.
2. What is wrong with this statement? ½ full glass = ½ empty glass ⇔ 1 full glass = 1 empty glass

Answer the following questions:

3. Determine the pattern revealed in this group of products:
   $1 \cdot 1089 = 1089$
   $2 \cdot 1089 = 2178$
   $3 \cdot 1089 = 3267$
   $4 \cdot 1089 = 4356$
   $5 \cdot 1089 = 5445$
   $6 \cdot 1089 = 6534$
   $7 \cdot 1089 = 7623$
   $8 \cdot 1089 = 8712$
   $9 \cdot 1089 = 9801$
4. Determine the pattern revealed in this group of products:
   $1 \cdot 142857 = 142857$
   $2 \cdot 142857 = 285714$
   $3 \cdot 142857 = 428571$
   $4 \cdot 142857 = 571428$
   $5 \cdot 142857 = 714285$
   $6 \cdot 142857 = 857142$
5. What is $7 \cdot 142857$?
6. State the Field Laws using mathematical symbols.

> Simply put, e is somehow built into the fabric or design of nature ... of the universe.
> Dan Umbarger, *Explaining Logarithms* (2006), p. 41.

> Mathematics is on the artistic side a creation of new rhythms, orders, designs, harmonies, and on the knowledge side, is a systematic study of various rhythms, orders, designs and harmonies. We may condense this into the statement that mathematics is, on the one side, the qualitative study of the structure of beauty, and on the other side is the creator of new artistic forms of beauty.
> James B. Shaw, cited in William L. Schaaf, *Mathematics: Our Great Heritage* (1948), p. 50.

Answer the following questions:

7. Let W = {0, 1, 2, 3, …}, the set of non-negative integers. Let + and × represent the usual operation of addition and multiplication. This structure satisfies all eleven Field Laws except #10 and #11. Confirm these exceptions by a few examples.
8. Let $\mathbb{Z}$ be the set of integers. Let + and × represent the usual operation of addition and multiplication. This structure satisfies all eleven Field Laws except #11. Confirm this exception by a few examples.
9. Let K be the set of non-negative rational numbers. Let + and × represent the usual operation of addition and multiplication. This structure satisfies all eleven Field Laws except #10. Confirm this exception by a few examples.

True or False: (If False, provide a counterexample.)

10. The Natural numbers are closed under addition.
11. The Integers are closed under addition.
12. The Rational numbers are closed under addition.
13. The Natural numbers are closed under multiplication.
14. The Integers are closed under multiplication.
15. The Rational numbers are closed under multiplication.
16. The Natural numbers are closed under subtraction.
17. The Integers are closed under subtraction.
18. The Rational numbers are closed under subtraction.
19. The Natural numbers are closed under division.
20. The Integers are closed under division.
21. The Rational numbers are closed under division.
22. The Natural numbers are closed under exponentiation.
23. The Integers are closed under exponentiation.
24. The Rational numbers are closed under exponentiation.
25. The Natural numbers are closed under extraction of roots.
26. The Integers are closed under extraction of roots.
27. The Rational numbers are closed under extraction of roots.

Figure 2. The construction of the Tower Bridge in London, England (1892). The engineers designed the suspension cables according to the parabola $f(x) = \frac{9x^2}{80}$. Graph this function and compare it with the picture. Source: Public Domain.

Law of Sines and Law of Cosines (ambiguous cases).

In Figure 3, we know one angle, 30°, and two sides of a triangle. One of the sides of length 20 is adjacent to the 30° and the other side of length 12 is opposite the same angle. We want to find the other angles and the third side. Answer these questions with the aid of a scientific calculator:

28. Why are ΔABC and $\Delta ABC'$ two valid configurations given the measurements we know?
29. Use the Law of Sines to find θ and θ'. Round to the nearest tenth of an angle.
30. Use the Law of Sines to find AC and AC'. Round to the nearest tenth.

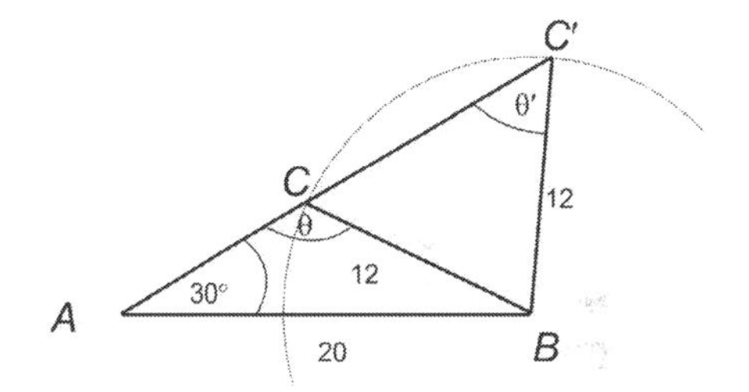

Figure 3.

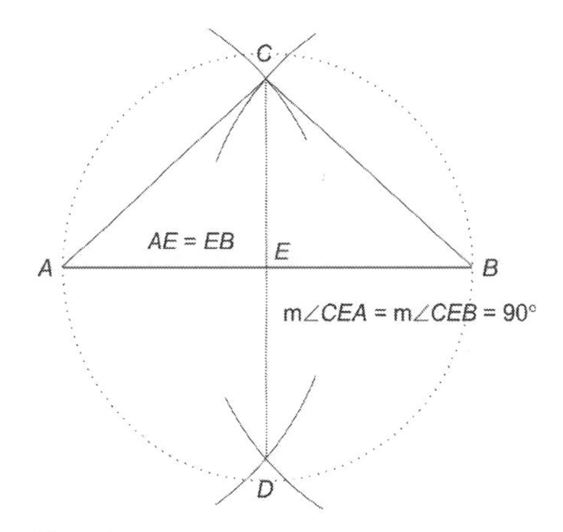

Figure 4.

Answer this question:

31. In Figure 4, explain why $\angle CEA$ and $\angle CEB$ are right angles. (Hint: Review the construction exercise in Lesson 5.2, the "Mysterious Island" section in Lesson 8.1, and the SSS Congruence Theorem[5] in the homework exercise in Lesson 12.12.)

Reproduce Table 2 and draw a check mark, where applicable, to indicate what type or types the number is column one is.

Table 2

	Prime	Positive	Negative	Integer	Rational	Odd	Even	Irrational	Real	Complex
32. 635										
33. -(4/7)										
34. π										
35. 0.005										
36. 22										
37. 15/0										
38. 30%										
39. $0.5 + 2i$										
40. $24\frac{1}{5}$										
41. 99/3										
42. 14.2×10^{-10}										
43. $0.5\overline{36}$										
44. -400										
45. -1221										
46. $\sqrt{7}$										
47. 22.8%										
48. 481										
49. $-\sqrt{121}$										
50. 41										
51. 62.25										
52. -43.921										
53. -(45/98)										
54. 2.2×10^{4}										
55. 1										
56. e										
57. 9^{2}										
58. $-3\frac{3}{4}$										
59. $\sqrt{-8}$										

[5] Euclid's Proposition 8 in Book I.

13.2 The Components of Deduction

Mathematicians use deductive logic to justify what, in many cases, is hinted to be true by the discovery of patterns. We have seen many examples of this search for patterns in this text. When we studied squares and square roots, we discovered that numbers that end in the digits 2, 3, 7, and 8 are not perfect squares. When we extract the square root of these numbers, we discover that they are irrational numbers. The type of thinking characterized by search for pattern is inductive thinking.

Terms & Concepts Introduced
1. Antecedent
2. Antithetical thinking
3. Argument (logic)
4. Asserting the consequent
5. Axiomatic-Deductive System
6. Biconditional statements
7. Boundary
8. Coherence statement
9. Conclusion
10. Conditional statement
11. Consequent
12. Contrapositive
13. Denying the antecedent
14. *Ex nihilo*
15. Existence statement
16. Exterior angle of a triangle
17. Figure
18. Formal statement
19. Heuristic argument
20. Hypothesis
21. Inductive thinking
22. Inverse (logic)
23. Law of Contradiction
24. Law of Contraposition
25. Law of Excluded Middle
26. Law of Identity
27. *Modus ponens*
28. *Modus tollens*
29. Negation
30. Postulate
31. Premise
32. Ratiocination
33. Recognition statement
34. Rigorous argument
35. *Stoicheia*

Inductive Thinking

Inductive thinking is a method of reasoning to a conclusion based on a limited set of observations. The nature of this method is that one observes repeated instances of the same phenomenon and concludes that the phenomenon will always occur. Using philosophical terms, it is reasoning from the particular to the general, from diversity to unity. This type of reasoning plays a part in operational science where scientists describe theories based on creational patterns using mathematical forms.[1]

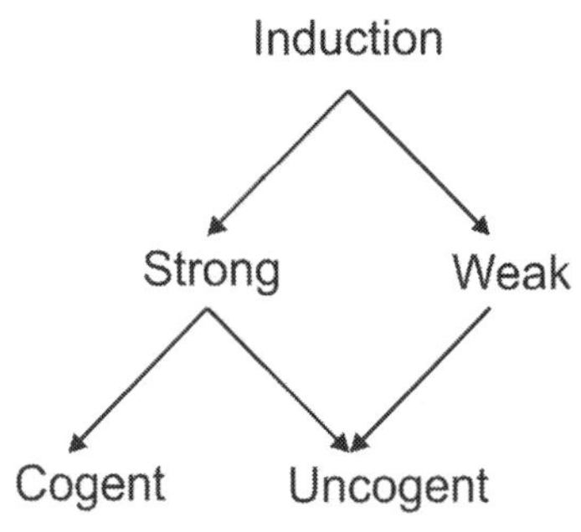

Figure 1.

An inductive **argument**[2] is cogent if it produces a true conclusion. An example of a weak inductive argument is the following reasoning. The last three times I watched my team play, they won. Tomorrow, I'm going to watch my team play, and they will win. Or, I tossed a fair coin four times in a row and got heads. I am certain that the fifth toss of the same coin will be heads. An example of a strong inductive argument are the many types we have illustrated in this text; e.g., numbers that end in the digits 2, 3, 7, and 8 are not perfect squares.

We often call a weak inductive argument the error of induction, or the error of generalization. It may surprise you to discover that many generalizations are weak inductive arguments. So, be careful when you see someone making a generalization from a few examples.

---

[1] Many of the mathematical forms that scientists generate are intuited from their intensive indwelling in the realities presented to them.

[2] In logic, an argument is a set of statements where one of those statements is affirmed based on one or more of the others.

Since mathematics is closely related to science, the search for pattern paradigm is also fundamental to mathematics. The essence of doing mathematics is the search for pattern, either in number relationships or scientific measurements. Mathematicians then employ deductive logic or **ratiocination**, close and careful reasoning, to justify the patterns discovered.

THE FOUNDATIONS OF DEDUCTIVE THINKING

EUCLID REVISITED

As we have noted (Lesson 2.7 and Lesson 5.1), the Greek mathematician Euclid (ca. 330-ca. 275 BC) wrote thirteen geometry books entitled *The Elements*, ***stoicheia*** in Greek.[3] Euclid organized all the known empirircal Geometry of his times[4] by first establishing basic or fundamental definitions, a total of twenty-three, all related to plane geometry. Each succeeding definition built upon what he had previously defined. He defined a point, a line, a plane surface, a plane angle (right, obtuse, acute), perpendicular lines, a **boundary**,[5] a **figure**,[6] a circle, its center, the diameter of a circle, semicircles,

Figure 3. Euclid.
Source: Public Domain.

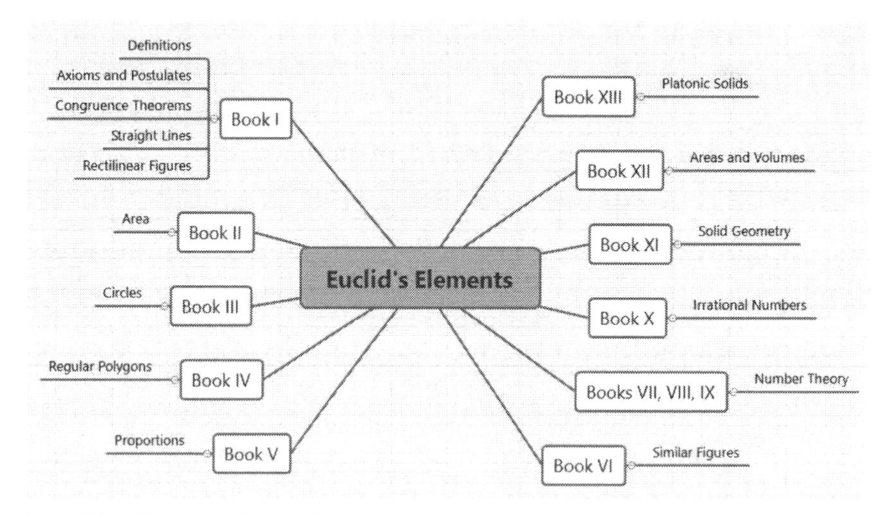

Figure 2. The Structure of Euclid's *Elements*.

---

[3] In the New Testament, *stoicheia* is used in four passages (Galatians 4:3-9; II Peter 3:10-12; Colossians 2:8-20; Hebrews 5:12). It means rudiments, fundamental principles, or first things. For example, the letters of the alphabet are the elements of speech. The onto-relational Trinity is the first principle, the element, the grammar of theology.

[4] For example, the Babylonian tradition bequeathed a tremendous amount of geometric/numeric principles to Greek mathematicians. Some of these principles include the properties of circles, the Pythagorean Theorem, area formula for a triangle, exponential functions used for the computation of compound interest, tables of squares and square roots, and tables of cubes and cube roots. Everything anyone needed to do necessary calculations was in the mathematical toolbox in ancient Babylon.

[5] Euclid defined boundary as "that which is an extremity of anything" meaning "something that surrounds something else."

[6] Euclid defined a figure as "that which is contained by a boundary."

rectilinear figures with three sides (trilateral: triangle), four sides (quadrilateral), and more (multilateral), and parallel lines.[7] His work is a *tour de force*[8] of logical structure.[9]

Second, Euclid stated five basic or general assumptions, i.e., axioms, which are also known as notions. Then he stated five geometric assertions, i.e. **postulates**.[10]

Third, he began to justify a wide variety of theorems, i.e., propositions, a total of 465 scattered throughout his thirteen books.[11] He invoked Aristotelian logic, i.e., deductive or syllogistic thinking, as his method of proof.

Axiom 1 is Euclid's way of stating the idea of the Transitive Property of Equality (Lesson 10.7). In symbols, we start by letting *a*, *b*, and

Euclid's Five Axioms:

Axiom 1. Things being equal to the same thing are also equal to each other.
Axiom 2. If equals are added to equals, the wholes are equal.
Axiom 3. If equals are subtracted from equals, the remainders are equal.
Axiom 4. Things which coincide with each other are equal to each other.
Axiom 5. The whole is greater than the part.

Euclid's Five Postulates:

Postulate 1. Any two points determine exactly one straight line.
Postulate 2. A finite straight line can be extended continuously as a straight line.
Postulate 3. A circle can be completely described given only its center and the measure of its radius.
Postulate 4. All right angles are equal to each other.
Postulate 5. Through a point not on a line, there is one unique line parallel to the given line. [This statement is a simplified version from the Scottish minister, scientist, and mathematician John Playfair (1748-1819).]

---

[7] Remember, parallel, in Greek, means "alongside each other." As his 23rd and last definition, Euclid specified parallel straight lines (Lesson 2.4) as "straight lines which, being in the same plane and being produced indefinitely in both directions, do not meet one another in either direction." He stated his fifth postulate (see above) this way, "That, if a straight line falling on two straight lines make the interior angles on the same side less than two right angles, the two straight lines, if produced indefinitely, meet on that side on which are the angles less than the two right angles." (T. L. Heath, *Euclid: The Thirteen Books of the Elements* [New York: Dover Publications, 1956], 1:155.) Here Euclid toyed gingerly with the idea of infinity.

[8] *Tour de force* is French for "feat of strength."

[9] The ancient Greeks were so good at deduction starting from abstract concepts that we could call them "the abstracts." The problem with abstraction absolutized, and this is the problem of the ancient Greek philosophy, is to dwell permanently in the abstract world. To the Greek philosopher Plato (427-347 BC) the abstract world is the ideal world, the world of forms only. As a corrective to this error, we must always remember that the world of abstraction serves as a tool to help us make links to and from the physical world, either through counting or by measuring. Number and geometric ideas close the gap between pure thought and objective existence. Number and geometric ideas, though, are not objective reality. They report on the nature of reality given the context governing the investigation. Number and geometric ideas recognize and describe objective reality, a reality independent of our thinking. This realism is why these mathematical ideas unify our thinking about objects independent of our thoughts. Number and geometric ideas are the perichoretic link, the interpenetration between what goes on in our head and what goes on outside our head. Abstraction, even though it is thinking apart from its concrete base, is grounded in the objective reality to which it is joined by the creative and sustaining Word of the Triune God.

[10] Postulate, from the Latin, means "a thing demanded." The Greeks made a fine distinction between axioms and postulates. An axiom is an assumption that is intuitively obvious and acceptable while a postulate is an assumption that is neither necessarily obvious nor necessarily acceptable. Also, an axiom is an assumption common to all sciences, while a postulate is an assumption specific to the science being studied. When the German mathematician David Hilbert (1862-1943) spotted loopholes in Euclid's logic, he shored up Euclid's foundations by increasing the number of postulates from five to twenty. See David Hilbert, *Foundations of Geometry* (*Grundlagen der Geometrie*), Leo Unger, trans. (La Salle: Open Court, 1971), pp. 3-28.

[11] For the definitive translation of Euclid's *Elements* into English, see Thomas L. Heath, ed. *The Thirteen Books of the Elements* (New York: Dover Publications, 1956). To mention the book and proposition number (e.g., Book I, Proposition 44 or I:44) is enough to identify its content for the mathematically literate person. In this naming sense only, propositions in *The Thirteen Books of the Elements* carry the same gravitas as a book, chapter, and verse of the Bible.

c represent any mathematical object. If $a = b$, and $b = c$, then $a = c$. Things equal to the same thing are equal to each other.

The Substitution Property and the Transitive Property of Equality are interrelated. In review, we let a and b represent any mathematical object. If $a = b$, then a can be substituted for b. Or, if $a = b$, then b can be substituted for a.

Deduction is a method of logical steps applied to basic facts, whether they be axioms, postulates, definitions, and other deductions. Deduction applied necessarily generates a true conclusion.[12] The English writer Sir Arthur Conan Doyle created a fictional character, the detective Sherlock Holmes who was particularly astute in using this type of analysis to solve criminal cases.[13] In contrast, induction is a method of reasoning that detects some ruling principle by exploring the empirical nature of reality. Induction starts from the particulars, diversity, and generates a universal, unity. Deduction starts from universals, unity, and generates particulars, diversity. Both methods are justified, philosophically, only in terms of the creation of man in the image of the Triune God as revealed by Jesus.[14] Both methods of reasoning work side by side. Induction generates axioms or postulates, i.e., rules, and deduction starts from these rules and generates new propositions. The balanced interplay between induction and deduction forms the basis of all reasoning both in science and its fundamental language tool, mathematics.

LOGIC AND STATEMENTS

In logic, there is a difference between a statement and a formal statement. We make statements all the time, sometimes true, sometimes false, sometimes uncertain. In contrast, a **formal statement** is a statement that can be adjudicated as either true or false. For example, the formal statement $27 + 74 = 100$ is false while the formal statement $699 + 743 = 1442$ is true. Since we can prove mathematical propositions as true or false, mathematical propositions are formal statements.

In logic, all formal statements are what they are; e.g., a spade is a spade. This observation sounds trivial, but it is an important element of logic. It is the **Law of Identity**. In symbols, if we represent a formal statement by b, then:

$$b = b$$

CONDITIONAL STATEMENT

A **conditional statement** is a formal statement that consists of two clauses, one of which begins with the word "if" or "when" or some equivalent word, while the other clause begins with "then."

The "if" clause is the **antecedent**, **premise**, what comes before or prior, or **hypothesis**. The "then" clause is the **consequent**, what comes after or the result, or **conclusion**.

A generalization or law is an "if-then" statement in which there is a variable or variables in the antecedent and consequent. For example, if $\frac{a}{b} = \frac{c}{d}$, then $ad = bc$ (Extreme/Mean Law). As

---

12 The nature of deduction is deterministic. The conclusion is necessarily true based upon assumptions and sound reasoning principles.

13 See Sir Arthur Conan Doyle, *The Complete Sherlock Holmes* (New York: Doubleday, nd).

14 The work of Christian philosopher/reformed theologian Cornelius Van Til (1895-1987) demonstrates that connection. Van Til was primarily concerned with theoretical philosophical principles (i.e., how to resolve the unity/diversity issue in philosophy using the Christian doctrine of the Trinity), but he overlooked the importance of onto-relations within the Trinity and the impact of these relationships on human thinking and life (Lesson 1.1). For an example of the fundamental absence of onto-relations in his thought, see Cornelius Van Til, *The Defense of the Faith* (Phillipsburg: Presbyterian and Reformed Publishing Company, [1955, 1963] 1967).

we have noted (Lesson 2.3), generalizations reflect on the unity in diversity principle and throughout this text, we have shown how Algebra is the generalizing principle of Arithmetic. A generalization states that something is always true, the unity, as in the cause of the Extreme/Mean Law. The diversity is that there are many particularities of this law, many specific revelations of it as in $\frac{6}{8}=\frac{3}{4}, \frac{4}{12}=\frac{1}{3}$, etc.

We use letters to represent a formal statement. Here we have Algebra extended where letters are used to represent clauses, not just numbers or algebraic expressions. If *a* and *b* are clauses and *a* is related to *b* in a formal way, we represent this relationship by stating: If *a*, then *b*, or *b* only if *a*. As we have seen, we can substitute the "if-then," with the symbol $\Rightarrow$ (Lesson 3.3) meaning implies. We can write "if *a*, then *b*" as follows:

$$a \Rightarrow b$$

> To *b* or not to *b*. That is the question.
> A logical interpretation of Shakespeare.

We can **negate** a statement by using the tilde symbol, ~. Let *b* represent a formal statement. By our definition of a formal statement, *b* is either true or false. $\sim b$ represents the negation, or the opposite, of *b*. Therefore, if *b* is true, then $\sim b$ is false, and if *b* is false, then $\sim b$ is true.

By this analysis, we cannot say that *b* and $\sim b$ are both true. The **Law of Contradiction** states that a formal statement cannot be true and false at the same time.[15] The **Law of Excluded Middle**[16] states that if *b* is a formal statement, then either *b* or $\sim b$.

Formal statements in mathematics, by their definition, invoke **antithetical thinking** or thinking in accord with thesis and antithesis. In other words, a formal statement is true, the thesis, or it is not true, the antithesis. Antithetical thinking subsumes the Law of Contradiction and the Law of Excluded Middle and is reflective of the rationality of number at its deterministic level. These laws are determined because we cannot escape their validity. We must assume them to deny them. For example, to deny the Law of Contradiction means that we are saying that the law is false. We are using this law to deny it. Pause and reflect. These two laws are prerequisite for coherence of the human experience as reflected in the determinate rationality of number. Without these laws, we cannot communicate anything intelligible in mathematics. For example, we could say $2 + 2 = 4$ and $2 + 2 \neq 4$.

How do we use conditional statements in mathematics? ***Modus ponens***[17] is a valid form of argumentation in which we affirm the antecedent of a conditional statement, thereby entailing the affirmation of the consequent, or:

If *a* then *b* and *a* is true, therefore, *b*.

Here are a two examples:

If $\frac{a}{b}=\frac{c}{d}$, then $ad = bc$.

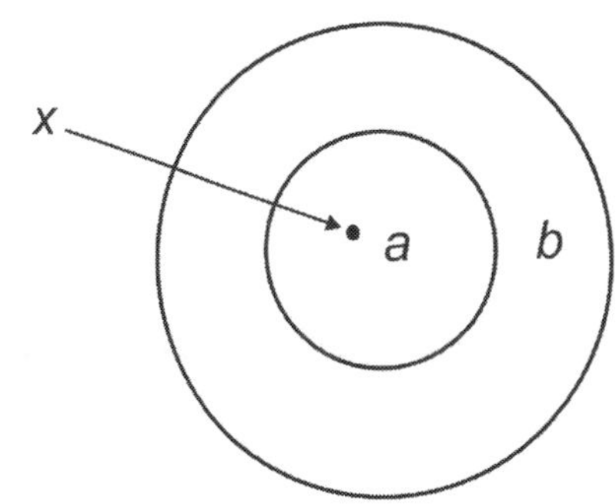

Figure 4. Conditional Statement: $a \Rightarrow b$

[15] The literature on logic sometimes names this law as the Law of Non-contradiction.
[16] In Latin, *teritum non datur*, no third (possibility) is given.
[17] *Modus pollens* is a Latin phrase meaning "mode that affirms."

$\frac{2}{3} = \frac{4}{6}$ is true, therefore $2 \times 6 = 3 \times 4$.

We can represent a conditional statement using Venn diagrams. In Figure 4, if x is in the circle represented by a (think geometric area), then x is also in the circle represented by b. If a then b, and x is in a, therefore x is in b.

CONVERSE

As we have already noted (Lesson 3.3), given the conditional statement $a \Rightarrow b$, the converse is $b \Rightarrow a$. It is important to point out that, if the conditional statement is true, the converse may be true, but it is not necessarily true. For example, if I live in Fresno, then I live in the state of California. We have a true conditional statement. Its converse, however, is not true, i.e., if I live in the state of California, then I live in Fresno.

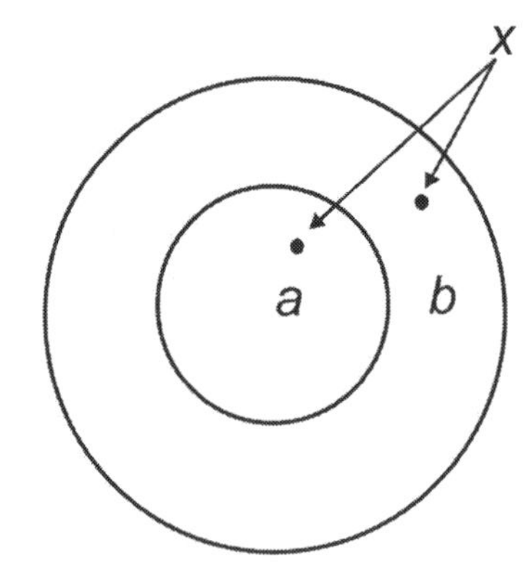

Figure 5. $b \Rightarrow a$?

Using a Venn Diagram (Figure 5), if $a \Rightarrow b$, for x to be in the area represented by b means:

(1) x could not be in the area represented by a.
Or:
(2) x could be in the area represented by a.

We have also noted (Lesson 3.3) that when a conditional statement and its converse are both true, we have logical equivalence, symbolized by $\Leftrightarrow$. We write:

$a \Leftrightarrow b$ means $a \Rightarrow b$ and $b \Rightarrow a$

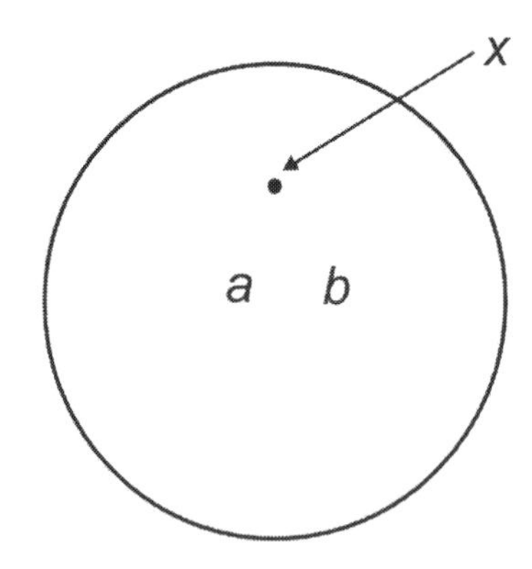

Figure 6. $a \Leftrightarrow b$

Note in the Venn Diagram (Figure 6) that the areas represented by a and b are identical.

We can also represent logical equivalence by stating, "a is both a necessary and sufficient condition for b." We have seen (Lesson 3.3 and Lesson 10.2) that logical equivalence, $a \Leftrightarrow b$, is another way to say "a if and only if b." The "if" clause is the *sufficient* condition ($a \Rightarrow b$), and the "only if" clause is the *necessary* condition ($b \Rightarrow a$). When logical equivalence is true, $a \Rightarrow b$ and $b \Rightarrow a$, logicians name these two statements **biconditional statements**.

In Geometry, if a triangle has three sides of equal length, then it is an equilateral triangle, and if a triangle is equilateral, then it has three sides of equal length. We have logical equivalence meaning a triangle having three sides of equal length is both a necessary and sufficient condition for it to be equilateral.

In Algebra, we used logical equivalence in solving equations. For example:

Example 1. $3x = 12 \Leftrightarrow x = 4$

$3x = 12$ is both a necessary and sufficient condition for $x = 4$; i.e., $3x = 12$ is a sufficient condition for $x = 4$ and $x = 4$ is a necessary condition for $3x = 12$.

Example 2. If $x = -3$, then $x^2 = 9$ or $x = -3 \Rightarrow x^2 = 9$

This is a true conditional statement but the converse is *not* true: $x^2 = 9 \Rightarrow x = -3$. Why? $x = 3$ is also a solution to $x^2 = 9$. Therefore, we say the following:

(1) $x^2 = 9 \Leftrightarrow x = -3$ is a *false* formal statement. Why? $x^2 = 9$ is a sufficient condition for $x = -3$, but $x = -3$ is *not* a necessary condition for $x^2 = 9$ because $x = 3$ is another condition that will generate the same result if we square both sides of the equation $x = 3$.

(2) $x^2 = 9 \Leftrightarrow x = 3$ or $x = -3$ is a *true* formal statement. Why? $x^2 = 9$ is a necessary and sufficient condition for $x = 3$ or $x = -3$.

INVERSE

Given $a \Rightarrow b$, the **inverse** is $\sim a \Rightarrow \sim b$. Again, the inverse may be true, but it is *not* necessarily true. If I live in Fresno, then I live in the state of California. Its inverse, however, is *not* true, i.e., if I do not live in Fresno, then I do not live in the state of California. If I live in Sacramento, I do not live in Fresno, but I am still living in the state of California.

Using a Venn Diagram (Figure 7), if $a \Rightarrow b$, for x to not be in the area represented by a means:

(1) x could be in the area represented by b.
Or:
(2) x could not be in the area represented by b.

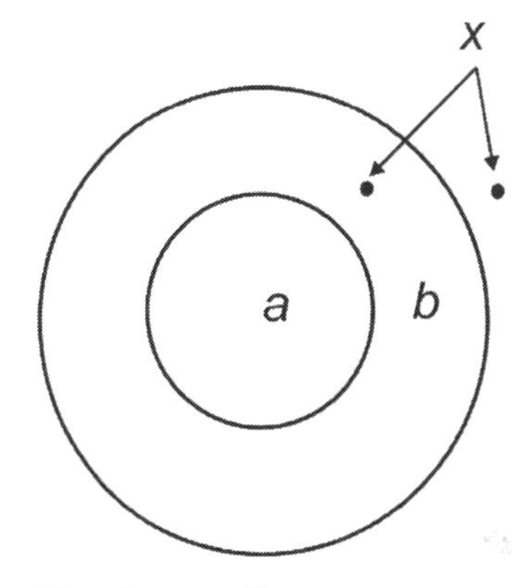

Figure 7. $\sim a \Rightarrow \sim b$?

CONTRAPOSITIVE

The ***modus tollens***[18] argument, or the **Law of Contraposition** argument, takes this form:

If a then b and not b, therefore not a.

Given $a \Rightarrow b$, the **contrapositive** is $\sim b \Rightarrow \sim a$. The contrapositive is necessarily true. If I live in Fresno, then I live in the state of California is logically equivalent to saying that if I do not live in the state of California, then I do not live in Fresno.

Using a Venn Diagram (Figure 8), if $a \Rightarrow b$, for x to not be in the area represented by b means x is not in the area represented by a.

We have logical equivalence between a conditional statement and its contrapositive:

$a \Rightarrow b \Leftrightarrow \sim b \Rightarrow \sim a$

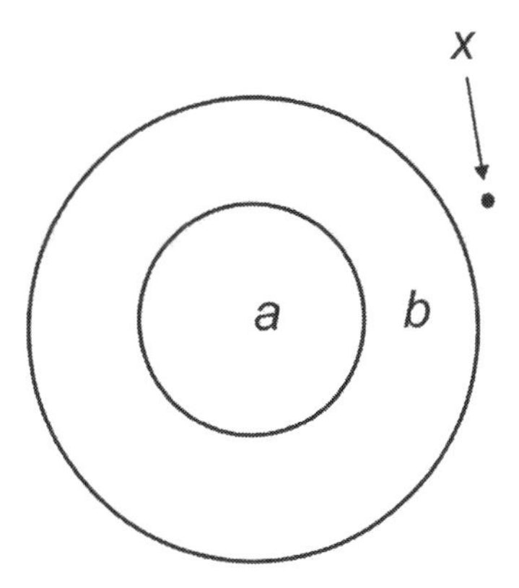

Figure 8. $\sim b \Rightarrow \sim a$

[18] *Modus tollens* is a Latin phrase meaning "mode that denies."

We also have logical equivalence between the converse and the inverse (Figure 9):

$b \Rightarrow a \Leftrightarrow \sim a \Rightarrow \sim b$

We will see several examples of this method of argumentation in Lesson 13.9 through Lesson 13.11.

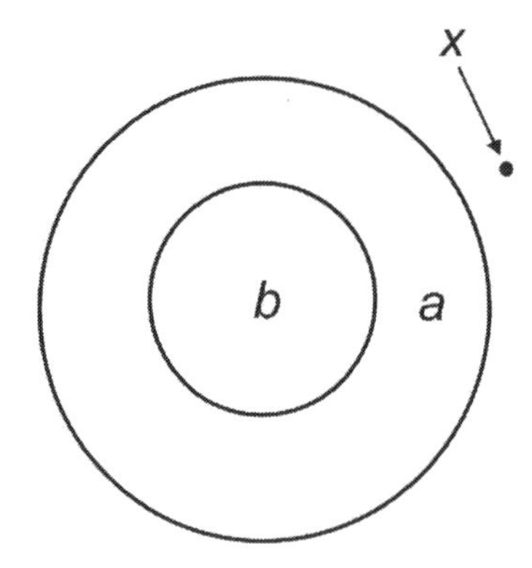

Figure 9. $\sim a \Rightarrow \sim b$

FORMAL LOGICAL FALLACIES

From these observations, we describe two formal logical fallacies, **asserting the consequent** (Figure 10) and **denying the antecedent** (Figure 11).

Given $a \Rightarrow b$, asserting the consequent, or the converse error, is stating that the converse, $b \Rightarrow a$, is always true. If I live in Fresno, then I live in the state of California. If I assert that I live in the state of California, i.e., if I assert the consequent, and then I conclude that I live in the city of Fresno, I am guilty of committing a logical fallacy.

This fallacy often appears in science. Some Theory P predicts that we will observe Q. Experimental observation shows Q. It is not necessarily true that theory P is true. Many times this assertion of the consequent is declared true by this false reasoning.

In symbols:

$a \Rightarrow b \not\Leftrightarrow b \Rightarrow a$ where $\not\Leftrightarrow$ means "not equivalent to."

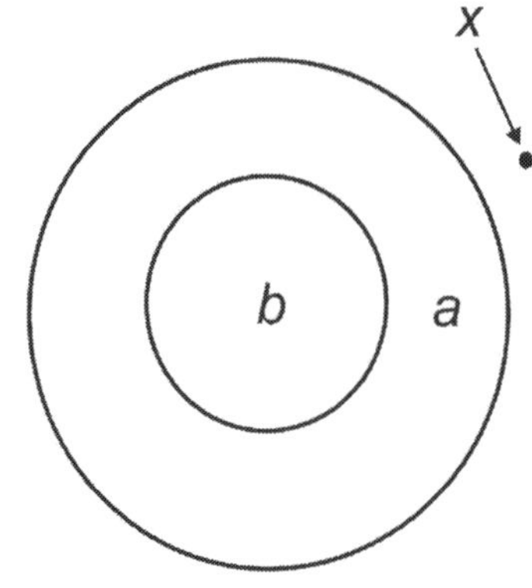

Figure 10. Asserting the consequent.

Given $a \Rightarrow b$, denying the antecedent, or the inverse error, is stating that the inverse, $\sim a \Rightarrow \sim b$, is always true. If I live in Fresno, then I live in the state of California. If I assert that I do not live in Fresno, denying the antecedent, to conclude that I do not live in the state of California is a logical fallacy. I could live in Sacramento, a city in the state of California.

In symbols:

$a \Rightarrow b \not\Leftrightarrow \sim a \Rightarrow \sim b$

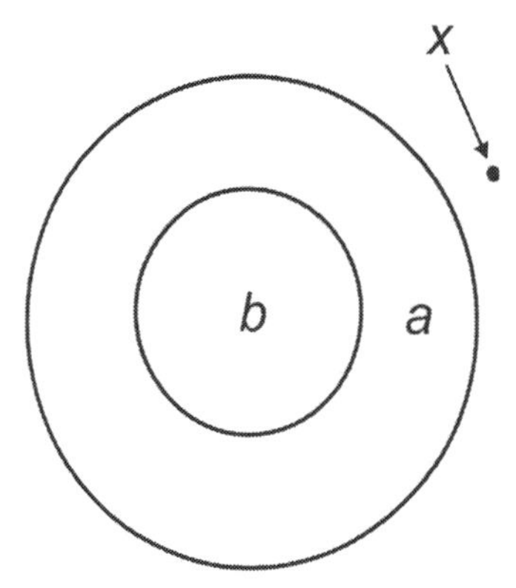

Figure 11. Denying the antecedent.

Table 1: If-then Syllogistic Structures				
Given the true conditional statement $a \Rightarrow b$				
Assume the truth of:	a	$\sim a$	b	$\sim b$
Conclusion	b	$\sim b$	a	$\sim a$
Validity of Conclusion	Valid (*modus ponens*)	Invalid (denying the antecedent; inverse error)	Invalid (affirming the consequent; converse error)	Valid (*modus tollens*)

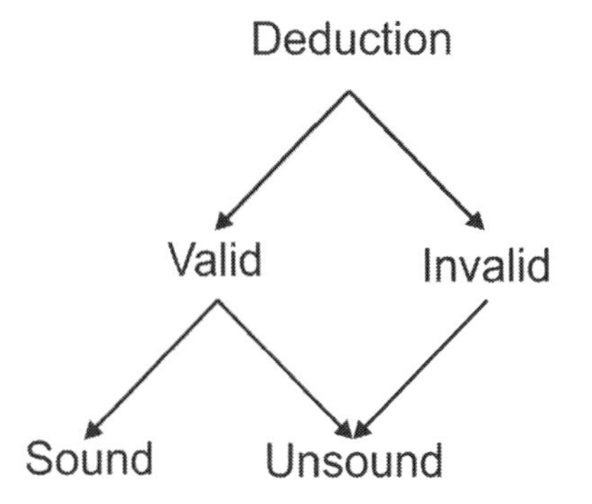

Figure 12.

> If you start with false premises, you can arrive at the wrong conclusion for all the right reasons.
> James D. Nickel

A strong deductive argument is a valid argumentation applied to true premises to generate a true conclusion. An invalid deductive argument is valid argumentation applied to false premises to produce a conclusion that is wrong. Invalid deductive arguments are also unsound when there is no logical equivalence between the conditional statement and its converse or inverse, thus either asserting the consequent or denying the antecedent.

All of this material, and much more is studied in a formal course in logic.[19] Mathematicians are required to master logic as a prerequisite to their studies. Since Euclid, mathematicians have followed his model, with an emphasis on axioms, postulates, and deduction, known as the development of **Axiomatic-Deductive Systems**.

> A mathematical **argument** is **rigorous** when it is logically valid and strong.
> A mathematical **argument** is **heuristic** (from a Greek word meaning "find") when it stresses the underlying meaning, the process of discovery, the motivating factors, and the applicability to reality.

EXISTENCE, COHERENCE, AND RECOGNITION STATEMENTS

Albert Einstein (1879-1955), in his essay "Geometry and Experience" (1921), expressed an enigma between the nature of reality, what goes on outside of us, and the nature of human thought, what goes on in our heads:

---

[19] See T. Ryan Byerly, *Introducing Logic and Critical Thinking: The Skills of Reasoning and the Virtues of Inquiry* (Grand Rapids: Baker Academic, 2017). For a more mathematically oriented study, see Warren W. Esty, *The Language of Mathematics, Nineteenth Edition* (Bozeman: Montana State University, 2011).

> ... it is mathematics which affords the exact natural sciences a certain measure of certainty, to which without mathematics they could not attain.
>
> At this point an enigma presents itself which in all ages has agitated inquiring minds. How can it be that mathematics, being after all a product of human thought which is independent of experience, is so admirably appropriate to the objects of reality? Is human reason, then, without experience, merely by taking thought, able to fathom the properties of real things?
>
> In my opinion, the answer to this question is, briefly, this: as far as the propositions of mathematics refer to reality, they are not certain; and as far as they are certain, they do not refer to reality. It seems to me that complete clarity as to this state of things became common property only through that trend in mathematics which is known by the name of "axiomatics." The progress achieved by axiomatics consists in its having neatly separated the logical-formal from its objective or intuitive content; according to axiomatics the logical-formal alone forms the subject matter of mathematics, which is not concerned with the intuitive or other content associate with the logical formal.[20]

Einstein is differentiating between existence statements and coherence statements.[21] **Existence statements** are statements that refer to external facts independent of them. The truth of existence statements lies in realities to which they point. They are usually discovered by one's interaction with the world outside of the mind. **Coherence statements** are logically coherent statements that put a system or discipline in harmony. These statements form the relational dance of a system. For example, the Axiomatic-Deductive System, used consistently by mathematicians since Euclid, is primarily concerned with coherence statements; i.e., how a system of statements interconnects logically.

Figure 13. Source: United States Postal Service.

Geometry, as understood by Euclid, is a purely theoretical discipline. It is only concerned with statements that are constructed into coherent patterns according to certain fixed axioms, postulates, definitions, and rules of reasoning. In themselves, geometric statements tell us nothing about the real world although they can, as with formal logic or Algebra, help us check the coherence of our existence statements with one another.

These observations apply to any system of thinking, especially any form of systematic theology, where coherence statements usually take precedence. Scripture, for example, consists of existence statements that refer ultimately to reality outside of its words, to the living Trinity because Jesus, the incarnate Son of God, is the ultimate Word of God. We must connect Scripture and systematic theology, our coherence statements, to the life of the Trinity. If we do not, we have a dead letter.[22]

In his essay "Science and Religion" (1939), Einstein said:

> Now, even though the realms of religion and science in themselves are clearly marked off from each other, nevertheless there exist between the two strong reciprocal relationships and dependencies. Though religion may be that which determines the goal, it has,

---

[20] Albert Einstein, *Ideas and Opinions* (New York: Wings Books, 1954), p. 233.

[21] For much of the analysis in this section, I am indebted to Thomas F. Torrance, *Theology in Reconstruction* (Grand Rapids: William B. Eerdmans, 1965), pp. 52-61. See also his extended discussion in *Theological Science* (Oxford: Oxford University Press, [1969] 1978), pp. 164-352.

[22] See II Corinthians 3 where the Apostle Paul compares dead letter to life in the Holy Spirit.

> nevertheless, learned from science, in the broadest sense, what means will contribute to the attainment of the goals it has set up. But science can only be created by those who are thoroughly imbued with the aspiration toward truth and understanding. This source of feeling, however, springs from that sphere of religion. To this there also belongs the faith in the possibility that the regulations valid for the world of existence are rational, that is, comprehensible to reason. I cannot conceive of a genuine scientist without that profound faith. The situation may be expressed by an image: science without religion is lame, religion without science is blind.[23]

In the coherence statements of science, mathematics, and theology, we must work with existence statements or else we are playing logical games. Rewording Einstein, coherence statements without existence statements are lame. Existence statements without coherence statements are blind. When applied to Geometry, the coherence statements of Euclidean geometry without existence statements are lame. Existence statements without coherence statements of Euclidean geometry are blind.

There is a gap between human thought and existence and the rationality of number transcends that divide. In this context, the kinds of statements mathematician make are **recognition statements**, statements they must make in the face of an order outside of themselves. Recognition statements acknowledge that there is reality outside of the human mind, an order that presses itself on our minds.[24] It is these recognition statements that resonate with the inherent rationality, the dance, of the universe.

Human beings create the symbols of mathematical language, but the symbols and syntax, the reasoning applied, report on a patterned reality that transcends the human mind at the same time the human mind reasons about them.[25] Therefore, recognition statements are not ultimately human constructs because they are pressed upon us by their ontological reality. These statements are by-products of the rational patterns of objective reality, the structure of the way things work, albeit, if only in the form of mathematical equations.[26]

> Number relationships underlie, unify, and reveal the order of nature.
>
> Morris Kline, *Mathematics: The Loss of Certainty* (1980), p. 15.

---

[23] Einstein, *Ideas and Opinions*, pp. 45-46. Einstein adapted these observations, especially the words "lame" and "blind" from the German philosopher Immanuel Kant (1724-1804).

[24] Recognition means "to know again," to "recall to the mind." It is to acknowledge the existence of something outside of ourselves. When we comprehend an infinitesimal portion of the fabric of the rationality of creation, we are re-cognizing a reality that has been antecedently thought by far exceeding intelligence, the wisdom of God the Father Almighty, thought actualized, i.e., spoken into existence, by His Son, the *logos*.

[25] There is, in a sense, immanence and transcendence in mathematical thought. Their interpenetration is perichoretic.

[26] Being and form (or structure) interpenetrate because both are created ***ex nihilo*** (from Latin meaning "out of nothing") through the free and lavish benevolence of the Triune God. For Euclid, form had nothing to do with being, form had nothing to do with existence. Without recognizing its ontological grounds, Euclid's geometry devolves into a formal game of logic. The applicability of mathematics to existence is what distinguishes mathematics as a science from mathematics as a game.

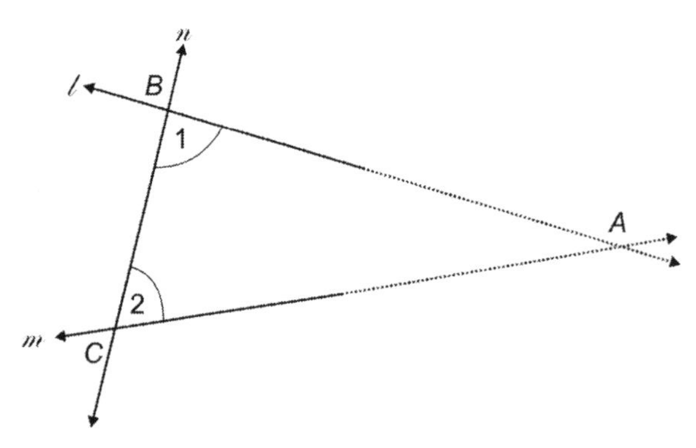

Figure 14. The Geometry of Euclid's Parallel Postulate where $m\angle 1 + m\angle 2 < 180°$. See footnote 7 of this lesson.

Listen carefully to the summary analysis of the theologian Thomas F. Torrance (1913-2007):

> It must be granted that all human knowledge and not least scientific knowledge is reached through a compromise between thought and being, but that does not entitle us to draw the conclusion that it is we human beings who impart order to nature or rationality to the universe. There could be no science at all if we were not up against an implacably objective rationality in things independent of any and all of us. Certainly we do not find ready-made equations in nature. We have to frame these ourselves, but we do so not by imposing patterns of our own creation upon nature but by acting in obedience to a rationality inherent in nature itself. Number, as a calm and sober reflection surely forces us to realize, represents something quite objective. Hence our basic statements in mathematics and physics are made by way of *recognition* or *reflection* of what is there independently rather than by invention or imposition on our part.[27]

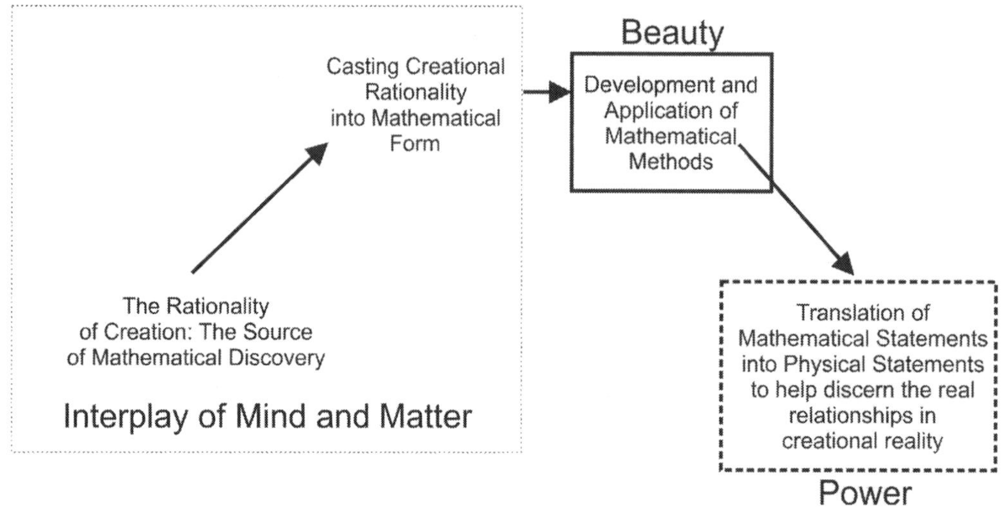

Figure 15. The Beauty and Power of Mathematics.

The integration of being and structure is why algebraic operations applied to these statements can generate new statements that are also dance with the way things work in the universe. This interpenetration, this perichoresis, is why, in the words of Einstein, human thought which is independent of experience, is so admirably appropriate to the objects of reality.

---

[27] Thomas F. Torrance, *Theology in Reconstruction*, pp. 275-276.

For example, we can use Geometry and Algebra to derive measurements impossible to make otherwise. The radius of the Earth is a measurement derived algebraically from the Earth's circumference, a measurement first approximated by Eratosthenes (3rd century BC) when he applied propositions of Euclidean geometry to the distance between two cities and shadow angles in a well (Lesson 8.7). Knowing the circumference of the Earth, we can find its radius because $C = 2\pi r \Leftrightarrow r = \frac{C}{2\pi}$. Knowing the radius of the Earth, we can apply algebraic operations to the Pythagorean Theorem and generate results that will tell an observer at a certain height above the Earth how many miles he can see to the horizon (Lesson 11.9).

When we study logic, we need to see a bigger picture, a picture that puts logic in the framework of existence, coherence, and recognition statements.

EXERCISES

Define the following terms:

1. Inductive thinking
2. Argument (logic)
3. Ratiocination
4. *Stoicheia*
5. Boundary
6. Figure
7. Postulate
8. Formal statement
9. Law of Identity
10. Conditional statement
11. Premise
12. Antecedent
13. Hypothesis
14. Consequent
15. Conclusion
16. Negation
17. Law of Contradiction
18. Law of Excluded Middle
19. Antithetical thinking
20. *Modus ponens*
21. Biconditional statements
22. Inverse
23. *Modus tollens*
24. Law of Contraposition
25. Contrapositive
26. Asserting the consequent
27. Denying the antecedent
28. Axiomatic-Deductive System
29. Rigorous argument
30. Heuristic argument
31. Existence statement
32. Coherence statement
33. Recognition statement

> ... mathematicians are explorers of patterns, and formal, logical proofs that can be methodically checked are the ultimate test of mathematical validity.
>
> Luke Heaton, *A Brief History of Mathematical Thought* (2015), p. 7.

34. *Ex nihilo*
35. Exterior angle of a triangle (See homework exercise below.)

> ... order is one of the ultimate beliefs which, while rational, cannot be proved – for we have to assume order either in trying to prove or disprove it – all rational order points beyond itself to an ultimate ground of order ... apart from God the transcendent ground of all order, there could be no rational thought, let alone any science.
>
> Thomas F. Torrance, *Theological and Natural Science* (2002), p. 33.

Answer the following questions:

36. What is the difference between an axiom and a postulate?
37. Is the inverse of a conditional statement logically equivalent to its converse?
38. Why is the nature of deduction deterministic? (Hint: Review the definition of determinism in Lesson 9.1.)
39. Explain why immanence and transcendence is in mathematical thought.
40. A conditional statement: If I drink sweet tea today, it will rain. It did not rain today. Therefore, I did not drink sweet tea. What is right about this argument? What is wrong about this argument?
41. Jean-Paul Sartre (1905-1980), a French existential philosopher once said, "If God exists, I cannot be free. I am free. Therefore, God does not exist." What is right about this argument? What is wrong about this argument?
42. Why is it possible to come to the wrong conclusion for all the right reasons?
43. Why is it important to understand the premises, the framework, of any system of thought?

True or False.

44. That a train runs on schedule is a sufficient condition for you to arrive on time at your destination.
45. That you arrive on time at your destination is a necessary condition for a train to run on schedule.
46. $8x = 3$ is a sufficient condition for $x = \frac{3}{8}$.
47. $x = \frac{3}{8}$ is a necessary condition for $8x = 3$.
48. $8x = 3$ is a sufficient and necessary condition for $x = \frac{3}{8}$.
49. $x = -2.5$ is a sufficient condition for $x^2 = 6.25$.
50. $x^2 = 6.25$ is a necessary condition for $x = 2.5$.
51. $x^2 = 121$ is a sufficient and necessary condition for $x = 11$ or $x = -11$.
52. The real number q is a sufficient and necessary condition for q to be a rational number.
53. Euclid's system of Geometry is an example existence statements.
54. Recognition statements report on the nature of existence statements.

Answer the following questions:

55. During World War II, physicist Richard Feynman (1918-1988) worked on the secret atomic bomb project in Los Alamos, New Mexico. He once wrote a letter to a friend about a peculiar decimal expansion involving the fraction 1/243. Project censors intercepted the letter

and returned it to Feynman because they thought it was some sort of secret code. If we divide 1 by 243, we get 0.004115226337 ….
(a) What is the pattern?
(b) Do you think this pattern continues *ad infinitum*?
(c) Why or why not?

56. Explain what is wrong with this reasoning: Since we know that "the lot is cast into the lap, but its every decision is from the LORD" (Proverbs 16:33, ESV), we conclude that God brings about all things, good and evil, in accordance with His will. God Himself brings about all evil aspects of the world, even the brutality of the Nazis at Birkenau and Auschwitz, for His glory and for His people's good. (Hint: Refer to the discussion of this verse in Lesson 9.1, especially how the Greek Septuagint translates the Hebrew.)
57. The Hungarian mathematician Abraham Wald (1902-1950) immigrated to the United States in 1938 when the Nazis became more active in persecuting Jews. During World War II he worked for the Statistical Research Group where he analyzed statistical data retrieved from airplanes that returned from combat missions in Europe. Specifically, he studied the number of bullet holes per square foot in different sections of these planes. The least number of holes occurred in the engine. To everyone's surprise, Wald recommended the military needed more reinforcement armor around the engine. Explain why he came to this conclusion.

The following set of questions illustrate the way Euclid reasoned in *The Elements*. These problems are a good introduction to the principles taught in Lesson 13.3.

58. Use Figure 16 to help you prove m$\angle DBF$ = m$\angle EBF$. (Hint: Refer to the Construction exercise in Lesson 5.3 and the last homework question in Lesson 13.1). This theorem is Euclid's Proposition 9, Book I.

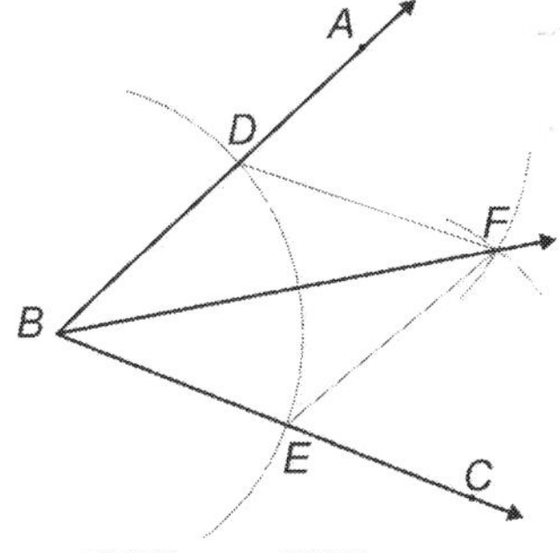

Figure 16. Bisecting an angle.

Let's see how Euclid proved Book I, Proposition 16, commonly known as the Exterior Angle Theorem. Euclid states it like this, "In any triangle, if one of the sides be produced, the exterior angle is greater than either of the interior and opposite angles." First, we define an **exterior angle of a triangle** as the angle that forms a linear pair (Lesson 8.7) with one of the angles of the triangle. In Figure 18, $\angle CBD$ is an exterior angle of ΔABC; it forms a linear pair with $\angle CBA$. Answer the following questions:

59. In Figure 17, if C is a jet aircraft and A and B are positions on the Earth in sight of C, what seems to be true about the relationship between $\angle 1$ and $\angle 2$?
60. We are going to prove, given ΔABC in Figure 18, that m$\angle CBD$ > m$\angle ACB$. What is the other inequality that we must prove?
61. Recreate ΔABC in your workbook. Make it large enough and allow for enough space to handle the construction extensions in the figure.

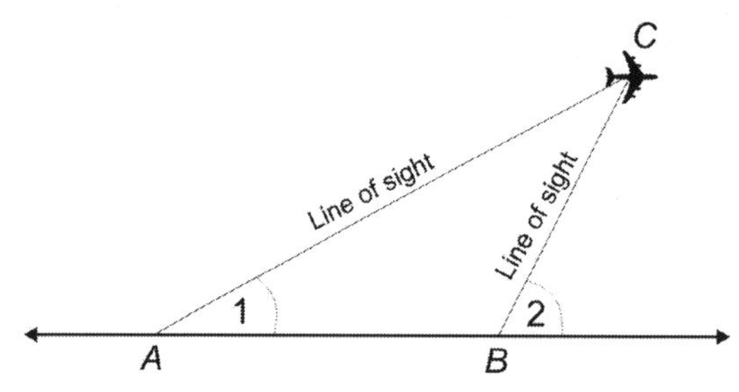

Figure 17. Line of sight.

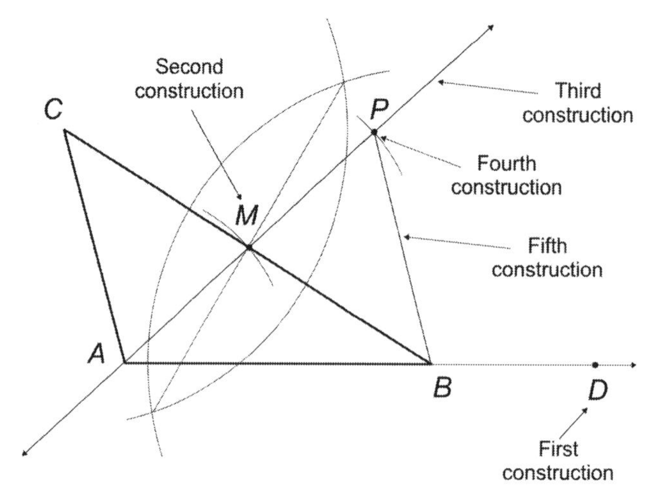

Figure 18. Exterior Angle Theorem.

62. First construction: Extend $\overline{AB}$ to make $\overrightarrow{AB}$ and mark D on $\overrightarrow{AB}$ such that $AD > AB$. We can do this by Euclid's first postulate. We now have $\angle CBD$, an exterior angle to ΔABC.
63. Second construction: Bisect $\overline{CB}$ and mark M as the point of bisection. We can do this by Euclid's Proposition 10 in Book I.
64. What can we say about CM and MB?
65. Third construction: Draw $\overleftrightarrow{AM}$. We can do this by Euclid's first postulate.
66. (a) Fourth construction: Mark P on $\overleftrightarrow{AM}$ such that $AM = MP$.
    (b) We can do this by Euclid's third postulate. Explain why.
67. Fifth construction: Draw $\overline{PB}$. We can do this by Euclid's first postulate.
68. Note the two triangles, ΔCMA and ΔBMP. Why are the two angles, $\angle CMA$ and $\angle BMP$, equal? (Hint: Refer to the text of Lesson 8.3, Lesson 8.7 homework, and Euclid's Proposition 15 of Book I.)
69. Since $m\angle CMA = m\angle BMP$, $CM = MB$ and $AM = MP$, what can we conclude about the relationship between ΔCMA and ΔBMP? (Hint: Think SAS Congruence Theorem, Book 1, Proposition 4.[28])
70. Why, therefore, is $m\angle ACM = m\angle PBM$? (Hint: What is always true about congruent triangles?)
71. Why is $m\angle CBD > m\angle PBM$? (Hint: Refer to Euclid's fifth axiom.)

---

[28] The German mathematician David Hilbert (1862-1943) preferred to state this proposition as an axiom, Congruence Axiom 6, because of the faulty way Euclid employed to prove it.

72. Why can we now conclude that m∠*CBD* > m∠*ACB*? (Note: We can apply the same logic to prove that that m∠*CBD* > m∠*CAB*.)
73. How would you prove that the exterior angle of a triangle is equal to the sum of the two opposite interior angles? (Hint: Draw a figure, establish the angles, and reason to the QED.)

Answer the following questions:

74. In the mystery *The Silver Blaze* renowned detective Sherlock Holmes is discussing a case with Dr. Watson while both are riding on a train. "We are going well," said Mr. Holmes, looking out of the window and glancing at his watch. "Our rate at present is 53.5 miles an hour." "I have not observed the quarter-mile posts," said Dr. Watson. "Nor have I. But the telegraph posts upon this line are sixty yards apart, and the calculation is a simple one." How did Mr. Holmes determine the speed of the train? (Note: You may use your calculator to assist you.)
75. Let's have some fun. Explain how this deduction is possible:

$$y = \frac{\ln\left(\frac{x}{m} - sa\right)}{r^2} \Leftrightarrow r^2 y = \ln\left(\frac{x}{m} - sa\right) \Leftrightarrow e^{r^2 y} = \frac{x}{m} - sa \Leftrightarrow me^{r^2 y} = x - sam \Leftrightarrow me^{rry} = x - mas$$

Explain the meaning of these sentences.

76. James Clerk Maxwell stressed embodied mathematics as mathematics in its fullness.
77. Euclidean geometry, as presented by Euclid, is empty of meaning even though its coherence statements are beautiful.

> The mathematicians who first discovered the theorems we now study did not start with a set of axioms or formulae and simply manipulate them until something 'came up'. They started from what they perceived to be a problem from comparison of different fields of study, or from paradoxes arising from previous results. From such observations (obtained by indwelling the various fields) plus, of course, a degree of manipulative ability, they extracted certain common properties as a formalised set. This set they then attempted to describe in the most economical way – they attempted to axiomatise it. But having axiomatised the system, new hypotheses are not derived by trial and error. Instead, hypotheses arising from the original intuitive grounds of the system may be proved by showing that they are derivable from the previously accredited axiom set. They then become *theorems*. Thus mathematicians, by a process of indwelling, extraction/abstraction and simplification/axiomatisation provide the world with a tool whereby to test new hypotheses. Belief in the universal validity of these results comes from the accrediting of their colleagues, and the richness of the implications of their results as they 'resonate' in other minds.
>
> John C. Puddefont, "Indwelling: Formal and Non-Formal Elements in Faith and Life." In *Belief in Science and in Christian Life* (1980), pp. 31-32.

13.3 The Direct Method of Proof

Terms & Concepts Introduced
1. Conclusion of an argument
2. Direct proof
3. Heron's formula for the area of a triangle
4. Incircle
5. Premises of an argument
6. Semi-perimeter of a triangle
7. Syllogism

Mathematicians use deductive logic, close and careful reasoning, to prove a proposition in three ways: (1) Direct, (2) Indirect, and (3) by Mathematical Induction. In this lesson, we will explain direct proof and illustrate it with several examples.

In a **direct proof** we start from certain givens, premises, and then reach a conclusion using steps that we can justify logically. We can thank the Greek philosopher Aristotle (384-322 BC) for teaching and writing about this method, a method used by his student Euclid and by mathematicians ever since.

In direct proof, we employ a chain of consequential reasoning. In symbols, if we know $a \Rightarrow b$ and we can reason that $b \Rightarrow c$, we conclude that $a \Rightarrow c$. The first two statements, $a \Rightarrow b$ and $b \Rightarrow c$ are the **premises of the argument** and the last statement, $a \Rightarrow c$, is the **conclusion of the argument**. By the nature of deduction, the conclusion is contained in the premises and the premises are contained in the conclusion, a perichoresis in logical-causal thinking.

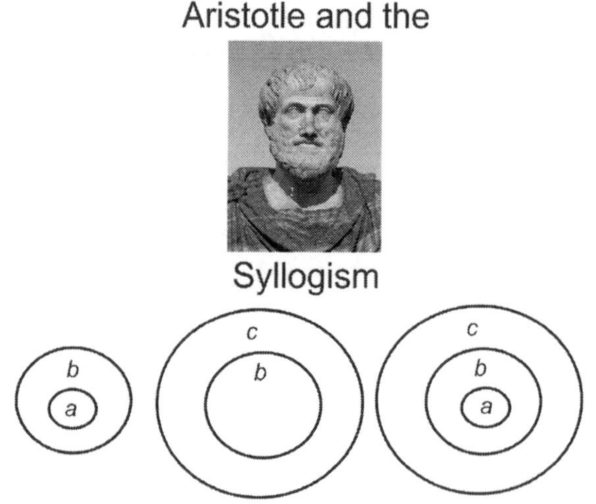

Figure 1.

Direct proof is also known as a **syllogism.**[1] Note how the geometric areas of the Venn Diagram (Figure 1) reveal syllogistic thinking: If a is in b and b is in c, then a is in c.

Proof of Extreme/Mean Law

Let's prove the Extreme/Mean Law by direct proof; i.e., in symbols, we want to prove:

$$\frac{a}{b} = \frac{c}{d} \Leftrightarrow ad = bc \text{ where } a, b, c, d \neq 0$$

(Note that we are establishing the truth of biconditional statements, or logical equivalence.)

Let's develop the proof step by step, following Euclid's logic in Proposition 18, Book VII, of *The Elements*. In his proof, Euclid worked with line segments instead of letters representing numbers. Our rendition of his proof, therefore, is purely algebraic.

We assume that a, b, c, and d are non-zero real numbers. Euclid first proved this implication:

$$\frac{a}{b} = \frac{c}{d} \Rightarrow ad = bc$$

[1] *Syllogism* is derived from the Greek word *syllogismos* which is derived from *syllogizesthai*, meaning to "reason with."

Step 1. Given: $\frac{a}{b}=\frac{c}{d}$. We must prove $ad = bc$.

Step 2. Starting from $\frac{c}{d}$, multiply both the numerator and denominator by a. We get:

$$\frac{ac}{ad}=\frac{c}{d}.$$

Step 3. From the given, $\frac{c}{d}=\frac{a}{b}$.

Step 4. Now consider $\frac{a}{b}$. Multiply both the numerator and denominator by c. We get:

$$\frac{a}{b}=\frac{ac}{bc}.$$

Step 5. Therefore, reasoning syllogistically from Step 1 to Step 3, $\frac{ac}{ad}=\frac{ac}{bc}$.

Step 6. Since $ac = ac$ (Law of Identity), $ad = bc$.

Step 7. Therefore, from Step 1 to Step 6, $\frac{a}{b}=\frac{c}{d}\Rightarrow ad=bc$.

QED

We are reasoned from Step 1 to Step 2, Step 2 to Step 3, Step 3 to Step 4, Step 4 to Step 5, and Step 5 to Step 6, where we have established what we wanted to prove; i.e., $ad = bc$. Here is our syllogism consisting of five premises and the conclusion:

Step 1 $\Rightarrow$ Step 2
Step 2 $\Rightarrow$ Step 3
Step 3 $\Rightarrow$ Step 4
Step 4 $\Rightarrow$ Step 5
Step 5 $\Rightarrow$ Step 6
Therefore, Step 1 $\Rightarrow$ Step 7

> Life is the art of drawing sufficient conclusions from insufficient premises.
> Samuel Butler (1835-1902), *Note-Books* (1912).

Following this chain of consequential reasoning, where each step passes on a baton to the next step, our conclusion is $ad = bc$.

The proof unfolds, indeed, like playing notes, one beat after another, of a symphony. There is a dance to proof!

Next, Euclid proved the converse; i.e., $ad = bc \Rightarrow \frac{a}{b}=\frac{c}{d}$ where $a, b, c, d \neq 0$.

Step 1. Given: $ad = bc$. We must prove $\frac{a}{b}=\frac{c}{d}$.

Step 2. Since $ac = ac$ (Law of Identity) and $ad = bc$, then $\frac{ac}{ad}=\frac{ac}{bc}$.

Step 3. But, $\frac{ac}{ad}=\frac{c}{d}$ since $\frac{a}{a}=1$.

Step 4. We can also conclude this: $\frac{ac}{bc}=\frac{a}{b}$ since $\frac{c}{c}=1$.

Step 5. Therefore, from Step 2 to Step 4, $\frac{a}{b} = \frac{c}{d}$.

QED

We have proved $\frac{a}{b} = \frac{c}{d} \Rightarrow ad = bc$ and $ad = bc \Rightarrow \frac{a}{b} = \frac{c}{d}$, a conditional statement and its converse. Therefore, we have logical equivalence; i.e., $\frac{a}{b} = \frac{c}{d} \Leftrightarrow ad = bc$. Since we have logical equivalence, $\frac{a}{b} = \frac{c}{d} \Leftrightarrow ad = bc$ is both a necessary and sufficient condition and what we wanted to prove.

QED

PROOF THAT THE SUM OF TWO EVEN INTEGERS IS ALWAYS EVEN

Let's do some more direct proofs by returning to some number theory. First, let's consider the sum of any two even integers. Let's see if we can determine a pattern:

$2 + 4 = 6$
$6 + 10 = 16$
$88 + 76 = 164$
$1{,}234{,}236 + 678{,}772 = 1{,}913{,}008$
$-18 + 22 = 4$
$-98 + -44 = -142$

What do you notice about the sums? Are the sums odd integers or even integers? Can we prove that the sum of any two even integers will always be even? To prove this statement inductively requires that we cover all possibilities which is an impossibility! Direct proof comes to our aid.

> No doubt there are proofs in mathematics. Proofs are the mathematician's coin in trade. The question is why there are none elsewhere.
>
> David Berlinski, *One, Two, Three: Absolutely Elementary Mathematics* (2011), p. 28.

We must first define an even integer algebraically. We do so by stating that an integer a is an even number if $a = 2b$, where b is any integer.[2] This equation means that every even number is divisible by 2 or that every even number has 2 as one of its factors. Of course, an important given in this definition is the truth that the sum of any two integers is an integer.[3] We want to prove that if x and y are even integers, then $x + y$ is an even integer. Follow along:

Step 1. If x is an even integer, then it can be written in the form $x = 2a$ where a is an integer.
Step 2. Likewise, if y is an even integer, then it can be written in the form $y = 2b$ where b is an integer.

---

[2] This definition means that every even integer can be related to two times a given integer. Evenness is, therefore, is a relationship between a given even integer and some other integer. Even integers are precisely understood in the context of a relationship, reflective of relational Trinitarian realities.

[3] The Closure Law of Addition holds for integers (Lesson 13.1). Another way to state it is to say that when we add any two integers, our sum will always be an integer.

Step 3. If $x = 2a$ and $y = 2b$, then, by adding both equations, left side to left side and right side to right side, $x + y = 2a + 2b$.
Step 4. $2a + 2b = 2(a + b)$ invoking the Distributive Law in reverse; i.e., factoring 2, the common factor of $2a$ and $2b$.
Step 5. $2(a + b)$ is an even integer because $a + b$ is in integer. If we let $k = a + b$, then $2k$ is an even integer by definition.
Step 6. If x and y are even integers, then $x + y$ is an even integer.
QED

Do you catch the rhythm of the logic? Go over this proof several times to make sure that you do. In six steps, we have proved a theorem that would take an eternity to prove if we had to cover all the possibilities. Such is the power of deductive logic.

PROOF THAT WE CAN WRITE ANY ODD INTEGER CAN AS $2N+1$

Let's see if we can proof this statement: If an integer is odd, then it can be written as $2n + 1$ where n is an integer.[4] First, let's look at some examples.

$3 = 2(1) + 1 = 2 + 1$
$9 = 2(4) + 1 = 8 + 1$
$235 = 2(117) + 1 = 234 + 1$
$-19 = 2(-10) + 1 = -20 + 1$
$-65 = 2(-33) + 1 = -66 + 1$

The relationship seems to hold true for these examples. What about every case? Deduction to our rescue! Here are the steps:

Step 1. If an integer is odd, then it is 1 more than an even integer. (Justification: The definition of an odd integer.)
Step 2. If an integer is 1 more than an even integer, then it is 1 more than a multiple of 2. (Justification: The definition of an even integer.)
Step 3. If an integer is 1 more than a multiple of 2, then it can be written as $2n + 1$.
Step 4. If an integer is odd, then it can be written as $2n + 1$.
QED

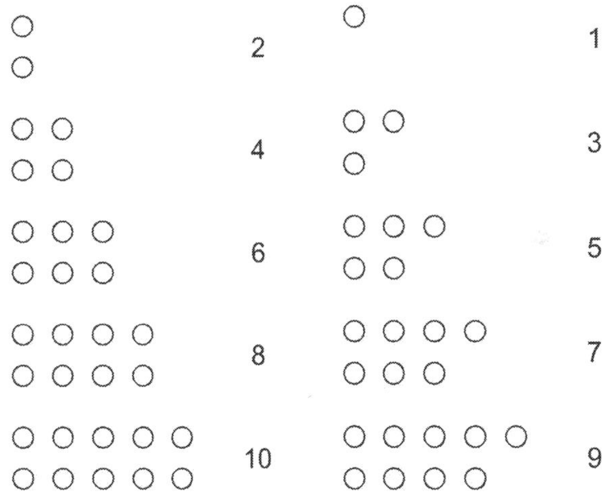

Figure 2. Pictures of even and odd positive integers.

The ancient Greeks were the first to generated these proofs. Their logic was limited to the set of natural numbers, or positive integers, not the set of integers. As we have seen in Lesson 5.1, they used the arrangement of pebbles to demonstrate these proofs (Figure 2). They saw that they could easily represent any even number as a rectangular arrangement of two rows of

[4] Again, as with our definition of an even integer, this definition means that every odd integer can be related to one plus two times a given integer. (Note: We could also define an odd integer as a number in the form $2n - 1$ where n is an integer.) Oddness is, therefore, is a relationship between a given odd integer and some other integer. Odd integers are precisely understood in the context of a relationship, reflective again of relational Trinitarian realities.

pebbles by any number of n columns, or $2n$. The two rows showed that any even number is divisible by 2 or that any even number has 2 as one of its factors. Odd numbers could be arranged as the rectangular arrangement of two rows of pebbles by any number of n columns with the addition of one more pebble, or $2n + 1$. Of course, to make the formula $2n + 1$ work for 1 (one pebble), the first odd natural number, we must have zero columns meaning no rectangular array or $n = 0$. Zero was not a number that the ancient Greeks could picture with their methods.

PROOF OF THE FINGER MULTIPLICATION METHOD

Let's now prove, in general, why our finger method of multiplication works. First, review the proof with numbers in Lesson 4.11. If, for example, we want to multiply 14 by 15 using 10 as our base, we change 14 into 10 + 4 and 15 into 10 + 5 and we change the multiplication to this:

$$14 \times 15 = (10 + 4)(10 + 5)$$

Using Algebra to reason to a general proof, we substitute 10 by a, 4 by b, and 5 by c. This means that a, b, and c can stand for *any* numbers. Therefore, $(a + b)(a + c)$. By applying the Distributive Law to this product, we get:

$$(a + b)(a + c) = a(a + c) + b(a + c) = a^2 + ac + ab + bc = a^2 + ab + ac + bc$$

Now, notice the first three terms of the final expression. Are there any common factors? Yes, a is a common factor to a^2, ac, and ab. Using the Distributive Law in reverse, i.e., factoring a, we get:

$$a^2 + ab + ac + bc = a(a + b + c) + bc$$

QED

This is exactly what we do in our finger method. Replacing a by 10, b by 4, and c by 5, we get:

$$10(10 + 4 + 5) + (4 \times 5) = 10 \times 19 + 20 = 190 + 20 = 210$$

Note also that b and c can represent either positive or negative values, i.e., integers, depending on whether they are above or below the base of operations.

We consider 14 × 15:

14 4

15 5

With the base of operations as 10, we write the 4 and 5 above the 14 and 15 respectively, representing positive integers. We cross add, 4 + 15 or 14 + 5, to get 19, multiply 19 by 10 to get 190 and then add 20 (4 × 5) to that to get 210.

Let's do the same with 20 as our base of operations. We write:

14 -6

15 -5

With the base of operations as 20, we write the 6 and 5 below the 14 and 15 respectively, representing negative integers. In our examples, we cross add, 15 + (-6) or 14 + (-5), to get 9. We next multiply 9 by 20 to get 180 and then add 30 (-6 × -5) to that to get 210.

What about 52 × 49? We use 50 as our base of operations and write:

52 2

49 -1

The 2 above the 52 is positive, but the 1 below the 49 is negative. We cross add: 52 + (-1) = 51 and 49 + 2 = 51. We next multiply 51 by 50, or 51 by 100 and divide by 2. Doing these two operations, we get:

$$\frac{5100}{2} = 2550$$

Therefore:

2 × (-1) = -2 and 2550 + (-2) = 2548 (Our product).

Using this method intelligently as a short-cut way to do some multiplication problems assumes working knowledge of signed numbers. Without knowing of how algebraic operations and signed numbers interpenetrate, we do not know what is going on. This knowledge is one example of the power of mathematic reasoning: it enables one to understand the why of a method, not just the how.

> Very few people appreciate more than some elementary aspects of mathematical beauty, much of it revealing itself only to mathematicians in the study and creation of intricately crafted proofs, barely within the reach of the most highly trained human minds. As a mathematician, I declare that I have established the truth of a theorem by writing at the end of its proof the three letters Q. E. D., an abbreviation for the Latin phrase *quod erat demonstrandum*, which translates as 'what had to be proved.' On the one hand, Q. E. D. is a synonym for truth and beauty in mathematics; on the other hand, it represents the seemingly inaccessible side of this ancient science.
>
> Burkard Polster, Australian mathematician, *Q. E. D. Beauty in Mathematical Proof* (2004), p. 1.

PROOF OF THE FORMULA FOR THE CIRCUMFERENCE OF A CIRCLE

In Lesson 8.4, we stated the formula for the circumference of a circle based on an experiment with a wheel. In Lesson 8.5, we used this formula in our derivation of the formula for the area of a circle. Let's prove the circumference formula in a way similar to our method for deriving the area formula. Before you continue, review the logic of the area proof in Lesson 8.5. We are going to use the results of this proof, i.e., $A = \pi r^2$, to prove the circumference formula.[5]

If r is the radius of a circle and C its circumference, we want to prove:

$$C = 2\pi r$$

[5] In Lesson 8.5, to prove the area formula, we used the circumference formula. Now, we prove the circumference formula using the area formula.

We first divide a circle O into n congruent triangles. Figure 3 shows the situation with eight such triangles. We establish:

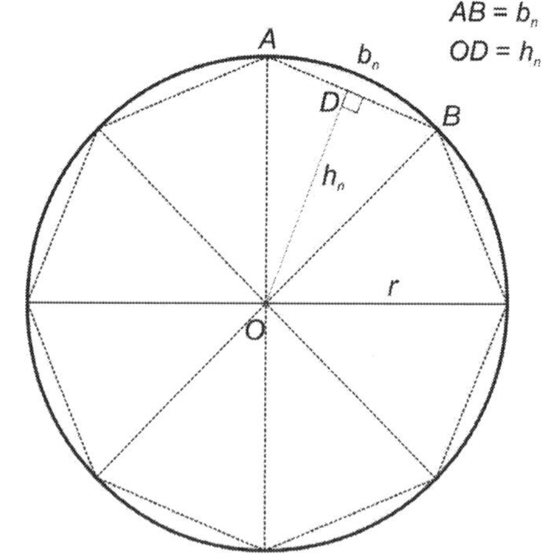

Figure 3.

$\overline{AB} \perp \overline{OD}$
$AB = b_n$
$OD = h_n$

The area, $\alpha(T_n)$, of each individual triangle, therefore, is:

$\alpha(T_n) = \frac{1}{2}b_nh_n$

Now, we let:

α_n = area of the n-gon
P_n = perimeter of the n-gon
α(circle O) = area of circle O

Therefore:

$\alpha_n = n\alpha(T_n) = \frac{1}{2}nb_nh_n$
$P_n = nb_n$

We substitute P_n with nb_n:

$\alpha_n = \frac{1}{2}P_nh_n$

We now let $n \to \infty$. Using limit notation, we conclude:

$\lim_{n\to\infty} h_n = r$

$\lim_{n\to\infty} P_n = C$

$\lim_{n\to\infty} \alpha_n = \alpha(\text{circle } O)$ [Note: We recall that $\alpha(\text{circle } O) = \pi r^2$]

Since $\alpha_n = \frac{1}{2}P_nh_n$, then, as $n \to \infty$:

$\alpha_n = \frac{1}{2}Cr$

Therefore, as $n \to \infty$, we have this equation:

$\pi r^2 = \frac{1}{2}Cr$

Solving for C, we get:

$$\pi r^2 = \tfrac{1}{2}Cr \Leftrightarrow C = \frac{2\pi \cancel{r^2}^{\,r}}{\cancel{r}_{\,1}} \Leftrightarrow C = 2\pi r \text{ (since } \frac{r^2}{r} = \frac{r^2}{r^1} = r^{2-1} = r\text{)}$$

QED

Table 1	
Words that Signify a Premise is Forthcoming	**Words that Signify a Conclusion is Forthcoming**
• If • Since • Because • Owning to • For • Inasmuch as • After all • As	• Then • Therefore • Hence • Consequently • So • Thus • Accordingly • It follows that • For this reason • Whence

EXERCISES

Define the following.

1. Direct proof
2. Premises of an argument
3. Conclusion of an argument
4. Syllogism
5. Semi-perimeter of a triangle. (See homework exercise below.)
6. Heron's formula for the area of a triangle (See homework exercise below.)
7. Incircle (See homework exercise below.)

Answer these questions:

8. We know, from Lesson 4.14 (Multiplication fingers) that 15×14 can be multiplied using this shortcut:
   $15 \times 14 = (10 + 5)(10 + 4) = 10(10 + 5 + 4) + 5 \times 4 = 10(19) + 20 = 190 + 20 = 210$
   In general, if we substitute 10 with a, 5 with b, and 4 with c, what is $(a + b)(a + c)$?
9. Factor a from your result in Question 8 to prove the shortcut method.
10. Prove that the product of two odd integers is always odd.
11. Prove that for any two real numbers a and b, the sum of half their sum and half their difference is a.

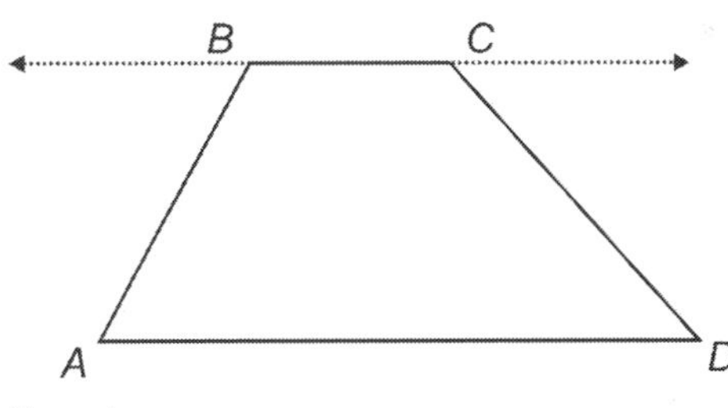

Figure 4.

Let's prove the area formula for a trapezoid. First, let's define our terms. The two legs, or sides, of a trapezoid $ABCD$, are $\overline{AB}$ and $\overline{CD}$. The two bases of a trapezoid are $\overline{BC}$ and $\overline{AD}$. These two bases are parallel to each other, i.e., $\overline{BC} \parallel \overline{AD}$.

12. What has been added to trapezoid $ABCD$ in Figure 4?

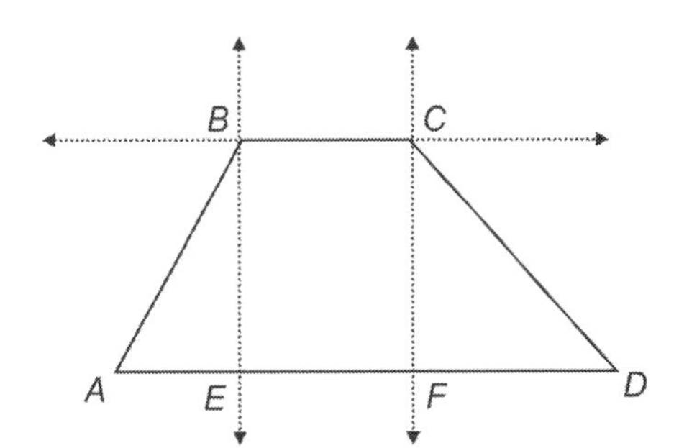

Figure 5.

13. From Figure 5, describe correctly the three parts of a trapezoid that comprise its area.
14. Write the general formula for the area of a right triangle.
15. Write the general formula for the area of a rectangle.
16. We let the height of the trapezoid be $h = BE = CF$. We let the bottom base, $b_1 = AD$ and the top base, $b_2 = BC = EF$. We want to develop a formula for the area A of trapezoid $ABCD$ in terms of h, b_1, and b_2. Write an equation for AD in terms of AE, EF, and FD.
17. Write the area of ΔABE, $\alpha(\Delta ABE)$, in terms of h and AE.
18. Write the area of ΔDCF, $\alpha(\Delta DCF)$, in terms of h and FD.
19. Write the area of rectangle $EBCF$, $\alpha(EBCF)$, in terms of h and EF.
20. Write an equation for A in terms of your answers to Question 17, 18, and 19.
21. Since $b_2 = EF$, substitute b_2 for EF and rewrite the equation you wrote in Question 20 with this substitution.
22. Multiply both sides of the equation you wrote in Question 21 by 2. This "removes" of the fractions on the right side of this equation.
23. Factor h in the equation you wrote in Question 22 and rewrite the equation including this factoring.
24. Since, in general, $2k = k + k$, rewrite the equation you wrote in Question 23, replacing a term that looks like $2k$ with $k + k$.
25. Since $b_2 = EF$, substitute b_2 for EF and rewrite the equation you wrote in Question 24 with this substitution.
26. In Question 16, you wrote an expression equal to AD. Since $b_1 = AD$, substitute b_1 for AD and rewrite the equation you wrote in Question 25 with this substitution.
27. Divide both sides of the equation you wrote in Question 26 by 2. If you followed all of these instructions correctly, you have derived the general formula for the area of a trapezoid. QED.

Heron of Alexandria, Egypt (ca. 10 AD), a Greek mathematician, proved a **formula** for finding the area of any triangle if you know its three sides a, b, and c (Figure 6). Let $s = \frac{1}{2}(a + b + c)$, the **semi-perimeter** of the triangle and A = area of the triangle. Heron showed that $A = \sqrt{s(s-a)(s-b)(s-c)}$.[6] Verify that this formula is true by justifying the following steps:

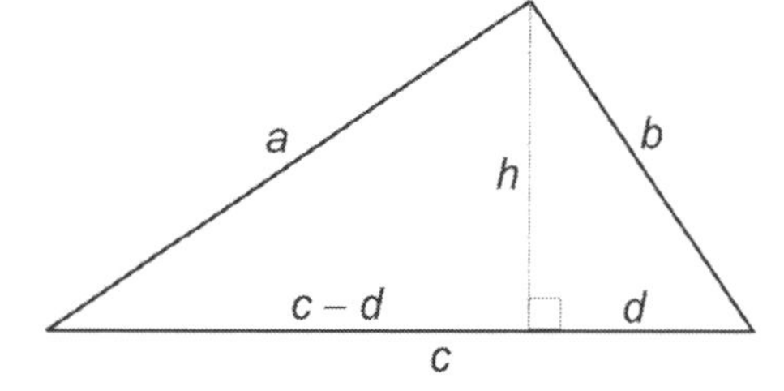

Figure 6.

28. $A = \dfrac{1}{2}hc$
29. $a^2 = b^2 + c^2 - 2cd$
30. $d = \dfrac{b^2 + c^2 - a^2}{2c}$
31. $h^2 = b^2 - d^2$
32. $h^2 = b^2 - \left(\dfrac{b^2 + c^2 - a^2}{2c}\right)^2$

[6] Surveyors use this formula to determine the area of any three-sided lot. Since we can partition lots with four or more sides into non-overlapping triangles, we can apply this formula to find the total area by summing the areas of these triangles.

33. $h^2 = b^2 - \dfrac{\left(b^2 + c^2 - a^2\right)^2}{4c^2}$ (Hint: The expression on the right is the difference of two squares. Use the algebraic identity $a^2 - b^2 = (a + b)(a - b)$ to simplify it as you work on Question 33.)

34. $h^2 = \dfrac{(a+b+c)(b+c-a)(a+b-c)(a-b+c)}{4c^2}$

35. $h^2 = \dfrac{2s(2s-2a)(2s-2c)(2s-2b)}{4c^2}$

36. $h^2 = \dfrac{16s(s-a)(s-b)(s-c)}{4c^2}$

37. $h^2 = \dfrac{4s(s-a)(s-b)(s-c)}{c^2}$

38. $h = \dfrac{2}{c}\sqrt{s(s-a)(s-b)(s-c)}$

39. $\mathrm{A} = \sqrt{s(s-a)(s-b)(s-c)}$

> In classical geometry ... form and being were held apart, so that the force of the demonstration lay in its purely formal connections and logical compulsion. On the other hand, when form and being are found to be not separate, but indivisibly united, the real force of the demonstration lies in its ontological compulsion. It is only through such an ontological grasp of things in their intrinsic intelligibility and truth that genuine advances in knowledge are made.
>
> Thomas F. Torrance, *The Christian Frame of Mind* (1989), p. 74.

Let's say we want to find the area of the unshaded region of the triangle in Figure 7. We know the lengths of the three sides of a triangle (we won't bother with the units) and that the circle is inscribed inside the triangle, the **incircle**; i.e., the circumference of the circle is tangent to the triangle at three points, one on each side.

40. To find the area of the unshaded region, what two areas must you find and how would you compute the area of the unshaded region if you know these two areas?
41. What is the formula for the area of the circle?

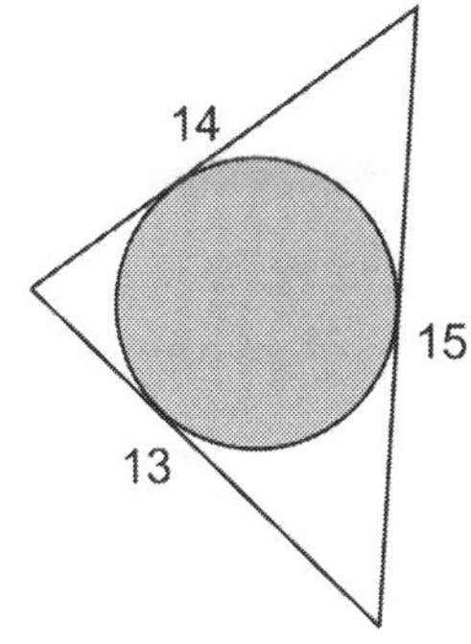

Figure 7.

How would we find the area of the triangle if we know its three sides? Inspect Figure 8 and then answer these questions:

42. What do we know about $\angle BC'I$, $\angle CB'I$, and $\angle BA'I$? (Hint: Refer to Lesson 11.9. We will prove why this relationship is true in Lesson 13.9.)
43. Write a formula for the area of ΔAIB, ΔBIC, and ΔAIC. Let r, the radius of circle I, be the height of each of these triangles.
44. From your results in Question 43, write a formula for the area of ΔABC by letting $s = \frac{1}{2}(a + b + c)$ where s is the semi-perimeter of the triangle.
45. Use Heron's formula for the area of a triangle to find:
    (a) The exact area of circle I.
    (b) The exact area of the unshaded region of ΔABC.

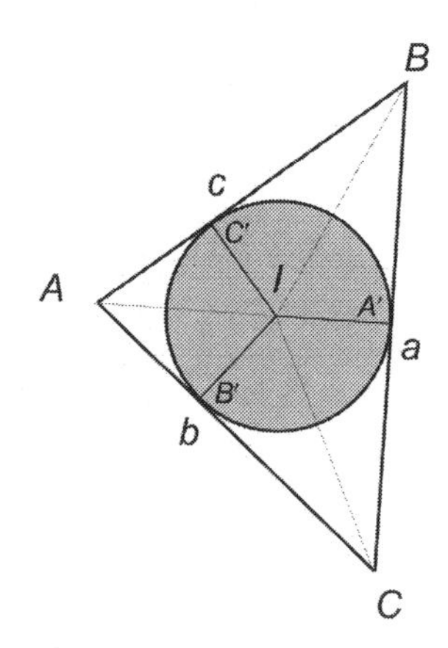

Figure 8.

The Quadrature of a Rectangle.

This construction exercise requires some background. The ancient Greeks loved the visual beauty and symmetries revealed through the logic and structure of geometry. In Euclid's *Elements*, he started from the simple and elementary (five axioms and five postulates) and proceeding to things complex and intricate. This enchantment with building the complex from the simple was also evident in the way the Greeks constructed their geometric figures. They had one simple rule: *you can only use a straightedge and a compass*, nothing more, nothing less. Remember too that for them, a straightedge was a ruler with no markings on it. They embraced this rule because these tools were all they had at their disposal. Because of their limited tool set, straight lines and circles were the order of the day. We have already seen some of their rich results in our constructions to date. What was uppermost in the minds of these ancient geometers, starting from the 5th century BC, was the problem of quadrature, the "the act of squaring," of a plane figure. In other words, given any plane figure, these geometers sought to construct a square equal to the area of this figure using only a straightedge and a compass. What motivated these geometers to do this was part practical and part philosophical. The practical motivation was to develop some rules for finding the areas of curved surfaces. The philosophical motivation was the appeal of replacing what appeared to be asymmetrical with the symmetrical, the imperfect with the perfect, the unreasonable with reason. For these geometers, successful quadrature demonstrated the triumph of human reason and revealed the simplicity, beauty, and symmetry of the universe. The grand goal at the mountaintop of symmetry was the quadrature of the circle (Lesson 11.5). In this and the next few lessons, we shall show you how these ancient geometers attempted to ascend this mountain.[7] We will begin with a relatively easy step: the quadrature of a rectangle.

[7] We will follow the logical and geometric methods of Hippocrates of Chios (ca. 470-ca. 410 BC), as reported by Eudoxus of Cnidus (ca. 390-ca. 337 BC), a report summarized by Simplicius of Cilicia (ca. 490-ca. 560 AD) ca. 530 AD. This Hippocrates is not to be confused with Hippocrates of Cos, the father of Greek medicine and the originator of the physicians' Hippocratic oath. We observe that there is nearly one thousand years between the original work by Hippocrates and the earliest extant manuscript of that work by Simplicius. The substantial number of years between originals and their extant manuscripts is a common occurrence that historians must reckon with as they piece together the writings that reveal the ancient Greek philosophical and mathematical heritage (ca. 600-300 BC). For a more detailed discussion of Greek methods of quadrature, see William Dunham, *Journey Through Genius: The Great Theorems of Mathematics* (New York: Penguin Books, [1990] 1991), pp. 1-26.

46. Draw rectangle *ABCD* (Figure 9). We must now construct, using a straightedge and compass only, a square having area equal to that of *ABCD*.
47. With the straightedge, extend $\overline{AD}$ to the right and use a compass to mark off $\overline{DE}$ such that $DE = CD$.
48. Bisect $\overline{AE}$ and mark the point of bisection *F*.
49. With the center at *F* and the radius $AF = FE$, construct a semicircle.

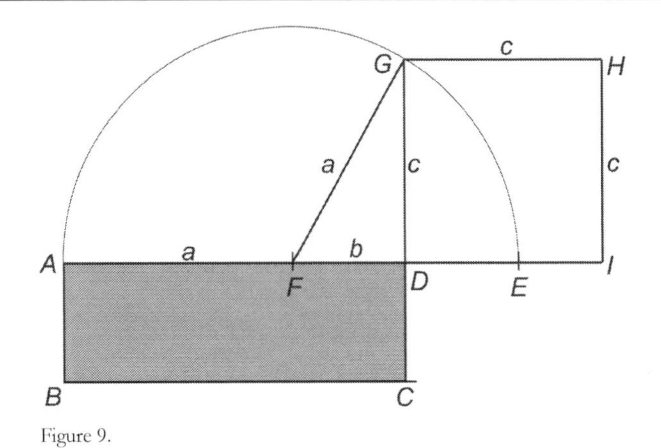

Figure 9.

50. At *D*, construct $\overline{DG}$ perpendicular to $\overline{AE}$ where point *G* is the point of intersection of the perpendicular and the semicircle.

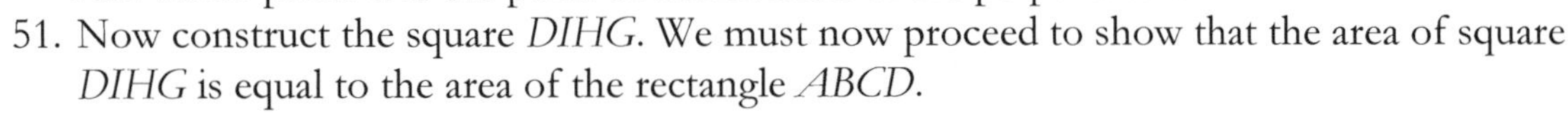

51. Now construct the square *DIHG*. We must now proceed to show that the area of square *DIHG* is equal to the area of the rectangle *ABCD*.
52. Consider ΔFGD. Label the lengths of its two legs $FD = b$ and $GD = c$ and the length of its hypotenuse $FG = a$. By the Pythagorean Theorem, $a^2 = b^2 + c^2$. Solve this equation for c^2.
53. Since all radii of a circle are equal, then $FG = AF = FE = a$. Since $FE = a$, determine the length of *DE* (Hint: since $FE = a$ and $FD = b$, then $DE = ?$)
54. In terms of *a* and *b*, determine *AD*.
55. Since the area of a rectangle is the product of its length and width, then the area of rectangle *ABCD* is (*AD*)(*DC*). Substitute *AD* with your answer for Question 54 and substitute *DC* with your answer for Question 53 (since $DE = DC$). In terms of *a* and *b*, what is the area of rectangle *ABCD*? (Remember that, in general, $(x + y)(x - y) = x^2 - y^2$.)
56. Compare your answer for Question 55 with the area of the square *DIHG* and your answer to Question 52. What have you proven? Your QED should state that the area of rectangle *ABCD* equals the area of square *DIHG*.

Trigonometric Identities: Compound-Angle Identities. In Figure 10, ΔDEA is a right triangle and *FCEB* is a rectangle.

Figure 10.

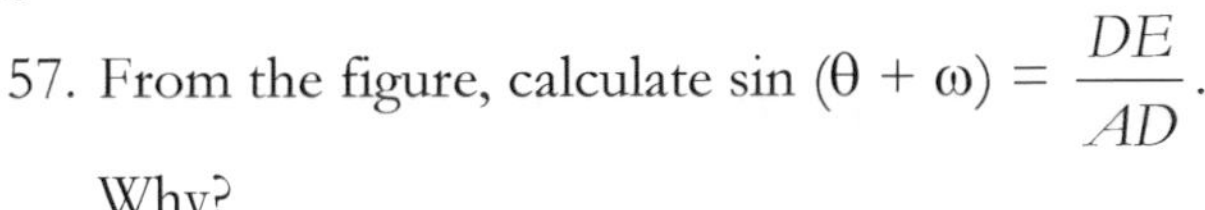

57. From the figure, calculate $\sin(\theta + \omega) = \dfrac{DE}{AD}$. Why?

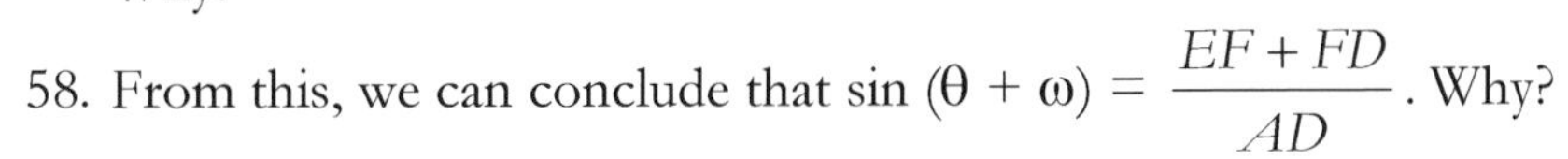

58. From this, we can conclude that $\sin(\theta + \omega) = \dfrac{EF + FD}{AD}$. Why?
59. From this, we can conclude that $\sin(\theta + \omega) = \dfrac{BC + FD}{AD}$. Why?
60. From this, we can conclude $\sin(\theta + \omega) = \dfrac{BC}{AD} + \dfrac{FD}{AD}$. Why?

61. From this, we can conclude sin (θ + ω) = $\frac{BC}{AD}\frac{AC}{AC}+\frac{FD}{AD}\frac{CD}{CD}$. Why?

62. From this, we can conclude sin (θ + ω) = $\frac{BC}{AC}\frac{AC}{AD}+\frac{FD}{CD}\frac{CD}{AD}$. Why?

63. Therefore, sin (θ + ω) = sin θ cos ω + cos θ sin ω. Why?

64. If we substitute ω with -ω, we get sin (θ – ω) = sin θ cos ω – cos θ sin ω. Why? (Hint: Use cos(-ω) = cos ω and sin(-ω) = -sin ω.)

65. From the figure, show that cos (θ + ω) = cos θ cos ω – sin θ sin ω. Why?

66. If we substitute ω with -ω, we get cos (θ – ω) = cos θ cos ω + sin θ sin ω. Why? (Hint: Use cos(-ω) = cosω and sin(-ω) = -sinω.)

67. Since $\tan(\theta+\omega)=\frac{\sin(\theta+\omega)}{\cos(\theta+\omega)}$, derive a formula for tan (θ + ω) and tan (θ – ω). (Hint: your formula must only consist of an arithmetical combination of tangent ratios.)

68. Since cotangent is the inverse of the tangent function, derive a formula for cot (θ + ω) and cot (θ – ω). (Hint: your formula must only consist of an arithmetical combination of tangent ratios.)

69. Rounded to four decimal places, find sin (π/12) using a Compound-Angle Identity.

70. Rounded to four decimal places, find sin (5π/12) using a Compound-Angle Identity.

In the days before calculators and computers, the sum and difference identities were invaluable in workplace calculations.

Knowing the trigonometric ratios for the basic radian/degree measures of 0, (π/6) (30°), (π/4)(45°), (π/3)(60°), and (π/2)(90°), one could work out the values of trig functions of (π/12)(15°) and (π/8)(22.5°) and other such angles by way of these identities.

In those days, trigonometry was both *pure math* and *applied math*, useful in many professions involving science, engineering, and architecture.

The tangent sum and tangent difference identities are used in many sophisticated mathematical proofs and in methods of calculating π to a large number of decimal places, e.g., to 1.24 trillion places!

13.4 Proof of Divisibility Laws

Number	Casting Out Nines	Sum of the Digits (and the Sum of the Sum of the Digits)	Divisible by 9?
4~~18~~	1 + 8	4	No
~~945~~	9 and 4 + 5	0	Yes
~~54~~,~~927~~	5 + 4, 9, 2 + 7	0	Yes
~~234~~,1~~18~~	2 + 3 + 4, 1 + 8	1	No
5,~~153~~,628	1 + 5 + 3	3	No
~~27~~,~~718~~,~~821~~	2 + 7, 1 + 8, 7 + 2, 8 + 1	0	Yes

Casting Out Nines

Term Introduced
1. Inscribed angle

How would we prove the divisibility by 9 rule (Lesson 5.4)? In general, let's consider a five-digit positive integer N:

$N = a_1a_2a_3a_4a_5$

In base 10, N looks like this:

$N = 10^4a_1 + 10^3a_2 + 10^2a_3 + 10a_4 + a_5$

Since $10 = 9 + 1$, we write:

$N = (9 + 1)^4a_1 + (9 + 1)^3a_2 + (9 + 1)^2a_3 + (9 + 1)a_4 + a_5$

Now we invoke some careful thinking. Look at the second term, $(9 + 1)^2a_3$. Let's find the square (Figure 1):

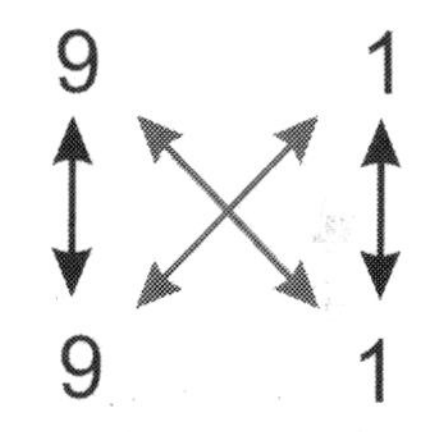

Figure 1.

$(9 + 1)^2 = 81 + 2(9)(1) + 1 = 81 + 18 + 1 = 99 + 1 = 100$

We note: 99 is divisible by 9.
Next, look at the third term, $(9 + 1)^3a_2$. Let's find the cube (Figure 2):

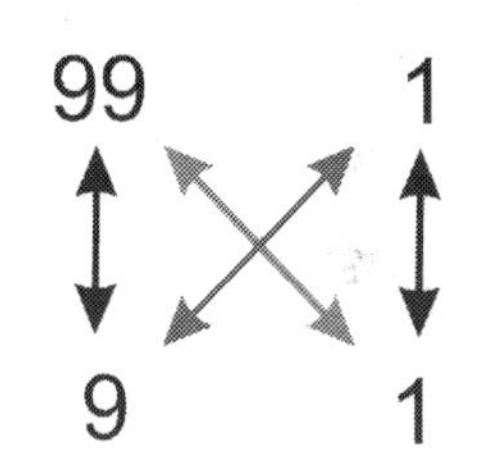

Figure 2.

$(9 + 1)^3 = (99 + 1)(9 + 1) = 891 + 9 + 99 + 1 =$
$891 + 108 + 1 = 999 + 1 = 1000$

We note: 999 is divisible by 9.
Finally, look at the fourth term, $(9 + 1)^4a_1$. Let's find the fourth power (Figure 3):

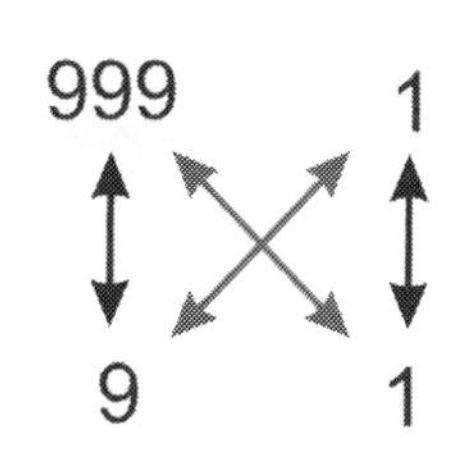

Figure 3.

$(9 + 1)^4 = (999 + 1)(9 + 1) = 8991 + 9 + 999 + 1 =$
$8991 + 1008 + 1 = 9999 + 1 = 10{,}000$

We note: 9999 is divisible by 9.
Let's return to our base 10 representation of N:

$N = (9 + 1)^4a_1 + (9 + 1)^3a_2 + (9 + 1)^2a_3 + (9 + 1)a_4 + a_5$

By our observations, we let $9M$ represent any number that is divisible by 9. We write:

$N = (9M + 1)a_1 + (9M + 1)a_2 + (9M + 1)a_3 + (9M + 1)a_4 + a_5$

Applying the Distributive Law, we get:

$N = 9Ma_1 + a_1 + 9Ma_2 + a_2 + 9Ma_3 + a_3 + 9Ma_4 + a_4 + a_5$

Applying the Commutative/Associative Laws of Addition, we get:

$N = 9Ma_1 + 9Ma_2 + 9Ma_3 + 9Ma_4 + a_1 + a_2 + a_3 + a_4 + a_5$

Factoring $9M$ (applying the Distributive Law in reverse), we get:

$N = 9M(a_1 + a_2 + a_3 + a_4) + a_1 + a_2 + a_3 + a_4 + a_5$

Note: $9M$ times any number is a number divisible by 9. If N is divisible by 9, $a_1 + a_2 + a_3 + a_4 + a_5$ must be divisible by 9, or the sum of the digits must be divisible by 9.
QED

To prove casting out nines for any n-digit number, we do this:

$N = a_n a_{n-1} a_{n-2} a_{n-3} \ldots a_3 a_2 a_1$

In base 10, N looks like this:

$$N = 10^n a_n + 10^{n-1} a_{n-1} + 10^{n-2} a_{n-2} + 10^{n-3} a_{n-3} + \ldots + 10^3 a_3 + 10^2 a_2 + 10^1 a_1$$

Since $10 = 9 + 1$, we write:

$$N = (9+1)^n a_n + (9+1)^{n-1} a_{n-1} + (9+1)^{n-2} a_{n-2} + (9+1)^{n-3} a_{n-3} + \ldots + (9+1)^3 a_3 + (9+1)^2 a_2 + (9+1)^1 a_1$$

We then invoke the same reasoning as above.

DIVISIBILITY BY 7

Here is our recursive algorithm to see if a number is divisible by 7:

1. Delete the last digit of the given number.
2. Subtract twice this deleted digit from the remaining number.
3. If the result is divisible by 7, the original number is divisible by 7.
4. Repeat Steps 1 to 3 if the result of Step 3 is too large for easy analysis.

Let's see if we can prove what this algorithm works using algebraic operations. Any multiple digit number can be rewritten, using base 10 knowledge, as:

$10x + y$

For example, $3176 = 317(10) + 6$
If $10x + y$ is divisible by 7 then $20x + 2y$ is divisible by 7. Why? $20x + 2y$ is twice the original number and doubling it does not affect its divisibility by 7 since 2 and 7 are relatively prime.
We subtract $20x + 2y$ from $21x$ without affecting its divisibility by 7. Why? $21x$ is divisible by 7 since 21 is divisible by 7. We write:

$21x - (20x + 2y) = 21x + -(20x + 2y) = 21x + -1(20x + 2y) =$
$21x + (-20x) + (-2y) = 21x - 20x - 2y = x(21 - 20) - 2y =$
$x - 2y$

So, $10x + y$ is divisible by 7 if we can show that $x - 2y$ is divisible by 7.
QED

DIVISIBILITY BY 11

Problem 1. Is 14,525,189 divisible by 11? We add the odd number digits and the even number digits separately:

Sum of even digits: $1 + 5 + 5 + 8 = 19$
Sum of odd digits: $4 + 2 + 1 + 9 = 16$

Then, we subtract the leser from the greater, the sum of the even digits from the sum of the odd digits:

$19 - 16 = 3$

The difference is not divisible by 11. This result means that 14,525,189 is not divisible by 11.

Problem 2. Is 57,642,816 divisible by 11? We add the odd number digits and the even number digits separately:

Sum of even digits: $5 + 6 + 2 + 1 = 14$
Sum of odd digits: $7 + 4 + 8 + 6 = 25$

Then, we subtract the lesser from the greater or the absolute value of the greater from the lesser, the sum of the even digits from the sum of the odd digits:

$25 - 14 = 11$
$|11 - 25| = |-11| = 11$

The difference is divisible by 11. This result means that 57,642,816 is divisible by 11.

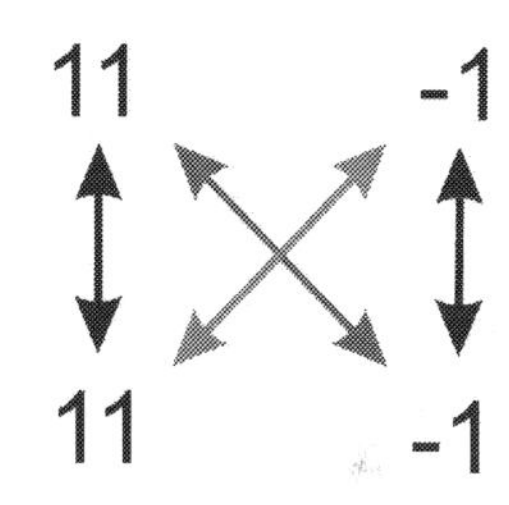

Figure 4.

Our proof of this law follows the same logic as the proof of the divisibility by 9 law. Why? $10 = 9 + 1$ and $10 = 11 - 1$.

In general, let's consider a five-digit positive integer N:

$N = a_1a_2a_3a_4a_5$

In base 10, N looks like this:

$N = 10^4a_1 + 10^3a_2 + 10^2a_3 + 10a_4 + a_5$

Since $10 = 11 - 1$, we write:

$N = (11 - 1)^4a_1 + (11 - 1)^3a_2 + (11 - 1)^2a_3 + (11 - 1)a_4 + a_5$

Apply the Algebraic Definition of Subtraction, we get:

$N = [11 + (-1)]^4a_1 + [11 + (-1)]^3a_2 + [11 + (-1)]^2a_3 + [11 + (-1)]a_4 + a_5$

Look at the second term, $(11 - 1)^2a_3$. Let's find the square (Figure 4):

$[11 + (-1)]^2 = 121 + 2(11)(-1) + (-1)^2 = 121 - 22 + 1 = 99 + 1 = 100$

We note: 99 is divisible by 11.

Next, look at the third term, $(11 - 1)^3a_2$. Let's find the cube (Figure 5):

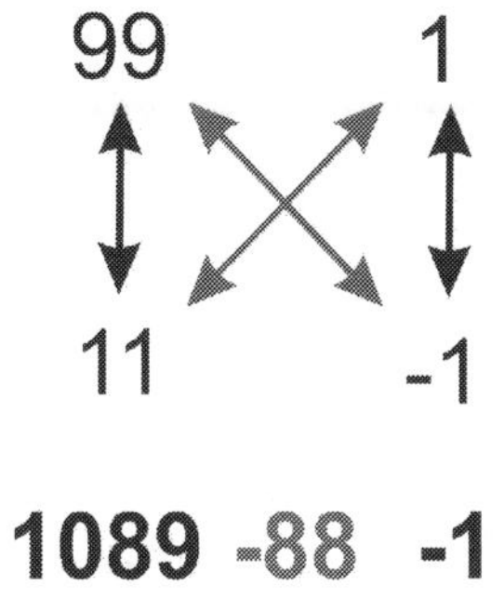

$[11 + (-1)]^3 = (99 + 1)[11 + (-1)] = 1089 + 11 + (-99) + (-1) =$
$1089 + (-88) + (-1) = 1001 + (-1) = 1000$

99 1
11 -1
1089 -88 -1

Figure 5.

We note: 1001 is divisible by 11.

Finally, look at the fourth term, $(11 - 1)^4a_1$. Let's find the fourth power (Figure 6):

$[11 + (-1)]^4 = [1001 + (-1)][11 + (-1)] =$
$11{,}011 + (-11) + (-1001) + 1 = 11{,}011 + (-1012) + 1$
$9999 + 1 = 10{,}000$

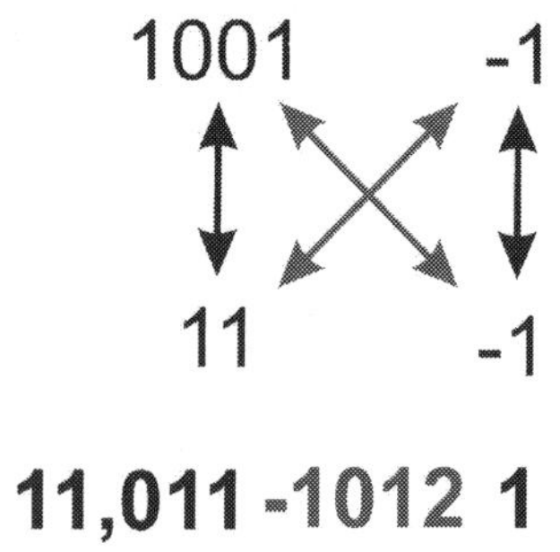

1001 -1
11 -1
11,011 -1012 1

Figure 6.

We note: 9999 is divisible by 11.
Let's return to our base 10 representation of N:

$N = [11 + (-1)]^4 a_1 + [11 + (-1)]^3 a_2 + [11 + (-1)]^2 a_3 +$
$[11 + (-1)]a_4 + a_5$

By our observations, we let $11M$ be any number that is divisible by 9. We write:

$N = [11M + 1]a_1 + [11M + (-1)\,]a_2 + [11M + 1]a_3 + [11M + (-1)]a_4 + a_5$

Applying the Distributive Law, we get:

$N = 11Ma_1 + a_1 + 11Ma_2 + (-1)a_2 + 11Ma_3 + a_3 + 11Ma_4 + (-1)a_4 + a_5$

Applying the Commutative/Associative Laws of Addition, we get:

$N = 11Ma_1 + 11Ma_2 + 11Ma_3 + 11Ma_4 + a_1 + (-1)a_2 + a_3 + (-1)a_4 + a_5$

Factoring $11M$ (applying the Distributive Law in reverse), we get:

$N = 11M(a_1 + a_2 + a_3 + a_4) + a_1 - a_2 + a_3 - a_4 + a_5$

Note: $11M$ times any number is a number divisible by 11. If N is divisible by 11, $a_1 - a_2 + a_3 - a_4 + a_5$ must be divisible by 9, or the sum of the even digits subtracted from the sum of the odd digits must be divisible by 11.
QED

To prove Divisibility by 11 for any n-digit number, we do this:

$N = a_n a_{n-1} a_{n-2} a_{n-3} \ldots a_3 a_2 a_1$

In base 10, N looks like this:

$$N = 10^n a_n + 10^{n-1} a_{n-1} + 10^{n-2} a_{n-2} + 10^{n-3} a_{n-3} + \ldots + 10^3 a_3 + 10^2 a_2 + 10^1 a_1$$

Since $11 = 10 + 1$, we write:

$$N = (10+1)^n a_n + (10+1)^{n-1} a_{n-1} + (10+1)^{n-2} a_{n-2} + (10+1)^{n-3} a_{n-3} + \ldots + (10+1)^3 a_3 +$$
$$(10+1)^2 a_2 + (10+1)^1 a_1$$

We then invoke the same reasoning as above.

EXERCISES

Define this term:

1. Inscribed angle (See homework exercise below.)

State why you can generate the equation on the right of the equals sign from the equation on the left of the equals sign:

2. $21x - (20x + 2y) = 21x + -(20x + 2y)$
3. $21x + -(20x + 2y) = 21x + -1(20x + 2y)$
4. $21x + -1(20x + 2y) = 21x + (-20x) + (-2y)$
5. $21x + (-20x) + (-2y) = 21x - 20x - 2y$

6. $21x - 20x - 2y = x(21 - 20) - 2y$
7. $x(21 - 20) - 2y = x - 2y$

Answer the following questions:

8. State the three methods to find the area of a triangle and the conditions necessary for these methods.
9. Using Heron's formula, prove that the area of an equilateral triangle with sides of length a is $\frac{a^2}{4}\sqrt{3}$.
10. What would be the rule to check for divisibility by 15?
11. What would be the rule to check for divisibility by 21?
12. What would be the rule to check for divisibility by 99?
13. Rearrange the digits in any whole number in any way you like. The difference between the first number and the new number will always be divisible by 9. Why?

A number trick. Find a friend and do the following:

14. (a) Ask your friend to write down any six-digit number so that you cannot see it.
(b) Tell your friend to scramble this six-digit number into a different number.
(c) Tell your friend to subtract the lesser number from the greater number.
(d) Tell your friend to cross out any single non-zero digit in the result and then state the remaining digits to you in any order
15. You should have no trouble naming the crossed-out digit. What truth about divisibility by nine that enables you to name this digit?

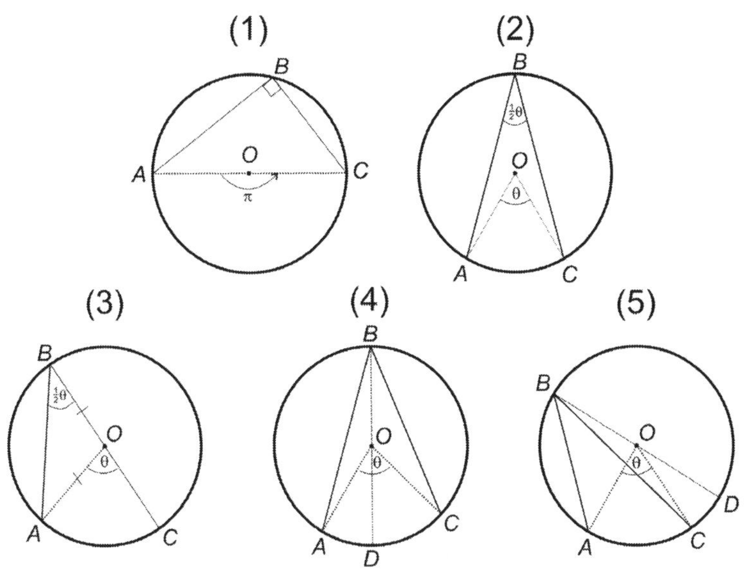

Figure 9.

An Excursion in Geometry.

An **inscribed angle** of a circle is an angle whose vertex is on a circle and each of whose sides intersect it in another point. In (2) of Figure 9, $\angle ABC$ is an inscribed angle of circle O. $\angle ABC$ intercepts $\overset{\frown}{AC}$ and inscribes $\overset{\frown}{ABC}$. We want to prove that an inscribed angle in $\overset{\frown}{ABC}$ of circle O equals one-half of the corresponding central angle (Lesson 12.6). In (2) of Figure 9, we want to show that $m\angle AOC = \frac{1}{2}m\angle ABC$. Review the relevant homework exercises in Lesson 11.3 and then answer these questions:

16. Why is this proposition true in (1) of Figure 9 where $\overline{AC}$ is the diameter of circle O?
17. Prove the proposition in (3) of Figure 9 where $\overline{BC}$ is the diameter of circle O.
18. Prove the other two cases, where the center of the circle lies inside (4) or outside (5) the inscribed angle in Figure 9, using the results from Question 17. (Note: $\overline{BD}$ is the diameter of circle O in both cases.)

19. In Figure 10, $\overline{AC}$ represents a screen in a movie theater. Based on what you have proved about inscribed angles in a circle, what can you say about angles α (Greek letter *alpha*), β (Greek letter *beta*), γ (Greek letter *gamma*), δ (Greek letter *delta*), and ε (Greek letter *epsilon*) where the points on the circle, i.e., B_1, B_2, B_3, B_4, and B_5, represent seats in the theater?

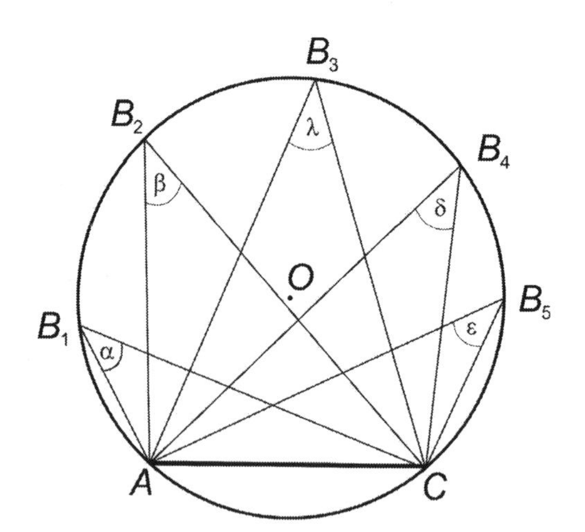

Figure 10.

The Quadrature of a Triangle. Use a straightedge and compass for the following questions:

20. Trace or approximate ΔABC (Figure 11) on a separate sheet of paper.
21. Construct a perpendicular from B meeting $\overline{AC}$ at D.
22. What is $\overline{BD}$ called in terms of ΔABC?
23. If we know the base b and height h of any triangle, we determine its area by the formula $bh/2$ or ½bh. Write an expression for the area of ΔABC, α(ΔABC), in terms of BD and AC.

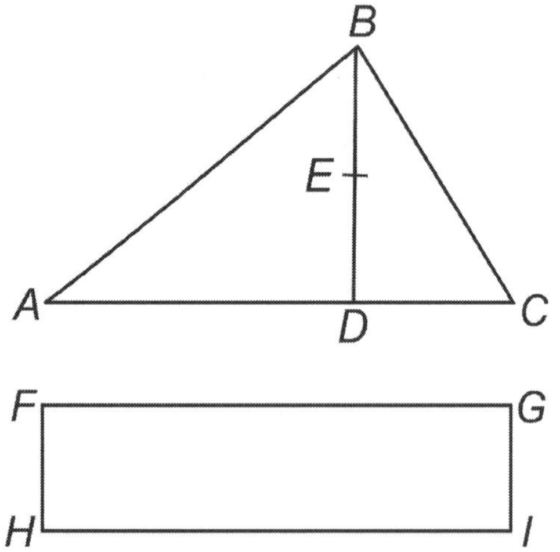

Figure 11.

24. (a) Bisect $\overline{BD}$ at E.
(b) Write an equation relating DE to BD.
25. Construct the rectangle $FGHI$ such that $HI = AC$ and $FH = DE$.
26. To simplify matters, let $x = FH$ and $y = HI$. In terms of x and y, write an expression for the area of rectangle $FGHI$, α($FGHI$).
27. Since $DE = FH$ and $AC = HI$, rewrite the expression for the area of rectangle $FGHI$ in terms of DE and AC.
28. Based on your answer to Question 24b, rewrite the expression for the area of rectangle $FGHI$ in terms of BD and AC.
29. What do you notice about your answer to Question 23 and your answer to Question 28?
30. (a) Since we have already proven that the area of a rectangle can be squared (Homework exercise in Lesson 13.3), what can we conclude about the area of a triangle being squared?
(b) Can we therefore QED the proposition that we can construct the quadrature of a triangle?

Trigonometric Identities: Double-Angle Identities (functions of 2θ).
Refer to the Compound-Angle Identity exercise in Lesson 13.1 and answer the following questions:

31. Show that if $\omega = \theta$, then $\sin(\theta + \omega) = \sin\theta\cos\omega + \cos\theta\sin\omega$ becomes $\sin 2\theta = 2\sin\theta\cos\theta$.
32. Show that if $\omega = \theta$, then $\cos(\theta + \omega) = \cos\theta\cos\omega - \sin\theta\sin\omega$ becomes $\cos 2\theta = \cos^2\theta - \sin^2\theta$. (Remember that $\cos^2\theta$ means the same as $(\cos\theta)^2$ and we say "cosine squared theta.")
33. Since $\sin^2\theta + \cos^2\theta = 1$ (The Pythagorean Identity), show that $\cos 2\theta = 2\cos^2\theta - 1$.
34. Show that from $\cos 2\theta = 2\cos^2\theta - 1$, you can derive $\cos 2\theta = 1 - 2\sin^2\theta$.
35. Since $\tan(\theta + \omega) = \dfrac{\tan\theta + \tan\omega}{1 - \tan\theta\tan\omega}$, then show that $\tan 2\theta = \dfrac{2\tan\theta}{1 - \tan^2\theta}$.
36. Since $\cot(\theta + \omega) = \dfrac{\cot\theta\cot\omega - 1}{\cot\theta + \cot\omega}$, then show that $\cot 2\theta = \dfrac{\cot^2\theta - 1}{2\cot\theta}$.

Trigonometric Identities: Half-Angle Identities.
Answer the following questions:

37. Cos 2θ = 1 – 2sin²θ can be rearranged as $\sin^2\theta = \frac{1-\cos 2\theta}{2}$. Why?

38. Show that we can arrange $\sin^2\theta = \frac{1-\cos 2\theta}{2}$ as $\sin^2\frac{\theta}{2} = \frac{1-\cos\theta}{2}$.

39. Now, show that $\sin\frac{\theta}{2} = \sqrt{\frac{1-\cos\theta}{2}}$ or $\sin\frac{\theta}{2} = -\sqrt{\frac{1-\cos\theta}{2}}$.

40. Show that from cos 2θ = 2 cos²θ – 1 you can derive $\cos\frac{\theta}{2} = \sqrt{\frac{1+\cos\theta}{2}}$ or $\cos\frac{\theta}{2} = -\sqrt{\frac{1+\cos\theta}{2}}$.

41. Show that $\tan\frac{\theta}{2} = \sqrt{\frac{1-\cos\theta}{1+\cos\theta}}$ or $\tan\frac{\theta}{2} = -\sqrt{\frac{1-\cos\theta}{1+\cos\theta}}$.

42. Show that $\cot\frac{\theta}{2} = \sqrt{\frac{1+\cos\theta}{1-\cos\theta}}$ or $\cot\frac{\theta}{2} = -\sqrt{\frac{1+\cos\theta}{1-\cos\theta}}$.

43. Use $\sin^2\left(\frac{\theta}{2}\right) = \frac{1-\cos\theta}{2}$ and $\cos^2\left(\frac{\theta}{2}\right) = \frac{1+\cos\theta}{2}$ to show that $\tan\frac{\theta}{2} = \frac{\sin\theta}{1+\cos\theta}$. (Hint: In one step of your proof, you will need to simplify the numerator using the algebraic identity $(a + b)(a - b) = a^2 - b^2$.)

Answer these questions using a scientific calculator:

44. Find the exact value of cos π/3 using three different Double-Angle Identities.
45. Find sin π/12 using a Half-Angle Identity. Round to the nearest ten-thousandths.
46. Find tan π/12 using a Half-Angle Identity you proved in Question 43. Round to the nearest ten-thousandths.

> ... while mathematics has to resort to abstractions to secure a foothold for a first peep into reality, it must continually transcend them and go beyond them by taking into account other aspects, previously ignored, to get a fuller view of reality.
> Jagjit Singh, *Modern Mathematics: Their Nature and Use* (1959), p. 299.

13.5 The Pythagorean Theorem Revisited

In this lesson, we will revisit the Pythagorean Theorem by adding two more proofs, one grounded in an algebraic derivation based upon a geometric principle and the other rooted entirely in Geometry.

Proof by Similarity

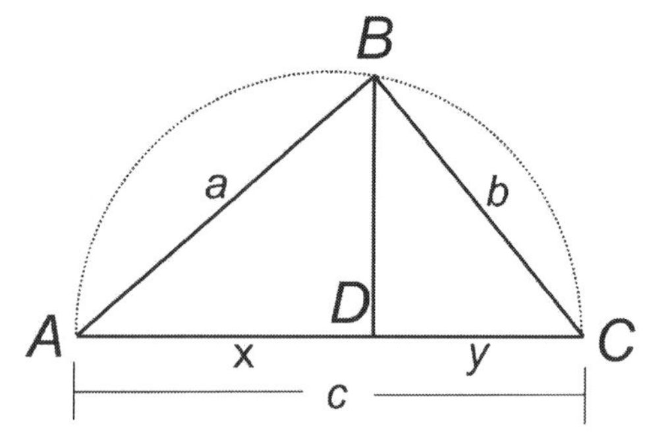

Figure 1.

Let's prove the Pythagorean Theorem using Algebra and what we know of similar triangles. In Figure 1, ΔABC is a right triangle since it is inscribed in a semicircle (Lesson 11.3), i.e., $m\angle ABC = 90°$. It has two legs $a = AB$ and $b = BC$. Its hypotenuse is $c = AC$.

We want to prove that $a^2 + b^2 = c^2$. Consider the altitude of ΔABC at point B. This altitude creates two additional right triangles: ΔADB and ΔBDC. Let $x = AD$ and $y = DC$. Note that $c = x + y$.

Why are ΔABC, ΔADB, and ΔBDC all similar to each other? (Proposition 8 of Book VI of Euclid's *Elements*)

1. $\Delta ABC \sim \Delta ADB$ because both are right triangles and both share $\angle A$ (AA Similarity Theorem) $\Rightarrow m\angle ACB = m\angle ABD$.
2. $\Delta ABC \sim \Delta BDC$ because both are right triangles and both share $\angle C$ (AA Similarity Theorem) $\Rightarrow m\angle BAC = m\angle DBC$.
3. $\Delta ABC \sim \Delta ADB$ and $\Delta ABC \sim \Delta BDC \Rightarrow \Delta ADB \sim \Delta BDC$, or $\Delta ABC \sim \Delta ADB \sim \Delta BDC$.

The three triangles are not congruent, the same shape and size, but similar, the same shape but resized proportionally.

If $\Delta ABC \sim \Delta ADB$, we write a proportion using the terms a, c, and x:

Equation 1. $\dfrac{x}{a} = \dfrac{a}{c}$ [Note: This proportion is the geometric mean (Lesson 11.6).]

If $\Delta ABC \sim \Delta BDC$, we write a proportion using the terms b, c, and y:

Equation 2. $\dfrac{y}{b} = \dfrac{b}{c}$ (Note: Another geometric mean.)

Applying the Extreme/Mean Law to Equation 1, we get:

Equation 3. $a^2 = xc$

Solving Equation 3 for x, we get:

Equation 4. $x = \dfrac{a^2}{c}$

Applying the Extreme/Mean Law to Equation 2, we get:

Equation 5. $b^2 = yc$

Solving Equation 5 for y, we get:

Equation 6. $y = \frac{b^2}{c}$

Since $c = x + y$, we write:

Equation 7. $c = \frac{a^2}{c} + \frac{b^2}{c}$

Multiplying both sides of Equation 7 by c, we get:

Equation 8. $c^2 = a^2 + b^2$

QED

LEONARDO DA VINCI'S PROOF

The painter, sculptor, architect, musician, mathematician, engineer, inventor, anatomist, geologist, cartographer, botanist, and writer Leonardo da Vinci (1452-1519), truly a Renaissance man, proved the Pythagorean Theorem based upon the congruency of geometric figures.

In Figure 2, he seeks to prove that $a^2 + b^2 = c^2$.

To follow along with his proof, photocopy Figure *A*, on page 819, on hard stock paper.

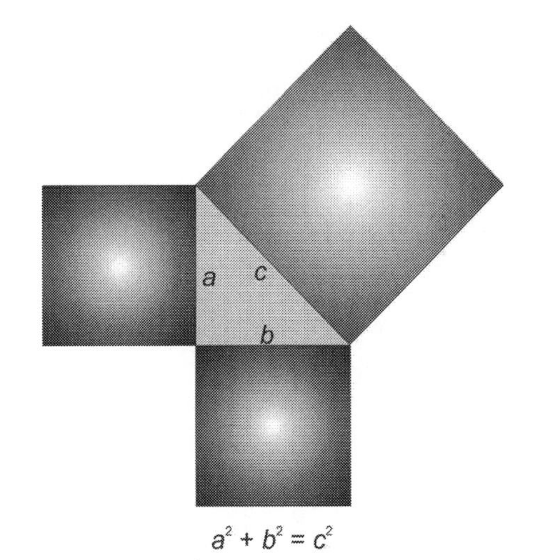

Figure 2.

Carefully cut out the three squares leaving the one right triangle. Duplicate the right triangle two more times.

Da Vinci added two triangles (labeled 1 and 2) congruent to the original triangle (Figure 3). Duplicate this with your cutouts.

He then constructed the six-sided polygon, cut in two along the line, to cover the original triangle, triangle 1 (congruent to the original), and the squares with area a^2 and b^2 (Figure 4). Photocopy Figure *B*, on page 820, on hard stock paper, cut it in two along the line and duplicate DaVinci's cover-up.

He then moved upper half of the six-sided polygon as shown in Figure 5. Duplicate DaVinci's move with your cut-outs.

Next, he moved the lower half of the six-sided polygon as shown in Figure 6. Duplicate DaVinci's move with your cut-outs.

This move was enough for DaVinci to QED his proof. Before reading on, carefully investigate what you have done explain why he could QED his proof.

The six-sided polygon (covers the original triangle, triangle 1, congruent to the original, and the squares with area a^2 and b^2. The same congruent six-sided polygon covers the original triangle, triangle 2, congruent to the original, and the square with area c^2. Therefore, by the principle of congruency:

$c^2 = a^2 + b^2$

QED

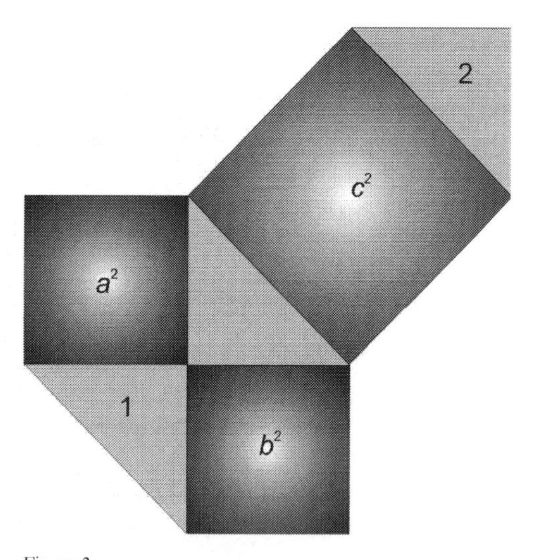

Figure 3.

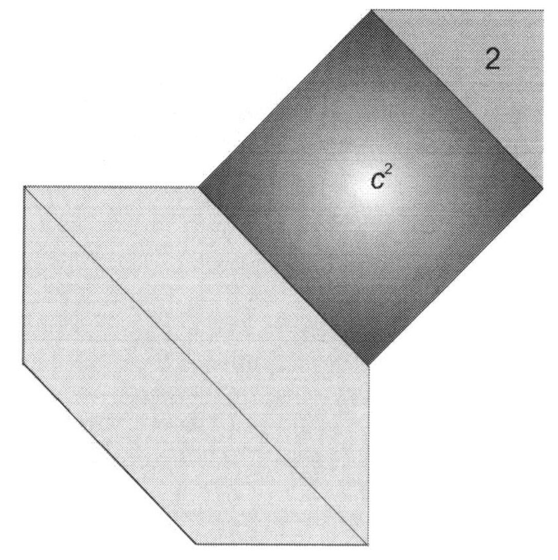

Figure 4.

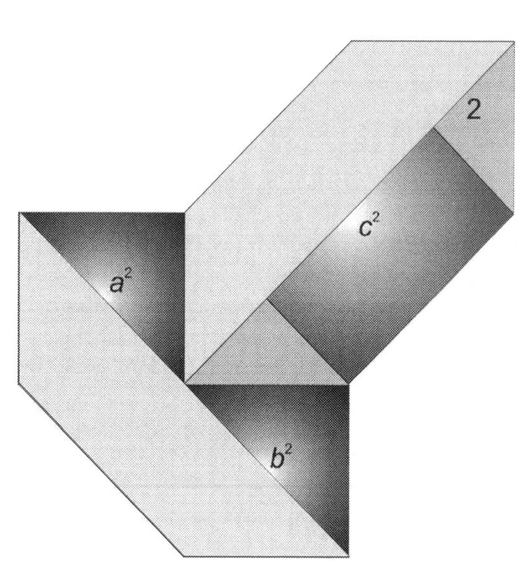

Figure 5.

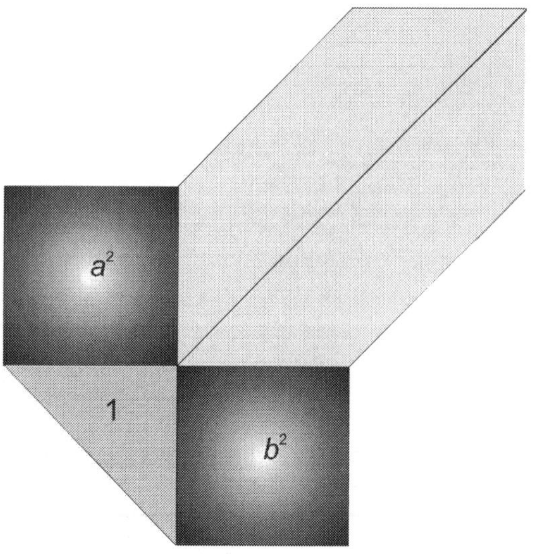

Figure 6.

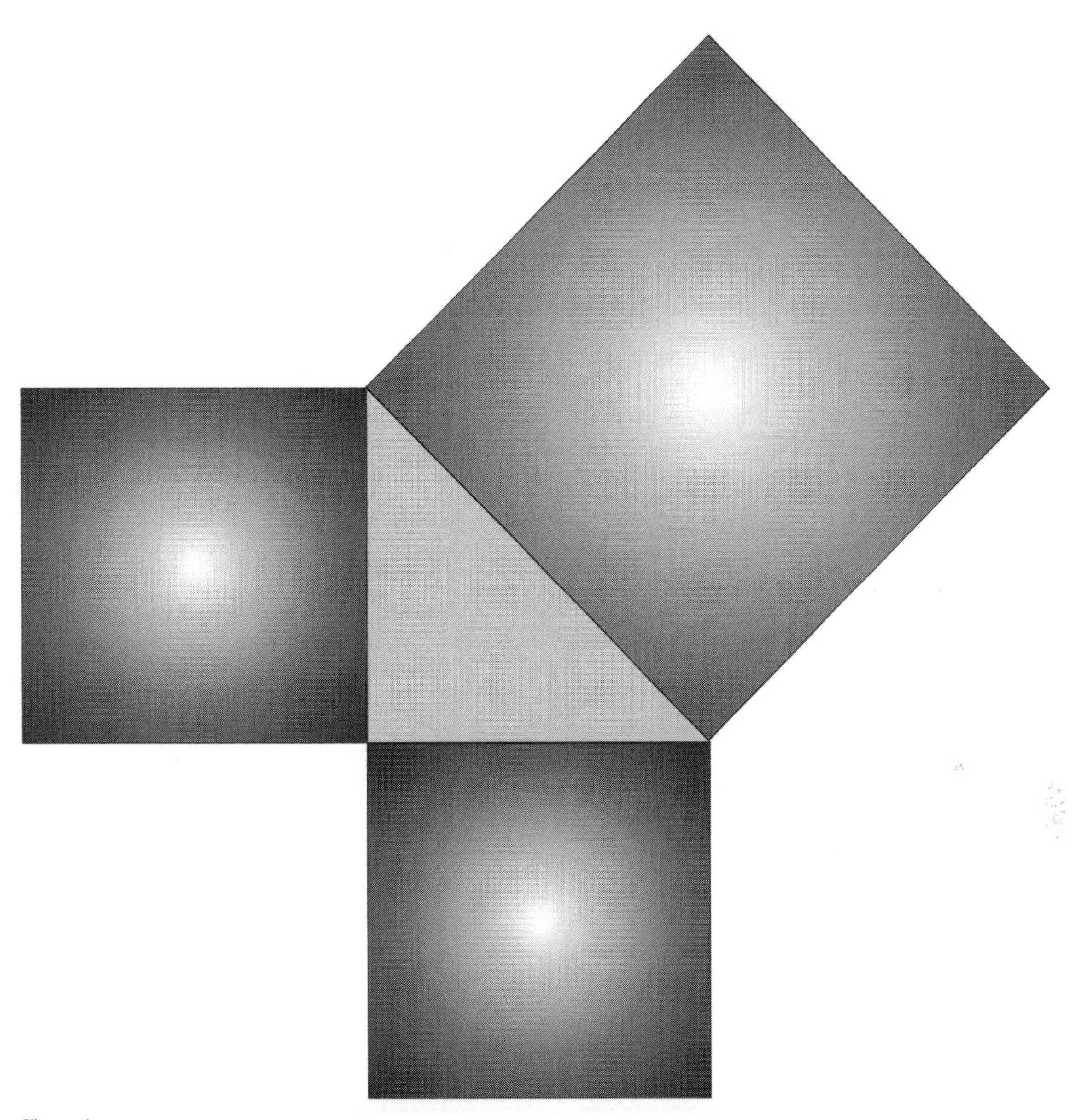

Figure *A*.

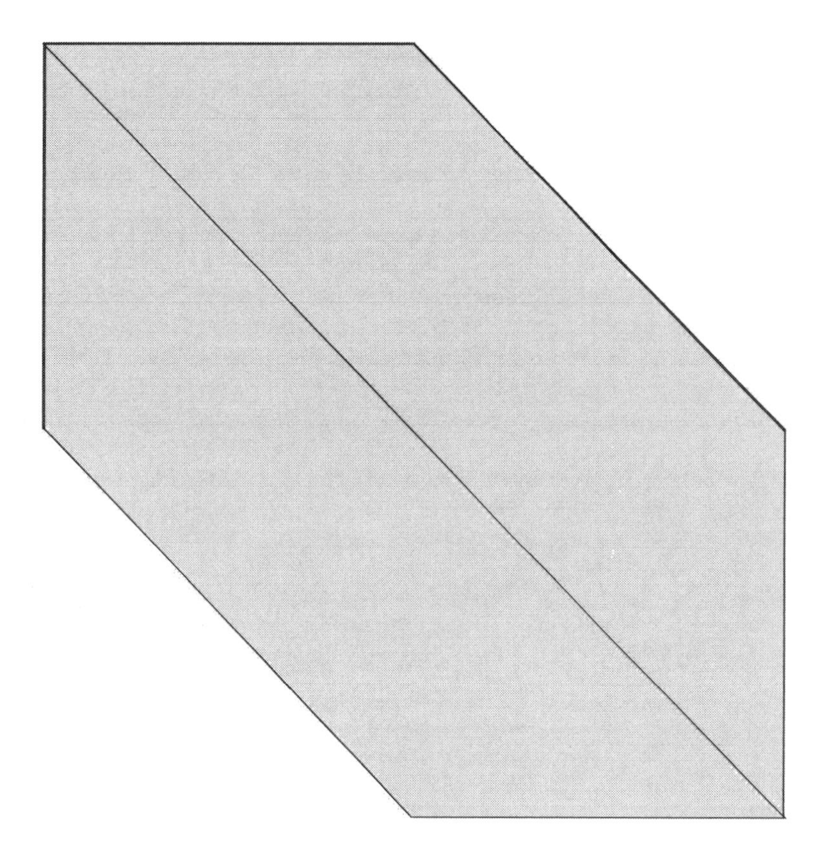

Figure *B*.

EXERCISES

1. A rope hangs from the top of a flagstaff and is two feet longer than the flagstaff. When pulled taut, it reaches a point on the ground 18 feet from the foot of the staff. What is the height of the flagstaff?
2. A bridge (Figure 7) of length one mile in winter expands two feet in the summer. Suppose the shape in summer is ΔACB (we are simplifying matters). How far, CD, does the center of the bridge collapse in summer? Round your answer to the nearest foot. You may use your calculator only to estimate the square root.

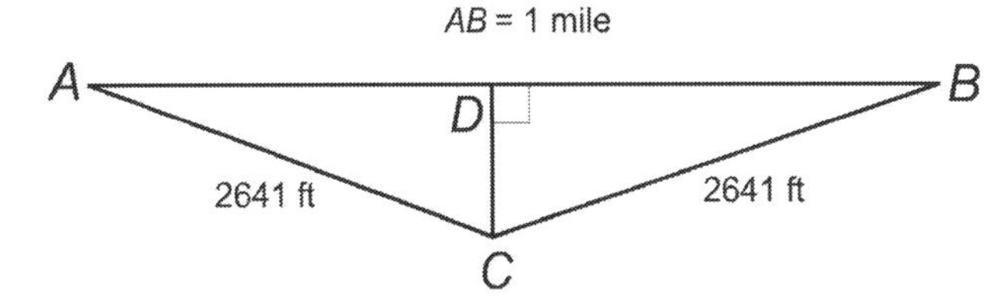

Figure 7.

3. Mr. City Slicker wanted to do some bow hunting on Mr. Farmer's land. Mr. Farmer happened to be in the city visiting an agricultural museum and offered to ride back with Mr. City Slicker on the bus since Mr. Farmer's only vehicle of transportation is his tractor. Mr. City Slicker grabbed his brand new five-foot long hunting bow and walked to the bus stop with Mr. Farmer. When the bus arrived, the driver told Mr. City Slicker that he could not take his bow on board since bus rules prohibit objects more than four feet long on the bus. Mr. City Slicker slunk back in despondency. "Don't worry," said Mr. Farmer to his brokenhearted friend, "I'll get your hunting bow on the bus." And he did without violating the rules or breaking or bending the bow. How did Mr. Farmer do it?

Euclid's Proof of the Pythagorean Theorem.

Let's reason with Euclid and write QED to one of the most famous geometric proofs in the history of mathematics. It is found in Book I, Proposition 47 of *The Elements*.

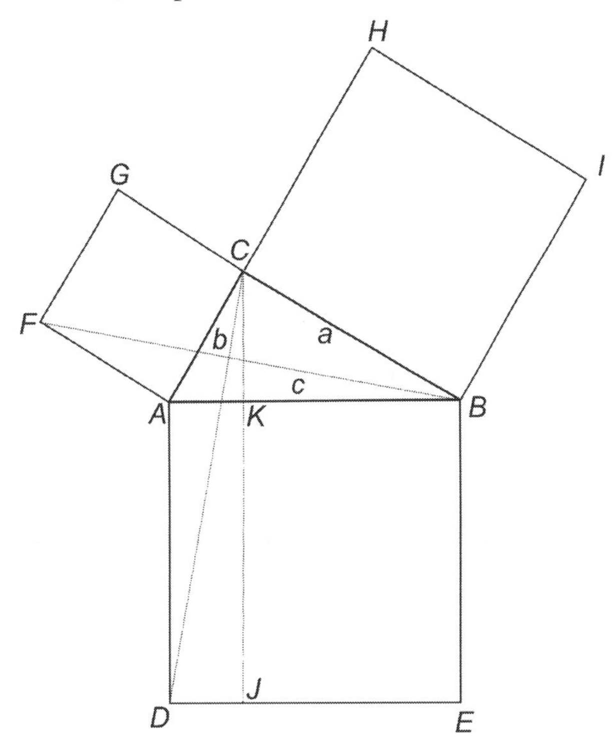

Figure 8. Euclid's proof of the Pythagorean Theorem. By the shape of the figure, this diagram is also known as the "windmill."

4. First, we construct a right triangle ΔABC where $m\angle ACB = 90°$ (Figure 8). We label its vertices and let $AB = c$ (the hypotenuse of ΔABC), $AC = b$, and $BC = a$. From the figure, explain why the Greek word hypotenuse means "to stretch under."

In Figure 8, we construct three squares, square *FGCA*, square *CHIB*, and square *DABE*. We note that two squares are on each leg and one square is on the hypotenuse. Euclid proved that the area of square *DABE* equals the sum of the areas of the square *FGCA* and square *CHIB* or, using symbolic algebra, $c^2 = a^2 + b^2$.

5. Euclid's ingenious strategy started with this construction. From the vertex of the right angle ($\angle C$ or $\angle ACB$), he constructed $\overline{CJ}$ perpendicular to $\overline{DE}$. We label points *K* and *J* as indicated. Note the two rectangles, rectangle *DAKJ* and rectangle *JKBE*. Euclid showed that the area of rectangle *DAKJ* equals the area of square *FGCA,* and the area of rectangle *JKBE* equals the area of square *CHIB*. How could this demonstration logically generate a QED?
6. If you draw $\overline{CD}$ and $\overline{BF}$, how do you know that $\overline{GB}$ is a straight line segment? (Hint: Show that $m\angle GCA + m\angle ACB = 180°$. This is the only place in the proof where Euclid made use of the fact that ΔABC is a right triangle.)
7. Observe the two triangles, ΔCAD and ΔBAF. Look at them carefully. Do not let the overlap confuse you. Try to see them as separate and distinct triangles. We are going to show that these two triangles are congruent by Euclid's SAS theorem (Book I, Proposition 4); i.e., when two sides and the included angle of one triangle are equal respectively to another triangle, then the two triangles are congruent.
   (a) What can you conclude about the length of two of its sides, *CA* and *FA*?
   (b) What can you conclude about the length of two of its sides, *AB* and *AD*?
8. Now consider the two angles, $\angle CAD$ and $\angle BAF$, the included angles. Note that $m\angle CAD = m\angle CAB + m\angle BAD$ and $m\angle BAF = m\angle BAC + m\angle CAF$.
   (a) What do you know about $\angle CAB$ and $\angle BAC$?
   (b) What do you know about $\angle BAD$ and $\angle CAF$? (Hint: Use Euclid's Postulate 4.
   (c) Why can you use the answer to question (b) to prove that $m\angle CAD = m\angle BAF$? (Hint: Use Euclid's Axiom 2.)
9. Since $m\angle CAD = m\angle BAF$, $CA = FA$, and $AB = AD$, then $\Delta CAD \cong \Delta BAF$ by Euclid's SAS theorem. Congruency means that the area of ΔCAD = the area of ΔBAF. Let $\alpha(\Delta CAD)$ = the area of ΔCAD and $\alpha(\Delta BAF)$ = the area of ΔBAF. Write an equation relating $\alpha(\Delta CAD)$ with $\alpha(\Delta BAF)$.
10. Next, Euclid noticed a connection between ΔCAD and rectangle *DAKJ*. What is it? (Hint: look at their base. To find the base of ΔCAD look at the projection of its altitude $\overline{CJ}$ to $\overline{DE}$. $\overline{DJ}$ is the base of ΔCAD.)
11. Since ΔCAD and rectangle *DAKJ* share the same base and since ΔCAD resides between the parallel lines formed by the line segments $\overline{AD}$ and $\overline{KJ}$, what can you conclude? Support you answer based on Euclid's Proposition 41 in Book I, which states that the area of a triangle is half that of any parallelogram sharing the triangle's base and having the same height. (Note. Rectangles are parallelograms.)
12. Let $\alpha(\Delta CAD)$ = area of ΔCAD and $\alpha(DAKJ)$ = area of rectangle *DAKJ*. Write an equation relating $\alpha(\Delta CAD)$ with $\alpha(DAKJ)$.
13. Similarly, observe that ΔBAF and square *FGCA* share the same base $\overline{FA}$. (This should be easy to see.) Euclid took particular note that since $\overline{GB}$ is a straight line segment, then the line segments formed by $\overline{GC}$ and $\overline{FA}$ are parallel. This situation is the only instance where Euclid used that fact

that ΔABC is a right triangle. From these two observations, what can we conclude based upon Euclid's Book I, Proposition 41? (Note: Squares are also parallelograms.)

14. Let $\alpha(FGCA)$ = area of square and $\alpha(\Delta BAF)$ = area of ΔBAF. Write an equation relating $\alpha(\Delta BAF)$ with $\alpha(FGCA)$.
15. We know from Question 9 that $\alpha(\Delta CAD) = \alpha(\Delta BAF)$. From Question 11, $\alpha(\Delta CAD) = \alpha(DAKJ)$. From Question 13, $\alpha(\Delta BAF) = \alpha(FGCA)$. By substitution:
    (a) Write an equation relating $\alpha(DAKJ)$ to $\alpha(FGCA)$.
    (b) In words, what have we shown?
16. By the same reasoning, we can show that the area of rectangle *JKBE* is equal to the area of square *CHIB*. Let $\alpha(JKBE)$ = area of rectangle *JKBE* and $\alpha(CHIB)$ = area of square *CHIB*. Write an equation relating $\alpha(JKBE)$ with $\alpha(CHIB)$.
17. We are ready to QED Euclid's proof. Let $\alpha(DABE)$ = area of square *DABE*. Write an equation relating $\alpha(DABE)$ to $\alpha(DAKJ)$ and $\alpha(JKBE)$.
18. By substitution, write an equation relating the $\alpha(DABE)$ to $\alpha(FGCA)$ and $\alpha(CHIB)$.
19. Write the equation you derived in Question 18 in terms of a, b, and c.

Proposition 48 of Book I: The Converse of Proposition 47.
Not as well-known as Proposition 47, Euclid's reasoning to demonstrate the converse is somewhat unique because he uses Proposition 47 in his proof. Let's investigate his ingenuity.

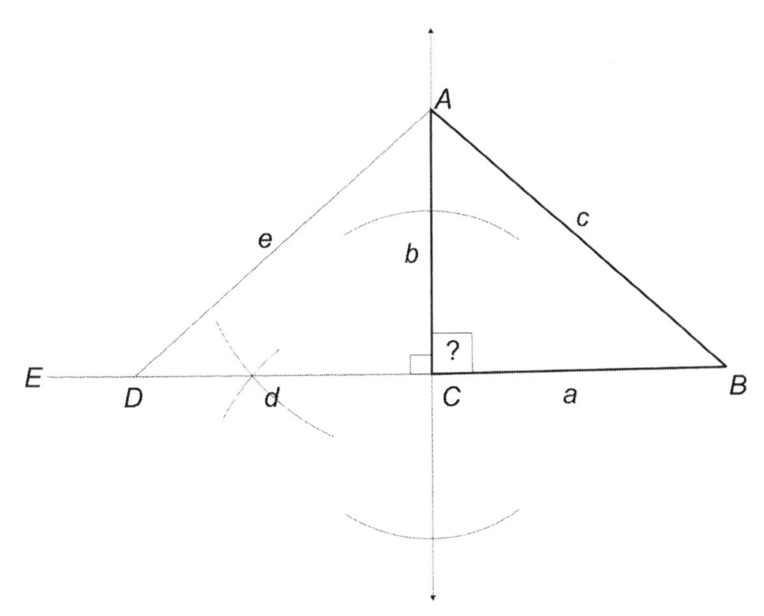

Figure 9.

20. Given ΔABC (Figure 9) with sides of length c, a, and b where $c^2 = a^2 + b^2$, Euclid must prove $m\angle ACB = 90°$. First, he constructed $\overline{CE}$ such that $\overline{CE} \perp \overline{AC}$; i.e., $m\angle ACE = 90°$. (Note the relevant construction arcs in the figure.) He did this by Proposition 11 of Book I, a proposition in the context of a given right angle. It is very similar to Proposition 12 of the same book. (Review Lesson 5.8.) He next constructed D so that $CD = CB$, or $d = a$. Finally, he drew $\overline{AD}$. His goal was to prove $\Delta ABC \cong \Delta ADC$. Doing this, he could conclude $m\angle ACB = 90°$. Why?
21. Euclid observed that $AC = AC$, or $b = b$, and, by construction $d = a$. If he could prove that $AB = AD$, or $c = e$, he could establish congruency between the two triangles. Why?

22. To show $c = e$, he made use of the fact that $m\angle ACE = 90°$. By Proposition 47, what is the relationship between b, d, and e?
23. Euclid now had enough information to QED his proof. Explain how he showed $c = e$.

Pythagoras and the President of the United States.

James Abram Garfield (1831-1881) became the 20th President of the United States on 4 March 1881. He was the last president to be born in a log cabin. He was the first president to have his mother present at his inauguration, and he was the first president to view the inaugural parade from a stand in front of the White House. He was ambidextrous and could entertain friends by writing a statement in Greek with one hand and in Latin with the other. (He was not the first president who could do this!) In 1876, while a member of the House of Representatives, he developed this simple and elegant proof of the Pythagorean Theorem, which was published in the *New England Journal of Education* (1 April 1876). Charles J. Guiteau, a disappointed office seeker, shot Garfield on 2 July 1881. Garfield died from infections from his wound on 19 September 1881.

> It is the high privilege and sacred duty of those now living to educate their successors and fit them, by intelligence and virtue, for the inheritance which awaits them.
> James A. Garfield, inaugural address, 4 March 1881.

Figure 10. Source: United States Postal Service (Dates of issue, top to bottom: 1922, 1938, 1986).

24. In this proof, Garfield invoked the truth that the area of a trapezoid is half the product of its altitude multiplied by the sum of the lengths of its parallel bases. From Figure 11, write a formula for the area of a trapezoid.

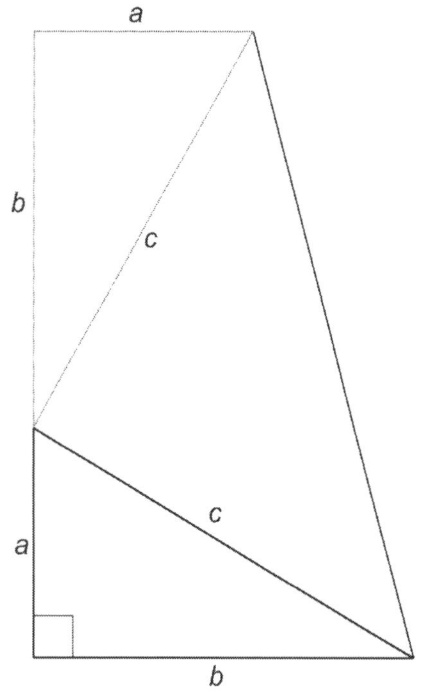

Figure 11.

25. Garfield constructed a right triangle with legs a and b and hypotenuse c. He sought to prove that $a^2 + b^2 = c^2$. From the three sides of the given right triangle, he constructed three right triangles to

form a trapezoid. The area of the trapezoid is the sum of the areas of the three triangles. Write this relationship as an equation.

26. Multiply both sides of the equation in Question 24 and the equation in Question 25 by 2.
27. Expand $(a + b)(a + b)$.
28. Set the two equations equal to each other and subtract $2ab$ from both sides.
29. QED the Pythagorean Theorem.

In Figure 12, we have a geometric proof of the Pythagorean Theorem. In Part a, we have a right triangle labeled 1. In Part b, we have created three duplicates right triangle 1, labeled 2, 3, and 4, and rearranged them to form a square. The square labeled 5 is the extra area generated by this rearrangement.

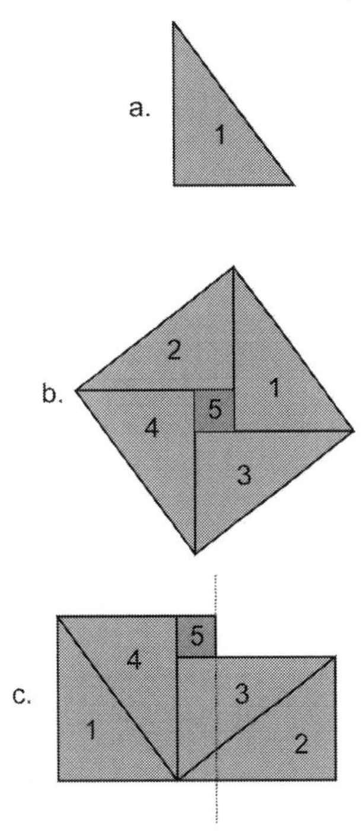

Figure 12.

30. Based on Part c, the rearrangement of the five figures created in Part b, QED the Pythagorean Theorem. (Hint: Use the dotted line segment as an aid in your reasoning.) Note: Some historians believe that this procedure was how Pythagoras originally proved the theorem.[1]

In Figure 13, we have partitioned the area of a square of sides $a + b$ into two congruent trapezoids. Answer these questions:

31. Show that ΔABC, ΔCED, and ΔACD are right triangles.
32. Prove $c^2 = a^2 + b^2$. (Hint: Start by stating an equation for the area of half the square and for the area of the three right triangles.)

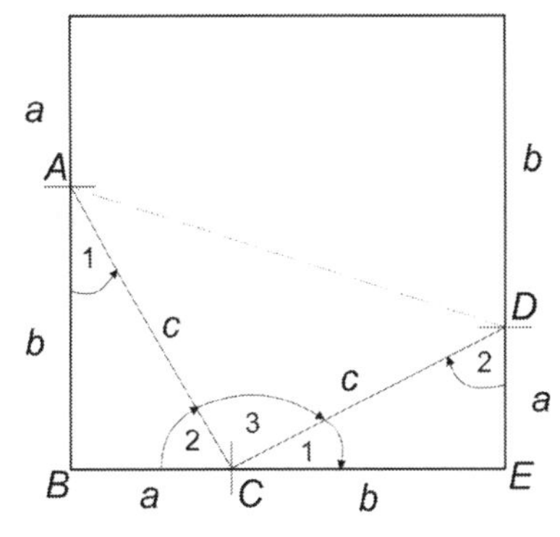

Figure 13.

[1] See Jacob Bronowski, *The Ascent of Man* (Boston: Little, Brown & Company, 1973), pp. 158-160.

Pons Asinorum Theorem.

Medieval geometers named Euclid's fifth proposition in Book I *pons asinorum* (Lesson 8.1 and Lesson 11.3), meaning "bridge of asses."[2] It states that if two sides of a triangle are equal (i.e., isosceles triangle), then the angles opposite them are equal. The proof is somewhat complicated because lines and angles must be added. Note Figure 14 where all Greek letters represent angle measures. Copy the following table and supply justifications for each step of the theorem:

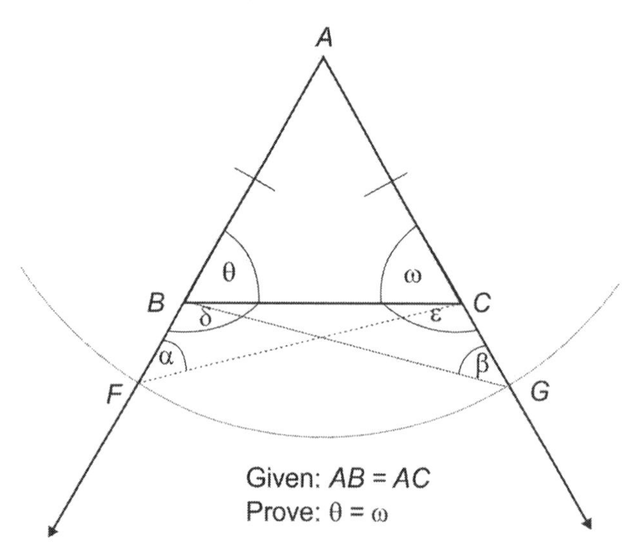

Figure 14. *Pons asinorum* theorem.

	Assertion	Justification
33. Step 1	Extend $\overline{AB}$ and $\overline{AC}$ indefinitely to form rays $\overrightarrow{AB}$ and $\overrightarrow{AC}$.	
34. Step 2	Draw $\overset{\frown}{FG}$ so the it intersects $\overrightarrow{AB}$ and $\overrightarrow{AC}$ at F and G respectively.	
35. Step 3	$AB = AC$	
36. Step 4	$AF = AG$	
37. Step 5	$m\angle FAC = m\angle GAB$	
38. Step 6	$\Delta FAC \cong \Delta GAB$	
39. Step 7	$\alpha = \beta$	
40. Step 8	$FC = BG$	
41. Step 9	$BF = CG$	
42. Step 10	$\Delta BFC \cong \Delta CGB$	
43. Step 11	$\delta = \varepsilon$	
44. Step 12	$\theta = \omega$	
	QED	

[2] Those who can cross this bridge, i.e., prove this theorem, can enter the geometric kingdom of deductive logic. The geometry of this period consisted only of the analysis of the first few theorems of Euclid (Book I).

The French mathematician Adrien-Marie Legendre (1752-1833) developed a much easier proof of the *pons asinorum* theorem. He knew the theorem that stated if the hypotenuse and a leg of one right triangle are equal to the corresponding parts of another right triangle, then the two triangles are congruent (The HL Congruence Theorem). In ΔABC (Figure 15), he constructed the altitude $\overline{AD}$ of the triangle; i.e., $\overline{AD} \perp \overline{BC}$.

45. Reason to the QED of the proof.

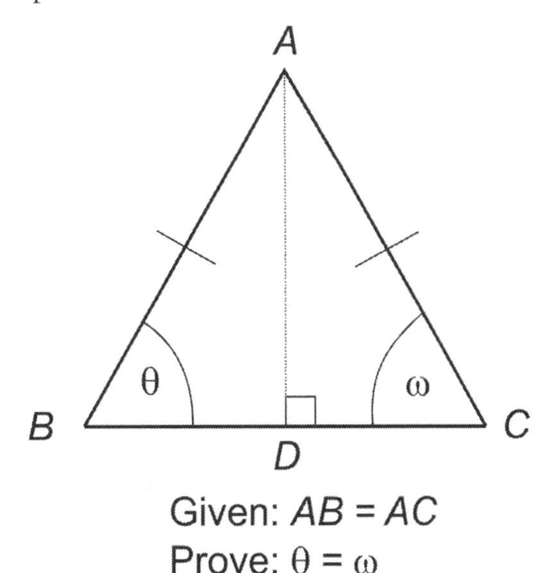

Figure 15. *Pons asinorum* theorem (simplified proof).

46. Based on the *pons asinorum* theorem, prove that if a triangle is equilateral, it must be equiangular. (Refer to Lesson 4.6.)

> Mathematical symbols, formulas, functions, properties, axioms, postulates, derivations, theorems ... never stand alone. They are connected to reality: to people, to history, to culture, to utility, to beauty.
>
> James D. Nickel

13.6 PEANO'S AXIOMS AND THE PROOF THAT $2 + 2 = 4$

Figure 1. Giuseppe Peano. Source: Public Domain.

Terms & Concepts Introduced
1. Completeness
2. Consistency
3. Formal mathematics
4. Independence

Mathematicians like to **formalize** topics in mathematics into a deductive system.[1] It was not until recently that mathematicians formulated a series of statements that defined the system of natural numbers. The reason it took so long is that mathematicians did not feel a need for such a system because of the universal and intuitive sense for numbers. It was the Italian mathematician Giuseppe Peano (1858-1932), in *Arithmetices principia, nova methodo exposita* (1899), who put together a series of arithmetical axioms (Lesson 3.7 and Lesson 13.2), statements that contain words or terms that are left undefined and simply accepted as foundational to the topic under consideration.[2]

Before we inspect the axioms Peano used to encompass the system of natural numbers, let us remind ourselves that Jesus, as the Light and Logos of the universe (John 1:1-14; 8:12), is the light and life of men; i.e., men know by the gift of Jesus Christ, their Creator and Redeemer. The ground of our ability to think rationally, what goes on inside of us, and that we find the created order embedded with rationality, what goes on outside of us, is the uncreated rationality of the Triune God revealed to us by and grounded in Jesus Christ.

> The idea of an axiomatic system stands to mathematics as a whole as the idea of the Gothic cathedral stands to medieval architecture. It is the form to which mathematicians have always aspired.
> David Berlinski, *One, Two, Three: Absolutely Elementary Mathematics* (2011), p. 41.

In the 19th century, mathematicians established three criteria governing the mathematical system they are trying to develop and understand.[3] Then, following the plan of Euclid, they laid out a set of axioms that form the basis for the application of logical thinking and logical derivations. They combined these axioms with a set of undefined terms or notions that appear to be intuitively obvious and used these axioms and undefined terms to justify the many propositions of the system under study, either a number system or a geometric system.

There are three preliminary criteria, axioms behind the axioms, three logical requirements that every system of axioms must aim to meet: (1) **consistency**, (2) **independence**, and (3) **completeness**.

Requirement 1. A set of axioms must be *consistent* in that they do not contradict each other. This consistency also implies that it is impossible to derive from these axioms results that will contradict each other. In other words, the system of axioms must comport both with each other and with all the results derived from this set. This requirement satisfies the Law of Contradiction. It should be impossible to derive both proposition P and its negation $\sim P$ from the given axioms; i.e. no proposition can be both proved *and* disproved within the system.

Requirement 2. Each axiom in the set must be *independent* of the other axioms in the set. In other words, an axiom in the set cannot be derived from the other axioms in the set. This stipulation guarantees that the set of axioms are both minimal and efficient.

Requirement 3. A set of axioms must be *complete*, meaning they are sufficient to generate all possible results of the given field of knowledge they seek to encompass. A system of axioms is complete if it is impossible to add consistent and independent axioms without introducing additional undefined

[1] Unfortunately, in this formalistic thrust there is a dualistic separation of form from being, number from ontology.

[2] Recall that axiom, in Greek, means "to reckon or think worthy."

[3] Most of them did not comprehend the light of Jesus Christ (John 1:5).

terms. The requirement of completeness satisfies the Law of Excluded Middle; i.e., every proposition can be proved *or* disproved within the system.[4]

With these preliminaries established, here is Giuseppe Peano's list:[5]

Axiom 1. 1 is a natural number.
Axiom 2. The successor of any natural number is a natural number.
Axiom 3. No two natural numbers have the same successor.
Axiom 4. 1 is not the successor of any natural number.
Axiom 5. If 1 has a particular property, and the successor of every natural number has the same property, then natural every number has that property.

Let's see if we can determine what words Giuseppe Peano considered to be foundational and therefore undefined. There are three. Think about it for a moment.

The three foundation assumptions are (1) natural number, (2) the number one, and (3) successor. Peano assumed these terms and therefore left them undefined. Because we have an intuitive sense of counting due to being made in the image of God, the *imago Dei*, we know what is meant by sequential counting starting from 1.

AXIOM ANALYSIS

When we combine Axiom 1 with Axiom 4, we conclude that 1 is the first number of the counting numbers.

Axiom 2 states that the successor of any natural number is a natural number. This axiom guarantees that the sequence of natural numbers *always* contains natural numbers.

Axiom 3 guarantees every natural number in the sequence is one greater than the preceeding natural number, the pattern, and that every natural number in the sequence is unique. Therefore, when we count we will not do something like this: $\{1, 2, 3, 2, 4, 5, 3, 6, 2, \ldots\}$.

Axiom 5 allows us to prove theorems about all natural numbers in the sequence of natural numbers even though there are an infinite number of them. This axiom is the method of proof we have already mentioned, Mathematical Induction.[6] We will explore the logic of this procedure in Lesson 13.16.

PROOF THAT $2 + 2 = 4$

These axioms are sufficient to define all the operations of arithmetic. Let's see how it works. First, consider addition. Let's prove $2 + 2 = 4$ using Giuseppe Peano's Axioms.

---

[4] Although we will not enter into a detailed discussion of the work of the logician and mathematician Kurt Gödel (1906-1978), he showed, in the early 1930s, that any axiomatic system of mathematics, even the system of natural numbers, can be either consistent or complete. The system cannot be both. One, either consistency or completeness, must be sacrificed to have the other. In short, the realm of infinity (e.g., the natural numbers are infinite in scope) generates such problems when one tries to develop perfectly logical systems. See Kurt Gödel, *On Formally Undecidable Propositions of Principia Mathematica and Related Systems* (Mineola: Dover Publications, [1931, 1962] 1992). For a clear, non-technical demonstration of Gödel's reasoning see Rózsa Péter, *Playing with Infinity: Mathematical Explorations and Excursions* (New York: Dover Publications, [1961] 1976), pp. 255-265. See also James D. Nickel, *Mathematics: Is God Silent?* (Vallecito: Ross House Books, [1990] 2001), pp. 183-194, Stanley L. Jaki, *The Relevance of Physics* (Edinburgh: Scottish Academic Press, [1966, 1970] 1993, pp. 127-130, and Thomas F. Torrance, *Transformation & Convergence in the Frame of Knowledge: Explorations in the Interrelations of Scientific and Theological Enterprise* (Grand Rapids: William B. Eerdmans Publishing Company, 1984), pp. 136-145.

[5] Cited in Calvin C. Clawson, *Mathematics Mysteries: The Beauty and Magic of Numbers* (Cambridge: Perseus Books, 1996), p. 17. Giuseppe Peano started with the number zero instead of the number 1.

[6] The French mathematician/theologian Blaise Pascal (1623-1662) first developed this method of proof.

Step	Justification	Assertion
	Given	2 + 2
1.	Write the first 2 as a successor of 1	(1 + 1) + 2
2.	Apply the Associative Law of Addition	1 + (1 + 2)
3.	Write the successor of 2 as 3	1 + 3
4.	Write the successor of 3 as 4	4
	QED	

PROOF THAT 3 + 4 = 7

Let's prove this proposition in the same way:

Step	Justification	Assertion
	Given	3 + 4
1.	Write 4 as a successor of 3	3 + (3 + 1)
2.	Write the second 3 as a successor of 2	3 + (2 + 1 + 1)
3.	Rearrange[7] the 1s by applying the Apply the Associative Law of Addition	(3 + 1) + (2 + 1)
4.	Write the successor of 3 as 4	4 + (2 + 1)
5.	Write the 2 as a successor of 1:	4 + (1 + 1 + 1)
6.	Apply the Associative Law of Addition	(4 + 1) + (1 + 1)
7.	Write the successor of 4 as 5	5 + (1 + 1)
8.	Apply the Associative Law of Addition	(5 + 1) + 1
9.	Write the successor of 5 as 6	6 + 1
10.	Write the successor of 6 as 7	7
	QED	

Likewise, we can prove the sum of any two numbers by this process, from 2 + 2 to 12,489,423,298 + 598,498,009,234. Fortunately, we do not need to perform all these steps to determine these sums; we just use our addition facts. The purpose of proving 3 + 4 = 7 is to show how Giuseppe Peano's axioms account for, or justify, the process of addition, an Order 1 operation, which is, as we have noted, really a faster way of counting forward.

The next order of operations, Order 2, is multiplication, or repeated addition if we limit ourselves to natural numbers: $4 \times 3 = 3 + 3 + 3 + 3$ or $4 + 4 + 4 = 12$. The next order, Order 3, exponentiation can be defined as repeated multiplication: $4^3 = 4 \times 4 \times 4 = 64$.

Subtraction and division are inverse operations of addition and multiplication respectively and extraction of roots/logarithms are the two inverses of exponentiation.

Enfolded in Giuseppe Peano's axioms is the fascination and wonder of realizing that tumbling out of the infinite set of natural numbers are all the characteristics of the basic operations of arithmetic.

EXERCISES

Define the following terms:

1. Formal mathematics
2. Consistency
3. Independence

[7] We invoke the Associative Law of Addition to do this.

4. Completeness

Use Peano's Axioms to prove:

5. $2 + 3 = 5$
6. $4 + 5 = 9$

Answer this question:

7. Review the construction in the homework exercise in Lesson 5.14 (Figure 2). Then, prove that *AJBHCI* is a regular hexagon. (Hint: Make use of the bisection of the three sides of the equilateral triangle *ABC* and the HL Congruence Theorem used in the homework in Lesson 13.5. You want to show that the six interior triangles, ΔAGJ, ΔJGB, ΔBGH, ΔHGC, ΔCGI, and ΔIGA, are equilateral and congruent.) Note: This proof requires many steps so be careful with your reasoning. Equality of sides and angles must be explicitly proved, not just assumed.

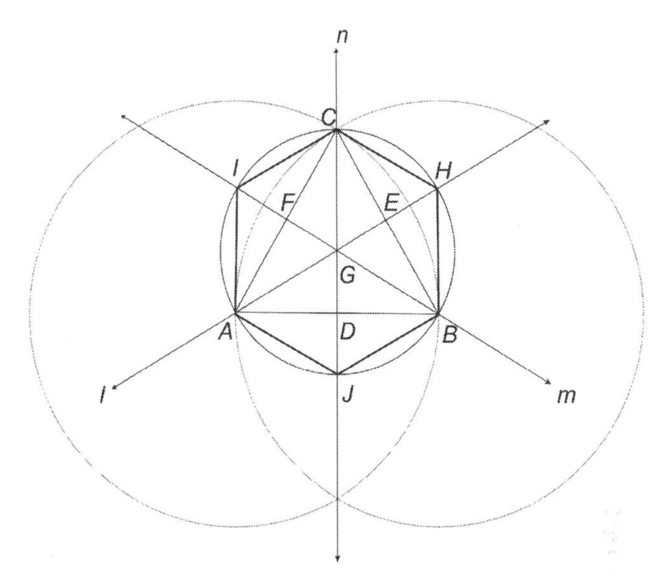

Figure 2.

Unity in Diversity in the Study of the Ellipse.

There are two diverse descriptions of the ellipse. The first definition relates this shape to a cone: We can generate an ellipse by intersecting a cone with a plane at less than a right angle to the central axis but more than the angle made by the curved or lateral side of the cone. The second description is the ellipse is a locus of points in the Cartesian coordinate plane: An ellipse is the locus of points the sum of whose distance to the two given points, the foci[8] of the ellipse, is constant. Are these two definitions connected? Study the Figure 3 carefully.

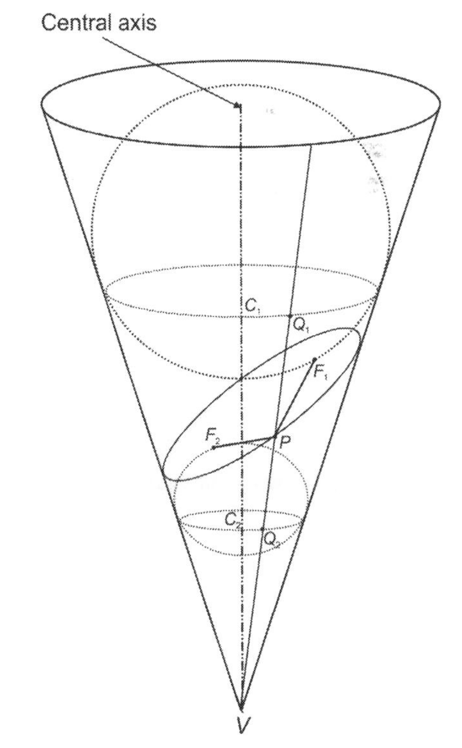

Figure 3. Ellipse and Circles in a Half-Cone.

In the figure, two spherical balls of different diameters, C_1 and C_2, have been placed in the cone (imagine that they are scoops of ice cream). One is above the plane that is cutting through the cone (and imaging an oval as it intersects with the cone) and the other below this plane. Each of these spheres fit snugly into the cone, and each is respectively tangent to the plane at one point; i.e., Sphere C_1 at point F_1 and Sphere C_2 at point F_2. We are going to prove an intriguing relationship; i.e., that F_1 and F_2 are the foci, the fixed points, of an ellipse.

Note that point P is on the surface of the cone and lies in the intersecting plane. Note also that points Q_1 and Q_2 are also on the surface of the cone such that Q_1, Q_2, and P all lie on the same line (i.e., they are collinear – Lesson 2.7). We can prove

[8] Foci (pronounced fo-seye in the United States, but fo-keye in the United Kingdom) is the plural of focus.

that given a circle and a point outside of or external to a circle, the tangent segments to a circle from that external point are equal. (See homework exercise in Lesson 13.9.) By analogous thinking, we can reason from a two-dimensional circle to a three-dimensional sphere and deduce that same; i.e., that the distances from an external point to any two tangent points are equal. Therefore, $PF_1 = PQ_1$ and $PF_2 = PQ_2$.

8. What happens to Q_1Q_2 as point P moves around the intersection of the plane and the cone (Q_1, Q_2, and P remain collinear)?
9. Show that $PF_1 + PF_2$ is independent of the P; i.e., no matter where P is, $PF_1 + PF_2$ remain constant. (Hint: from Question 8, we know that $PQ_1 + PQ_2$ is constant regardless of the location of P.)
10. From Question 9, show that the cross section of the intersection of the plane with the cone is indeed an ellipse.

Prove this Proposition: Two nonvertical lines are perpendicular ⇔ the product of their slopes is -1. (See Homework exercises in Lesson 10.7.)

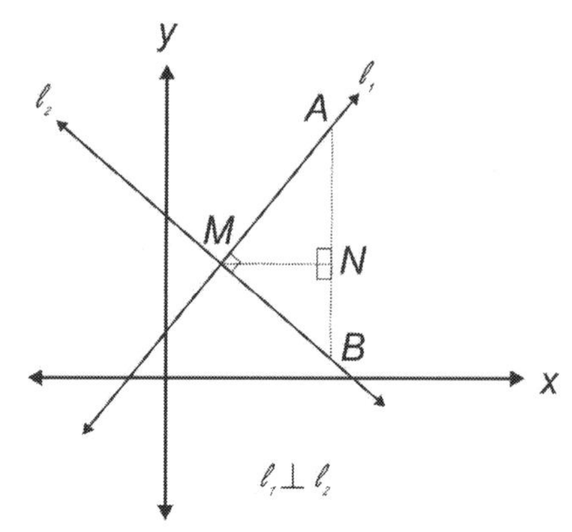

Figure 4.

11. In Figure 4, which line, l_1 or l_2, has this slope: $\frac{-NB}{MN}$?
12. What is the slope of the other line?
13. Why is $\frac{AN}{MN} = \frac{MN}{NB}$?
14. If $\frac{-NB}{MN} = a_2$, what does $\frac{MN}{NB}$ equal in terms of a_2?
15. If $\frac{AN}{MN} = a_1$, why is $a_1 = -\frac{1}{a_2}$?
16. Why is $a_1a_2 = -1$?

Let's invoke trigonometry to prove that if a nonvertical line has slope $m \neq 0$, then any line perpendicular to it has slope $n = -\frac{1}{m}$ (Figure 5).

17. Given $m = \tan\theta$, we want to prove that $n = \frac{1}{m}$. We let n = slope of the line perpendicular to m. Will n be negative or positive?
18. Write an equation for n in terms of the tangent of $90° - \theta$.
19. What is the trig identity for $\tan(90° - \theta)$? (Hint: See Lesson 12.6.)
20. Substitute the identity you found in Question 19 into the equation you wrote in Question 18.
21. Based on Question 20, reason to the QED of the proof.

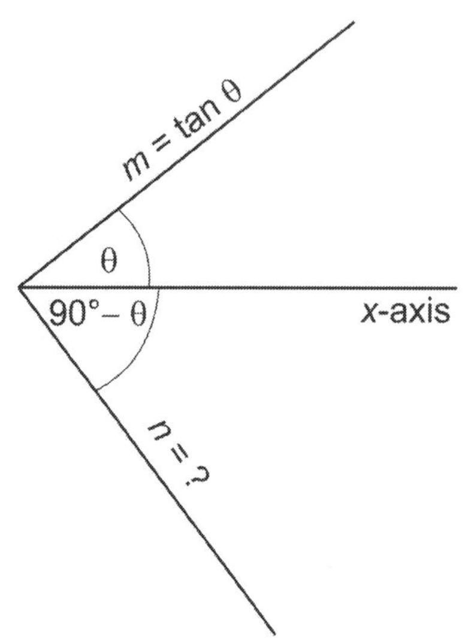

Figure 5.

The Quadrature of a Polygon: A "Thought" Construction.

22. Start with any general type polygon of five sides as shown in Figure 6. By drawing diagonals, we can subdivide its area into a set of triangles with areas A, B, and C respectively. Write the expression for the area of the polygon.
23. From Lesson 13.4 homework, we have shown that triangles are quadrable, so we can construct squares with sides a, b, and c with areas A, B, and C (i.e., $A = a^2$, $B = b^2$, and $C = c^2$). We then could

construct a right triangle with legs of length a and b and whose hypotenuse is of length x. Write an expression in terms of a, b, and x using the Pythagorean Theorem.

24. Next, we could construct another right triangle with legs of x and c and hypotenuse y. Write an expression in terms of x, c, and y using the Pythagorean Theorem.
25. Next, we could construct a square with side y. Write an expression in terms of y for the area of this square.
26. We must now prove that y^2 (the area of the square) $= A + B + C$ (the area of the given polygon). From Question 24, write an expression for y^2.
27. From Question 25, write an expression for x^2.
28. Substitute the expression for x^2 in Question 27 with your answer to Question 26.
29. (a) Since $A = a^2$, $B = b^2$, and $C = c^2$, the, by substitution, write an expression for y^2.
    (b) Can we therefore QED the proposition that we can construct the quadrature of a polygon?
30. Reason that, in general, *any* polygon (of n sides) is quadrable. (Hint: show that any polygon can be subdivided into a set of triangles. Your reasoning should be inductive.)

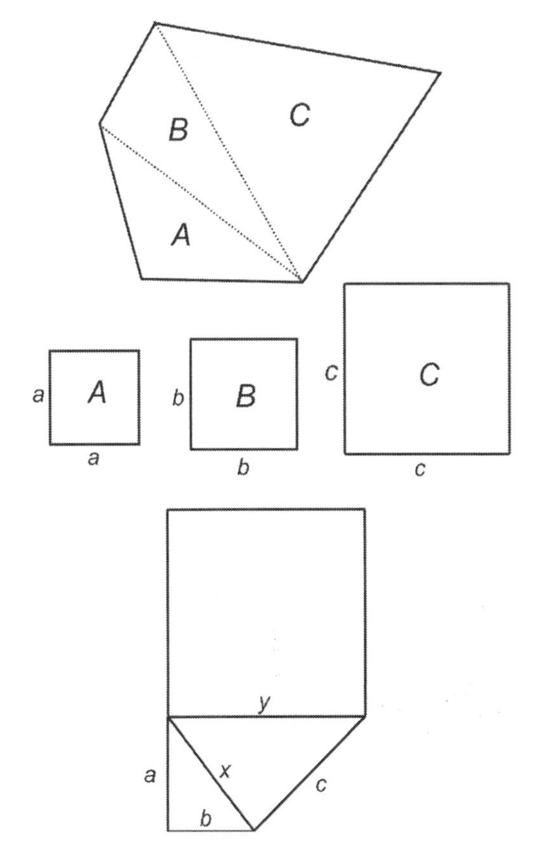

Figure 6.

Proving the Pythagorean Theorem from Heron's Formula. We start with the right triangle in Figure 7 where all we know are the sides a, b, and c. By Heron's formula, we know:

$$s \text{ (semi-perimeter)} = \frac{a+b+c}{2}$$

$$\alpha \text{ (area of triangle)} = \sqrt{s(s-a)(s-b)(s-c)}$$

From this information, we want to prove $c^2 = a^2 + b^2$; i.e., we will show that the Pythagorean Theorem is perichoretically embedded in Heron's formula. Get ready for some intense Algebra!

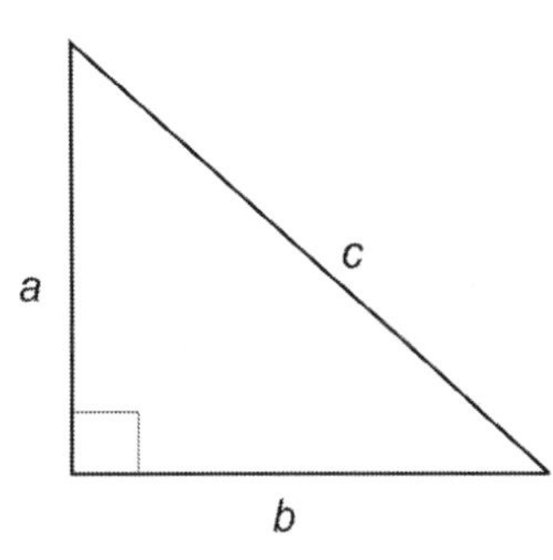

Figure 7.

31. Use $s = \dfrac{a+b+c}{2}$ to find an expression for $s - a$.
32. Use $s = \dfrac{a+b+c}{2}$ to find an expression for $s - b$.
33. Use $s = \dfrac{a+b+c}{2}$ to find an expression for $s - c$.

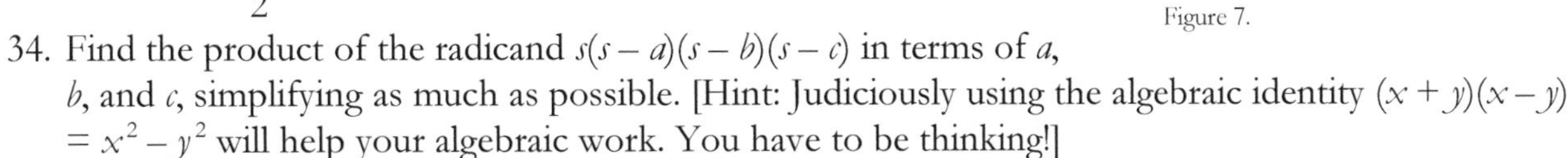

34. Find the product of the radicand $s(s - a)(s - b)(s - c)$ in terms of a, b, and c, simplifying as much as possible. [Hint: Judiciously using the algebraic identity $(x + y)(x - y) = x^2 - y^2$ will help your algebraic work. You have to be thinking!]
35. From your results to Question 34, write the formula for α in terms of a, b, and c.
36. Looking at Figure 7, use the area formula for a triangle to generate another formula for α.

37. Equate the two formulas for α (Question 35 and Question 36) and apply algebraic operations to QED the proof. [Hint: To do this will take more algebraic ingenuity. Again, think carefully. At a key point in your algebraic work, you will need to use this algebraic identity: $(x - y)^2 = x^2 - 2xy + y^2$.]

Trigonometric Product Identities.

These product identities gave John Napier that idea that multiplication can be converted into addition. (Refer to Lesson 12.1, footnote 1.) From the homework of Lesson 13.1, we know these four Compound-Angle Identities:

- $\sin(\theta - \omega) = \sin\theta\cos\omega - \cos\theta\sin\omega$
- $\sin(\theta + \omega) = \sin\theta\cos\omega + \cos\theta\sin\omega$
- $\cos(\theta - \omega) = \cos\theta\cos\omega + \sin\theta\sin\omega$
- $\cos(\theta + \omega) = \cos\theta\cos\omega - \sin\theta\sin\omega$

Using $a = b + c$ and $d = e + f \Leftrightarrow a + d = b + c + e + f$, prove the following Product Identities:

38. $\cos\theta\cos\omega = \dfrac{\cos(\theta-\omega)+\cos(\theta+\omega)}{2}$

39. $\sin\theta\sin\omega = \dfrac{\cos(\theta-\omega)-\cos(\theta+\omega)}{2}$

40. $\sin\theta\cos\omega = \dfrac{\sin(\theta-\omega)+\sin(\theta+\omega)}{2}$

41. $\cos\theta\sin\omega = \dfrac{\sin(\theta+\omega)-\sin(\theta-\omega)}{2}$

Answer the following questions:

42. From the Binomial Theorem $(n + 1)^2 = n^2 + 2n + 1$, state an expression for the difference of squares of two natural numbers whose difference is 1.
43. State a factored expression for the difference of squares of two natural numbers whose difference is 2.
44. State a factored expression for the difference of squares of two natural numbers whose difference is k.
45. Use the expression in Question 44 to calculate $32^2 - 25^2$.
46. Confirm your answer to Question 45 using the algebraic identity $a^2 - b^2 = (a + b)(a - b)$.

We have discovered another way to find the difference of two squares, a way that expresses the beautiful relationships that are hidden in the natural numbers. It is the treasure of these hidden relationships that sometimes makes possible modern wonders. See Lesson 13.12 for one example.

> Mathematics explains the meaning and provides the justification. The theories that result demand the same combination of art and sophistication that is characteristic of any great intellectual endeavor.
>
> David Berlinski, *One, Two, Three: Absolutely Elementary Mathematics* (2011), p. 4.

13.7 Number Property Proofs

Term Introduced
1. Lune

In Lesson 4.12, we reasoned from pattern investigation to conclude that a negative number times a negative number is positive. To clarify matters, we used inductive thinking to reach this conclusion. How would a mathematician employ deductive logic to reach the same conclusion? In this lesson, we will demonstrate the way Giuseppe Peano would prove this proposition involving the multiplication of signed numbers. Whether by induction or by deduction, this property undergirds the way numbers work in the world of the Triune God's making.

We assume the following laws in this proof:

1. Commutative Law of Multiplication: $ab = ba$
2. Associative Law of Multiplication: $(ab)c = a(bc)$
3. Law of \Multiplying by Zero: $0a = 0$
4. Law of Multiplying by One, the Identity Element for Multiplication: $1a = a$
5. Law of Adding Zero to any number, the Identity Element for Addition: $0 + a = a$
6. Law of Adding Opposites: $a + (-a) = 0$
7. Distributive Law: $a(b + c) = ab + ac$ and $(b + c)a = ba + ca$
8. Factoring, or the Distributive Law in reverse: $ab + ac = a(b + c)$ and $ba + ca = (b + c)a$

Before we prove that a negative number times a negative number is a positive number, we demonstrate the proof of a few of these propositions using deductive logic.

First, we prove that $0a = 0$ and we will use laws concerning multiplication and the laws of addition to do this.

Proof That Zero Times Any Number Is Zero

Proposition 1. Prove $0a = 0$.

We start with $0a$ and add a to it. From this, we reason as follows:

Step	Assertion	Justification
1.	$0a + a = 0a + 1a$	We invoke the Law of Multiplication by 1, i.e., $a = 1a$.
2.	$0a + 1a = (0 + 1)a$	We apply the Distributive Law in reverse, or we factor a in $0a + 1a$.
3.	$(0 + 1)a = 1a$	We add or we invoke the Identity Element for Addition; i.e., $0 + 1 = 1$.
4.	$1a = a$	We invoke the Law of Multiplication by 1.
5.	$0a + a = a$	The conclusion of a syllogism starting with Step 1 and ending with Step 4.
6.	$0a + a + (-a) = a + (-a)$	We add $-a$ to both sides of the equation.
7.	$0a + a - a = a - a$	We invoke the Algebraic Definition of Subtraction, i.e., $a - b = a + (-b)$ for any a and b.
8.	$0a + 0 = 0$	We subtract; i.e., $a - a = 0$.
9.	$0a = 0$	We invoke the Identity Element for Addition; i.e., $k + 0 = k$ for any number $k \Rightarrow 0a = 0$.
		QED

Make sure you follow the dance of this logic. Note that we can skip Step 7 and go directly from Step 6 to Step 8 invoking $a + (-a) = 0$.

Now, let's prove $(-1)a = -a$. Knowing this law is just as important as knowing $1a = a$. Experienced students of Algebra invoke this law without thinking twice about it.

PROOF THAT -1 TIMES ANY NUMBER IS THE OPPOSITE OF THAT NUMBER

Proposition 2. Prove $(-1)a = -a$.

We reason as follows:

Step	Assertion	Justification
1.	$(-1)a$	Given.
2.	$(-1)a + a$	We add a to $(-1)a$.
3.	$(-1)a + a = (-1)a + 1a$	We invoke the Law of Multiplication by 1, i.e., $a = 1a$.
4.	$(-1)a + 1a = (-1 + 1)a$	We apply the Distributive Law in reverse, or we factor a in $(-1)a + 1a$.
5.	$[(-1) + 1]a = 0a$	We know that $(-1) + 1 = 0$; i.e., the sum of any number and its opposite is zero, the Law of Opposites. Or, in general, $(-k) + k = 0$ for any k.
6.	$0a = 0$	We invoke Proposition 1.
7.	$(-1)a + a = 0$	The conclusion of a syllogism starting with Step 3 and ending with Step 6.
8.	$(-1)a = -a$	We invoke the Law of Addition of opposites; i.e., $(-k) + k = 0$ for any k.
QED		

Another great dance step! Go over it carefully until you understand it.

Next, we are going to prove $-(ab) = (-a)b$. For example, $-(2 \times 3) = (-2)3$. Both sides of this equation, when evaluated, generate -6. Our logic will prove that any negative number times any positive number will always be a negative number.

PROOF THAT A NEGATIVE NUMBER TIMES A POSITIVE NUMBER IS A NEGATIVE NUMBER

Proposition 3. Prove $-(ab) = (-a)b$.

We must show that $(-a)b$ is the opposite, or negative, of ab. In other words, we must show that $ab + (-a)b = 0$. We reason as follows:

Step	Assertion	Justification
1.	ab	Given.
2.	$ab + (-a)b$	Add $(-a)b$ to ab.
3.	$ab + (-a)b = [a + (-a)]b$	We apply the Distributive Law in reverse, or we factor b in $ab + (-a)b$.
4.	$[a + (-a)]b = 0b$	By the Law of Opposites, $a + (-a) = 0$.
5.	$0b = 0$	We invoke Proposition 1.
6.	$ab + (-a)b = 0$	The conclusion of a syllogism starting with Step 3 and ending with Step 5.
QED		

By the same logic, we prove:

Proposition 4. $-(ab) = a(-b)$ You will do this proof as a homework exercise.

We are ready to prove $(-a)(-b) = ab$, or a negative number times a negative number is a positive number.

PROOF THAT A NEGATIVE NUMBER TIMES A NEGATIVE NUMBER IS A POSITIVE NUMBER

Proposition 5. Prove $(-a)(-b) = ab$.

We know Proposition 3 and Proposition 4: $-(ab) = (-a)b$ and $-(ab) = a(-b)$. From this, we reason as follows:

Step	Assertion	Justification
1.	$-(ab) = (-a)b$ and $-(ab) = a(-b) \Rightarrow (-a)b = a(-b)$	We make a substitution. (Make sure you see this.)
Inspect $(-a)b = a(-b)$ carefully in the context that the opposite of an opposite, or the negative or a negative is positive; i.e., $-(-k) = k$.		
2.	$(-a)(-b) = ab$	The Opposite of an Opposite Law; i.e., $-(-k) = k$.
	QED	

What is the justification for Step 2? Given $(-a)b = a(-b)$, we think this way. On the left side of the equation, the opposite of b is $-b$. The product $(-a)b$ becomes $(-a)(-b)$ by taking the opposite of b. To invoke the Balance Beam Principle, we must also take the opposite of $-b$ on the right side of the equation. Since $-(-b) = b$, then $a(-b)$ becomes ab. Therefore, $(-a)(-b) = ab$. Pretty nifty dance logic, isn't it?

Let's conclude this lesson by proving a definition that we have invoked quite a bit in previous work.

THE ALGEBRAIC DEFINITION OF SUBTRACTION

Let's see how we can prove this definition. We first invoke the Closure Law of Addition for real numbers. We write, by the Symmetric Law of Equality:

$$b + x = a \Leftrightarrow a = b + x$$

By the Balance Beam Principle, we subtract b from both sides:

$$a = b + x \Leftrightarrow a - b = x$$

If we can prove that $a + (-b) = x$, then, by substitution, $a - b = a + (-b)$. We reason as follows:

Step	Assertion	Justification
1.	$a + (-b) = (-b) + a$	We invoke the Commutative Law of Addition.
2.	$(-b) + a = (-b) + b + x$	We substitute, since $a = b + x$.
3.	$(-b) + b + x = [(-b) + b] + x$	We invoke the Associative Law of Addition.
4.	$[(-b) + b] + x = 0 + x$	We invoke the Law of Addition of opposites; i.e., $(-b) + b = 0$
5.	$0 + x = x$	We invoke the Additive Identity.
6.	$a + (-b) = x$	The conclusion of a syllogism starting with Step 1 and ending with Step 5.
	QED	

Most elementary Arithmetic and Algebra textbooks establish definitions like this, as we have done in the first three volumes of this textbook series. It is worthy to note that many of these definitions are theorems that we can prove.

EXERCISES

1. Master the proofs of Proposition 1, Proposition 2, Proposition 3, and Proposition 5.
2. Prove Proposition 4 in the lesson.
3. Prove the Algebraic "Definition" of Division.
4. Show that $a - b$ is equal to the opposite of $b - a$. [Hint: $-(b - a) = -1(b - a)$]

5. Use $x^2 = |x|^2$ to show that $(a - b)^2 = |a - b|^2$.

Assume that $a, b \in \mathbb{Z}$. Prove these propositions:

6. $a + b = 0 \Leftrightarrow b = -a$ and $a = -b$ (Hint: You must prove $a + b = 0 \Leftrightarrow b = -a$ and $a + b = 0 \Leftrightarrow a = -b$)
7. $a = -(-a)$ (Hint: Use what you proved in Question 6.)
8. $-(a + b) = -a - b$
9. $a + b = c \Leftrightarrow a = c - b$
10. $a + b = c \Leftrightarrow b = c - a$

The Shape of a Lune.

11. Let's construct a **lune**,[1] a crescent moon shape, so that we can see what it looks like (Figure 1). First, construct a semicircle with center at point O and diameter $\overline{AB}$.
12. Draw $\overline{OC}$ perpendicular to $\overline{AB}$ and label C at the point of intersection of the semicircle.

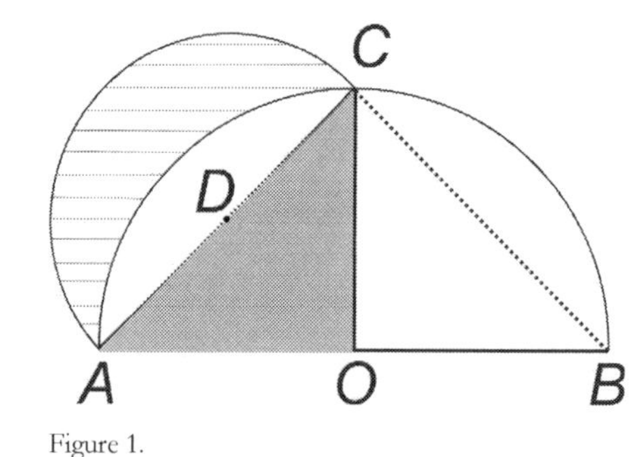

Figure 1.

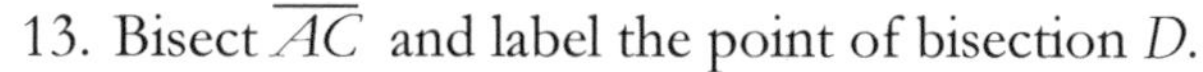

13. Bisect $\overline{AC}$ and label the point of bisection D.
14. From D, draw a semicircle that intersects the first semicircle at A and C. The crescent moon-like figure with horizontal markings is a lune. Its crescent shape mirrors one of the lunar phases, waxing or waning, of the Moon.

Before we can analyze the quadrability of a lune is, we must make an extended observation about the Pythagorean Theorem. As you do the following questions, refer to the last homework question in Lesson 11.3.

15. Construct a right ΔABC where $m\angle C = 90°$ (Figure 2). From this, we know from the Pythagorean Theorem that $c^2 = a^2 + b^2$ where $c = AB$, $b = AC$, and $a = BC$. The extension of this theorem is that the area of *any* figure drawn on the hypotenuse of a right-angle triangle is equal to the sum of the areas of *similar figures* drawn on the other two legs. We are going to prove this in a *particular* case when the similar figures are triangles.

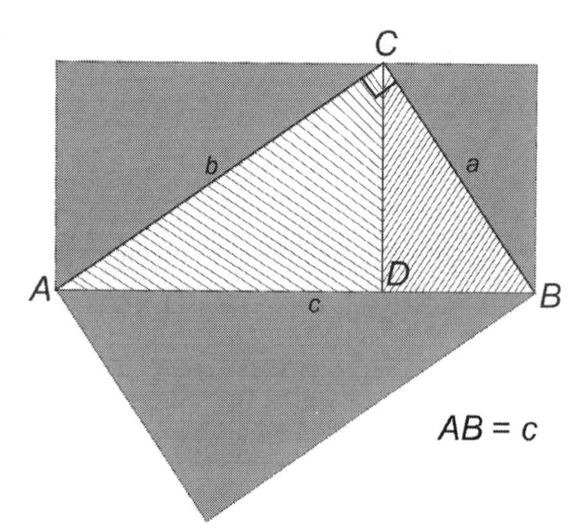

Figure 2.

16. Construct the perpendicular $\overline{CD}$ that intersects $\overline{AB}$ at D. We observe that $\overline{CD}$ divides ΔABC into two triangles, ΔACD and ΔCDB. What do you notice about the relationship between ΔACD and ΔCDB? They are not congruent, but they are similar. Why? [Hint: (a) We know that $m\angle CDB = m\angle CDA = 90°$ (by construction), (b) we know that $m\angle A + m\angle B = 90°$ (Why?) and $m\angle DCB + m\angle B = 90°$ (Why?). Therefore, $m\angle A = m\angle DCB$. (Why?) (c) Likewise, we know that $m\angle A + m\angle ACD = 90°$. Therefore, $m\angle B = m\angle ACD$. Since corresponding angles of two similar triangles are equal to each other (Lesson 8.1), we know that $\Delta ACD \sim \Delta CDB$.]
17. (a) What do you notice about the relationship between ΔABC and ΔACD? (b) Why?
18. (a) What do you notice about the relationship between ΔABC and ΔCDB? (b) Why?

[1] *luna* is Latin for "moon."

19. From Question 16, 17, and 18, we have shown that $\Delta ABC \sim \Delta ACD \sim \Delta CDB$. Now, imagine the figure as a right triangle with these three similar triangles drawn on its three sides (These triangles are shaded in the figure.), *but drawn inwards from the sides.* This means that the triangle on the hypotenuse is the original triangle (Make sure you can visualize this.) and the similar triangles drawn on the two legs are the two triangles, ΔACD and ΔCDB, into which ΔABC was divided by the perpendicular line segment $\overline{CD}$. From this case of similar triangles, we have verified the more general statement of the Pythagorean Theorem. How have we done this? (Hint: what do we know about the areas of ΔABC, ΔACD, and ΔCDB?)

Hippocrates of Chios, living in the 5th century BC, was a member of the school of Pythagoras and developed the first proof that a lune, a curved figure, is quadrable. We shall make use of our observation in the previous four questions to prove this.

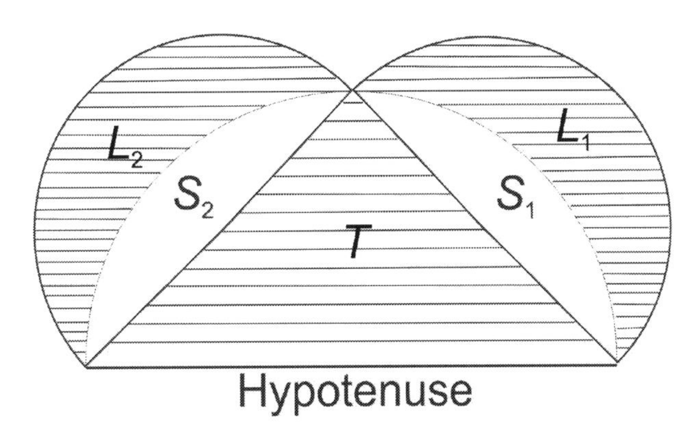

Figure 3.

20. Following the construction in Questions 11 to 14, construct two lunes as shown in Figure 3. Let T represent the area of the right triangle in the figure and L_1 and L_2 represent the areas of the two lunes. Note that the semicircle on the hypotenuse is drawn *inwards* while the other two semi-circles on the legs of the right triangle are drawn *outwards.* These three semicircles, like the three triangles in in the previous four questions, are similar to each other. Let A_S represent the area of the semicircle on the hypotenuse. Write an equation for the A_S in terms of S_1, S_2, and T where S_1 and S_2 represent the two respective unshaded areas.
21. Let A_1 represent the area of the semicircle containing S_1 and L_1. Let A_2 represent the area of the semicircle containing S_2 and L_2.Write an equation for the areas of the two other semicircles.
22. From Question 20, we have $A_S = S_1 + S_2 + T$. From Question 21, we have $A_1 = S_1 + L_1$ and $A_2 = S_2 + L_2$. From exercise 26, we know that $A_S = A_1 + A_2$. Write a new equation using substitution to replace A_S, A_1, and A_2.
23. (a) From Question 22, solve for T. (b) What have we shown?
24. (a) Since we have shown that the area of a triangle is equal to the sum of the area of two lunes, what can we conclude about a lune being quadrable? It was because of this proof of the quadrature of lunes that Greek mathematicians became convinced that a circle is quadrable. (b) Why do you think they made this conclusion?

Euclid's construction of a line segment congruent to a given line segment (Book I, Proposition 2; see the related construction and the discussion of the collapsing compass in Lesson 5.1). It states, "To place at a given point (as an extremity) a straight line equal to a given straight line." To follow his construction, answer these questions:

25. First, Euclid marked the given point A and then drew $\overline{BC}$ (Figure 4). He wanted to generate another line segment equal to BC with A as its endpoint, i.e., its extremity. He drew $\overline{AB}$. Why could he do that?
26. Next, he constructed equilateral ΔABD. How did he do that? (Hint: Review the relevant homework exercise in Lesson 5.8.)
27. He extended $\overline{DA}$ and $\overline{DB}$. Why could he do that?
28. (a) He then constructed a circle with center at B with radius BC. Why?
    (b) He marked E on the extension of $\overline{DB}$. Why is $BC = BE$?
29. (a) Again, he constructed a circle with center at D with radius DE. Why?
    (b) He marked F on the extension of $\overline{DA}$. Why is $DF = DE$?
30. From this work, reason to the conclusion, i.e., $AF = BC$.

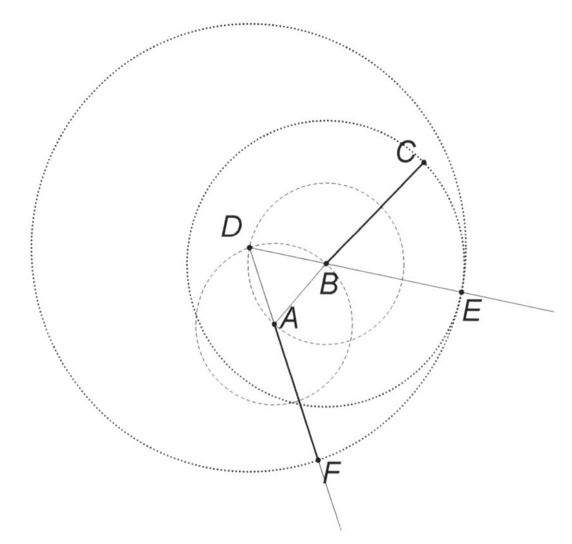

Figure 4.

Generalized Projectile Motion.

Let's genearlize projectile motion (Homework exercise in Lesson 12.8) and ask some questions about the relationships revealed. In Figure 5, a function $y = f(x)$ describes the parabolic motion of a projectile shot from a cannon at angle θ, starting from its initial propulsion and following its position until it impacts the ground. The coordinates (x, y) represent the projectile's horizontal and vertical positions. Thanks to the insight of Galileo Galilei, we can parse and then investigate this motion into two components or two parametric equations, horizontal and vertical; i.e., $x = f(t)$ is the horizontal component, position as a function of time t, and $y = g(t)$ is the vertical component, position as a function of time t.

Note the construction of a parallelogram $OQRP$, specifically a rectangle. The distance traveled in one second is represented the radius vector $\overrightarrow{OR}$. The horizontal distance traveled in one second is OP and is represented by the radius vector $\overrightarrow{OP}$. The vertical distance traveled in one second is OQ and is represented by the radius vector $\overrightarrow{OQ}$. Suppose that the angle of fire of a cannon is θ and it shoots a shell with an initial velocity of $\mathbf{V}$. (Note: the bold notation means that the velocity is a vector; it has magnitude and

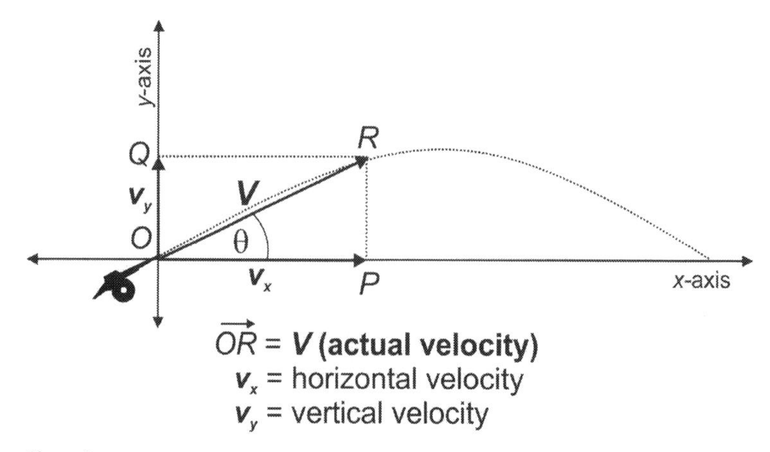

Figure 5.

direction. Another way to denote a vector is $\vec{V}$, but we will use the bold notation. We can also parse the velocity vector **V** into its horizontal and vertical component velocity vectors: $\mathbf{v_x}$ and $\mathbf{v_y}$. If we let the distance traveled for one second ($t = 1$) to be OR, answer these questions relating velocity to trig functions:

> The supreme task of the physicist is to arrive at those elementary universal laws from which the cosmos can be built up by deduction. There is no logical path to these laws; only intuition resting on sympathetic understanding of experience, can reach them ... There is no logical bridge between phenomena and their theoretical principles; that is what Leibnitz described so happily as a 'preestablished harmony.'
>
> Albert Einstein, *The World as I See It* (1949), p. 125f.

31. Write an equation for $\cos \theta$ in terms of $\mathbf{v_x}$ and $\mathbf{V}$.
32. Since $RP = OQ$, Write an equation for $\sin \theta$ in terms of $\mathbf{v_y}$ and $\mathbf{V}$.
33. Solve the equation you wrote in Question 31 for $\mathbf{v_x}$, the x-component of velocity in ft/s.
34. Solve the equation you wrote in Question 32 for $\mathbf{v_y}$, the y-component of velocity in ft/s
35. Gravity pulls the projectile downward at a velocity of 32 feet per second every second (32 ft/s^2).[2] If the vertical velocity, in ft/s, is defined by $\mathbf{v_y}$:
    (a) Write an equation for $\mathbf{v_y}$ in terms of $\mathbf{V}$, θ, and the downward velocity adjustment of $32t$.
    (b) Why must the adjustment to velocity be $32t$?
36. We define the horizontal distance (distance is rate multiplied by time) traveled in t seconds by $x = f(t)$. Write an equation for by $x = f(t)$ in terms of $\mathbf{V}$, θ, and t. (Note: Make sure that the expression representing the function looks like $\mathbf{V}t$ multiplied by the trig function in terms of θ.)
37. By experimenting with balls rolling down inclined planes (See the relevant homework exercises in Lesson 12.12.), Galileo discovered that the force of gravity pulls the projectile downward at a distance of $16t^2$ ft/s. If the vertical distance traveled in t seconds is defined by $y = g(t)$, write an equation for by $y = g(t)$ in terms of $\mathbf{V}$, θ, t, and the downward distance adjustment of $16t^2$.
38. Using your equations, $x = f(t)$ in Question 36 and $y = g(t)$ in Question 37:
    (a) Write an equation in the form $y = f(x)$ and write it in the form of $y = ax^2 + bx + c$.
    (b) In the quadratic form, what is the value of a, b, and c?
39. When the projectile reaches its maximum height, its vertical velocity, $\mathbf{v_y}$, will be zero. Write a formula for:
    (a) t, the time it takes for the projectile reach that height.
    (b) y, the maximum height at that time. (Note: Simplify your answers as much as possible.)
40. (a) How long will it take the projectile to reach the ground again? (Hint: We know that when the projectile strikes the ground, or when $y = g(t) = 0$.)
    (b) What is the vertical velocity of the projectile when it hits the ground?
    (c) What does your answer to part b mean?
41. Compare your result in Question 40a with your result in Question 39a. What do you notice?
42. If you know the initial velocity $\mathbf{V}$ and the range x, solve for θ, the angle of fire. (Hint: You must use a Double-Angle identity, proved in Lesson 13.1.)

---

[2] 9.8 m/s^2 in the Metric System.

43. If $V = 750$ ft/s and $x = 15{,}000$ ft, find θ to the nearest hundredth of a degree using a scientific calculator.
44. There is second angle of fire that answers Question 43. To find it, rounded to the nearest hundredth of a degree, reason carefully invoking complementary angle trig identities (Lesson 12.6). (Hint: Use Figure 6.)

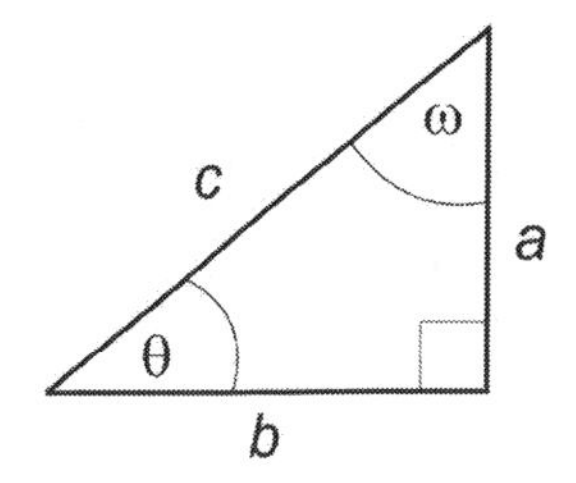

Figure 6.

45. What angle of fire will result in the maximum distance?[3] [Hint: You will need to determine when $\sin\theta\cos\theta$ is maximum. Use Figure 7, where $\overline{AB}$ is the diameter of the circle, and the *pons asinorum* theorem (Lesson 13.5 homework) to help you.]

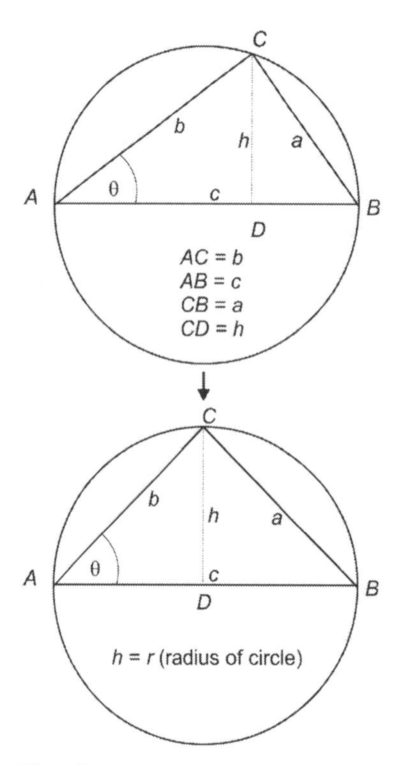

Figure 7.

[3] It was the Italian mathematician Niccolò Fontana Tartaglia (1499-1557) who first gave the theoretical reason for this angle of fire. His answer surprised the experts of his day since they thought the angle should be less than the angle derived in this question.

13.8 Quadratic Deductions

Terms & Concepts Introduced
1. Circumscribe
2. Cosmology
3. Equilateral hyperbola
4. Generatrix
5. Inscribe
6. Major axis of an ellipse
7. Minor axis of an ellipse
8. Nappes

Linear equations and line graphs are two diversified expressions of the same concept. Underlying the manifold variety of linear equations is an underlying unity, i.e., the general form $y = ax + b$. All linear equations have a family likeness.

We generate curved graphs from equations like this:

$y = 2^x, y = x^2$, or $y = 12/x \Leftrightarrow xy = 12$

In this lesson, one longer than usual, we will deductively derive the standard equations that are generated by the intersection of a cone with a plane, the four Conic Sections: the circle, parabola, ellipse, and hyperbola. The algebraic operations are meticulous, so mental vigilance is required.

The Circle

Let's see if we can find any family likeness in the conics by first considering the circle. To the ancient Greeks, the circle was the basic geometric shape. Reflecting Pythagorean metaphysical convictions, many Greek philosophers understood the circle as a generating power. For example, they understood the Earth to be the center of a series of concentric[1] circles (Lesson 8.5) where he Sun and all the planets orbited this center point in perfect circles.[2] Circles to the Greeks reflected the perfection of celestial motion.

> While painting the Sistine Chapel, Michelangelo (1475-1564) was asked by the Pope to demonstrate his legendary artistic talent. Michelangelo took a piece of paper, picked up a writing instrument and drew (freehand) a perfect circle.

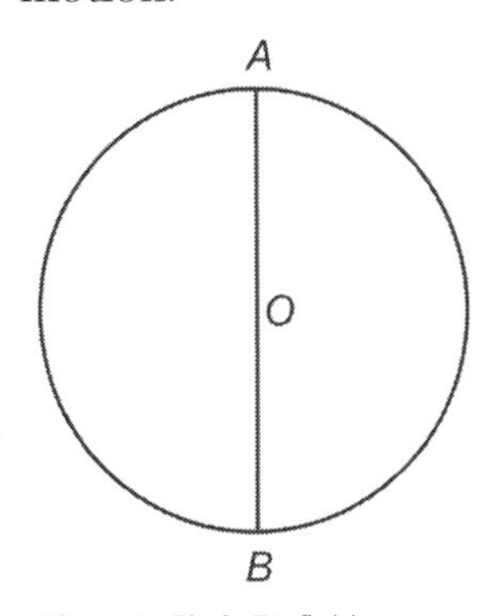

Figure 1. Circle Definitions.

Since the Greeks had no knowledge of the Cartesian coordinate plane, their study of the nature of circles, although profound, was limited. Let's first review the parts and structure of a circle. The point labeled O is the center of the circle (Figure 1). The distance between A and O, AO, is the radius of the circle and the distance between A and B, AB, is the diameter of the circle. The Greeks discovered that the ratio of the circumference to the diameter of the circle is always a constant no matter what the size of the circle. The Greek mathematician, engineer, and physicist Archimedes (ca. 287-212 BC) used an ingenious method of calculating this number, i.e., π. (See homework exercises in Lesson 14.7.) To estimate π's lower limit, he **inscribed**[3] a 96-side regular polygon within a given circle and calculated its perimeter. To estimate π's upper limit he then **circumscribed**[4] a 96-side regular polygon outside the same circle and calculated its perimeter. Using modern decimal notation, Archimedes calculated that π could not be greater than 3.1429 or less than 3.1408. In symbols, $3.1408 < \pi < 3.1429$. This boundary condition was a remarkably accurate estimate.

---

[1] Recall that concentric (Lesson 8.5) is derived from two Latin words meaning "common center."

[2] This **cosmology**, meaning "word concerning the cosmos," is denoted as geocentrism, meaning "earth centered."

[3] A regular polygon is inscribed within a circle when its vertices touch, but do not intersect, the circle at one point. Inscribe is from the Latin meaning "to write into."

[4] A regular polygon is circumscribed around a circle when its sides touch, but do not intersect, the circle at one point. Circumscribe is from the Latin meaning "to write around."

In review, if d = diameter of a circle, r = radius of a circle, C = circumference of a circle, and A = area of a circle, then the following formulas describe the nature and structure of a circle:

$d = 2r$, $C/d = \pi$, $C = \pi d$, $C = 2\pi r$, $A/r^2 = \pi$, $A = \pi r^2$

Let's plot a circle using the Cartesian coordinate plane where the center of the circle is the origin (0, 0) and the radius of the circle is 5 units (Figure 2).

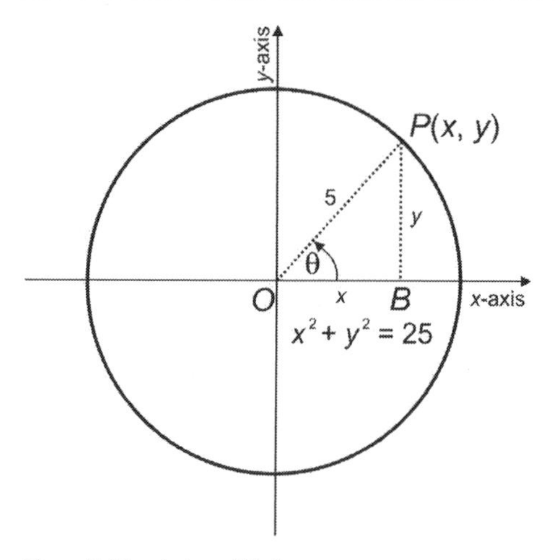

Figure 2. The circle and Pythagoras.

What kind of equation describes this curve? We choose any point P on the circumference of the circle and draw the radius from O to P at 5 units. What is the x-coordinate, OB, and the y-coordinate, BP, of the point P? We can immediately infer that ΔOBP is a right triangle. Therefore, the Pythagorean Theorem governs the determination of OB and BP where 5 is the length of the hypotenuse:

$5^2 = OB^2 + BP^2$

Since OB is the x-coordinate and BP is the y-coordinate, we can rewrite this equation:

$5^2 = x^2 + y^2 \Leftrightarrow 25 = x^2 + y^2 \Leftrightarrow x^2 + y^2 = 25$

In general, if r = radius of a circle and its center is at the origin, then the equation of the circle is:

$x^2 + y^2 = r^2$

This equation is a second-degree or quadratic equation. We can solve this equation for y as follows:

$x^2 + y^2 = r^2 \Leftrightarrow y^2 = r^2 - x^2 \Leftrightarrow y = \sqrt{r^2 - x^2}$ or $y = -\sqrt{r^2 - x^2}$

This equation tells us that for every value of x there are two values of y, a positive and a negative value. It is a one-to-many mapping, a relation, not a function. We confirm the existence of these two values by observing the behavior of the graph. For example, when $x = 0$, then $y = r$ or $y = -r$.

THE PARABOLA

The equation of a circle whose center is at the origin is not the simplest type of quadratic equation. As we have noted, the simplest quadratic equation is:

$y = x^2$

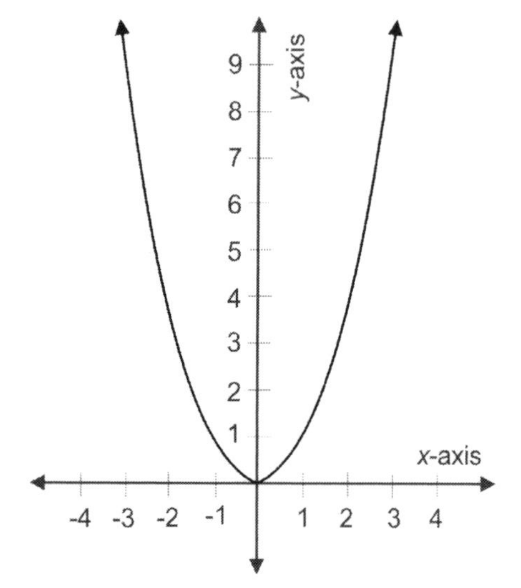

Figure 3. Parabola.

Figure 3 is the graph of this function, the parabola.[5] Note that in this case the y-axis serves as a mirror, or line of symmetry. The portion of the graph of the left side of the y-axis is a mirror image, a reflection (Lesson 10.5), of the portion of the graph on the right side of the y-axis. Note also that both

[5] Parabola comes from two Greek words, *para* and *bola*. *Para* means "equal to" or "alongside" and *bola* means "to throw." As a figure of speech, a parable is a story that illustrates truth; i.e., you can equate the story with a truth. Christ used this figure of speech many times when He taught the multitudes (e.g., Matthew 13).

sides continue indefinitely getting steeper and steeper, approaching vertical lines. Although both the equation for a circle and the equation for the parabola are quadratic, the graphs are not like each other.

Let's continue our investigation of a parabola. We selected this curve by an arbitrary choice of $y = x^2$. How did the ancient Greeks[6] define this curve?

The Greek geometers started with a fixed point F and a fixed line d (Figure 4). Then they considered the locus[7] (Lesson 2.7) of points, each of which is equally distant from F and d. Thus, for any point P on the parabola, $PF = PD$. The locus of all points, each of which is equidistant from F and d generates the parabola. The point F is the focus[8] (Lesson 8.5) of the parabola and the line d is the directrix (Lesson 11.7).[9]

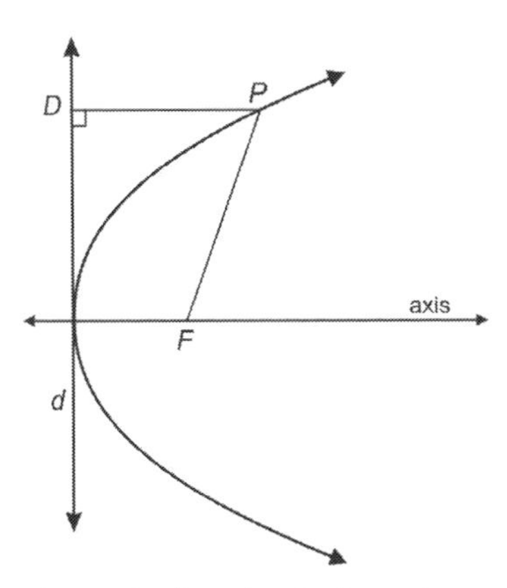

Figure 4. Starting points for the parabola.

Let's now park a parabola on the Cartesian coordinate plane by rotating it 90° counterclockwise (Figure 5).

By definition, $PF = PD$. We choose the y-axis to be the line through F and perpendicular to d. The x-axis is drawn such that it is halfway between F and d. We let $FB = 2k$. Therefore, $OF = OB = k$. The coordinates of F are $(0, k)$. We now want to express $PF = PD$ in terms of an equation involving x and y. The vertex of the parabola, where the curve reaches a minimum, is the origin $(0, 0)$, or O in the figure. The vertex is also the point on the parabola closest to the directrix. Note that the vertex is on the perpendicular line from F to the directrix. This line is the line of symmetry of the parabola,[10] or simply the axis of the parabola. In the figure, the line of symmetry of the parabola is the y-axis.

Let's determine the equation for this parabola. We let P be any point on the parabola with coordinates (x, y). PF is, therefore, the hypotenuse of a right triangle with legs x and $y - k$. By the Pythagorean Theorem, we write:

$$PF = \sqrt{x^2 + (y-k)^2}$$

Since $PD = y + k$ and $PF = PD$, then, by substitution:

$$\sqrt{x^2 + (y-k)^2} = y + k$$

Figure 5. The parabola and the Cartesian coordinate system.

We now have rewritten $PF = PD$ as an equation in terms of y and x. Let's see if we can simplify it. First, let's get rid of the square root by squaring both sides of the equation. By the Binomial Theorem, we note:

$$(y + k)^2 = y^2 + 2ky + k^2$$

---

[6] Euclid apparently wrote about this curve in a book separate from *The Elements*. Unfortunately, no copies of this book have survived. We do have copies of a book written by another Greek geometer Apollonius (ca. 262-ca. 190 BC). He analyzed this curve and the other curves that we will meet in this lesson.

[7] To review, locus, in Latin, means a "locale or a place." In mathematics, locus means the set of all points whose coordinates satisfy an equation or some other condition.

[8] There are historical, perhaps legendary reports that the Greek mathematician Archimedes constructed a giant parabolic mirror and focused the rays from the Sun on a single point, an enemy ship in the harbor. Since the rays of the Sun intensify at the focus, the ship caught fire and burned in flames.

[9] In review, the directrix is the fixed curve or standard by which the parabola is generated.

[10] The axis of symmetry is a line that acts as a mirror in which one half of the parabola exactly reflects the other half.

$(y-k)^2 = y^2 - 2ky + k^2$

By squaring both sides of the equation we get:

$\sqrt{x^2+(y-k)^2} = y+k \Rightarrow x^2 + (y-k)^2 = y^2 + 2ky + k^2$ (Note: We do not have logical equivalency.)

Expanding $(y-k)^2$ we get:

$x^2 + (y-k)^2 = y^2 + 2ky + k^2 \Leftrightarrow x^2 + y^2 - 2ky + k^2 = y^2 + 2ky + k^2$

We can simplify this equation by subtracting y^2 from both sides:

$x^2 + y^2 - 2ky + k^2 = y^2 + 2ky + k^2 \Leftrightarrow x^2 - 2ky + k^2 = 2ky + k^2$

Now subtract k^2 from both sides of the equation:

$x^2 - 2ky + k^2 = 2ky + k^2 \Leftrightarrow x^2 - 2ky = 2ky$

Finally, we add $2ky$ to both sides of the equation:

$x^2 - 2ky = 2ky \Leftrightarrow x^2 = 4ky \Leftrightarrow 4ky = x^2$

Let's solve for y by dividing both sides of the equation by $4k$:

$4ky = x^2 \Leftrightarrow y = \frac{x^2}{4k}$ or $y = \frac{1}{4k}x^2$

This equation is much simpler than $\sqrt{x^2+(y-k)^2} = y+k$. Note also that in our derivation we squared both sides of an equation. Since squaring does not produce an equivalent equation, we may have a problem with our solutions; i.e., there is a possibility that we introduced values of x and y that satisfy $\sqrt{x^2+(y-k)^2} = y+k$ but do not satisfy $y = \frac{1}{4k}x^2$, i.e., an extraneous solution (Lesson 11.12, the last homework problem). It can be shown that this is not the case; i.e., the values of x and y that satisfy $\sqrt{x^2+(y-k)^2} = y+k$ do satisfy $y = \frac{1}{4k}x^2$. We will not demonstrate this reasoning.

The equation $y = \frac{1}{4k}x^2$ is similar to $y = x^2$. Note also that $4k$ in the denominator is twice the distance from F to d. In general, let the distance from F to d be p. Therefore, $4k = 2p$. Now we have a general formula for a parabola in terms of p:

$y = \frac{1}{2p}x^2$ where p is the distance from the parabola's focus to its directrix.

For the equation $y = x^2$, we solve for p this way:

$\frac{1}{2p} = 1 \Leftrightarrow 2p = 1 \Leftrightarrow p = \frac{1}{2}$

This means that the coordinates of the focus of the parabola governed by the equation $y = x^2$ are (0, ¼) since ¼ is ½ of ½. The directrix of this curve is the line $y = -¼$.

We can also write the general equation for a parabola like this:

$x^2 = 2py \Leftrightarrow x^2 - 2py = 0$

To generate a parabola that faces right, the one we started with in Figure 4, we find the inverse of $y = f(x) = \frac{1}{2p}x^2$ by solving for x (Lesson 10.5):

$$y = \frac{1}{2p}x^2 \Leftrightarrow x^2 = 2py \Leftrightarrow x = \sqrt{2py} \text{ or } x = -\sqrt{2py}$$

To graph the inverse, we exchange x with y, since they are placeholders. We get:

$$y = f^{-1}(x) = \sqrt{2px} \text{ or } y = f^{-1}(x) = -\sqrt{2px}$$

We will graph this inverse in a homework problem.

THE ELLIPSE

Another very widely used curve is the ellipse.[11] This curve looks like a flattened circle or an oval. The ancient Greeks defined an ellipse by starting with two fixed points, F and F', and any constant quantity greater than FF'. In our example, $FF' = 2c$. Let's choose $2a$ as our constant quantity where $2a > 2c$.[12] The reason why we choose $2c$ and $2a$ rather than c and a will become evident soon. We consider all points P in the plane whose distances from F and F' sum to $2a$.[13] In other words, an ellipse is the locus of points P such that $PF + PF' = 2a$. F and F' are the *foci*, the plural of focus, of the ellipse.

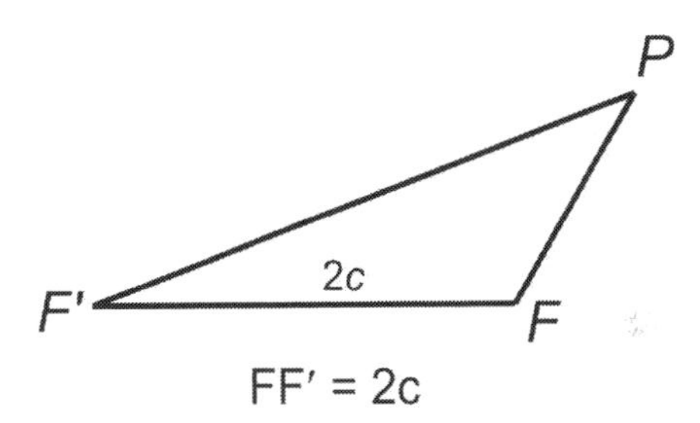

Figure 6. Starting points for the ellipse.

As with a parabola, let's park an ellipse on the Cartesian coordinate plane. In Figure 7, note how we set up the four coordinates $(a, 0)$, $(-a, 0)$, $(0, b)$, and $(0, -b)$. Note also that $\overline{FF'}$ lies on the x-axis and that the y-axis lies halfway between F and F'. Since $FF' = 2c$, then the coordinates of F and F' are $(c, 0)$ and $(-c, 0)$ respectively.

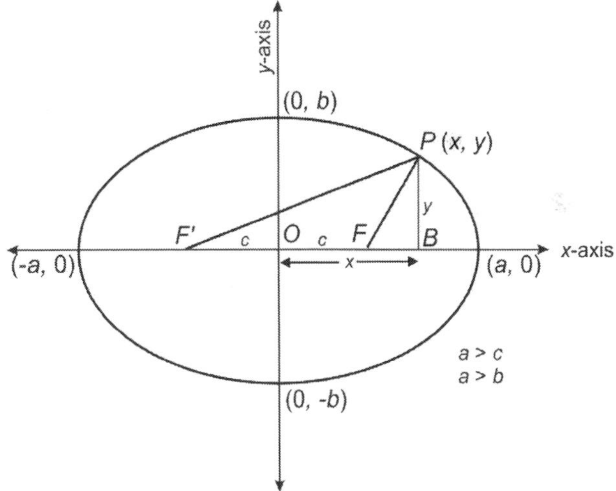

Figure 7. The ellipse and the Cartesian coordinate system.

As with the parabola, let's see if we can write an equation of an ellipse in terms of x and y. Let P be any point on the curve denoted by the coordinates (x, y). We know that $PF + PF' = 2a$. Note that PF is the hypotenuse of the right triangle with legs $x - c$ and y. By the Pythagorean Theorem, we write:

---

[11] Ellipse means "to fall short or deduct" in the Greek. As we have already noted (Lesson 2.3), an ellipsis (signified by…) is the omission of a word or phrase necessary for a complete syntactical construction of a sentence but not necessary for understanding. For example, "He drove … home." In mathematics, the understanding is similar: $\{1, 2, 3, \ldots\}$.

[12] We note that $2a > 2c \Leftrightarrow a > c$.

[13] As we can see from the triangle, $2a > 2c$ by the Triangle Inequality Theorem (Lesson 10.7). This theorem is also known as Proposition 20 in Book I of Euclid's *Elements*, Book 1. Thomas L. Heath, *Euclid: The Thirteen Books of The Elements* (New York: Dover Publications, [1925] 1956), 1:286-288.

$PF = \sqrt{(x-c)^2 + y^2}$

Note also that PF' is the hypotenuse of the right triangle with legs $x + k$ and y. By the Pythagorean Theorem, we write:

$PF' = \sqrt{(x+c)^2 + y^2}$

Since $PF + PF' = 2a$, then:

$\sqrt{(x-c)^2 + y^2} + \sqrt{(x+c)^2 + y^2} = 2a$

To simplify this equation requires some intense algebraic work. Let's see if we can do it step by step. You need to follow along with pencil and paper.

First, let's simplify matters by letting:

$m = (x - c)^2 + y^2$
$n = (x + c)^2 + y^2$

We now have this equation:

$\sqrt{m} + \sqrt{n} = 2a$

We subtract $\sqrt{m}$ from both sides of the equation. We get:

$\sqrt{m} + \sqrt{n} = 2a \Leftrightarrow \sqrt{n} = 2a - \sqrt{m}$

Now, square both sides of the equation. Using the Binomial Theorem, we first note:

$\left(2a - \sqrt{m}\right)^2 = 4a^2 - 4a\sqrt{m} + m$

Square both sides, we get:

$\sqrt{n} = 2a - \sqrt{m} \Rightarrow n = 4a^2 - 4a\sqrt{m} + m$ (Note: We do not have logical equivalency.)

Next, add $4a\sqrt{m}$ to both sides of the equation:

$n = 4a^2 - 4a\sqrt{m} + m \Leftrightarrow 4a\sqrt{m} + n = 4a^2 + m$

Next, subtract n from both sides of the equation:

$4a\sqrt{m} + n = 4a^2 + m \Leftrightarrow 4a\sqrt{m} = 4a^2 + m - n$

At this point, let's go ahead and determine what $m - n$ is:

$m = (x - c)^2 + y^2 = x^2 - 2cx + c^2 + y^2$
$n = (x + c)^2 + y^2 = x^2 + 2cx + c^2 + y^2$

Subtracting n from m, we get:

$m - n = x^2 - 2cx + c^2 + y^2 - (x^2 + 2cx + c^2 + y^2) = x^2 - 2cx + c^2 + y^2 - x^2 - 2cx - c^2 - y^2 = -4cx$

Now our equation looks like this:

$4a\sqrt{m} = 4a^2 + m - n \Leftrightarrow 4a\sqrt{m} = 4a^2 - 4cx$

Are you still with me? If not, go back and retrace the steps. We are not out of the woods yet. There is more algebraic work to do. Let's square both sides of the equation to get rid of the square root.

Using the Binomial Theorem, we note:

$(4a^2 - 4cx)^2 = 16a^4 - 32a^2cx + 16c^2x^2$

Squaring both sides of $4a\sqrt{m} = 4a^2 - 4cx$, we get:

$4a\sqrt{m} = 4a^2 - 4cx \Rightarrow 16a^2m = 16a^4 - 32a^2cx + 16c^2x^2$ (Note: We do not have logical equivalency.)

Since $m = (x - c)^2 + y^2 = x^2 - 2cx + c^2 + y^2$, then:

$16a^2m = 16a^2(x^2 - 2cx + c^2 + y^2) = 16a^2x^2 - 32a^2cx + 16a^2c^2 + 16a^2y^2$

Now, since $16a^2m = 16a^4 - 8a^2cx + 16c^2x^2$, then:

$16a^2x^2 - 32a^2cx + 16a^2c^2 + 16a^2y^2 = 16a^4 - 32a^2cx + 16c^2x^2$

Can we simplify? Yes, let's first add $32a^2cx$ to both sides of the equation. We get:

$16a^2x^2 - 32a^2cx + 16a^2c^2 + 16a^2y^2 = 16a^4 - 32a^2cx + 16c^2x^2 \Leftrightarrow$
$16a^2x^2 + 16a^2c^2 + 16a^2y^2 = 16a^4 + 16c^2x^2$

We note (a) that the terms of the expressions are reducing in number and (b) that 16 is a common factor of all factors because of our choice of $2a$ and $2c$. Dividing by sides by 16, we get:

$16a^2x^2 + 16a^2c^2 + 16a^2y^2 = 16a^4 + 16c^2x^2 \Leftrightarrow a^2x^2 + a^2c^2 + a^2y^2 = a^4 + c^2x^2$

Now, subtract c^2x^2 from both sides of the equation. We get:

$a^2x^2 + a^2c^2 + a^2y^2 = a^4 + c^2x^2 \Leftrightarrow a^2x^2 - c^2x^2 + a^2c^2 + a^2y^2 = a^4$

Let's now subtract a^2c^2 from both sides to get a constant number on the right side and all the variable-related terms on the left side:

$a^2x^2 - c^2x^2 + a^2c^2 + a^2y^2 = a^4 \Leftrightarrow a^2x^2 - c^2x^2 + a^2y^2 = a^4 - a^2c^2$

Let's factor next, x^2 from the first two terms on the left side and a^2 from the two terms on the right side:

$a^2x^2 - c^2x^2 + a^2y^2 = a^4 - a^2c^2 \Leftrightarrow x^2(a^2 - c^2) + a^2y^2 = a^2(a^2 - c^2)$

We see that the expression $a^2 - c^2$ occurs on the left and right side of the equation. Since $a > c$, we know that $a^2 - c^2 > 0$. We choose b, the length of the semi-minor axis of the ellipse (Lesson 8.5), such that:

$a^2 - c^2 = b^2$

We substitute:

$x^2(a^2 - c^2) + a^2y^2 = a^2(a^2 - c^2)$ and $a^2 - c^2 = b^2 \Rightarrow x^2b^2 + a^2y^2 = a^2b^2$

Dividing both sides by a^2b^2, we get:

$x^2b^2 + a^2y^2 = a^2b^2 \Leftrightarrow$

$\frac{x^2}{a^2} + \frac{y^2}{b^2} = 1$ (General form of an ellipse)

Is it not a wonder that such a complex algebraic procedure results in an equation that is beautiful in its simplicity?

Note that in our derivation we squared both sides of an equation twice. Since squaring does not produce an equivalent equation, we may have a problem with our solutions; i.e., there is a possibility that we introduced values of x and y that satisfy $\sqrt{(x-c)^2+y^2}+\sqrt{(x+c)^2+y^2}=2a$ but do not satisfy $\frac{x^2}{a^2}+\frac{y^2}{b^2}=1$ where $a^2-b^2=c^2$, i.e., an extraneous solution. It can be shown that this is not the case; i.e., the values of x and y that satisfy $\sqrt{(x-c)^2+y^2}+\sqrt{(x+c)^2+y^2}=2a$ do satisfy $\frac{x^2}{a^2}+\frac{y^2}{b^2}=1$ where $a^2-b^2=c^2$. Again, we will not demonstrate this reasoning.

Solving for y in terms of x, we get:

$$x^2b^2+a^2y^2=a^2b^2 \Leftrightarrow a^2y^2=a^2b^2-x^2b^2 \Leftrightarrow y^2=\frac{a^2b^2-x^2b^2}{a^2} \Leftrightarrow$$

$$y^2=b^2-\frac{x^2b^2}{a^2} \Leftrightarrow y^2=b^2-\frac{b^2}{a^2}x^2 \Leftrightarrow y^2=b^2\left(1-\frac{x^2}{a^2}\right) \Leftrightarrow$$

$$y=b\sqrt{1-\frac{x^2}{a^2}} \text{ or } y=-b\sqrt{1-\frac{x^2}{a^2}}$$

This means that when $x = 0$, then $y = b$ or $y = -b$. From this, we know that $(0, b)$ and $(0, -b)$ are coordinates of the ellipse. The line connecting these two points, the chord (Lesson 12.6), is the **minor axis of an ellipse**, of length $2b$.

We can also solve for x in terms of y:

$$x^2b^2+a^2y^2=a^2b^2 \Leftrightarrow x^2b^2=a^2b^2-a^2y^2 \Leftrightarrow x^2=\frac{a^2b^2-a^2y^2}{b^2} \Leftrightarrow$$

$$x^2=a^2-\frac{a^2y^2}{b^2} \Leftrightarrow x^2=a^2-\frac{a^2}{b^2}y^2 \Leftrightarrow x^2=a^2\left(1-\frac{y^2}{b^2}\right) \Leftrightarrow$$

$$x=a\sqrt{1-\frac{y^2}{b^2}} \text{ or } x=a\sqrt{1-\frac{y^2}{b^2}}$$

If $y = 0$, then $x = a$ or $x = -a$. From this, we know that $(a, 0)$ and $(-a, 0)$ are coordinates of the ellipse. The chord connecting these two points is the **major axis of an ellipse**,[14] of length $2a$. Note that the two foci lie on the major axis which is on the x-axis.

In general, the equation of an ellipse, where $2a$ and $2b$ are the major and minor axes respectively, is the quadratic:

$$\frac{x^2}{a^2}+\frac{y^2}{b^2}=1 \text{ where } a \geq b > 0$$

To find the inverse of the general form of the ellipse, we simply interchange the x and y, generating this equation:

---

[14] There are two axes for every ellipse (Lesson 8.5). The longer axis is the major axis and it contains the two foci of the ellipse. The shorter axis is the minor axis.

$$\frac{y^2}{a^2}+\frac{x^2}{b^2}=1 \text{ where } a \geq b > 0$$

We will show why this is so in a homework problem.

In this case, the foci lie in the y-axis. The graph in Figure 9 is the inverse of the graph in Figure 8.

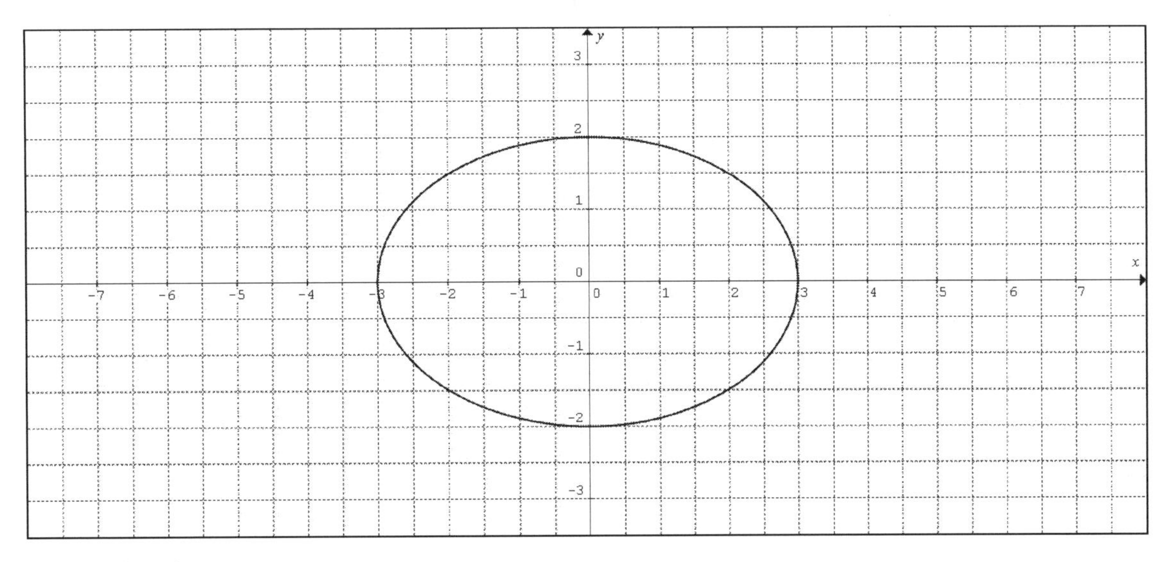

Figure 8. $\frac{x^2}{3^2}+\frac{y^2}{2^2}=1$ with foci on the x-axis.

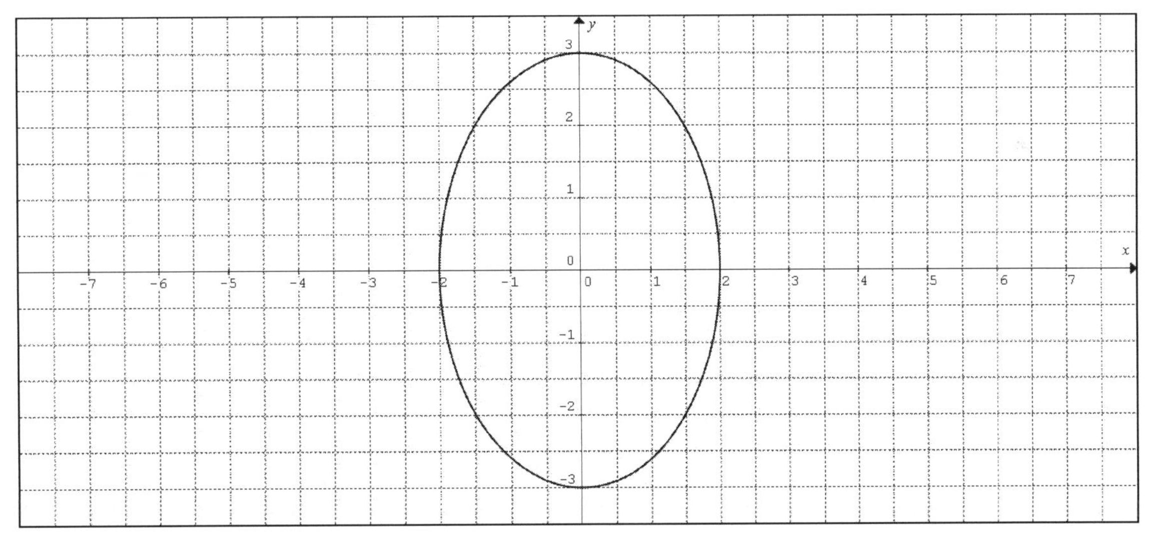

Figure 9. $\frac{y^2}{3^2}+\frac{x^2}{2^2}=1$ with foci on the y-axis.

THE HYPERBOLA

The hyperbola[15] is also a quadratic equation. Our example of a hyperbola was $y = 12/x$, an equation that represents an inverse proportion. This equation can be rewritten as $xy = 12$ since:

---

[15] Hyperbola, in Greek, literally means "to throw above." It speaks, as we saw in Lesson 8.8, to the idea of "greater than." In grammar, a hyperbole is a statement that is an exaggeration; it is not meant to be taken literally.

$y = 12/x \Leftrightarrow xy = 12$

This equation has two unknowns embedded in the term xy. Since the sum of the exponents of the two unknowns (e.g., x^1y^1) is 2, we regard it as a quadratic, a second-degree equation.

The ancient Greeks defined the hyperbola by starting with two fixed points, F and F' at a fixed distance apart (Figure 10). Like the ellipse, F and F' are the foci of the hyperbola. We note that $FF' = 2c$. The Greeks defined the hyperbola as the locus of points P such that the distances from F and F' differ by a constant amount.

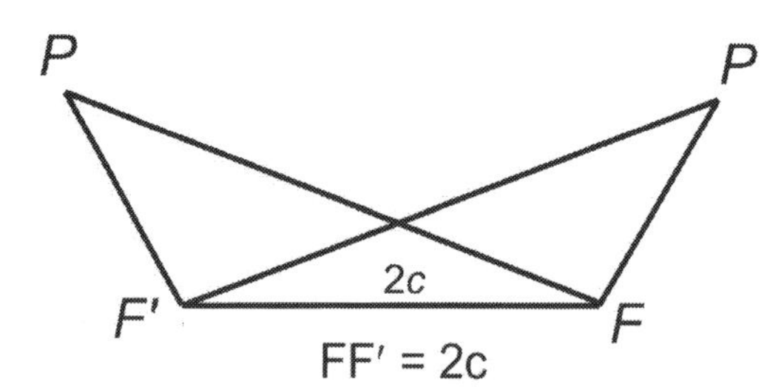

Figure 10. Starting points for the hyperbola.

Let's park a general hyperbola on the Cartesian coordinate plane (Figure 11). We will let the constant difference be $2a$. Therefore, $PF - PF' = 2a$ or $PF' - PF = 2a$. We note that $2a < 2c$.[16] Why? If P is a point on the hyperbola, then $|PF' - PF|$ must be less than FF' because the difference of any two sides of a triangle must be less than the third side, an inference from the Triangle Inequality Theorem (Lesson 10.7).

As with the parabola and the ellipse, let's see if we can write an equation of the hyperbola in terms of x and y. In Figure 11, note how we set up the two coordinates $(a, 0)$ and $(-a, 0)$. We determine the coordinates $(0, b)$ and $(0, -b)$ by drawing a circle with center at O with radius c. b is the length of the semi-major axis of the hyperbola while a is the length of the semi-minor axis of the hyperbola. We assume, from the figure, that $a < b$.

Let P be any point on the curve denoted by the coordinates (x, y). For any point P on the hyperbola either:

$$PF - PF' = 2a \text{ or } PF' - PF = 2a$$

Note again that $\overline{FF'}$ lies on the x-axis and that the y-axis lies halfway between F and F'. Because $FF' = 2c$, the coordinates of F and F' are $(c, 0)$ and $(-c, 0)$ respectively.

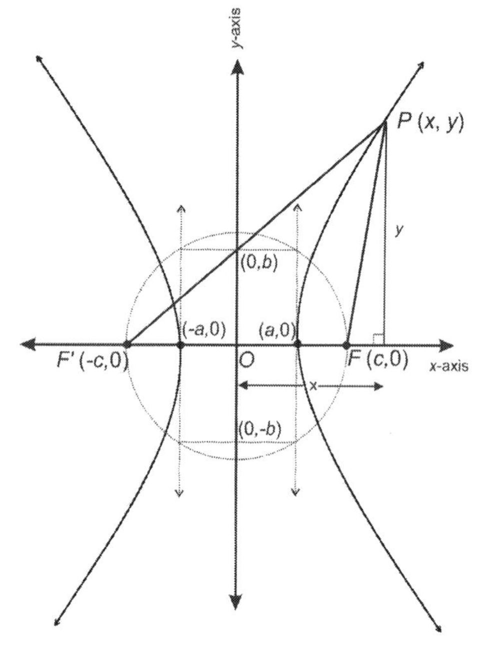

Figure 11. The hyperbola and the Cartesian coordinate system.

Again, PF is the hypotenuse of a right triangle whose legs are $x - c$ and y. PF' is the hypotenuse of a right triangle whose legs are $x + c$ and y. By the Pythagorean Theorem, we get:

$$PF = \sqrt{(x-c)^2 + y^2}$$

$$PF' = \sqrt{(x+c)^2 + y^2}$$

[16] We note that $2a < 2c \Leftrightarrow a < c$.

Since $PF - PF' = 2a$ or $PF' - PF = 2a$, then:[17]

$$(1)\sqrt{(x-c)^2+y^2}-\sqrt{(x+c)^2+y^2}=2a$$

or

$$(2)\sqrt{(x+c)^2+y^2}-\sqrt{(x-c)^2+y^2}=2a$$

In our derivation, just to change the pace a little, we will *not* make use of this substitution:

$m = (x - c)^2 + y^2$
$n = (x + c)^2 + y^2$

Are you ready to try your algebraic skills again? Hold on, get out your pencil and paper … here we go. Let's simplify the Equation (1) as follows:[18]

$$\sqrt{(x-c)^2+y^2}-\sqrt{(x+c)^2+y^2}=2a \Leftrightarrow \sqrt{(x-c)^2+y^2}=2a+\sqrt{(x+c)^2+y^2}$$

Let's apply the Binomial Theorem the expressions within the parentheses:

$(x - c)^2 = x^2 - 2xc + c^2$
$(x + c)^2 = x^2 + 2xc + c^2$

Squaring both sides of $\sqrt{(x-c)^2+y^2}=2a+\sqrt{(x+c)^2+y^2}$, we get:

$$\sqrt{(x-c)^2+y^2}=2a+\sqrt{(x+c)^2+y^2} \Rightarrow (x-c)^2+y^2=4a^2+4a\sqrt{(x+c)^2+y^2}+(x+c)^2+y^2$$

(Note: We do not have logical equivalency.)

Applying the binomial expansion of $(x - c)^2$ and $(x + c)^2$, we get:

$$(x-c)^2+y^2=4a^2+4a\sqrt{(x+c)^2+y^2}+(x+c)^2+y^2 \Leftrightarrow$$

$$x^2-2xc+c^2+y^2=4a^2+4a\sqrt{(x+c)^2+y^2}+x^2+2xc+c^2+y^2$$

Subtracting x^2, c^2, and y^2 from both sides of the equation, we get:

$$x^2-2xc+c^2+y^2=4a^2+4a\sqrt{(x+c)^2+y^2}+x^2+2xc+c^2+y^2 \Leftrightarrow$$

$$-2xc=4a^2+4a\sqrt{(x+c)^2+y^2}+2xc$$

Now, we add $2xc$ to both sides of the equation:

$$-2xc=4a^2+4a\sqrt{(x+c)^2+y^2}+2xc \Leftrightarrow 0=4a^2+4a\sqrt{(x+c)^2+y^2}+4xc$$

Next, we next subtract $4a^2$ and $4xc$ from both sides of the equation:

$$0=4a^2+4a\sqrt{(x+c)^2+y^2}+4xc \Leftrightarrow -4xc-4a^2=4a\sqrt{(x+c)^2+y^2}$$

---

[17] Since the difference can be negative and distance is always positive, we can restate the definition of the hyperbola using absolute value: $|PF - PF'| = 2a$.

[18] It can be shown that it does not make any difference which equation we start with because our derived equation will be the same in both cases. (See the homework problem in this lesson.)

We divide both sides of the equation by 4:

$$-4xc - 4a^2 = 4a\sqrt{(x+c)^2 + y^2} \Leftrightarrow -xc - a^2 = a\sqrt{(x+c)^2 + y^2}$$

Squaring both sides of the equation again, we get:

$$-xc - a^2 = a\sqrt{(x+c)^2 + y^2} \Rightarrow x^2c^2 + 2xca^2 + a^4 = a^2[(x + c)^2 + y^2]$$

(Note: We do not have logical equivalency.)

Expanding $(x + c)^2$ we get:

$$x^2c^2 + 2xca^2 + a^4 = a^2[(x + c)^2 + y^2] \Leftrightarrow x^2c^2 + 2xca^2 + a^4 = a^2(x^2 + 2xc + c^2 + y^2)$$

Applying the Distributive Law to the right side of the equation, we get:

$$x^2c^2 + 2xca^2 + a^4 = a^2(x^2 + 2xc + c^2 + y^2) \Leftrightarrow x^2c^2 + 2xca^2 + a^4 = a^2x^2 + 2xca^2 + a^2c^2 + a^2y^2$$

We subtract $2xca^2$ from both sides of the equation:

$$x^2c^2 + 2xca^2 + a^4 = a^2x^2 + 2xca^2 + a^2c^2 + a^2y^2 \Leftrightarrow x^2c^2 + a^4 = a^2x^2 + a^2c^2 + a^2y^2$$

Let's get all the variables, terms of x or y, on the left side and the constant values on the right side. We first subtract a^2x^2 and a^2y^2 from both sides of the equation:

$$x^2c^2 + a^4 = a^2x^2 + a^2c^2 + a^2y^2 \Leftrightarrow x^2c^2 - a^2x^2 - a^2y^2 + a^4 = a^2c^2$$

Next, we subtract a^4 from both sides of the equation:

$$x^2c^2 - a^2x^2 - a^2y^2 + a^4 = a^2c^2 \Leftrightarrow x^2c^2 - a^2x^2 - a^2y^2 = a^2c^2 - a^4$$

On the left side, we have a common factor of x^2 in the first two terms. Factoring, we get:

$$x^2c^2 - a^2x^2 - a^2y^2 = a^2c^2 - a^4 \Leftrightarrow x^2(c^2 - a^2) - a^2y^2 = a^2c^2 - a^4$$

On the right side, we have a common factor of a^2 in the first two terms. We factor again:

$$x^2(c^2 - a^2) - a^2y^2 = a^2c^2 - a^4 \Leftrightarrow x^2(c^2 - a^2) - a^2y^2 = a^2(c^2 - a^2)$$

Since $a < c \Leftrightarrow c - a > 0$, we can choose $b > 0$, the length of the semi-minor axis of the hyperbola, such that:

$$c^2 - a^2 = b^2$$

Substituting, we get:

$$x^2(c^2 - a^2) - a^2y^2 = a^2(c^2 - a^2) \text{ and } c^2 - a^2 = b^2 \Rightarrow x^2b^2 - a^2y^2 = a^2b^2$$

Dividing both sides of the equation by a^2b^2, b^2 cancels with the b^2 in the numerator of the first term and a^2 cancels with the a^2 in numerator of the second term, we get:

$$x^2b^2 - a^2y^2 = a^2b^2 \Leftrightarrow$$

$$\frac{x^2}{a^2} - \frac{y^2}{b^2} = 1$$ (This is the general equation for the hyperbola, a quadratic equation.)

Again, note that in our derivation we squared both sides of an equation twice. Since squaring does not produce an equivalent equation, we may have a problem with our solutions; i.e., there is a possibility that we introduced values of x and y that satisfy $\sqrt{(x-c)^2 + y^2} - \sqrt{(x+c)^2 + y^2} = 2a$ but do not satisfy

$\frac{x^2}{a^2} - \frac{y^2}{b^2} = 1$ where $c^2 - a^2 = b^2$, i.e., an extraneous solution. It can be shown that this is not the case; i.e., the values of x and y that satisfy $\sqrt{(x-c)^2 + y^2} - \sqrt{(x+c)^2 + y^2} = 2a$ do satisfy $\frac{x^2}{a^2} - \frac{y^2}{b^2} = 1$ where $c^2 - a^2 = b^2$. Again, we will not demonstrate this reasoning.

Solving for y in terms of x, we get:

$$x^2b^2 - a^2y^2 = a^2b^2 \Leftrightarrow x^2b^2 = a^2b^2 + a^2y^2 \Leftrightarrow a^2y^2 = x^2b^2 - a^2b^2 \Leftrightarrow y^2 = \frac{x^2b^2 - a^2b^2}{a^2} \Leftrightarrow$$

$$y^2 = \frac{b^2}{a^2}\left(x^2 - a^2\right) \Leftrightarrow y = \frac{b}{a}\sqrt{x^2 - a^2} \text{ or } y = -\frac{b}{a}\sqrt{x^2 - a^2}$$

This means that when $x = 0$, there are no real values for y. Why? The radicand is negative. From this, we know that $(0, b)$ and $(0, -b)$ are not coordinates of the hyperbola, but a and b tell us something about the slant, or oblique, asymptotes of the hyperbola (Lesson 14.3).

We note:

$$\lim_{x \to +\infty} \sqrt{x^2 - a^2} = x$$

or

$$\lim_{x \to -\infty} \sqrt{x^2 - a^2} = x$$

(As $x \to \pm\infty$, a becomes insignificant in both situations.)

Therefore:

$$\lim_{x \to +\infty} \frac{b}{a}\sqrt{x^2 - a^2} = \frac{b}{a}x, \quad \lim_{x \to -\infty} \frac{b}{a}\sqrt{x^2 - a^2} = \frac{b}{a}x$$

$$\lim_{x \to +\infty} -\frac{b}{a}\sqrt{x^2 - a^2} = -\frac{b}{a}x, \quad \lim_{x \to -\infty} -\frac{b}{a}\sqrt{x^2 - a^2} = -\frac{b}{a}x$$

The two slant asymptotes are $y = \frac{b}{a}x$ and $y = -\frac{b}{a}x$ (Figure 12). We also note that the hyperbola opens around the horizontal axis, the x-axis. In this graph, $a < b$.

If we want the hyperbola to open around the vertical axis, the y-axis, we find its inverse by simply interchanging x and y. The inverse of the general form is:

$$\frac{y^2}{a^2} - \frac{x^2}{b^2} = 1$$

We will show why this is so in a homework problem.

Figure 13 shows an example of what happens when $a < b$. The graph is the inverse of the hyperbola graphed in Figure 12.

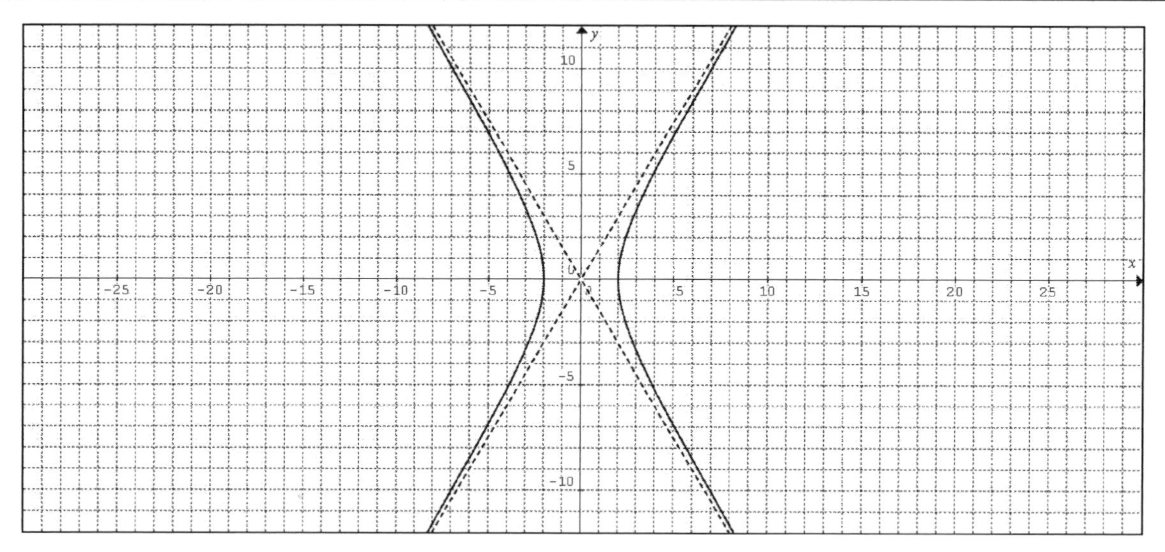

Figure 12. $\frac{x^2}{2^2} - \frac{y^2}{3^2} = 1$ opens around the horizontal axis with slant asymptotes $y = 1.5x$ and $y = -1.5x$.

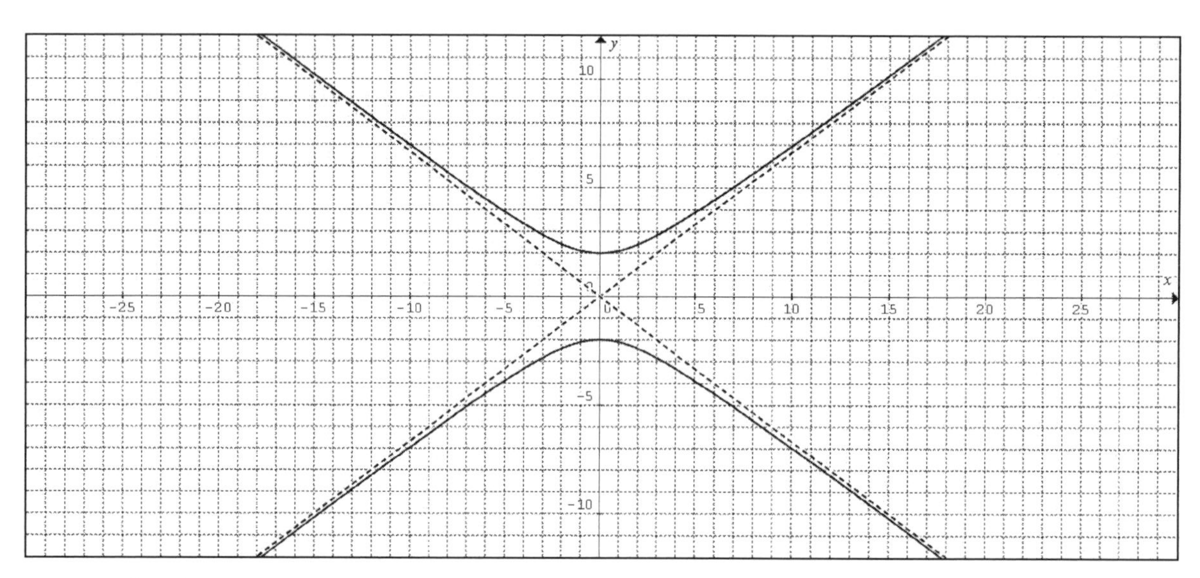

Figure 13. $\frac{y^2}{2^2} - \frac{x^2}{3^2} = 1$ opens around the vertical axis with slant asymptotes $y = (2/3)x$ and $y = -(2/3)x$.

In this case, the slant asymptotes are:

$$y = \frac{a}{b}x \text{ and } y = -\frac{a}{b}x$$

Why? Because the graph in Figure 13 is the inverse of the graph in Figure 12, we exchange y with x in the equations that generate the slant asymptotes in $\frac{x^2}{a^2} - \frac{y^2}{b^2} = 1$, i.e., $y = \frac{b}{a}x$ and $\frac{x^2}{2^2} - \frac{y^2}{3^2} = 1$. This interchange gives us:

$$x = \frac{b}{a}y \Leftrightarrow y = \frac{a}{b}x$$

$$x = -\frac{b}{a}y \Leftrightarrow y = -\frac{a}{b}x$$

If we compare $\frac{x^2}{a^2} - \frac{y^2}{b^2} = 1$ with the equation of the ellipse, $\frac{x^2}{a^2} + \frac{y^2}{b^2} = 1$, the only difference is a change in sign. Yet that little change generates two remarkably different curves.

EQUILATERAL HYPERBOLA

How does $xy = 12$ fit into the form of the hyperbola? It does so when the semi-axes of the hyperbola are equal; i.e., $a = b$. If this is the case, we have, in general:

$$\frac{x^2}{a^2} - \frac{y^2}{a^2} = 1 \Leftrightarrow x^2 - y^2 = a^2$$

When the hyperbola is of this form, it is an **equilateral hyperbola**.[19] For any $p > 0$, the solution set to $xy = p$ is also an equilateral hyperbola. Why?

We graph $xy = p$ and introduce a new Cartesian coordinate plane (Figure 14), the X-axis and Y-axis, both rotated 45° counterclockwise about the origin of the traditional x-axis and y-axis. In this new arrangement, the x-axis and y-axis are the slant asymptotes. What is the relationship between the old coordinates (x, y) of P and its new coordinates (X, Y)? We will use the answer to show that this hyperbola is of the form $\frac{x^2}{a^2} - \frac{y^2}{a^2} = 1$.

We first note the following relationships:

$\overline{PQ} \perp X$-axis
$\overline{PS} \perp x$-axis
$x = OS$
$y = PS$
$X = OQ$
$Y = PQ$
$PS = PR + RS$[20]
$OQ = OR + RQ$
$RS = OS$ (ΔORS is a 45° isosceles triangle.)
$OR = \sqrt{2}OS$ (ΔORS is a 45° isosceles triangle. Review Lesson 11.4 and Lesson 12.6, the *Special Angles* section.)
$RQ = PQ$ (ΔPQR is a 45° isosceles triangle. Do you see why?)
$PR = \sqrt{2}PQ$ (ΔPQR is a 45° isosceles triangle.)

Therefore, by careful substitution:

Equation 1. $y = \sqrt{2}Y + x$
Equation 2. $X = \sqrt{2}x + Y$

[19] Recall that the ellipse becomes a circle when the semi-axes are equal.
[20] If three points A, B, and C, are collinear, signified A-B-C (B is between A and C), there is a geometric theorem that states what is intuitively obvious: $AB + BC = AC$.

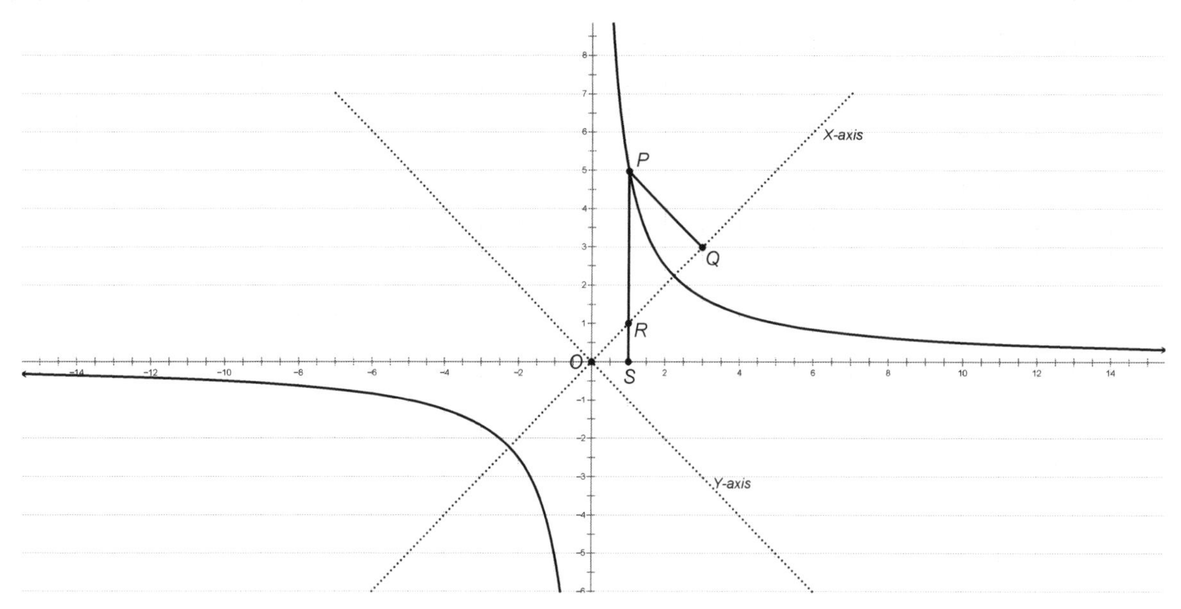

Figure 14. Rotating the x-y axis 45° counterclockwise about the origin to generate the new X-Y axis.

From these two equations, we need to show that the hyperbola $xy = p$ is of the form $\frac{x^2}{a^2} - \frac{y^2}{a^2} = 1$. To do this, we need to solve for x and y in terms of X and Y. Follow along carefully for the algebraic work is intense:

Let's multiply Equation 1 by $\sqrt{2}$:

$y = \sqrt{2}Y + x \Leftrightarrow \sqrt{2}y = 2Y + \sqrt{2}x$

We rewrite Equation 2 as follows:

$X = \sqrt{2}x + Y \Leftrightarrow X = Y + \sqrt{2}x$

We have a system of two equations:

$\sqrt{2}y = 2Y + \sqrt{2}x$
$X = Y + \sqrt{2}x$

If we subtract the second equation from the first, term by term, we get:

$\sqrt{2}y - X = Y$

Solving for y, we get:

$\sqrt{2}y - X = Y \Leftrightarrow \sqrt{2}y = X + Y \Leftrightarrow y = \frac{X+Y}{\sqrt{2}}$ (Nice, isn't it?)

Now, we multiply Equation 2 by $\sqrt{2}$:

$X = \sqrt{2}x + Y \Leftrightarrow \sqrt{2}X = 2x + \sqrt{2}Y$

We rewrite Equation 1 as follows:

$y = \sqrt{2}Y + x \Leftrightarrow y = x + \sqrt{2}Y$

We, again, have a system of two equations:

$\sqrt{2}X = 2x + \sqrt{2}Y$
$y = x + \sqrt{2}Y$

We subtract the second equation, term by term, from the first. We get:

$\sqrt{2}X - y = x$

We need to get an equation for x in terms of X and Y. Since $x = \sqrt{2}X - y$ and $y = \dfrac{X+Y}{\sqrt{2}}$, we substitute:

$$x = \sqrt{2}X - \left(\frac{X+Y}{\sqrt{2}}\right) \Leftrightarrow x = \frac{2X}{\sqrt{2}} - \left(\frac{X+Y}{\sqrt{2}}\right) \Leftrightarrow x = \frac{2X-(X+Y)}{\sqrt{2}} \Leftrightarrow$$

$$x = \frac{X-Y}{\sqrt{2}}$$

(This equation is another beautiful conclusion.)

We have derived these two equations:

Equation 1. $y = \dfrac{X+Y}{\sqrt{2}}$

Equation 2. $x = \dfrac{X-Y}{\sqrt{2}}$

We started with $xy = p$. By substitution, we get:

$$\left(\frac{X-Y}{\sqrt{2}}\right)\left(\frac{X+Y}{\sqrt{2}}\right) = p \Leftrightarrow \frac{(X+Y)(X-Y)}{2} = p \Leftrightarrow \frac{X^2-Y^2}{2} = p \Leftrightarrow \frac{X^2}{2} - \frac{Y^2}{2} = p \Leftrightarrow \frac{X^2}{2p} - \frac{Y^2}{2p} = 1$$

If we let $a = \sqrt{2p}$, we know:

$a = \sqrt{2p} \Rightarrow a^2 = 2p$

Since $\dfrac{X^2}{2p} - \dfrac{Y^2}{2p} = 1$, we substitute and get:

$$\frac{X^2}{a^2} - \frac{Y^2}{a^2} = 1$$

Starting from $xy = p$, we have derived an equation in the form of an equilateral hyperbola, i.e., $\dfrac{x^2}{a^2} - \dfrac{y^2}{a^2} = 1$.

QED

In review, this equilateral hyperbola interpenetrates the inverse proportion (Lesson 8.8). One of this proportion's scientific applications is Boyle's Law of gases: The product of pressure and volume is constant or $pv = k$.

ALL TOGETHER NOW

We have investigated the equations of four curves: the circle, the parabola, the ellipse, and the hyperbola. The general form of each curve, with the central symmetric point being the origin, is summarized in Table 1.

Table 1	
Curve	**General Form**
Circle	$x^2 + y^2 = r^2$
Parabola (smiling)	$x^2 - 2py = 0$
Ellipse	$\frac{x^2}{a^2} + \frac{y^2}{b^2} = 1$
Hyperbola	$\frac{x^2}{a^2} - \frac{y^2}{b^2} = 1$

Each equation is quadratic and we have exhausted the possible curves for these equations. That is, we can graph every quadratic equation in two unknowns as a circle, a parabola, an ellipse, or a hyperbola. Yet, these curves are very different from each other. Some are finite and closed, i.e., the circle and the ellipse. (We note that circle is a special form of the ellipse where the major axis equals the minor axis.) Some wander off to infinity, i.e., the parabola and the hyperbola. Three are in one piece, i.e., the circle, the parabola, and the ellipse. One is in two pieces, i.e., the hyperbola.

Is there a family likeness? Is there a unity in this diversity? The family name for the four curves is Conic Sections, coming from the shape of a cone (Lesson 8.4 and Figure 15). Again, think of the traditional ice cream cone and you have a correct image of this three-dimensional figure. As we have noted, the sharp point or tip at the bottom of the ice cream cone is the apex of the cone. We can generate three of the Conic Sections, the circle, ellipse, and parabola, from a single cone. We generate the hyperbola from the double-cusped cone. We can think of generating the double-cusped cone by first imaging a horizontal disk and a slanting straight line segment, the **generatrix**,[21] leaning over the center of the disk and touching the disk at one point, i.e., tangent to

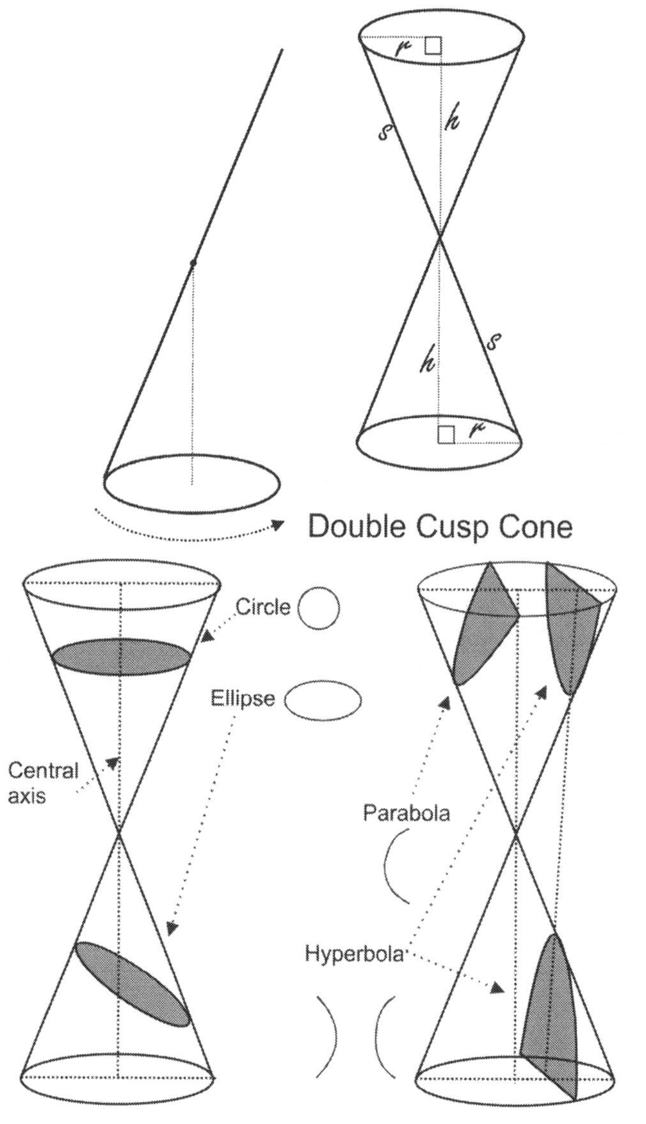

Figure 15. The Conic Sections.

[21] A generatrix is a point, line, or surface that is moved to form a line, surface, or solid.

the disk. Now imagine taking this line segment and rotating it around the disk while holding it fast at the apex lying above the center of the disk. This rotation will generate a cone above and below this apex. The generated cone, in this instance, is the directrix. The two individual cones are its **nappes**.[22]

If we intersect these two cones with a plane in various positions (Table 2), the four Conic Sections appear along the edges of the truncated pieces.

Table 2	
A plane cutting the cone ...	**Conic Section**
orthogonal (at a right angle) to the central axis of the cone.	Circle
between the orthogonal to the central axis of the cone and parallel to the generatrix.	Ellipse
parallel to the generatrix.	Parabola
between a plane parallel to the generatrix and a plane parallel to the central axis of the cone.	Hyperbola

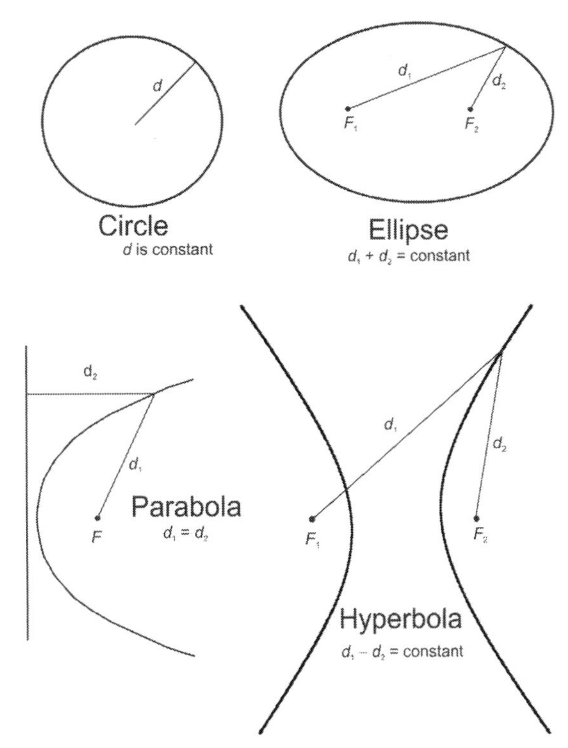

Figure 16.

If we think of the locus of all points for each Conic Section, we can describe these curves in Table 3.

Table 3	
The curve of	**is the locus of points**
the circle	that have the *same distance* to the center of the circle.
the ellipse	whose distances to two given foci have a *constant sum*.
the parabola	that have the *same distance* to a focus and the directrix.

[22] *Nappe* (singular), in French, means "sheet or surface."

Table 3	
The curve of	**is the locus of points**
the hyperbola	whose distances to two given foci have a *constant difference*.

ECCENTRICITY

Another way to define the Conic Sections is in terms of eccentricity (Lesson 8.6).[23]

Given the focus, F, the directrix d, a point P on the curve, $r = PF$, and $a = PD$, eccentricity, E, is:

$$E = \frac{r}{a}$$

For a parabola, since $r = a$, $E = 1$. For an ellipse, since $r < a$, $E < 1$. For the hyperbola, since $r > a$, $E > 1$. It is this eccentricity that provides the etymological foundation for the respective names[24] of these three Conic Sections, as we can see in Table 4.

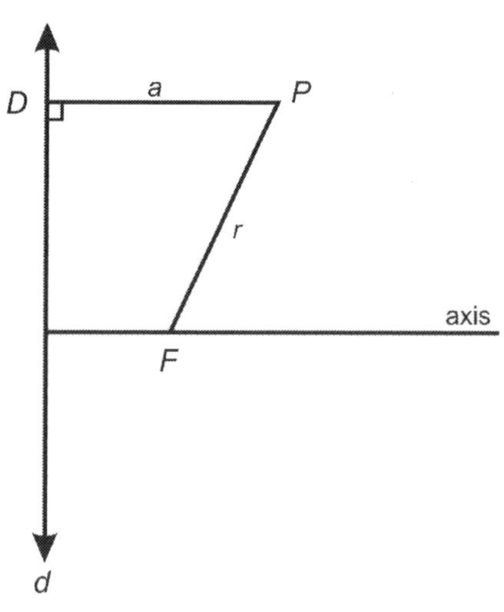

Figure 17. Starting points for understanding eccentricity.

Table 4: Eccentricity		
E	**Curve**	**Meaning**
$E = 1$	Parabola	equal to
$E < 1$	Ellipse	to fall short
$E > 1$	Hyperbola	in excess of

Since a circle is not off center, $E = 0$. Since $r =$ the radius of the circle, then, for $E = 0$, a, the distance from P to the directrix, must be at infinity. In symbols, using the limit concept:

$$\lim_{a \to \infty} \frac{r}{a} = 0$$

Since an ellipse with eccentricity of 0 becomes a circle, the complete qualification for the possible values of E for an ellipse is $0 < E < 1$.

These curves have another geometric property, reflection (Table 5), a property that can be used to concentrate or reflect light rays or sound beams. We've already seen how Archimedes used a parabolic mirror to concentrate the rays of the Sun.

Table 5: Physical Properties	
Curve	**Reflects rays coming from the focus ...**
Circle	back to the center of the circle
Ellipse	into the other focus
Parabola	as a parallel outgoing ray or beam
Hyperbola	as if coming from the other focus

[23] Eccentricity comes from the Greek word *ekkentros* meaning "out of" or "off center."

[24] As we have noted, these words are also used in grammar: the parable, the ellipsis, and the hyperbole.

THE CONIC SECTIONS AND REALITY

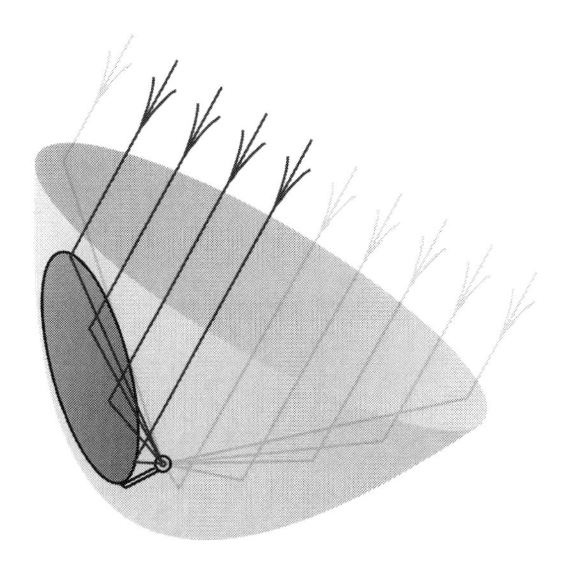

Figure 18. Principle of an off-axis parabolic reflector used, for example, in satellite dishes. The shape is an elliptic paraboloid. Source: Wikimedia Commons.

Let's review some of places where the Conic Sections interpenetrate reality. Because of the reflective property of parabolas, they are used in automobile headlights or searchlights. The mirror in each headlight has a curved surface formed by rotating a parabola about its line of symmetry. If a light is placed at the focus of the mirror, it is reflected in rays parallel to the axis. In this way, a straight beam of light is formed. The opposite principle is used in the giant mirrors of reflecting telescopes, radar transmitters, solar furnaces, sound reflectors, and in satellite or radio wave dishes. With these instruments the beam is reflected off the parabolic surface and is concentrated at the focus.

In Lesson 11.7, we saw how civil engineers use parabolic girders to build bridges.

Figure 19. Johannes Kepler. Source: Public Domain.

The reflective property of an ellipse is used in the creation of whispering galleries. If you are at one focal point in a room shaped in the size of an ellipse, you will be able to hear the whispers of a person located at the other focal point even if other conversations are going on in the room. As we noted in Lesson 8.5, the Statuary Hall in the United States Capitol and the whispery gallery of St. Paul's Cathedral in London are two examples.

In the 17th century, the German astronomer and mathematician Johannes Kepler (1571-1630) augmented the heliocentric cosmology of the Polish astronomer Nicholas Copernicus (1473-1543). He did this by showing that the planets orbit the Sun in a curve that resembles an ellipse where the Sun is at one focus (Lesson 8.6 and Lesson 12.4).

When a projectile is launched from the Earth with a velocity between the orbital velocity of the Earth, about 17,000 miles per hour, and escape velocity, about 25,000 miles per hour, its path will resemble an ellipse.

The path of an electron follows an elliptical path as it whirls around the nucleus of an atom. In this ordered dervish, the appearance of pentagons is evident (Figure 20).

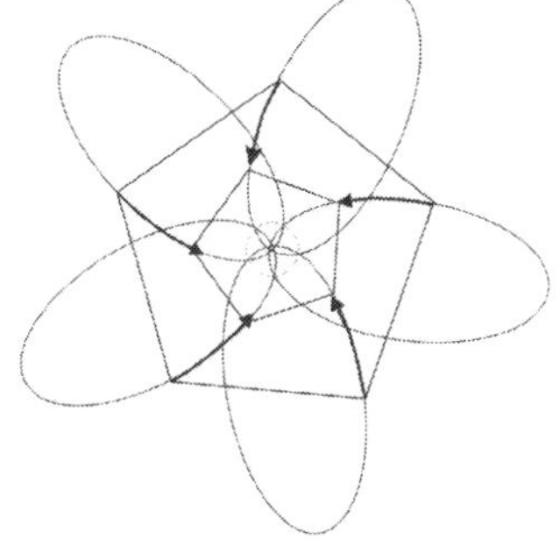

Figure 20. Path of an electron.

The Italian mathematician Galileo Galilei (1564-1642) showed that the motion of a projectile follows the path of a parabola that is frowning. And, we have already noted that when a projectile is launched from the Earth with a velocity less than the orbital velocity of the Earth, its path will be parabolic.

The hyperbola is also known as a shock wave curve (Lesson 10.8). When an airplane flies faster than the speed of sound, it creates a shock wave heard on the ground as a sonic boom. This wave has a shape of a cone with its apex located at the front of the airplane and it intersects the ground in the shape of the hyperbola. When a projectile is launched from the Earth with a velocity greater than escape velocity, its path will resemble the hyperbola. The hyperbola is also essential to understanding LORAN (stands for LOng RAnge Navigation), a technique used

Figure 21. Galileo Galilei. Source: Public Domain.

for locating ships at sea. The Cassegrain telescope makes special use of both parabolic and hyperbolic mirrors (Figure 22).

The circle has so many applications in our world that to list them all would take a book.[25]

UNSUSPECTED PERICHORESIS

The ancient Greeks understood the Conic Sections as useful in some ways, but playful toys in many other ways.[26] They would have never envisioned, even in a dream, how useful and essential their playful games would become. As history unfolded, their thoughts interpenetrated with a multiplicity of scientific and technological applications.

The quadratic equations reflecting the geometric behavior of the Conic Sections serve two purposes in the world of the Triune God's making:

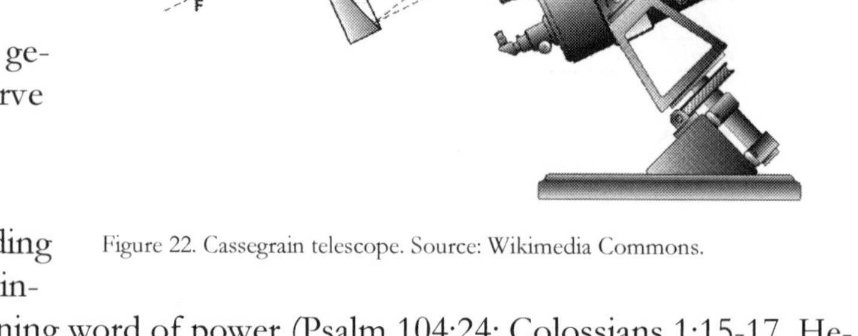

Figure 22. Cassegrain telescope. Source: Wikimedia Commons.

1. They are essential for an understanding of the harmonious order of the Trinity's creative design and His sustaining word of power (Psalm 104:24; Colossians 1:15-17, Hebrews 1:3).
2. They serve as tools that enable us to take effective dominion over the creation (Genesis 1:26-28).

This lesson has provided us the logical and algebraic basis for appreciating and enjoying the mathematical wonders of God's world as revealed by the Conic Sections.

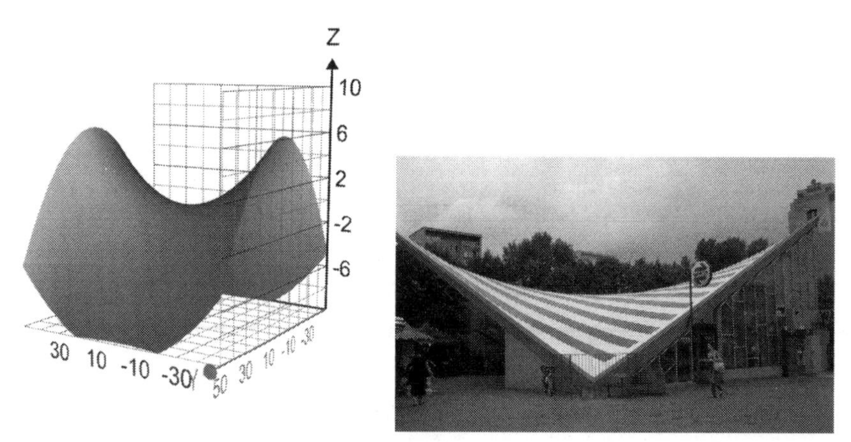

Figure 23. The geometry of three dimensions on the x-y-z axes; the hyperbolic paraboloid (saddle-shaped curve): $\frac{y^2}{16} - \frac{x^2}{9} = 25z$. The Warszawa-Ochota railway station in Poland. Source: Wikimedia Commons.

---

[25] See Ernest Zebrowski, *A History of the Circle: Mathematical Reasoning and the Physical Universe* (London: Free Association Books, 1999).

[26] Renowned antiquities science historian Otto Neugebauer (1899-1990) believed that the conic sections were first analyzed in the context of the nature and construction of sundials.

EXERCISES

Define the following terms.

1. Cosmology
2. Inscribe
3. Circumscribe
4. Major axis of an ellipse
5. Minor axis of an ellipse
6. Equilateral hyperbola
7. Generatrix
8. Nappes

Answer the following questions:

9. Why are the two triangles denoted in Figure 14 equilateral right triangles?
10. Define the terms ellipsis, parable, hyperbole, ellipse, parabola, and hyperbola and explain how the latter three terms from geometry are related to their counterparts in grammar.
11. True or False. $a = \sqrt{2p} \Leftrightarrow a^2 = 2p$
12. What shape does the ellipse become when its semi-major axis is equal to its semi-minor axis?
13. What shape does the hyperbola become when its semi-major axis is equal to its semi-minor axis?
14. Use the distance formula to find the distance from (0, 0) to (3, 4) on the Cartesian coordinate plane.
15. Use the distance formula to find the distance from (0, 0) to (x, y) on the Cartesian coordinate plane.
16. Consider this rhetorical sentence: The distance from (0, 0) to (x, y) is 5. Use your answer to Question 15 to write this sentence using symbolic algebra.

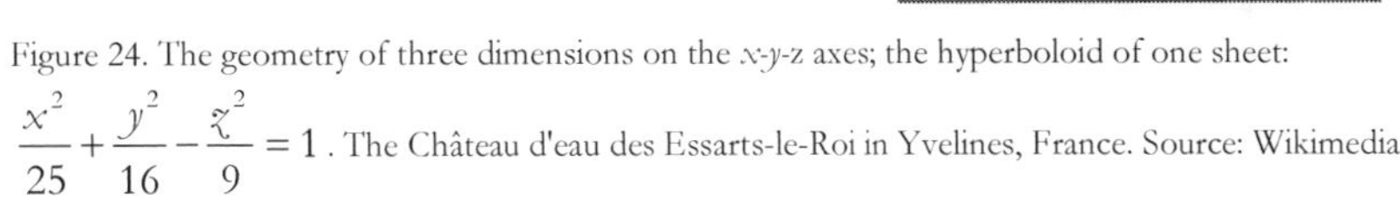

Figure 24. The geometry of three dimensions on the x-y-z axes; the hyperboloid of one sheet: $\frac{x^2}{25}+\frac{y^2}{16}-\frac{z^2}{9}=1$. The Château d'eau des Essarts-le-Roi in Yvelines, France. Source: Wikimedia Commons.

17. Consider this rhetorical sentence: The point (x, y) lies on the circle of radius 5 with center at (0, 0).
    (a) Explain why this sentence has exactly the same meaning as the sentence in the previous question.
    (b) Rewrite this sentence using symbolic algebra.
18. Consider this algebraic expression: $x^2 + y^2 = 25$.
    (a) Explain why this sentence logically implies that $\sqrt{x^2 + y^2} = 5$.
    (b) Explain why $\sqrt{x^2 + y^2} = 5$ means that (x, y) lies on the circle of radius 5 with center at (0, 0).
    (c) Synthesize your answers to part a and part b to explain why $x^2 + y^2 = 25$ means that (x, y) lies on the circle of radius 5 with center at (0, 0).
    (d) Explain carefully in what sense $x^2 + y^2 = 25$ connects with a circle of radius 5 with center at (0, 0).

Restate the following rhetorically in the context of a circle:
19. $x^2 + y^2 = 49$
20. $x^2 + y^2 = 36$
21. $x^2 + y^2 = 25$
22. $x^2 + y^2 = 9$
23. $x^2 + y^2 = 1$

Answer these questions:
24. What is the exact radius and the coordinates of the center of a circle when $x^2 + y^2 = 2$?
25. What is the exact radius and the coordinates of the center of a circle when $(x - 3)^2 + y^2 = 2$? [Hint: Think translation. You are subtracting 3 from the argument of the function $y = f(x)$.]
26. What is the exact radius and the coordinates of the center of a circle when $x^2 + (y + 5)^2 = 2$? [Hint: Think translation. You are adding 5 to the image of the function $y = f(x)$.]
27. What is the exact radius and the coordinates of the center of a circle when $(x - 3)^2 + (y + 5)^2 = 2$?
28. In general, what is the radius and the coordinates of the center of a circle when $(x - h)^2 + (y - k)^2 = r$?

Restate the following using algebraic symbolism:
29. The distance from (x, y) to $(\pi, 3)$ is 5.
30. (x, y) lies on the circle of radius 5 centered at $(\pi, 3)$.
31. The distance from (x, y) to $(2, 3)$ is 5.
32. (x, y) lies on the circle of radius 5 centered at $(2, 3)$.
33. (x, y) lies on the circle of radius $\sqrt{2}$ centered at $(1, 0)$.
34. (x, y) lies on the circle of radius 3 centered at $(-2, 5)$.
35. (x, y) lies on the circle of radius r centered at (a, b).

Restate the following rhetorically in the context of a circle.
36. $(x + 2)^2 + (y - 5)^2 = 9$
37. $(x - 2)^2 + (y + 5)^2 = 9$
38. $x^2 + (y - 2)^2 = 3$
39. $9x^2 + 9y^2 = 18$ (Hint: Divide both sides of the equation by 9 first.)
40. $10(x + 2)^2 + 10(y - 4)^2 = 250$

Answer the following questions:
41. The simplest hyperbola is $xy = 1$.
   (a) Sketch the graph of this hyperbola.
   (b) What is the domain and range of this hyperbola?
   (c) Is this graph a graph of a function?
42. Consider the parabola whose focus F is at $(0, 2)$ and whose directrix D is the line with equation $y = -2$.
   (a) What are the coordinates of the vertex of this parabola?
   (b) What is the line of symmetry of this parabola?
   (c) Write an equation for this parabola.
   (d) Graph this equation.
43. Consider the parabola whose focus F is at $(0, p)$ and whose directrix is the line whose equation is $y = -p$. Write an equation for this parabola.
44. Given the parabola represented by the equation $y = \frac{x^2}{4}$:
   (a) What is the value of p?

(b) What are the coordinates of its focus?
(c) What is the equation of its directrix?

45. Consider that the point (x, y) is on a parabola with focus $F = (0, 1)$ and whose directrix D is the line $y = -1$.
(a) Construct of graph marking the F and D.
(b) The vertex, V, is halfway between F and D. What are the coordinates of V?
(c) The axis of the parabola is the line through F and V. What is the axis of this parabola?

By the definition of a parabola, the distance (x, y) to F is the same as the distance (x, y) to D.
(d) What are the coordinates of F?
(e) What are the coordinates of *any* point on D?
(f) Write an algebraic expression for the distance between (x, y) and F.
(g) Write an algebraic expression for the distance between (x, y) and D.
(h) Why are the expressions in part f and g equal?
(i) Set the two expressions in part f and g equal to each other.
(j) Simplify the radicand expressions as much as possible.
(k) Square both sides of the equation to remove the radical sign.
(l) Using algebraic operations, solve the equation for y in terms of x and graph the result.
(m) Graph the parabola, its inverse, and $y = x$ together on one graph (Hint: Solve the equation derived in part l for x in terms of y. Interchange x with y to graph y in terms of x.)

46. The eccentricity, E, of a Conic Section is defined in terms of a ratio.
(a) Write the ratio for E in terms of the distance from (x, y) to F and the distance from (x, y) to a point on D.
(b) What is E in the case of a parabola?
(c) What is E in the case of a circle?
(d) What are the limits (lower and upper bounds) for E in the case of an ellipse?
(e) What is the limit (lower bound) for E in the case of a hyperbola?

47. Consider the hyperbola whose focus F is $(0, 1)$, whose directrix D is the line with equation $y = -1$, and whose eccentricity is 2.
(a) Construct a graph marking the F and D.
(b) Write an equation for this hyperbola. [Hint: Since $E = 2$, then the distance from (x, y) to $(0, 1)$ is *twice* the distance from (x, y) to a point on D $(x, -1)$. Why? Set these two distances equal to each other (remember, one is twice the other) and proceed to simplify the equation. Your answer should be of the form $ax^2 - by^2 + cy + d = 0$.]
(c) Graph the hyperbola.
(d) Is the point $(0, -3)$ on this hyperbola?
(e) Is the point $(0, -\frac{1}{3})$ on this hyperbola?

48. Consider the ellipse whose focus F is $(0, 1)$, whose directrix D is given by the line $y = -1$, and whose eccentricity is $\frac{1}{2}$.
(a) Construct a graph marking the F and D.
(b) Write an equation for this ellipse. (Hint: Your answer should be of the form $ax^2 + by^2 + cy + d = 0$.)
(c) Graph the ellipse.
(d) Is the point $(0, -3)$ on this ellipse?
(e) Is the point $(0, -\frac{1}{3})$ on this ellipse?

49. (a) Graph the three curves, the parabola in Question 45, the hyperbola in Question 47, and the ellipse in Question 48 on the same Cartesian coordinate plane, labelling the three curves with their associated eccentricities; i.e., 1, 2, and $\frac{1}{2}$ respectively.

(b) The German scientist and mathematician Johannes Kepler once observed that "the parabola is trying to be like both an ellipse and a hyperbola." From your graph, why does this appear to be so?

From the preceding exercises, we can state a more general definition of the Conic Sections given the general quadratic equation of the form:

$$ax^2 + bx + cy^2 + dy + k = 0$$

The important parameters are a and c, the coefficients, respectively of the x^2 and y^2 terms.

Table 6: The Conics and the General Quadratic

Conditions on a and c	then curve is a(n)
If a and c have the same sign,	ellipse
If a and c have the same sign and a = c,	circle
If a and c have the opposite signs,	hyperbola
If a and c have the opposite signs and a = c,	equilateral hyperbola
If a = 0 or c = 0 [XOR or "exclusive or"(Lesson 5.15)]	parabola

Based on this table, answer these questions:

50. What type of Conic Section is $8x^2 + 8y^2 + 10y - 3 = 0$?
51. What type of Conic Section is $8x^2 + 2y^2 - 3y + 3 = 0$?
52. What type of Conic Section is $2x^2 - y^2 - 2y + 2 = 0$?
53. What type of Conic Section is $2y - x^2 = 0$?
54. (a) True or False. $2x^2 + 2y^2 + 10x + 7y - 10 = 0$ is the equation of a circle.
    (b) If your answer is True, what is the circle's exact center and exact radius? (Hint: You will need to complete the square twice. Review Lesson 11.11 homework.)

Answer the following questions:

55. The coordinates of the center of the ellipse $\frac{x^2}{9} + \frac{y^2}{16} = 1$ is (0, 0).

(a) What are the coordinates of the center of the ellipse $\frac{(x-4)^2}{9} + \frac{y^2}{16} = 1$?

(b) What are the coordinates of the center of the ellipse $\frac{x^2}{9} + \frac{(y-1.5)^2}{16} = 1$?

(c) What are the coordinates of the center of the ellipse $\frac{(x+8)^2}{9} + \frac{(y+2)^2}{16} = 1$?

(d) In general, what are the coordinates of the center of the ellipse $\frac{(x-h)^2}{a^2} + \frac{(y-k)^2}{b^2} = 1$?

56. A U.S. Geological Survey map of Washington, DC shows that there is an elliptical park in front of the White House. The map is drawn to scale 1:31,680. On the map, the major axis of the ellipse, a, measures $\frac{13}{64}$ inch. The minor axis, b, measures $\frac{11}{64}$ inch. Given that the area of an ellipse is given

by the formula πab, compute, to the nearest acre, the number of acres in the elliptical park. (Hint: Recall that, from Lesson 7.10, 1 acre = 4840 yd^2. You may use your calculator.)

57. If $x^2 - 2py = 0$ represents the equation of a parabola smiling, ∪, where the vertex is at the origin of the Cartesian coordinate plane, write the equation of a parabola where the vertex at the origin of the Cartesian coordinate plane for the following situations: (Hint: If you need to, experiment with a graphics software package with a given value of p.)
   (a) Frowning, ∩
   (b) Facing right, ⊂
   (c) Facing left, ⊃
58. (a) Solve $\frac{x^2}{a^2} + \frac{y^2}{b^2} = 1$ for x^2.
   (b) Then, exchange x with y and derive this equation: $\frac{y^2}{a^2} + \frac{x^2}{b^2} = 1$
59. On the same Cartesian coordinate plane, graph:
   (a) $25x^2 + 16y^2 = 400$
   (b) The inverse of $25x^2 + 16y^2 = 400$
   (c) $y = x$
60. (a) Solve $\frac{x^2}{a^2} - \frac{y^2}{b^2} = 1$ for x^2.
   (b) Then, exchange x with y and derive this equation: $\frac{y^2}{a^2} - \frac{x^2}{b^2} = 1$
61. On same Cartesian coordinate plane, graph:
   (a) $x^2 - 4y^2 = 36$
   (b) the inverse of $x^2 - 4y^2 = 36$
   (c) $y = x$
62. Show that the inverse of a circle of the form $x^2 + y^2 = r^2$ is $x^2 + y^2 = r^2$; i.e., any circle is the inverse of itself.

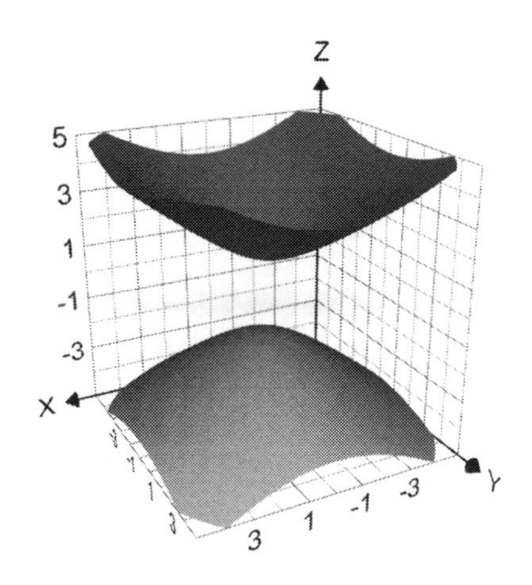

Figure 25. The geometry of three dimensions on the x-y-z axes; the hyperboloid of two sheets: $\frac{z^2}{2} - \frac{x^2}{3} - \frac{y^2}{4} = 1$.

63. Beginning with the equation $\sqrt{(x+c)^2+y^2}-\sqrt{(x-c)^2+y^2}=2a$, derive the equation for the hyperbola, i.e., $\frac{x^2}{a^2}-\frac{y^2}{b^2}=1$.

64. A point $P(x, y)$ moves so that the difference of the distances from A (2, 2) and B (-2, -2), the two foci, is always 4. Derive its equation. (Hint: Begin with $PA - PB = 4$).

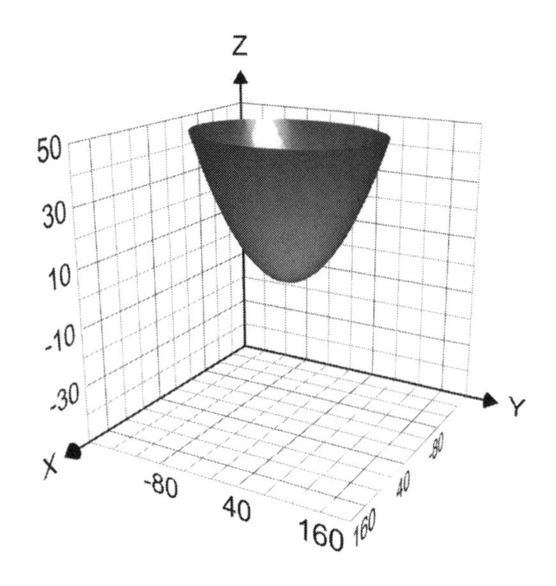

Figure 26. The geometry of three dimensions on the x-y-z axes; the elliptic paraboloid: $\frac{x^2}{9}+\frac{y^2}{16}=25z$.

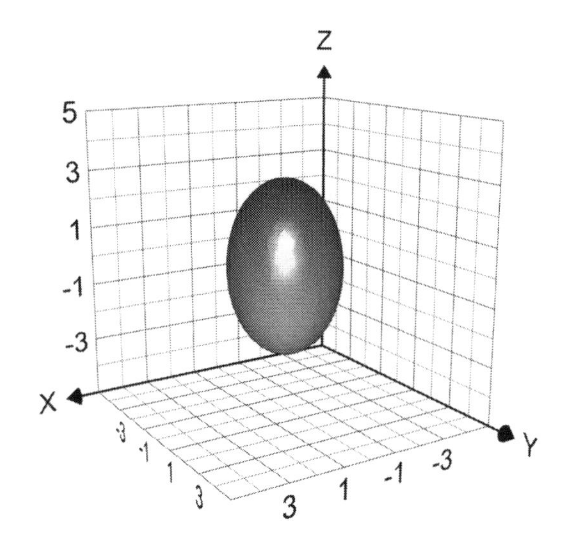

Figure 27. The geometry of three dimensions on the x-y-z axes; the egg-shaped ellipsoid: $\frac{x^2}{4}+\frac{y^2}{4}+\frac{z^2}{9}=1$.

13.9 THE INDIRECT METHOD OF PROOF

> The first person he met was Rabbit. "Hello, Rabbit," he said, "is that you?" "Let's pretend it isn't," said Rabbit, "and see what happens."
>
> Alan Alexander Milne (1882-1956), *Winnie-The-Pooh.*

Terms, Concepts & Symbols Introduced
1. $\rightarrow\leftarrow$
2. Incommensurable ratio
3. Indirect proof
4. NAND
5. NOR
6. NOT
7. *Reductio ad absurdum*
8. XNOR

Direct proof uses a series of implications in a chain of consequential reasoning.[1]

Step 1. $a \Rightarrow b$

Step 2. $b \Rightarrow c$

Step 3. $c \Rightarrow d$

Therefore, $a \Rightarrow d$

INDIRECT PROOF

We cannot prove some propositions this way, so mathematicians have developed a second way to prove formal statements indirectly using the Law of Contraposition (Figure 1 taken from Lesson 13.2). **Indirect proof** is the application of that law.[2]

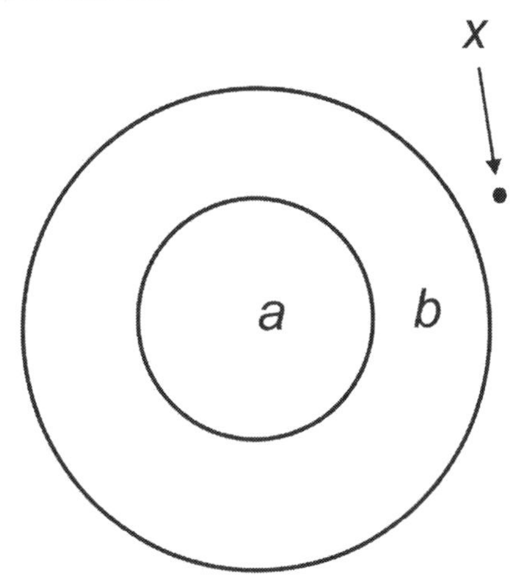

Figure 1. Law of Contraposition $a \Rightarrow b \Leftrightarrow \sim b \Rightarrow \sim a$

Let P be the statement you want to prove. We assume $\sim P$ and then reason to a particular statement Q that is a contradiction, i.e., Q is a statement that is *not* true. This method of reasoning is also known as ***reductio ad absurdum***, a Latin phrase meaning "to reduce to absurdity."[3]

Using symbols, we do this:

$\sim P \Rightarrow Q$

Since Q is *not* true, $\sim Q$ is true. By the Law of Contraposition, we know:

$\sim P \Rightarrow Q, \Leftrightarrow \sim Q \Rightarrow P$

---

[1] These implications can be equivalencies.

[2] Mathematics historians credit Hippocrates of Chios (ca. 470-ca. 410 BC) with introducing the indirect method of proof into mathematical thinking. He is not to be confused with his contemporary, Hippocrates of Cos (460-370 BC), the founder of Greek medicine.

[3] Recall from Lesson 11.4 that surd means irrational. To reason to a contradiction, to absurdity, is to show that a statement is irrational, i.e., without reason.

By negating Q, we have proved P; i.e., P is true.
QED

How about that dance? Go over the logic several times to let it sink into your thinking.[4]

> [Aristotle's] basic principles of logic – the law of contradiction, which asserts that a proposition cannot be both true and false, and the law of excluded middle, which maintains that a proposition must be either true or false – are the heart of the indirect method of mathematical proof.
>
> Morris Kline, *Mathematical Thought from Ancient to Modern Times* (1972), p. 53.

[4] The Reformed apologist Cornelius Van Til (1895-1987) developed an indirect proof for the existence of God, named TAG, an acronym standing for the **T**ranscendental **A**rgument for **G**od's existence. Van Til wanted to prove the statement P that "God exists." For him, this God is the Christian God, i.e., the ontological Trinity. To summarize and simplify his nifty piece of deductive reasoning, we state that if God does not exist ($\sim P$), then we have no precondition for intelligibility ($\sim P \Rightarrow Q$). This conclusion is not only an absurdity; it is an impossibility since all people can reason intelligibly, i.e., $\sim Q$ is true. Since the consequent Q is absurd, the antecedent $\sim P$ is false. Therefore, by *reductio ad absurdum*, God exists ($\sim Q \Rightarrow P$). One problem with this reasoning is that it does not start with Jesus Christ who, as the exact representation of the Father's nature (John 1:18; Hebrews 1:3), makes known the nature of the *onto-relational* Trinity (Lesson 1.1), i.e., the loving relationship between the Father and the Son (Matthew 3:17; Matthew 12:18; Matthew 17:5; John 3:35; John 5:20; John 10:17; John 10:38; John 14:10-11, 20, 31; John 15:9-10; John 17:23-26), not a non-relational definition of the ontological Trinity as we see in Van Til's section entitled "The Doctrine of God" in *The Defense of the Faith* (Phillipsburg: Presbyterian and Reformed Publishing Company, [1955, 1963], 1967) where he makes no mention of onto-relations, just an ontological definition. Like the Roman Catholic theologian Thomas Aquinas (1225-1274), Van Til employs Aristotelian logic to develop a philosophical construct that proves, with objective certainty, the existence of God. Both men engaged logical principles to prove that God exists, to them the Christian God, but not the onto-relational Trinity revealed uniquely by Jesus, the Incarnate and beloved Son of the Father. Therefore, both methodologies overlook Christ-logic, that which is inherent to God's own rationality, and introduce an alien rationality in the attempt to prove God exists. Instead of asking "Does God exist?" the question should be "*Who* is this God revealed by Jesus Christ?" The arguments of Aquinas and Van Til do not center on Jesus as the Son of the Father, who, by the Holy Spirit, savingly encounters us in the void of the darkness of our self-will and alienated mind. Therefore, their arguments rarely convert the committed atheist, even if the atheist mentally agrees with their possible validity. We must always remember that the only point of contact between God and humanity is the mediator between God and man, Jesus Christ, the union of divine and human natures in one person (I Timothy 2:5-6). We, therefore, proclaim Christ we truly know in the demonstration of the Spirit and power, not in the cogency of a logical argument, i.e., employing the wisdom of the world (I Corinthians 1:18-2:5). If not, belief is justified by the works of a logical argument, not by the grace of the living Christ. In the context of troubling suffering and a query about the evidence of an unearthly confidence, I Peter 3:15 states that we set apart the Lord in our hearts, always ready for ἀπολογίαν (literally, "from word") to everyone asking you a λόγον, a word, concerning the hope in you. *Who* is the source, the word, of this hope? "Christ in you, the hope of glory" (Colossians 1:27). Here we see that the focal point of the cardinal passage that supports the discipline known as apologetics is not on the rational argumentation of Aristotelian logic, either direct or indirect, but in an explanatory proclamation of and a bearing witness to a living relationship with the transcendent reality that is logos-centric, i.e., thinking and living centered in the authenticity of Christ-logic, in the belief that Jesus Christ authenticates Himself.

Let's explore an example of applying this reasoning. First, let's review Table 1, the table of squares and square roots.

Table 1: Squares and Square Roots

Positive Integer	Square	Square Root		Positive Integer	Square	Square Root		Positive Integer	Square	Square Root
1	1	1		21	441	4.583		41	1681	6.403
2	4	1.414		22	484	4.690		42	1764	6.481
3	9	1.732		23	529	4.796		43	1849	6.557
4	16	2		24	576	4.899		44	1936	6.633
5	25	2.236		25	625	5		45	2025	6.708
6	36	2.449		26	676	5.099		46	2116	6.782
7	49	2.646		27	729	5.196		47	2209	6.856
8	64	2.828		28	784	5.292		48	2304	6.928
9	81	3		29	841	5.385		49	2401	7
10	100	3.162		30	900	5.477		50	2500	7.071
11	121	3.317		31	961	5.568		51	2601	7.141
12	144	3.464		32	1024	5.657		52	2704	7.211
13	169	3.606		33	1089	5.745		53	2809	7.280
14	196	3.742		34	1156	5.831		54	2916	7.348
15	225	3.873		35	1225	5.916		55	3025	7.416
16	256	4		36	1296	6		56	3136	7.483
17	289	4.123		37	1369	6.083		57	3249	7.550
18	324	4.243		38	1444	6.164		58	3364	7.616
19	361	4.359		39	1521	6.245		59	3481	7.681
20	400	4.472		40	1600	6.325		60	3600	7.746

What can you conclude about the squares of numbers that are even? Take some time to investigate all of the relationships in Table 1. Your verdict should be that if a square is even, then its positive square root is even. Table 2 is the evidence.

Table 2

Positive Integer	Square		Positive Integer	Square		Positive Integer	Square
2	4		22	484		42	1764
4	16		24	576		44	1936
6	36		26	676		46	2116
8	64		28	784		48	2304
10	100		30	900		50	2500
12	144		32	1024		52	2704
14	196		34	1156		54	2916
16	256		36	1296		56	3136
18	324		38	1444		58	3364
20	400		40	1600		60	3600

PROOF THAT IF P^2 IS EVEN, P IS EVEN

The problem with this evidence is that it is scant; it is not exhaustive. We would have the cover all the possibilities which, again, is an impossibility. How could we prove, beyond a shadow of a doubt, that if p^2 is even, then p is even?[5] We could try different avenues of direct reasoning, but sometimes direct reasoning does not suffice. When direct proof appears to be inadequate, mathematicians resort to indirect reasoning.

First, we are given that p^2 is even. Second, we look at what we want to prove, p is even, and assume its negation, its opposite, is true. In other words, we assume that p is odd and begin to reason on that basis. We know that if a number is odd, it will be of the form $2n + 1$ where n is an integer. If $p = 2n + 1$, then what is p^2? Or, wheat is $(2n + 1)^2$? We apply our mastery of the extended Distributive Law to find out (Figure 2). We get:

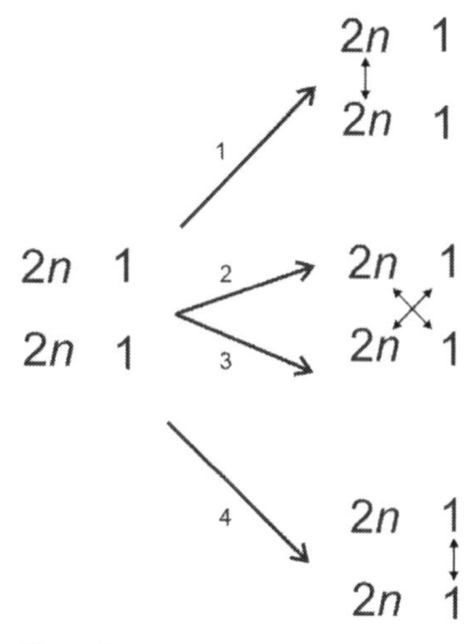

Figure 2.

$(2n + 1)^2 = (2n + 1)(2n + 1) = 2n(2n + 1) + 1(2n + 1) =$
$4n^2 + 2n + 2n + 1 = 4n^2 + 4n + 1$

Note that $2n + 2n = 4n$ because, applying the Distributive Law in reverse (i.e., factoring n), $2n + 2n = n(2 + 2) = n4 = 4n$. We know that $4n^2$ is certainly even no matter what n is. Why? 4 is divisible by 2. Therefore, $4n^2$ has to be even. By the same reasoning, we know for certain that $4n$ has to be even. The algebraic expression $4n^2 + 4n + 1$ now represents an even number plus an even number plus 1. Since we have already proved that an even number added to an even number is an even number, then $4n^2 + 4n + 1$ must be an odd number. Since $p^2 = 4n^2 + 4n + 1$, then p^2 is an odd number. But, we are given that p^2 is an even number. We have reasoned to a contradiction, an absurdity. We have proven that if p^2 is even, then p cannot be odd; i.e., it has to be even.

QED

Logically, we have proved our proposition in an indirect or roundabout way. The Law of Contraposition states, as we have already noted, that we have logical equivalence between a conditional statement and its contrapositive. In symbols:

$$P \Rightarrow Q \Leftrightarrow \sim Q \Rightarrow \sim P$$

This equivalency means that if we can prove $\sim Q \Rightarrow \sim P$, we can conclude that $P \Rightarrow Q$.

In our example, we want to prove p^2 is even $\Rightarrow p$ is even. We let P be the statement "p^2 is even" and Q be the statement "p is even." Substituting, we want to prove $P \Rightarrow Q$. We can prove $P \Rightarrow Q$ if we can prove that the contrapositive, $\sim Q \Rightarrow \sim P$ is true. The statement $\sim Q$ means, in our example, p is odd. Our reasoning from this assumption led us to conclude that p^2 is odd. To state that p^2 is odd is $\sim Q$ where Q stands for "p^2 is even." Therefore,.we have proved that $\sim Q \Rightarrow \sim P$ is true. Since $\sim Q \Rightarrow \sim P$ is true, then $P \Rightarrow Q$ is true.

QED

Make sure you read this paragraph as many times as necessary to understand the exquisite dance of logical reasoning that is the indirect method of proof.

[5] Of course, we are assuming that p is a positive integer.

PROOF THAT $\sqrt{2}$ IS IRRATIONAL

With this type of reasoning, we are going to embrace one of the Top Ten proofs in the history of mathematics, originally derived by the mathematicians of ancient Greece.[6] In Lesson 11.4, when we discussed irrational numbers, we asserted that $\sqrt{2}$, the length of the diagonal of a unit square, is irrational. We are now going to prove this assertion beyond a shadow of a doubt. We have already noted that the positive integers 1, 4, 9, 16, 25, 36, 49, etc. are perfect squares and their positive square roots are positive integers, and we can dress any integer as a rational number; i.e., $2 = 2/1$. What about the numbers in between? Are they rational or irrational? Let's zero in on the positive square root of 2. We seek some number, x, such that:

$$x = \sqrt{2}$$

Squaring both sides, we get:

$$x = \sqrt{2} \Rightarrow x^2 = 2$$

What is x? We assert the x is irrational, or $\sqrt{2}$ is irrational. Let's start by assuming that x is rational, more specifically, x is a proper fraction reduced to lowest terms. Then, let's see if we can reason to a contradiction, i.e., *reductio ad absurdum*. If we can do this, then we will know for certain that $\sqrt{2}$ is irrational by the Law of Contraposition. We write this assumption as follows:

$x = \dfrac{m}{n}$, where m is the hypotenuse of a right isosceles triangle, n is one of the legs (Figure 3), and the GCF of m and n is 1. Since the GCF is 1, this means that 2 is not a common factor, an observation that we will use to our reasoning benefit.

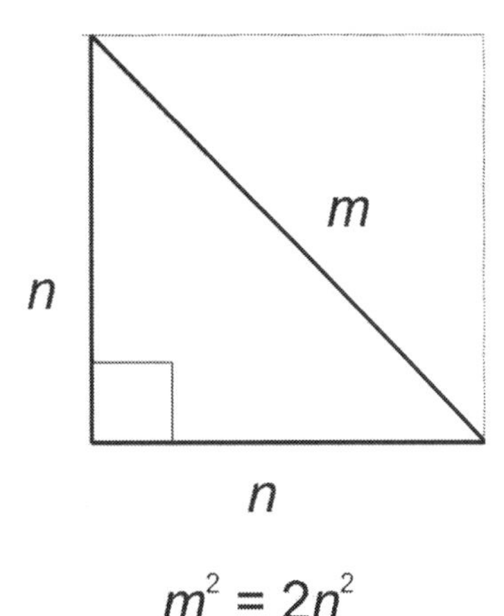

Figure 3.

Squaring both sides, we get:

$$x = \frac{m}{n} \Rightarrow x^2 = \left(\frac{m}{n}\right)^2$$

[6] This proof is generally credited to Euclid, but it was probably developed long before his time (3rd century BC), maybe by the Pythagoreans (6th century BC).

We note:

$$\left(\frac{m}{n}\right)^2 = \frac{m^2}{n^2}$$

Since $x^2 = 2$, we substitute and get:

$$2 = \frac{m^2}{n^2}$$

Multiplying both sides of this equation by n^2, we get:

$2n^2 = m^2$

(Note: We can get this equation directly from applying the Pythagorean Theorem to the isosceles right triangle in Figure 3; i.e., $n^2 + n^2 = m^2 \Leftrightarrow 2n^2 = m^2$. We see, therefore, that the ancient Greek need to understand the nature of $\sqrt{2}$ is related to the nature of the measure of the diagonal of a square.)

It looks like we can work with this. We seek two positive integers, m and n, such that the square of one is twice the square of the other. Since the set of perfect squares is infinite, the squares begin with 1 and proceed as such:

1, 4, 9, 16, 25, 36, 49, 64, 81, 100, 121, 144, 169, 196, 225…

We see that 49 is almost twice 25 (50 – 49 = 1). 196 is 4 less than 200, which is twice 100. Surely, there has to be one perfect square, somewhere in this infinite collection, that is exactly twice another one. There is no such number and the proof is not that difficult.

In the equation $2n^2 = m^2$, we know that the left side, $2n^2$, has to be even based upon our definition of an even number; i.e., all multiples of 2 are even. Therefore, the right side, since it is equal to $2n^2$ must also be even; i.e., m^2 is even. We just proved that since m^2 is even, then m is even. If m is even, then it has to be a multiple of 2. Therefore, m^2, since it contains 2 as a factor twice, must be a multiple of 4. By this reasoning, we can say that $m^2 = 4k$ for some positive integer k. By substitution, we get:

$2n^2 = 4k$

Dividing both sides by 2, we get:

$n^2 = 2k$

Since $n^2 = 2k$, we know that n^2 has to be even. Since n^2 is even, then n has to be even. Thus, we have reasoned to the conclusion that both m and n must be even. But, we assumed that $\frac{m}{n}$ is reduced to lowest terms, i.e., the GCF of m and n is 1. If m and n are both even, then 2 is a common factor of both. We have reasoned to a contraction[7] and therefore, by the Law of Contraposition, our assumption is false and, indeed, $\sqrt{2}$ is irrational.

QED

How does the Law of Contraposition establish our proof? We want to prove that $\sqrt{2}$ is irrational. We let P be the statement that $\sqrt{2}$ is irrational. We assume $\sim P$, or $\sqrt{2}$ is rational, or $\sqrt{2} = \frac{m}{n}$ where the GCF of m and n is 1. We reasoned to a statement Q, i.e., m and n are both even, a contradiction, i.e., Q is

[7] We signify contradiction using two arrows pointed toward each other: $\rightarrow\leftarrow$.

false. If Q is false, then, by the Law of Excluded Middle, $\sim Q$ is true. By the Law of Contraposition, $\sim P \Rightarrow Q \Leftrightarrow \sim Q \Rightarrow P$. By our reasoning, we have therefore proved P; i.e., P is true. Make sure that you understand this dance of reasoning.

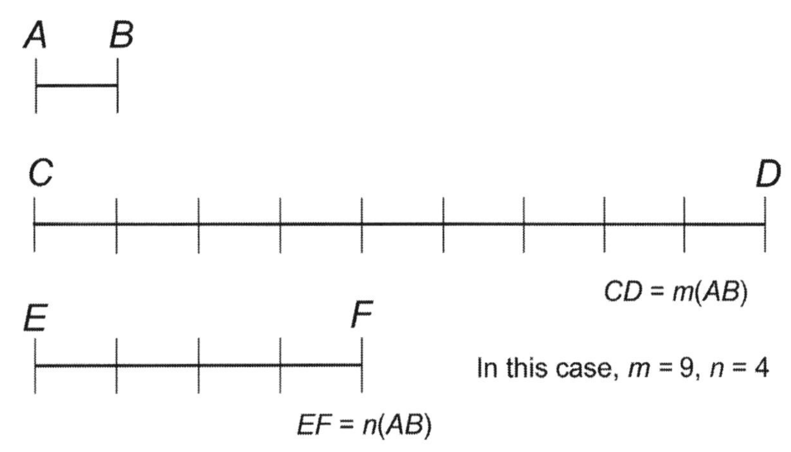

Figure 4.

INCOMMENSURABILITY

Pythagoras defined a rational numbers as commensurate using a geometric argument (Figure 4), the typical method of Greek mathematicians. Given $\overline{AB}$, we can construct $\overline{CD}$ and $\overline{EF}$ as positive integer multiples, respectively, of $\overline{AB}$, i.e., the multiples are m and n. We, therefore, write:

$CD = m(AB)$
$EF = n(AB)$

Using these equations, the ratio of CD to EF is:

$$\frac{CD}{EF} = \frac{m\left(\overset{1}{\cancel{AB}}\right)}{n\left(\underset{1}{\cancel{AB}}\right)} = \frac{m}{n}$$

Since $\frac{m}{n}$ is the *ratio* of two positive integers, the ratio of the lengths of two commensurable line segments is a *ratio*nal number.

The ratio of the hypotenuse to the leg of a right isosceles triangle of one unit, $\sqrt{2}$, is an **incommensurable ratio**, meaning that there is no common basis, measure, or standard of comparison. There is no $\overline{AB}$ that is the constructible unit for the ratio $\frac{\sqrt{2}}{1}$; i.e., there is no AB such that $\sqrt{2} = m(AB)$ for some positive integer m. There is no EF such that:

$$\frac{\sqrt{2}}{1} = \frac{m\left(\overset{1}{\cancel{AB}}\right)}{n\left(\underset{1}{\cancel{AB}}\right)} = \frac{m}{n} \Leftrightarrow \sqrt{2} = \frac{m}{n}$$

The ancient Greeks used incommensurable to denote irrational numbers. Thinking outside of geometry, i.e., using a pure algebraic argument, for any ratio $\frac{m}{n}$ to be rational, is a necessary and sufficient condition for the existence of some rational number k, and integers a and b, such that:

$$m = ak \text{ and } n = bk \Rightarrow \frac{m}{n} = \frac{a\cancel{k}^{1}}{b\cancel{k}_{1}} = \frac{a}{b}$$

Let's look at some examples:

Example 1. 8, or $\frac{8}{1}$, is a rational number because $8 = 16\left(\frac{1}{2}\right)$ and $1 = 2\left(\frac{1}{2}\right)$. Since $k = \frac{1}{2}$, $a = 16$, and $b = 2$, 8 is commensurable.

Example 2. $\frac{2}{3}$ is a rational number because $2 = 6\left(\frac{1}{3}\right)$ and $3 = 9\left(\frac{1}{3}\right)$. Since $k = \frac{1}{3}$, $a = 6$, and $b = 9$, $\frac{2}{3}$ is commensurable.

Example 3. $\frac{3}{4}$ is a rational number because $3 = 12\left(\frac{1}{4}\right)$ and $4 = 16\left(\frac{1}{4}\right)$. Since $k = \frac{1}{4}$, $a = 12$, and $b = 16$, $\frac{3}{4}$ is commensurable.

By the above indirect proof, we have shown that $\sqrt{2} \neq \frac{m}{n}$. This means we cannot find k, a, and b such that $m = ak$ and $n = bk$. Therefore, $\sqrt{2}$ is incommensurable.

EXERCISES

Define the following terms/symbols.
1. Indirect proof
2. *Reductio ad absurdum*
3. $\rightarrow\leftarrow$
4. Incommensurable ratio
5. NAND (See homework exercise below.)
6. NOT (See homework exercise below.)
7. NOR (See homework exercise below.)
8. XNOR (See homework exercise below.)

> When you have excluded the impossible, whatever remains, however improbable, must be the truth.
> Sherlock Holmes, *The Adventure of the Beryl Coronet.*

Answer these questions:

9. Master the two proofs in the text. Be able to write them without reference to the text.
10. Figure 5 shows a concave hexagon (Lesson 4.6). We see that one line intersects all six sides. Can you create a convex heptagon where one line connects all seven sides? (Hint: Assume that the answer is yes. Change perspectives. Instead of drawing a heptagon and then a straight line. Draw a straight line first and try to draw the heptagon.)
11. Is 1.414 a rational number? (Hint: show that it is equal to a ratio of two integers.)
12. Is 2 a rational number?
13. Is it true that $\sqrt{2} = 1.414$?
14. Is $\sqrt{4}$ an irrational number?
15. Is $\sqrt{9}$ an irrational number?

Figure 5.

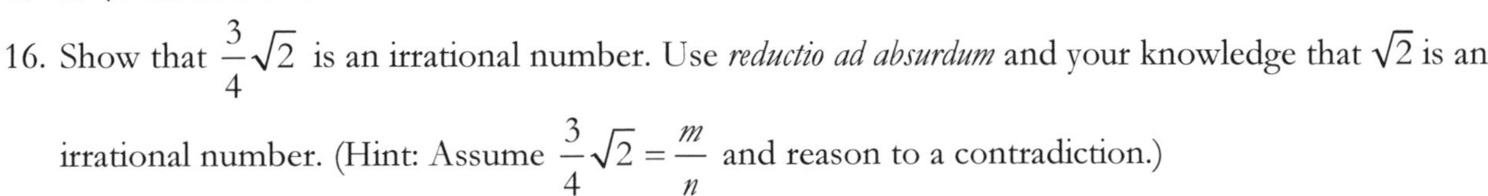

16. Show that $\frac{3}{4}\sqrt{2}$ is an irrational number. Use *reductio ad absurdum* and your knowledge that $\sqrt{2}$ is an irrational number. (Hint: Assume $\frac{3}{4}\sqrt{2} = \frac{m}{n}$ and reason to a contradiction.)
17. Show that $\frac{5}{13}\sqrt{2}$ is an irrational number.
18. Show that, in general, $\frac{a}{b}\sqrt{2}$ is an irrational number if $a \neq 0$, and $b \neq 0$. What happens when a or $b = 0$?
19. Show that $5\sqrt{2}$ is an irrational number.
20. Show that $2 + \sqrt{2}$ is an irrational number. (Hint: Assume $2 + \sqrt{2} = \frac{m}{n}$ and reason to a contradiction.)
21. Show that $2 - \sqrt{2}$ is an irrational number.
22. Prove that $\sqrt{3}$ is an irrational number. Use the *reductio ad absurdum* method.
23. Prove that $\sqrt{5}$ is an irrational number. Use the *reductio ad absurdum* method.
24. Is the sum of two irrational numbers always an irrational number? (Hint: Look for a counterexample.).
25. Is the sum of two rational numbers always a rational number? Explain why or why not.
26. Is the product of two rational numbers always a rational number? Explain why or why not.
27. Is the product of two irrational numbers always an irrational number? Explain why or why not.
28. Prove that log 2 is irrational. (We promised to do this in Lesson 12.3.) Use the *reductio ad absurdum* method. [Hint: Use what you know of logs and working with powers. At some point in your proof, you must set $10 = 2 \times 5$. (1) You want to be able to show that the number on one side of an equation is odd and the number on the other side is even, indicating a contradiction, or (2) according to the Fundamental Theorem of Arithmetic (Lesson 6.1), every composite number can be partitioned into a unique product of primes.]
29. Prove that log 3 is irrational. Use the *reductio ad absurdum* method.

In Book III, Proposition 18, Euclid showed that if a line is tangent to a circle, it is perpendicular to the radius drawn to the point of contact (Figure 6). We have applied this theorem already, especially in Lesson 12.10.

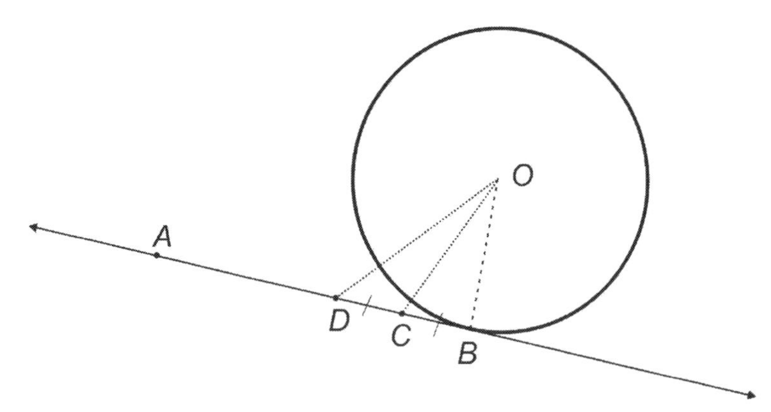

Figure 6.

30. Given: $\overleftrightarrow{AB}$ is tangent to Circle O at point B (Note: A line tangent to a circle intersects it at exactly one point). We need to prove that $\overleftrightarrow{AB} \perp \overline{OB}$. We are going to apply the Sherlock Holmes principle (*reductio ad absurdum*) and suppose that opposite of what we want to prove; i.e., $\overleftrightarrow{AB} \sim\perp \overline{OB}$ ($\sim$ stands for "not"). Let's choose a point C on $\overleftrightarrow{AB}$ such that $\overleftrightarrow{AB} \perp \overline{OC}$. Why?
31. Choose D on $\overleftrightarrow{AB}$ such that $CD = CB$. We draw $\overline{OD}$. Therefore, $\triangle OCB \cong \triangle OCD$. Why?
32. By congruency of two triangles, $OB = OD$. Since OB is the radius of the circle, then D must also be on the circle. Therefore, we have a contraction. What is it?
33. QED the proof that $\overleftrightarrow{AB} \perp \overline{OB}$.

Because of the above theorem, we can prove another which states that the tangent segments to a circle from an external point are equal.

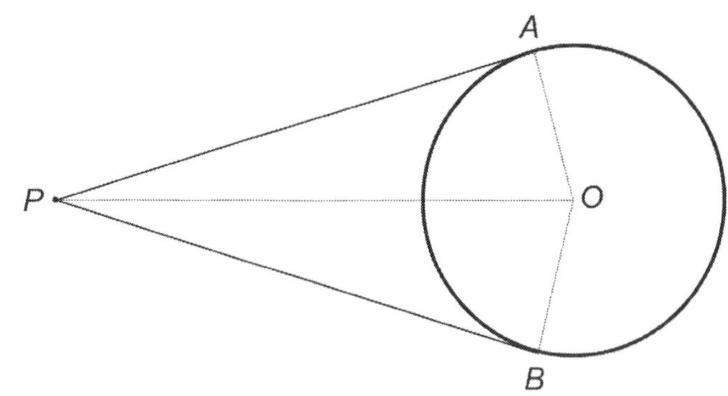

Figure 7.

Given: Circle O with tangent segments $\overline{PA}$ and $\overline{PB}$ (Figure 7). Prove: $PA = PB$.

34. We know that $\triangle PAO \cong \triangle PBO$.

    Why? (Hint: Use the *pons asinorum* theorem from Lesson 13.5.)
35. QED the proof that $PA = PB$.

The Sherlock Holmes principle ("When you have eliminated the impossible, whatever remains, however improbable, must be the truth") applied to the *reductio ad absurdum* method of proof means that you first consider all of the possibilities. Then you eliminate all but one by showing that the others lead to logical contradictions. In the mathematics context, we usually think of the possibility that the *opposite* of what we want to prove is true. Assuming this, we try to reason to a contradiction. Having found the contradiction, we can conclude that the *opposite* of what we want to prove is false, and this enables us to deduce that what we wanted to prove is true.

36. Let's try this method on a non-mathematical problem. Matthew, Mark and Luke are different heights. Who is the tallest and who is the shortest if *only one* of the following is true? (1) Matthew is the tallest, (2) Mark is not the tallest, (3) Luke is not the shortest. Consider all possibilities and eliminate all but one by showing that the others lead to logical contradictions.
37. Study Figure 8. Then, use the Sherlock Holmes principle to prove the converse of the Pythagorean Theorem, i.e., another way to prove Proposition 48 of Book I of Euclid's *Elements*; i.e., If, in a triangle with three sides a, b, and c, $c^2 = a^2 + b^2$, then the triangle is a right triangle. (Note: the lengths a and b are respectively the same in all three cases.)

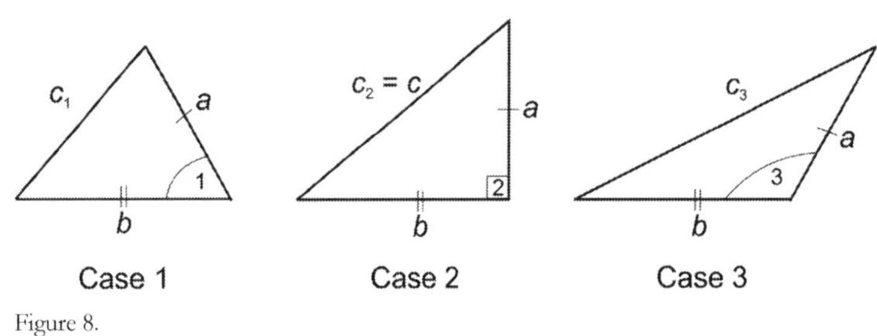

Figure 8.

Answer this question about the optics light rays:

38. Heron of Alexandria (ca. 10 AD) first discovered this theorem about the behavior of light rays. In Figure 9, let B look at a mirror and see the reflection of A. Prove that only one ray from A will be reflected to B, i.e., $\overrightarrow{AP}$. [Hint: Reason indirectly by making use of the figure and invoke the Law of Reflection (Lesson 8.13).]

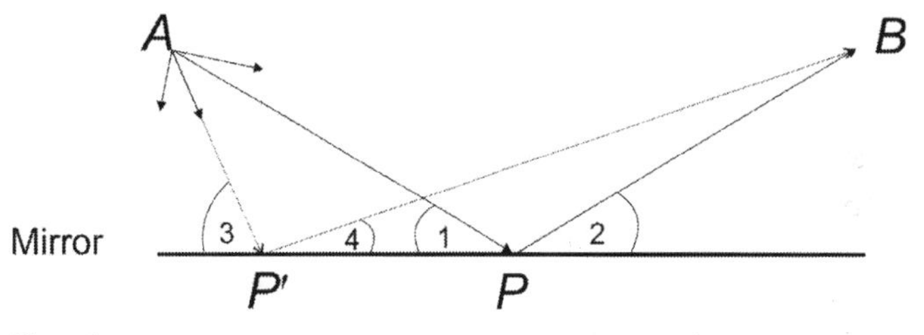

Figure 9.

Addendum: Scientists have developed two physical theories to account for the behavior of light. One theory states that light consists of tiny, invisible particles that move along rays. Figure 10 shows light of wavelength λ hitting an opaque barrier with a hole of diameter d. In configuration (a), when $d > \lambda$, light emerges from the hole moving in a straight line like a ray. The other theory states that light is wavelike,

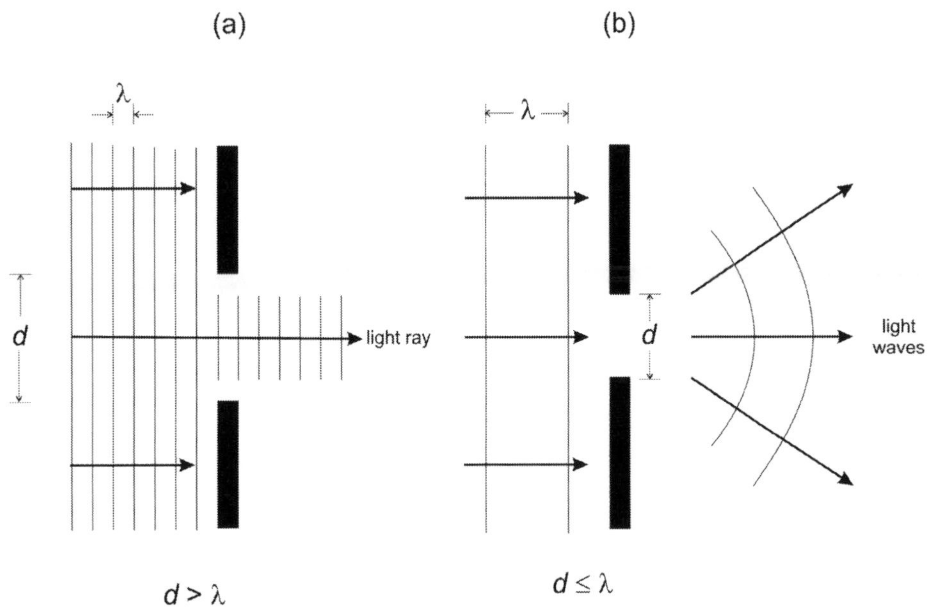

Figure 10.

moving like waves generated when dropping a pebble in a still pond. In configuration (b), when $d \leq \lambda$, the interference causes light to bend like a wave, called the diffraction of light. Wave theory accounts for the diffraction of light better than the ray theory.

Answer the following question based on a study of Figure 11:

39. Show that $\theta = 30°$.

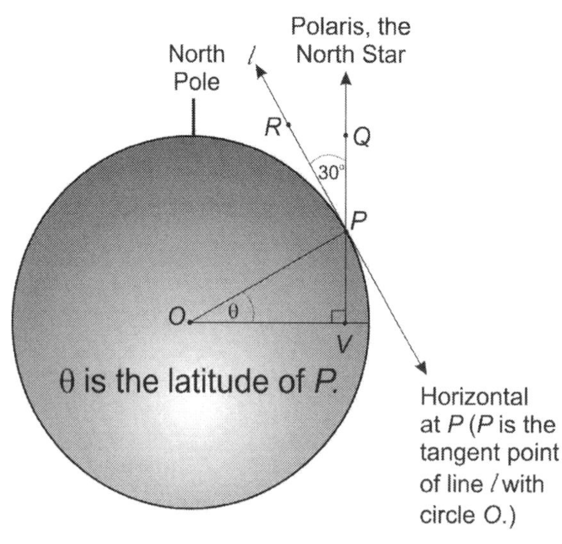

Figure 11.

All information processing of computers, no matter how complex, can be reduced to three logical functions on binary digits 0 and 1 (representing off or on, no or yes, false F or true T). There can be either one or two inputs to these functions. Each function generates only one output.

- The AND function (Lesson 5.2, logical conjunction) generates the output of 1 if A and B are both 1. Otherwise, the output is 0. Any circuit or device that performs this rule is and AND gate. In electricity (Figure 12), if two switches are connected in series and a closed switch and a lit bulb is the logical 1, then both switches must be closed for the bulb to be on.
- The OR function (Lesson 5.15, logical disjunction) generates the output of 0 if A and B are both 0. Otherwise, the output is 1. Mathematicians always use OR in this way. We can state "inclusive or" function by saying that the output is 1 if A is 1 and B is 1, A is 1, but B is 0, or A is 0, but B is 1. Putting electrical switches in parallel makes a lightbulb circuit into an OR gate (Figure 13).

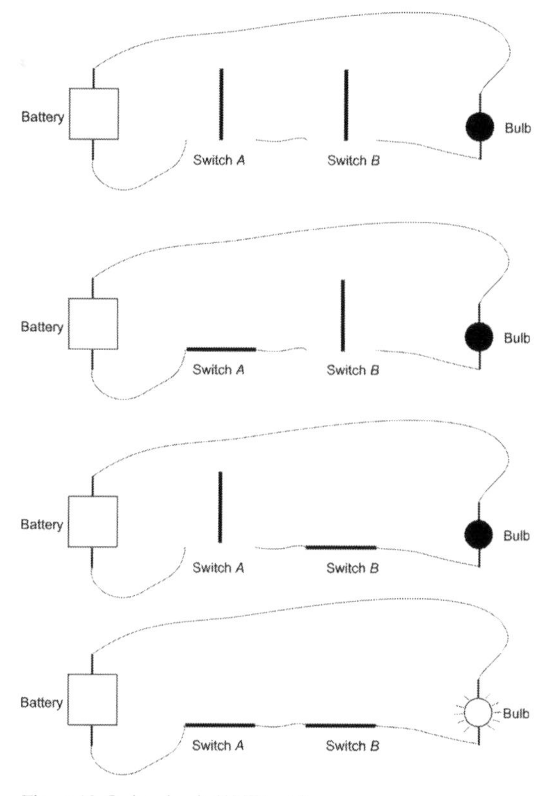

Figure 12. Series circuit (AND gate).

- The NOT function (this lesson combined with Lesson 9.5, complementary events) has only one input. It is also known as the inversion function and generates the output of 1 is *A* is 0 and output of 0 if *A* is 1. In electricity, we add a resistor to the circuit to prevent too much current from flowing through a switch when it is closed (Figure 14), thus turning off (logical 0) the circuit (logical 1). When the switch is on, the resistor causes the circuit to flow through the shorter path from *B* to *C*, thus bypassing the bulb. The resistor, therefore, acts as a NOT gate. It inverts the input. Let's envision another example. When you open the knob on a faucet, water flows (logical 1). When you close the knob, water stops (logical 0). Let's say that we add a stopper in the pipe, connected in such a way that when you open the knob, the stopper closes and when you close the know, the stopped opens. The stopper, therefore, inverts the function of the knob; i.e., when you open the knob, water stops (logical 0) and when you close the knob, water flows (logical 1).

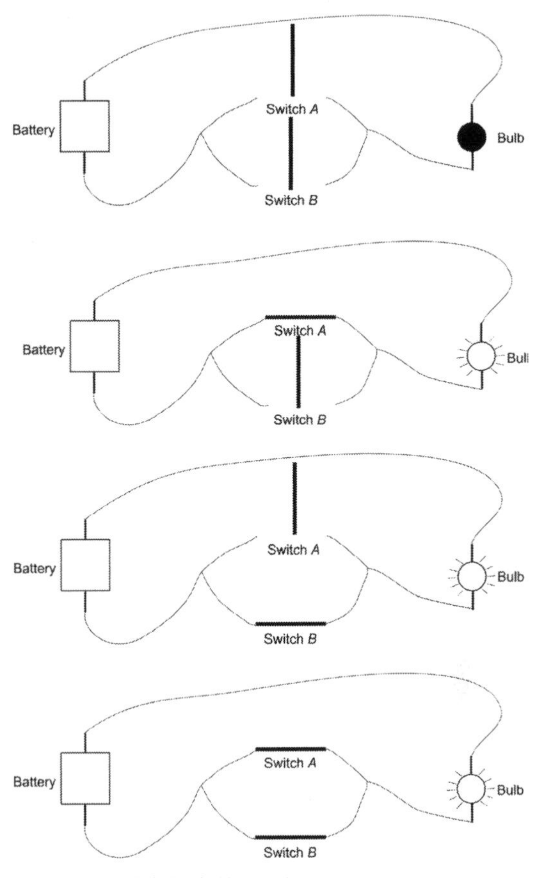

Figure 13. Parallel circuit (OR gate).

In computer technology, it is easier to make and work with NAND and NOR gates. The outputs of these functions are the opposite of the AND and OR gates, respectively. We say, "not AND" and "not OR." If we connect the two inputs at either gate together, i.e., we combine the two gates when they have the same logical value, we get a NOT gate. Answer these questions:

40. Show how connecting the two inputs at the NOR gate gives us the NOT gate.
41. Show how connecting the two inputs at the NAND gate gives us the NOT gate.

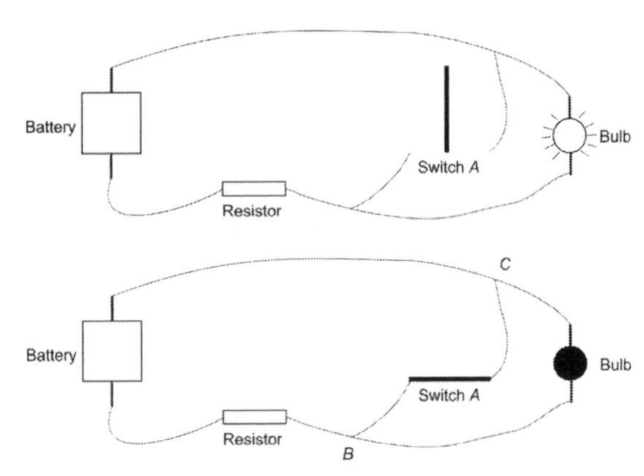

Figure 14. Inversion circuit (NOT gate).

Table 3: Logic Gates and the Computer World (Truth Tables)								
A	***B***	$A \wedge B$	$A \vee B$	$A \oplus B$	$\sim A$	$\sim(A \wedge B)$	$\sim(A \vee B)$	$\sim(A \oplus B)$
Computer Symbol		AND	OR	XOR	NOT	NAND	NOR	XNOR
Logic Symbol								
T	T	T	T	F		F	F	T
T	F	F	T	T	F	T	F	F
F	T	F	T	T	T	T	F	F
F	F	F	F	F		T	T	T

Therefore, we do not need a NOT gate. We can build it from either the NOR or NAND gate. In fact, we only need NOR or NAND gates to build all possible logic circuits. The next question will show us how using multiple NAND gates generate a different gate:

42. Figure 15 shows a logical circuit diagram.
    (a) Generate a truth table for all possible inputs *A* and *B* using Table 3 (NAND) as a guide.
    (b) What type of gate does this figure demonstrate? (Hint: Check your results with Table 3).

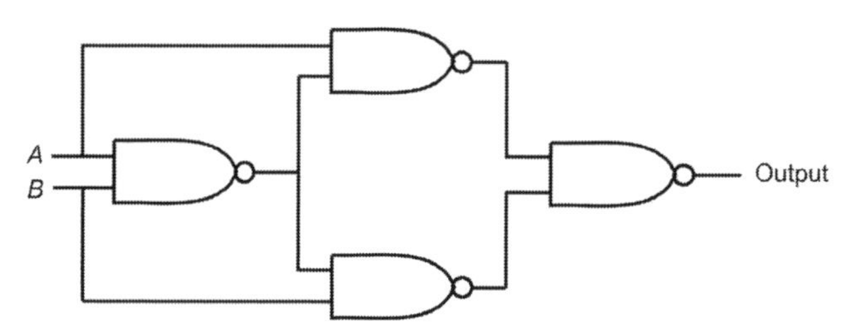

Figure 15. Gate constructed from four NAND gates.

These logical ideas interpenetrate, starting with the classical logic of Aristotle (384-322 BC), the work in symbolic logic by the German mathematician Gottfried Wilhelm Leibniz (1646-1716), the English mathematician George Boole's (1815-1864) propositional logic,[8] the German mathematician Gottlob Frege's (1848-1925) predicate logic, and finally the incorporation of these ideas in the design of computer circuity. The application of mathematical logic has, indeed, transformed the technological world in which we live, starting from the 1940s to the present, and beyond.

Figure 16. Source: United States Postal Service.

[8] See Peter M. D. Gray, *Logic, Algebra and Databases* (Chichester: Ellis Horwood Limited, 1984) for a discussion of the perichoretic interpenetration of Boolean Algebra with computer databases.

13.10 Proof that the Number of Primes is Infinite and a Caveat

Terms & Concepts Introduced
1. Momentum
2. Three Laws of Motion
3. Quantum logic
4. Uncertainty principle

In Step 6, we introduced prime and composite numbers. The ancient Greeks, notably Euclid, wanted to know one question about the set of prime numbers. Is the set finite or infinite? Euclid proved the set infinite. He proved this assertion by reasoning indirectly. He assumed the set was finite; i.e., there was a largest prime number. Then, he showed that there had to be a prime number greater than the chosen prime number.

Euclid's Proof

> To master a sustained closely reasoned mathematical argument, to grasp fully a new idea, is to acquire a brand new skill.
>
> M. M. Schiffer and L. Bowden, *The Role of Mathematics in Science* (1984), p. 1.

Follow along with the beautiful dance of Euclid's thinking in Proposition 20 of Book IX of *The Elements.*

Step 1. The number of prime numbers is either infinite or finite. We will assume the number of primes is finite where P is the largest prime number.

Step 2. We list this finite number of primes and multiply all of them together to get a very large positive integer N. We write:

$N = 2 \cdot 3 \cdot 5 \cdot 7 \cdot \ldots \cdot P$

Step 3. Consider N + 1.

First, $N + 1 > P$.

> One has to be blind to beauty to not be able to see it in a mathematical proof (e.g., Euclid's proof of the infinity of the primes) for "an elegantly executed proof is a poem in all but the form in which it is written."
>
> Morris Kline, *Mathematics in Western Culture* (1953), p. 470.

Second, every prime number, from 2 to P, is a factor of N, but none of those prime numbers individually, or products of two or more, are factors of $N + 1$. Make sure you see this.

For example, if we assume P is 7, then $N = 210 = 2 \cdot 3 \cdot 5 \cdot 7$. Since $N + 1 = 211$, then $211 > 7$ and, although 2, 3, 5, 7, and all combinations of their products are factors of 210, none are factors of 211. Therefore, either 211 is prime, or 211 is divisible by some prime number greater than 7. In this case, 211 is prime.

If we assume P is 13, then $N = 30{,}030 = 2 \cdot 3 \cdot 5 \cdot 7 \cdot 11 \cdot 13$. Since $N + 1 = 30{,}031$, then $30{,}031 > 13$ and, although 2, 3, 5, 7, 11, 13, and all combinations of their products are factors of 30,030, none are factors of 30,031. Therefore, either 30,031 is prime or 30,031 is divisible by some prime number greater than 13. In this case, 30,031 is not prime since $30{,}031 = 59 \times 509$. Therefore, 30,031 is divisible by 59 and 509. Both are prime numbers greater than 13.

Likewise, in general, either $N + 1$ itself is prime or $N + 1$ is divisible by some prime number that has to be greater than P. In either case, we have discovered a prime number greater than P and here lies our contradiction. Therefore, our assumption is false, and the number of primes is infinite.

QED

Reread this proof as many times as possible until you understand it. It qualifies as one of the Top Ten mathematical proofs of all time. If you grasp it, congratulations!

An Important Caveat to the Dance of Logic

We have explored a few of the wonders revealed by the dance of reason. In upcoming lessons, we will continue to demonstrate the beauty of mathematical reasoning, with a focus on the dance of reasoning to infinity.

Aristotelian logic governed the geometric and number theory work of Euclid. As we noted in Lesson 13.6, in the late 19th century, Giuseppe Peano invoked the axiomatic-deductive framework to justify the operations of arithmetic. In the mid to late 17th century Isaac Newton (1642-1727) wrote *Principia* (*Mathematical Principles of Natural Philosophy*) grounding his deductions on **three basic laws**, or axioms, of **motion**:

Axiom 1. Law of inertial motion: A body will continue to be in a state of rest or of uniform velocity, speed and straight-line direction, unless acted upon by an external force. Newton's rendering: "Every body perseveres in its state of rest, or of uniform motion in a right line, unless it is compelled to change that state by forces impressed thereon."[1]

Axiom 2. The acceleration a, the rate of change of velocity, produced in a body of mass m is in direct proportion to the force F applied. Mathematically expressed, $F = ma$. Newton's rendering: "The alteration of motion is ever proportional to the motive force impressed; and is made in the direction of the right line in which that force is impressed."[2]

Axiom 3. When two bodies experience an interaction, the force of the first body on the second is equal and opposite to the force of the second body on the first. Newton's rendering: "To every action there is always opposed an equal reaction: or the mutual actions of two bodies upon each other are always equal, and directed to contrary parts."[3]

Newton's system of the world placed the world of science on mechanistic, logical cause and effect, foundations. Being deterministic, mathematics, the dance of number, is a servant to this world.[4] Since Newton, the scientific mind came under subjugation to a purely mechanistic cosmology due to the quantitative successes of measurement in Physics.

Figure 1. James Clerk Maxwell. Source: Public Domain.

It wasn't until the work of James Clerk Maxwell (1831-1879) that Newton's deterministic world came into question. Unable to apply Newtonian mechanics to the world of electromagnetism, Maxwell developed partial differential equations, equations consequential to the methods of Calculus, to describe the dynamic interrelations, the dance between electrical and magnetic fields.[5]

Figure 2. Source: United States Postal Service.

[1] Isaac Newton, *The Principia*, Andrew Motte, trans. (Amherst: Prometheus Books, [1687, 1848] 1995), p. 19.

[2] *Ibid.*

[3] *Ibid.*

[4] Number relations are deterministic. For example, in base 10, the sum of 2 and 2 is always 4. The effect, 4, results from the cause, 2 + 2.

[5] James Clerk Maxwell, *The Dynamical Theory of the Electromagnetic Field*, Thomas F. Torrance, ed. (Eugene: Wipf and Stock Publishers, 1983). See also Nancy Forbes and Basil Mahon, *Faraday, Maxwell, and the Electromagnetic Field* (Amherst: Prometheus Books, 2014). Maxwell submitted the theories of the English scientist Michael Faraday (1791-1867) to mathematical analysis.

Maxwell's field theories led to Albert Einstein's (1879-1955) gravitational field theories of the early 20th century.[6] To Einstein, there is a dynamic dance between space, matter, and time. Space and time form a continuum and exist in an inseparable relation to mass-energy structures, structures governed by his famous mass-energy equation $E = mc^2$: energy is equivalent to the product of the mass of an object times the speed of light squared.

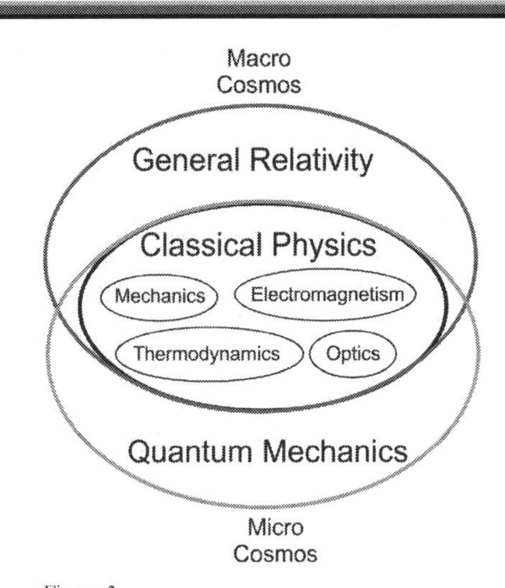

Figure 3.

Using intuition, imagination, the belief in a rational harmony of the universe, and the tools of mathematics, Einstein showed that this unity means that mass-energy objects determine the curvature of space-time and that curvature in turn controls the motion of the masses.[7] In other words, matter moves by the structure of space and space curves by the mass of matter.[8] Thus mass-energy structure and space-time geometry are dynamically and integrally related. They indeed dance in beautiful harmony!

Einstein's work dethroned the logical-causal determinacy of Newton. Concurrent with Einstein's work with the macro cosmos,[9] as a consequence of intense experimental study of the micro cosmos or quantum world, there arose another challenge to the necessary cause and effect world, the syllogistic world, of Aristotelian logic. This challenge became known as the **Uncertainty Principle** first conceptualized by German physicist Werner Karl Heisenberg (1901-1976) in 1927.[10]

Figure 4. Werner Heisenberg, left, with Danish physicist Niels Bohr (1885-1962). Source: Public Domain.

[6] Note that in the year Maxwell died, Einstein was born. This death-birth relationship has occurred before in the history of science. In the year that Galileo Galilei died (1642), Isaac Newton was born.

[7] Space-time curvature requires a geometry other than Euclid's (i.e., non-Euclidean geometry), the geometry of a curved surface, where there exist no lines through a point *P* not on line *l* that are parallel to *l*. In 1916, Einstein discovered that the geometry developed by the German mathematician Georg Friedrich Bernhard Riemann (1826-1866), elliptical geometry, interpenetrated his theory perfectly. Why is Riemann's geometry known by the name elliptical? His geometry is one of two non-Euclidean ones. The other is hyperbolic geometry, developed by the Russian mathematician Nikolai Ivanovich Lobachevsky (1792-1856) and the Hungarian mathematician János Bolyai (1802-1860), both working independently of each other. In hyperbolic geometry, there exist at least two lines through *P* parallel to *l*. In the context of elliptical and hyperbolic geometries, Euclidean geometry is parabolic geometry because there exists exactly one line through *P* parallel to *l*. Mathematicians use the relationship of these geometries to Euclid's fifth postulate, the Parallel Postulate, as a means of naming, and nothing else: Elliptical (less than one, or zero), Parabolic (equal to one), and Hyperbolic (greater than one).

[8] Instead of saying that the gravity of the Earth pulls an object of mass *m* down, the field of curved space is pushing the object down. Gravity is the curvature.

[9] The cosmos is the physical universe (Lesson 1.1), "everything that exists."

[10] Werner Heisenberg, *The Physical Principles of the Quantum Theory*, C. Eckart and F. C. Hoyt, trans. (Chicago: University of Chicago Press, 1930). This principle is also known as the Indeterminacy Principle. Heisenberg spoke of the necessity to tune into "the Central Order" (his phrase for God) in his attempt to unravel the beauties of the quantum world via the complexities of mathematical analysis.

Through experimentation, scientists discovered that their tools of measurement, their probing into the relations of atomic particles, changed the conditions of the experiment. They discovered an inherent limitation in the precision of their measurements; i.e., they could not measure the **momentum**[11] and position of an atomic particle at the same time.[12] The uncertainty principle states that if we know the momentum of an atomic particle, we cannot determine that it is definitely at a particular place. And, if we know the position of an atomic particle, we cannot measure its momentum. Consequently, scientists must resort to the Law of Large Numbers (Lessons 9.1 and 9.5), probabilities based on statistical averages, to understand the momentum and position of an atomic particle.

> If logic is right quantum theory must be wrong, and if quantum theory is right (in particular the uncertainty relation), then classical logic must be wrong (in particular the law of excluded middle).
>
> Friedrich Waismann, *How I See Philosophy* (1968), p. 232.

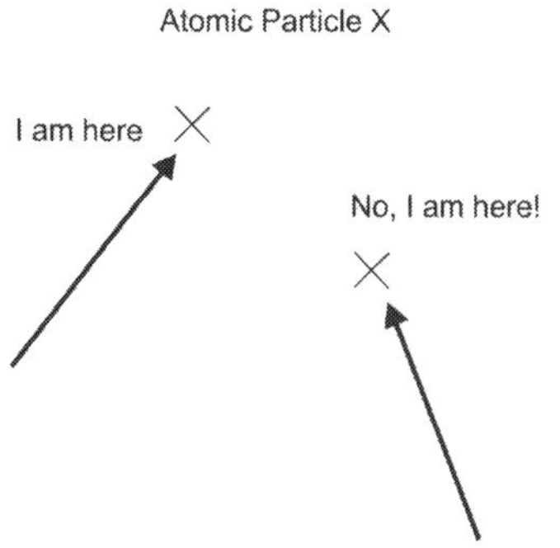

Figure 5.

Scientists could not say, with certainty, whether an atomic particle was there, at a particular position, or not there. To understand the Law of Excluded Middle (Lesson 13.1) as universally applicable in every situation is not guaranteed by the discoveries of sub-atomic world. Revealed in the realm of quantum mechanics was another kind of logic, **quantum logic**.[13] This revelation is why it may be appropriate to embrace multi-level logic, i.e., Aristotelian (Euclidean) logic for one situation and quantum logic for another.[14] We then come to understand that both levels of logic give adequate rational expression to distinctive kinds of connection between the geometric and dynamic aspects of reality. Both levels of logic are rational tools appropriate for the specific context of study.

It may be that behind the physics of quantum mechanics lies a higher degree of unity and harmony that our current instrumentation cannot yet measure.[15] The wisdom and logic of the quantum realm may be so complex that we may never be able to unravel it. The only instrumentality to help us describe this realm is the tools that mathematics gives us.

What William Shakespeare (1564-1616) said through Hamlet is appropriate for Newton's logical-causality:

> There are more things in heaven and earth, Horatio, than are dreamt of in your philosophy.[16]

---

[11] Momentum, in physics, is the product of a body's mass m and its velocity v, or mv.

[12] Every measurement requires light waves/rays; i.e., to observe results, we must read a needle on a scale, if the scale is analog. We read a measurement by light reflecting off that needle into our eyes. When scientists do experiments determining the position of atomic particles, they discover that when a light wave reflects from a particle, momentum is transferred to it. Observing position now becomes the simultaneous observation of position and momentum, and the Heisenberg Uncertainly Principle sets a limit to the precision that the scientist can achieve.

[13] Quantum logic does not assert that the Law of Excluded Middle is false, contrary to the above quote by Waismann. It asserts that this law may not be applicable in the sub-atomic realm.

[14] There are other valid logics; e.g., modal logic is where a statement is qualified by "it is necessarily true," "it is possibly true," "it is not possibly true," or "it is possibly but not necessarily true."

[15] The Copenhagen/Göttingen version of Quantum Theory grounded its interpretation in statistics and probability, leading to the unfortunate idea that chance governs the micro-universe. Albert Einstein refused to go that far stating that the primary function of science is not merely to apply statistics to observations, but to unfold, as far as possible, the multivariate structure of reality.

[16] William Shakespeare, *Hamlet* Act 1, Scene 5, 159-167.

Or, as Blaise Pascal (1623-1662) noted:

> The last proceeding of reason is to recognize that there is an infinity of things which are beyond it.[17]

Trinitarian theologian Thomas F. Torrance (1913-2007) warns:

> If all knowledge could be reduced to explicit formal relations, impersonal logical operations would take over completely and knowledge would be mechanised.[18]

> The great science [mathematics] occupies itself at least as much with the power of the imagination as with the power of logical conclusion.
>
> Johann Friedrich Herbart, *Werke* (1890), Bk. 1, p. 174.

What quantum theory has shown us is that logical-causal relations, logical connections assumed by Aristotle, Euclid, the scientific and mathematical world, and even by many in the world of theology, need not be the only type of relations revealed in the rational order of creation or the plan and purposes of the Triune God. It is not necessary, therefore, to immutably entrench logical-causal relations in our minds as the necessary framework for understanding all things. If we can explain everything through an axiomatic-deductive approach, then we engage in rationalism (Lesson 8.8).[19]

Some of the leaders in the early church, especially those from Cappadocia[20] and Athanasius of Alexandria (ca. 296-373), asserted that a dynamic and very real relationship existed between the freedom of the Triune God and authentic human beings. These theologians believed that another level of logic exists between human beings and their Creator, a logic not confined solely to Aristotelian syllogisms,[21] but to the relational dynamism between the Triune God, the gentle persuasions of the Holy Spirit, and human beings.[22] The message of the New Testament is that the Gospel is a Trinitarian dance that we join or resist.[23]

---

[17] Blaise Pascal, *Pensées* (New York: E. P. Dutton & Co., Inc., 1958), #267, p. 77.

[18] Thomas F. Torrance, *Christian Theology & Scientific Culture* (New York: Oxford University Press, 1981), p. 66.

[19] No argument, no logico-deductive system, can operate rationally outside a framework of fundamental beliefs. See Thomas F. Torrance, ed. *Belief in Science and in Christian Life* (Eugene: Wipf & Stock, [1980] 1998), pp. 1-27, 143.

[20] Some of the Cappadocian leaders responsible for the Nicene Creed were Basil the Great (330-379), who was bishop of Caesarea, Basil's younger brother Gregory of Nyssa (ca. 332-395), who was bishop of Nyssa, and a close friend, Gregory of Nazianzus (329-389), who became Patriarch of Constantinople.

[21] For example, the Incarnation, the union of God and man in the person of Jesus Christ, eludes all logical categories of thinking. It is inconceivable, yet true. The salvation of the cosmos is negated if we deny the reality of the union of God and man in the person of Jesus Christ. See Thomas F. Torrance, *Incarnation: The Person and Life and Christ*, Robert T. Walker, ed. (Downers Grove: InterVarsity Press, 2008) and Thomas F. Torrance, *Atonement: The Person and Work of Christ*, Robert T. Walker, ed. (Downers Grove: InterVarsity Press, 2009).

[22] See James E. Loder and W. Jim Neidhart, *The Knight's Move: The Relational Logic of the Spirit in Theology and Science* (Colorado Springs: Helmers & Howard, 1992).

[23] In contrast to this dynamic, some theological systems assert that there is logical-causal relationship between the death of Christ and the salvation of sinners, a correlation that cannot be ultimately resisted by some human beings called the elect. The logical-causal system developed by the followers of the Protestant reformer John Calvin (1509-1564) is one example of the framework of the logical-causality of Aristotle applied to soteriological doctrines, i.e., the doctrine of salvation, specifically the order of salvation (in Latin, *ordus salutis*). It was Theodore Beza (1519-1605), Calvin's successor in Geneva, who introduced Aristotelian logic to the curriculum of Geneva Academy to systematize Calvin's soteriological thinking, following the method established by Euclid. Beza introduced a framework of cause-effect thinking that prevails in some branches of Christianity to this day, a way of understanding doctrine known as scholastic Calvinism. For a brief introduction, see Donald Fairbairn, *Life in the Trinity: An Introduction to Theology with the Help of the Church Fathers* (Downers Grove: IVP Academic, 2009), pp. 195-198. See also Thomas F. Torrance, *Scottish Theology from John Knox to John McLeod Campbell* (Edinburgh: T & T Clark, 1996) and James B. Torrance, "Strengths and Weakness of the Westminster Theology." In *The Westminster Confession in the Church Today*, ed. Alasdair I. C. Heron (Edinburgh: The Saint Andrew Press, 1982), pp. 40-54.

So, we seek to understand, appreciate, and continue to use logic in mathematics all the while recognizing that impersonal logical operations are not the end all and be all of life. There is a beautiful dance to life and the dance of number is only a subset of the fullness of that beauty given to us by the Triune God.

> ... the electric field theory of Faraday and Maxwell represents probably the most profound transformation which has been experienced by the foundations of physics since Newton's time.
>
> Albert Einstein, *Out of My Later Years* [1956, 1984] 1991, pp. 75-76.

EXERCISES

Define the following terms and concepts:

1. Three laws of motion
2. Uncertainty principle
3. Momentum
4. Quantum logic

Answer the following questions:

5. Be able to prove Euclid's proof of the infinitude of prime numbers without reference to the text.
6. Prove that there are an infinite number of natural numbers.
7. Let p be a prime number greater than 2. Reason to the conclusion that $p + 1$ cannot be a prime number.
8. Reason to the conclusion that it is impossible to have three consecutive natural numbers that are prime numbers.
9. Reason to the conclusion that if you take any prime number greater than 11 and add 3 to it, that sum is not a prime number.
10. Determine a consecutive list of five natural numbers, none of which is a prime number by showing that you can do this by starting with this number: $6! + 2 = (1 \cdot 2 \cdot 3 \cdot 4 \cdot 5 \cdot 6) + 2$.

> Maxwell's electromagnetic laws ... are manifestations of one underlying mathematical scheme. This theory, which is at once so profound and so comprehensive that it beggars the imagination, has revealed a plan and an order in nature that speaks more eloquently to humanity than nature herself.
>
> Morris Kline, *Mathematics and the Search for Knowledge* (1985), p. 145.

11. True or False. If in the prime factorization of a positive integer x there is at least one factor that occurs an odd number of times, then $\sqrt{x}$ is irrational.
12. True or False. If in the prime factorization of a positive integer x each factor occurs an even number of times, then $\sqrt{x}$ is irrational.

Euclid developed two indirect proofs as background preparation for his proof of the Triangle Angle Sum Theorem (Lesson 8.7). First, let's look at his proof of Proposition 27 in Book I: If a straight line falling on two straight lines make the alternate angles equal to one another, the straight lines will be parallel to one another.

13. What is another word for this straight line that "falls" on two straight lines? (Hint: Refer to Lesson 8.7.)
14. In Figure 6, assuming $m\angle 1 = m\angle 2$, Euclid had to prove $m \parallel n$. According to Definition 23 (Lesson 13.2), he had to prove that these lines never meet. He invoked indirect reasoning. What, therefore, did he first assume? Use *A* in Figure 6 in your statement of this assumption.

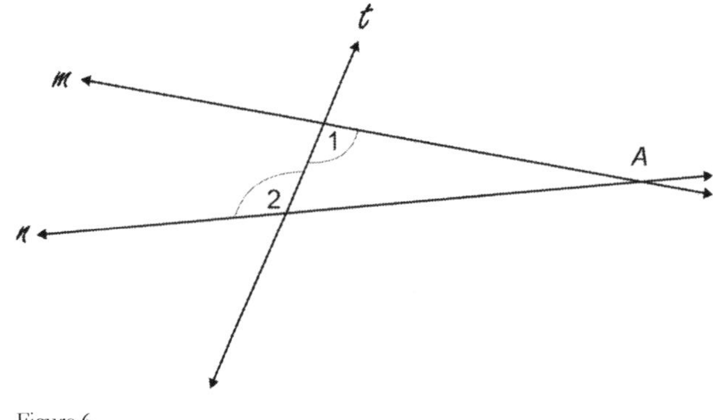

Figure 6.

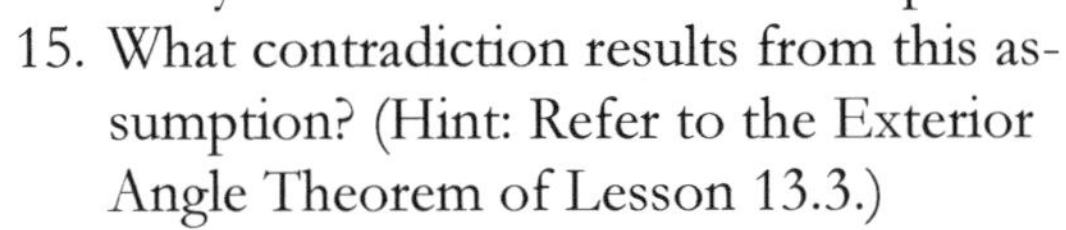

15. What contradiction results from this assumption? (Hint: Refer to the Exterior Angle Theorem of Lesson 13.3.)

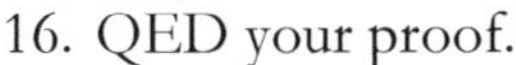

16. QED your proof.

Next, let's look at his proof of Proposition 29 in Book I, the converse of Proposition 27 of the same book: A straight line falling on parallel straight lines makes the alternate angles equal to one another.

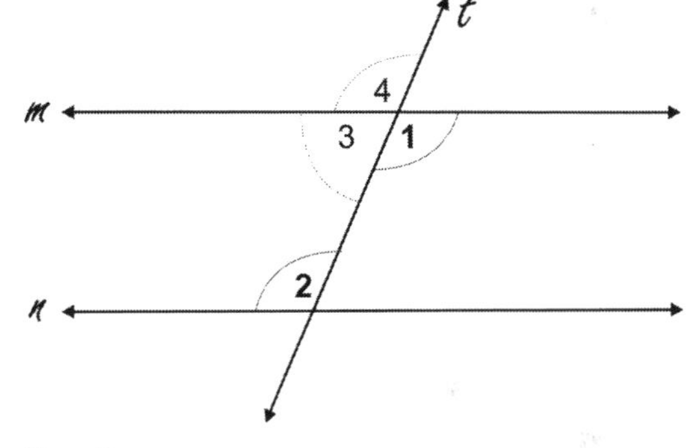

Figure 7.

17. In Figure 7, assuming $m \parallel n$, Euclid had to prove $m\angle 1 = m\angle 2$. He invoked indirect reasoning. hat, therefore, did he first assume?
18. We can state this assumption as an inequality; i.e., either let $m\angle 1 > m\angle 2$ or $m\angle 2 > m\angle 1$. We assume $m\angle 1 > m\angle 2$. Write an inequality that results from adding $m\angle 3$ (Figure 7) to both sides.
19. What is true about the sum of the measure of $\angle 1$ and $\angle 3$?
20. Substitute your answer to Question 19 into your inequality in Question 18.
21. What contradiction results from this assumption? (Hint: Refer Postulate 5, Euclid's version, Lesson 13.3.)
22. QED your proof.

As a corollary to Proposition 29 in Book I, we can now prove that if two parallel lines are cut by a transversal, their corresponding angles are equal (Lesson 8.7).

23. (a) What is true about the measure of $\angle 1$ and $\angle 4$?
    (b) Why?
24. What can you conclude about the measure of the corresponding angles, $\angle 2$ and $\angle 4$?
25. How would you prove the converse; i.e., if two lines are cut by a transversal so that their corresponding angles are equal, the two lines are parallel?

Construction of a line parallel to a given line through a point not on that line.

Answer these questions that explain and apply the construction of a line parallel to a given line through a given point (Figure 8), Proposition 31 of Book I of Euclid's *Elements*:

26. Construct line n and a point A not on line n.
27. Choose any point B on line n somewhat to the left of A and draw $\overleftrightarrow{AB}$. Label the angle formed as $\angle 1$.
28. Place the tip of the compass at B and draw $\overset{\frown}{CD}$.
29. Without changing the orientation of the compass, place the tip on A and draw a similar arc labeling E as the point of intersection the arc with $\overleftrightarrow{AB}$.
30. Place the tip of the compass on C and the other end on D. Without changing the orientation of the compass, place the tip on E and draw an arc that intersects the arc previously dawn. Label the point of intersection F.
31. Draw line m through the points A and F. Label the angle formed as $\angle 2$.
32. Why is $m \parallel n$?

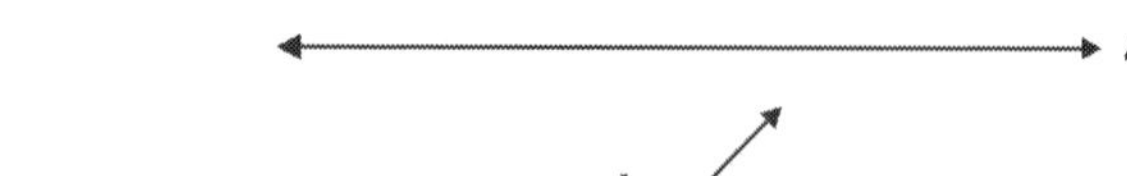

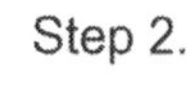

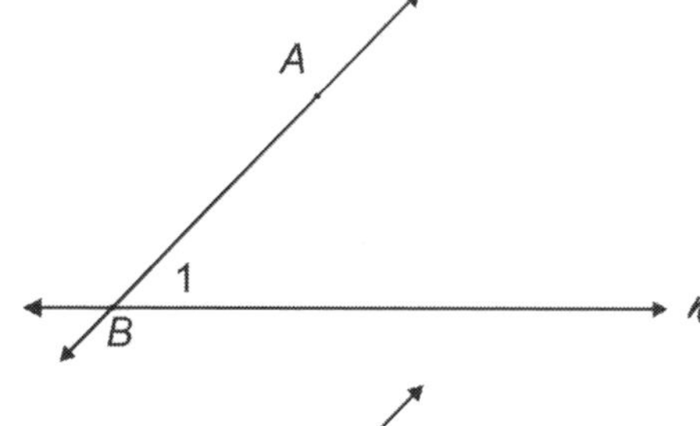

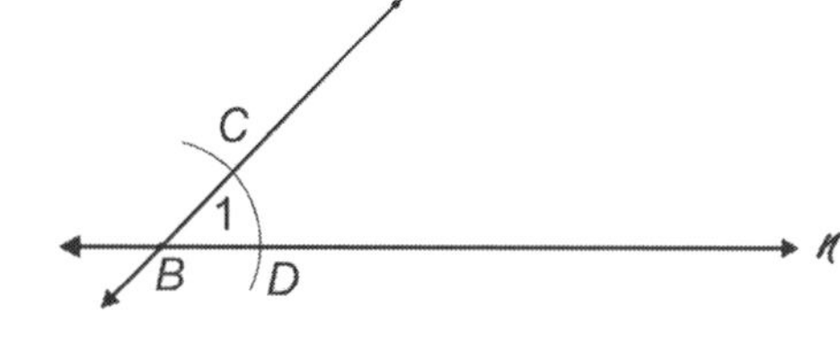

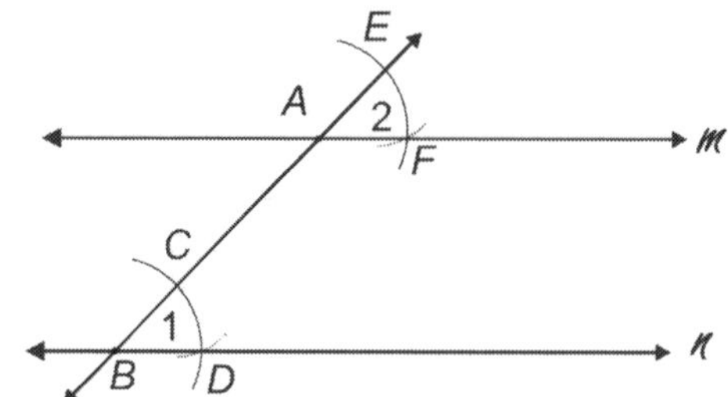

Figure 8.

Finally, let's look at his proof of Proposition 32 in Book I, the Triangle Angle Sum Theorem: In any triangle … the three interior angles of the triangle are equal to two right angles.

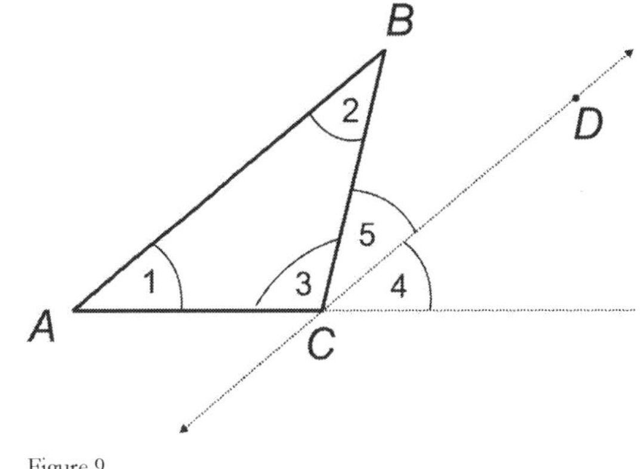

Figure 9.

33. Starting with ΔABC (Figure 9), Euclid had to prove $m\angle 1 + m\angle 2 + m\angle 3 = 180°$. By Proposition 31, Book I, he constructed $\overleftrightarrow{CD} \parallel \overline{AB}$ at C. He also extended $\overline{AC}$ to generate $\angle 4$.
    (a) What did he conclude about $\angle 2$ and $\angle 5$ by this construction?
    (b) Why? (Note how the Parallel Postulate, Postulate 5, interpenetrates the logic this theorem.)
34. (a) What did he, therefore, conclude about $\angle 1$ and $\angle 4$?
    (b) Why?
35. (a) What is true about the sum of the measures of $\angle 3$, $\angle 5$, and $\angle 4$?
    (b) Why?
36. From Question 33, Question 34, and Question 35, QED the proof.

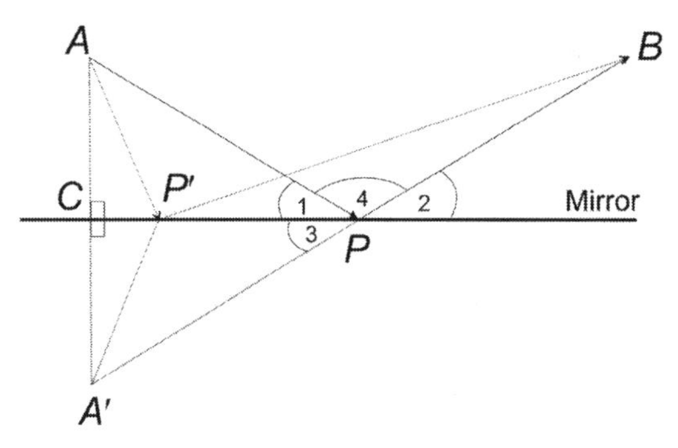

Figure 10.

In Figure 10, when we at B look into a straight-line mirror along $\overrightarrow{PB}$, we see the image of A at A', an image that appears to be as far behind the mirror as A is in front of the mirror. In addition, $\overline{AA'} \perp \overleftrightarrow{CP}$. From this physical observation we can state that $AC = CA'$. Heron of Alexandria (ca. 10 AD) used this observation to prove a very important theorem in optical Physics about light rays; i.e., the path $\overrightarrow{AP}$ to $\overrightarrow{PB}$ is the shortest possible path a light ray can take. Another way to state this theorem is that $AP + PB$ is shorter than any other path such at $AP' + P'B$ where P' is a point on the mirror. To follow Heron's reasoning, answer these questions:

37. Why is $\Delta ACP' \cong \Delta A'CP'$?

> … geometry cannot be pursued simply as an axiomatic-deductive system detached from actual knowledge of physical processes or be developed as an independent science antecedent to physics, but must be pursued in indissoluble unity with physics, as the science of its internal rational structure and as an essential part of empirical and theoretical interpretation of nature.
>
> Thomas F. Torrance, *Space, Time & Incarnation* (1969), p. 69.

38. From Question 37, what can we say about the relationship between AP' and $A'P'$?
39. Why is $ACP \cong \Delta A'CP$?
40. From Question 39, what can we say about the relationship between AP and $A'P$?
41. We want to compare $AP + PB$ with $AP' + P'B$ and prove $AP + PB < AP' + P'B$.
    (a) Why is $AP' + P'B = A'P' + P'B$?
    (b) Why is $AP + PB = A'P + PB$?
42. Since the eye at B looks along $\overline{BA'}$, this suggest that the points A', P, and B are collinear. If this is true, then $AP + PB < AP' + P'B$. Why? (Hint: Review Lesson 10.7.)
43. We need to prove A', P, and B are collinear; i.e., we need to show that $m\angle 3 + m\angle 1 + m\angle 4 = 180°$. We know that $m\angle 1 + m\angle 4 + m\angle 2 = 180°$. Why?
44. Why is $m\angle 1 = m\angle 3$?
45. Why is $m\angle 1 = m\angle 2$?
46. From Question 43 to Question 45, QED the proof.
47. Think about the game of billiards. How does our knowledge of the behavior of light rays interpenetrate this game?

Answer the following questions:

48. Where is the flaw in the following algebraic derivation? (Hint: It is not division by zero.)

Assertion	**Justification**
$(x + 1)^2 = x^2 + 2x + 1$	Expand $(x + 1)^2$.
$(x + 1)^2 - (2x + 1) = x^2$	Subtract $(2x + 1)$ from both sides.
$(x + 1)^2 - (2x + 1) - x(2x + 1) = x^2 - x(2x + 1)$	Add $-x(2x + 1)$ to both sides.
$(x + 1)^2 - (x + 1)(2x + 1) + \frac{1}{4}(2x + 1)^2 =$ $x^2 - x(2x + 1) + \frac{1}{4}(2x + 1)^2$	Add $\frac{1}{4}(2x + 1)^2$ to both sides.
$[(x + 1) - \frac{1}{2}(2x + 1)]^2 = [x - \frac{1}{2}(2x + 1)]^2$	Factor both sides (being squares).
$(x + 1) - \frac{1}{2}(2x + 1) = x - \frac{1}{2}(2x + 1)$	Extract the square root of both sides.
$x + 1 = x$	Add $\frac{1}{2}(2x + 1)$ to both sides.
$1 = 0$	Subtract x from both sides.

49. In the Sherlock Holmes mystery entitled *The Gloria Scott,* the detective cracks the hidden message behind the following riddle: "The supply of game for London is going steadily up. Head keeper Hudson, we believe, has been now told to receive all orders for fly paper and for preservation of your hen pheasant's life." Given that Hudson was the name of a sailor under investigation determine the key to the riddle and crack the secret message contained therein.

50. Match each symbolic representation in column one with its corresponding logical law in column two:

(a) $P \vee \sim P$	(g) Law of Contraposition
(b) $[(P \Rightarrow Q) \wedge (Q \Rightarrow R) \Rightarrow (P \Rightarrow R)$	(h) Law of Double Negation
(c) $P \Leftrightarrow \sim(\sim P)$	(i) Law of Excluded Middle
(d) $(P \Rightarrow Q) \Leftrightarrow (\sim Q \Rightarrow \sim P)$	(j) Law of Contradiction
(e) $\sim(P \wedge \sim P)$	(k) Law of Syllogism
(f) $(Q \Rightarrow P) \Leftrightarrow (\sim P \Rightarrow \sim Q)$	

Foundations of Chaos Theory.

Chaos Theory, a new branch of mathematics developed in the 20th century, asserts as its fundamental presupposition that small changes in initial conditions can lead to unpredictable behavior in the future. As example, let's compare 1 with 1.001. The difference is small, only 0.001, and it seems to be insignificant. We know that $1^1 = 1$. Use a scientific calculator to check the degree to which the following indicated powers of 1.001 differ from 1^1.

51. 1.001^{100} (Answer in as many digits as your calculator will display.)
52. 1.001^{1000} (Answer in as many digits as your calculator will display.)
53. $1.001^{20,000}$ (Estimate using Scientific Notation with the mantissa rounded to the nearest tenth.)
54. $1.001^{100,000}$ (Estimate using Scientific Notation with the mantissa rounded to the nearest tenth.)

> A ruggedly independent way of thinking, influenced by his Christian faith, had enabled Maxwell to breach the mechanistic structure of Newtonian science and open up a new way of understanding the universe.
>
> Charles E. Hummel, *The Galileo Connection* (1986), pp. 263-264.

13.11 The Power of the Continuum

Concepts and Symbol Introduced
1. c
2. Fundamental Property of Decimal Expansions
3. Power of the Continuum

In Lesson 9.6, we discovered that the set of integers and the set of rational numbers are countable, i.e., denumerable.[1] By denumerable, we mean that the cardinality of these sets is aleph-null, $\aleph_0$. We write:

$c(\mathbb{Z}) = \aleph_0$ (Meaning: the cardinality of the set of integers is $\aleph_0$.)

$c(\mathbb{Q}) = \aleph_0$

We have expanded the set of rational numbers to real numbers, the union of the set of rational numbers and irrational numbers. How many irrational numbers are there? Can we count them? That is, are they denumerable like the set of integers and the set of rational numbers?

Maybe the cardinality of the set of rational numbers equals the cardinality of the set of irrational numbers. That fact that $\mathbb{Q}$ and I are distinct, i.e., $\mathbb{Q}$ is not a proper subset of I, ought to make us wonder about that supposition. Let's return to the work of the German mathematician Georg Cantor (1845-1918) and see how he resolved the question, "Are the irrational numbers denumerable?"

Cantor's Proof

Cantor's method has been hailed as one of the most elegant and ingenious proofs in the history of mathematics. First, let's consider the set of real numbers and let us imagine all of them in their unique decimal expansions. Of these numbers, let us restrict ourselves to the real numbers between 0 and 1; i.e., to the numbers that look like $0.a_1a_2a_3 \ldots$. Cantor showed that even this portion of real numbers is more numerous than all the natural numbers; i.e., we cannot arrange these numbers in a natural number sequence without leaving some real numbers out of it.

To prove this, Cantor used the *reductio ad absurdum* approach. He assumed that we can count the real numbers between 0 and 1 and then reasoned to a contradiction. Follow his reasoning carefully. Your mind needs to be fully engaged.

The set of real numbers between 0 and 1 has the form $0.a_1a_2a_3 \ldots$, where the digits after the decimal point terminate (e.g., 0.215), repeat infinitely (e.g., 0.333 …), or are infinite but not repeatable (e.g., irrational numbers like $\frac{\sqrt{2}}{2} \approx 0.7071$). Let's assume that we can establish a one-to-one correspondence between the real numbers between 0 and 1 and the natural numbers. If we can show that there is a real number that has not been counted by this method, then our assumption, the real numbers between 0 and 1 are denumerable, is false and what we want to prove, the real numbers between 0 and 1 are not denumerable, is true.

We now prepare our arrangement of real numbers. Each real number has a unique decimal expansion unless the expansion terminates after a finite number of decimal places. In this case, it may be represented by an infinite decimal expansion involving the sequence .999999 …. For example:

$0.245 = 0.244999999\ldots$

To avoid these two ways of writing the same number, we invoke the principle known as the **Fundamental Property of Decimal Expansions**:

---

[1] Recall that an infinite set of numbers is denumerable if a one-to-one correspondence can be created between the given set and the set of natural numbers, where $c(\mathbb{N}) = \aleph_0$.

If a number has an infinite decimal expansion, no other infinite decimal expansion can represent that number.

This property implies that a difference in any one digit in two infinite decimal expansions means that the expansions represent two distinct numbers.

Here is our general list:[2]

Row											
1	0.	a_1	a_2	a_3	a_4	a_5	a_6	a_7	a_8	a_9	...
2	0.	b_1	b_2	b_3	b_4	b_5	b_6	b_7	b_8	b_9	...
3	0.	c_1	c_2	c_3	c_4	c_5	c_6	c_7	c_8	c_9	...
4	0.	d_1	d_2	d_3	d_4	d_5	d_6	d_7	d_8	d_9	...
5	0.	e_1	e_2	e_3	e_4	e_5	e_6	e_7	e_8	e_9	...
6	0.	f_1	f_2	f_3	f_4	f_5	f_6	f_7	f_8	f_9	...
⋮	0.	⋮	⋮	⋮	⋮	⋮	⋮	⋮	⋮	⋮	⋮

Figure 1.

Cantor showed that a decimal lying between 0 and 1 does not appear anywhere on this list.

We first consider the number ζ, the Greek letter *zeta*, and the construction of its decimal expansion, namely $\zeta = 0.\zeta_1\zeta_2\zeta_3\zeta_4\ldots$. We compare ζ with our first row; i.e., $0.a_1a_2a_3a_4\ldots$. We now create a method by which we can determine what digit to put in tenths position of ζ; i.e., ζ_1. Our method:

If a_1 is 0, 1, 2, 3, 4, 5, 6, or 7, then $\zeta_1 = 8$. If a_1 is 8 or 9, then $\zeta_1 = 1$.

ζ is now different from the number represented in the first row.

Now consider the second row; i.e., $0.b_1b_2b_3b_4\ldots$. We use the same method to determine what digit to put in the hundredths position of ζ; i.e., ζ_2.

If b_2 is 0, 1, 2, 3, 4, 5, 6, or 7, then $\zeta_2 = 8$. If b_2 is 8 or 9, then $\zeta_2 = 1$.

ζ is now different from the number represented in the second row.

Now consider the third row; i.e., $0.c_1c_2c_3c_4\ldots$. Again, by the same method, we determine what digit to put in the thousandths position of ζ; i.e., ζ_3.

If c_3 is 0, 1, 2, 3, 4, 5, 6, or 7, then $\zeta_3 = 8$. If c_3 is 8 or 9, then $\zeta_3 = 1$.

ζ is now different from the number represented in the third row.

We continue this reasoning *ad infinitum*. The number ζ we have constructed lies between 0 and 1, but is it contained in our enumerated list? It cannot be equal to the number in the first row since, by construction, ζ_1 differs from a_1. It cannot be equal to the number in the second row since, by construction, ζ_2 differs from b_2. It cannot be equal to the number in the third row since, by construction, ζ_3 differs

[2] A homework exercise will examine a specific list.

from c_3. And, ζ cannot be equal to the number in the nth row since, by construction, ζ_n differs from n^{th} digit of the decimal in the nth place in the enumeration.

By this marvelous piece of logic, Cantor constructed a number not on our list. He therefore reached a contradiction and concluded that the real numbers between 0 and 1 are not denumerable. If we were to try to match the real numbers between 0 and 1 with the natural numbers 1, 2, 3, 4, 5, ... by writing them in a sequence, a real number would always be left out. In this sense, we can say that the real numbers are more numerous than the natural numbers. Cantor denoted the number of real numbers by a symbol that resembles the letter $\mathfrak{c}$, representing the **power, the cardinality of the continuum.**[3] We write:

$$c(\mathbb{R}) = \mathfrak{c} > \aleph_0$$

He then went on to show that there is no infinite set, of whatever aleph, which cannot be transcended by another set of a higher aleph. By this reasoning, Cantor showed there are an infinite number of infinities, i.e., $\aleph_0$, $\aleph_1$, $\aleph_2$, $\aleph_3$, $\aleph_4$, ...![4] The stunning meaning of our observation encapsulated by these symbols is that there are different orders of infinites in mathematics. The Hungarian poet Mihály Babits (1883-1941) created a phrase for these numbers, towering higher and higher forever, as "the towering battlements of infinity."[5] The Argentine writer, Jorge Luis Borges (1899-1986), named them "terrible dynasties."[6]

SUMMARY

> Cantor showed that $\mathfrak{c}$ was the number of such infinite sets as ... the number of points on a line of infinite length, the number of points on any plane figure or on the infinite plane, and the number of points in any solid figure or in all of three-space. Going into higher dimensions does not increase the number of points. The points on a line segment one inch long can be matched one to one with the points in any higher-dimensional solid, or with the points in the entire space of any higher dimension.
>
> Martin Gardner, "The Hierarchy of Infinities and the Problems It Spawns." In *Mathematics: An Introduction to Its Spirit and Use* (1966), p. 76.

Our proof establishes the non-denumerability of $\mathbb{R}$. We already know that the rational numbers are countable. By implication, the irrational numbers are not countable since if we can write these numbers

[3] Cantor originally designated the power of the continuum as aleph-one, $\aleph_1$.
[4] See Martin Gardner, "The Hierarchy of Infinities and the Problems It Spawns," *Mathematics: An Introduction to Its Spirit and Use*, Morris Kline, ed. (San Francisco: W. H. Freeman, 1979), pp. 74-78. Cantor conjectured that there is no aleph between $\aleph_0$ and $\mathfrak{c}$, the power of the continuum. In 1938, Kurt Gödel showed that we could assume that Cantor's conjecture, the continuum hypothesis, is true. In 1963, a twenty-nine year old mathematician at Stanford University, Paul J. Cohen (1934-2007), showed that we could also assume that the *negation* of the continuum hypothesis is true; i.e., one can conjecture that $\mathfrak{c}$ is not $\aleph_1$, the next aleph after $\aleph_0$, that there is at least one aleph between $\aleph_0$ and $\mathfrak{c}$. By Cohen's reasoning, Cantor's conjecture is undecidable.
[5] Cited in Rózsa Péter, *Playing with Infinity: Mathematical Explorations and Excursions* (New York: Dover Publications, [1961] 1976), p. 229.
[6] Cited in Gardner, p. 74.

in the form of a sequence then we can unite the two sequences by taking numbers alternatively from each to make a new countable sequence. To illustrate this, we can unite the set of positive integers {1, 2, 3, 4, …} with the set of negative integers {-1, -2, -3, -4, …} producing a countable set as we did in Lesson 9.6:

1, -1, 2, -2, 3, -3, 4, -4, …

If we could construct a countable sequence consisting of union of the set of rational numbers and the set of irrational numbers, then we could count the set of real numbers. Cantor proved that we cannot do this. Therefore, the set of irrational numbers cannot be counted; this set is not denumerable. There are more irrational numbers than rational numbers on the number line.

As we stated in Lesson 11.4, the irrational numbers spread continuously over the entire number line even though the rational numbers are everywhere dense. The set of natural numbers, when compared with the set of rational numbers, appear, on the surface, to be as a few insignificant needles in a haystack infinitely full of straw (since $\mathbb{N} \subset \mathbb{Q}$). Yet, we discovered that the number of needles equals the number of straws of hay; i.e., a one-to-one correspondence exists between these two infinite sets. In other words, the set of natural numbers and the set of rational numbers are equally denumerable. From Cantor's proof demonstrated in this lesson, we can picture the set of rational numbers as only a few insignificant needles in an infinite haystack of irrational numbers.

> The fact that one cannot carry out an infinite procedure no more diminishes the reality or usefulness of Cantor's alephs than the fact that one cannot fully compute the value of pi diminishes the reality or usefulness of pi.
>
> Martin Gardner, "The Hierarchy of Infinities and the Problems It Spawns." In *Mathematics: An Introduction to Its Spirit and Use* (1966), p. 78.

EXERCISES

Define the following concepts:

1. Fundamental Property of Decimal Expansions
2. Power of the continuum

Answer these questions:

3. Explain $c(\mathbb{R}) = \mathfrak{c} > \aleph_0$.
4. Find an irrational number between 0 and $\frac{1}{1{,}000{,}000}$. (Hint: Set $a = 1$ in $\frac{a}{b}\sqrt{2}$. Find b such that $\frac{a}{b}\sqrt{2} < \frac{1}{1{,}000{,}000} = 0.000001$ and note that, from the homework of Lesson 13.9, $\frac{a}{b}\sqrt{2}$ is an irrational number.)
5. Use the *reductio ad absurdum* argument to show that there is no smallest positive irrational number. Assume that there is a smallest positive rational number. (Hint: Let that number = $\frac{a}{b}\sqrt{2}$ where a = 1 and $b > a$.)

6. Are there infinitely many irrational numbers between 0 and $\frac{1}{1,000,000}$? Explain why or why not.

   (Hint: Start with the irrational number $\frac{a}{b}\sqrt{2}$ where $a = 1$ and $b = 1,000,000$.)
7. Are there infinitely many irrational numbers between any two rational numbers? Explain why or why not. (Hint: Use the reasoning in the previous question.)

Cantor's proof that the real numbers are uncountable or *not denumerable* (without all those symbols)
Let's make an endless list of real numbers, fixed once and for all, that we *assume* can be matched one-to-one with the natural numbers (Figure 2):

8. Reproduce Figure 2 and underline the first digit to the right of the decimal point in the first number in the list.
9. Underline the second digit in the *second* number in the list.
10. Underline the third digit in the *third* number in the list.
11. Underline the fourth digit in the *fourth* number in the list.
12. Underline the fifth digit in the *fifth* number in the list.

$1 \leftrightarrow 15.587213 \ldots$

$2 \leftrightarrow 8.971145 \ldots$

$3 \leftrightarrow 0.369000 \ldots$

$4 \leftrightarrow 98.333432 \ldots$

$5 \leftrightarrow 0.962863 \ldots$

$\vdots \leftrightarrow \quad \vdots \quad \cdots$

Figure 2.

Ignore the digits not underlined. Focus on the digits that are underlined. Note that these digits form an endless left-to-right downward diagonal. Cantor now used that number to construct a number x that he shows *cannot* be on the list. This number looks like $x = 0.\_\_\_\_\_\ldots$

13. We now must deduce what digits go into these empty places. Write the underlined digits in order.
14. Below each of these digits write a digit that is different from it. To automate this process, let's make a rule: *If the underlined digit is 6, write 7; if the underlined digit is not 6, then write 6*. By this rule, we generate x. Write out the results in our case.
15. Think about this number carefully. Can this number be anywhere on our list? Answer these questions:
    (a) Could it be the first number?
    (b) The second number?
    (c) The third number?
    (d) The fourth number?
    (e) The fifth number?
    (f) In general, could it be the nth number?
16. Since our argument applies to all possible lists that you could create, what must be our conclusion in accordance with *reductio ad absurdum*?

Figure 3. Georg Cantor. Source: Public Domain. Although his work gained little acknowledgement in his lifetime, it permeates modern mathematics, particularly logic, topology (the study of the properties of stretched geometric figures [Lesson 14.4]), set theory, and analysis, the study of infinite processes.

> ... most of the points on the number axis [line – JN] are irrational and ... the rational numbers are vanishing exceptions.
>
> Friedrich Waismann, *Introduction to Mathematical Thinking* ([1951, 1959, 1966] 2003), p. 8.

13.12 KEEPING SECRETS

This lesson will describe one of the many ways prime numbers interpenetrate modern life, i.e. the use of secret codes. It is an exemplary example of the power of deduction.

SECRET CODES

One of the pleasant memories of childhood is playing hide and seek or making up secret codes so that only you and your closest friend can communicate in complete privacy. Maybe some of you tried something like this with your secret pal. You rearranged the alphabet at random, setting each letter of the alphabet to some other letter, let's say, as Table 1 reveals.

Table 1

A	B	C	D	E	F	G	H	I	J	K	L	M
T	*L*	*P*	*A*	*W*	*J*	*F*	*M*	*Q*	*B*	*X*	*H*	*O*
N	O	P	Q	R	S	T	U	V	W	X	Y	Z
C	*K*	*V*	*Z*	*D*	*R*	*Y*	*N*	*G*	*U*	*E*	*I*	*S*

Only you and your friend have this key. Using it, you could change any sentence into unintelligible gibberish:

Want to watch cartoons on Saturday morning?

becomes:

Utcy yk utypm ptdkkcr kc Rtyndati okdcqcf?

You might even remove the capital letters, spaces, and punctuation marks to really confuse the uninitiated:

utcyykutypmptdkkcrkcrtyndatiokdcqcf

After decoding this message with your key, you reply:

quqhhrwwiknymwc (I will see you then)

Terms, Symbols & Concepts Introduced
1. ≡
2. Asymmetric cryptosystem
3. Cryptanalysis
4. Cryptography
5. Decryption
6. Decryption function
7. Encryption
8. Encryption function
9. Fermat's Little Theorem
10. Modulus of RSA code
11. phi-function
12. Plain text
13. Public encryption key
14. Random sample
15. Secret decryption key
16. Symmetric cryptosystem
17. Trapdoor one-way function

CRYPTOGRAPHY

In this childhood example is found all the elements of the science of **cryptography**.[1] We classify a cryptographic system in three ways:

1. We develop some operation, either randomly as in our example or mathematical, by which we can conceal important information that is either text or numbers. We call this information **plain text**. We conceal the plain text with the use of an **encryption**[2] key.
2. The sender and receiver either use the same key, **symmetric**[3] **cryptosystem**, or different keys, **asymmetric**[4] (two-key or public-key) **cryptosystem**.

---

[1] Cryptography combines two Greek roots, *crypto* meaning "to hide" and *graph* meaning "to write." It literally means "hidden writing." It is the science of codes and ciphers.

[2] Encrypt literally means to "hide in" or to put into a cipher.

[3] Symmetric is Greek for "like measure."

[4] Asymmetric is Greek for "unlike measure."

3. Using one or the other key system, we produce a message cipher. The sender transmits a key-encrypted cipher to the receiver. The receiver **decrypts**[5] the cipher according to the given key and the information is confirmed: The two will watch cartoons on Saturday morning.

The uninitiated who wants to understand the message must break the cipher either by obtaining the key or by determining the key by mathematical analysis. Breaking ciphers by analysis is known as the science of **cryptanalysis**. The simple key devised above is easy to break. Anyone skilled in cryptanalysis can do this because they know the nature and structure of language. Given an encrypted message that is lengthy enough, we can invoke the statistical Law of Large Numbers (Lesson 9.8). For example, in the English language, a **random sample**[6] of prose contains *e* as the most common letter. It appears 12% of the time, 12 out of every 100 letters, followed by *t* (9%), *a* and *o* (8% each), *i, n,* and *s* (7% each), and *r* (6%). The least used letters are *j, k,* and *x* (0.5%, one out of every 200 letters) and *q* and *z* ($^1/_3$%, i.e., one out of every 300 letters).

Combinations of letters reveal more. Using the Fundamental Counting Principle (Lesson 9.2), we can tabulate the percentage of occurrence of the $26 \cdot 26$ (676) different possible two-letter combinations in the English alphabet and really narrow the field. Certain letters are never doubled in English; e.g., *hh, ii, jj, kk, qq, uu, ww, xx, yy*. The vowels *a, e, i, o,* and *u* appear far more frequently adjacent to other letters than they do to one another. The letter *n* is far more likely to be preceded by a vowel than by a consonant. Certain pairs of letters occur frequently in one order but rarely or never in the reverse; e.g., *ea* versus *ae*, *lm* verses *ml*, *rn* verses *nr*. From this discussion, a cryptanalyst must be skilled in language analysis, logical analysis, and mathematical analysis. It is a challenging vocation.

Civil governments throughout history have recognized the need to keep state secrets, especially in time of war. During war, the ability of one nation to break the code of another nation is the source of critical and strategic intelligence. For example, in World War II the ability of American cryptanalysts to break the Japanese naval code *JN25* was pivotal to the American victory over a superior Japanese fleet at the battle of Midway (3-6 June 1942). Later in the Pacific Theater of Operations (PTO), American cryptanalysts identified the whereabouts of a small group of Japanese planes carrying Admiral Isoroku Yamamoto (1884-1943), the officer who conceived of the surprise attack on the United States naval base at Pearl Harbor on 7 December 1941. A squadron of Lockhead P-38 Lightnings ambushed and shot down Yamamoto's plane over Bougainville Island in the Solomon Islands on 18 April 1943. After Yamamoto's plane fell in flames to the tropical forest below, a "pop goes the weasel" cipher was sent to American naval Admiral William F. "Bull" Halsey (1882-1959) signifying "mission accomplished."

British cryptanalysts broke the key to the German *Enigma* ciphering machine allowing German communications to be read virtually at will. The intelligence unearthed in this manner significantly altered World War II's outcome in the European Theater of Operations (ETO).[7]

CIPHER SYSTEMS

All cipher systems, except the one we will soon investigate, suffer from two serious defects. First, the recipient of the message must possess a secret key to decipher it. The problem with keys is that all potential recipients of a message must possess it. We would also need a trusted dispatcher to hand deliver the key. Second, how do we know that the message has not been intercepted in transit? Someone may have obtained the key fraudulently and changed the message. We need a guarantee of authenticity.

---

[5] Decrypt means the same as "decode or decipher." We convert the cipher back to its original plain text or numbers.

[6] A random sample is a group or subset of items taken from a given population; whether English prose or English people (Lesson 9.5).

[7] For a history of code breaking in World War II, see Stephen Budiansky, *Battle of Wits* (New York: The Free Press, 2000).

A unique type of code, named public-key code, i.e., asymmetric cryptosystem, resolves both issues. How does it work? First, Mr. Receiver makes *public* to all potential senders an enciphering key. Using this key, Mr. Sender encodes, or enciphers, a message and transmits it to Mr. Receiver. Mr. Receiver has a *secret* deciphering key whereby he can decode, or decipher, the message. The uniqueness about this system is that the enciphering key only works in one direction; i.e., it only works to encrypt a message and is known as the **trapdoor one-way function**. This key is made public to all. No special couriers are needed. Anyone can use it. Deciphering this message is only possible using the secret deciphering key. The one who sends the message cannot accidentally or deliberately reveal the deciphering key to any would-be interlopers or spies.

How is this done in detail?[8] This amazing technique is accomplished by means of the mathematics of prime numbers and modular arithmetic.[9] Let's first look at how a message is enciphered. Each alphabetic letter is assigned a two-digit number. This step is the substitution step. Next, this two-digit number is shuffled or scrambled according to a mathematical rule. This step is the transposition step. Note the interpenetration of algebraic ideas: substitution and rule, i.e., function. Doing this involves modular arithmetic. To discover how this arithmetic works, let's first set up a five-column array of numbers in Table 2.

Table 2

1	**2**	3	**4**	5
6	7	**8**	9	10
11	12	13	14	15
16	17	18	19	20
21	22	23	24	25
26	27	28	29	30
31	**32**	33	34	35
36	37	38	39	40
41	42	43	44	45
46	47	48	49	50

Note that each number in **bold** is a power of 2, i.e., 2, 4, 8, 16, and 32. Note their column placement:

- 2 (2^1) is in column 2.
- 4 (2^2) is in column 4.
- 8 (2^3) is in column 3.
- 16 (2^4) is in column 1.
- 32 (2^5) is in column 2.

In what column is 2^6 (64)? Think about it first; then extend the rows of the table to confirm your conjecture

- 64 (2^6) is in column 4.
- 128 (2^7) will be in column 3.

---

8 I am summarizing some of the structured thought of Edward Burger and Michael Starbird, *The Heart of Mathematics: An Invitation to Effective Thinking* (Emeryville: Key Curriculum Press, 2000), pp. 96-111. Many thanks to these men for the homework ideas. For a more technical exposition, I am indebted to W. W. L. Chen, "Public Key Cryptography," in *Discrete Mathematics*, lecture notes, Macquarie University, 1997.

9 Modular arithmetic is also known as the arithmetic of remainders (Lesson 5.2).

- 256 (2^8) will be in column 1, and 512 (2^9) will return to column 2.

An obvious pattern of the columns is developing; i.e., 2, 4, 3, 1, 2, 4, 3, 1, etc.

Let's investigate how 5, i.e., the number of columns, interpenetrates this scheme. In Table 3, the third column contains modular, of mod, arithmetic notation. Recall (Lesson 5.2) that $14 \equiv 4 \pmod 5$ means that "14 divided by 5 results in a remainder of 4." The symbol $\equiv$ means "is equivalent to." In general, $a \equiv r \pmod n$ means $^a/_n$ leaves a remainder of r. In mod arithmetic, we are not concerned with the quotient of a division problem; we are only concerned with the remainder. The modulus n is the divisor, a the dividend, and r the remainder. If we know a and n, we can find a unique r. If we know r and n, a is not unique because there may be many dividends that give a remainder of r when divided by n. Example: $32 \equiv 2 \pmod 5$ means that $\frac{32}{5}$ leaves a remainder of 2. We also note that $37 \equiv 2 \pmod 5$ means that $\frac{37}{5}$ leaves a remainder of 2. We see this relationship in our study of Table 3.[10]

Table 3

Powers of 2	Remainder When Divided by 5	Mod Arithmetic
$2^1 = 2$	2	$2^1 \equiv 2 \pmod 5$
$2^2 = 4$	4	$2^2 \equiv 4 \pmod 5$
$2^3 = 8$	3	$2^3 \equiv 3 \pmod 5$
$2^4 = 16$	1	$2^4 \equiv 1 \pmod 5$
$2^5 = 32$	2	$2^5 \equiv 2 \pmod 5$
$2^6 = 64$	4	$2^6 \equiv 4 \pmod 5$
$2^7 = 128$	3	$2^7 \equiv 3 \pmod 5$
$2^8 = 256$	1	$2^8 \equiv 1 \pmod 5$
$2^9 = 512$	2	$2^9 \equiv 2 \pmod 5$
$2^{10} = 1024$	4	$2^{10} \equiv 4 \pmod 5$

We discover that the remainder of the powers of 2 when divided by 5 is the column number. A similar pattern can be discerned using any base, e.g., 2, 3, 4, 5, etc., and any number of columns with this proviso: The number of columns must be a prime number and the base does not have this number as a factor. Let's try base 8 with 5 columns. [We note that 5 is not a factor of 8; i.e., the greatest common factor of 5 and 8 is 1 or 5 and 8 are relatively prime (Lesson 6.8).] Remember, to find the remainder, all we need to do is look at the last digit of the number remembering a number is a multiple of 5 if its last digit is 0 or 5. If the digit is greater than 5, then we subtract 5 from the digit to get the remainder. If the digit is less than 5, that digit is the remainder. Investigate Table 4.

Table 4

Powers of 8	Remainder When Divided by 5	Mod Arithmetic
$8^1 = 8$	3	$8^1 \equiv 3 \pmod 5$
$8^2 = 64$	4	$8^2 \equiv 4 \pmod 5$
$8^3 = 512$	2	$8^3 \equiv 2 \pmod 5$

[10] Note, for all numbers k in column 5 of Table 2, we write: $k \equiv 0 \pmod 5$ because k is divisible by 5; i.e., the remainder is zero. All the remainders for the numbers in column 4 will be 4 when divided by 5, 3 in column 3, 2 in column 2 and 1 in column 1.

Table 4

Powers of 8	Remainder When Divided by 5	Mod Arithmetic
$8^4 = 4096$	1	$8^4 \equiv 1 \pmod 5$
$8^5 = 32{,}768$	3	$8^5 \equiv 3 \pmod 5$
$8^6 = 262{,}144$	4	$8^6 \equiv 4 \pmod 5$
$8^7 = 2{,}097{,}152$	2	$8^7 \equiv 2 \pmod 5$
$8^8 = 16{,}777{,}216$	1	$8^8 \equiv 1 \pmod 5$
$8^9 = 134{,}217{,}728$	3	$8^9 \equiv 3 \pmod 5$
$8^{10} = 1{,}073{,}741{,}824$	4	$8^{10} \equiv 4 \pmod 5$

Let's try one more, base 10 with 7 columns. We note that 7 is not a factor of 10; 7 and 10 are relatively prime. Investigate Table 5.

Table 5

Powers of 10	Remainder When Divided by 7	Mod Arithmetic
$10^1 = 10$	3	$10^1 \equiv 3 \pmod 7$
$10^2 = 100$	2	$10^2 \equiv 2 \pmod 7$
$10^3 = 1000$	6	$10^3 \equiv 6 \pmod 7$
$10^4 = 10{,}000$	4	$10^4 \equiv 4 \pmod 7$
$10^5 = 100{,}000$	5	$10^5 \equiv 5 \pmod 7$
$10^6 = 1{,}000{,}000$	1	$10^6 \equiv 1 \pmod 7$
$10^7 = 10{,}000{,}000$	3	$10^7 \equiv 3 \pmod 7$
$10^8 = 100{,}000{,}000$	2	$10^8 \equiv 2 \pmod 7$
$10^9 = 1{,}000{,}000{,}000$	6	$10^9 \equiv 6 \pmod 7$
$10^{10} = 10{,}000{,}000{,}000$	4	$10^{10} \equiv 4 \pmod 7$

Note again that the remainder pattern starts to repeat itself based upon the number of columns. Inspecting the last two tables, the remainder sequence has a repeating pattern of four digits in mod 5 (3, 4, 2, 1) and six digits (3, 2, 6, 4, 5, 1) in mod 7.

From the previous three tables, we note:

- In mod 5, the fourth sequence gives a remainder of 1 [$2^4 \equiv 1 \pmod 5$ and $8^4 \equiv 1 \pmod 5$].
- In mod 7, the sixth sequence also gives a remainder of 1 [$10^6 \equiv 1 \pmod 7$].

FERMAT'S LITTLE THEOREM

In 1640, the French mathematician Pierre de Fermat (1601-1665) confirmed this pattern in what is today known, in number theory, as **Fermat's Little Theorem**. If p is a prime number and n is any integer that does not have p as a factor, then:

Figure 1. Pierre de Fermat. Source: Public Domain.

$n^{p-1} \equiv 1 \pmod p$

(These symbols mean n^{p-1} will always have a remainder of 1 when divided by p.)

If we subtract one from both sides of the equivalence relation, another way of saying the same thing is:

$n^{p-1} - 1 \equiv 0 \pmod{p}$
(These symbols mean $n^{p-1} - 1$ is divisible by p.)

In our examples:

- $2^{5-1} = 2^4 \equiv 1 \pmod{5} \Leftrightarrow 2^4 - 1 \equiv 0 \pmod{5}$
- $8^{5-1} = 8^4 \equiv 1 \pmod{5} \Leftrightarrow 8^4 - 1 \equiv 0 \pmod{5}$
- $10^{7-1} = 10^6 \equiv 1 \pmod{7} \Leftrightarrow 10^6 - 1 \equiv 0 \pmod{7}$

EULER'S PHI-FUNCTION

In 1760, the Swiss mathematician Leonhard Euler (1707-1783) observed another interesting pattern in prime numbers. First, Euler defined a **phi-function**, where *phi* is a Greek letter φ, as follows:

Given any natural number n, $\varphi(n)$ represents the number of natural numbers less than n that have no factor in common with n.

Figure 2. Leonhard Euler.
Source: Public Domain.

For example, for the natural number 6, there are only two numbers less than 6, 1 and 5, that have no factor in common with 6. The ordered pair (1, 6) and (5, 6) are relatively prime. Therefore, $\varphi(6) = 2$.

Table 6 contains the values of $\varphi(n)$ from $n = 2$ to 15. To augment your familiarity with Euler's definition, verify the results in each instance.

Table 6: Phi-Function

	$\varphi(6) = 2$	$\varphi(11) = 10$
$\varphi(2) = 1$	$\varphi(7) = 6$	$\varphi(12) = 4$
$\varphi(3) = 2$	$\varphi(8) = 4$	$\varphi(13) = 12$
$\varphi(4) = 2$	$\varphi(9) = 6$	$\varphi(14) = 6$
$\varphi(5) = 4$	$\varphi(10) = 4$	$\varphi(15) = 8$

Look carefully at the phi-function of prime numbers in this table and note the pattern:

- $\varphi(2) = 1$
- $\varphi(3) = 2$
- $\varphi(5) = 4$
- $\varphi(7) = 6$
- $\varphi(11) = 10$
- $\varphi(13) = 12$

We conclude, via induction, i.e., search for pattern:

If p is prime, then $\varphi(p) = p - 1$.

Now let's suppose that the numbers p and q are distinct primes. For example, let $p = 7$ and $q = 17$. What is $\varphi(pq) = \varphi(7 \cdot 17)$?

Consider first the number $7 \cdot 17$. We will not calculate its product for reasons that will become obvious. To calculate $\varphi(7 \cdot 17)$ we start with the numbers 1, 2, 3, 4, 5, 6, 7, 8, 9, …, $7{\cdot}17$ and eliminate all the multiples of 7 and 17. We note that among these $7 \cdot 17$ numbers, there are 17 multiples of 7 and 7 multiples of 17. We can then eliminate $7 + 17 = 24$ numbers from the total of $7 \cdot 17$. The only common multiple of both 7 and 17 is $7 \cdot 17$. Therefore, we subtract 1 from 24 to get 23. What we have left is the number we are looking for; i.e., $\varphi(7 \cdot 17) = 7 \cdot 17 - 23$. We can write our analysis as follows to explain how we got 23:

$\varphi(7 \cdot 17) = 7 \cdot 17 - 7 - 17 + 1$

Let's apply the Distributive Law of Multiplication over Subtraction to the expression $7 \cdot 17 - 7$. We are essentially factoring 7 from the two terms, $7 \cdot 17$ and -7. Factoring 7 from $7 \cdot 17$ ($7 \cdot 17$ divided by 7) gives us 17. Factoring 7 from -7 (-7 divided by 7) gives us -1. We get:

$7 \cdot 17 - 7 = 7(17 - 1) = 7(16)$

We now have $7(16) - 17 + 1$. Looking at the last two terms, we apply our rule for adding integers:

$-17 + 1 = -16$

Therefore:

$7(16) - 17 + 1 = 7(16) - 16$

We factor 16 from the two terms, $7(16) - 16$. We get:

$7(16) - 16 = 16(7 - 1) = 16(6)$

Therefore:

$\varphi(7 \cdot 17) = 6(16) = 96$

Euler noted that, in general, if p and q are distinct primes, we can use this nifty formula to calculate $\varphi(pq)$:

$\varphi(pq) = (p - 1)(q - 1)$

EULER'S EXTENSION OF FERMAT'S LITTLE THEOREM

Also in 1760, **Euler extended Fermat's Little Theorem** using φ notation. If p and q are relatively prime, then:

$p^{\varphi(q)} \equiv 1 \pmod{q}$

Don't get lost in the symbols. Seek to understand what they mean. If $p = 7$ and $q = 17$, then $\varphi(17) = 16$. Why? If p is prime, then $\varphi(p) = p - 1$. Therefore, $7^{16} \equiv 1 \pmod{17}$.

Let's try one more example. If $p = 7$ and $q = 9$ (We note that both are relatively prime but 9 is not a prime number.), then, from Table 6, $\varphi(9) = 6$. Therefore, $7^6 \equiv 1 \pmod{9}$. To confirm this, note that $7^6 = 117{,}649$ and $117{,}649/9 = 13{,}072$ with remainder 1. If we can cast out nines (Lesson 5.4) in 117,649, we get 1, the remainder when 117,640 is divided by 9.

Here is a list, five to be exact, of our theorems, observations, and definitions so far:

1. Fermat's Little Theorem: If p is a prime number and n is any integer that does not have p as a factor, then
   $n^{p-1} \equiv 1 \pmod{p}$.
2. phi-function: Given any natural number n, $\varphi(n)$ represents the number of natural numbers less than n that have no factor in common with n.
3. If p is prime, then $\varphi(p) = p - 1$.
4. If p and q are distinct primes, then $\varphi(pq) = (p - 1)(q - 1)$.

5. Euler's extension of Fermat's Little Theorem: If p and q are relatively prime, then $p^{\varphi(q)} \equiv 1 \pmod{q}$.

RSA DATA SECURITY METHODOLOGY

These relationships were fixed in the mathematical landscape by the middle of the 18th century.[11] In 1977, three mathematicians, Ronald Rivest (1947-), Adi Shamir (1952-), and Leonard Adleman (1945-), developed a commercial public-key encryption methodology. In 1982, these men founded RSA Data Security, Inc. of Redwood City, California, to market the system.[12] The ground of the extraordinary success of the RSA public-key code in the late 20th century business world is the observations of Fermat and Euler, discoveries made over 200 years before the founding of RSA Data Security, Inc.

The RSA code exploits Euler's extension of Fermat's Little Theorem. Even though modern computers are extremely fast, we know that it still takes them an enormous amount of time to factor numbers that are about 200 digits in length.

Let's see how the RSA code works. Suppose that p and q are two very large prime numbers, each about 100 digits.[13] Mr. Rishad[14] Clandestine picks them and he tells no one else their values. The numbers p and q, therefore, are the **secret decryption key**.[15] Mr. Rishad Clandestine announces the product $n = pq$ to Mr. General Q. Public. n is the **modulus**, the divisor, of the RSA code, the **public encryption key**. Since Mr. Rishad Clandestine knows the value of p and q, he also knows the value of $\varphi(n)$.

Mr. Rishad Clandestine also gives Mr. General Q. Public the public encryption key e, a natural number that it is relatively prime to $\varphi(n)$.

Mr. General Q. Public now wants to encrypt the message, "Math sure is fun but it takes a lot concentration." He assigns a unique number x to each letter of the message such that $x < n$. There will be no trouble doing this for any text since n is a 200-digit number. Each number x is encrypted to another number c, also a natural number that is less than n, using this **encryption function**:

$$x^e \equiv c \pmod{n}$$

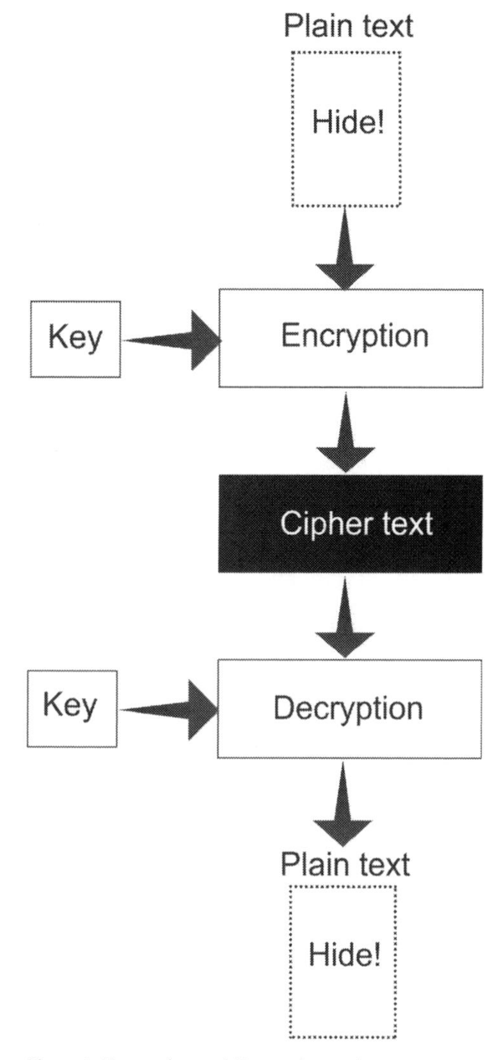

Figure 3. Encryption and Decryption cycle.

[11] When I studied number theory in university in the early 1970s, I, along with my professors, had no idea of the impact these five statements would have in the unfolding of the history of computers.

[12] RSA is an acronym formed from the first letters of these mathematicians last names: Rivest, Shamir, and Adleman.

[13] The product of two 100-digit numbers will have a maximum number of 200 digits.

[14] Rishad, Mr. Clandestine's first name, is a secret code that honors the first two letters of Ronald Rivest, Adi Shamir, and Leonard Adleman's last names.

[15] To break the code, one must know p and q. Factorizing n to obtain p and q in any systematic way when n is 200 digits takes years of computer time. When computers become fast enough to factor 200-digit numbers, all Mr. Rishad Clandestine must do is select greater prime numbers p and q. Since the number of prime numbers is infinite (Lesson 13.10), Mr. Rishad Clandestine will always be in business.

In other words, he knows n, e, and x. He divides x^e by n to get the remainder c.

Mr. General Q. Public sends his message, the value of c, to Miss Math Student. Mr. Rishad Clandestine has given Miss Math Student a private decryption key d, known only to her, where d is a natural number such that:

$$ed \equiv 1 \; [\text{mod } \varphi(n)]$$

Because of the secrecy of $\varphi(n)$, it would take many years of computer time to calculate d from e. Therefore, Mr. Rishad Clandestine must tell Miss Math Student the value of d. When Miss Math Student receives an encrypted c, she decrypts it to another number y, also a natural number that is less than n, by using this **decryption function**:

$$c^d \equiv y \; (\text{mod } n)$$

In other words, she knows n, c, and d. She divides c^d by n to get the remainder y.

DEDUCTION AT WORK

We invoke algebraic deduction to show that $y \equiv x$ (mod n); i.e., the deciphered number y is equivalent to Mr. General Q. Public's original number x, or y divided by n gives a remainder of x.

We first note that since $ed \equiv 1$ (mod $\varphi(n)$), there exists, by the definition of division, another natural number k such that:

$$ed = k[\varphi(n)] + 1$$

Although these symbols may look like nothing but comical hieroglyphics, i.e., brackets, parentheses, Greek letter φ, the number 1, +, =, and letters e, d, k, and n, what we are saying, using an example, is a statement that is easy to understand:

If $41 \equiv 1$ (mod 5), then $41 = 8 \cdot 5 + 1$

The symbols ed represent the product of two numbers, a number. The symbols $k[\varphi(n)] + 1$ also represent the product of two numbers, a number, plus 1. The symbols $ed = k[\varphi(n)] + 1$ mean "the product of two numbers equals the product of two other numbers plus 1." Or, using different symbols, we can say that if x and y are the first two numbers, and k and z are the next two numbers, then:

$$xy = kz + 1$$

Go slow with the following. Seek to understand. You may need read this algebraic analysis several times until that understanding comes.

Since we are using mod n arithmetic [i.e., $c^d \equiv y$ (mod n)] we can state this equivalence without adding the mod notation:

Equivalence 1. $y \equiv c^d$

We want to show $y \equiv x$ (mod n) or $c^d = x$ (mod n).

Since we are using mod n arithmetic [i.e., $x^e \equiv c$ (mod n)], we state this equivalence:

Equivalence 2. $x^e \equiv c$

Substituting x^e for c in Equivalence 1, we get:

Equivalence 3. $y \equiv (x^e)^d$

The Power of a Power Law of exponents (Lesson 11.1) states that $(a^m)^n = a^{mn}$. By this law, we conclude that $(x^e)^d = x^{ed}$. Therefore, Equivalence 3 becomes:

Equivalence 4. $y \equiv x^{ed}$

We know that $ed = k[\varphi(n)] + 1$. Let's tone down the proliferation of symbols by letting $\varphi(n) = z$. Therefore, $ed = kz + 1$. Substituting $kz + 1$ for ed in Equivalence 4, we get:

Equivalence 5. $y \equiv x^{kz+1}$

The Product of Powers Law of exponents (Lesson 11.1) states that $a^m a^n = a^{m+n}$. By this law, Equivalence 5 becomes:

Equivalence 6. $y \equiv x^{kz}x^1 = x^{kz}x$ (Recall that $x^1 = x$.)

By the Power of a Power Law of exponents, Equivalence 6 becomes:

Equivalence 7. $y \equiv (x^z)^k x$

Let's now replace z with $\varphi(n)$. In mod n arithmetic, what is $(x^{\varphi(n)})^k x$ equivalent to? From Euler's extension of Fermat's Little Theorem, we know:

$x^{\varphi(q)} \equiv 1 \pmod{n}$ or $x^{\varphi(q)} \equiv 1$

By the Commutative Law of Multiplication, we can rewrite $(x^{\varphi(n)})^k x$ as follows:

$(x^{\varphi(n)})^k x = x\,(x^{\varphi(n)})^k$

Now, we substitute 1 for $x^{\varphi(n)}$. We are applying Euler's extension:

$(x^z)^k x = x(1)^k$

Since $1^k = 1$ for all integers k, then we know that $(1)^k = 1$. Substituting, we write:

$(x^z)^k x = x(1)$

We also know that $x(1) = 1x = x$ since the $1x = x$. Therefore, replacing $(x^z)^k x$ in Equivalence 7 with x, we write:

Equivalence 8. $y \equiv x$

Since we are using mod n arithmetic, we state Equivalence 8 in full:

Equivalence 9. $y \equiv x \pmod{n}$

QED

We have proved what we set out to prove; i.e., $y \equiv x \pmod{n}$, the deciphered number y is equivalent to Mr. General Q. Public's original number x, or y divided by n gives a remainder of x.

AN EXAMPLE

Let's replace the symbols with some numbers to illustrate how the procedure works. We will pick small numbers to work with. High-speed computers can compute those 100-digit and 200-digit numbers faster and more accurately than we could ever do but we need to see how the principle is applied.

Mr. Rishad Clandestine chooses two prime numbers, $p = 5$ and $q = 11$. These numbers are the secret decryption keys. Therefore, n (the public enciphering key) $= pq = 5 \cdot 11 = 55$ and $\varphi(n) = (p - 1)(q - 1) = 4 \cdot 10 = 40$. We have all the variables to begin the procedure:

- $p = 5$
- $q = 11$

- $n = 55$
- $\varphi(n) = 40$

To keep things simple, let's say that Mr. General Q. Public wants to send the number 2 to Miss Math Student. So, we let $x = 2$.

Next, Mr. Rishad Clandestine must give Mr. General Q. Public a public encryption key e. Remember, e is a natural number that is relatively prime to 40. We can choose several and we choose $e = 23$. Next, Mr. Rishad Clandestine must give Miss Math Student a secret decryption key d. Remember, d is a natural number such that $23d \equiv 1 \pmod{40}$. We let $d = 7$ since $23 \cdot 7 = 161$ and $161 \equiv 1 \pmod{40}$.

We are ready to transmit. Mr. General Q. Public must scramble or encrypt the number 2 to another number c according to the encryption function $x^e \equiv c \pmod{n}$. Since $x = 2$, $e = 23$ and $n = 55$, then:

$$2^{23} \equiv c \pmod{55}$$

You can use your scientific calculator to find c. $2^{23} = 8{,}388{,}608$ and $\dfrac{8{,}388{,}608}{55} = 152{,}520$ with remainder of 8. Therefore $2^{23} \equiv 8 \pmod{55}$. Mr. General Q. Public transmits $c = 8$ to Miss Math Student.

After receiving 8 from Mr. General Q. Public, Miss Math Student must decrypt 8 to another number y according to the decryption function $c^d \equiv y \pmod{n}$. Since $c = 8$, $d = 7$, and $n = 55$, then:

$$8^7 \equiv y \pmod{55}$$

Engage your scientific calculator again to find y. $8^7 = 2{,}097{,}152$ and $\dfrac{2{,}097{,}152}{55} = 38{,}130$ with remainder of 2. Therefore $8^7 \equiv 2 \pmod{55}$. Miss Math Student has decoded Mr. General Q. Public's message as $y = 2$. Message received!

With this simple example, we found ourselves working with large numbers, e.g., 2^{23} and 8^7. Imagine starting with two prime numbers that are 100 digits in length! The RSA code provides a safe and secure way to transmit data between companies, people, governments, schools, etc. It is the basis for securing data transmitted across the World Wide Web, i.e., the Internet, a phenomenon that burst on the historical scene in the 1990s. Until some ingenious mathematician finds a way to break this coding scheme, it will remain safe. Maybe there is no way to break this scheme. Who knows for sure?

This is a challenging lesson. We started from grade school codes to some impressive number theory. We note that mathematicians generated the RSA code from these simple mathematical principles:

- Division and remainders (mod arithmetic)
- The laws of exponents
- Basic prime number theorems
- The deductive flow of algebraic operations

PERICHORESIS

The ingenious innovation of mathematical principles can interpenetrate the world in which we live. Perichoresis can appear in surprising situations!

EXERCISES

Define the following words/symbol:

1. Cryptography
2. Plain text

Figure 4. Clock arithmetic is mod 12 arithmetic. Source: James D. Nickel.

$2 + 3 = 5$. On our clock, this means that 3 hours after 2 o'clock is 5 o'clock. In mod 12, we write: $2 + 3 \equiv 5 \pmod{12}$.

$7 + 6 = 1$. On our clock, 6 hours after 7 o'clock is 1 o'clock. In mod 12, we write: $7 + 6 \equiv 1 \pmod{12}$.

$6 + 6 = 0$. On our clock, 6 hours after 6 o'clock brings us to 12 o'clock or 0. In mod 12, we write: $6 + 6 \equiv 0 \pmod{12}$.

Clock arithmetic is a way of circular counting, a way of envisioning the straight number line as a circle.

3. Encryption
4. Symmetric cryptosystem
5. Asymmetric cryptosystem
6. Decryption
7. Cryptanalysis
8. Random sample
9. Trapdoor one-way function
10. $\equiv$
11. Fermat's Little Theorem
12. phi-function
13. Secret decryption key
14. Modulus of the RSA code
15. Pubic encryption key
16. Encryption function
17. Decryption function

Answer this question:

18. In the Sherlock Holmes mystery entitled *The "Gloria Scott"* the detective cracks the hidden message behind the following riddle: "The supply of game for London is going steadily up. Head keeper Hudson, we believe, has been now told to receive all orders for fly paper and for preservation of your hen pheasant's life." Given that Hudson was the name of a sailor under investigation and Hudson is in this message, determine the key to the riddle and crack the secret message contained therein.

Using Fermat's Little Theorem [$n^{p-1} \equiv 1 \pmod{p}$ when p is prime and n is a natural number], find k:

19. $2^4 \equiv k \pmod{5}$ (Hint: $2^4 = 16$. $\frac{16}{5}$ has what remainder?)
20. $3^6 \equiv k \pmod{7}$
21. $5^6 \equiv k \pmod{7}$
22. $5^{600} \equiv k \pmod{7}$. [Hint: $5^6 \pmod{7} \equiv 1 \pmod{7}$.]
23. $5^{668} \equiv k \pmod{7}$. (Hint: use the Product of Powers Law of exponents.)
24. $4^{10} \equiv k \pmod{11}$
25. $5^{12} \equiv k \pmod{13}$
26. For any n, $n^{12} \equiv k \pmod{13}$
27. For any n, $n^{10} \equiv k \pmod{11}$
28. For any n, $n^6 \equiv k \pmod{7}$
29. For any n, $n^4 \equiv k \pmod{5}$
30. $8^{1{,}000{,}000} \equiv k \pmod{11}$

Calculate the phi-function:

31. $\varphi(16)$
32. $\varphi(17)$
33. $\varphi(18)$
34. $\varphi(19)$
35. $\varphi(97)$
36. $\varphi(101)$

Let's try sending and receiving a number using the RSA security algorithm.

Let's choose two prime numbers, 3 and 7. Therefore, $p = 3$ and $q = 7$ (the *secret* deciphering keys).

First, we calculate the *public* enciphering key, $n = pq = 3 \cdot 7 = 21$.

Second, we calculate $\varphi(n) = (p - 1)(q - 1) = \varphi(21) = \varphi(2 \cdot 6) = 12$.

Third, we choose a public encryption key, e, such that e and $\varphi(n)$ are relatively prime. Since $\varphi(21) = 12$, we let $e = 5$. (Note: Other numbers are possible.)

Fourth, we choose a secret decryption key d such that $5d \equiv 1 \pmod{12}$. Since $5 \cdot 5 = 25$ and $\frac{25}{12} = 2$ with remainder of 1, we can set $d = 5$.

We've got all our numbers: n (public enciphering key) = 21, e (public encryption key) = 5, and d (secret decryption key) = 5.

Use a calculator to help you answer the following. Using $x^e \equiv c \pmod{n}$, let $x = 2$ and find c. (i.e., encrypt 2 to c). Using $c^d \equiv y \pmod{n}$, find y; i.e., decrypt c back to 2. Here is how we do it: Since $x = 2$, then we need to find c such that $2^5 = 32 \equiv c \pmod{21}$. $\frac{32}{21} = 1$ with remainder of 11. Therefore $c = 11$.

Now find y such that $11^5 = 161{,}051 \equiv y \pmod{21}$. With your calculator, determine $\frac{161{,}051}{21}$. The answer will be 7669.095238. The decimal expansion (i.e., 095238) is the remainder y divided by 21. From this, we know that $21 \cdot 7669 + y$ (the remainder) = 161,051. Since $21 \cdot 7669 = 161{,}049$, then y (the remainder) = 2. Success!

37. Do the same process sending 3; i.e., $x = 3$.
38. Do the same process sending 4; i.e., $x = 4$.
39. Do the same process sending 5; i.e., $x = 5$.
40. Do the same process sending 6; i.e., $x = 6$.

Answer the following questions:

41. Devise your own RSA coding scheme. Let $p = 3$ and $q = 5$. Compute n and then find smallest possible values for e and d.
42. Use your coding scheme from Question 41 to show your secret pal how to decode a secret message from you. The message you want to send is "hide". Assign each letter with a number: replace A with 1, B with 2, C with 3, ..., Z with 26. Convert your message to 4 numbers, code the message, decode it, and covert your numeric answer back to letters. Did you return to your original "hide"?

For the following questions, make use of this information:

$73^7 \equiv 83 \pmod{143}$	$83^{143} \equiv 58 \pmod{103}$	$8^{103} \equiv 83 \pmod{143}$
$74^7 \equiv 35 \pmod{143}$	$74^{143} \equiv 51 \pmod{103}$	$74^{103} \equiv 61 \pmod{143}$
$61^7 \equiv 74 \pmod{143}$	$38^{143} \equiv 29 \pmod{103}$	$73^{103} \equiv 73 \pmod{143}$
$83^7 \equiv 8 \pmod{143}$	$35^{143} \equiv 5 \pmod{103}$	$38^{103} \equiv 103 \pmod{143}$
$38^7 \equiv 25 \pmod{143}$	$8^{143} \equiv 72 \pmod{103}$	$35^{103} \equiv 74 \pmod{143}$

43. Let n (public enciphering key) = 143 and e (public encryption key) = 7.
    (a) Encrypt 61.
    (b) If d (secret decryption key) = 103, how would you decrypt the message encrypted from 61?
44. Let $n = 143$, $e = 7$, and $d = 103$.
    (a) Encrypt 74.
    (b) Decrypt the message encrypted from 74.
45. Let $n = 143$, $e = 7$, and $d = 103$, decrypt a message received from 8.

Answer this final question:

46. What algorithm (procedure) must you follow to break the RSA security algorithm? That is, if you know the public numbers n and e, then how can you determine d?

The 666 Cipher

Probably one of the most famous of all ciphers is found in the book of Revelation, chapter 13, verse 18. It reads:

> Here is wisdom. Let him who has understanding calculate the number of the beast, for it is the number of a man: His number is 666.

Because of the numerical nature of ancient alphabets (letters were associated with numbers), riddles employing numbers that concealed names were common. In fact, in the ruins of Pompeii, destroyed by the violent eruption of Mount Vesuvius in AD 79, graffiti on the buildings of the walls have been noted to say, in essence, "I love her whose number is 545."

In the English translation of Revelation 13:18 from the Greek, 666 is a number in base 10, a numerical system *unknown to the ancients*. Therefore, the ancient would have understood this number in the context of Greek letters that represent numbers.

In the Greek text, 666 is written χξϛ′ where χ = 600, ξ = 60, and ϛ′ = 6. χ is the Christian symbol for Christ where χ is the first letter of the Greek word *christos*. ϛ′ is the Christian symbol for Cross where ϛ′ is the first sound [st] of the Greek word *stauros* meaning "cross." ξ, pronounced as "x" in relax, is the symbol and sound for serpent. Can you hear the "hiss"? In these three Greek letters we see symbolized (1) the guaranteed victory of the Cross of Christ over the machinations of Satan and (2) there is a real battle, a 666 satanically inspired battle, against the people of God and the Lord Jesus Christ.

New Testament scholars have determined that the John the Revelator, banished to the island of Patmos by the authorities of the Roman Emperor Domitian (81-96), wrote Revelation ca. 90 AD and chapter 13 is John's prophetic interpretation for seven churches in Asia Minor (present-day Turkey) of the persecuted life of the early Christians under the savage reign of the Emperor Nero (54-68). To protect John's readers from governmental authorities, the identity of the beastly nature of Rome is coded in Hebrew. Neron Kaiser (*Nrwn Qsr*), written and read from right to left, is:

נֵרוֹנ קֵסַר

The sum (calculation) of the number values of these letters, from right to left, is:

$$50 + 200 + 6 + 50 + 100 + 60 + 200 = 666$$

13.13 Dancing in Addition

An **arithmetic sequence** is a list of numbers that follow a particular pattern; after the first term, each successive term is obtained by the addition of a constant number to the preceding term.

Terms & Concepts Introduced
1. Arithmetic sequence
2. Arithmetic series
3. Gaussian formula
4. Series

Finite arithmetic sequence: 1, 2, 3, 4
Infinite arithmetic sequence: 1, 2, 3, 4, …

What is the pattern to these sequences? Add 1.

When we sum a sequence, it becomes a **series**. An **arithmetic series** is a sum of numbers in which we obtain each term by the addition of a constant number to the preceding term. A series is a sequence of terms combined by addition. An arithmetic series is the dance of addition.

Finite arithmetic series: 1 + 2 + 3 + 4
Infinite arithmetic series: 1 + 2 + 3 + 4 + …

Ancient Greek mathematicians dressed properties of numbers in geometric clothes. For example, we can view the sum of the first four natural numbers as two-dimensional squares placed on top of each other (Figure 1). One new square is added to the configuration to illustrate 1 + 2 + 3 + 4. How can we determine the sum without counting the squares one by one? We double the configuration to create a rectangle, multiplying to find the area of the rectangle, and then dividing that result by 2.

Figure 1.

The resulting configuration is a 4 by 5 rectangle (Figure 2). The area is 20 square units. Dividing 20 by 2 gives us 10, the sum of the first four natural numbers.

1 + 2 + 3 + 4 = 10

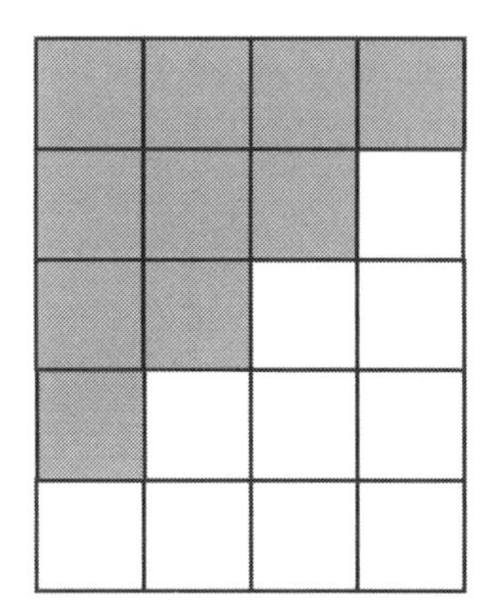

Figure 2.

Mr. City Slicker once visited Mr. Farmer and asked him how many cows he had in his pasture. The farmer responded, "Why, that is easy. I simply count the number of legs and divide by four." In a similar way, this is what ancient Greek mathematicians did to find the sum of 1 + 2 + 3 + 4. They doubled the sum of the count and then divided by 2.

Figure 3. Source: Public Domain.

One day in arithmetic class, the teacher of the renowned mathematician Carl Friedrich Gauss (1777-1855), must have needed a break from the stresses and strains of the day, so he decided to give his class some busy work. Of course, we know that no teacher ever gives busy work to students. He wrote this problem on the blackboard, "Add up all the numbers from 1 to 100." As soon as he removed his chalk from the blackboard, the teacher sat down at his desk thinking confidently, "Ah, some rest, finally. This problem ought to keep these pesky children busy for some time." No luck, Mr. Teacher, you forgot that Carl Friedrich Gauss was in your class.

Figure 4. Carl Friedrich Gauss. Source: Public Domain.

Within seconds, student Gauss got up, walked forward, and placed his slate face down on the teacher's desk. Incredulously, the teacher turned the slate over and saw written on it just one number: 5050. Gauss was right, but how did he do it so fast? Can you figure it out? Review the relevant homework exercise in Lesson 4.7.

Here is how Gauss reasoned. We must find the sum of:

$1 + 2 + 3 + 4 + 5 + \ldots + 96 + 97 + 98 + 99 + 100$

Instead of proceeding from left to right, like all of Gauss's fellow students did, Gauss paused to think first. He did this in his mind:

$1 + 2 + 3 + 4 + 5 + \ldots + 96 + 97 + 98 + 99 + 100$
$100 + 99 + 98 + 97 + 96 + \ldots + 5 + 4 + 3 + 2 + 1$

He saw these relationships:

$1 + 100 = 101$
$2 + 99 = 101$
$3 + 98 = 101$
$4 + 97 = 101$
$3 + 98 = 101$
etc.

How many of these sums are there? There are 50. (Note: The last sum is $50 + 51$.) After 50 such additions, the sums taken from the beginning and the end finally meet in the middle. Therefore, we have 50 sums all totaling 101. The product is:

$50 \times 101 = 50(100 + 1) = 5000 + 50 = 5050$

SUM OF A FINITE ARITHMETIC SERIES

Here is another version of the type of problem that Gauss solved. Consider the sum of the first nine natural numbers:

$1 + 2 + 3 + 4 + 5 + 6 + 7 + 8 + 9$

We see the same sort of pattern as Gauss encountered summing up the first 100 numbers with one important difference. We are summing an odd number of terms.

The process that Gauss used works until we get to the middle number in the series, 5. It stands there by itself. We do not get a constant number of sums that equal 10. Since five stands by itself, can we discover a sum rule around it? We see this:

$1 + 9 = 10$
$2 + 8 = 10$
$3 + 7 = 10$
$4 + 6 = 10$

We have got four tens and five more. Therefore, our sum is 45. How does 45 relate to 5? $45/5 = 9$. Do you see a connection? There are nine terms, the middle term, the mode, is 5, and $9 \times 5 = 45$, the sum of the nine terms.

To show how this will always work for the sum of any odd number of consecutive terms, rewrite the series as follows:

$1 + 2 + 3 + 4 + 5 + 6 + 7 + 8 + 9 = 45$
$9 + 8 + 7 + 6 + 5 + 4 + 3 + 2 + 1 = 45$

Let's compare the first row with the second. Look at Table 1.

Table 1

1	2	3	4	5	6	7	8	9
+8	+6	+4	+2	0	-2	-4	-6	-8
9	8	7	6	5	4	3	2	1

To get the first term in the second row, we add 8 to the first term in the first row. To get the last term in the second row, we subtract 8 to the last term in the first row. Both terms sum to 10. We then add 6 to the second term of the first row to get the second term of the second row and subtract 6 from the eighth term of the first row to get the eighth term of the second row. For the second time, both terms sum to 10. Next, we add 4 to the third term of the first row to get the third term of the second row and subtract 4 from the seventh term of the first row to get the seventh term of the second row. The pattern still holds: For the third time, both terms sum to 10. Next, we add 2 to the fourth term of the first row to get the fourth term of the second row and subtract 2 from the sixth term of the first row to get the sixth term of the second row. For the fourth time, both terms sum to 10. The fifth term of both rows is 5. Summing, we get 10 for the fifth time. By this method, we have rewritten the given series as a multiplication problem, i.e., nine groups of 10. Dividing this product by 2, we get $90/2 = 45$, the sum of $1 + 2 + 3 + 4 + 5 + 6 + 7 + 8 + 9$.

We have seen two principles illustrated: one for the sum of an even number of consecutive terms and the other for the sum of an odd number of consecutive terms. Is there a way that we can unite these two procedures? We can, if we use Mr. Farmer's approach.

Let's consider these sums:

$1 + 2 + 3 + 4 + 5 + 6$
$1 + 2 + 3 + 4 + 5 + 6 + 7$

Let's write down each addition problem twice:

Group 1:
$1 + 2 + 3 + 4 + 5 + 6$
$6 + 5 + 4 + 3 + 2 + 1$

Group 2:
$1 + 2 + 3 + 4 + 5 + 6 + 7$
$7 + 6 + 5 + 4 + 3 + 2 + 1$

Now, sum up the numbers by columns:

Group 1:
$1 + 2 + 3 + 4 + 5 + 6$
$\underline{6 + 5 + 4 + 3 + 2 + 1}$
$7 + 7 + 7 + 7 + 7 + 7$

Group 2:
$1 + 2 + 3 + 4 + 5 + 6 + 7$
$\underline{7 + 6 + 5 + 4 + 3 + 2 + 1}$
$8 + 8 + 8 + 8 + 8 + 8 + 8$

In the first group of sums, we have 6 groups of 7, or $6 \times 7 = 42$. Note the sum of the first and last term: $1 + 6 = 7$ and there are 6 terms (6×7). In the second group of sums, we have 7 groups of 8, or $7 \times 8 = 56$. Note the sum of the first and last term: $1 + 7 = 8$ and there are 7 terms (7×8).

In the first group, since 42 is twice the sum of the series, all we need to do is divide by 2 to get the sum of each series: 42/2 = 21. In the second group, since 56 is twice the sum of the series, all we need to do is divide by 2 to get the sum of each series: 56/2 = 28.

We have our rule:

Sum the first and the last term, multiply this sum by the number of terms, and then divide that answer by 2.

Let's try this rule on the series Gauss solved. Sum the first and last terms:

$$1 + 100 = 101$$

Multiply by the number of terms and then divide by 2:

$$\frac{101 \times 100}{2}$$

Of course, we can cancel:

$$\frac{101 \times \overset{50}{\cancel{100}}}{\underset{1}{\cancel{2}}}$$

We end up with 101 × 50 = 5050.

Let's do some exploring. This rule works for summing consecutive numbers. Will it also work for sums of numbers that succeed each other by equal steps? For example, consider 4 + 8 + 12 + 16 + 20. Note that every succeeding term is 4 more than the previous term, or we add 4 to a given term to get the next term.

Calculate the sum of the first and last terms:

$$4 + 20 = 24$$

Multiply 24 by the number of terms, 5 in this case, and divide the result by 2:

$$\frac{24 \times 5}{2}$$

Cancel:

$$\frac{\overset{12}{\cancel{24}} \times 5}{\underset{1}{\cancel{2}}} = 60$$

Does it work? Is 60 the sum? You bet it works because 4 + 8 + 12 + 16 + 20 = 60.

We can now write this formula algebraically. We first let the letter S_n represent the sum of a finite arithmetic series with n terms. We represent that series, in general and in subscript notation, as $t_1 + t_2 + t_3 + \ldots + t_n$. We read the first term, t_1, as "t sub 1." Therefore:

$S_n = t_1 + t_2 + t_3 + \ldots + t_n$

Applying our law, we have this nifty formula, the **Gaussian Formula**, in symbols where the letter n represents the number of terms in the series:

$$S_n = \frac{n(t_1 + t_n)}{2}$$

The Key Elements of the Arithmetic Series:

- The common difference
- The first term
- The last term
- The number of terms
- The sum of the series

Make sure you understand the symbols and make sure you note the condition that makes the formula work; i.e., the difference between each term in the sum must be constant.

THE AREA OF A TRAPEZOID

What is amazing in mathematics is the discovery of interpenetrating, indeed, perichoretic connections. The Gaussian Formula should remind you of the formula a trapezoid that we proved for in the homework of Lesson 13.1. The formula for the area of the trapezoid $ABCD$ (Figure 5), or $\alpha(ABCD)$, with height h and bases b_1 and b_2 is:

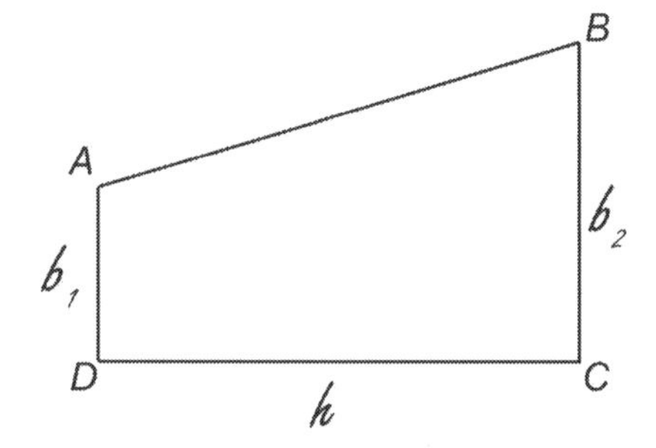

Figure 5.

$$\alpha(ABCD) = \frac{1}{2}h(b_1 + b_2) = \frac{h(b_1 + b_2)}{2}$$

Compare this formula with the Gaussian Formula. They are the same. This observation means that the area of the trapezoid, the area under $\overline{AB}$, is the sum of the arithmetic series containing h terms. Amazing, isn't it? You will revisit this connection again when you study Integral Calculus, a method the enables you to find areas, not just under straight line segments, but under curves.

FREE-FALL MOTION

In physics, we encounter arithmetic sequences on a regular basis. This sequence is embedded in the analysis of free-fall motion. In the 17th century, Galileo Galilei (1564-1642) used inclined planes to study the motion of falling bodies. (See the relevant homework exercises in Lesson 12.12.) He slowed down the motion in this way so that he could time what was happening with either his heartbeat or a water clock. Figure 6 shows the results of one of his experiments. He divided the inclined plane into equal units of distance and noted that after one heartbeat, a spherical ball
"falls" one unit. After two heartbeats, it falls three units for a sum of four units fallen altogether. After three heartbeats, it falls five units for a sum of nine units. We can summarize Figure 6 in Table 2.

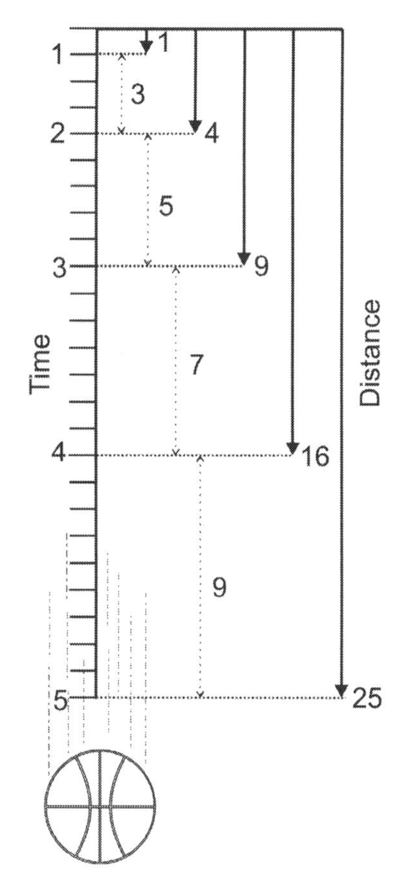

Figure 6.

Table 2		
Time (heartbeats)	Units Traveled During that Interval	Total Units Travelled
1	1	$1 = 1^2$
2	3	$4 = 2^2$
3	5	$9 = 3^2$
4	7	$16 = 4^2$
5	9	$25 = 5^2$

What is fascinating about this table is the appearance of the sequence of positive odd integers that represent the units travelled in a given time interval associated with the sequence of positive squares that represent the total units travelled. The sequence of natural numbers (1, 2, 3, 4, 5, …), the sequence of positive odd integers (1, 3, 5, 7, 9, …), and the sequence of the squares of the sequence of natural numbers (1, 4, 9, 16, 25, …) interpenetrate.

Suppose Galileo timed the fall by two heartbeats instead of one. After two heartbeats, one unit of two heartbeats, the ball falls four units. After four heartbeats, two units of two heartbeats, it falls 12 (5 + 7) units for a sum of 16 units fallen altogether. After six heartbeats, three units of two heartbeats, it falls 20 (9 + 11) units for a sum of 36 units. We can summarize our analysis in Table 3.

Table 3		
Time (heartbeats)	Units Traveled During that Interval	Total Units Travelled
2	4	$4 = 2^2$
4	12	$16 = 4^2$
6	20	$36 = 6^2$
8	28	$64 = 8^2$
10	36	$100 = 10^2$

Note again how the total units travelled are perfect squares, the squares of 2, 4, 6, 8, 10, …. Note also that the distances 4, 12, 20, 28, 36, … coinhere in the sequence 1, 3, 5, 7, 9, …. We see this by noting:

$1 \times 4 = 4$

$3 \times 4 = 12$

$5 \times 4 = 20$

$7 \times 4 = 28$

$9 \times 4 = 36$

It doesn't matter what time interval we choose, we find the dance of the sequence of positive odd integers embedded in units travelled in that interval, a beautiful perichoretic relation.

> We cannot grasp connections in math unless we grasp perichoresis and we can only grasp perichoresis in the light of the personal relations known from eternity in the Trinity.
>
> James D. Nickel

Galileo also discerned that a number acted as a constant in his experimentation, a number that coordinated everything about his observations. We let that number be g. In Table 2, $g = 2$, the constant difference between the numbers in column two. In Table 3, $g = 8$, the constant difference between the numbers in column two.

From his experiments and using trigonometry, Galileo was able to determine what happens in true free-fall. Study Table 4 where time is in seconds, distance is in feet, and the second and third columns are arithmetic sequences.

Table 4

Term	Time (s)	Distance Traveled (ft) During that Second	Total Distance Travelled
1st	1	16	16
2nd	2	48	64
3rd	3	80	144
4th	4	112	256
5th	5	144	400

In column three, the sequence of numbers is again related to the sequence of positive odd integers:

$1 \times 16 = 16$

$3 \times 16 = 48$

$5 \times 16 = 80$

$7 \times 16 = 112$

$9 \times 16 = 144$

The common difference in the third column is 32 (Lesson 10.6), the value of g in free-fall. Do you see that the common difference in columns two and three are equivalent to our delta analysis, Δx and Δy, for linear equations or linear functions? Every arithmetic sequence is revealing this linear relationship. Let's recast Table 4 to Table 5 to demonstrate this connection.

Table 5

x	Δx	y	Δy
1		16	
2	1	48	32
3	1	80	32
4	1	112	32
5	1	144	32

What is the formula relating y, the distance travelled in each second, to x? See it?

$y = 32x - 16$

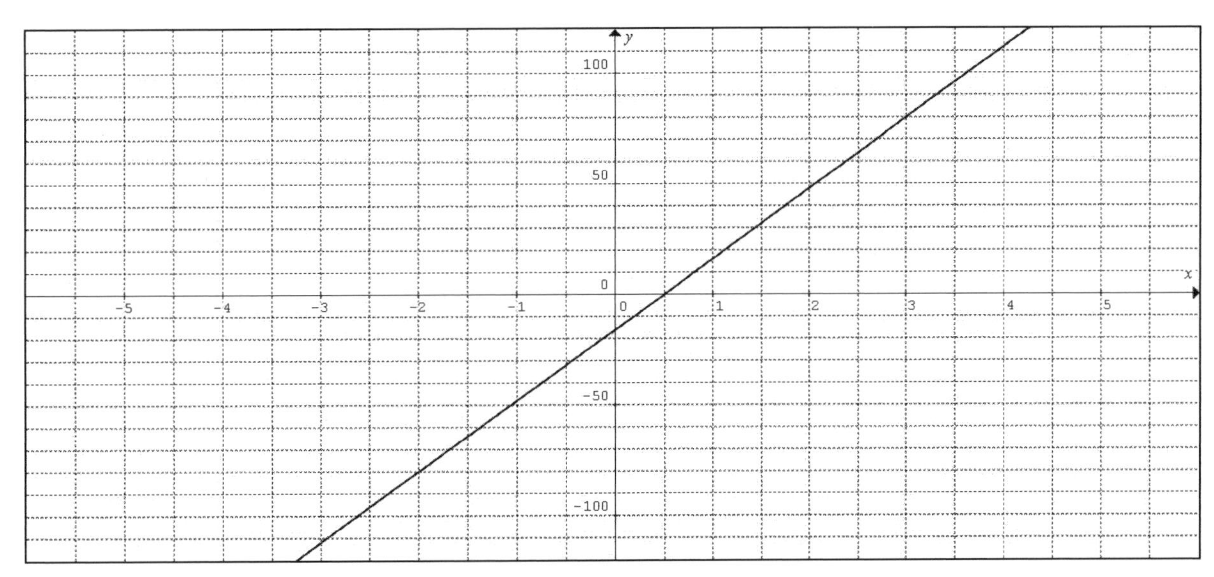

Figure 7. $y = 32x - 16$ (This continuous graph is valid only in Quadrant I.)

Since $\frac{\Delta y}{\Delta x} = \frac{32}{1} = 32$, the rate of change is the slope of the line. In an arithmetic sequence, the slope is revealed as the common difference between terms or $\frac{\Delta y}{\Delta x}$, the constant of proportionality. For now, just remember that an arithmetic sequence reveals a linear pattern, a linear function. An arithmetic sequence coinheres, therefore, in a linear function. This coinherence is a truly beautiful mathematical connection, a revelation of perichoresis in action.

In physics, 32, the rate of change, represents the acceleration on an object in free fall due to the downward pull of the gravity of the Earth. In the words of Galileo, "velocity goes on increasing, after departure from rest, in simple proportionality to the time."[1] In other words, in free-fall motion where air resistance is disregarded, the velocity of an object, its change in distance over time (Δy in column four of Table 5), increases at a constant rate of 32 feet per second every second. In symbols, we write 32 ft/s^2 where s^2 means "per second every second." We can write a function to determine this velocity v in terms of time t. It is a simple linear function:

$v = 32t$

Table 6 reveals this linear relationship, where Δv is the change in velocity, the proportionality constant equal to g, the gravitational of acceleration constant.[2]

Table 6

t	v	Δv
0	0	0
1	32	32
2	64	32
3	96	32

[1] Galileo Galilei, *Dialogues Concerning Two New Sciences* (New York: Dover Publications, [1914] 1954), p. 167.

[2] Of course, in free-fall motion, velocity does not increase forever. There is a terminal velocity that every object in free-fall eventually reaches, if it does not hit the ground first.

Table 6		
t	v	Δv
4	128	32
5	160	32

In the equation $y = 32x - 16$, y represents the distance travelled in each second. Can we develop a formula for the total distance d travelled in time t? We want to find a formula that gives us the last column in Table 4. We know that this formula will involve a square function. Let's begin by writing the basic square function forming the parabola:

$d = t^2$

Using this formula, we get Table 7.

Table 7		
t	d	Total Distance Travelled
0	0	0
1	1	16
2	4	64
3	9	144
4	16	256
5	25	400

Our values for d are too small. We know that g is related to this function and the relationship must be multiplicative. If $g = 32$, we have this formula:

$d = 32t^2$

Table 8 gives us our results.

Table 8		
t	d	Total Distance Travelled
0	0	0
1	32	16
2	128	64
3	288	144
4	512	256
5	800	400

Our values for d are now too large. Do you see what how to fix things? Divide by 2, or multiply by ½. Our final formula becomes, a formula that Galileo also determined:

$$d = \left(t^2\right)\left(\frac{1}{2}\right)(32) \Leftrightarrow d = 16t^2$$

For any value of g, we can relate time to velocity to total distance travelled using the relationships in Table 9.

Table 9

t	0	1	2	3	4	5		
v	0	g	$2g$	$3g$	$4g$	$5g$	...	gt
d	0	$\frac{1}{2}g$	$4\cdot\frac{1}{2}g$	$9\cdot\frac{1}{2}g$	$16\cdot\frac{1}{2}g$	$25\cdot\frac{1}{2}g$	...	$\frac{1}{2}gt^2$

The velocity row represents an arithmetic sequence with a common difference of g. The distance row represents the famous time-squared law that Galileo discovered governed the distance an object freely falls in time t.

EXERCISES

Define the following terms:

1. Series
2. Arithmetic sequence
3. Arithmetic series
4. Gaussian formula

Answer the following questions:

5. What does Chaos Theory teach us about making small errors in our starting assumption(s) if we want build an axiomatic-deductive system from them? (Hint: Refer to the homework question in Lesson 13.10.)
6. What is the relationship between arithmetic sequences and linear equations?
7. Solve $S_n = \frac{n(t_1 + t_n)}{2}$ for n.
8. Solve $S_n = \frac{n(t_1 + t_n)}{2}$ for t_1.
9. Solve $S_n = \frac{n(t_1 + t_n)}{2}$ for t_n.
10. How many gifts are given for the traditional twelve days of Christmas? On the first day of Chrismas, my true love gave to me: a partridge in a pair tree …

t_1

$t_2 = t_1 + d$

$t_3 = t_1 + 2d$

$t_4 = t_1 + 3d$

$t_5 = t_1 + 4d$ $\quad d$ = common difference

$t_6 = t_1 + 5d$

$t_7 = t_1 + 6d$

$t_8 = t_1 + 7d$

Figure 8.

11. (a) In a soccer league of six teams, for each team to play all the other teams the teams must play in how many games?

(b) If there are seven teams, the teams must play in how many games?
(c) If there are 12 teams, the teams must play in how many games?

12. Derive a formula for finding the nth term of an arithmetic sequence. (Hint: Use Figure 8 to help you.)
13. Find the 16th term of the sequence 123, 120, 117, 114, …
14. In the arithmetic sequence 1, 4, 7, 10, 13, 16, find the arithmetic mean of:
    (a) The first and third term.
    (b) The second and fourth term.
    (c) The third and fifth term.
    (d) The fourth and sixth term.
    (e) What conclusion can you draw from these observations?

Table 10: Summary of Arithmetic Sequence Analysis	
Common Difference	$d = t_n - t_{n-1}$
Recursive Formula	If we know t_1, $t_n = t_{n-1} + d$ for $n \geq 2$
Explicit Formula	$t_n = t_1 + (n - 1)d$

Answer these questions about important relationships in the physics of free-fall motion:

15. Solve $v = gt$ for t.
16. Rewrite $d = \frac{1}{2}gt^2$ as d in terms of g and v.
17. Solve the equation you derived in Question 16 for v in terms of g and d. Solve only for the positive root. This equation did not occur to Galileo. The Dutch mathematician and scientist Christiaan Huygens (1629-1695) was probably the first person to appreciate its significance for further scientific study.

What number(s) must be substituted for the variable(s) in the following arithmetic sequences?

18. 9, 12, 15, x
19. 13, x, 23, 28
20. 9, x, y, 57
21. x, 25, 20, y
22. 18, x, 0, y
23. 9, x, y, 10
24. -3, x, y, z, 17
25. $\frac{3}{10}, x, \frac{1}{2}, \frac{3}{5}$

Figure 9. Count the number of windows, the Gaussian way. Source: Wenatchee, Washington, James D. Nickel

Using the Gaussian formula, find the sum of the following.

26. 3 + 9 + 15 + 21 + 27 + 33
27. 7 + 14 + 21 + 28 + 35 + 42
28. 20 + 25 + 30 + 35 + 40
29. 15 + 18 + 21 + 24 + 27 + 30
30. 1 + 2 + 3 + 4 + … + 64
31. 8 + 16 + 24 + … + 200
32. -46 + -43 + -40 + … + 2

In the following arithmetic sequences, find the term indicated:

33. 1, 7, 13, … ; 15th term
34. 15, 22, 29, …; 8th term
35. 90, 87, 83, …; 25th term
36. 19, 8, -3, …; 40th term

37. -15, -15, -15, …; 118th term

Find the sum of indicated arithmetic sequences:
38. The first 8 terms of 8, 14, 20, …
39. The first 10 terms of 41, 45, 49, …
40. The first 20 terms of 19, 14, 9, …
41. The first 100 terms of 90, 89.5, 89, …

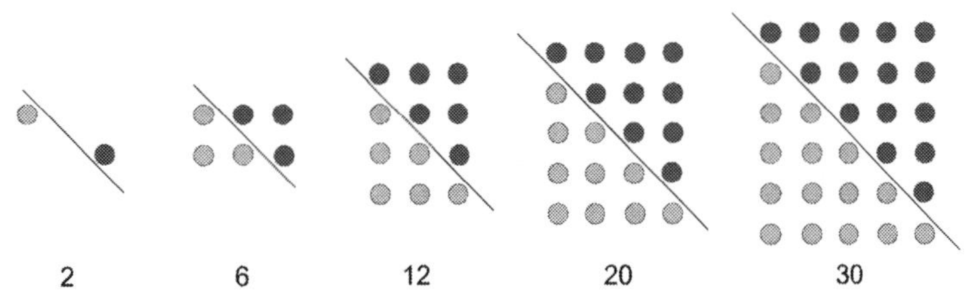

Figure 10. The first five oblong numbers.

For the following questions, use the oblong numbers depicted in Figure 10 as an aid:
42. (a) Generate a two-column table representing the first six oblong numbers.
(b) Extend this table by using delta analysis to determine the formula for finding the nth oblong number. (Hint: Review the relevant homework problems in Lesson 11.6 and 11.11.)
43. Graph your formula on the x-y coordinate plane.

Figure 11. Signature of 17-year-old Carl Friedrich Gauss (ca. 1794). Source: Public Domain

13.14 DANCING IN MULTIPLICATION

Terms & Concepts Introduced
1. φ
2. Chromatic scale
3. Exponential function
4. Exponential model (base e)
5. Geometric sequence
6. Geometric series
7. Golden ratio
8. Logistics model
9. Standard form of the exponential decay function
10. Standard form of the exponential growth function

What is the difference between Sequence 1 and Sequence 2?

Sequence 1. 2, 4, 6, 8
Sequence 2. 1, 2, 4, 8, 16

Sequence 1 is arithmetic because the common difference is 2. In Sequence 2, instead of a common difference, there is a common ratio between each term in the sequence. The common ratio, or common multiplier, is 2.

In a **geometric sequence**, there is a common ratio or common multiplier between terms. We determine each successive term by multiplying by the same number. The sum of a geometric sequence is a **geometric series**.

We continue Sequence 2 by adding several terms.

1, 2, 4, 8, 16, 32, 64

As a series, we have:

$1 + 2 + 4 + 8 + 16 + 32 + 64$

Can you use the Gaussian Formula to find the sum? No. Is there something special about the terms? Yes, they are powers of 2. We could rewrite the series as follows:

$2^0 + 2^1 + 2^2 + 2^3 + 2^4 + 2^5 + 2^6$

EXPONENTIAL FUNCTION

The formula for the nth term of this geometric sequence, i.e., just the listing of the terms, is 2^{n-1}. In functional notation, we write:

$y = f(x) = 2^{x-1}$ (See Figure 1 for a graph of this function.)

This function is an **exponential function.** Scientists use these types of functions to understand problems of growth and decay. (See Lesson 12.5, especially the last homework question.)

EXPONENTIAL GROWTH AND DECAY

The **standard form of the exponential growth and decay function**, where a and b are parameters, is:

$y = f(x) = ab^x$

For growth, the conditions on the parameters are:

$a > 0, b > 1$

We also note that the general form of the compound interest model (Lesson 8.16) matches the standard form:

$A = P(1 + r)^t$, where P replaces a and $1 + r$, where r is the percentage growth as a decimal, replaces b.

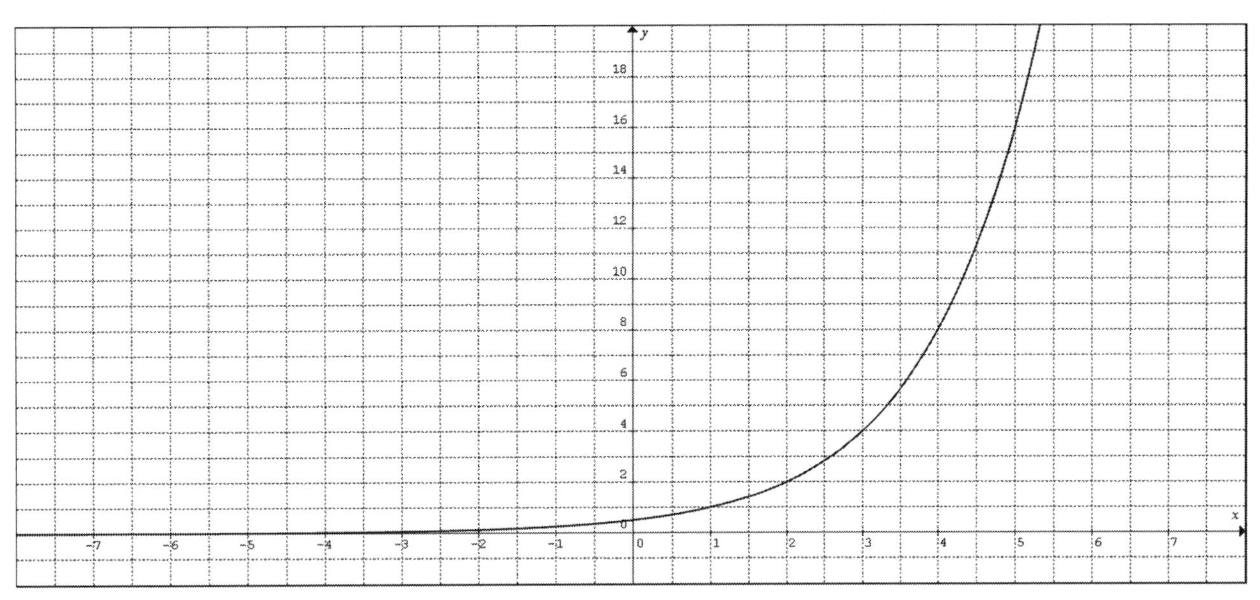

Figure 1. $y = f(x) = 2^{x-1}$ (The exponential function as a continuous curve.)

For decay, the conditions on the parameters are:

$a > 0, 0 < b < 1$

The boundary condition on b mean that the base is a proper fraction. When we compute increasing powers of a fraction, the result, the image, becomes lesser and lesser.

We graph two simple examples of these grown models (Figure 2), $y = f(x) = 3(2^x)$ and $y = f(x) = 3(0.5^x)$. The line of symmetry, the y-axis acting as a line of reflection, exists because 2 is the reciprocal of $0.5 = \frac{1}{2}$.

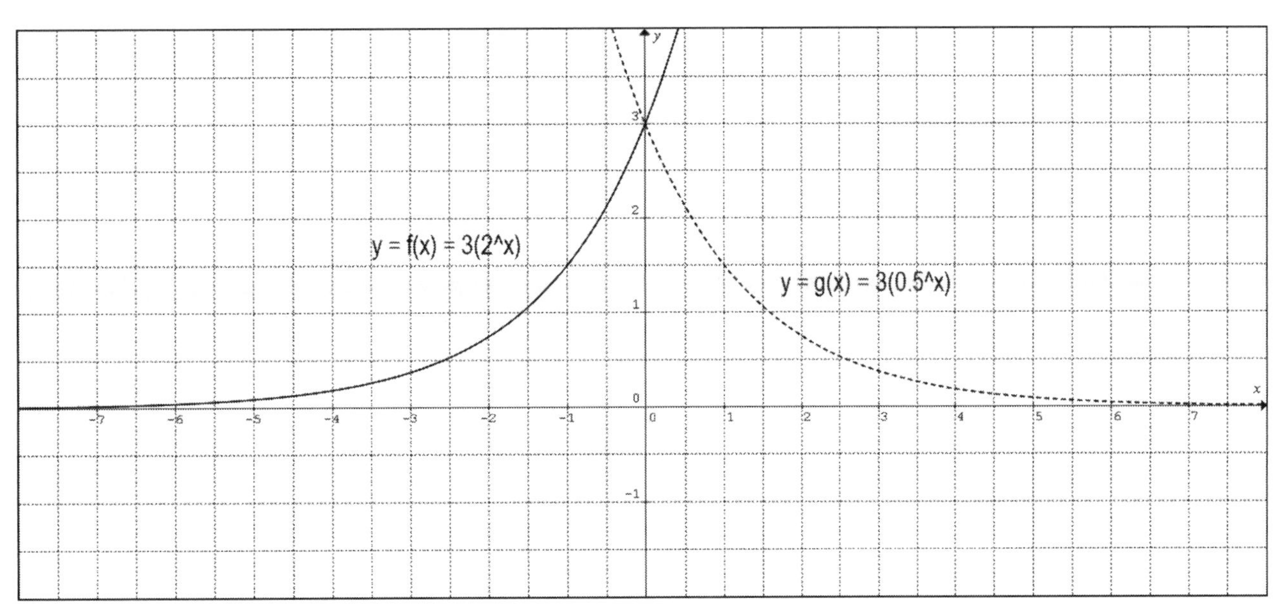

Figure 2. Growth and Decay functions.

Since interest compounded continually converges to e, the base of the natural logarithms, or $\lim_{n\to\infty}\left(1+\frac{1}{n}\right)^n = e$ (Lesson 8.16), we can use e to model both growth and decay in time.

The **exponential model with *e* as the base** for an amount $P(t)$, at time t is:

$P(t) = P(0)e^{kt}$

This model has two parameters, $P(0)$, the initial amount, and k, the exponential growth/decay parameter.

The equation models growth when $e^k > 1$ and this happens when $k > 0$.

The equation models decay when $e^k < 1$ and this happens when $k < 0$.

Of course, when $k = 0$, there is no growth or decay, the initial amount does not change over time; i.e., $P(t) = P(0)$ for all t.

Figure 3 is an example of growth and decay using this model.

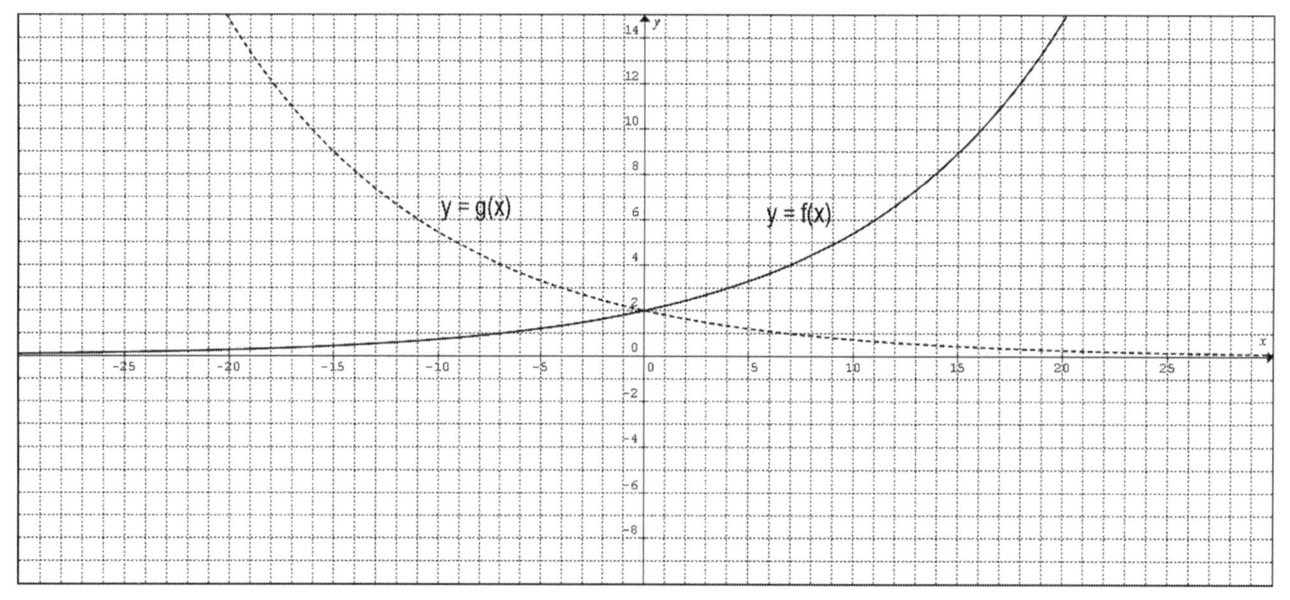

Figure 3. Growth [$y = f(x) = 2e^{0.1x}$] and Decay [$y = g(x) = 2e^{-0.1x}$] functions with e as base.

LOGISTICS MODEL

Is there a limit to exponential growth or decay? In the world that we know, populations that are given unlimited resources, whether they be people, animals, or bacteria, will grow exponentially. In most situations, though, resources are limited. If a chemist puts bacteria in a petri dish with a good environment and plenty of food, the bacteria will grow exponentially until they fill the dish. As resources deplete, growth slows until the population reaches a maximum number that the petri dish can hold. In this context, scientists use mathematical methods to develop a formula, the **Logistics model**, that recognizes growth with restraints. If p is the population at time $t = 0$, b is the limiting population, and k is the parameter for growth rate, the population at time t, $P(t)$, is determined by this formula:

$$P(t) = \frac{bp}{p+(b-p)e^{-kt}}$$

If t is very large, i.e., as $t \to \infty$, what is the value of $P(t)$? We suspect it should be b, the limiting population. Let's see how we can confirm our conjecture by first inspecting the term in the denominator involving t, i.e., e^{-kt}. We know that as $t \to \infty$, $e^{-kt} \to 0$. Let $k = 1$, and note what happens when you graph $y = e^{-x}$. Using limit notation, we write:

$$\lim_{t \to \infty} e^{-kt} = 0$$

We now use algebraic operations to find $P(t)$. We write:

$$P(t) = \frac{bp}{p + (b - p)0} \Leftrightarrow P(t) = \frac{b\cancel{p}^{1}}{\cancel{p}_{1}} \Leftrightarrow P(t) = b$$

As we have intuited, the value of $P(t) \to b$, the limiting population, as $t \to \infty$. Our algebraic work confirms our intuition. Using limit notation, we write:

$$\lim_{t \to \infty} \frac{bp}{p + (b - p)e^{-kt}} = b$$

If $k = 0.2$, $b = 10{,}000$, and $p = 2000$, Figure 4 is the graph of this situation.

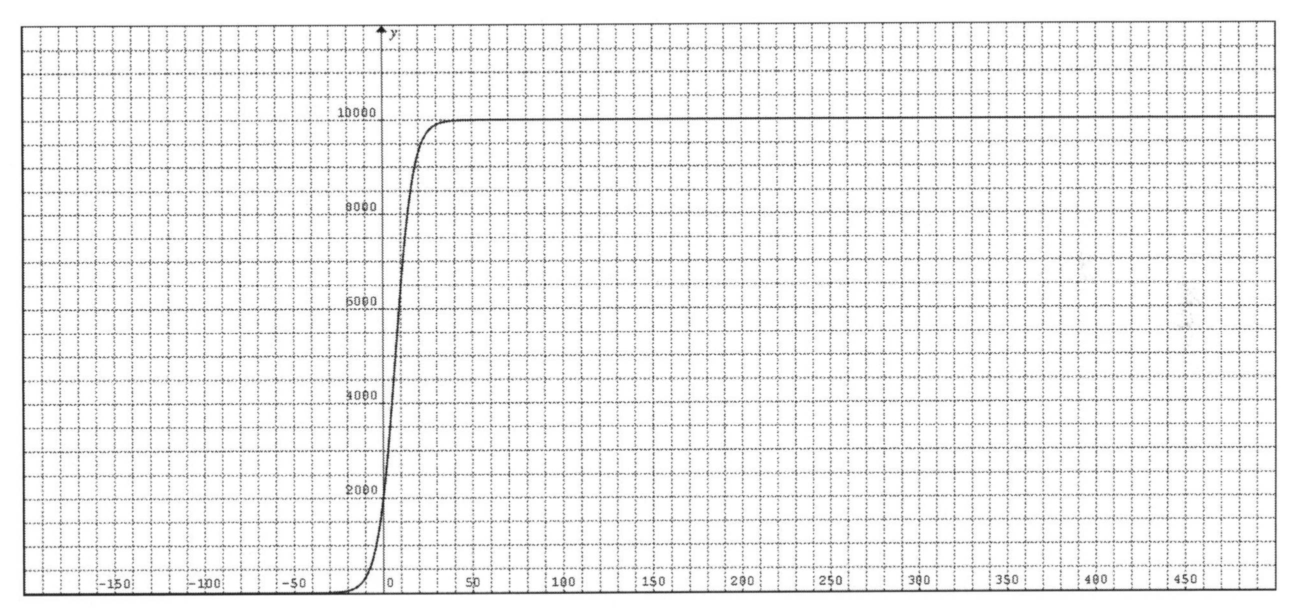

Figure 4. Logistics Model.

When $t = 0$, the initial population is 2000. This population grows at an exponential rate until it reaches a maximum of 10,000. The domain of this function is restricted: $[0, \infty)$. In this representation, ∞ means unlimited time which, according to the context, would be unnecessary. The range is also restricted: $[2000, 10{,}000)$.
Since the function reaches 10,000 as a limit,) is used in the boundary notation instead of].

Suppose we want to find the time it takes for the population to reach 9000. We let $P(t) = 9000$ and solve for t. Assuming t is in hours, follow along:

$$9000 = \frac{20{,}000{,}000}{2000 + 8000e^{-0.2t}} \Leftrightarrow 9000\left(2000 + 8000e^{-0.2t}\right) = 20{,}000{,}000 \Leftrightarrow$$

$9\left(2000+8000e^{-0.2t}\right)=20,000 \Leftrightarrow 18,000+72,000e^{-0.2t}=20,000 \Leftrightarrow$

$18+72e^{-0.2t}=20 \Leftrightarrow 9+36e^{-0.2t}=10 \Leftrightarrow 36e^{-0.2t}=1 \Leftrightarrow$

$\ln 36 + (-0.2t) = \ln 1 \Leftrightarrow -0.2t = 0 - \ln 36 \Leftrightarrow -0.2t = \ln 36 \Leftrightarrow t = \dfrac{-\ln 36}{-0.2} \Leftrightarrow$

$t \approx 17.917$ (about 17.9 hours)

POWER AND EXPONENTIAL FUNCTIONS COMPARED

Note the difference in the graph of a square or power function and an exponential function (Figure 5). In the square function, the variable is the base but in the exponential function, the variable is in the exponent. The two base functions, $y = x^2$ (square function) and $y = 2^x$ (exponential function) have two respective inverses: extraction of roots and logarithms (Lesson 13.1).

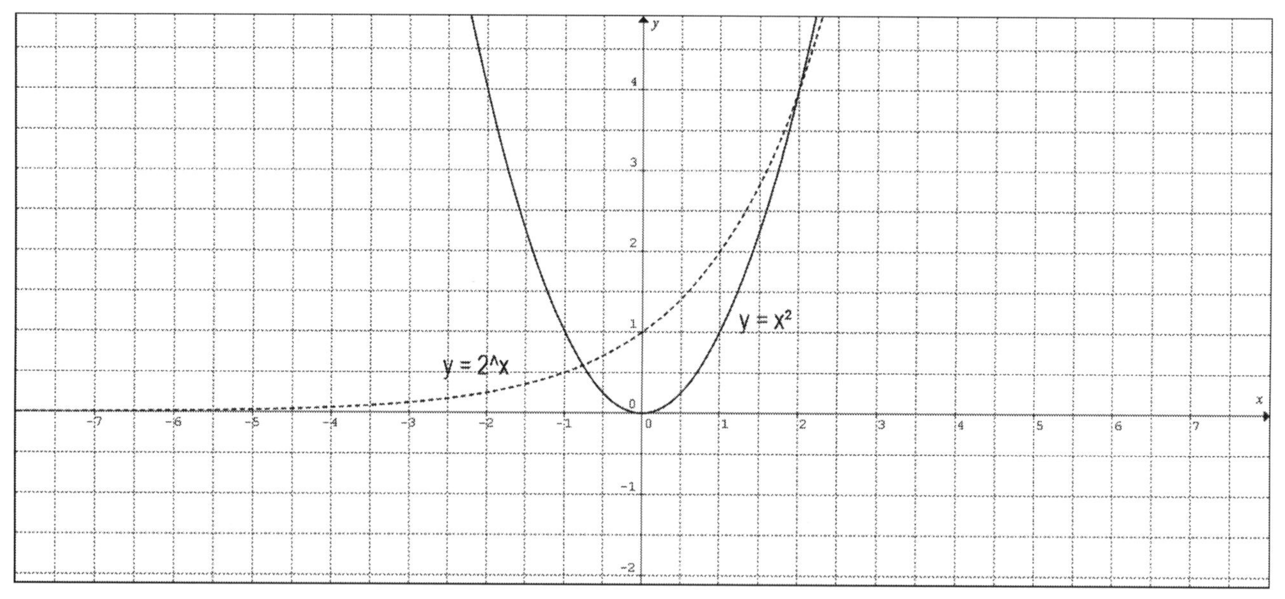

Figure 5. Power vs. Exponential Function.

Table 1 shows a few arguments with their associated images for the function $y = f(x) = 2^x$ (Lesson 11.13), a growth situation where $a = 1$ and $b = 2$.

Table 1			
x	$y = 2^x$		
-3	2^{-3}	=	$\frac{1}{2^3} = \frac{1}{8}$
-2	2^{-2}	=	$\frac{1}{2^2} = \frac{1}{4}$
-1	2^{-1}	=	$\frac{1}{2^1} = \frac{1}{2}$
0	2^0	=	1
1	2^1	=	2
2	2^2	=	4
3	2^3	=	8

BACK TO SEQUENCES

Some sequences that neither arithmetic nor geometric. For example, what is the pattern of this sequence?

$$\frac{1}{12}, \frac{2}{11}, \frac{3}{10}, \frac{4}{9}$$

What is the next term?

$$\frac{5}{8}$$

But, the sequence is neither arithmetic nor geometric.
Is this sequence geometric? If yes, what is the common multiplier?

4, 16, 64

Since there is a common multiplier, 4, the sequence is geometric. What is the formula for the nth term of this sequence?

4^n

What is the formula for the nth term of this sequence? Is it geometric? If yes, what is the common multiplier?

$$1, \frac{1}{4}, \frac{1}{9}, \frac{1}{16}, \frac{1}{25}$$

The formula is $\frac{1}{n^2}$. Since there is no common multiplier, this sequence is not geometric.

THE KING, A CHESSBOARD, AND GRAINS OF WHEAT

There is a famous legend from India that invokes the use of this series:

$2^0 + 2^1 + 2^2 + 2^3 + 2^4 + 2^5 + 2^6$

A certain King of India wanted to reward his grand vizier for inventing and presenting to him the game of chess. The clever vizier responded as he knelt before the king, "Majesty, give me a grain of wheat to put on the first square of this chessboard, and two grains to put on the second square, and four grains to put on the third, and eight grains to put on the fourth. And so, oh King, doubling the number for each succeeding square, give me enough grains to cover all 64 squares of the board." Kneading a bag of wheat with his fingers, the King replied, "You do not ask for much, oh my faithful servant. I will certainly grant your wish."

How many grains of wheat will the King need? The answer to the problem consists in summing the powers of two, from 0 to 63:

$2^0 + 2^1 + 2^2 + 2^3 + 2^4 + \ldots + 2^{63}$

Table 2 shows the number of grains of wheat in each square. If we subtract 1 from the exponent of the numbers in bold, we have Mersenne primes (Lesson 6.1).

Table 2							
2^{0}	2^{1}	2^{2}	**2^{3}**	2^{4}	2^{5}	2^{6}	2^{7}
2^{8}	2^{9}	2^{10}	2^{11}	2^{12}	2^{13}	2^{14}	2^{15}
2^{16}	2^{17}	2^{18}	2^{19}	2^{20}	2^{21}	2^{22}	2^{23}
2^{24}	2^{25}	2^{26}	2^{27}	2^{28}	2^{29}	2^{30}	2^{31}
2^{32}	**2^{33}**	2^{34}	2^{35}	2^{36}	2^{37}	2^{38}	2^{39}
2^{40}	2^{41}	2^{42}	2^{43}	2^{44}	**2^{45}**	2^{46}	**2^{47}**
2^{48}	2^{49}	2^{50}	**2^{51}**	2^{52}	2^{53}	2^{54}	2^{55}
2^{56}	**2^{57}**	2^{58}	**2^{59}**	2^{60}	**2^{61}**	**2^{62}**	2^{63}

Figure 6.

How do we find the answer? Let's revisit Zeno first by reviewing a homework question in Lesson 11.2. A resolution of his paradox will show us the way.

ZENO REVISITED

In review, one of the famous paradoxes of Zeno of Elea, the ancient Greek mathematician involves this situation: Let's say that Mr. Zeno is standing one meter from a door. Every step he takes leaves him ½ as far from the door. How far would he travel in five steps? If we let S_5 = the distance traveled in five steps, we must compute this:

Equation 1. $S_5 = \frac{1}{2} + \frac{1}{4} + \frac{1}{8} + \frac{1}{16} + \frac{1}{32}$

Follow along now because we are going to develop a formula for this sum and we are going to find it in an indirect way, similar to, but different from Mr. Farmer's technique of counting cows. Let's multiply both sides of Equation 1 by ½. We get this equation:

Equation 2. $\frac{1}{2}S_5 = \frac{1}{4} + \frac{1}{8} + \frac{1}{16} + \frac{1}{32} + \frac{1}{64}$

Now, we are going to subtract Equation 2 from Equation 1.[1] Note what disappears when we do this: $\frac{1}{4}, \frac{1}{8}, \frac{1}{16},$ and $\frac{1}{32}$ since $\frac{1}{4} - \frac{1}{4} = 0, \frac{1}{8} - \frac{1}{8} = 0,$ etc. We get:

Equation 3. $S_5 - \frac{1}{2}S_5 = \frac{1}{2} - \frac{1}{64}$

We know what to do with the left side of Equation 3. We factor the S_5 because S_5 is a common factor of both terms. We get:

[1] Adding equals to equals or subtracting equals from equals is a valid algebraic method. Euclid's Axiom 2 states, "If equals are added to equals, the whole are equal." Axiom 3 states, "If equals are subtracted from equals, the remainders are equal." Consider 5 = 5, a true statement. Subtracting 3 from both sides, we get 2 = 2, also a true statement. Adding 2 to both sides gives us 7 = 7, a true statement. We have, therefore, justified the principle of subtracting equations from equations or adding equations to equations.

$$S_5 - \frac{1}{2}S_5 = S_5\left(1 - \frac{1}{2}\right) = \frac{1}{2}S_5$$

Since $\frac{1}{64} = \frac{1}{2^6}$, we can write the right side of Equation 3 as $\frac{1}{2} - \frac{1}{2^6}$. In this expression, we note that ½ is a common factor of both terms. Factoring, we get:

$$\frac{1}{2} - \frac{1}{2^6} = \frac{1}{2}\left(1 - \frac{1}{2^5}\right)$$

We can now write Equation 4:

Equation 4. $\frac{1}{2}S_5 = \frac{1}{2}\left(1 - \frac{1}{2^5}\right)$

We can now solve for S_5 by dividing both sides of Equation 4 by ½. We get:

Equation 5. $S_5 = \dfrac{\frac{1}{2}\left(1 - \frac{1}{2^5}\right)}{\frac{1}{2}}$

We cancel on the right side:

$$\frac{\cancel{\frac{1}{2}}^{1}\left(1 - \frac{1}{2^5}\right)}{\cancel{\frac{1}{2}}_{1}}$$

We have our formula and our sum:

Equation 6. $S_5 = 1 - \frac{1}{2^5} = 1 - \frac{1}{32} = \frac{31}{32}$

Can we develop a general formula for any geometric series consisting of n terms? Let's try. As we do, we will follow what we did in Equations 1 to Equation 6 above.

First, we define some symbols. Consider the first n terms of a geometric series where the first term is t_1 and the common multiplier, or common ratio, is r. We let S_n be the sum of this series. We write:

Equation 1. $S_n = t_1 + t_1r + t_1r^2 + t_1r^3 + ... + t_1r^{n-1}$

Let's see if we can make sense of this. Given $S_5 = \frac{1}{2} + \frac{1}{4} + \frac{1}{8} + \frac{1}{16} + \frac{1}{32}$, the first term is ½ or t_1 = ½. The common multiplier or common ratio is ½ or r = ½. There are five terms so n = 5. Let's substitute $S_n = t_1 + t_1r + t_1r^2 + t_1r^3 + ... + t_1r^{n-1}$ with these numbers. We get:

$$S_5 = \frac{1}{2} + \frac{1}{2}\cdot\frac{1}{2} + \frac{1}{2}\cdot\frac{1}{2^2} + \frac{1}{2}\cdot\frac{1}{2^3} + \frac{1}{2}\cdot\frac{1}{2^4}$$

Simplifying, we get:

$$S_5 = \frac{1}{2} + \frac{1}{4} + \frac{1}{8} + \frac{1}{16} + \frac{1}{32}$$

As we did with our example, let's now multiply both sides of Equation 1 by r. Note what happens when we multiply the last term of Equation 1 by r:

$$\left(r^{n-1}\right)r = \left(r^{n-1}\right)r^1 = r^{n-1+1} = r^{n+(-1)+1} = r^{n+0} = r^n$$

We get:

Equation 2. $rS_n = t_1r + t_1r^2 + t_1r^3 + t_1r^4 + ... + t_1r^n$

As we did with our example, let's subtract Equation 2 from Equation 1. We get:

Equation 3. $S_n\left(1-r\right) = t_1\left(1-r^n\right)$

Make sure you see how this works, especially factoring of the left and right side, as we did with our example. Now, to solve for S_n, we divide both sides of Equation 3 by $(1 - r)$. We get:

Equation 4. $S_n = \dfrac{t_1\left(1-r^n\right)}{1-r}$

The key elements of the geometric series:

- The common ratio
- The first term
- The number of terms
- The sum of the series

Are there any conditions for our formula? Look at the denominator. If $r = 1$, then the denominator is zero and we cannot divide by zero. If $r = 1$, what happens to Equation 1? It becomes this:

$S_n = \underbrace{t_1 + t_1 + t_1 + t_1 + ... + t_1}_{n\ times}$ or:

$S_n = nt_1$

By our definition of multiplication, this result makes sense. But, this geometric series is not very interesting.

In our example, $r = ½$, $t_1 = ½$, and $n = 5$. Substituting these values into Equation 4, we get:

$$S_5 = \frac{\frac{1}{2}\left(1-\left(\frac{1}{2}\right)^5\right)}{\frac{1}{2}} = 1-\left(\frac{1}{2}\right)^5 = 1-\frac{1}{32} = \frac{31}{32}$$

BACK TO THE KING

Let's try the formula with the King and the grains of wheat. In this case, $r = 2$, $t_1 = 1$, and $n = 64$. Substituting these values into Equation 4, we get:

$$S_{64} = \frac{1\left(1-2^{64}\right)}{1-2} = \frac{1-2^{64}}{-1}$$

Note: $1 - 2^{64} < 0 \Rightarrow \dfrac{1-2^{64}}{-1} > 0$

Can we make $\frac{1-2^{64}}{-1}$ look a little better? We can, if we divide by -1:

$$\frac{1-2^{64}}{-1} = -(1-2^{64}) = 2^{64} - 1$$

Since 2^{64} is by far the dominant term, we can state:

$$S_{64} \approx 2^{64}$$

What is 2^{64}?
Let's use logs (Lesson 12.5). We let $x = S_{64}$. We take the log of both sides:

$$\log x = \log 2^{64} \Leftrightarrow$$
$$\log x = 64(\log 2) \Leftrightarrow$$
$$\log x = 64(0.301) \Leftrightarrow$$
$$\log x = 19.264$$

In Scientific Notation, 19 is the characteristic and 0.264 is the log of the mantissa. To find the mantissa, we must take the inverse log. From our log tables (Lesson 12.5), we know that $0.264 \approx \log 1.84$. To three significant figures, we have this equivalency:

$$10^{0.264} = 1.84 \Leftrightarrow \log 1.84 = 0.264$$

Therefore: $x = S_{64} \approx 1.84 \times 10^{19}$

1.84×10^{19} grains would be enough to cover the entire surface of the Earth with a layer of wheat one-half inch (1.3 cm) in height. If we placed that many grains in an unbroken line, the line would be two light-years in length. Remember, we define a light-year as the distance light travels in one year (Lesson 7.11). Light travels at a speed of about 186,000 mi/s (300,000 km/s). The distance of two light-years is about half the distance from Earth to the nearest star beyond our solar system, Proxima Centauri.[2] Legend tells us that when the king found out how much grain he needed to give his servant, he ordered his soldiers to behead the servant. Sometimes, it does not pay to know math.

SUMMARY

Summarizing this lesson and the last lesson:

1. We know a sequence is arithmetic if there is a constant difference between terms. Arithmetic sequences, when graphed, are linear equations or linear functions.
2. We know a sequence is geometric if there is a constant multiplier or ratio between terms. Geometric sequences, when graphed, are exponential equations or exponential functions.
3. When we sum a sequence, it is a series.
4. The formula for the sum of a finite arithmetic series is the Gaussian Formula:

$$S_n = \frac{n(t_1 + t_n)}{2}$$

[2] If we make a scale model of our solar system, and we set the Earth to be the size of a pea, the distance of Proxima Centauri to the Earth would be about 10,000 miles.

5. The formula for the sum of a finite geometric series is:

$$S_n = \frac{t_1\left(1-r^n\right)}{1-r}$$

Table 3: Powers of x						
x	**½**	**2**	**3**	**4**	**5**	**6**
x^2	$\frac{1}{4}$	4	9	16	25	36
x^3	$\frac{1}{8}$	8	27	64	125	216
$x^4 = (x^2)^2$	$\frac{1}{16}$	16	81	256	625	1296
x^5	$\frac{1}{32}$	32	243	1024	3125	7776
$x^6 = (x^2)^3$	$\frac{1}{64}$	64	729	4096	15,625	46,656
x^7	$\frac{1}{128}$	128	2187	16,384	78,125	279,936
$x^8 = (x^2)^4$	$\frac{1}{256}$	256	6561	65,536	390.625	1,679,616
x^9	$\frac{1}{512}$	512	19,683	262,144	1,953,125	10,077,696
$x^{10} = (x^2)^5$	$\frac{1}{1024}$	1024	59,049	1,048,576	9,765,625	60,466,176

EXERCISES

Define the following terms:

1. Geometric sequence
2. Geometric series
3. Exponential function
4. Golden Ratio (See homework exercise below.)
5. φ (See homework exercise below.)
6. Chromatic scale (See homework exercise below.)

Justify the following equivalencies:

7. $9000 = \frac{20,000,000}{2000 + 8000e^{-0.2t}} \Leftrightarrow 9000\left(2000 + 8000e^{-0.2t}\right) = 20,000,000$
8. $9000\left(2000 + 8000e^{-0.2t}\right) = 20,000,000 \Leftrightarrow 9\left(2000 + 8000e^{-0.2t}\right) = 20,000$
9. $9\left(2000 + 8000e^{-0.2t}\right) = 20,000 \Leftrightarrow 18,000 + 72,000e^{-0.2t} = 20,000$
10. $18,000 + 72,000e^{-0.2t} = 20,000 \Leftrightarrow 18 + 72e^{-0.2t} = 20$
11. $18 + 72e^{-0.2t} = 20 \Leftrightarrow 9 + 36e^{-0.2t} = 10$
12. $9 + 36e^{-0.2t} = 10 \Leftrightarrow 36e^{-0.2t} = 1$
13. $36e^{-0.2t} = 1 \Leftrightarrow \ln 36 + -0.2t = \ln 1$
14. $\ln 36 + -0.2t = \ln 1 \Leftrightarrow -0.2t = 0 - \ln 36$
15. $-0.2t = 0 - \ln 36 \Leftrightarrow t = \frac{-\ln 36}{-0.2}$
16. $t = \frac{-\ln 36}{-0.2} \Leftrightarrow t \approx 17.917$

Using the logistics model, answer the following questions:

17. Let $b = 200$, $p = 300$ and $k = 0.15$.
    (a) Graph $P(t)$.
    (b) State the domain and range of the function using boundary notation.
18. Let $b = 400$, $p = 300$ and $k = 0.15$.
    (a) Graph $P(t)$.
    (b) State the domain and range of the function using boundary notation.
19. Let $b = 300$, $p = 300$ and $k = 0.15$. Graph $P(t)$.
20. Explain what the three graphs in Questions 17-19 mean in relation to growth and/or decay.

Answer the following questions:

21. What is the difference between a square function and an exponential function?
22. Explain why $1 - 2^{64} < 0 \Rightarrow \frac{1-2^{64}}{-1} > 0$ is a true conditional statement.
23. Solve $S_n = \frac{t_1\left(1-r^n\right)}{1-r}$ for t_1.
24. In general, does the function $y = ab^x$ where $a > 0$ and $b > 1$ represent growth or decay?
25. In general, does the function $y = ab^x$ where $a > 0$ and $0 < b < 1$ represent growth or decay?
26. What conditions are necessary for the function $y = p(1 + r)^x$ to represent growth?
27. What conditions are necessary for the function $y = p(1 + r)^x$ to represent decay?
28. Solve $\frac{e^{-0.5k}}{5} = 0.3$ for k. You may use your scientific calculator and round your answer to the nearest hundredth.

t_1

$t_2 = t_1 r$

$t_3 = t_1 r^2$

$t_4 = t_1 r^3$

$t_5 = t_1 r^4$ $\quad r$ = common ratio

$t_6 = t_1 r^5$

$t_7 = t_1 r^6$

$t_8 = t_1 r^7$

Figure 7.

29. Derive a formula for finding the nth term of a geometric sequence. (Hint: Use Figure 7 to help you.)
30. In the geometric sequence 1, 4, 16, 64, 256, 1024, calculate the geometric mean (Lesson 11.6) of:
    (a) the first and third term.
    (b) the second and fourth term.
    (c) the third and fifth term.
    (d) the fourth and sixth term.
    (e) What conclusion can you draw from these observations?

31. If a geometric sequence when the nth is given by $t_n = \frac{1}{2}4^{n-1}$:
    (a) What are the first four terms of the sequence?
    (b) What is the ratio of two successive terms?
    (c) What is the expression representing the 20th term?
    (d) What is the expression representing the 200th term?
32. An automobile depreciates in value, i.e., decreases in value, one-fifth of its initial cost every year. After n years, what is the value of an automobile that initially cost $40,000?

Table 4: Summary of Geometric Sequence Analysis	
Common Ratio	$r = t_n/t_{n-1}$ for $n \geq 2$
Recursive Formula	If we know t_1, $t_n = rt_{n-1}$ for $n \geq 2$
Explicit Formula	$t_n = t_1r^{n-1}$

What number(s) must be substituted for the variable(s) in the following geometric sequences?
33. 4, 20, 100, x
34. 10, x, 22.5, 33.75
35. 1, x, y, 512
36. x, -18, 36, y
37. 3^{-1}, x, y, 3^2
38. $\frac{8}{13}, \frac{4}{13}, \frac{2}{13}, x, y$

Write the formula for the nth term of the following geometric sequences:
39. 8, 16, 32, …
40. 128, 16, 2, …
41. 15, -15, 15, …
42. 5, 12.5, 31.25, …
43. 3, $3\sqrt{3}$, 9, …
44. 500, -50, 10, …

Find the sum of the first:
45. ten terms of 5, 15, 45, …
46. seven terms of 1, 5, 25, …
47. ten terms of 3, -6, 12, …
48. seven terms of 4, 16, 64, …
49. ten terms of $\frac{1}{2}, \frac{1}{4}, \frac{1}{8}$, … (Write the sum as a rational number.)
50. 50 terms of 15, 15, 15, …

Answer these questions about your biological ancestors:
51. Write ten terms of the geometric series, beginning with two, that represents the number of your biological ancestors ten generations back.
52. How many biological ancestors do you have:
    (a) 10 generations back?
    (b) 20 generations back?
53. Write a formula for the number of biological ancestors in the nth generation preceding you.
54. Write a formula to find the total number of your biological answers for n generations.

A rubber ball is known to rebound half the height it drops. If we drop the ball from a height of 200 feet, how far will it have traveled by the time it hits the ground?

55. The first time?
56. The second time?
57. The third time?
58. The fourth time?
59. The fifth time?
60. (a) Determine the pattern revealed.
    (b) Develop a formula to determine the total distance traveled by the ball after it hits the ground for the nth time. (Hint: Make a table and develop the expressions for your answers using powers of ½.)
61. Is there a maximum distance the ball will travel if we assume it will bounce "forever"? (Hint: Refer to a homework question in Lesson 8.8. We are anticipating the answer to Zeno's door paradox that we will discuss in Lesson 13.15.)
62. A ball is dropped from a height of 10 meters and bounces freely, rebounding 50% each time. Find the total distance of the *downward* falls if it bounces "forever."

The Ancient Greek Ratio φ.

Figure 8. The Parthenon. Source: Wikimedia Commons.

Greek mathematicians constructed a rectangle and derived a ratio from it, a ratio that that Greek builders used in construction of temples like the Parthenon. To find the rectangle's length and width, a and b (Figure 9), they started with a line segment and divided in into two segments of length a and b, $a > b$, such that:

$$\frac{a+b}{a} = \frac{a}{b}$$

In Euclid's *Elements*, Book VI, Definition 3, he stated this proportion in words, "A straight line is said to have been cut in extreme and mean ratio when, as the whole line is to the greater segment, so is the greater to the less."[3]

[3] T. L. Heath, *Euclid: The Thirteen Books of the Elements* (New York: Dover Publications, 1956), 2:188.

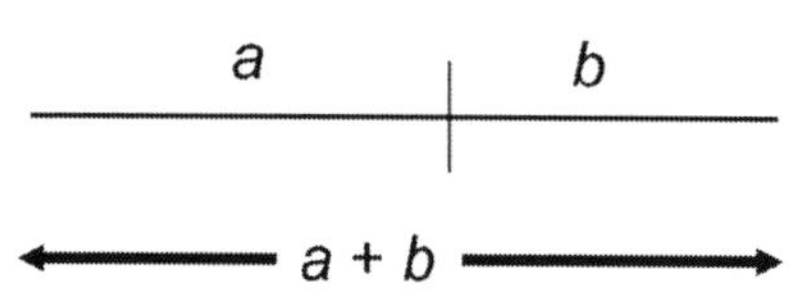

Figure 9. Extreme and mean ratio.

In the 20th century, mathematicians denoted this ratio as φ, the Greek letter *phi*, after the first letter of Phidias (ca. 480-430 BC), a sculptor, painter, and architect.[4] Let's use what we know of quadratic equations to find an expression for φ:

63. We set $\frac{a+b}{a} = \frac{a}{b} = \varphi$. Solve $\frac{a}{b} = \varphi$ for a.
64. Substitute your expression for a into $\frac{a+b}{a} = \frac{a}{b}$.
65. From your answer to Question 64, write a quadratic in φ in the form $a\varphi^2 + b\varphi + c = 0$.

> Geometry has two great treasures: one is the Theorem of Pythagoras, and the other the division of a line into extreme and mean ratio; the first we may compare to a measure of gold, the second we may name a precious jewel.
> Johannes Kepler (1571-1630).

66. Solve the quadratic you derived in Question 65 for the exact value(s) of φ.
67. Use your scientific calculator to round your answer(s) in Question 66 in the nearest thousandths.
68. Using computer software, graph the quadratic to confirm your solution(s).
69. State (a) exact expression(s) and (b) the rounded value(s) for the reciprocal of φ. (c) What do you notice?
70. Refer to the homework in Lesson 8.8, Lesson 8.11, and Lesson 10.8 related to the Fibonacci Sequence. What do you notice about these exercises and φ?

[4] The ancient Greeks called φ the **Golden Ratio**. The Italian mathematician Luca Pacioli (1445-1517) first used divine proportion in a book by that title in 1509. Two quantities a and b, where $b > a$, are in a *golden ratio* if their ratio a/b is the same as the ratio of their sum to the greater of the two quantities, or $(a + b)/b$.

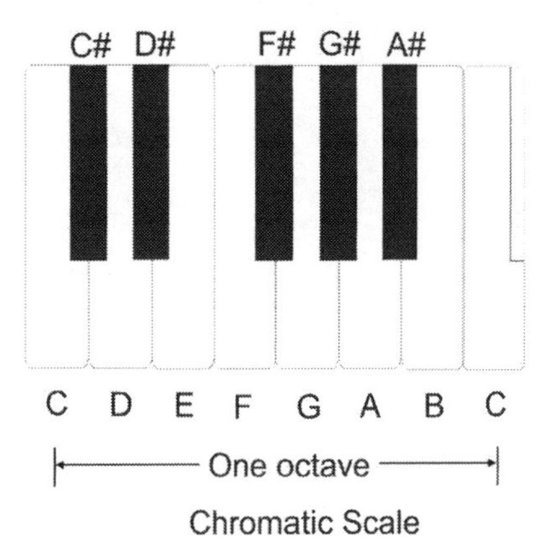

Figure 10.

The Chromatic Musical Scale.

As we have noted, every octave of the piano contains thirteen notes, based upon a **chromatic scale,**[5] from C to C (Figure 10): The thirteen notes consist of eight white keys – octave means "eighth part" – and five black keys – two and three. Note: Two, three, eight, and thirteen are Fibonacci Numbers. Modern pianos are tuned so that the ratios of the frequencies of the consecutive notes are constant. That is, the ratio of the frequencies from C to C# is the same as the ratio of frequencies from C# to D, from D to D#, etc. Let r represent this ratio and f_n represent the frequency of the nth note of the scale starting from middle C.

71. What type of sequence is this?
72. Write an equation describing how f_n is related to f_1.
73. The frequency of middle C is approximately 261.6 cycles per second. What is the frequency of the C above middle C in hertz (Hz)?
74. Using these two frequencies, find the value of the common ratio r between the notes of the scale (to 10 significant figures). [Hint: From the formula in Question 72, set f_n equal to your answer to Question 73 and set $f_1 = 261.6$. We know that $n = 12$ (12 notes from middle C to the C above middle C). Now, take the log of both sides and solve for r.]
75. Simply your answer in Question 74 in terms of a radical $\sqrt{}$. (Hint: Recall that $6 = r^4 \Leftrightarrow r = 6^{1/4} = \sqrt[4]{6}$.)
76. With your scientific calculator, determine the frequencies for each note in the octave. Make a two-column table and plot the results on a graph (Hint: Let 1, 2, 3, etc. replace C, C#, D, etc.). Round the frequency to the nearest tenth.
77. What is the domain of your graph?
78. What is the range of your graph?
79. Given r as determined in Question 74, verify that f_{13} (the frequency of C above middle C) is as you determined in Question 73.
80. Extend the domain of the table to include the frequencies for next octave above the middle octave of a piano.
81. What is the frequency of F in the next octave of a piano?
82. What is the frequency of upper C in the next octave above the middle octave of a piano?
83. Describe two different methods for finding the frequency in the previous question.

---

[5] The chromatic scale is a musical scale with twelve pitches (C to B), each a musical interval above or below another. On a modern piano or other equal-tempered instrument, all the intervals have the same size, as the subsequent exercises will demonstrate. By equal size we mean that the notes of an equal-tempered chromatic scale are equally spaced.

84. How is the frequency of F in the middle octave of a piano related to the frequency of F in the next octave above?

Answer these questions:

85. This list is contained in the Rhind Papyrus from ancient Egypt (Lesson 12.10):

Household	7
Cats	49
Mice	343
Barley	2301
Hekats	16,807

Do the numbers in this list form a geometric sequence?

86. *As I was going to St. Ives* is a traditional nursery rhyme (ca. 1730) in the form of a riddle. Answer the question in the last line.

As I was going to St. Ives,
I met a man with seven wives,
Each wife had seven sacks,
Each sack had seven cats,
Each cat had seven kits:
Kits, cats, sacks, and wives,
How many were there going to St. Ives?

A proof that $\sqrt{-1}$ cannot be a real number.

We first establish that, according to the Trichotomy Principle (Lesson 6.7), that a real number r can be in one of three states:

Case 1. $r > 0$ (r is positive)
Case 2. $r < 0$ (r is negative)
Case 3. $r = 0$ (r is zero)

We assume that $\sqrt{-1}$ is a real number k. Therefore:

$$k = \sqrt{-1} \Rightarrow k^2 = -1$$

Case 1. If $k > 0$, then $k^2 > 0$. Therefore, $k^2 \neq -1$.

Case 2. If $k < 0$, we set $k = -a$ where $a > 0$. (Note: if a is positive, $-a$ is negative. Therefore, we must state $a > 0$. If not, a could be negative and if a is negative, $-a$ is positive.) Therefore, $k^2 = (-a)(-a) = a^2$ where $a^2 > 0$. Therefore, $k^2 > 0 \Rightarrow k^2 \neq -1$.

Case 3. If $k = 0$, then $k^2 = 0$. Therefore, $k^2 \neq -1$.

We conclude, that if $\sqrt{-1}$ is a real number k, $k^2 = -1$ is impossible. By *reductio ad absurdum*, our assumption is false and $\sqrt{-1}$ cannot be a real number.

QED

13.15 Dancing to Infinity

Terms & Concepts Introduced
1. Convergent series
2. Divergent series
3. The convergence of an infinite series to a limiting value

So far, we have learned how to sum a series like these:

Example 1. $5 + 13 + 21 + 29 + 37 + 45$

Example 2. $16 + 48 + 144 + 432$

Example 3. $18 + 9 + 4.5 + 2.25 + 1.125$

Example 4. $\frac{1}{2}+\frac{1}{4}+\frac{1}{8}+\frac{1}{16}+\frac{1}{32}$

In general, an arithmetic series consisting of n terms, t_1 is the first term, and an additive factor d is:

$t_1 + (t_1 + d) + (t_1 + 2d) + (t_1 + 3d) + \ldots + [t_1 + (n - 1)d]$

A geometric series consisting of n terms t, t_1 is the first term, and a multiplicative factor r is:

$t_1 + t_1r + t_1r^2 + t_1r^3 + t_1r^4 + \ldots + t_1r^{n-1}$

How would we find sum of this series?

$\frac{1}{2}+\frac{1}{4}+\frac{1}{8}+\frac{1}{16}+\frac{1}{32}+\ldots$

Or this?

$5 + 13 + 21 + 29 + 37 + 45 + \ldots$

Divergent Series

As we recall, the ellipsis (…) indicates that the series continues *ad infinitum*. Can we find the sum of such a series? It is the goal of this lesson to find out if we can.

First, inspect this series:

$1 + 2 + 4 + 8 + 16 + \ldots$

It should be no surprise that as we add subsequent terms to this series, the sum of the series gets greater and greater. This series, as a sum of an infinite number of terms, has no sum. Why? Since every term is greater than the previous term, adding this greater number to the previous sum makes the sum greater. Doing this *ad infinitum* means we can never explicitly write the sum of this series. If a series has no sum, it is a **divergent series**.

Convergent Series

Second, inspect this series:

$\frac{1}{2}+\frac{1}{4}+\frac{1}{8}+\frac{1}{16}+\frac{1}{32}+\ldots$

Again, as we add subsequent terms to this series, the sum of the series gets greater and greater. But, what we are adding gets lesser and lesser. Although every term is greater than the previous term, adding this ever-decreasing greater number to the previous sum makes the sum greater, but at a lesser rate. If a series acts like this, it is a **convergent series**. When a series is convergent, we can calculate its infinite sum. Impossible, you may say, but we have already shown this to be the case in Lesson 7.8. Review that lesson now.

What is the decimal expansion of 1/3? It is periodic, so we write:

$\frac{1}{3} = 0.\overline{3}$ (Note that 3 is the repetend.)

But, what does $0.\overline{3}$ mean?

$$0.\overline{3} = \frac{3}{10} + \frac{3}{100} + \frac{3}{1000} + \frac{3}{10,000} + \ldots$$

As you can see, 3 is in every place value: tenths, hundredths, thousandths, etc. The right side of this equation a geometric series. The first term, t_1, is:

$$t_1 = \frac{3}{10}$$

What is r, the common multiplier or common ratio?

$$r = \frac{1}{10}$$

We cannot invoke the formula we discovered in the last lesson to find the sum because this series is an infinite geometric series (Lesson 7.8). But, we know the sum already:

$$0.\overline{3} = \frac{1}{3}$$

Note that every subsequent term is lesser than the term before it, lesser by a factor of 1/10. Doing this *ad infinitum* means that the sum is getting greater, but, as we have already noted, it is getting greater at a lesser rate. When a series acts like this, it is convergent, and we can calculate its infinite sum, which, in our example, is 1/3.

It is, therefore, possible to add ever-decreasing quantities to a sum until we reach a point at which the sum ceases to grow. Mathematicians call this **the convergence of an infinite series to a limiting value.**

Here are more examples:

Example 1. $\frac{2}{3} = 0.\overline{6} = \frac{6}{10} + \frac{6}{100} + \frac{6}{1000} + \frac{6}{10,000} + \ldots$

Example 2. $\frac{1}{9} = 0.\overline{1} = \frac{1}{10} + \frac{1}{100} + \frac{1}{1000} + \frac{1}{10,000} + \ldots$

Example 3. $1 = 0.\overline{9} = \frac{9}{10} + \frac{9}{100} + \frac{9}{1000} + \frac{9}{10,000} + \ldots$

Example 4. $11\frac{1}{9} = 11.\overline{1} = 11 + \frac{1}{10} + \frac{1}{100} + \frac{1}{1000} + \frac{1}{10,000} + \ldots$ (Recall that $11\frac{1}{9}$ is our answer for Zeno's paradox of Achilles and the Tortoise. See the homework exercise in Lesson 10.1.)

INFINITE GEOMETRIC SERIES

We have already discovered the sum of this infinite geometric series:

$$\frac{1}{2} + \frac{1}{4} + \frac{1}{8} + \frac{1}{16} + \frac{1}{32} + \ldots$$

This sum is the answer to another paradox devised by Zeno, discussed in the last lesson. To review, let's say that Mr. Zeno is standing one meter from a door. Every step he takes leaves him 1/2 as far from the door. Will he ever reach the door if he takes an infinite number of steps? Zeno said, "No," because there would always be a little bit left, no matter how infinitesimally small, to traverse. But, the mathematics of the infinite geometric series proves him wrong.

> ... half-of-half could still be halved,
> with limitless division less and less.
> Lucretius, *De rerum natura* (ca. 50 BC).

We can derive a formula to find the sum of a series like this so hold on to the hat of your mind. We are entering the wonderful world of Calculus in our following explorations.

We already know how to sum a *finite* geometric series if we know its first term, t_1, and its common multiplier or common ratio, r. Our formula is:

$$S_n = \frac{t_1\left(1-r^n\right)}{1-r}$$

What happens to this formula as n, the number of terms, getting greater and greater? As we have already noted, mathematicians have a particular way of writing this rhetoric in symbols. It is concise, and it gets the message across. Here it is:

$$n \to \infty$$

The symbols mean "as n approaches infinity." Recall that in mathematics infinity is not a number. Infinity is a concept meaning "to increase beyond bounds." We can consider an infinite collection of objects like the set of natural numbers. This set continues indefinitely, without end, *ad infinitum*. It is an infinite set. A process, like an infinite geometric series, continues indefinitely, without end, *ad infinitum*.

We want to find out what happens to this formula as $n \to \infty$. As we look at the formula, we see that there is only one term in it that involves n, namely r^n. So, to answer our question, we need to find out what happens to r^n as $n \to \infty$.

CASE 1: $R \geq 1$

Let's first consider some values of r. If $r = 1$, then $r^n = 1^n = 1$ no matter what the value of n. But, when $r = 1$, our formula blows up because the denominator, $1 - r$, is zero. So, we can rule out 1 as a valid common ratio.

What happens when $r > 1$? If $r = 2$, what happens to 2^n as $n \to \infty$? 2^n gets very, very large and we cannot determine how large this number will be. This information tells us, if $r > 1$, we have something like this when $r = 2$:

2, 4, 8, 16, ...

And, this series is divergent. So, we can rule out $r > 1$ as a valid common ratio.

CASE 2: $R \leq -1$

What about negative values of r? That is possible. If $r = -1$, then $r^n = (-1)^n$. If n is even, $(-1)^n = 1$, but if n is odd, $(-1)^n = -1$. If $r = -1$, either our formula blows up because the denominator, $1 - r$, is zero or the numerator is zero. (Be sure to check this.) As $n \to \infty$, we will never set foot in either camp, 1 or -1. If $r = -1$, we must throw it out because we do not know what will happen.

What happens when $r < -1$. If $r = -3$, what happens to $(-3)^n$ as $n \to \infty$? $(-3)^n$ gets very, very large, either positive or negative, and we cannot determine how large this number will be. This information tells us, if $r < -1$, we have something like this when $r = -3$:

-3, 9, -27, 81, -243, …

This series, when $r = -3$, bounces all over the positive and negative planet. So, we can rule out $r < -1$ as a valid common ratio.

OUNDARY CONDITIONS: $-1 < R < 1$

What values of r are left to consider? $-1 < r < 1$, our boundary conditions (Figure 1).

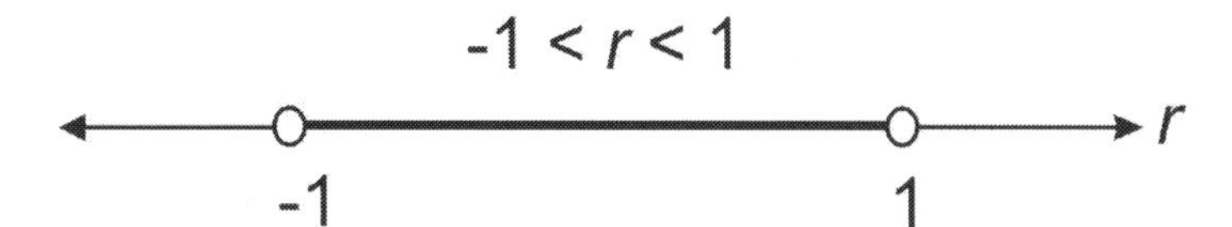

Figure 1.

Recall from Lesson 10.8, $-c < x < c \Leftrightarrow |x| < c$. Therefore:

$-1 < r < 1 \Leftrightarrow |r| < 1$

Let's now investigate some of the values of r within this range.

If $r = 0$, our formula $S_n = \frac{t_1(1-r^n)}{1-r}$ becomes:

$$S_n = \frac{t_1(1-0^n)}{1-0} = \frac{t_1(1)}{1} = t_1$$

That makes sense, doesn't it? If $r = 0$, you only have one term in the series, the first term, but this is not that exciting. In this case, we don't even have a series.

What happens if $0 < r < 1$? If $r = \frac{1}{2}$, what happens to $\left(\frac{1}{2}\right)^n$ as $n \to \infty$? Think about it. Let $n = 1, 2, 3, 4, 5, 6, 7, 8, 9, 10$. Do the calculations. What is your conclusion? We can demonstrate your conclusion on a continuous graph if we graph the exponential function $y = \left(\frac{1}{2}\right)^x$ (Figure 2).[1] We see immediate that as $x \to \infty$, $y \to 0$. This obervation means that as $n \to \infty$, $\left(\frac{1}{2}\right)^n \to 0$. Make sure that you understand the meaning of the symbols. Using limit notation, we write:

$$\lim_{n \to \infty}\left(\frac{1}{2}\right)^n = 0$$

---

[1] In physics, this graph is used to demonstrate exponential decay, like radioactive half-life. See the homework both in Lesson 12.5 and in Lesson 13.13.

We read it as follows: The limit, or the threshold, that $\left(\frac{1}{2}\right)^n$ reaches as n approaches infinity is zero. The symbols say it all.

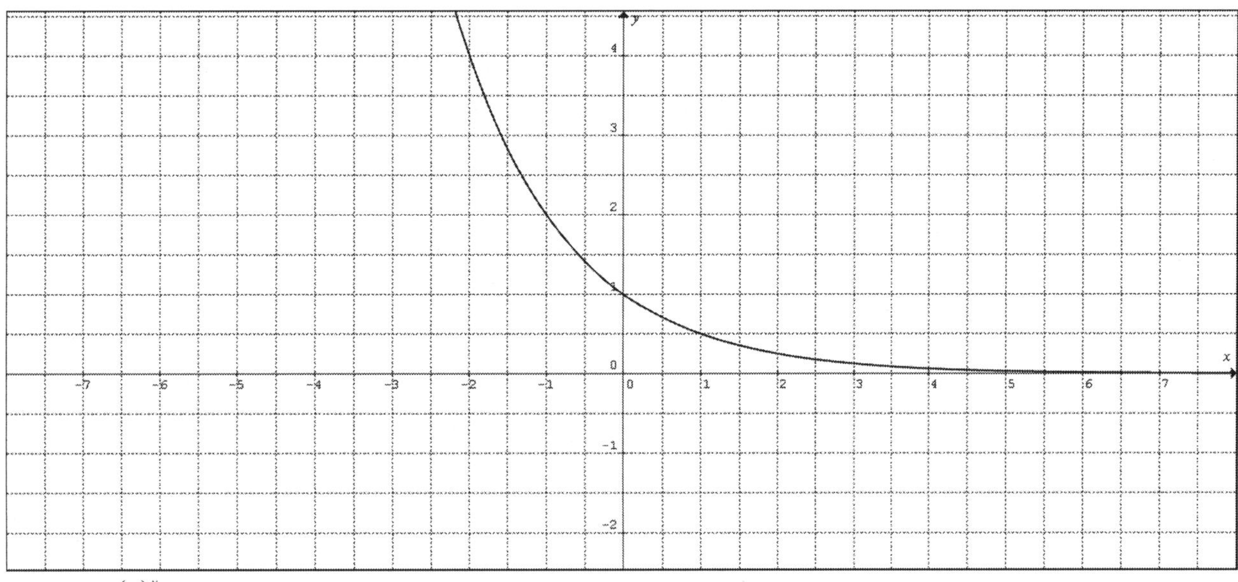

Figure 2. $\lim_{x \to \infty} \left(\frac{1}{2}\right)^x = 0$

If $r = \frac{1}{2}$ and as $n \to \infty$, our formula $S_n = \dfrac{t_1(1-r^n)}{1-r}$ becomes:

$$\lim_{n\to\infty} S_n \Leftrightarrow \lim_{n\to\infty} \frac{t_1(1-r^n)}{1-r} = \frac{t_1(1-0)}{1-\frac{1}{2}} = \frac{t_1}{\frac{1}{2}} = 2t_1$$

We now have an answer for Zeno. In the infinite geometric series $\frac{1}{2}+\frac{1}{4}+\frac{1}{8}+\frac{1}{16}+\frac{1}{32}+\ldots$, $t_1 = \frac{1}{2}$. Therefore:

$$\lim_{n\to\infty} S_n = 2t_1 = 2\left(\frac{1}{2}\right) = 1$$

We do reach the door. Our answer confirms the analysis we did in the homework problem in Lesson 11.2. We have invoked two ways to get the same answer, one geometric and the other algebraic. Again, we see this unity in diversity principle embedded mathematics like an exquisite jewel. It is a principle that drives almost all work in mathematics and science, a principle that mathematicians describe using one word: beautiful. And, it is the Triune God revealed by Jesus, the ultimate Unity in Diversity, the interpenetrating Dance of the beautiful and Holy Trinity, who is the ground of these types of unexpected perichoretic connections. What He creates and sustains, the invisible realm of thought and the visible realm of matter, will reflect, in a proximate way, the interpenetrating nature of His being.

Now, let's consider negative values of r. What happens if $-1 < r < 0$? If $r = -\frac{1}{2}$, what happens to $\left(-\frac{1}{2}\right)^n$ as $n \to \infty$?

Let's see what happens with some values of n:

1	2	3	4	5	6	...	n
$-\frac{1}{2}$	$\left(-\frac{1}{2}\right)^2 = \frac{1}{4}$	$\left(-\frac{1}{2}\right)^3 = -\frac{1}{8}$	$\left(-\frac{1}{2}\right)^4 = \frac{1}{16}$	$\left(-\frac{1}{2}\right)^5 = -\frac{1}{32}$	$\left(-\frac{1}{2}\right)^6 = \frac{1}{64}$	...	$\left(-\frac{1}{2}\right)^n$

The values of $\left(-\frac{1}{2}\right)^n$ are converging to zero from two directions, negative and positive. Therefore:

$$\lim_{n\to\infty}\left(-\frac{1}{2}\right)^n = 0$$

We conclude from this analysis that if $|r| < 1$, the r^n term in the formula $S_n = \frac{t_1\left(1-r^n\right)}{1-r}$ approaches zero as n gets very, very large. In symbols, $r^n \to 0$ as $n \to \infty$ when $|r| < 1$ or:

$$\lim_{n\to\infty} r^n = 0 \text{ when } |r| < 1$$

Therefore, when $|r| < 1$, $S_n = \frac{t_1\left(1-r^n\right)}{1-r} = \frac{t_1}{1-r}$ as $n \to \infty$ or, written in two different ways:

1. $\lim\limits_{n\to\infty}\frac{t_1\left(1-r^n\right)}{1-r} = \frac{t_1}{1-r}$ when $|r| < 1$

2. Since $S_n = \frac{t_1\left(1-r^n\right)}{1-r}$, $\lim\limits_{n\to\infty} S_n = \frac{t_1}{1-r}$ when $|r| < 1$

This is our formula to find the sum of an infinite geometry series when r, the common multiplier or common ratio, is between -1 and 1 exclusive, $-1 < r < 1$, or $|r| < 1$. This is, indeed, a beautiful formula resulting from careful mathematical reasoning.[2]

If we let $t_1 = 2$, replace r with x, $\lim\limits_{n\to\infty} S_n$ with y, we can investigate what happens to the limit when $|x| < 1$ by graphing $y = \frac{2}{1-x}$ (Figure 3). The graph is a hyperbola, the positive images the region between the two dotted vertical lines are the only valid limits of the infinite geometric series. For example, when $x = -0.5$, the limit is $1\frac{1}{3}$. When $x = 0.5$, the limit is 4.

[2] For a fascinating study of the mathematics of infinite processes, see Eli Maor, *To Infinity and Beyond: A Cultural History of the Infinite* (Princeton: Princeton University Press, [1987] 1991).

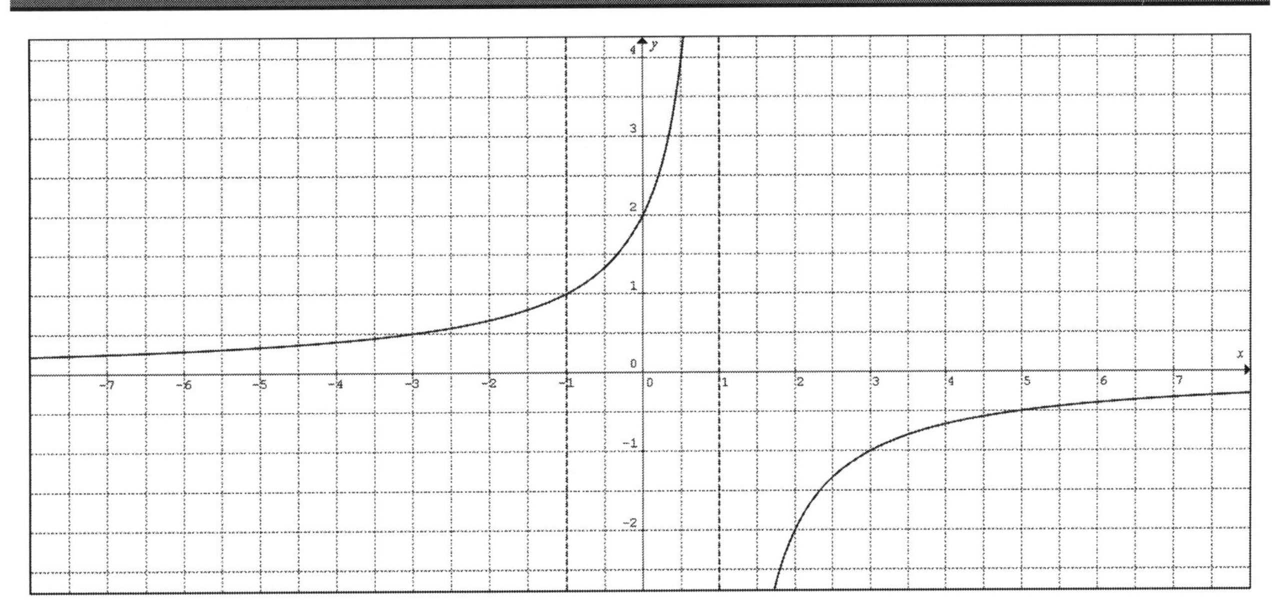

Figure 3. $y = \frac{2}{1-x}$.

Table 1: Series Formula Summary	
Finite Arithmetic Series	$S_n = \frac{n(t_1 + t_n)}{2}$
Finite Geometric Series	$S_n = \frac{t_1(1-r^n)}{1-r}$
Infinite Geometric Series	$\lim_{n \to \infty} S_n = \frac{t_1}{1-r}$ when $\|r\| < 1$

We conclude this lesson showing two different revelations of the infinite geometric series, one exploring its interpenetration of periodic decimals and the other in the calculation of π, the ratio of the circumference to the diameter of a circle.

Periodic Decimals

Consider this infinite geometric series:

$$0.\overline{3} = \frac{3}{10} + \frac{3}{100} + \frac{3}{1000} + \frac{3}{10{,}000} + \ldots$$

We could write the same series like this:

$$0.\overline{3} = \frac{3}{10} + \frac{3}{10^2} + \frac{3}{10^3} + \frac{3}{10^4} + \ldots$$

From these representations, we see that:

$r = 1/10$ and $t_1 = 3/10$

Substituting these values into our formula, we get:

$$S_n = \frac{\frac{3}{10}}{1-\frac{1}{10}} = \frac{\frac{3}{10}}{\frac{9}{10}} = \frac{\cancel{3}^{1}}{\cancel{10}_{1}} \cdot \frac{\cancel{10}^{1}}{\cancel{9}_{3}} = \frac{1}{3}$$

Therefore: $0.\overline{3} = \frac{1}{3}$

Note how division, 1 divided by 3, and the formula $S_n = \frac{t_1}{1-r}$ coinhere. They generate the same answer, but by different methods. The methods interpenetrate in perichoretic fashion.

By the formula $S_n = \frac{t_1}{1-r}$, we can also prove $0.4\overline{9} = 0.5$ and, as a byproduct of our mathematical reasoning, $0.\overline{9} = 1$. We write:

$$0.4\overline{9} = \frac{4}{10} + 0.0\overline{9} = \frac{4}{10} + \frac{1}{10}\left(0.\overline{9}\right) = \frac{4}{10} + \frac{1}{10}\left(\frac{9}{10} + \frac{9}{10^2} + \frac{9}{10^3} + \ldots\right)$$

In the infinite geometric series $\frac{9}{10} + \frac{9}{10^2} + \frac{9}{10^3} + \ldots$, $r = 1/10$ and $t_1 = 9/10$.

Substituting these values into our formula, we get:

$$S_n = \frac{\frac{9}{10}}{1-\frac{1}{10}} = \frac{\frac{9}{10}}{\frac{9}{10}} = 1$$

Since $\frac{9}{10} + \frac{9}{10^2} + \frac{9}{10^3} + \ldots = 1$, i.e., $0.\overline{9} = 1$, then:

$$0.4\overline{9} = \frac{4}{10} + \frac{1}{10}(1) = \frac{4}{10} + \frac{1}{10} = \frac{5}{10} = 0.5$$

QED

Every rational number, therefore, can be written as the sum of an infinite geometric series. Why? We can rewrite the decimal expansion of a rational number that terminates as a decimal expansion with repeating digits (Figure 4).

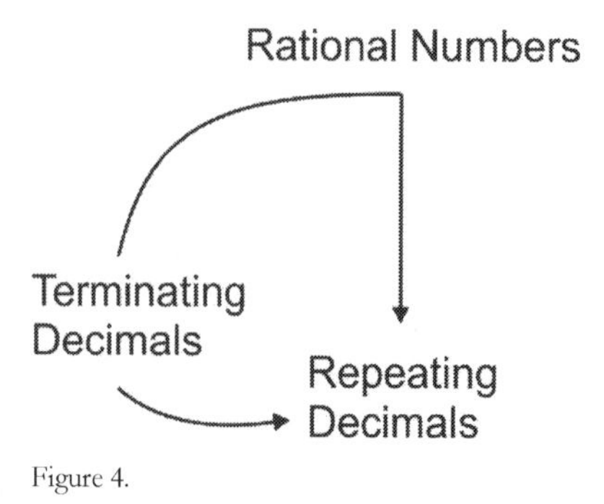

Figure 4.

By the same reasoning, we can show:

$7 = 6.\overline{9}$
$-15 = -14.\overline{9}$

Since $0.\overline{9} = 1$, every integer is the sum of an infinite geometric series. The fact the infinite geometric series interpenetrates $\mathbb{Z}$ should not surprise us since $\mathbb{Z} \subset \mathbb{Q}$.

π AND THE INFINITE GEOMETRIC SERIES

In Lesson 8.3, we stated that mathematicians have shown that $\frac{\pi}{4} = 1 - \frac{1}{3} + \frac{1}{5} - \frac{1}{7} + \frac{1}{9} - \ldots$

Familiar to the mathematicians from India in 1500, the discovery of this infinite expression of π occurred much earlier. Discovered in the West by James Gregory in 1671 and Gottfried Wilhelm Leibniz in 1673, there are several ways to proof this equation. We will follow the logic developed in India.

To prove this relationship, we must know some things:

1. Similar triangles and proportional analysis
2. The sum of an infinite geometric series
3. The behavior of a specific quotient

Follow the dance of this logic carefully. This proof will employ a host of principles that we have learned throughout this course, along with a result that we will prove in Lesson 14.2, and engage some intensive algebraic analysis.

That we have an infinite expression for $\frac{\pi}{4}$ indicates that we are finding the measure of one-eighth of the circumference of a circle with radius of 1 (Figure 5). Why? Since $C = 2\pi r$ and $r = 1$, then:

$$\frac{\pi}{4} = \frac{2\pi}{8} = m\overset{\frown}{AD}$$

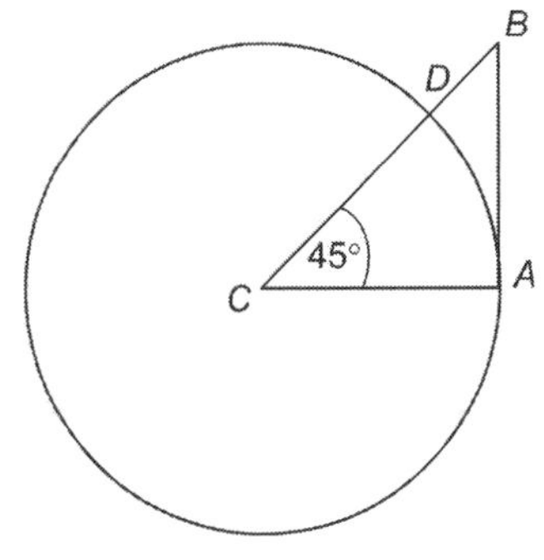

Figure 5.

In Figure 5, we construct a 45° right ΔABC, where $CD = CA = AB = 1$, $\angle BAC$ is the central angle in circle C, an angle that intercepts $\overset{\frown}{AD}$, and D, a point on its hypotenuse, is also a point on the circumference of circle C. [Note: $45° = \frac{1}{8}(360°) \Rightarrow m\overset{\frown}{AD} = \frac{1}{8}(2\pi) = \frac{\pi}{4}$]

Our strategy is to generate estimates of $m\overset{\frown}{AD}$ and observe how these estimates behave as they get closer and closer to the actual arc length. We do this by dividing $\overline{AB}$ into sections of equal length. This

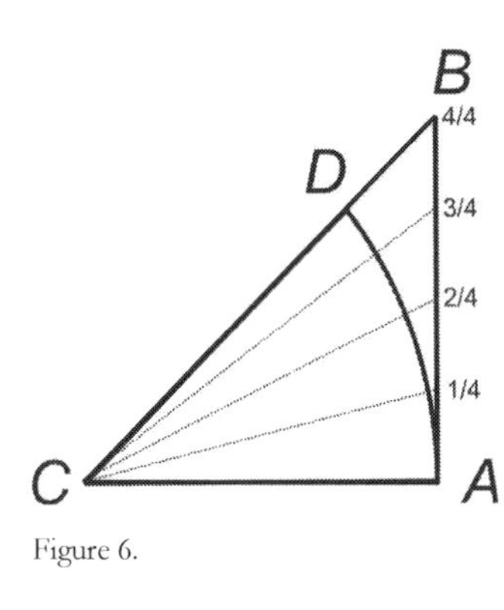

Figure 6.

division will divide $\overset{\frown}{AD}$ into small arcs, but they will *not* be equal in length. We will proceed to estimate the length of each of these small arcs. The sum of these estimates will be an estimate of $m\overset{\frown}{AD}$.

Let's start by dividing $\overline{AB}$ into four equal lengths. Since $AB = 1$, the measure of each segment will be ¼ (Figure 6).

SIMILAR TRIANGLES AND PROPORTIONAL ANALYSIS

In Figure 7, let's see if we can estimate $m\overset{\frown}{GH}$ corresponding to $\overline{EF}$ where $EF = FE = $ ¼. In Figure 8, we draw $\overleftrightarrow{GI}$ tangent to $\overset{\frown}{AD}$ at G. Therefore,

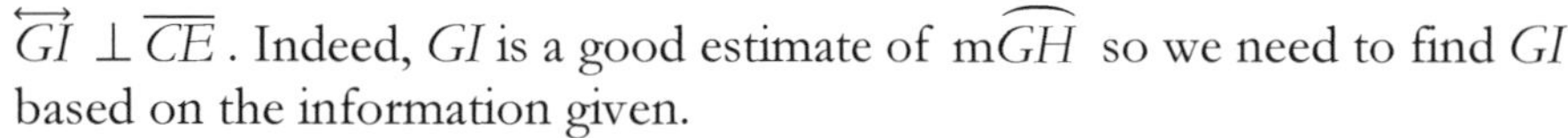

$\overleftrightarrow{GI} \perp \overline{CE}$. Indeed, GI is a good estimate of $m\overset{\frown}{GH}$ so we need to find GI based on the information given.

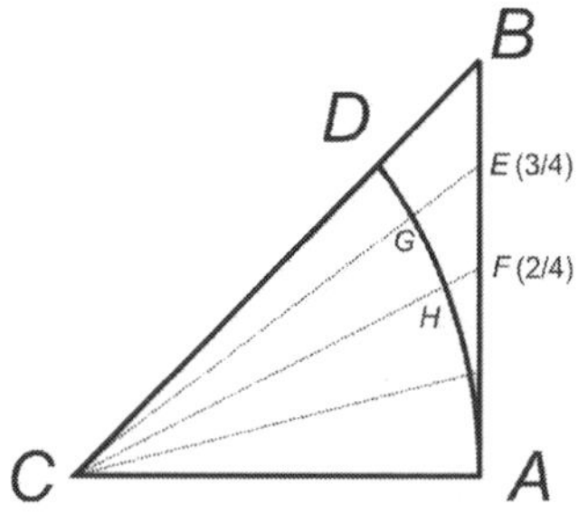

Figure 7.

We draw $\overline{JF} \perp \overline{CE}$ and note two pairs of similar right triangles:

$\Delta CGI \sim \Delta CJF$

$\Delta FJE \sim \Delta CAE$

Based on the second similarity, we get this proportion:

$$\frac{FJ}{CA} = \frac{FE}{CE}$$

Since $CA = 1$ and $FE = $ ¼, then, by substitution:

$$FJ = \frac{\frac{1}{4}}{CE}$$

From $\Delta CGI \sim \Delta CJF$, we get this proportion:

$$\frac{GI}{JF} = \frac{CG}{CJ}$$

Since $CG = 1$, then, by substitution:

$$GI = \frac{JF}{CJ}$$

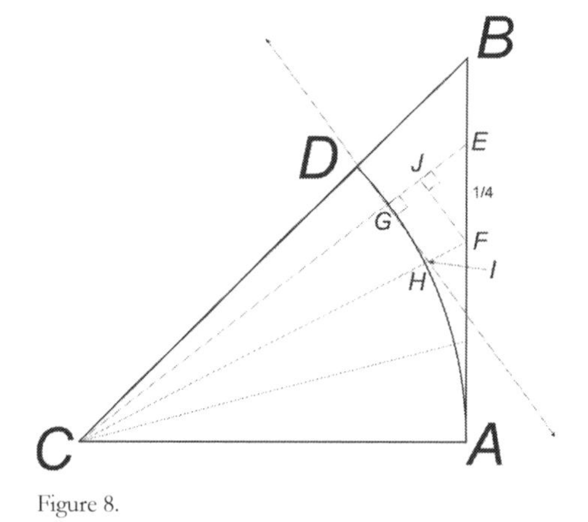

Figure 8.

What can we say about CJ? If we keep on dividing $\overline{AB}$ into 8 equal parts, then equal 16 parts, etc., to n equal parts, EF gets lesser and lesser, and so does JE. Therefore, as n gets greater and greater, CE becomes a good approximation of CJ ($CE \approx CJ$) since $\frac{CE}{CJ} \approx 1$. Therefore, by substitution:

$$GI = \frac{JF}{CE}$$

Since $FJ = \frac{\frac{1}{4}}{CE}$, then, by substitution (Note: $FJ = JF$):

$$GI = \frac{\frac{1/4}{CE}}{CE} \Leftrightarrow GI = \frac{1/4}{CE^2}$$

Since $\overline{CE}$ is the hypotenuse of right ΔCAE, then, by the Pythagorean Theorem:

$CE^2 = CA^2 + AE^2$

Since $CA = 1$ and $AE = 3/4$, we get:

$$CE^2 = CA^2 + AE^2 \Leftrightarrow CE^2 = 1 + \left(\frac{3}{4}\right)^2$$

We substitute for CE^2 in $GI = \frac{1/4}{CE^2}$ to get:

$$GI = \frac{1/4}{1+\left(\frac{3}{4}\right)^2}, \text{ which means } m\widehat{GH} = \frac{1/4}{1+\left(\frac{3}{4}\right)^2}$$

We can apply this same reasoning to the four individual arc lengths that comprise $\widehat{AD}$. We get:

$$\frac{\pi}{4} = m\widehat{GH} = \frac{1/4}{1+\left(\frac{1}{4}\right)^2} + \frac{1/4}{1+\left(\frac{2}{4}\right)^2} + \frac{1/4}{1+\left(\frac{3}{4}\right)^2} + \frac{1/4}{1+\left(\frac{4}{4}\right)^2}$$

If we divide $\overline{AB}$ into n equal parts, then:

Observation 1. $$\frac{\pi}{4} = m\widehat{AD} = \frac{1/n}{1+\left(\frac{1}{n}\right)^2} + \frac{1/n}{1+\left(\frac{2}{n}\right)^2} + \frac{1/n}{1+\left(\frac{3}{n}\right)^2} + \frac{1/n}{1+\left(\frac{4}{n}\right)^2} + \ldots$$

$$+ \frac{1/n}{1+\left(\frac{n-1}{n}\right)^2} + \frac{1/n}{1+\left(\frac{n}{n}\right)^2}$$

Factoring $\frac{1}{n}$, we get:

Observation 2. $$\frac{\pi}{4} = m\overset{\frown}{AD} = \frac{1}{n}\left[\frac{1}{1+\left(\frac{1}{n}\right)^2} + \frac{1}{1+\left(\frac{2}{n}\right)^2} + \frac{1}{1+\left(\frac{3}{n}\right)^2} + \frac{1}{1+\left(\frac{4}{n}\right)^2} + \ldots + \frac{1}{1+\left(\frac{n-1}{n}\right)^2} + \frac{1}{1+\left(\frac{n}{n}\right)^2}\right]$$

To find $\frac{\pi}{4} = m\overset{\frown}{AD}$, we find the limit of Observation 2 as $n \to \infty$, i.e., as we divide $\overline{AB}$ into lesser and lesser equal parts. We write:

$$\lim_{n\to\infty}\left\{\frac{1}{n}\left[\frac{1}{1+\left(\frac{1}{n}\right)^2} + \frac{1}{1+\left(\frac{2}{n}\right)^2} + \frac{1}{1+\left(\frac{3}{n}\right)^2} + \frac{1}{1+\left(\frac{4}{n}\right)^2} + \ldots + \frac{1}{1+\left(\frac{n-1}{n}\right)^2} + \frac{1}{1+\left(\frac{n}{n}\right)^2}\right]\right\}$$

By careful inspection of Observation 1, we should see problems because $\lim_{n\to\infty}\frac{1}{n} = 0$. Therefore, the numerators of each term are all zero as $n \to \infty$. The implication is $\frac{\pi}{4} = m\overset{\frown}{AD} = 0$. We know that $m\overset{\frown}{AD} > 0$, so we must try something else. We invite the infinite geometric series into the dance of our reasoning.

INFINITE GEOMETRIC SERIES

The sum, S_n, of an infinite geometric series is:

$$S_n = \sum_{k=0}^{\infty} t_1 r^k = t_1 + t_1 r + t_1 r^2 + t_1 r^3 + t_1 r^4 + t_1 r^5 + \ldots = \frac{t_1}{1-r} \text{ when } |r| < 1$$

If we let t_1, the first term of the series, be 1, we have a series of this form, i.e., $S_n = 1 + r + r^2 + r^3 + r^4 + r^5 + \ldots$. If $|r| < 1$, the sum is:

$$1 + r + r^2 + r^3 + r^4 + r^5 + \ldots = \frac{1}{1-r}$$

If we replace r by $-s$ where $|s| < 1$, we get:

$$1 - s + s^2 - s^3 + s^4 - s^5 + \ldots = \frac{1}{1+s}$$

Note that the denominators in Observation 2 are of the form $\frac{1}{1+s}$. We can, therefore, turn these denominators into an infinite geometric series of the form $1 - s + s^2 - s^3 + s^4 - s^5 + \ldots$. Let's consider all the terms in the brackets in Observation 2 except the last term since $\frac{n}{n}=1$. We can rewrite each term as an infinite geometric series:

$$\frac{1}{1+\left(\frac{1}{n}\right)^2}=1-\left(\frac{1}{n}\right)^2+\left(\frac{1}{n}\right)^4-\left(\frac{1}{n}\right)^6+\left(\frac{1}{n}\right)^8-\left(\frac{1}{n}\right)^{10}+\ldots$$

$$\frac{1}{1+\left(\frac{2}{n}\right)^2}=1-\left(\frac{2}{n}\right)^2+\left(\frac{2}{n}\right)^4-\left(\frac{2}{n}\right)^6+\left(\frac{2}{n}\right)^8-\left(\frac{2}{n}\right)^{10}+\ldots$$

$$\vdots$$

$$\frac{1}{1+\left(\frac{n-1}{n}\right)^2}=1-\left(\frac{n-1}{n}\right)^2+\left(\frac{n-1}{n}\right)^4-\left(\frac{n-1}{n}\right)^6+\left(\frac{n-1}{n}\right)^8-\left(\frac{n-1}{n}\right)^{10}+\ldots$$

The last term is $\frac{1}{1+\left(\frac{n}{n}\right)^2}=\frac{1}{1+1}=\frac{1}{2}$. If we multiply that term by $\frac{1}{n}$, we get:

$$\frac{1}{n}\left(\frac{1}{2}\right)=\frac{1}{2n}$$

We note:

$$\lim_{n\to\infty}\frac{1}{2n}=0$$

We now have $n-1$ equations to sum. We sum the expression on the right of each equation term by term; i.e., we sum the first terms together, the second terms together, the third terms together, etc. The sum of the first terms, always 1, is:

$$1(n-1)=n-1$$

The sum of the second terms is:

$$-\left(\frac{1}{n}\right)^2-\left(\frac{2}{n}\right)^2-\ldots-\left(\frac{n-1}{n}\right)^2=-\left(\frac{1^2+2^2+\ldots+(n-1)^2}{n^2}\right)$$

The sum of the third terms is:

$$\left(\frac{1}{n}\right)^4+\left(\frac{2}{n}\right)^4+\ldots+\left(\frac{n-1}{n}\right)^4=\frac{1^4+2^4+\ldots+(n-1)^4}{n^4}$$

We continue, generating similar expressions with signs alternating positive, negative, positive, negative, etc.. Therefore:

$$\frac{\pi}{4} = \text{m}\widehat{AD} = \frac{1}{n}\left[(n-1) - \left(\frac{1^2 + 2^2 + \ldots + (n-1)^2}{n^2}\right) + \frac{1^4 + 2^4 + \ldots + (n-1)^4}{n^4} - \ldots\right]$$

Applying the Distributive Law, we get:

$$\frac{\pi}{4} = \text{m}\widehat{AD} = \left(\frac{n-1}{n}\right) - \left(\frac{1^2 + 2^2 + \ldots + (n-1)^2}{n^3}\right) + \frac{1^4 + 2^4 + \ldots + (n-1)^4}{n^5} - \ldots$$

What happens as $n \to \infty$? For the first term:

$$\lim_{n\to\infty} \frac{n-1}{n} = 1$$

For the second term, we ask this question:

$$\lim_{n\to\infty} -\left(\frac{1^2 + 2^2 + \ldots (n-1)^2}{n^3}\right) = ?$$

THE BEHAVIOR OF A SPECIFIC QUOTIENT

To help us answer this question, let's take an interlude and look at the behavior of a specific quotient as $n \to \infty$:

$$\frac{1^k + 2^k + \ldots + n^k}{n^{k+1}} = \frac{1^k}{n^{k+1}} + \frac{2^k}{n^{k+1}} + \ldots + \frac{n^k}{n^{k+1}} \text{ where } k \in +\mathbb{Z}$$

We want to find this limit:

$$\lim_{n\to\infty} \frac{1^k}{n^{k+1}} + \frac{2^k}{n^{k+1}} + \ldots + \frac{n^k}{n^{k+1}} = ?$$

Look at the last term, $\frac{n^k}{n^{k+1}}$. We note:

$$\frac{n^k}{n^{k+1}} = \frac{1}{n}$$

Therefore:

$$\lim_{n\to\infty} \frac{1}{n} = 0$$

Since the last term drops out, we have:

$$\lim_{n\to\infty} \frac{1^k}{n^{k+1}} + \frac{2^k}{n^{k+1}} + \ldots + \frac{(n-1)^k}{n^{k+1}} \Leftrightarrow \lim_{n\to\infty} \frac{1^k + 2^k + \ldots + (n-1)^k}{n^{k+1}}$$

We want to find:

$$\lim_{n\to\infty} \frac{1^k + 2^k + \ldots + (n-1)^k}{n^{k+1}} = ?$$

If $k = 1$, we apply the Gaussian formula:

$$\frac{1+2+\ldots+(n-1)}{n} = \frac{n-1}{2n}$$

Therefore:

$$\lim_{n\to\infty}\frac{n-1}{2n} \Leftrightarrow \lim_{n\to\infty}\left(\frac{n}{2n}-\frac{1}{2n}\right) \Leftrightarrow \text{(The Distributive Law interpenetrates limits of sum and differences.)}$$

$$\lim_{n\to\infty}\frac{n}{2n}-\lim_{n\to\infty}\frac{1}{2n} \Leftrightarrow \lim_{n\to\infty}\frac{1}{2}-\lim_{n\to\infty}\frac{1}{2n} \Leftrightarrow \frac{1}{2}-0=\frac{1}{2}$$

Therefore:

$$\lim_{n\to\infty}\frac{1^k+2^k+\ldots+(n-1)^k}{n^{k+1}} = \frac{1}{k+1} \text{ when } k = 1$$

If $k = 2$, we have:

$$\frac{1^2+2^2+\ldots+(n-1)^2}{n^3}$$

In Lesson 14.2, we will prove, using methods taught in the next lesson, this relationship:

$$1^2+2^2+\ldots+(n-1)^2 = \frac{1}{6}(n-1)n(2n-1)$$

By substitution, we get:

$$\frac{\frac{1}{6}(n-1)n(2n-1)}{n^3} = \frac{(n-1)n(2n-1)}{6n^3} = \frac{(n-1)(2n-1)}{6n^2} = \frac{2n^2-3n+1}{6n^2} = \frac{2n^2}{6n^2}-\frac{3n}{6n^2}+\frac{1}{6n^2} =$$

$$\frac{1}{3}-\frac{1}{2n}+\frac{1}{6n^2}$$

Let's find the limit:

$$\lim_{n\to\infty}\left(\frac{1}{3}-\frac{1}{2n}+\frac{1}{6n^2}\right) = \lim_{n\to\infty}\frac{1}{3}-\lim_{n\to\infty}\frac{1}{2n}+\lim_{n\to\infty}\frac{1}{6n^2} = \frac{1}{3}-0+0=\frac{1}{3}$$

Therefore:

$$\lim_{n\to\infty}\left[\frac{1^2+2^2+\ldots+(n-1)^2}{n^3}\right] = \frac{1}{3} = \frac{1}{k+1}$$

Do you see a pattern developing?

In general, although we will not prove it for all k (Note: We are reasoning by induction.), we have this relationship:

$$\lim_{n\to\infty}\frac{1^k+2^k+\ldots+(n-1)^k}{n^{k+1}} = \frac{1}{k+1}$$

Let's apply this result to conclude our dance of reasoning. We know:

$$\frac{\pi}{4} = \mathrm{m}\overset{\frown}{AD} = \lim_{n\to\infty}\left[\left(\frac{n-1}{n}\right) - \left(\frac{1^2+2^2+\ldots+(n-1)^2}{n^3}\right) + \frac{1^4+2^4+\ldots+(n-1)^4}{n^5} - \ldots\right]$$

We already know this:

$$\lim_{n\to\infty}\frac{n-1}{n} = 1$$

We now need to find this:

$$\lim_{n\to\infty} -\left(\frac{1^2+2^2+\ldots+(n-1)^2}{n^3}\right) = -\lim_{n\to\infty}\frac{1^2+2^2+\ldots+(n-1)^2}{n^3} = ?$$

Since $k = 2$:

$$\lim_{n\to\infty}\frac{1^2+2^2+\ldots+(n-1)^2}{n^3} = \frac{1}{3}$$

Therefore:

$$\lim_{n\to\infty} -\left(\frac{1^2+2^2+\ldots+(n-1)^2}{n^3}\right) = -\frac{1}{3}$$

In the same way, since $k = 4$, we get:

$$\lim_{n\to\infty}\frac{1^4+2^4+\ldots+(n-1)^4}{n^5} = \frac{1}{5}$$

For $k = 6$:

$$\lim_{n\to\infty} -\left(\frac{1^6+2^6+\ldots+(n-1)^6}{n^7}\right) = -\frac{1}{7}$$

Do you see what is happening? The reciprocals of the odd numbers, the odd terms of the Harmonic Series (Lesson 9.9), trot to infinity changing signs as they step their way into a dance of astonishing perichoretic beauty.

Therefore:

$$\frac{\pi}{4} = \mathrm{m}\overset{\frown}{\mathrm{AD}} = 1 - \frac{1}{3} + \frac{1}{5} - \frac{1}{7} + \frac{1}{9} - \ldots$$

QED

An eighth portion, an arc, of the circumference of a circle of radius 1 interpenetrates the odd terms of the Harmonic Series, the dance of the sum of the reciprocals of the positive odd integers, signs alternating, positive, negative, positive, negative, etc. *ad infinitum*.

EXERCISES

Define the following terms/concepts:

1. Divergent series
2. Convergent series
3. The convergence of an infinite series to a limiting value

Write the following rational numbers in the form of a repeating decimal:

4. 0.2
5. -18
6. 6.25
7. -3.125

Find the next term for the following sequences. Classify each as arithmetic, geometric, or neither.

8. $-\frac{1}{2}$, 1, -2, 4, -8, ___
9. $-\frac{2}{5}, -\frac{1}{5}, -\frac{1}{10}, -\frac{1}{20}$, ___
10. $\frac{1}{5}, \frac{1}{10}, \frac{1}{15}, \frac{1}{20}$, ___
11. $-\frac{1}{2}$, -1, $-\frac{3}{2}$, -2, ___
12. $\frac{1}{4}, \frac{1}{7}, \frac{1}{10}, \frac{1}{13}$, ___
13. $\frac{1}{3}, \frac{1}{10}, \frac{1}{17}, \frac{1}{24}$, ___

Determine (a) the multiplicative factor *r* for each of these geometric sequences and (b) whether the sequence is convergent or divergent:

14. 6, 7.2, 8.64, 10.368, …
15. 10, 9, 8.1, 7.29, …
16. 18, -9, 4.5, …
17. 3, 3, 3, 3, …
18. 5, -5, 5, -5, …
19. -3, -3.03, -3.0603, -3.090903, …

> Mathematics is indeed the dance of reason.
>
> James D. Nickel

If possible, find the following sums:

20. 225, 45, 9, …
21. $\frac{1}{4}+\frac{1}{12}+\frac{1}{36}+\ldots$
22. 90, 45, 22.5,
23. $\frac{1}{5}-\frac{1}{10}+\frac{1}{20}-\frac{1}{40}+\ldots$
24. $\left(\frac{1}{3}\right)+\left(\frac{1}{3}\right)^2+\left(\frac{1}{3}\right)^3+\left(\frac{1}{3}\right)^4+\ldots$
25. $\left(\frac{1}{4}\right)+\left(\frac{1}{4}\right)^2+\left(\frac{1}{4}\right)^3+\left(\frac{1}{4}\right)^4+\ldots$
26. $\left(\frac{1}{5}\right)+\left(\frac{1}{5}\right)^2+\left(\frac{1}{5}\right)^3+\left(\frac{1}{5}\right)^4+\ldots$

27. $\left(\frac{1}{6}\right)+\left(\frac{1}{6}\right)^2+\left(\frac{1}{6}\right)^3+\left(\frac{1}{6}\right)^4+\ldots$
28. $\left(\frac{2}{3}\right)+\left(\frac{2}{3}\right)^2+\left(\frac{2}{3}\right)^3+\left(\frac{2}{3}\right)^4+\ldots$
29. $\left(\frac{3}{2}\right)+\left(\frac{3}{2}\right)^2+\left(\frac{3}{2}\right)^3+\left(\frac{3}{2}\right)^4+\ldots$
30. $\left(\frac{2}{5}\right)+\left(\frac{2}{5}\right)^2+\left(\frac{2}{5}\right)^3+\left(\frac{2}{5}\right)^4+\ldots$
31. $\left(\frac{3}{5}\right)+\left(\frac{3}{5}\right)^2+\left(\frac{3}{5}\right)^3+\left(\frac{3}{5}\right)^4+\ldots$
32. $\left(\frac{8}{17}\right)+\left(\frac{8}{17}\right)^2+\left(\frac{8}{17}\right)^3+\left(\frac{8}{17}\right)^4+\ldots$
33. $2^0+2^1+2^2+2^3+2^4+\ldots$

Algebraic Laws of Limits
Let f(x) and g(x) represent algebraic expressions.

- $\lim\limits_{x\to a}\left[f(x)+g(x)\right]=\lim\limits_{x\to a}f(x)+\lim\limits_{x\to a}g(x)$
- $\lim\limits_{x\to a}\left[f(x)-g(x)\right]=\lim\limits_{x\to a}f(x)-\lim\limits_{x\to a}g(x)$
- $\lim\limits_{x\to a}\left[cf(x)\right]=c\lim\limits_{x\to a}f(x)$
- $\lim\limits_{x\to a}\left[f(x)g(x)\right]=\lim\limits_{x\to a}f(x)\cdot\lim\limits_{x\to a}g(x)$
- $\lim\limits_{x\to a}\left[\frac{f(x)}{g(x)}\right]=\frac{\lim\limits_{x\to a}f(x)}{\lim\limits_{x\to a}g(x)}$ if $\lim\limits_{x\to a}g(x)\neq 0$

Given $\left(\frac{x}{y}\right)+\left(\frac{x}{y}\right)^2+\left(\frac{x}{y}\right)^3+\left(\frac{x}{y}\right)^4+\ldots$, answer these questions:

34. Write a general formula for determining the sum.
35. This formula will only work if what relationship exists between x and y?
36. If this relationship does not exist, what happens to the sum?

Using the formula for the sum of a geometric series, express the following repeating decimals as a rational number in lowest terms:

37. $0.\overline{7}$ (Hint: $0.\overline{7}=\frac{7}{10}+\frac{7}{100}+\frac{7}{1000}+\frac{7}{10{,}000}+\frac{7}{100{,}000}+\ldots$)
38. $0.\overline{45}$
39. $0.\overline{148}$
40. $0.0\overline{2}$
41. $0.0\overline{65}$

Answer the following questions:

42. Using Figure 8, explain why $\Delta CGI \sim \Delta CJF$ and $\Delta FJE \sim \Delta CAE$.
43. Explain why $1+r+r^2+r^3+r^4+r^5+\ldots=\frac{1}{1-r}$ becomes $1-s+s^2-s^3+s^4-s^5+\ldots=\frac{1}{1+s}$ when we replace r with $-s$.
44. Show that $\frac{1+2+\ldots+(n-1)}{n}=\frac{n-1}{2n}$.
45. $1^3+2^3+\ldots+(n-1)^3=\frac{n^2(n-1)^2}{4}$. Show that $\lim\limits_{n\to\infty}\left(\frac{\frac{n^2(n-1)^2}{4}}{n^4}\right)=\frac{1}{4}$.

46. $1^4 + 2^4 + \ldots + (n-1)^4 = \dfrac{6(n-1)^5 + 15(n-1)^4 + 10(n-1)^3 - (n-1)}{30}$. Show that

$$\lim_{n\to\infty}\left(\frac{\dfrac{6(n-1)^5 + 15(n-1)^4 + 10(n-1)^3 - (n-1)}{30}}{n^5}\right) = \frac{1}{5}.$$

[Hint: Review the Binomial Theorem as discussed in Lesson 4.13, where $(1 + x)^n = {}_nC_0 + {}_nC_1x + {}_nC_2x^2 + \ldots + {}_nC_nx^n$. (Recall the combinatorial analysis of Lesson 9.4.) You must determine what to do with the signs of a binomial expansion for the powers of $n - 1$).]

Figure 9.

Figure 9 pictures an infinite sequence of squares formed by joining the midpoints of the sides of each square to create the next smallest square. Each side of the original square is 8 inches, and the area of each successive square is half the area of the preceding square. Answer these questions:

47. What are the areas of the four largest squares?
48. What is the sum of the areas of the four largest squares?
49. Assuming this process continues *ad infinitum*, what is the area of all the squares?

We can now return to our work with the Koch curve in the homework of Lesson 12.12. For the following questions, if possible, state your answer as a rational number.

50. For Question 49 in Lesson 12.12, find the area of the Koch curve.
51. For Question 50 in Lesson 12.12, find the perimeter of the Koch curve.

The Harmonic Series.

The medieval Bishop and mathematician Nicole Oresme (ca. 1323-1382) studied the musical ratios that form the Harmonic Sequence (Lesson 9.9), the reciprocals of the sequence of natural numbers:

$$1, \frac{1}{2}, \frac{1}{3}, \frac{1}{4}, \frac{1}{5}, \frac{1}{6}, \frac{1}{7}, \frac{1}{8}, \frac{1}{9}, \frac{1}{10}, \frac{1}{11}, \frac{1}{12}, \frac{1}{13}, \frac{1}{14}, \frac{1}{15}, \frac{1}{16} \ldots$$

He noted that each succeeding term gets lesser and lesser. At infinity, the terms approach 0. If each succeeding term gets lesser and lesser, he asked, "Can we *always* conclude that the sum of the infinite series converges?" The answer to his question eventually shaped the framework of the development of the theory undergirding differential and integral calculus, a mathematical method that is the ground of the success of Western technology. We can write the Harmonic Series as follows:

$$1 + \frac{1}{2} + \frac{1}{3} + \frac{1}{4} + \frac{1}{5} + \frac{1}{6} + \frac{1}{7} + \frac{1}{8} + \frac{1}{9} + \frac{1}{10} + \frac{1}{11} + \frac{1}{12} + \frac{1}{13} + \frac{1}{14} + \frac{1}{15} + \frac{1}{16} + \ldots$$

52. Is this series a geometric series?

Oresme found the sum this series using a brilliant technique. Starting with the third term, $\frac{1}{3}$, he grouped $\frac{1}{3}$ with $\frac{1}{4}$ (two terms), then the next four, then the next eight, etc., as follows:

$$1+\frac{1}{2}+\underbrace{\frac{1}{3}+\frac{1}{4}}_{\text{two terms}}+\underbrace{\frac{1}{5}+\frac{1}{6}+\frac{1}{7}+\frac{1}{8}}_{\text{four terms}}+\underbrace{\frac{1}{9}+\frac{1}{10}+\frac{1}{11}+\frac{1}{12}+\frac{1}{13}+\frac{1}{14}+\frac{1}{15}+\frac{1}{16}}_{\text{eight terms}}+\ldots$$

53. Based on this pattern, copy Table 2 and write addends for each row. (Note: The table shows the first three rows as complete.)

Table 2	
Terms summed	**Sum**
1st	1
2nd	$\frac{1}{2}$
3rd and 4th	$\frac{1}{3}+\frac{1}{4}$
5th to 8th	
9th to 16th	
17th to 32nd	

Oresme focused on the terms that are summed, starting with the first group, $\frac{1}{3}+\frac{1}{4}$. When comparing two fractions with the same numerator (e.g., $\frac{1}{3}$ and $\frac{1}{4}$), he noted the fraction with the greater denominator is lesser; i.e., $\frac{1}{4}<\frac{1}{3}$ or if we cut a pie into more slices, each slice will be lesser. Given this understanding, consider the first partial sum $\left(\frac{1}{3}+\frac{1}{4}\right)$. If we compare this sum to $\left(\frac{1}{4}+\frac{1}{4}\right)$, we know that the second sum is lesser than the first sum. Or, the first sum is greater than the second sum. Note:

$$\frac{1}{3}+\frac{1}{4}>\left(\frac{1}{4}+\frac{1}{4}\right)\Leftrightarrow\frac{1}{3}+\frac{1}{4}>2\left(\frac{1}{4}\right)\Leftrightarrow\frac{1}{3}+\frac{1}{4}>\frac{1}{2}$$

Consider the next partial sum $\left(\frac{1}{5}+\frac{1}{6}+\frac{1}{7}+\frac{1}{8}\right)$. If we compare this sum to $\left(\frac{1}{8}+\frac{1}{8}+\frac{1}{8}+\frac{1}{8}\right)$, we know that the first sum is greater than the second sum:

$$\frac{1}{5}+\frac{1}{6}+\frac{1}{7}+\frac{1}{8}>\frac{1}{8}+\frac{1}{8}+\frac{1}{8}+\frac{1}{8}\Leftrightarrow\frac{1}{5}+\frac{1}{6}+\frac{1}{7}+\frac{1}{8}>4\left(\frac{1}{8}\right)\Leftrightarrow\frac{1}{5}+\frac{1}{6}+\frac{1}{7}+\frac{1}{8}>\frac{1}{2}$$

54. In Table 3, continue this comparison with the succeeding partial sums. (Note: The table shows the first three rows as complete.)

Table 3	
Terms summed	**Sum**
1st	1
2nd	$\frac{1}{2}=\frac{1}{2}$
3rd and 4th	$\frac{1}{3}+\frac{1}{4}+\frac{1}{4}>2\left(\frac{1}{4}\right)=\frac{1}{2}$
5th to 8th	
9th to 16th	
17th to 32nd	

We have a new series to consider:

$$1+\frac{1}{2}+\underline{\frac{1}{4}+\frac{1}{4}}+\underline{\frac{1}{8}+\frac{1}{8}+\frac{1}{8}+\frac{1}{8}}+\underline{\frac{1}{16}+\frac{1}{16}+\frac{1}{16}+\frac{1}{16}+\frac{1}{16}+\frac{1}{16}+\frac{1}{16}+\frac{1}{16}}+\ldots$$

We note that the value of the partial sums of this series is, one after another is:

$$\frac{1}{4}+\frac{1}{4}=2\left(\frac{1}{4}\right)=\frac{1}{2}$$

$$\frac{1}{8}+\frac{1}{8}+\frac{1}{8}+\frac{1}{8}=4\left(\frac{1}{8}\right)=\frac{4}{8}=\frac{1}{2}$$

$$\frac{1}{16}+\frac{1}{16}+\frac{1}{16}+\frac{1}{16}+\frac{1}{16}+\frac{1}{16}+\frac{1}{16}+\frac{1}{16}=8\left(\frac{1}{16}\right)=\frac{8}{16}=\frac{1}{2}$$

etc.

We see that the sum of every group is $\frac{1}{2}$.

55. If we construct 10 of these groups, what would be the sum?
56. If we construct 100 groups, what would be the sum?
57. If we construct 1000, what would be the sum?
58. If we construct 1,000,000 groups, what would be the sum?
59. Since the partial sums get greater and greater as we walk leisurely toward infinity, what kind of series is $1+\frac{1}{2}+\frac{1}{4}+\frac{1}{4}+\frac{1}{8}+\frac{1}{8}+\frac{1}{8}+\frac{1}{8}+\frac{1}{16}+\frac{1}{16}+\frac{1}{16}+\frac{1}{16}+\frac{1}{16}+\frac{1}{16}+\frac{1}{16}+\frac{1}{16}+\ldots$?
60. Based on your answer to Question 59, (a) what kind of series is $1+\frac{1}{2}+\frac{1}{3}+\frac{1}{4}+\frac{1}{5}+\frac{1}{6}+\frac{1}{7}+\frac{1}{8}+\frac{1}{9}+\frac{1}{10}+\frac{1}{11}+\frac{1}{12}+\frac{1}{13}+\frac{1}{14}+\frac{1}{15}+\frac{1}{16}+\ldots$? (b) Why?

Are the following sequences harmonic? Why or why not?

61. $\frac{1}{8},\frac{1}{4},\frac{1}{2},1,2,\ldots$
62. $1,\frac{1}{2},\frac{1}{3},\frac{1}{4},\frac{1}{5},\ldots$

63. $\frac{1}{2}, \frac{1}{5}, \frac{1}{8}, \frac{1}{11}, \ldots$

64. $2, \frac{2}{3}, \frac{2}{5}, \frac{2}{7}, \ldots$

65. $\frac{1}{5}, -\frac{1}{25}, \frac{1}{125}, -\frac{1}{625}, \ldots$

66. $\frac{3}{4}, \frac{1}{2}, \frac{1}{3}, \frac{2}{9}, \ldots$

Figure 10. Victoria Falls Bridge, Victoria Falls, Zimbabwe and Livingstone, Zambia. The engineers designed the arch according to the parabola $f(x) = \frac{116 - 21x^2}{120}$. Graph this function and compare it with the picture at left. Source: Public Domain.

> In his scientific autobiography, Werner Heisenberg tells us that again and again when the mathematics of quantum theory proved to be as difficult as they were intricate, he would go away for three or four weeks at a time to play the piano or the violin in order, as he put it, to tune in to the 'Central Order' – the name he used in that context for God. When his whole being was tuned in to that Central Order he would come back to find his mathematical equations working out more easily.
>
> Thomas F. Torrance, "The Reconciliation of the Mind." In *Atonement: The Person and Work of Christ* (2009), p. 447.

13.16 THE INFINITE DANCE OF THE DOMINO EFFECT

Concept Introduced
1. Equiangular spiral
2. Logarithmic spiral
3. Mathematical Induction

Giuseppe Peano's fifth axiom, sometimes known as the Domino Effect, is:

If 1 has a particular property, and the successor of every natural number has the same property, then every natural number has that property.

In this lesson, we will demonstrate how we use this axiom to prove propositions about all numbers in the sequence of natural numbers even though there are an infinite number of them.

SUM OF CONSECUTIVE POSITIVE INTEGERS

First, let's revisit the ancient Greek geometric method of finding the sum of consecutive positive integers. Using Mr. Farmer's method of counting, we get (Figure 1):

$$1 + 2 = \frac{\overset{1}{\cancel{2}} \times 3}{\underset{1}{\cancel{2}}} = 3$$

$$1 + 2 + 3 = \frac{3 \times \overset{2}{\cancel{4}}}{\underset{1}{\cancel{2}}} = 6$$

$$1 + 2 + 3 + 4 = \frac{\overset{2}{\cancel{4}} \times 5}{\underset{1}{\cancel{2}}} = 10$$

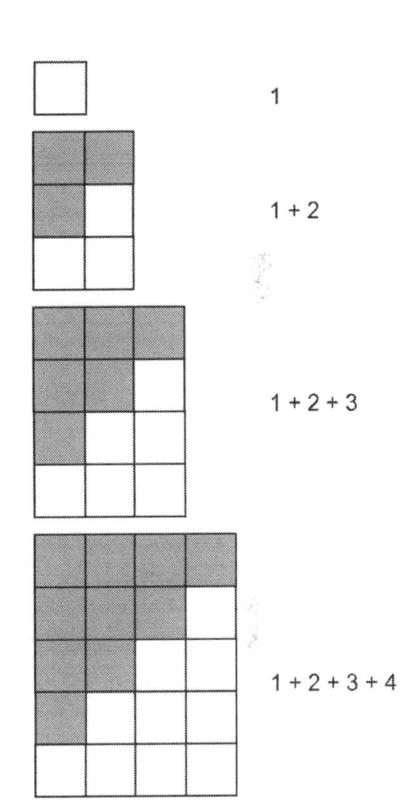

Figure 1.

In general, where $t_1 = 1$ and $t_n = n$, we have a special application of the Gaussian Formula for summing the first n natural numbers:

$$1 + 2 + 3 + \ldots + (n-2) + (n-1) + n = \frac{n(n+1)}{2}$$

Let's see if we can derive this formula using algebraic operations. First, we let $S_n =$ the sum of the first n natural numbers. We get:

Equation 1. $S_n = 1 + 2 + 3 + \ldots + (n-2) + (n-1) + n$

Next, we reverse the terms in the sum. We get:

Equation 2. $S_n = n + (n-1) + (n-2) + \ldots + 3 + 2 + 1$

Now, we add Equation 1 to Equation 2. We get:

Equation 3. $2S_n = \underbrace{(n+1) + (n+1) + \ldots + (n+1) + (n+1)}_{n \text{ times}}$ (Make sure you see this. It is one example of the beautiful dance of Algebra.)

Invoking the principle that multiplication is repeated addition, we get:

Equation 4. $2S_n = n(n+1)$

Dividing both sides of Equation 4 by 2, we get our formula:

Equation 5. $S_n = \frac{n(n+1)}{2}$

Pythagoras showed that the sum of the first n odd integers is a square number. We can demonstrate this proposition geometrically using pebbles (Figure 2).

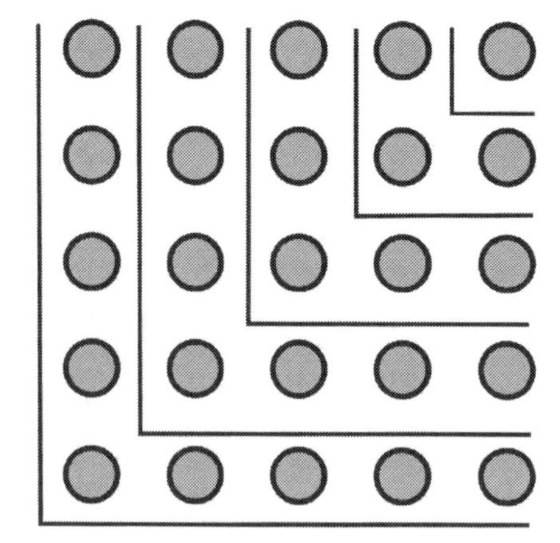

Figure 2.

Follow these observations:

1. The first square number is 1.
2. The second square number is 4 = 1 + 3
3. The third square number is 9 = 1 + 3 + 5
4. The fourth square number is 16 = 1 + 3 + 5 + 7
5. The fifth square number is 25 = 1 + 3 + 5 + 7 + 9
6. etc., *ad infinitum.*

It is the *ad infinitum* that causes mathematicians headaches. The pattern seems to work. We should be able to conclude that that the sum of the first n odd integers is a square number. But, how do we know for certain?

We need to invoke deductive logic. In this case, Giuseppe Peano's fifth axiom, the axiom of **Mathematical Induction** or the Domino Effect, enables us to prove propositions about all numbers in the sequence of natural numbers even though there are an infinite number of them. We call this method of reasoning the Domino Effect because if you erect a set of dominos in order, equally spaced, all you need to do is trip the first one and all the rest come tumbling down.

Figure 3. Source: iStockPhoto.

MATHEMATICAL INDUCTION

Suppose we wish to prove an assertion A about a pattern involving the natural numbers. We let $A(n)$, read "A of n," denote this assertion regarding any natural number n.[1] By doing this, we have generalized the situation. Instead of looking at a specific natural number like 5 or 789, we consider any natural number, and we represent this natural number using the letter n. To prove that $A(n)$ is true for all n (the infinite set of dominoes), it is sufficient to prove two things:

Step 1. *The Step of Induction*: We must show the $A(1)$ is true; i.e., the assertion is true when $n = 1$. Using our domino illustration, this is equivalent to toppling the first domino.

[1] $A(n)$, stated "A of n," is similar to the mathematical notation for functions, i.e., $f(x)$. See Lesson 10.2.

Step 2. *The Step of Inheritance*: We next assume that $A(k)$ is true for all k. Then, all we must do is prove that this assertion is true for $A(k + 1)$, the next number in the sequence of natural numbers. If we can do this, then the initial assertion, $A(k)$ is true. Using our domino illustration, this is equivalent to the toppling of all the dominoes.

These two steps comprise the logical process of Mathematical Induction. Both steps, the induction step and the inheritance step, are necessary; neither is sufficient alone. Step 1 gives us a starting point; i.e., we knock down the first domino. Step 2 shows us that we can prove $A(2)$ from $A(1)$ or the first domino has knocked down the second, then $A(3)$ from $A(2)$ or the second domino has knocked down the third, etc., *ad infinitum*. Truly a stunning dance of logic, isn't it?

SUM OF CONSECUTIVE ODD INTEGERS

From our analysis of square and odd numbers, we see this pattern, the dance of free-fall motion (Lesson 13.13):

1. $1 = 1 \times 1 = 1^2$ $(n = 1)$
2. $1 + 3 = 4 = 2 \times 2 = 2^2$ $(n = 2)$
3. $1 + 3 + 5 = 9 = 3 \times 3 = 9 = 3^2$ $(n = 3)$
4. $1 + 3 + 5 + 7 = 16 = 4 \times 4 = 16 = 4^2$ $(n = 4)$

We conjecture that, in general, this proposition is true:

$A(n) = 1 + 3 + 5 + \ldots + (2n - 1) = n^2$

Make sure that you see that $(2n - 1)$ represents the last odd number. See how it works for $n = 1, 2, 3$, and 4 before you continue.

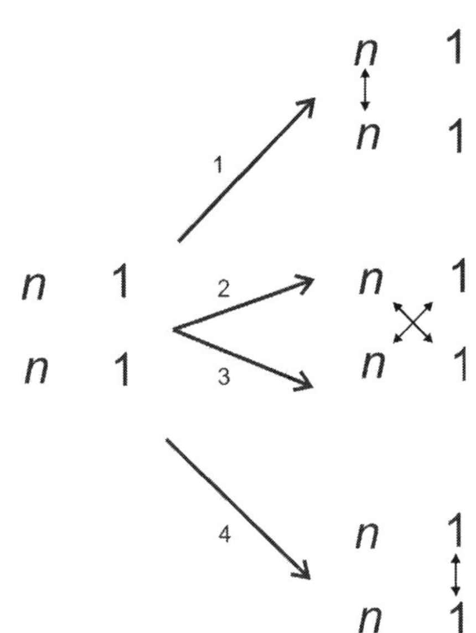

Figure 4.

Back to our assertion, $A(n)$. Can we prove that this pattern is always true? We invoke Mathematical Induction:

Step 1. *The Step of Induction*: Is it true when $n = 1$ or for $A(1)$?
Since $A(n) = 1 + 3 + 5 + \ldots + (2n - 1) = n^2$, is $A(1)$ true? We substitute n with 1 and find out. When $n = 1$, we get:

$1 = 1 \times 1 = 1^2 = 1$. $A(n)$ is true when $n = 1$.

Step 2. *The Step of Inheritance*: We shall now assume $A(k)$ is true for some k in general; i.e., we assume the truth of this statement:
$A(k) = 1 + 3 + 5 + \ldots + (2k - 1) = k^2$
We ask, "Does this pattern now hold for the successor of k, i.e., $k + 1$?" Or, "Is $A(k + 1)$ true?" Given $1 + 3 + 5 + \ldots + (2k - 1) = k^2$, we need to add $2k+ 1$, the next odd number in the series, to both sides of this equation. We get:

$A(k + 1) = 1 + 3 + 5 + \ldots + (2k - 1) + (2k + 1) = k^2 + 2k + 1$

We note:

Observation 1. $2k + 1 = 2k + 2 - 1 = 2(k + 1) - 1$
Observation 2. $k^2 + 2k + 1 = (k + 1)^2$ since (Figure 4):
$(k + 1)^2 = (k + 1)(k + 1) =$
$k(k + 1) + 1(k + 1) =$
$k^2 + k + k + 1 =$
$k^2 + 2k + 1$

We should also know this relationship from our algebraic identity $(a + b)^2 = a^2 + 2ab + b^2$.

We substitute $2(k + 1) - 1$ for $2k + 1$ and $(k + 1)^2$ for $k^2 + 2k + 1$ and get:

$A(k + 1) = 1 + 3 + 5 + \ldots + (2k - 1) + [2(k + 1) - 1] = (k + 1)^2$

Do you see what is happening? By adding the next odd number, $2k + 1$, we get the next square number because $(k + 1)^2$ is the next square number after k. What is true for k is also true for k + 1 or $A(k + 1)$ is true. In other words, the sum of the first n odd numbers is n^2 and the sum of the first $(k + 1)$ odd numbers is $(k + 1)^2$.

Therefore, by Mathematical Induction, the sum of all odd numbers up to $2n - 1$ will always equal n^2.

QED

An exploration like this demonstrates the power of mathematical thinking, using algebraic methods, to corral the infinite. What wonder! What beauty!

GAUSSIAN FORMULA

Let's try Mathematical Induction on the Gaussian Formula to show that there is more than one way to prove a proposition in mathematics. We want to prove:

$$A(n) = 1 + 2 + 3 + \ldots + n = \frac{n(n+1)}{2}$$

Step 1. *The Step of Induction*: $n = 1 \Rightarrow \dfrac{1(1+1)}{2} = \dfrac{1(2)}{2} = \dfrac{2}{2} = 1 \Rightarrow A(1)$ is true.

Step 2. *The Step of Inheritance*: We assume that $A(k)$ is true for k; i.e., $1 + 2 + 3 + \ldots + k = \dfrac{k(k+1)}{2}$ is true. Then, for $k + 1$, we get, by adding $(k + 1)$ to both sides:

$$A(k+1) = 1 + 2 + 3 + \ldots + k + (k+1) = \frac{k(k+1)}{2} + (k+1)$$

Let's apply algebraic operations to the right side to see if we can simplify it. We are summing two terms. Any common factors? Yes: $(k + 1)$. Factoring $(k + 1)$, we get:

$$(k+1)\left(\frac{k}{2} + 1\right)$$

Make sure you see this.

Note: $\dfrac{k}{2} + 1 = \dfrac{k+2}{2}$ (We are adding fractions by finding the common denominator.) Substituting, we get:

$$(k+1)\left(\frac{k+2}{2}\right) = \frac{(k+1)(k+2)}{2}$$

Since $k + 2 = k + 1 + 1$, we get:

$$\frac{(k+1)(k+2)}{2} = \frac{(k+1)[(k+1)+1]}{2}$$

> The principle of mathematical induction contains an infinite number of syllogisms compressed, as it were, into one formula.
>
> Henri Poincaré, *Science and Hypothesis* (1905), pp.10-11.

We now have this:

$$A(k+1)=1+2+3+\ldots+k+(k+1)=\frac{(k+1)\left[(k+1)+1\right]}{2}$$

We have established the truth of $A(k+1)$. Do you see it? Look carefully: "$k + 1$" has replaced "n".

Compare $A(k + 1)$ with $A(n)$ to make sure.

Here is $A(n)$ again:

$$A(n)=1+2+3+\ldots+n=\frac{n(n+1)}{2}$$

Ponder carefully until you see the substitution.

Therefore, by Mathematical Induction, $A(n)$ is true for any natural number n.

QED

We have again demonstrated the beautiful principle of unity in diversity revealed in different methods of logical proof. Both methods result in the same QED. Both procedures interpenetrate the proposition. We see in this interpenetration the perichoretic nature of mutual indwelling. This wonder of reasoning should lead us to worship the Triune God, the ultimate ground of rationality in the universe, visible and invisible.

EXERCISES

1. Explain the two steps of Mathematical Induction.

From the exercises below, define these terms:

2. Equiangular spiral
3. Logarithmic spiral

Key Algebraic Identities:

1. $ax^2 + bx = x(ax + b)$
2. $(x + b)^2 = x^2 + 2bx + b^2$
3. $(x - b)^2 = x^2 - 2bx + b^2$
4. $(x + b)(x - b) = x^2 - b^2$
5. $(x + d)(x + e) = x^2 + (d + e)x + de$
6. $(ax + d)(bx + e) = abx^2 + (ae + db)x + de$

Review Lesson 11.12 and then, showing your algebraic reasoning in detail, factor the following algebraic expressions into a product of expressions or a single expression: (Hint: Use the algebraic identities given below to help.)

4. $64x - 16x^2$
5. $5x^3 + 15x$
6. $9x - 27$
7. $z^2 - c^2$
8. $x^4 - 9x^2$
9. $2x^2 - 32$
10. $3x + 7x$
11. $x^2 + 8x + 7$

12. $x^2 + 2x - 3$
13. $x^3 - 6x^2 + 8x$
14. $d^2 + 2de + e^2$
15. $4x^2 + 12x + 9$
16. $x^2 - 2xy + y^2$
17. $7x^2 + 12x - 4$
18. $2x^2 + 15x + 7$
19. $2x^2 + 13x - 7$
20. $6x^2 + 17x + 5$

Answer the following questions:

21. Explain how adding these two equations, (1) $S_n = 1+2+3+\ldots+(n-2)+(n-1)+n$ and (2) $S_n = n+(n-1)+(n-2)+\ldots+3+2+1$, produces this equation: $2S_n = \underbrace{(n+1)+(n+1)+\ldots+(n+1)+(n+1)}_{n \text{ times}}$

22. Explain how we can simplify the equation $2S_n = \underbrace{(n+1)+(n+1)+\ldots+(n+1)+(n+1)}_{n \text{ times}}$ to the equation $2S_n = n(n+1)$.

23. Substitute k with $k + 1$ to show that $A(k) = 1+2+3+\ldots+k = \frac{k(k+1)}{2}$ becomes $A(k+1) = 1+2+3+\ldots+k+(k+1) = \frac{(k+1)[(k+1)+1]}{2}$.

24. Prove that $1^3 + 2^3 + \ldots + n^3 = \left[\frac{n(n+1)}{2}\right]^2$.

25. Prove that $1^2 + 3^2 + 5^2 + \ldots + (2n-1)^2 = \frac{1}{3}(4n^3 - n)$. (Hint: Factor $\frac{1}{3}(4n^3 - n)$ first.)

26. Prove that $1^3 + 2^3 + \ldots + n^3 = (1 + 2 + \ldots + n)^2$ (See Lesson 11.11 where we derived this relationship by looking at geometric patterns.)

27. (a) Determine a formula for the sum $\frac{1}{1\cdot 2} + \frac{1}{2\cdot 3} + \ldots + \frac{1}{n(n+1)}$ by searching for a pattern and (b) prove that this formula is true. (Refer to the homework in Lesson 8.5.)

28. What is the sum of $\frac{1}{1\cdot 2} + \frac{1}{2\cdot 3} + \ldots + \frac{1}{n(n+1)} + \ldots$? (Hint: Invoke limit notation in your analysis.)

Figure 5. Azimuthal equidistant map projection. Source: United States Postal Service.

In the homework exercises in Lesson 13.14, we discovered the connection between $\sqrt[12]{2}$ (≈ 1.059463094) and the notes of the chromatic scale, a geometric sequence, on a piano. We graphed this relationship on the Cartesian coordinate plane. We are now going to graph these values in polar coordinates (Lesson 12.12).

In review, polar coordinates are of the form $(r, \theta.)$ The first coordinate r represents the distance of a point from the pole, the center of the graph (0, 0). The second coordinate θ represents the measure of the angle of rotation or the counterclockwise angle formed between the positive polar axis, an axis equivalent to the x-axis, and a ray connecting the pole to the point. In Figure 6, the point (2, 90°) is located 2 units from the pole at a counterclockwise rotation of 90° from the positive polar axis.

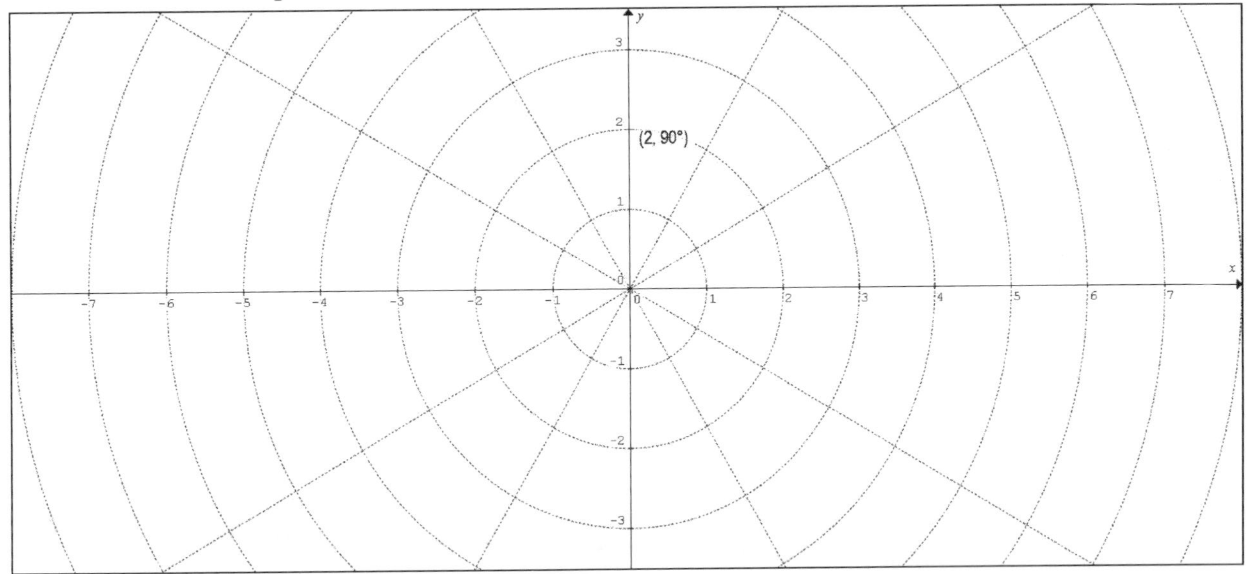

Figure 6. Polar coordinate system whereby (r, θ) can be plotted.

29. The polar coordinates of our musical graph take the form $\left(\left(\sqrt[12]{2}\right)^n, n(15°)\right)$. In other words, from $n = 1$ to 20, we are going to find the value of $\left(\sqrt[12]{2}\right)^n$ and plot these values on the polar coordinate graph using arbitrary increments of 15°. Create a table for the values of $\left(\sqrt[12]{2}\right)^n$ from n from 1 to 20 matching each increment with 15° intervals. Use a scientific calculator and write your answer rounded to ten significant figures. You can also create a spreadsheet to do the calculations.

30. Plot each point on the polar coordinate graph and then connect the points of your graph. (Note: You will need to use software where you can plot points on a polar coordinate graph or use polar graph paper. If necessary, photocopy Figure 7.)

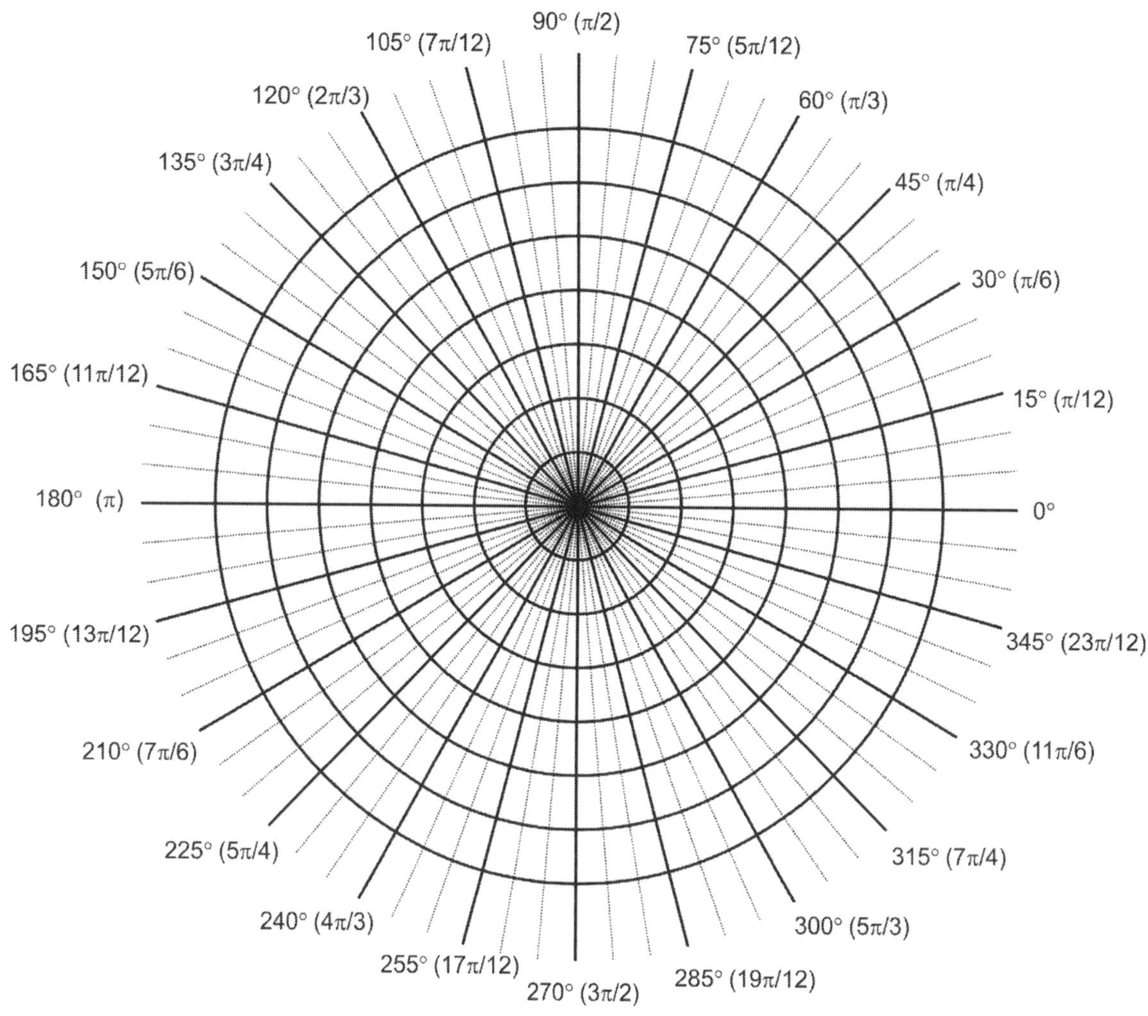

Figure 7. Polar coordinate grid.

31. This graph is an **equiangular spiral**. Why? If you look at Figure 8, you will discover that each radius vector, or the radii from the pole through each point on the graph, intersects the graph at the same angle α. This angle is approximately 77.6°. We see this shape in many places of created reality, e.g., the chambered nautilus (Figure 8), the webs of some spiders, and specific galaxy forms. Mathematicians also name this graph the **logarithmic spiral** because the angles the radii make with the polar axis are proportional to the logarithms of the lengths of the corresponding radii, i.e., $\frac{\theta_n}{\theta_{n+1}} = \frac{\log r_n}{\log r_{n+1}}$.

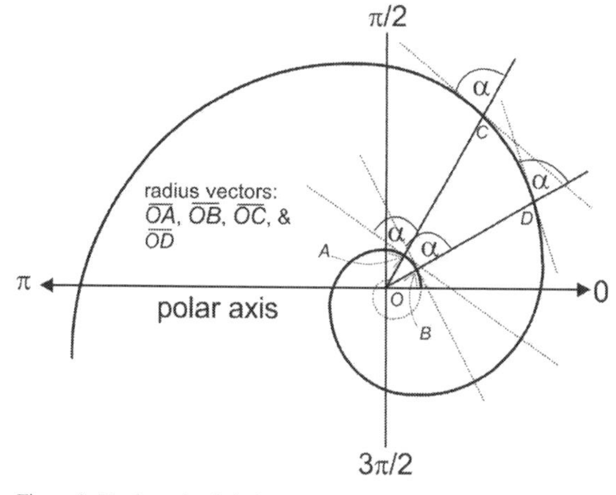

Figure 8. Equiangular Spiral.

With a scientific calculator:

(a) Show that this proportion is true for (1.059463094, 15°) and (1.122462048, 30°).

(b) Show that this proportion is true for (1.122462048, 30°) and (1.189207115, 45°)

32. Find the polar coordinates of a point on the musical spiral for $n = 40$. Use a scientific calculator and round r to nine significant figures.
33. Find the polar coordinates of a point on the musical spiral for $n = 100$. Use a scientific calculator and round r to ten significant figures.
34. Theoretically, does the musical spiral ever end?
35. The general equation for a point (r, θ) in polar coordinates on a logarithmic spiral is $r = e^{\theta \cot \alpha}$ where α is the measure of the angle that any radius vector makes with the spiral curve and e = 2.718281828. Isn't it amazing that e, like π, both of which are irrational numbers, interpenetrate creational realities, including the chromatic scale, in such a dramatic fashion? Approximate α for the point $(1.059463094, \frac{\pi}{12})$. Remember, $\frac{\pi}{12} = 15°$. (Hint: Set up the equation substituting 1.059463094 for r and $\frac{\pi}{12}$ for θ. Take the natural logarithm of both sides and apply your logarithm rules. Solve for α recognizing that $\cot \alpha = \frac{1}{\tan \alpha}$ using a scientific calculator. Your answer, rounded to the nearest tenth of a degree, should equal the angle measure given in Question 31.)

Figure 9. Chambered Nautilus. Source: James D. Nickel.

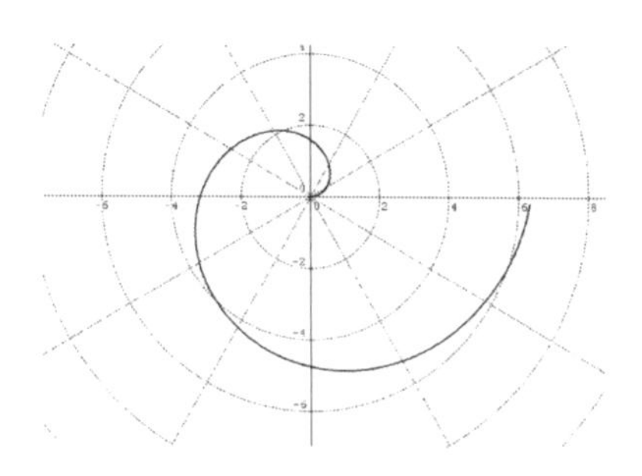

Figure 10. $r = e^{k\theta}$, where $k = 0.01$. Logairthmic spiral.

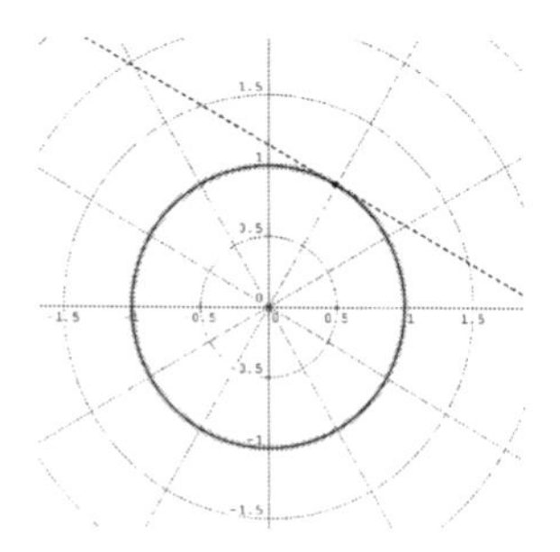

Figure 11. $r = 1$. A circle is a logarithmetic spiral; i.e., $r = e^{k\theta}$, where $k = 0$. (The growth rate is zero.) Why? [Note: The angle of tangent line at every point on the circumference of the circle to the radius of the circle at that point is $\pi/2$ (90°).]

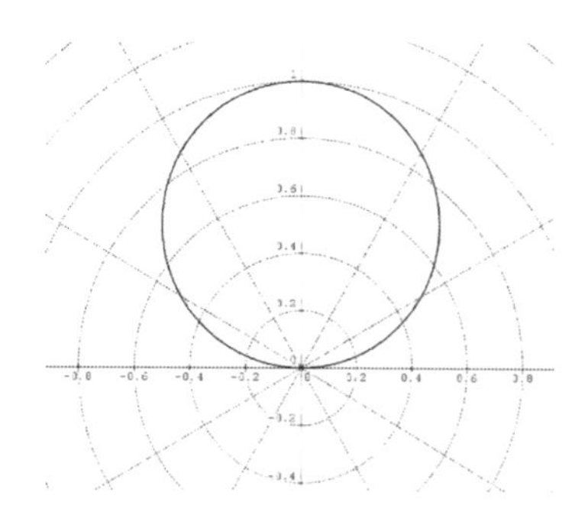

Figure 12. $r = \sin\theta$. Do you see why? (Let θ range from 0 to 2π.)

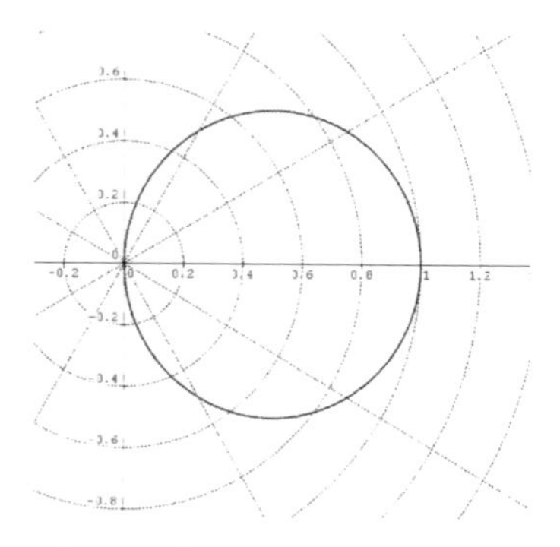

Figure 13. $r = \cos\theta$. Do you see why? (Let θ range from 0 to 2π.)

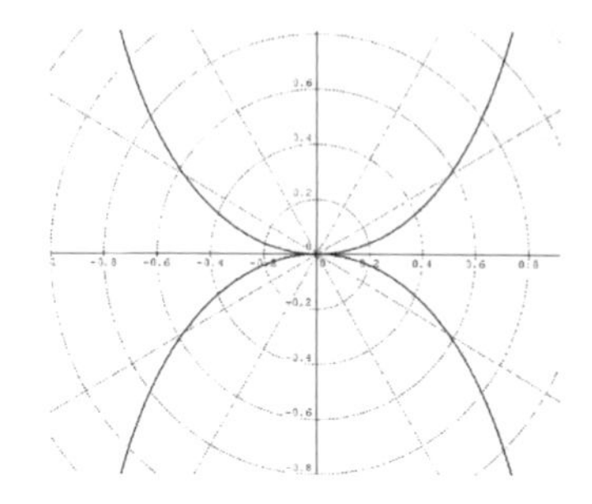

Figure 14. $r = \tan\theta$. Do you see why? (Let θ range from 0 to 2π.)

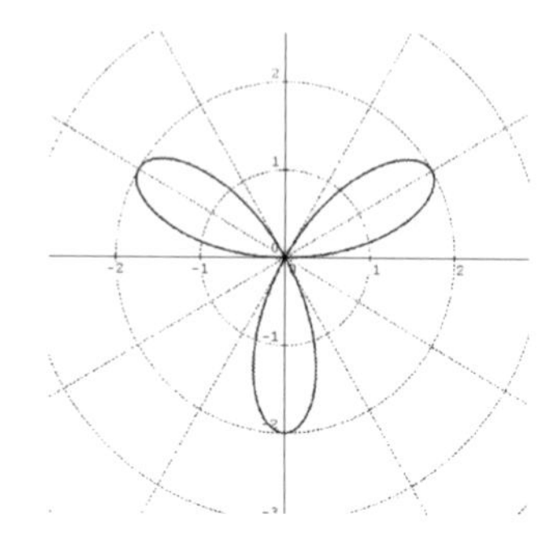

Figure 15. $r = 2\sin 3\theta$. The three-leaved "sine clover."

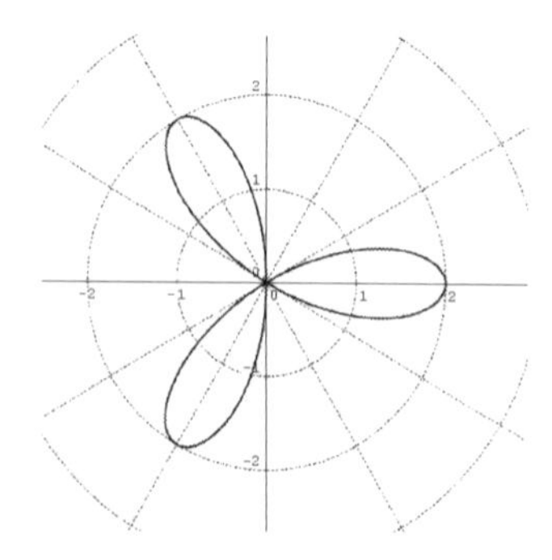

Figure 16. $r = 2\cos 3\theta$. The three-leaved "cosine clover."

13.17 An Introduction to Calculus Reasoning

Terms, Symbols & Concepts Introduced
1. Calculus
2. $\frac{dy}{dx}$
3. $f'(x)$
4. *horror infiniti*
5. Method of increments
6. $\dot{y}$
7. y'

The Babylonian Algorithm

In Lesson 11.7, we investigated the Babylonian algorithm as a way to calculate square roots. In review, here are the steps:

Step 1. Estimate the square root of the given positive integer.
Step 2. Calculate the average of that guess and the given positive integer divided by that guess.
Step 3. Recursion step: Use your answer to Step 2 as your new guess and repeat Step 2 until you obtain the desired degree of accuracy.

Using symbols, we let A = positive integer. We want to find $\sqrt{A}$. Let x_n be our first estimate where n = 1. The formula for the recursive algorithm is:

$$x_{n+1} = \frac{x_n + \frac{A}{x_n}}{2}$$

The symbols show us how the input, x_n, generates the output, x_{n+1}. This output becomes the input for the next iteration of the algorithm.

Babylonian Algorithm Extended

In Lesson 11.10, we extended the Babylonian algorithm to include the calculation of cube roots.

Step 1. Estimate the cube root of the given positive integer.
Step 2. Sum twice the estimate with the given positive integer divided by the square of the estimate and then divide that sum by 3.
Step 3. Recursion Step: Use your answer to Step 2 as your new guess and repeat Step 2 until you obtain the desired degree of accuracy.

Let A represent the positive integer and x_n the initial estimate. We want to find $\sqrt[3]{A}$. Again, we let x_n be our first estimate where n = 1. The formula for the recursive algorithm is, using the symbols x_n for the input and x_{n+1} for the output, is:

$$x_{n+1} = \frac{2x_n + \frac{A}{(x_n)^2}}{3}$$

Newton's Perichoretic Discovery

Using Sir Isaac Newton's (1642-1727) newly invented Differential Calculus,[1] both Newton and the English mathematician Joseph Raphson (1648-1715) developed an algorithm, the Newton-Raphson

[1] Historians consider both Newton and the German mathematician Gottfried Wilhelm Leibniz (1646-1716), pronounced "liebnits," as immediate co-founders of Calculus. Newton was the first to put the ideas together while Leibniz was the first to publish his ideas. The great controversy of their time was over who was to receive the honor of priority in the founding of Calculus. Note: Many mathematics books speak of *the* Calculus to distinguish this branch of mathematics from the name of a

method, that interpenetrates the Babylonian method. To show this connection, we first need to develop some elementary Calculus concepts, and we will spend some time deriving lots of Calculus ideas as part of this preparatory work. Enjoy this excursion into the Calculus realm of reasoning.

> Further dim chambers lighted by sullen, sulphurous fires were reputed to contain a dragon called the 'Differential Calculus.'
>
> Winston Churchill, "Examinations," *My Early Life: 1874-1904* ([1930, 1958] 1996), p. 26.

HISTORICAL DEVELOPMENT

We trace the historical roots of Calculus back to the paradoxes of Zeno of Elea (5th century BC) in which he concluded the impossibility of motion. The convergence of an infinite series to a limiting value (Lesson 13.15), a foundational concept of Calculus, resolved Zeno's conundrum. Archimedes (3rd century BC) anticipated another method of Calculus when he calculated the lower and upper limits of π, known as the method of exhaustion (Lesson 14.7 homework).

Calculus came into its own in 17th century Europe, primarily in England and Germany. Before we investigate the history behind this fruitful development, let's briefly review the motivations for the development of the branches of mathematics that provide the foundation for the methods of Calculus, namely Algebra, Geometry, and Trigonometry.

Algebraic operations provided solutions to simple physical problems that in their mathematical form called for solving first, second, and higher degree equations with one or two unknowns. The plane and solid geometry of Euclid tackled problems dealing with the calculation of perimeters, areas, and volumes of common figures. Plane geometry also defined the conditions under which two figures, e.g., two triangles, are congruent or similar. Trigonometry, along with the invention of the sextant and transit, enabled scientists to determine immeasurable distances, either across a river or the heavens. The coordinate or analytic geometry of René Descartes (1596-1650) and Pierre de Fermat (1601-1665) simplified the study of important curves such as the paths of projectiles, planets, and light rays.

---

more general method describing the formal development of a theory, i.e., "a" calculus. Historically, this branch of mathematics was named "the calculus of infinitesimals."

Although the ancient Greeks anticipated Calculus methods, they could not advance the subject to its fullest for two reasons. First, they had trouble with one concept, infinity. When Archimedes exhausted the circumference of the circle with inscribed and circumscribed regular polygons, he calculated his solution using finite sums. The word infinity never appeared in any of his arguments. In the case of Zeno, he concluded the impossibility of motion because he could not accept the fact that an infinite sum of numbers could converge to a limit. The transcendent nature of infinity rattled the Greek mind. In this context, transcendence means that the concept of infinity goes beyond the limits of the human intellect and for that reason, the Greeks were horrified by it (in Latin, ***horror infiniti***). The Greek worldview erred in one of two ways; either they absolutized number as in the case of Pythagoras, or they absolutized reason as in the case of their philosophers. When a culture absolutizes or deifies, any aspect of God's creation, then nothing can transcend deity. Since the concept of infinity transcended Greek deity, i.e., human reason, then the Greeks, shrinking before its silence, swept this intruder under the proverbial rug.

Figure 1. François Viète. Source: Public Domain.

Second, since the Greeks tied form to number in the context of plane and solid geometry, they had an inadequate understanding of algebraic processes. Because the rhetorical nature of their algebra, they did not develop a collection of symbols and a set of rules to operate upon these symbols. The reason why they failed to embrace symbolic algebra is again worldview related. They grounded their geometric commitments on their static view of the world. In plane geometry, all lengths have fixed, or static, magnitudes. In the symbolic algebra fully developed in Western Europe, letting x equal a variable quantity presupposes a dynamic view of the world; i.e., the domain that x can assume can range across the real number continuum. Greek geometry, with its static line segments and angles, serves its intended purpose quite well, but it is alien to the dynamics of the real number continuum. Greek geometry cannot express continuous relations among variable quantities.

Nearly two millennia after Archimedes, François Viète (1540-1603), the founder of symbolic algebra, in a work on trigonometry published in 1593, discovered a remarkable formula involving π:

$$\frac{2}{\pi} = \frac{\sqrt{2}}{2} \cdot \frac{\sqrt{2+\sqrt{2}}}{2} \cdot \frac{\sqrt{2+\sqrt{2+\sqrt{2}}}}{2} \cdot \ldots$$

Note the ellipsis $\ldots$ indicating that $\frac{2}{\pi}$ is an infinite product. As far as mathematics historians can ascertain, this was the first time someone wrote an infinite process in mathematical formula. Viète's use of the ellipsis signaled an acceptance by the mathematical world of infinite processes and opened this method to widespread use.

Viète, from France, can cite Nicole Oresme (ca. 1323-1382), not only as a fellow countryman but as one of his mathematical ancestors. Oresme anticipated the coordinate geometry of Descartes (Lesson 10.3) and a profound understanding of the divergence of the harmonic series (Lesson 13.15 homework). Oresme also pioneered mathematical methods that dealt quantitatively with change and rate of change. His work in this area foreshadowed many of the methods of Calculus. He, like many medieval theologians, did not shy away from using the concept of infinity in mathematical processes. Why? Since infinity,

Infinite series formulas involving π:

$$\frac{\pi}{4}=1-\frac{1}{3}+\frac{1}{5}-\frac{1}{7}+\frac{1}{9}-\frac{1}{11}+\frac{1}{13}+\ldots \text{ (Gregory,1671)}$$

$$\frac{\pi^2}{6}=1+\frac{1}{1^2}+\frac{1}{2^2}+\frac{1}{3^2}+\frac{1}{4^2}+\ldots \text{ (Euler,1736)}$$

$$\pi=16\left(\frac{1}{5}-\frac{1}{3\cdot5^3}+\frac{1}{5\cdot5^5}-\frac{1}{7\cdot5^7}+\frac{1}{9\cdot5^9}-\ldots\right)-4\left(\frac{1}{239}-\frac{1}{3\cdot239^3}+\frac{1}{5\cdot239^5}-\ldots\right)$$

(Machin,1706)

$$\pi=2\sqrt{3}\left(1-\frac{1}{3\cdot3}+\frac{1}{5\cdot3^2}-\frac{1}{7\cdot3^5}+\ldots\right) \text{ (Sharp,1717)}$$

Some of these formulas were developed in the Hindu/Arabic cultures, but failed to make their way to the West. European mathematicians "re-discovered" them on their trek to the development of Calculus.

The relationship between π, the ratio of the circumference to the diameter of a circle, and these infinite series formulas is a constant source of wonder because, as they stand, they are as remote from geometry as anything imaginable. Yet, the connection exists, another wonderful commentary on the perichoretic unity and diversity that constitutes the structure of mathematics.

meaning without bounds, was an attribute of the Biblical God, medieval theologians, known as scholastics,[2] contra Greek philosophers, were not afraid of the concept.

Concerning the meditations of the scholastic philosophers, mathematics historian Howard Eves (1911-2004) observes:

> ... [they] led to subtle theorizing on motion, infinity and the continuum, all of which are fundamental concepts in modern mathematics. The centuries of scholastic disputes and quibblings may, to some extent, account for the remarkable transformation from ancient to modern mathematical thinking.[3]

The medieval theorizing on motion reflected a change in worldview: from the static view of the Greeks to a dynamic view, a view that led to the development of symbolic algebra. In this context, science historian Stanley L. Jaki (1924-2009) adds to the list of ideas embraced by medieval theologians:

> Inertia, momentum, conservation of matter and motion, the indestructibility of work and energy – conceptions which completely dominate modern physics – all arose under the influence of theological ideas.[4]

Mathematics historian Carl Boyer (1906-1976) remarks that, in this theorizing, "there was perhaps as much originality in medieval times as there is now."[5] The application of the concept of infinity to the study of change in motion is foundational to Calculus. Boyer comments about the impact of the input of the scholastics in this area:

---

[2] Scholastic theologians have received bad historical press in some quarters. Although they did err in some aspects of theology (See footnote 8.), they deposited an indispensable heritage for Western civilization, especially in science and mathematics.

[3] Howard Eves, *An Introduction to the History of Mathematics* (New York: Holt, Rhinehart and Winston, [1953, 1964, 1969] 1976), p. 213.

[4] Stanley L. Jaki, *The Road of Science and the Ways to God* (Edinburgh: Scottish Academic Press, 1978), p. 157.

[5] Carl Boyer, *The History of the Calculus and Its Conceptual Development* (New York: Dover Publications, [1949] 1959), p. 65.

> The blending of theological, philosophical, mathematical, and scientific considerations which has so far been evident in Scholastic thought is seen to even better advantage in a study of what was perhaps the most significant contribution of the fourteenth century to the development of mathematical physics ... a theoretical advance was made which was destined to be remarkably fruitful in both science and mathematics, and to lead in the end to the concept of the derivative.[6]

We will define the concept of the derivative shortly. In the light of these quotes, given modernity's loathing of anything that smacks of the supernatural and its arrogant premise that those who believe in Scripture believe in fairy tales, how then, could the theology of Scripture, a fairy tale at best, be the source of such remarkable fruit in science and mathematics? The answer of modernity is an answer of silence.

In his autobiography, historian Arnold Toynbee (1889-1975) notes the significance of Calculus:

> Looking back, I feel sure that I ought not to have been offered the choice [whether to study Greek or Calculus – JN] ... calculus ought to have been compulsory for me. One ought, after all, to be initiated into the life of the world in which one is going to live. I was going to live in the Western World ... and the calculus, like the full-rigged sailing ship, is ... one of the characteristic expressions of the modern Western genius.[7]

Using Toynbee's words, the "characteristic expression of the modern Western genius" finds its roots in theology. Without the Biblical revelation of the infinite, personal, and Triune God, Western man, with his culture impacted by the Gospel of Christ, could never have embraced the infinitesimal nature of Calculus. Christ is the Savior, in an historical sense, and Lord, in an epistemic sense, of science and mathematics.[8]

A TASTE OF CALCULUS

For the successful launch of Calculus, it needed an acceptance and use of the concept of infinite processes, symbolic algebra, coordinate or analytic geometry along with trigonometry, and the presence of reliable measuring tools, including mechanical clocks.[9] All of these ideas and instruments were on the launching pad in Western Europe at the dawn of the 17th century. The scientists of this century were trying to solve a whole new group of problems and Newton invented Calculus to quantify and resolve the following:

1. The study of the motion of celestial bodies.
2. The study of projectile motion and rays of light striking the surface of a telescopic lens. To do this, they had to determine of tangent lines to various curves. Why? These lines represent the direction of the curve at the tangent point. A problem of pure geometry, i.e., tangent lines, became of great importance for scientific applications.

---

6 *Ibid.*, pp. 70-71.

7 Arnold Toynbee, *Experiences* (New York: Oxford University Press, 1969), pp. 12-13.

8 See Stanley L. Jaki, *The Savior of Science* (Grand Rapids: Eerdmans, 2000). Although the overall thrust of medieval theology for the development of mathematics and science was positive, this theology had cracks in it. For example, the immensely influential theologian Thomas Aquinas (1225-1274), in his massive work, *Summa Theologiae*, divided theology into two parts: *De Deo Uno* (on the One God) and *De Deo Trino* (on the Triune God). By rational argument, he attempted to prove the existence of the One God (footnote 4 of Lesson 13.9), while postulating that the Trinity is accepted only by revealed faith. He, therefore, laid the foundation for the split between reason and revelation and an unfortunate bifurcation between the One God and the Triune God. The speculative theology of Thomas Aquinas, along with subsequent medieval scholasticism, asserted that we can consider the divine *ousia* (being) of God in the abstract apart from the Triune Persons. In contrast, because of the revelation of Jesus, the Triune Persons in their perichoretic interrelations are the *ousia* of God. The fellowship of the Father, Son and Holy Spirit, dwelling eternally in mutually reciprocal delight, is the *ousia* of God, and we cannot consider *ousia* apart from that divine fellowship.

9 See Donald Cardwell, *Wheels, Clocks, and Rockets: A History of Technology* (New York: W. W. Norton, 1995). Cardwell documents the strategic advances in technology that were made during the medieval period.

3. Optimization or maxima and minima problems. In warfare applications, a method was needed to determine the maximum range and angle of elevation for artillery cannon. Concerning planetary motion, scientists needed a method to determine the maximum and minimum distances of a planet from the Sun.
4. The study of lengths of curves. For example, the distance covered by a planet, moving in an elliptical orbit, in a given period.
5. The areas and volumes of figures bounded by curves and surfaces.
6. The centers of gravity of bodies.
7. The gravitational attraction that a planet exerts on another planet.

In the exposition that follows, we will focus on the second point, lines explicitly tangent to a curve at a given point. As we journey through this kingdom of mathematics, we will discover how much that we have already learned will come to fruition in this exciting branch of knowledge.

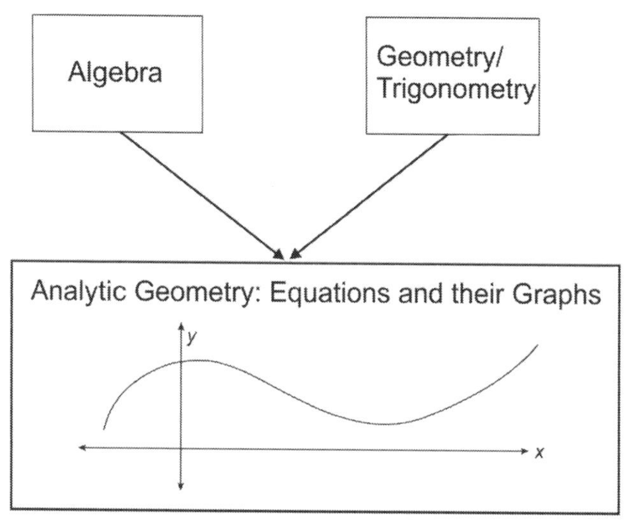

Figure 2. The spadework for Calculus.

THE CALCULUS LINEUP

Many men contributed to the development of Calculus. We can only list them now. The medieval heritage was transmitted through Nicholas of Cusa (1401-1464), Leonardo da Vinci (1452-1519), Niccolò Fontana Tartaglia (ca. 1499-1557), Geronimo Cardano (1501-1576), Rafael Bombelli (ca. 1526-1573), François Viète (1540-1603), Simon Stevin (1548-1620), Galileo Galilei (1564-1642), Johannes Kepler (1571-1630), and Evangelista Torricelli (1608-1647). Building on this foundation were Pierre de Fermat (1601-1665), René Descartes (1596-1650), Blaise Pascal (1623-1662), Gilles Persone de Roberval (1602-1675), Bonaventura Cavalieri (1598-1647), Isaac Barrow (1630-1677), James Gregory (1638-1675), Christiaan Huygens (1629-1695), John Wallis (1616-1703), Sir Isaac Newton (1642-1727), and Gottfried Wilhelm Leibniz (1646-1716).

From the late 17th and lasting throughout the 18th century, Calculus was refined by Jakob Bernoulli (1654-1705), Johann Bernoulli (1667-1748), Michel Rolle (1652-1719), Brook Taylor (1685-1731), Colin Maclaurin (1698-1746),[10] Leonhard Euler (1707-1783), Jean Le Rond d'Alembert (1717-1783), and Joseph-Louis Lagrange (1736-1813).

> Every textbook on calculus today borrows, more or less, from Euler.
>
> William McGowen Priestley, *Calculus: A Liberal Art* ([1974] 1998), p. 302.

In the 19th century, Bernhard Bolzano (1781-1848), Augustin-Louis Cauchy (1789-1857), Karl Weierstrass (1815-1897), Georg Friedrich Bernhard Riemann (1826-1866), and Julius Wilhelm Richard Dedekind (1831-1916) made final clarifications in the logical and rigorous sense.

Calculus is Latin for pebble, and it carries the meaning of counting or calculation. The derivative and the integral are fundamental concepts in this branch of mathematics. The foundation of both is the

[10] In the introduction to one of his books, Colin MacLaurin, a Scot, wrote that he undertook his labors to understand and bring forth the glory of God's creation.

limit concept, namely the convergence of an infinite series to a limiting value. We will only explore the nature of the derivative in this lesson and the next two lessons.

THE DERIVATIVE: FIRST STEPS IN A LINEAR DIRECTION

When we graph functions, we are never capable of entirely depicting a function because of the limits of graphic technology; we can only represent the way a function behaves for a given range of arguments. We need a more precise method of understanding the behavior of curves to any desired degree of accuracy. The derivative is such a tool.[11]

We define the derivative as the limiting value of the ratio of the change in the dependent value of a function to the corresponding change in its independent variable, Δy over Δx. We, therefore, encounter the derivative every time we calculate the slope of a straight line. In review, given two points on a straight line, (x_1, y_1) and (x_2, y_2), we define the slope a of a straight line as:

$$a = \frac{\Delta y}{\Delta x} = \frac{y_2 - y_1}{x_2 - x_1}$$

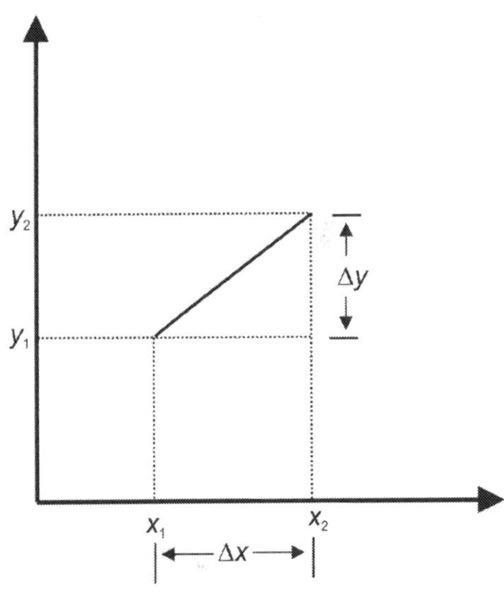

Figure 3. $y = f(x) = 2x$

We can also define the derivative of a function as the slope of the graph of the function *at a given point*. Note the phrase "given point." With a straight line, we need two points to determine the slope. To find the slope at a given point in Calculus, we take two points infinitesimally close to each other.

For example (Figure 3), consider a small portion of the line representing the function $y = f(x) = 2x$. We want to find the slope of the line at a point, say $x_1 = 2$. Let y_1 be the value of the function at this point. Therefore, $y_1 = 2x_1 = 4$. If we just consider the slope at this coordinate (2, 4), we run into trouble. At that instant, there is no change in y, Δy, and no change in x, Δx. No change in y means $\Delta y = 0$ and no change in x means $\Delta x = 0$. The slope, therefore, is:

$$\frac{\Delta y}{\Delta x} = \frac{0}{0}$$

This expression is indeterminate (Lesson 5.15) because "Thou shalt not divide by 0." Here is where the founders of Calculus, Leibniz primarily, introduced the concept of the infinitesimal, known as the **method of increments**.[12] Let's choose another coordinate (x_2, y_2). Therefore, $\Delta x = x_2 - x_1$. Since we know the first coordinates (2, 4), then:

$$\Delta x = x_2 - 2$$

Likewise, $\Delta y = y_2 - y_1$ and, since $y_1 = 4$, then:

$$\Delta y = y_2 - 4$$

At (x_2, y_2) this equation is true:

---

[11] Other words for derivative are the differential coefficient, meaning "difference number," or fluxion, Isaac Newton's word. Fluxion, in Latin, means "a flow or flowing."

[12] An increment, in this context, means "a very small increase or addition."

$y_2 = 2x_2$

We now solve for x_2 and y_2 respectively:

$\Delta y = y_2 - 4 \Leftrightarrow y_2 = \Delta y + 4$
$\Delta x = x_2 - 2 \Leftrightarrow x_2 = \Delta x + 2$

By substitution, we get this equation:

$\Delta y + 4 = 2(\Delta x + 2) \Leftrightarrow \Delta y + 4 = 2\Delta x + 4$

Subtracting 4 from both sides of the equation, we get:

$\Delta y + 4 = 2\Delta x + 4 \Leftrightarrow \Delta y = 2\Delta x$

This equation says that the "change in y" is always 2 times the "change in x." Since we define the slope as $\frac{\Delta y}{\Delta x}$, we write:

Figure 4. Gottfried Wilhelm Leibniz. Source: Public Domain.

$$\frac{\Delta y}{\Delta x} = 2$$

As we let Δx get lesser and lesser, Δy gets lesser and lesser. No matter how infinitesimally small Δx gets, $\frac{\Delta y}{\Delta x}$ is always 2. Therefore, 2 is the *limiting value of the ratio of the change in the dependent value of a function to the corresponding change in its independent variable*. In other words, the limit of $\frac{\Delta y}{\Delta x}$ as Δx approaches 0 is 2. By using the limit concept in this way, the founders of Calculus *avoided division by zero*. In limit notation, we write:

$$\lim_{\Delta x \to 0} \frac{\Delta y}{\Delta x} = 2$$

This symbolism means that the slope of the line $y = 2x$ is 2 *for every given point on the straight line*. Therefore, the derivative, symbolized as y' (say "y prime" meaning "instantaneous rate of change"), of the function $y = 2x$ is:

$$y' = \lim_{\Delta x \to 0} \frac{\Delta y}{\Delta x} = 2$$

The derivative, therefore, of $y = f(x)$ at any point x on its graph, not just of a linear function, but of almost all functions that are continuous[13] (i.e., has no breaks in it), is:

$$y' = \lim_{\Delta x \to 0} \frac{\Delta y}{\Delta x}$$

Congratulations! You have solved your first problem in Calculus. Not the "sulphurous" dragon Churchill thought it was, was it? It is as easy as calculating the slope. We can, therefore, state a general formula for calculating the derivative of any linear function of the form $y = ax$:

$$y = ax \Rightarrow y' = a$$

[13] There are functions that are continuous everywhere but differentiable nowhere; $y = |x|$ is one example.

The French mathematician Joseph-Louis Lagrange (1736-1813) used the y' notation for the derivative. Other mathematicians used other symbols. Isaac Newton used the dot notation $\dot{y}$ ("*y* dot"). Gottfried Wilhelm Leibniz symbolized the derivative as $\frac{dy}{dx}$. This symbol means "the ratio of the change in *y* over the change in *x*" or "a little bit of *y* over a little bit of *x*." We say, "*dy* over *dx*." For $y = 2x$, we write, using limit notation:

$$\frac{dy}{dx} = \lim_{\Delta x \to 0} \frac{\Delta y}{\Delta x} = 2$$

Using the function notation $f(x)$ invented by Leonhard Euler (1707-1783), we write:

$f(x) = ax + b$

The notation of the derivative is $f'(x)$. We say, "*f* prime of *x*." Therefore:

$$\boxed{f(x) = ax \Rightarrow f'(x) = a}$$

There is no agreed convention on the use of these four ways of symbolizing the derivative. We note:

y' means the same as $\dot{y}$, $\frac{dy}{dx}$, and $f'(x)$.

The Leibniz notation is used the most because of the way it pictures the meaning of the derivative. The least used is Newton's dot notation. Because Newton was a physicist, some physics textbooks still use the dot notation in his honor.

What would be the derivative of $y = 3$? The graph (Figure 5) of this relationship is a straight line parallel to the *x*-axis intercepting the *y*-axis at (0, 3). What is the slope of this line? It is 0, because Δy is always 0. As we let Δx approach 0, the ratio of $\frac{\Delta y}{\Delta x}$ is 0. In general, if $y = b$, then $y' = 0$. The derivative of a constant is always 0.

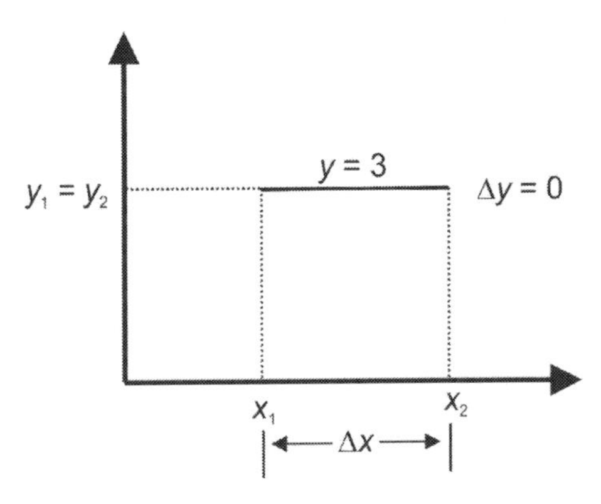

Figure 5. Derivative analysis: $y = 3$

To take the derivative of the two-stage composite function $h(x) = ax + b$, we take the derivative of each term and sum the result. We first set $f(x) = ax$ and $g(x) = b$. Taking their respective derivatives, we get:

$f(x) = ax \Rightarrow f'(x) = a$
$g(x) = b \Rightarrow g'(x) = 0$
(This means that *b*, the *y*-intercept, does not impact the slope of the line defined by $h(x) = ax + b$, a truth we have learned from our work in Step 10.)

Therefore:

$h'(x) = f'(x) + g'(x) = a + 0 = a$

We can, therefore, state a general formula for calculating the derivative of a linear function of the form $y = ax + b$:

$$\boxed{y = ax + b \Rightarrow y' = a}$$

Or:

$$f(x) = ax + b \Rightarrow f'(x) = a$$

Physically, the straight line pictures constant speed or, better yet, constant velocity.[14] It was in the analysis of the dynamism, or flow, of motion that Newton interpreted the derivative concept. He named it the method of fluxions. He denoted the variable x as the fluent, and when he calculated the rate of change of the variable, he used the expression "finding the fluxion of a given fluent." The variable *time*, seen as a flowing continuum, formed the basis of his physical theories.

LET'S GO FOR A DRIVE

Let's say that I'm driving my car southbound on a freeway. At 2:00 PM my odometer[15] reading is 50,250. Three hours later, my odometer reading is 50,430. Let's assume that I had my cruise control button turned on during these three hours. Table 1 reflects this situation.

Table 1		
t (hours)	t_1 = 2:00 PM	t_2 = 5:00 PM
d (distance)	d_1 = 50,250	d_2 = 50,430

How fast was I driving? In other words, what was my velocity v due South? We find velocity by calculating the ratio of the change in distance, Δd, over the change in time, Δt:

$$v = \frac{\Delta d}{\Delta t} = \frac{50,430 - 50,250}{5 - 2} = \frac{180}{3} = 60$$

In general:

$$v = \frac{\Delta d}{\Delta t} = \frac{d_2 - d_1}{t_2 - t_1}$$

So, if our velocity is constant, the graph of the situation is a straight line and the velocity, which is the slope of the line, is the derivative. In real life, however, velocity is not steady since it is continually changing. Things, therefore, are not this simple. We use this formula $r = \frac{d}{t}$ to determine the average velocity over time, where r = average rate, d = distance traveled, and t = time of travel. Calculus studies velocity *at an instant*. In other words, Calculus looks at the speedometer[16] and tells us how fast we are driving at a given instant of time.

---

[14] Remember that speed is a scalar quantity in Physics while velocity is a vector quantity involving magnitude *and* direction (Lesson 3.2).

[15] Odometer is Greek meaning "measure of the way."

[16] Speedometer means "measure of speed." In Calculus, the speedometer represents the derivative, the velocity at an instant of time. The distance travelled between two instants of time is integration, the inverse of differentiation. Although, as noted, we will not explore integration in these lessons, it is worthy to note at this point of our study that inverse relationships interpenetrate not only Arithmetic, but also Calculus.

Since velocity is a vector, it can be negative. What would that mean? In the case of a car, it would mean driving backward. If we throw a stone straight up, its velocity is positive as it travels upward; negative as it goes downward. We will investigate a differential understanding of velocity and its rate of change, acceleration, in Lesson 13.19.

> Alice looked around her in great surprise. "Why I do believe we've been under this tree the whole time! Everything's just as it was!"
> "Of course it is," said the Queen. "What would you have it?"
> "Well, in our country, "said Alice, still panting a little, "you'd generally get to somewhere else – if you ran very fast for a long time as we've been doing."
> "A very slow sort of country!" said the Queen. "Now, here, you see, it takes all the running you can do, to keep in the same place."
> Charles Lutwidge Dodgson (Lewis Carroll)
> *Through the Looking Glass.*

EXERCISES

Define the following words:

1. *horror infiniti*
2. Static view of the world
3. Dynamic view of the world
4. Calculus
5. Method of increments

Using Pascal's Triangle, expand following the following two-term, or binomial, expressions: (Review the relevant material in Lesson 9.4 to help you.)

6. $(a + b)^2$
7. $(a + 2b)^2$ (Hint: Let $x = 2b$)
8. $(a + b)^3$
9. $(2x + 3y)^3$
10. $(a + b)^4$
11. $(a + b)^5$
12. $(x + y)^6$
13. $(m + n)^7$
14. $(c + d)^8$

Answer the following questions:

15. Explain how the ancient Greeks dealt with the concept of infinity.
16. Explain how medieval theologians dealt with the concept of infinity.
17. What branches of mathematics and other technologies were foundational to the successful launch of Calculus?

18. What groups of physical problems, requiring Calculus to solve, faced scientists and mathematicians in the 17th century?
19. What is the technical definition of the derivative as given in this lesson?

Answer the next group of three connected questions:

20. Compare:
    (a) 3^2 to $2 \cdot 4$
    (b) 4^2 to $3 \cdot 5$
    (c) 5^2 to $4 \cdot 6$
    (d) 87^2 to $86 \cdot 88$
21. From these inductive observations, write a general observation rhetorically for any natural number x.
22. Let $x \in \mathbb{N}$, write this general observation using algebraic symbols.

For the next ten questions, use the derivative of y with respect to x, $\frac{dy}{dx}$, to determine the slope, if possible, of the following linear equations:

23. $y = -\frac{3}{2}x + 8$
24. $y = 6x - 12$
25. $3x + 4y = 8$
26. $6x - 2y = 15$
27. $2x + 3y = 12$
28. $9x - 6y = 22$
29. $3y + 2x = 98$
30. $5y - 6x - 36 = 0$
31. $y = 8$
32. $x = 3$

33. For Questions 23 to 32, (a) solve for x, if possible, and (b) find $x' = \frac{dx}{dy}$, if possible.
34. If you exchange x with y, (a) what do your answers to Question 33a represent? (b) What is the relationship between the derivatives x' in Question 33b with their respective derivatives y' in Questions 23 to 32?

> In the mathematical field, a single notion precisely learned is worth a textbook of partially digested material.
> Jerry P. King, *Mathematics in 10 Lessons: The Grand Tour* (2009), p. 17.

13.18 Catch a Falling Star

Terms, Symbols & Concepts Introduced
1. $\forall$
2. $\exists$
3. Characteristic triangle
4. Difference quotient
5. Epsilon-Delta Definition of a Limit
6. Inertia
7. Infinitesimal
8. Intermediate Value Theorem

"Catch a falling star and put it in your pocket. Never let it fade away..." were words of a popular song sung by Perry Como (1913-2001) in the 1950s.

Let's now consider motion where velocity is changing; i.e., our falling star. Instead of stars falling from the sky, we will consider Mr. Delta dropping a stone from the top of a building. How can we describe this situation? Enter the Italian mathematician Galileo Galilei (1564-1642).

Science historian Stanley L. Jaki (1924-2009) summarizes Galileo's foundations for scientific work:

> The creative science of Galileo was anchored in his belief in the full rationality of the universe as the product of the fully rational Creator, whose finest product was the human mind, which shared in the rationality of its Creator.[1]

Galileo's analytical skills incorporated three principles in his study of the magnificent book of God's creation. They are:

Principle 1. Obtain basic principles through observation and experimentation. Sometimes his experiments were thought experiments based upon what he observed.

Principle 2. Major on the major; i.e., strip away incidental or minor effects.[2] Galileo tried to understand what was happening with falling objects by stripping away air resistance by assuming these objects fall in a vacuum.

Principle 3. Apply the derived principles and other mathematical demonstrations back to the real world with all its limitations, i.e., air resistance.

Above all, Galileo sought quantitative descriptions using mathematical equations and formulas. His commitment to quantitative analysis was the fruit of the nearly one thousand years of the leavening influence of the Christian Gospel in Europe that began with the fall of the Western Roman Empire in the 5th century AD.[3] His appreciation of an orderly and understandable creation presupposes the "God who created everything according measure, number and weight" (Wisdom of Solomon 11:20-21), even in a world of motion.[4]

---

1 Stanley L. Jaki, *The Road of Science and the Ways to God* (Edinburgh: Scottish Academic Press, 1978), p. 106.

2 What can happen in this abstraction stage is the separation of surface patterns, i.e., form, from their objective foundation in reality, i.e., being. When radical separation appears, we have dualistic thinking. In the 20th century, scientists like Albert Einstein emphasized that we understand surface patterns in the light of their coherence with reality. This is unitary thinking, the unity of form and being.

3 We cannot ignore the revolutionary theological groundwork spoken to the Greek and Roman culture by the great Creeds of the Christian faith, primarily the Nicene-Constantinopolitan Creed (325, 381).

4 The *Wisdom of Solomon* is a book in the Apocrypha. In Latin, "measure, number, and weight" is *"omnia in mensura, numero et pondere disposuisti."* This phrase was the most often quoted and alluded to phrase in Medieval Latin texts. See E. R. Curtius, *European Literature and the Latin Middle Ages*, W. R. Trask, trans. (London: Routledge and Kegal Paul, 1953), p. 504. See also Ivor Grattan-Guiness, *The Rainbow of Mathematics: A History of the Mathematical Sciences* (New York: W. W. Norton, [1997] 2000), p. 127.

A CORRECTIVE TO ARISTOTLE

Let's envision Mr. Delta as he drops a stone from the top of a building. As Professor Galileo watches, he first notices that the stone's velocity is not constant; i.e., it increases with time. Stop the motion for a second! Freeze the frame! At the juncture, Galileo's theorizing, now known as the theory of **inertia**,[5] departs from the ancient Greek theory of motion, popularized by Aristotle (384-322 BC). Among other assertions, Aristotle postulated that an object, like a thrown ball, keeps moving only as long as something was actually in contact with it, imparting motion to it all the time. Aristotle thought this something was air closing behind the ball. He said that it continually pushed the object along.[6]

The theologian John Philoponus (ca. 490-ca. 570), by Christian convictions, first challenged this idea in the 6th century.[7] Contrary to Aristotelian dogma and amazingly similar to Galileo's principles,[8] Philoponus resolved that:

Point 1. All bodies would move in a vacuum with the same speed regardless of their weight, or mass as we would now describe these bodies

Point 2. Bodies of differing weights, falling from the same height, hit the ground at the same time, an observation easy to validate experimentally, but something Aristotle never tried.[9]

Point 3. Projectiles move across the air, not because the air keeps closing behind them, but because they were imparted with a quantity of motion, an "oomph," that is technically termed momentum.[10]

MEDIEVAL SCHOLARSHIP

The ideas of Philoponus were transmitted into the thinking of some key medieval theologians, particularly the French theologians Jean Buridan (ca. 1295-1358) and Nicole Oresme (ca. 1323-1382), via the work of the Arabic thinkers and translators.[11] These two medieval scholars refined the thoughts of Philoponus, especially his impetus[12] theory of motion (Point 3), thus building the foundation for Galileo's work in momentum and inertia and Isaac Newton's (1642-1727) formulation of the first law of motion.[13]

Mathematician Lipman Bers (1914-1993) was born in Latvia, the Baltic region of Northern Europe. In late 1938, just before the commencement of World War II in Europe, he migrated to the United States on an emergency visa given to political refugees who were living in Marseilles, France. In his Calculus text first published in 1969, he reflected on the Greek view of motion and the corrected view of Galileo, without recognizing the input of Philoponus, Buridan, or Oresme:

---

[5] Inertia, from Latin, means "idleness." The theory of impetus is also known as the theory of *momentum* (Latin for movement).

[6] Herbert Butterfield, *The Origins of Modern Science* (New York: The Macmillan Company, 1961), pp. 3-4.

[7] Philoponus spent most of his adult life in Alexandria, Egypt.

[8] Stanley L. Jaki, *Science and Creation: From Eternal Cycles to an Oscillating Universe* (Edinburgh: Scottish Academic Press, 1974), pp. 185-187.

[9] On 2 August 1971, astronaut Dave Scott (1932-), Apollo 15 commander, released a hammer and a feather near the surface of the Moon, a near vacuum. Both objects reached the ground at the same time, confirming the conjectures of both Philoponus and Galileo.

[10] Momentum, in Physics, means the quantity of motion of a moving body, measured as a product of its mass and velocity (Lesson 13.10).

[11] See Fritz Zimmermann, "Philoponus's Impetus Theory in the Arabic Tradition," in *Philoponus and the Rejection of Aristotelian Science*, Richard Sorabji, ed. (Cornell: Cornell University Press, 1987).

[12] Impetus, in Latin, means "to attack against."

[13] As we have noted (Lesson 13.10), Newton's first law of motion states that "every object persists in a state of rest or a state of uniform motion in a straight line unless acted upon by an external force that changes that initial state."

The ancient Greeks were excellent mathematicians; they also developed a sophisticated statics (that part of mechanics which deals with bodies at rest). But their ideas of dynamics (the mechanics of moving bodies) were naïve. Aristotle taught that the motion of falling bodies is uniform, and that the heavier the body, the faster it falls. Since Aristotle's authority acquired an almost religious character, his statement was unchallenged until the sixteenth century. The true law of falling bodies was discovered by Galileo, who thereby founded modern physics. Because his work involved an analysis of the idea of velocity, he became one of the pioneers of calculus.[14]

Mr. Delta interrupts, "Excuse me, this history lesson is illuminating, but I'm still waiting for the stone to hit the ground." "Hold on for a few more minutes," replies Professor Galileo, "Let's develop some mathematics before we start the motion again."

GALILEO'S QUANTITATIVE ANALYSIS

Concerning this falling motion, how did Galileo quantify this relationship? He sought to measure it with a mathematical formula. Noting that the velocity v increased in direct proportion to the lapse of time t, he wrote the equation:

$$v = kt$$

What was the value of k? Using an ingenious method of rolling a ball down an inclined plane and measuring time elapsed with a water clock (See the relevant homework exercises in Lesson 12.12.), Galileo determined the constant to be 32 feet per second every second,[15] written as we have already noted, this way:

$$32 \text{ ft/s}^2$$

In the Metric System, this constant is 9.8 meters/second every second, written 9.8 m/s^2.[16] Later, Isaac Newton determined this quantity to be the gravitational force, or gravitational acceleration (Lesson 8.4), of the Earth pulling the stone down.[17] In the British Imperial System, Galileo's formula becomes this:

$$v = 32t$$

Galileo now considered the quantitative answer to another question: How far does the stone fall in a given amount of time? He discovered that a ball rolling down an inclined plane covered a distance proportional to the square of the time (Lesson 13.13). In other words, doubling the time increased the distance four-fold, tripling the time increased the distance nine-fold, and so on. For the free-fall motion of a stone dropped from the top of a building, the equation relating distance d and time t, where g = the gravitational force of the Earth acting upon the stone, is:

$$d = \frac{1}{2}gt^2$$

---

[14] Lipman Bers with Frank Karal, *Calculus, Second Edition* (New York: Holt, Rinehart and Winston, [1969] 1976) , p. 96.

[15] In five significant figures, the gravitational acceleration on Earth is 32.174 ft/s^2. On the Moon, the gravitational acceleration is approximately 5.4 ft/s^2.

[16] In six significant figures, the gravitational acceleration on Earth is 9.80665 m/s^2. On the Moon, the gravitational acceleration is approximately 160 cm/s^2.

[17] We are considering this downward movement as a positive vector even though the downward pull of the gravitational force of the Earth on an object is technically, in Physics, negative. We should, therefore, write $v = -kt$, but for the sake of our argument in this section we will consider the downward pull of gravity as positive. A homework exercises, Question 8, will use the negative sign when describing physical situations like projectile motion.

Since $g = 32$, we get this quadratic equation:

$$d = \frac{1}{2}gt^2 \text{ and } g = 32 \Rightarrow d = 16t^2$$

Let's construct Table 1 with some images d for the arguments $t = 0, 1, 2,$ and 3. Then, let's change variables, y for d and x for t, and graph $y = 16x^2$ where, because of physical constraints, we are only interested in the images in Quadrant I.

Table 1

t	0	1	2	3
d	0	16	64	144

This graph (Figure 1) should be familiar to you. It is the "smiling" parabola. The images in Quadrant II mirror the images in Quadrant I through the line of symmetry, the y-axis (Lesson 11.14). We again note that negative arguments of t are values that physically makes no sense in our situation. The ancient Greeks would never have considered that the parabola could quantitatively describe falling motion. Unlike the straight-line graph for constant velocity, the graph of ever-increasing velocity curves sharply upward in Quadrant I. The Differential Calculus gives us a tool whereby we can analyze this changing velocity; it tells us what the velocity is *at an instant in time.*[18]

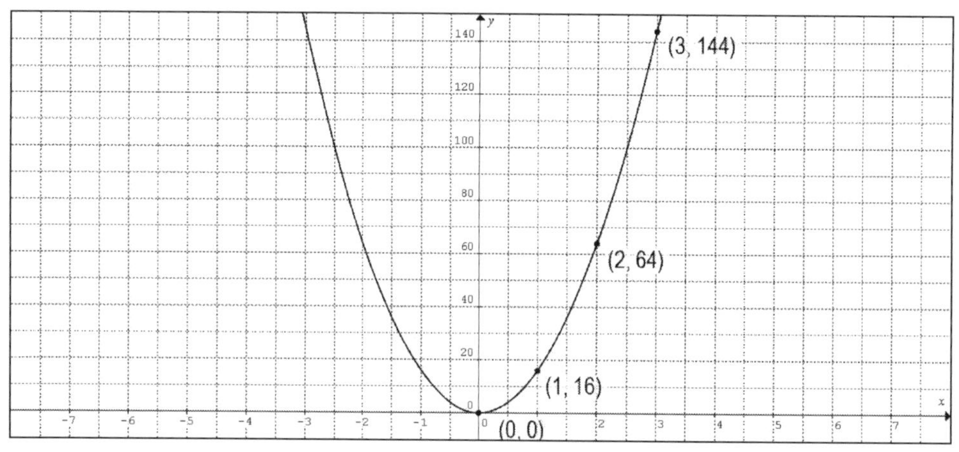

Figure 1. The graph of $d = 16t^2$ on the x-y coordinate plane.

For now, let's assume that we do not know the equation $v = 32t$. Given the equation $d = 16t^2$, let's apply the method of increments, the reasoning of Leibniz, to find the velocity of the falling stone since at $t = 2$ seconds. It is essential that you understand the next section in conjunction with Figure 1. The derivation of the derivative of a curved line is foundational to Calculus, so study this reasoning carefully.

[18] The algebraic formula for falling motion and its associated graph on the Cartesian coordinate plane now describe time and space in the context of the real number continuum, a truly astounding interpenetration, if you pause to think about it.

THE CHARACTERISTIC TRIANGLE

In Figure 2, we have magnified a portion of the curve where $P(x_1, y_1)$ represents an image on the graph of $y = 16x^2$. At $x_1 = 2$ seconds, $y_1 = 64$ feet. We draw a line tangent to P and consider a nearby point T on that line. From this, we get ΔPRT. Leibniz named this triangle the **characteristic triangle**. The lengths of the two legs of this triangle, PR and RT, are increments in the x and y coordinates as we move from P to T. Following the procedure of Leibniz, we denote these "little increases" as dx and dy respectively. Leibniz then argued that if we let dx and dy get sufficiently small, the tangent line to the graph at P will be nearly identical to the graph of $y = 16x^2$ in this infinitesimally small neighborhood of P. In more precise words, $\overline{PT}$ will *nearly* be "in sync" with the curved arc PQ. To find the slope of the tangent line at P, we find:

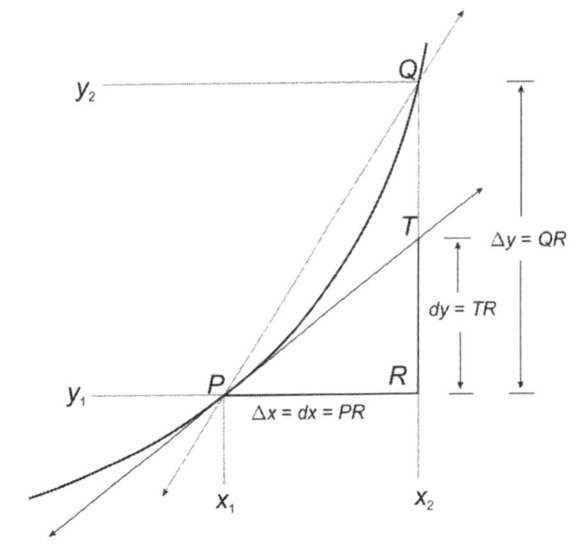

Figure 2. The characteristic triangle.

$$\frac{dy}{dx}$$

For Leibniz, since dx and dy are "little bits" or "infinitely small," the ratio of dy to dx represents both the slope of the tangent line at P and the steepness of the graph at P. The ratio of $\frac{dy}{dx}$ measures the rate of change of the curve at an instant. This idea parallels Newton's fluxions.

There is a flaw in this argument. The Irish prelate and philosopher George Berkeley (1685-1753) noted this in his satirical work *The Analyst* written in 1734.[19] The tangent line will nearly be in sync with the curve at P; *it will not coincide with it*. If they coincide, then the characteristic triangle disappears meaning $dy = 0$ and $dx = 0$. The ratio again becomes $\frac{0}{0}$, an indeterminate expression. In the 19th century, mathematicians rigorously developed the limit concept to circumvent this problem. Let's see, briefly but not rigorously, how they did it.

THE DIFFERENCE QUOTIENT

Referring again to the characteristic triangle in Figure 2, we choose two neighboring images P and Q on the graph of the curve $y = 16x^2$. Next, for the triangle-like shape PRQ, we name the sides $\overline{PR}$ and $\overline{QR}$ Δx and Δy respectively. Note that $\Delta y > dy$ because Q is above T and that $\Delta x = dx$. The "slope" of the arc between P and Q is:

[19] He coined a phrase for these ratios, naming them the "ghosts of departed quantities." George Berkeley, "The Analyst," in James R. Newman, ed., *The World of Mathematics* (New York: Simon and Schuster, 1956), 1:292.

$$\frac{\Delta y}{\Delta x}$$

As we let Δx approach 0 as a limit ($\Delta x \to 0$), Q moves back toward P along the arc. Δy also approaches 0 as a limit, i.e., $\Delta y \to 0$. The ratio of $\frac{\Delta y}{\Delta x}$ is the **difference quotient**, and it is the slope of the secant[20] line between P and Q. As Δx approaches 0, the secant line turns slightly (Figure 3), until, at the limiting value, it coincides with the tangent line. Leibniz denoted this limit as the derivative $\frac{dy}{dx}$:

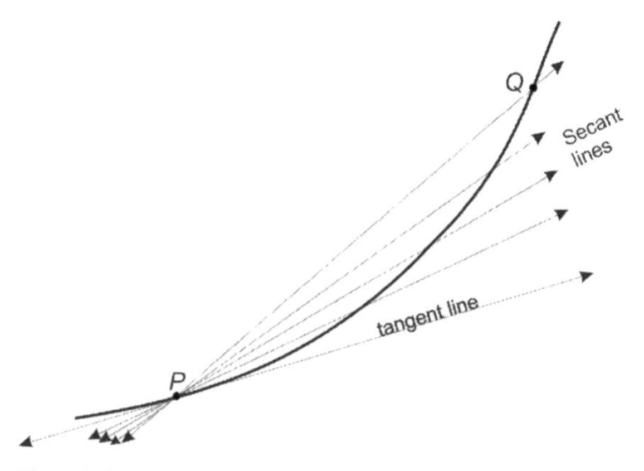

Figure 3. Secant lines approaching the tangent line.

$$\frac{dy}{dx} = \lim_{\Delta x \to 0} \frac{\Delta y}{\Delta x}$$

Mr. Delta is waiting patiently at the top of the building for us to calculate the velocity of the stone at precisely 2 seconds after he dropped it. If $x_1 = 2$ seconds, then $y_1 = 64$ feet. We let $\Delta x = PR$ and $\Delta y = QR$. We consider $x_2 = 2 + \Delta x$. Therefore, $y_2 = 64 + \Delta y$.

Using $y = 16x^2$ and making use of Binomial Theorem along with the Distributive Law, we do the following algebraic operations:

For the argument of $x_2 = 2 + \Delta x$, the image is $y_2 = 64 + \Delta y$. Therefore:

$$64 + \Delta y = 16(2 + \Delta x)^2 \Leftrightarrow$$
$$64 + \Delta y = 16[4 + 4\Delta x + (\Delta x)^2] \Leftrightarrow$$
$$64 + \Delta y = 64 + 64\Delta x + 16(\Delta x)^2$$

Solving for Δy, we subtract 64 from both sides of the equation:

$$64 + \Delta y = 64 + 64\Delta x + 16(\Delta x)^2 \Leftrightarrow \Delta y = 64\Delta x + 16(\Delta x)^2$$

Next, we divide both sides of the equation by Δx to get the difference quotient:

$$\Delta y = 64\Delta x + 16(\Delta x)^2 \Leftrightarrow \frac{\Delta y}{\Delta x} = 64 + 16\Delta x$$

The ratio $\frac{\Delta y}{\Delta x}$ is the slope of PQ, the secant line. To find the derivative $\frac{dy}{dx} = y'$ at $x = 2$, we conclude:

$$\frac{dy}{dx} = y' = \lim_{\Delta x \to 0} \frac{\Delta y}{\Delta x} = \lim_{\Delta x \to 0} \left(64 + 16\Delta x\right) = \lim_{\Delta x \to 0} 64 + \lim_{\Delta x \to 0} 16\Delta x = 64 + 0 = 64$$

Note that $16\Delta x$ drops out if we let Δx approach 0, or Δx gets infinitesimally small. Therefore, the velocity of the stone at 2 seconds is 64 feet/second. 64 is also the slope of the line tangent to the curve at P. In general:

---

[20] Remember that a secant is a straight line that intersects a curve in two or more points (Lesson 12.6). Secant, as we have already noted, is Latin meaning "to cut."

$y = 16x^2 \Rightarrow y' = 32x$

"Let the stone continue its fall!" cries Professor Galileo. "Thank you; it's about *time*," replies Mr. Delta.

Let's now resurrect Galileo's formula for the velocity for a falling object:

$v = 32t$

(Note the similarity between $y' = 32x$ and $v = 32t$. The same rule, multiply by 32, applies to both representations.)

If we let $t = 2$, then $v = 64$. We shall explore the remarkable differential connection between the two formulas $d = 16t^2$ and $v = 32t$ in the next lesson.

DELVING DEEPER INTO THE LIMIT NOTION

Figure 4. Augustin-Louis Cauchy. Source: Public Domain.

Let's review the limit concept, the driving idea of Calculus, from a different angle. The idea behind a limit is the idea of getting closer and closer to something; the limit of a sequence of numbers is converging upon a point, a goal, or a target; i.e., a number. As a Biblical illustration, when Jesus said, "The time is fulfilled, and the kingdom of God is at hand" (Mark 1:14-15), the Greek word for "at hand" is employing the limit concept. The long-promised kingdom of Messiah is about to cross the threshold, or limit, of time and space. The wave of the promised and coming kingdom of God is about to crash upon the surf like a tsunami.

We can corral the limit concept in a precise manner, and it took mathematicians nearly two thousand years to do so. The man primarily responsible for this definition was the French mathematician and devout Roman Catholic Augustin-Louis Cauchy (1780-1857). Mathematician David Berlinski (1942-) remarks about Cauchy's deep faith, "… the common assumption that scientific genius inevitably inclines a man toward agnosticism in his religious or political convictions is little more than a modern myth."[21]

Let's start with a sequence of terms S_n that converges to a limit L. This sequence converges to a limit as we extend it *ad infinitum*. We can coordinate two critical mathematical ideas in the unity of this basic idea: (1) extension of a sequence and (2) convergence to a limit. Rewording this definition, we say that a sequence S_n converges to L if, by extending the sequence, we may decrease the distance between S_n and L indefinitely; i.e., we can make the difference between S_n and L arbitrarily small. Take careful note that the mathematical operation of subtraction, taking the difference, is subordinated to the idea of approaching a limit.

Imagine a magnet drawing an iron hammer inexorably toward itself. With every passing moment, the hammer gets closer and closer to the attracting force, the distance between the two methodically sliced away. This suggests, as it has suggested to generations of mathematicians, that convergence hinges only upon some fixed but very, very small distance. Another word for this very, very small distance is the **infinitesimal**. What the ancient Greeks feared, the *horror infiniti*, raises its head, either as a demon or as an angel, depending upon your perception, and enters the conversation. The brilliance of Cauchy tamed the Greek demon *horror infiniti* in his definition of a limit.

Cauchy set the Greek letter epsilon to be a positive real number; i.e., $\varepsilon > 0$ where $\varepsilon \in \mathbb{R}$. Returning to our magnet illustration, as we decrease the distance between the hammer and the magnet indefinitely by whatever the value of ε, some electromagnetic force will eventually attract the hammer to a position

[21] David Berlinksi, *A Tour of the Calculus* (New York: Vintage Books, 1995), p. 126.

whose distance from the magnet is less than ε. In other words, whatever the distance between the magnet and the hammer currently is, the force from the magnet will draw the hammer closer. Carry this thought over to our sequence S_n. S_n converges toward a limit L if whatever the value of ε, we can find some point in the sequence such that for all points beyond in the sequence, the intervening distance is less than ε.

Let's state it again: For any positive number ε, there is some value δ (the lower case Greek letter delta), such that for all terms in the sequence beyond δ, the distance between S_n and L is less than ε. This statement is both a mouthful and a revelation of Cauchy's genius.

Figure 5. Karl Weierstrass. Source: Public Domain.

Let's consider our familiar geometric sequence, one of Zeno's paradoxes, $\frac{1}{2}, \frac{1}{4}, \frac{1}{8}, \ldots, \frac{1}{2^n}$ (Lesson 13.14). We set $S_n = \frac{1}{2^n}$. This sequence approaches $L = 0$ as the limit. Let's arbitrarily set $\varepsilon = \frac{1}{64}$, a value very close to L. The requisite δ then occurs at $\frac{1}{128}$. That is, for $\delta = \frac{1}{128}$ and all terms in the sequence beyond, the difference between $\frac{1}{128}$ and 0 is less than $\frac{1}{64}$.

Read the previous five paragraphs again and again until everything "sinks in." Remember, it took mathematicians two thousand years to finally grasp the infinitesimal.

THE WEIERSTRASS DEFINITION

In 1854, the German mathematician Karl Weierstrass (1815-1897) shored up some of the weak points of Cauchy's argument and defined the limit of a continuous function with a finely nuanced complexity that has since become a blight to the understanding of every beginning Calculus student. You will detect many of Cauchy's ideas about the limit of a sequence in this formal definition.

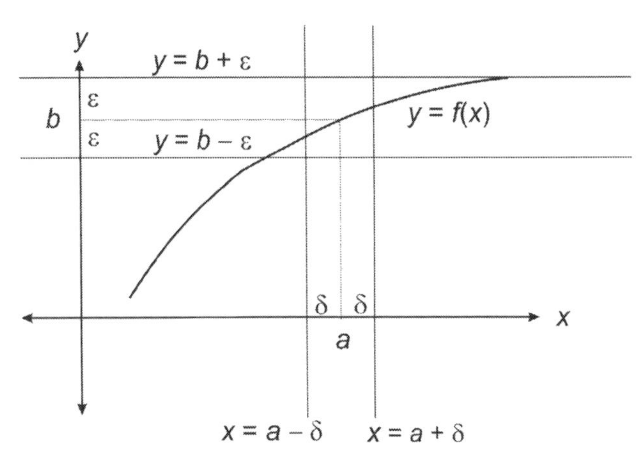

Figure 6. The Weierstrass definition of continuity and limits.

As a preliminary reminder, $|x - y|$ means the absolute value of $x - y$ or the distance, a positive amount, between x and y. Here comes a mouthful. Are you ready? In Figure 6, Weierstrass stated that if

$y = f(x)$ is continuous at $x = a$, where $f(a) = b$, given any positive number ε, there exists a δ (i.e., Whatever the choice of ε, some suitable choice of δ can be made.) such that for all x in the interval $|x - a| < \delta$, $|y - b| < \varepsilon$. (A principle in Lesson 10.8 returns to help us!) In rhetoric, if the distance between x and a is less than δ, then the distance between y and b is less than ε. A function $f(x)$ is continuous at a if it has a limit at a. In symbols:

$$\lim_{x \to a} f(x) = f(a) = b$$

Let's restate this definition another way. Given a continuous function $y = f(x)$, i.e., we replace $f(x)$ with y, then $\lim_{x \to a} y = b$ means for every $\varepsilon > 0$, there exists a $\delta > 0$ such that if x differs from a by less than δ, then y differs from b by less than ε. Or, there is some δ such that for all arguments that are within δ of a, the images are within ε of b. (Inspect Figure 6 to help you understand this rhetorical statement.) Reducing this definition to pure symbols, where ∀ means "for every" or "for any," ∃ means "there exists," and ∋ means "such that,"[22] we write:

$$\lim_{x \to a} y = b \text{ means } \forall \varepsilon > 0, \exists \delta > 0 \ni |x - a| < \delta \Rightarrow |y - b| < \varepsilon$$

These symbols include two logical qualifiers, absolute values, inequalities, and one implication. They encapsulate the **Epsilon-Delta Definition of a Limit**. They say that for every challenge $\varepsilon > 0$, you can find a response $\delta > 0$ that meets a specific condition, i.e., the difference in distances.

> To say that the distance between y and b is less than ε is to say that y lies somewhere between $b + \varepsilon$ and $b - \varepsilon$. Using symbols, $b - \varepsilon < y < b + \varepsilon$ (as the figure reveals). Subtracting b from each part of the inequality gives us: $-\varepsilon < y - b < \varepsilon$. This inequality is the same as $|y - b| < \varepsilon$ where $|y - b|$ represents the absolute value of $y - b$.

We demonstrate this definition using the function $y = f(x) = x^2$. In this function, y approaches 16 as a limit, the challenge, as x gets closer and closer to 4, the response.

After digesting the reasoning of Weierstrass, I give you permission to take your brain to a doctor and get a prescription for stress relief.

22 We recall that | also means "such that" from our discussion of set builder notation in Lesson 9.5.

THE INTERMEDIATE VALUE THEOREM

That a function is continuous guarantees that we will always find an image between any two non-equal images. Geometrically, this truth is demonstrated by the fact that a continuous curve has no breaks in it; it consists of one piece. In Calculus, this property is the **Intermediate Value Theorem.**[23] Follow the mathematical definition as you inspect with Figure 7.

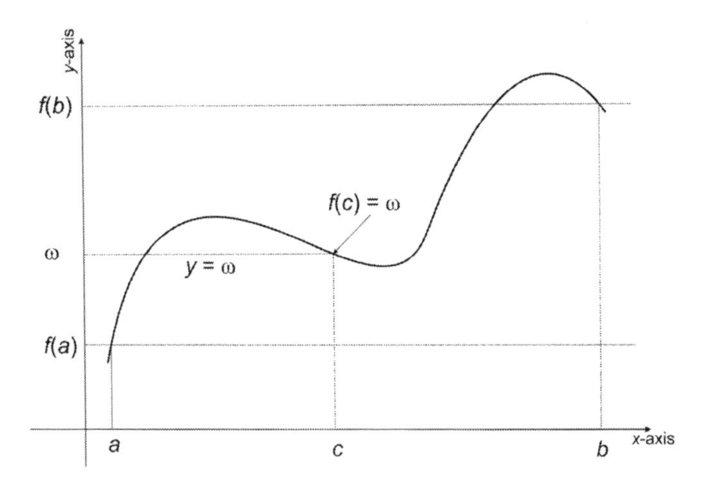

Figure 7. The Intermediate Value Theorem.

We let $f(x)$ be a continuous function between two arguments a and b; i.e., $a \leq x \leq b$. We assume $f(a) \neq f(b)$. If ω, the Greek letter omega, is any image strictly between $f(a)$ and $f(b)$, i.e., $f(a) < \omega < f(b)$ or $f(a) > \omega > f(b)$,[24] then there is an argument c such that $f(c) = \omega$.

Mathematicians use this theorem to find the zero, or zeroes, of a function that is continuous. If such a function has a negative image for some argument a and a positive image for another argument b, then there is a root, a zero, between a and b (Figure 8).

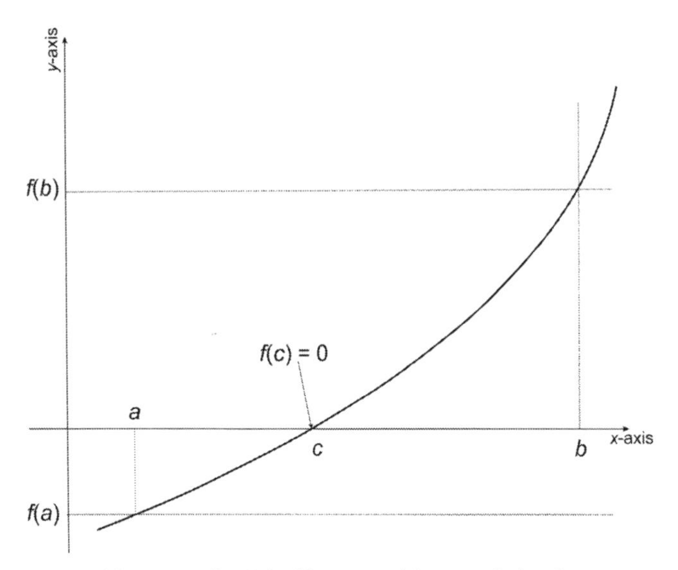

Figure 8. The Intermediate Value Theorem and the root of a function.

EXERCISES

Define the following words:

1. Inertia
2. Characteristic triangle
3. Difference
4. Infinitesimal

---

[23] The proof of this theorem has some fine nuances involving properties of numbers that is beyond the scope of this text.

[24] The two images have either increased or decreased between their two respective arguments a and b.

5. The Epsilon-Delta definition of the limit (in symbols)
6. Intermediate Value Theorem

Answer the following questions:

7. In review, the domain of a function $y = f(x)$ consists of all permissible values of x and the range consists of all corresponding values of y. Since there are three ways of looking at a function, table, rule, and graph, then there are three ways of thinking about a function's domain and range. Explain what is meant by domain and range in terms of these three viewpoints.
8. Suppose that the height, or position, of a projectile shot from a cannon is given by the formula $f(t) = 320t - 16t^2$ where t represents time in seconds. (Note: In this equation, $-16t^2$ represents a downward pull, a negative vector, affecting the projectile's height.)
   (a) Estimate the domain of this function.
   (b) Create a two-column table [t and $f(t)$] letting t range in integer values starting from 0 to 20. Notice what is happening to the height.
   (c) After you complete the table, redefine, if necessary, the domain of this function.
   (d) Define the range of this function.

The domain or range of a function can be defined rhetorically, graphically, or using inequalities (Figure 9). For example, if the domain of a function $f(x)$ consists of all real numbers x greater than 0, we would write this as the domain of $f(x)$ is $x > 0$ where $x \in \mathbb{R}$. Using set-builder notation (Lesson 3.2), we write: $\{x \in \mathbb{R} \mid x > 0\}$. Graphically, we could express this domain on the number line where the open circle indicates that the value 0 is *excluded* from the domain. If the domain of $f(x)$ is $x \geq 0$ where $x \in \mathbb{R}$, then the representation of the domain on the number line would have a closed circle indicating that the value of 0 in *included* in the domain. Using set-builder notation, we write: $\{x \in \mathbb{R} \mid x \geq 0\}$. If the domain of a function $f(x)$ is $0 \leq x < 5$ where $x \in \mathbb{R}$, then the graph would have an closed circle on 0 and an open circle on 5. Using set-builder notation, we write: $\{x \in \mathbb{R} \mid 0 \leq x < 5\}$.

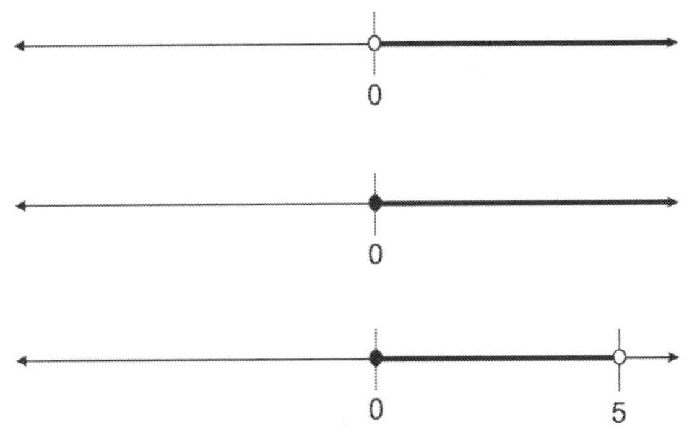

Figure 9.

Specify the domain of each of the following real-valued functions by both (a) an inequality or other appropriate symbolic representation, (b) set-builder notation), and (c) a line graph.

9. $f(x) = \sqrt{x}$
10. $f(x) = \dfrac{1}{x}$
11. $f(x) = 7x + \dfrac{48}{x}$
12. $f(h) = \dfrac{h^2 + 2h}{h}$
13. $f(t) = \sqrt{1 + t^2}$
14. $f(s) = (s - 1)(s - 2)$
15. $f(x) = \sqrt{x + 1}$

16. $f(x) = \dfrac{1}{x-1}$

17. $f(x) = 600x - \dfrac{1}{2}x^2$

18. $f(h) = h + 2$

19. $f(x) = \dfrac{x^2}{x^2 - 1}$

20. $f(s) = \sqrt{s-1}$

Answer these questions:

21. (a) Is the function specified by $f(h) = \dfrac{h^2 + 2h}{h}$ the same as the function specified by $g(h) = h + 2$? Why or why not?
    (b) Using graphing software to graph them to compare.
22. Distinguish between the change in distance d which results when an object moves for some interval of time t and the rate of change of distance compared to time in that interval.
23. Explain the difference between average velocity and instantaneous velocity.
24. What mathematical concept is used to define instantaneous velocity?
25. If the positive distance, d, in meters, which a body falls in t seconds is given by the formula $d = 4.9t^2$, calculate the average speed of the body:
    (a) during the first five seconds of fall.
    (b) during the fifth second of fall.
26. If the positive distance, d, in meters, which a body falls in t seconds is $d = 4.9t^2$, calculate the instantaneous velocity of the body at the end of the fifth second of fall; i.e., when $t = 5$.

> ... Athanasius' own writings reveal a remarkable understanding of the scientific approach and its heuristic method .... The discussion of this goes back as far as Clement's [of Alexandria – JN] *Stromateis* where, in the concluding book, he offered a careful analysis of what scientific questioning and scientific proof are about. There are two kinds of demonstration he claimed: that which we use in geometry and kindred sciences in which we argue necessarily to certain conclusions from fixed premisses or axioms, and a different kind of demonstration in which through questioning we allow our minds to fall under the compelling evidence of the reality of things, where it is the basic assent of the mind to the evidence which is the decisive factor – that is to say, the sheer fidelity of mind (what we today call the 'scientific conscience' ...) to the nature of what we are investigating.
>
> Thomas F. Torrance, *Theology in Reconciliation* (1976), pp. 216-217.

13.19 The Babylonian Algorithm Revisited

Terms, Symbols & Concepts Introduced
1. $\frac{d^2y}{dx^2}$
2. Chain rule for differentiation
3. Difference rule for differentiation of a polynomial
4. Newton-Raphson method
5. Second derivative
6. Sum rule for differentiation of a polynomial
7. Turning point

In this lesson, we will use what we have discovered about the Differential Calculus to re-investigate the Babylonian Algorithm that calculates both square and cube roots.

The Derivatives of Simple Algebraic Functions

The derivative of a real-valued function determines precisely, i.e., with perfect accuracy, the behavior, or direction, of a continuous curve at every one of its infinitude of points. It is no wonder that mathematicians have applied the method of increments to virtually every kind of mathematical function. These derivatives, therefore, are an essential tool in the hands of physicists in their analysis and work with these functions.

Let's return to the function $y = 16x^2$ where, from the previous lesson, we showed that $y' = 32x$. This time, to complete the full picture of the parabola, we will consider negative values of x. By method of increments, we can also calculate the derivative of this function at several specific points. Verify the derivative answers in your notebook.

Investigate Table 1.

Table 1							
x	-8	-4	-2	0	2	4	8
y = f(x)	1024	256	64	0	64	256	1024
y' = f'(x)	-256	-128	-64	0	64	128	256

This table tells us several facts about the curve. The y row reveals the y-coordinate for each x-coordinate, the image for each argument. We can plot these points. The y' row shows the slope of the line tangent to the curve at these images. By doing so, the derivative gives us information about (1) the direction the curve is going and (2) how steep it is.

- A slope of -256 means that the tangent line is pointing very steeply downward (\) at the coordinate (-8, 1024).
- A slope of -128 means that the tangent line is still pointing downward but not as steep at the coordinate (-4, 256).
- A slope of -64 means that the tangent line is still pointing downward but not as steep at the coordinate (-2, 64); i.e., the curve is rounding out as the argument approaches 0 from the left.
- A slope of 256 means that the tangent line is pointing very steeply upward (/) at the coordinate (8, 1024).
- A slope of 128 means that the tangent line is still pointing upward but not as steep at the coordinate (4, 256).
- A slope of 64 means that the tangent line is still pointing upward but not as steep at the coordinate (2, 64); i.e., the curve is rounding out as the argument approaches 0 from the right.

A slope of 0 means that the tangent line at (0, 0) is parallel (—) to the x-axis.[1] The tangent line, in this case, is the x-axis. The curve is turning directions at this point. This point is, therefore, a **turning point**.[2] Positive slopes mean that the tangent line is pointing upward (/). An analysis of the derivative tells us the shape of the parabola *without plotting its points*. With this example, by analyzing the derivative of a function, a mathematician or physicist can quantify the behavior of any curve at any point.

Fortunately, we do not have to apply the method of increments at every point to determine the derivative at that point. We can use the method of increments to derive general formulas that apply to different types of functions. Let's see how this works.

We already determined how to find the derivative of a linear function, i.e., $y = f(x) = ax + b \Rightarrow y' = a$.

Let's begin with a simple parabola, $y = f(x) = x^2$. Let's add Δx, a little bit of x, to x, which adds a little bit of y, Δy, to y. We get:

$$y + \Delta y = (x + \Delta x)^2$$

Applying the Binomial Theorem to the right side of the equation, we get:

$$y + \Delta y = (x + \Delta x)^2 \Leftrightarrow y + \Delta y = x^2 + 2x\Delta x + (\Delta x)^2$$

Since $y = x^2$, we can cancel these terms, i.e., subtract them, from both sides of the equation:

$$y + \Delta y = x^2 + 2x\Delta x + (\Delta x)^2 \Leftrightarrow \Delta y = 2x\Delta x + (\Delta x)^2$$

Next, we divide both sides of the equation by Δx to get the difference quotient:

$$\Delta y = 2x\Delta x + (\Delta x)^2 \Leftrightarrow \frac{\Delta y}{\Delta x} = 2x + \Delta x$$

Let's now let Δx get infinitesimally small. We get:

$$\frac{dy}{dx} = y' = \lim_{\Delta x \to 0} \frac{\Delta y}{\Delta x} = \lim_{\Delta x \to 0} (2x + \Delta x) = \lim_{\Delta x \to 0} 2x + \lim_{\Delta x \to 0} \Delta x = 2x + 0 = 2x$$

We conclude: Given $y = f(x) = x^2$, then $y' = f'(x) = 2x$.

Let's now differentiate $y = f(x) = x^3$. First, add Δx to x:

$$y + \Delta y = (x + \Delta x)^3$$

Applying the Binomial Theorem/Pascal's Triangle to the right side of the equation (Review the relevant homework from Lesson 13.17.), we get:

$$y + \Delta y = (x + \Delta x)^3 \Leftrightarrow y + \Delta y = x^3 + 3x^2\Delta x + 3x(\Delta x)^2 + (\Delta x)^3$$

Since $y = x^3$, we can cancel these terms, i.e., subtract them, from both sides of the equation:

$$y + \Delta y = x^3 + 3x^2\Delta x + 3x(\Delta x)^2 + (\Delta x)^3 \Leftrightarrow \Delta y = 3x^2\Delta x + 3x(\Delta x)^2 + (\Delta x)^3$$

Next, we divide both sides of the equation by Δx to get the difference quotient:

---

[1] This observation turns out to be very important in solving maximum/minimum problems. See the relevant homework exercises in this lesson.

[2] The turning point is also known as the point of infection. In Latin, infection means a "slight dip."

$\Delta y = 3x^2\Delta x + 3x(\Delta x)^2 + (\Delta x)^3 \Leftrightarrow \dfrac{\Delta y}{\Delta x} = 3x^2 + 3x(\Delta x) + (\Delta x)^2$

Let's now let Δx get infinitesimally small. We get:

$$\frac{dy}{dx} = y' = \lim_{\Delta x \to 0} \frac{\Delta y}{\Delta x} = \lim_{\Delta x \to 0} \left(3x^2 + 3x\Delta x + (\Delta x)^2\right) = \lim_{\Delta x \to 0} 3x^2 + \lim_{\Delta x \to 0} 3x\Delta x + \lim_{\Delta x \to 0} (\Delta x)^2 =$$
$$3x^2 + 0 + 0 = 3x^2$$

We conclude: Given $y = f(x) = x^3$, then $y' = f'(x) = 3x^2$.

We can apply the same process to $y = f(x) = x^4$. Try it on your own. The derivative y' should look like this:

$y' = f'(x) = 4x^3$

What pattern do we see?

Table 2

Function	y' = f'(x)
$y = f'(x) = x^2$	$2x$
$y = f'(x) = x^3$	$3x^2$
$y = f'(x) = x^4$	$4x^3$

Do you think differentiating x^5 gives $5x^4$? Differentiating x^6 gives $6x^5$? You are right. In general:

$$y = x^n \Rightarrow y' = f'(x) = nx^{n-1}$$

What if n is negative or if n is a fraction? Try a few examples, e.g., $n = -2$ and $n = \dfrac{1}{2}$. The formula holds.[3] It is thrilling to see how working knowledge of the arithmetic of negative numbers and fractions bears such fruit in situations like these.

We have already noted that the derivative of a constant is 0; i.e., $y = f(x) = 5 \Rightarrow y' = f'(x) = 0$. The slope of the graph of $y = 5$ is a straight line parallel to the x-axis and intersects the y-axis at (0, 5). The slope of this line is 0. What about differentiating $y = f(x) = x^2 + 5$? Intuitively, we would think to sum the derivatives of the individual terms; i.e., $2x + 0 = 2$. Let's apply the method of increments to make sure. First add Δx to x:

$y + \Delta y = (x + \Delta x)^2 + 5$

Applying the Binomial Theorem to the right side of the equation, we get:

$y + \Delta y = (x + \Delta x)^2 + 5 \Leftrightarrow y + \Delta y = x^2 + 2x\Delta x + (\Delta x)^2 + 5$

Since $y = x^2 + 5$, we can cancel these terms, i.e., subtract them, from both sides of the equation:

$y + \Delta y = x^2 + 2x\Delta x + (\Delta x)^2 + 5 \Leftrightarrow \Delta y = 2x\Delta x + (\Delta x)^2 + 5$

We proceed as before to calculate the derivative as $2x$.

Returning to our free-fall function, what happens in the case of $y = f(x) = 16x^2$? Our work will follow the algebraic derivation in the last lesson.

---

[3] If $n < 0$, we must assume $x \neq 0$. Can you explain why?

First, we add Δx to x:

$y + \Delta y = 16(x + \Delta x)^2$

Applying the Binomial Theorem to the right side of the equation, we get:

$y + \Delta y = 16(x + \Delta x)^2 \Leftrightarrow y + \Delta y = 16[x^2 + 2x\Delta x + (\Delta x)^2]$

Applying the Distributive Law to the right side of the equation, we get:

$y + \Delta y = 16[x^2 + 2x\Delta x + (\Delta x)^2] \Leftrightarrow y + \Delta y = 16x^2 + 32x\Delta x + 16(\Delta x)^2$

Since $y = 16x^2$, we can cancel these terms, i.e., subtract them, from both sides of the equation:

$y + \Delta y = 16x^2 + 32x\Delta x + 16(\Delta x)^2 \Leftrightarrow \Delta y = 32x\Delta x + 16(\Delta x)^2$

Next, we divide both sides of the equation by Δx to get the difference quotient:

$$\Delta y = 32x\Delta x + 16(\Delta x)^2 \Leftrightarrow \frac{\Delta y}{\Delta x} = 32x + 16(\Delta x)$$

Let's now let Δx get infinitesimally small. We get:

$$\frac{dy}{dx} = y' = \lim_{\Delta x \to 0} \frac{\Delta y}{\Delta x} = \lim_{\Delta x \to 0} (32x + 16\Delta x) = \lim_{\Delta x \to 0} 32x + \lim_{\Delta x \to 0} 16\Delta x = 32x + 0 = 32x$$

POSITION, VELOCITY, AND ACCELERATION FUNCTIONS

Therefore, $y = f(x) = 16x^2 \Rightarrow y' = f'(x) = 32x$. Here is our connection that we mentioned at the end of the last lesson. These equations match Galileo's observations. If x = time, and y = distance, then y', the derivative of distance concerning time, is the formula for velocity. That is, $v = y'$ where v = velocity. The derivative, in this case, represents the rate at which the distance, the position function, is changing in relation to time, exactly what velocity means.

Now let $v = 32x$. What is the derivative of v? That is, what is the rate at which the velocity is changing in relation to time? Since $v = 32x$ is a linear equation, then $v' = 32$. The constant 32 is the rate at which the velocity is increasing every second, the acceleration constant. If a = acceleration, then $a = v' = 32$. Galileo discovered this constant experimentally (See the relevant homework exercises in Lesson 12.12.). It represents the pull of the force of Earth's gravity upon a falling object. The Earth pulls an object down at a rate of 32 feet per second every second, or 9.8 meters per second every second. We note this relationship in Table 3, where $y = f(x) = 16x^2$ and we let $x = 0, 1, 2, 3, 4, 5$ seconds.

Table 3

x	0	1	2	3	4	5
y	0	16	64	144	256	400
v = y'	0	32	64	128	160	192
a = v'	0	32	32	32	32	32

Think about what this table reveals. The Differential Calculus accounts for what happens when we drop a stone from a building, a dramatic connection between mathematics and the physical world.

In summary, the position function representing the distance y a stone falls in a certain amount of time x is:

$y = f(x) = 16x^2$ [The rule is (1) square, then (2) multiply by 16.]

Differentiating y with respect to x gives us the velocity v, the rate at which the distance is changing in relation to time, which interpenetrates the slope of the tangent line to the graph of the function $y = f(x) = 16x^2$:

$v = y' = f'(x) = 32x$ (The rule is multiply by 32.)

Isn't this wonderful perichoresis? The derivative is the answer to two seemingly unrelated problems:

1. How do we draw a tangent line to a curve?
2. How do we compute the velocity of an object in motion?

Differentiating v with respect to x gives us the acceleration a, the rate at which the velocity is changing in relation to time:

$a = v' = y'' = f''(x) = 32$ (The rule is always 32.)

Note the y'' and $= f''(x)$ symbol. We say, "y double prime" and "f double prime of x." These symbols mean the second derivative. y', by implication, means the first derivative. Using the symbolism of Leibniz, we write the **second derivative** as follows:

$$a = \frac{d^2y}{dx^2}$$

The constant of acceleration, the second derivative of position, gives commentary to the way the universe of the Triune God's making coheres. The Father, Son, and Holy Spirit faithfully sustain the movement of bodies in the heavens and on the Earth in such a way that the second derivative of position unveils a constant that is an echo of the Triune God's covenant faithfulness in Christ the Son, the *logos*, who upholds all things (Hebrews 1:1-3; Colossians 1:15-17).

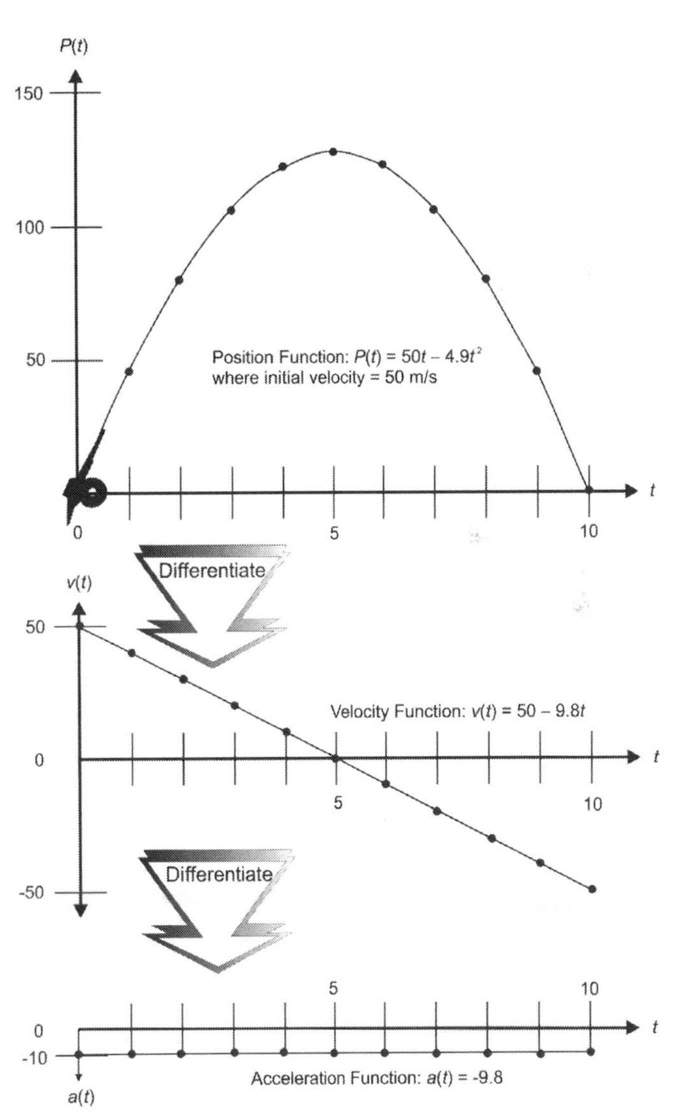

Figure 1. Physics equations for projectile motion where the pull of gravity, acceleration force in metric units, is a negative vector.

> In the context of the calculus, change in position is change that takes place along the spatial axis of a coordinate system, but the spatial axis itself may serve as a stand-in for *any change* that is made measurable by the real numbers, so that change in position functions as a large, a fabulously *general* concept, one standing in for change in *something*. It is the miracle of the calculus that change in something and change in time may be coordinated by means of the vastly greater abstraction of a function, purely an intellectual object, the key to the calculus, the key, in fact, to mathematics ....
>
> David Berlinski, *A Tour of the Calculus* (1995), pp. 63-64.

GENERAL DERIVATIVE FORMULA

Until you reach a constant, you can differentiate any function of the form ax^n as many times as you want. We can extend our derivation formula. In general:

$$y = f(x) = ax^n \Rightarrow y' = f'(x) = nax^{n-1}$$

With this formula in hand, we can calculate the first to the sixth derivatives of $y = f(x) = x^6$ as follows:

$y' = 6x^5$ (first derivative)

$y'' = \frac{d^2y}{dx^2} = 30x^4$ (second derivative)

$y''' = \frac{d^3y}{dx^3} = 120x^3$ (third derivative)

$y'''' = \frac{d^4y}{dx^4} = 360x^2$ (fourth derivative)

$y''''' = \frac{d^5y}{dx^5} = 720x$ (fifth derivative)

$y'''''' = \frac{d^6y}{dx^6} = 720$ (sixth derivative)

Although we compute these derivatives in mechanical fashion, we always need to remember that the nth derivative function expresses the instantaneous rate of change of the $(n-1)^{th}$ function.

PERICHORESIS IN THE POLYNOMIAL WORLD

In the polynomial world (Lesson 12.11), when the derivative of a function is a constant, e.g., $y = f(x) = ax + b \Rightarrow y' = f'(x) = a$, the derivative ordinal tells us the degree of the function, the degree defined as the highest power of the polynomial's terms.[4] In our example, the first derivative is a constant. Therefore, the function is a linear equation of the first degree.

[4] We will do more work with polynomials in Lesson 14.3.

Inspect Table 4.

Table 4: General Polynomial Functions			
	Linear	**Quadratic**	**Cubic**
Form	$y = ax + b$	$y = ax^2 + bx + c$	$y = ax^3 + bx^2 + cx + d$
First Derivative	$y' = a$ (Constant)	$y' = 2ax + b$	$y' = 3ax^2 + 2bx + c$
Second Derivative		$y'' = 2a$ (Constant)	$y'' = 6ax + 2b$
Third Derivative			$y''' = 6a$ (Constant)
Degree of Polynomial	1	2	3

For a first degree polynomial, the first derivative is constant. For a second degree polynomial, the second derivative is constant. For a third degree polynomial, the third derivative is constant. In general, for an nth degree polynomial, the nth derivative is constant. We can also state that the derivative of a polynomial of degree $n > 0$ is a polynomial of degree $n - 1$. These observations are in perichoretic sync with our delta analysis work in Lesson 10.6, Lesson 11.6, and Lesson 11.11. Review that respective work now.

BACK TO BABYLON

We finally have the tools to use the Newton-Raphson method to finding the square root of a number. We have used many techniques to solve a quadratic equation of the form $ax^2 + bx + c = 0$. For example, we can use the inverse method, factoring, or completing the square/quadratic formula. A less complicated approach using Calculus leads us to a technique that solves not only quadratic equations, but even more complicated equations like cubics, quartics (fourth-degree polynomials), etc. All we need to do is write the equation in the form $f(x) = 0$ and find $f'(x) = 0$. This method interpenetrates the ancient Babylonian recursion formula for calculating square roots. In review, here are the steps to find $\sqrt{2}$ using this ancient method, where x_n and x_{n+1} are exchanged with I and O respectively:

Step 1. Let I = input, the initial guess of $\sqrt{2}$.

Step 2. Let O = the output where $O = \dfrac{I + \frac{2}{I}}{2}$.

(Note: We expect O to be a better approximation than I.)

Step 3. Recursive Step: Set the output equal to the input, $I = O$, and go to Step 2.

As we repeat this process, we approach the value of $\sqrt{2}$ as a limit. In theory, we can run this algorithm forever, but in practice, we stop it in a finite number of steps when we are satisfied with the degree of precision obtained.

DERIVATION OF THE NEWTON-RAPHSON METHOD

In functional terms, we set $f(x) = x^2 - 2$ and we seek a positive solution to x when $f(x) = 0$, i.e., we solve this equation for x:

$$x^2 - 2 = 0$$

Graphically (Figure 2), we seek to obtain the x-coordinate of the image where the curve intersects the x-axis. Given an initial guess I of this x-coordinate, i.e., x_1, the figure shows how to use the idea of a tangent line to generate a better guess O. Note how much closer O is to the desired solution than I. In other words, the graph tells us how to get the better estimate O, i.e., x_2, that is closer to the actual solution at x. Given I, we let O equal the x-intercept of the line tangent to the graph of the function at

$[I, f(I)]$. Since this tangent line is the line of the slope $f'(I)$ passing through $(x_1, y_1) = ([I, f(I)]$, the equation of this line is:

$$y - f(I) = f'(I)(x - I)$$

{Note: We have replaced (x_1, y_1) with $([I, f(I)]$.}

Why? Remember that the slope a is measured by the ratio of Δy over Δx, or:

$$a = \frac{\Delta y}{\Delta x} = \frac{y_2 - y_1}{x_2 - x_1}$$

Therefore, solving for $y_2 - y_1$, we get:

$$a = \frac{y_2 - y_1}{x_2 - x_1} \Leftrightarrow y_2 - y_1 = a(x_2 - x_1)$$

In our case, we know one point $(x_1, y_1) = ([I, f(I)]$ and the value of the derivative $f'(I)$ at I.

The better estimate O is the x-coordinate x_2 of $(x_2, 0)$, where the tangent line intersects the x-axis. (Please do not get the "zero" and "O" mixed up!) Thus, the x-coordinate of O must satisfy $y_2 - y_1 = a(x_2 - x_1)$. We substitute these values into this equation:

$x_1 = I$
$y_1 = f(I)$
$x_2 = O$
$y_2 = 0$
$a = f'(I)$

From $y_2 - y_1 = a(x_2 - x_1)$, we get:

$$0 - f(I) = f'(I)(O - I)$$

Our object is to find O if we are given I. We apply these algebraic operations:

$$0 - f(I) = f'(I)(O - I) \Leftrightarrow$$
$$-f(I) = f'(I)(O - I)$$

Assuming $f'(I) \neq 0$, we divide both sides of the equation by $f'(I)$ and get:

$$-f(I) = f'(I)(O - I) \Leftrightarrow -\frac{f(I)}{f'(I)} = O - I$$

Solving for O, we get:

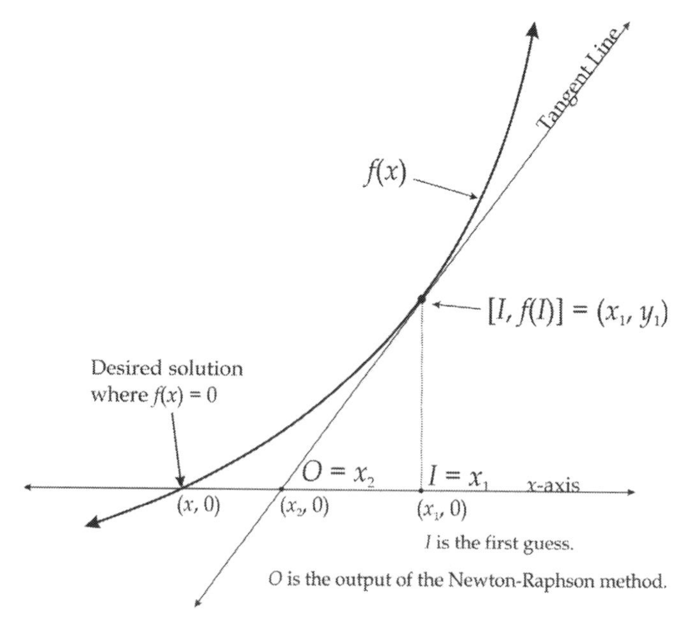

Figure 2. First iteration of the Newton-Raphson method.

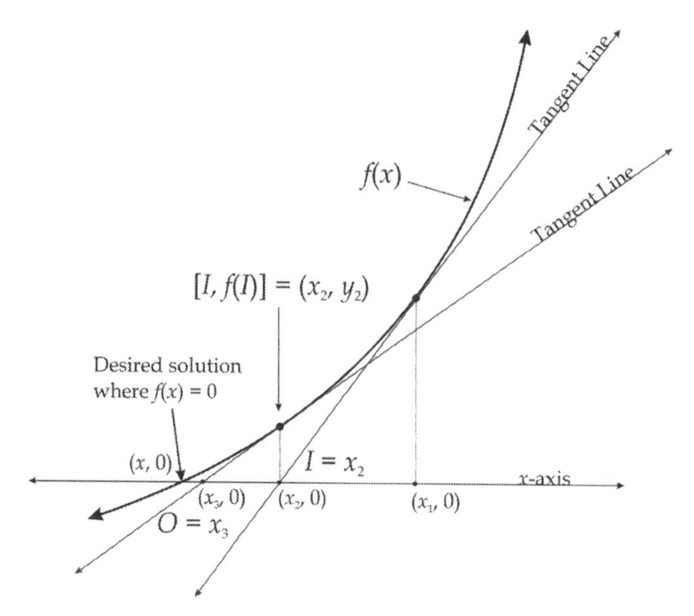

Figure 3. Second iteration of the Newton-Raphson method.

$$-\frac{f(I)}{f'(I)} = O - I \Leftrightarrow I - \frac{f(I)}{f'(I)} = O \Leftrightarrow$$

$$O = I - \frac{f(I)}{f'(I)}$$

The last equation expresses in Calculus terms the **Newton-Raphson method**, a recursive algorithm, of computing a better guess O for a given guess I as a solution to the equation $f(x) = 0$. We apply the Newton-Raphson method to solve an equation $f(x) = 0$ is as follows:

Step 1. Let I = the initial guess of the solution.

Step 2. Let O = output where $O = I - \frac{f(I)}{f'(I)}$.

(Note: We expect O to be a better approximation than I.)

Step 3. Recursive Step: Set the output equal to the input, $I = O$, and go to Step 2.

INSIGHT AND WARNING

We can apply the Newton-Raphson method, in principle, to any function $f(x) = 0$ if we know $f'(x)$. In practice, it is wise to sketch the curve first to make sure that it intersects the x-axis; i.e., it has a real number solution. If the curve does not intersect the x-axis, the method will give you garbage. Also, it is advisable to choose your initial guess I so that $f(I)$ is already close to 0. When you do this, the method will work with astonishing speed.

THE SQUARE ROOT OF 2

Let's apply the Newton-Raphson method to find $\sqrt{2}$, i.e., the positive square root of 2. First, we let $x = \sqrt{2}$. Squaring both sides, we get:

$$x = \sqrt{2} \Rightarrow x^2 = 2$$

Subtracting 2 from both sides, we get:

$$x^2 = 2 \Leftrightarrow x^2 - 2 = 0$$

We set $f(x) = x^2 - 2 \Rightarrow f'(x) = 2x$

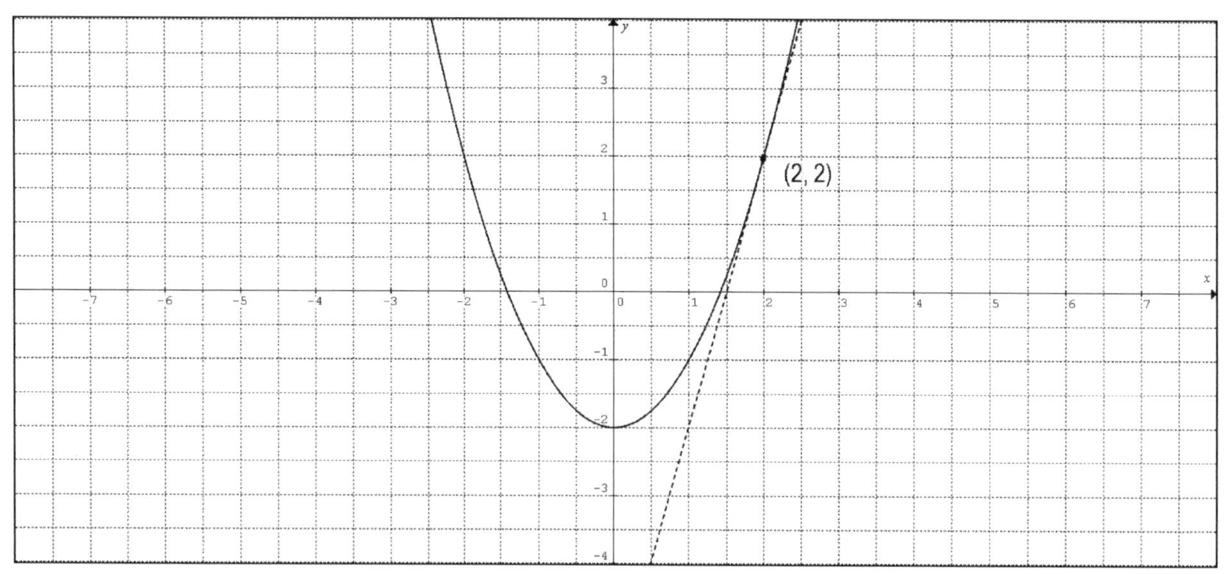

Figure 4. $y = x^2 - 2$

Since $f(x) = 0$, we invoke the Newton-Raphson method. First, we graph $y = x^2 - 2$. Good graphics software will plot the tangent line to any curve at a specific point. In Figure 4, we have shown the tangent line to the graph at (2, 2). We know by inspection that the positive solution is between 1 and 2. We choose 2 as our first guess.

Substituting the appropriate values into the Newton-Raphson algorithm, we do our first iteration:

$$O = I - \frac{f(I)}{f'(I)},\ I = 2, f(2) = 2, \text{ and } f'(2) = 4 \Rightarrow O = 2 - \frac{2}{4} = 2 - \frac{1}{2} = \frac{4-1}{2} = \frac{3}{2} = 1.5$$

Using the Babylonian algorithm, we get:

$$O = \frac{I + \frac{2}{I}}{2} \text{ and } I = 2 \Rightarrow O = \frac{2 + \frac{2}{2}}{2} = \frac{2+1}{2} = \frac{3}{2} = 1.5$$

The same result!

Now, for our second iteration. First, the Newton-Raphson algorithm:

$$O = I - \frac{f(I)}{f'(I)} \text{ and } I = 1.5, f(1.5) = 0.25, \text{ and } f'(1.5) = 3 \Rightarrow$$

$$O = 1.5 - \frac{0.25}{3} = 1.5 - 0.08\overline{3} = 1.41\overline{6}$$

Now, the Babylonian algorithm:

$$O = \frac{I + \frac{2}{I}}{2} \text{ and } I = 1.5 \Rightarrow O = \frac{1.5 + \frac{2}{1.5}}{2} = \frac{1.5 + 1.\overline{3}}{2} = \frac{2.8\overline{3}}{2} = 1.41\overline{6}$$

Again, the same result!

We continue with our third iteration. First, the Newton-Raphson algorithm:

$$O = I - \frac{f(I)}{f'(I)} \text{ and } I = 1.41\bar{6}, f(1.41\bar{6}) = 0.0069\bar{4}, \text{ and } f'(1.41\bar{6}) = 2.8\bar{3} \Rightarrow$$

$$O = 1.41\bar{6} - \frac{0.0069\bar{4}}{2.8\bar{3}} \approx 1.4142$$

Now, the Babylonian algorithm:

$$O = \frac{I + \frac{2}{I}}{2} \text{ and } I = 1.41\bar{6} \Rightarrow O = \frac{1.41\bar{6} + \frac{2}{1.41\bar{6}}}{2} \approx 1.4142$$

PERICHORESIS IN RECURSION

Both algorithms generate a very accurate and identical approximation of $\sqrt{2}$, iteration by iteration. The two algorithms, $O = \frac{I + \frac{2}{I}}{2}$ and $O = I - \frac{f(I)}{f'(I)}$ interpenetrate in stunning perichoresis! Why? Let's do more Algebra to prove that the two algorithms act in perichoresis because they represent the same expression.

First, let's simply the Babylonian algorithm:

$$O = \frac{I + \frac{2}{I}}{2} \Leftrightarrow O = \frac{\frac{I^2 + 2}{I}}{2} \Leftrightarrow O = \frac{I^2 + 2}{I} \div 2 \Leftrightarrow O = \frac{I^2 + 2}{2I}$$

Now, let's work the Newton-Raphson algorithm to see if we can get the same result. We do this:

$$O = I - \frac{f(I)}{f'(I)}, f(I) = I^2 - 2, \text{ and } f'(I) = 2I \Rightarrow O = I - \frac{I^2 - 2}{2I} \Leftrightarrow O = \frac{2I^2 - \left(I^2 - 2\right)}{2I} \Leftrightarrow$$

$$O = \frac{2I^2 - I^2 + 2}{2I} \Leftrightarrow O = \frac{I^2 + 2}{2I}$$

QED

Applying algebraic operations to both algorithms generates $O = \frac{I^2 + 2}{2I}$ and, therefore, our algebraic work reveals the reason for the perichoresis; i.e., $O = \frac{I^2 + 2}{2I}$ is contained in both $O = \frac{I + \frac{2}{I}}{2}$ and $O = I - \frac{f(I)}{f'(I)}$. $O = \frac{I + \frac{2}{I}}{2}$ and $O = I - \frac{f(I)}{f'(I)}$ interpenetrate each other in the form $O = \frac{I^2 + 2}{2I}$.

Pause to wonder!

CONCLUSION

In the last three lessons, we toured the landscape of Differential Calculus. Many university Calculus textbooks run over 1000 pages. In these lessons, we have given you a basic introduction to the way mathematicians reason about the infinitesimal. You have learned the elementary procedures of driving the Calculus car by traveling some backcountry roads. University Calculus is like driving on a freeway during rush hour traffic. In these courses, you will learn how to find derivatives of logs, exponential functions, and trigonometric functions. You will also learn a good number of differential techniques. Then, you will explore the inverse of differentiation, i.e., integration, and much, much more.

All this work is preparatory ground for the exploring more advanced methods like differential equations, i.e., equations with derivatives as terms (e.g., $\frac{dy}{dx} = 5x + 3$). From these equations, you will learn many techniques that open the workings of the physical world in manifold ways. For example, you will learn how Isaac Newton, in the 17th century, used differential equations to pinpoint the velocity needed for a ballistic-type rocket to escape the gravitational pull of the Earth, well before the invention of such rockets in the 20th century. The initial velocity applied to such rockets (e.g., in the NASA moon program in the 1960s and 1970s) confirmed that these objects do, indeed, escape the gravitational pull of the Earth according to Newton's mathematical analysis and predictions.

From differential equations, we enter the world of partial derivatives of surfaces. In the 19th century, the Scottish scientist James Clerk Maxwell (1831-1879) used this type of mathematics to derive a series of beautiful and symmetric equations, equations that describe the laws of electricity and magnetism. He used these equations to predict the existence of electromagnetic waves and the speed of light. In 1887, the German physicist Heinrich Hertz (1857-1894) confirmed Maxwell's equations by generating and receiving electromagnetic waves in his laboratory. In 1901, the Italian inventor Guglielmo Marconi (1874-1937) transmitted radio waves across the Atlantic Ocean using the telegraph. Also, around this time, in the early 20th century, Albert Einstein (1879-1955) employed Maxwell's work to develop his Special and General Theories of Relativity.

Electromagnetism is a fundamental force in the universe. It is the underlying reason for the way things work in the micro- and macro-realms. It is essential in technology, from microwave ovens to electronic watches to personal computers to smart phones to the World Wide Web. We can even explain our bodies, from electrochemical nerve impulses to the electric signals controlling our heartbeat, using Maxwell's principles.

Such wonders await you if you accept the challenge to continue your mathematical studies. I hope you do! One of you might be the next Maxwell!

> ... this vast branch of mathematics, partial differential equations serves the purpose of expressing the basic physical principles of such prevalent and vital phenomena as sound, heat, the various forms of electromagnetic waves, water waves, vibrations in rods, the flow of fluids and gases, and so forth, and that from these differential equations we can deduce by mathematical methods alone a vast amount of information about these phenomena. In fact, it is fair to say that the subject of differential equations is today the heart of mathematics and it is certainly the most useful branch for the study of the physical world.
>
> Morris Kline, *Mathematics and the Physical World* ([1959] 1981), p. 422.

EXERCISES

Define the following words:

1. Turning point
2. Second derivative
3. Newton-Raphson method
4. Sum rule for differentiation of a polynomial
5. Difference rule for differentiation of a polynomial
6. Chain rule for differentiation of a polynomial

Prove the following by the method of increments unless stated otherwise:

7. $y = bx \Rightarrow \frac{dy}{dx} = b$.
8. $y = c$ (a constant) $\Rightarrow \frac{dy}{dx} = 0$.
9. $y = ax^3 \Rightarrow \frac{dy}{dx} = 3ax^2$.
10. $y = ax^2 + bx \Rightarrow \frac{dy}{dx} = 2ax + b$ (**Sum rule for differentiation.**)
11. $y = ax^2 - bx \Rightarrow \frac{dy}{dx} = 2ax - b$ (**Difference rule for differentiation.**)
12. $y = x^n \Rightarrow \frac{dy}{dx} = nx^{n-1}$ (Use Mathematical Induction.)

Answer these questions:

13. Why must x be non-zero when $n < 0$ in Question 12?
14. Find the derivative, the instantaneous rate of change of the dependent variable compared to the independent variable, of:
    (a) $y = \sqrt{z}$
    (b) $y = \sqrt[3]{v}$
    (Hint: Write your answer using exponents that are positive. Convert $\sqrt{z}$ and $\sqrt[3]{v}$ to fractional exponents first.)
15. (a) Apply the method of increments to find the instantaneous rate of change of $y = x^2 + 7$ and compare the result with the instantaneous rate of change of $y = x^2$.
    (b) What general conclusion do your results suggest?
16. Explain geometrically why the functions $y = x^2$ and $y = x^2 + 7$ should have the same derivative at, say, $x = 2$.
17. What is the slope of the line tangent to the following curves at $x = -1$:
    (a) $2x^2 - 3y = 8$
    (b) $2x^3 - 3y = 8$
    (c) $y = 3x^3 - 2x^2 - 6x + 2$
    (d) Graph all three functions together along with $x = -1$. Justify the slopes you calculated based on what you see on the graphs.

Find the derivative for the following functions:

18. $y = 3x^2$

19. $y = (2/3)x^4$
20. $d = 2t^2$
21. $y = \frac{1}{2}x^2$
22. $k = 0.5p^4$
23. $y = 4x^3$
24. $y = -3x^2$
25. $d = -16t^2$
26. $y = x^{\frac{5}{2}}$
27. $y = x^{\frac{3}{2}} + 5x + 6$
28. $h = -4.9t^2 + 39.2t$
29. $h = 128t - 16t^2$

> One cannot escape the feeling that these mathematical formulas [Maxwell's equations – JN] have an independent existence and an intelligence of their own, that they are wiser than we are, wiser even than their discoverers, that we get more out of them than was originally put into them.
>
> Heinrich Hertz, cited in Eric Temple Bell, *Men of Mathematics* ([1937, 1965] 1986), p. 16.

Write your answer using exponents that are positive when you find the derivative of:
30. $y = x^{-1}$
31. $k = 2t^{-2}$
32. $m = -6d^{-5}$
33. $y = 1.5x^{-(2/3)}$

Calculate the second derivative $\left(\frac{d^2y}{dx^2}\right)$ for the following functions:

34. $y = 4x^3$
35. $y = 128x - 16x^2$
36. $y = 8x^2$
37. $y = 32x$
38. $y = -19x^5$
39. $y = -2x^{-2}$ (State with positive exponent.)
40. $y = 3x^{-(4/5)}$ (State with positive exponent.)

Answer these questions:
41. The instantaneous acceleration of a moving object is by definition the instantaneous rate of change of the velocity with respect to the time. Suppose an object falls a distance d in t seconds governed by the formula $d = -4.9t^2$, where d is in meters. (Note: We are taking into account the downward motion of the object by the negative sign.) What is the instantaneous acceleration of the object at any time t?
42. If an object is thrown upward with the initial velocity of 100 ft/s, then the distance d it falls in t seconds is given by the formula $d = 100t - 16t^2$. Calculate the velocity of the object at the end of the fourth second of fall.
43. Suppose that an uphill path can be represented by the equation $y = \left(\frac{1}{100}\right)x^2$.
    (a) What is the slope of the hill at $x = 3$?
    (b) Is the slope significantly steeper or more gradual at $x = 3$ or $x = 5$?
    (c) Determine the slope at $x = 0$ and interpret the result geometrically.
44. Suppose that the path of a projectile is represented by the quadratic equation $y = 4x - x^2$.
    (a) What direction does the projectile have when $x = 1$?
    (b) What direction does the projectile have when $x = 3$?

(c) At what value of x is the direction of the projectile horizontal; i.e., slope = 0?

45. Figure 5 illustrates the variation of a certain function. Describe how the derivative of y with respect to x varies as x increases from A to B.

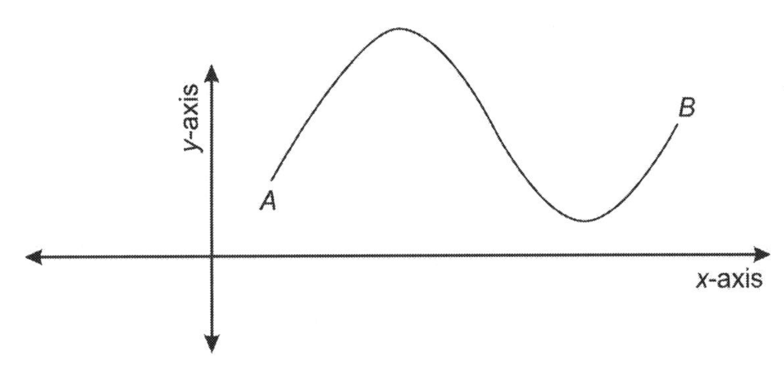

Figure 5.

How would you differentiate this function, $y = \sqrt{x^2 + a^2}$, where a is a constant? We can rewrite this function as follows: $y = \left(x^2 + a^2\right)^{\frac{1}{2}}$. This function is a three-stage composite function (Lesson 11.13) and the rule is (1) square, (2) add a^2, then (3) extract the square root of the sum. We can consider this three-stage function in two parts, (1) the two-stage function in the radicand $x^2 + a^2$ and (2) raising to the power of 1/2. Instead of trying to differentiate this function *in toto*, mathematicians attack it in two parts.

If we let $u = x^2 + a^2$, the problem becomes $y = u^{\frac{1}{2}}$. Differentiating y with respect to u gives us $y' = \frac{dy}{du} = \frac{1}{2}u^{-\frac{1}{2}}$. Next, differentiating u with respect to x gives us $u' = \frac{du}{dx} = 2x$. Then, $\frac{dy}{dx} = \frac{dy}{du} \cdot \frac{du}{dx}$. The derivatives appear to act like fractions, and they are in that they represent ratios, where we can cancel du from the equation: $\frac{dy}{dx} = \frac{dy}{\cancel{du}_1} \cdot \frac{\cancel{du}^1}{dx} = \frac{dy}{dx}$

This process is the **chain rule for differentiation**, a very useful short cut when differentiating complex functions. Applying the chain rule to our composite function, we get:

$$\frac{dy}{dx} = \frac{1}{2}u^{-\frac{1}{2}}2x = \frac{1}{2}\left(x^2 + a^2\right)^{-\frac{1}{2}}2x = x\left(x^2 + a^2\right)^{-\frac{1}{2}} = \frac{x}{\sqrt{x^2 + a^2}}$$

(Remember: $x^{-\frac{1}{2}} = \frac{1}{x^{\frac{1}{2}}} = \frac{1}{\sqrt{x}}$).

Find the first derivative of the following functions, where a is a constant, using the chain rule: (Note: These problems will give you a flavor of the intense algebraic work involved in Calculus.)

46. $y = \left(x^2 + a^2\right)^{\frac{3}{2}}$

47. $y = \left(2x^2 + a^2\right)^{\frac{5}{2}}$

48. $y = \sqrt{x - a}$

49. $y = \dfrac{1}{\sqrt{a + x^2}}$

50. $y = \dfrac{1}{\sqrt{x^3 - a^2}}$

51. $y = \left(x + \sqrt{x^2 + x + a}\right)$

52. Here is a superficial proof of the chain rule in terms of demonstrating how it works. Let's say, we have three children, Joy, Susan, and Charlotte. Joy grows twice as fast as Susan and Susan grows three times as fast as Charlotte. How much faster is Joy growing than Charlotte?

Prove the following:

53. Show how the Babylonian algorithm $O = \dfrac{2I + \dfrac{5}{I^2}}{3}$ for finding the cube root of 5 interpenetrates the Newton-Raphson method $O = I - \dfrac{f(I)}{f'(I)}$ for finding the cube root of 5.

Create Microsoft spreadsheet programs that apply the Newton-Raphson method to find the positive real number solution, unless otherwise indicated, to the following when $f(x) = 0$: (Write your answer to fifteen decimal places.)

54. $f(x) = x^2 - 3$
55. $f(x) = x^2 - 5$
56. $f(x) = x^2 - 92$
57. $f(x) = x^3 - 2$
58. $f(x) = x^3 - 3$
59. $f(x) = x^3 - 5$
60. $f(x) = x^3 - 24$
61. (a) $f(x) = -16x^2 - 50x + 200$ (Find all real number solutions.)
    (b) Graph to verify your results.

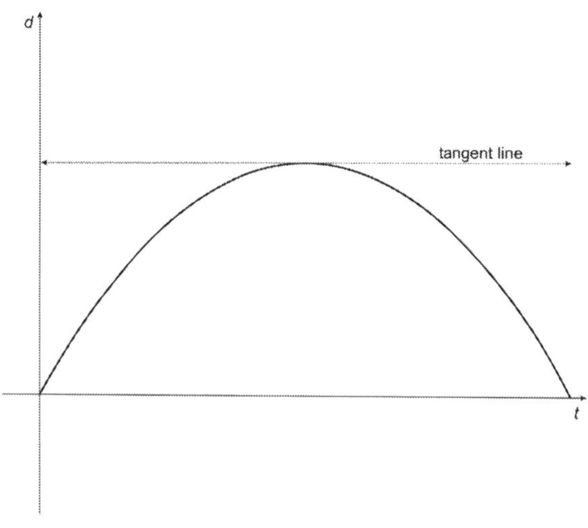

Figure 6.

Answer the following questions:

62. I pick up the stone and drop it into a "stone" cannon. I point the cannon straight up, ignite the gunpowder, and pull the trigger. Let's say that the cannon thrusts the stone upward with an initial velocity of 96 ft/s. Figure 6 is a general graph of the shape of a position function.
(a) Write the position function d in terms of time t, taking in account the downward pull of gravity on the stone.
(b) Inspect the figure and determine a method, using differential calculus, for finding the coordinates of the maximum height of the stone; i.e., the time t at which the distance d is the highest.
(c) Using the method in (b) to find (t, d) where d is maximum.
(d) Graph to verify your results.

63. Mr. City Slicker wants to build an ancient Egyptian amusement park on some property next to the Mr. Farmer's land. Mr. City Slicker is entertaining the nifty idea of transporting the park visitors around on camels. In fact, he has bought a herd of camels and wants to fence them in near a river that runs through his property. Mr. City Slicker can only afford 800 feet of fencing for his camel herd and he wants to enclose them in a rectangular field one side of which is bounded by the river. He finds a straight section of the river and figures that his idea is great because he doesn't have to worry about watering the camels. His problem is that he doesn't know how to get the most area out

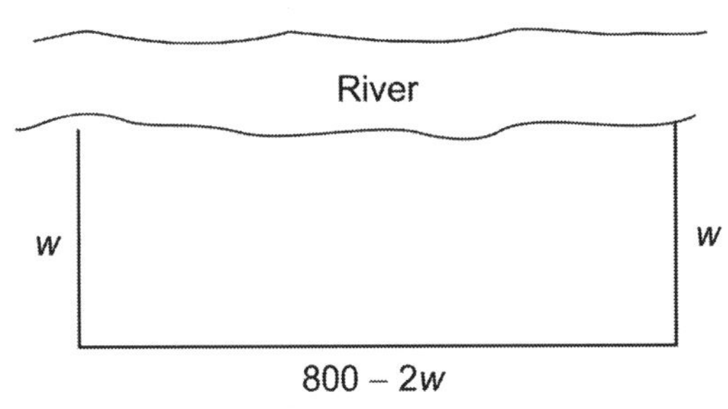

Figure 7.

of his 800 feet of fencing. He needs to know what to do before he starts to dig holes for his fence posts. "Mr. Farmer surely would know how to do this since he had such a nifty way of counting the number of cows in his pasture," thinks Mr. City Slicker to himself as he approaches Mr. Farmer's house and knocks on the screen door (Lesson 13.13). Mr. Farmer listens to Mr. City Slicker explain the situation. At the end of the account, Mr. Farmer pulls on his graying beard a few times in deep contemplative thought. Suddenly he exclaims, "Derivative!" He quickly retreats to his study. In the meantime, Mr. City Slicker stands in dumbfounded silence thinking, "Did I hear him right? I'm sure that he said "drive a Tiv." But I drive a Tercel! Is there a new model car that's out? And, how can driving a 'Tiv' solve my problem? I guess I'll have to trust Mr. Farmer because he sure knows how to count cows!" Meanwhile, back in the study, Mr. Farmer is drawing a diagram. Let's peak over his shoulder to find out what he is doing (Figure 7). Fortunately for us, Mr. Farmer always thinks out loud when he works in his study so we get to hear his reasoning. "Let's see," says Mr. Farmer, "I've got 800 feet of fence and three sides to work with. I've got to make a rectangular field for the camels so I'll let the width of the field be w. That takes care of two of the three sides and I've used up $2w$ feet of fence. I have $800 - 2w$ feet left. That's for the third side. The area of a rectangle is its length multiplied by its width, so I've got this equation:

$$A = w(800 - 2w) = 800w - 2w^2$$

(a) Finish Mr. Farmer's reasoning by finding w that gives the maximum area A.
(b) Graph to verify your results.

64. A farmer wishes to use 100 m of fencing to enclose a rectangular area and to divide the area into two rectangles by running a fence down the middle. (Hint: Draw a picture to represent the situation and then write down all relevant formulas.)
(a) What dimensions should he choose to enclose the maximum total area?
(b) Graph to verify your results.
65. We want to fence a small rectangular pen containing 24 square yards. The front, to be made of stone, will cost \$10 per yard of fencing, while each of the other three wooden sides will cost only \$4 per yard. What is the least amount of money that will pay for the fencing?
(a) Let $L =$ the length of the front and $C =$ cost. Determine a formula for C is terms of L.
(b) Find the minimal cost rounded to the nearest penny. (Note: Round L to the nearest hundredth.)
(c) Graph to verify your results.
66. In the previous question, C (total cost) can be expressed either in terms of L (length) alone or W (width) alone while L and W are connected in that $LW = 24$.
(a) Write again the formula for C in terms of L.
(b) Write a formula for L in terms of W.
(c) By substitution, write a formula for C in terms of W.
(d) Notice how the equations in (a) and (b) are links in a chain producing to the equation in (c). In other words, the equation is (a) is C as a function of L, i.e., $C(L)$, the equation in (b) is L as a function of W, i.e., $L(W)$, and the equation in (c) is C as a function of W, i.e., $C(W)$. Note the chain: $C \rightarrow L$, then $L \rightarrow W$, then $C \rightarrow W$. This chain illustrates, pun intended, the chain rule for differentiation. Calculate the three derivatives: $\frac{dC}{dL}, \frac{dL}{dW}$, and $\frac{dC}{dW}$.
(e) Apply the chain rule and show that $\frac{dC}{dL} \cdot \frac{dL}{dW} = \frac{dC}{dW}$. Isn't this a delightful connection?
67. To illustrate the power and efficiency of Calculus, we are going to prove that to maximize the area of a rectangle of perimeter p, then it must be a square.
(a) Let x and y be the dimensions of any rectangle, then write a formula for p in terms of x and y.
(b) Solve this formula for y.
(c) The area of any rectangle is given by $A = xy$. Express A as a function of x only and apply Calculus to find the maximum area. We can prove this relationship using Euclidean geometry, but this method is much more direct.
68. Does the function $y = x^3$ have a maximum or minimum value at $x = 0$? Plot the function using graphing software to assist you with your answer.

HOW A LITTLE MATHEMATICS BOOK INTERSECTED MY LIFE

Hungarian born Rózsa Péter (1905-1977) grew up in a land torn by war and civil strife. What we take for granted in terms of everyday living was for her *never easy*. Péter enrolled in Eötvös Loránd University in 1922 with the goal to earn a degree in chemistry. It did not take her long to discover the enchantment that mathematics offered. After changing majors, she studied under many professors who were world-famous mathematicians. She received her undergraduate degree in 1927, continued graduate studies, and earned her living by tutoring and teaching high school. She received her Ph. D. degree summa cum laude in 1935 and her studies pioneered the development of a new field of mathematics named recursive functions.

Figure 8. Rózsa Péter. Source: Wikimedia Commons.

World War II began in Europe in 1939. The Nazi juggernaut soon occupied Hungary and fascist laws forbade Péter to teach. She was even briefly confined in the Budapest ghetto. Amid suffering many hardships, including the painful loss of her brother along with many friends, students, and fellow mathematicians, she continued studying and writing. In the autumn of 1943, she finished a short mathematics manuscript. It was really a collection of letters she wrote to a friend explaining the nature of mathematics. Since no books could appear during the censorship imposed by the Nazis and since allied bombing destroyed many copies of this manuscript, the few copies that remained first appeared in 1945, on the first free book day.

Shortly after the end of the war, Budapest Teachers' College hired her. In 1951, she published an award-winning monograph on recursive functions. When the college closed in 1955, she became a mathematics professor at Eötvös Loránd University holding this post until her retirement in 1975. She would often speak on mathematics to general audiences. She entitled her lectures "Mathematics is Beautiful" saying, "No other field can offer, to such an extent as mathematics, the joy of discovery, which is perhaps the greatest human joy."[5]

In 1976 she published a book entitled *Recursive Functions in Computer Theory*. She died on the eve of her birthday in 1977. In her eulogy, one of her students recalled that she taught "that facts are only good for bursting open the wrappings of the mind and spirit" in the "endless search for truth."

What happened to that little manuscript that Péter wrote during the war years? It was finally published in Hungarian in 1957. The English translation was made by Dr. Z. P. Dienes and published in England by G. Bell and Sons, Ltd., in 1961. Simon and Schuster published it on the other side of the Atlantic in 1962. Dover Publications of New York, the great reprinter of out of print books, produced a wonderful paperback version in 1976 entitled *Playing with Infinity: Mathematical Explorations and Excursions*.

[5] For a transcript of one of these lectures, see Rózsa Péter, "Mathematics is Beautiful," *The Mathematical Intelligencer*, 12 (1990): 58-64.

I first encountered[6] the Dover version of this book in 1984 while teaching high school mathematics in the little Australian hamlet of Booleroo Centre. A small farming town with a population of 300 but serving a district population of nearly 2000, it still had hitching posts in front of local stores, individual stores where you could buy meat from a butcher, bread from a baker, everything else from Prests, a general merchandiser and grocer, and get a great meal at the local pub attached to the Booleroo Centre Hotel. It is in the state of South Australia, located in the southern Flinders Ranges, and about a hundred or so miles south of the start of the famous Australian outback territory.

Back to Péter's little book … At once I recognized her rare ability not only to explain mathematical topics but also to recognize and organize its intricate structure. Compared to the mathematical drivel taught by much of high school mathematics textbooks, this book was like "streams in the desert." After finishing its delightful read, this thought came to the forefront in my mind, "If only high school textbooks would teach mathematics this way!" The book had serious limitations in the textbook context. Professor Péter only wanted to explain the exquisite structure of mathematics; her purpose was not to teach anyone mathematical skills or techniques. Despite these limitations, this book warrants reading by every math teacher and math student.

> … Mathematics is an organic whole: wherever we touch it, connecting links from all other branches come crowding into our minds.
>
> Rózsa Péter, *Playing with Infinity* ([1957, 1961] 1976), p. 41.

For about two decades I have toyed with the idea of writing a textbook based upon her approach. You have in your hands my attempt at doing this. I have enhanced many of her ideas while, based on my teaching experience and research, added much, much more. I hope what I have written has followed the same delight of mathematical exposition as exhibited by Professor Péter. By it, I give honor to both her memory and insight, a wonderful woman known affectionately by her students as Aunt Rózsa.

Figure 9. *Playing With Infinity*, G. Bell and Sons Ltd. edition.

Figure 10. *Playing With Infinity*, Dover Publications edition.

[6] As a relatively new math teacher, I wanted to learn as much as I could from master teachers. Her title appeared in a book catalogue that I had ordered. Discovering Péter was like discovering gold.

STEP 14. THE DANCE OF THREE DIMENSIONS

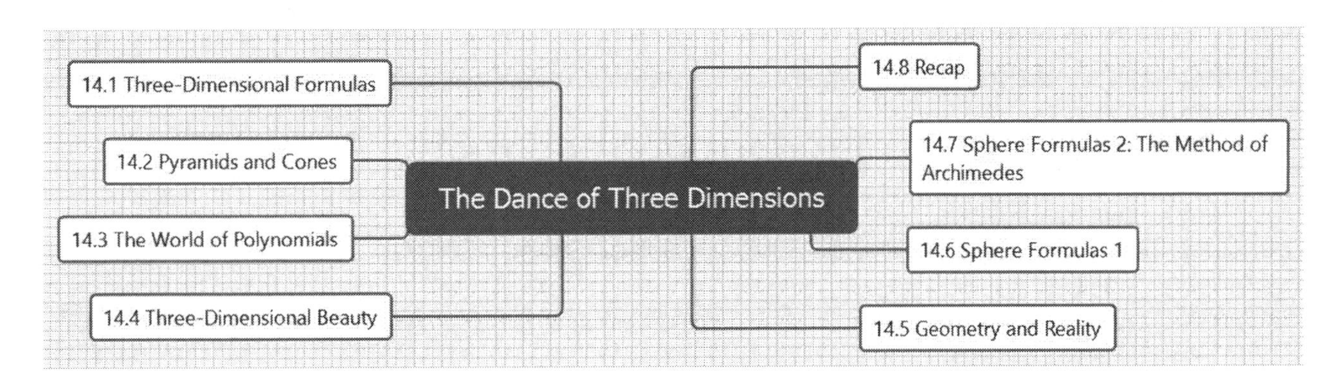

> There are three ruling ideas, three so to say, spheres of thought, which pervade the whole body of mathematical science, to some one or other of which, or to two or all three of them combined, every mathematical truth admits of being referred; these are the three cardinal notions, of Number, Space and Order. Arithmetic has for its object the properties of number in the abstract. In algebra, viewed as a science of operations, order is the predominating idea. The business of geometry is with the evolution of the properties of space, or of bodies viewed as existing in space.
>
> J. J. Sylvester, *A Probationary Lecture on Geometry, York British Association Report* (1844), Part 2; Collected Mathematical Papers, 2:6.

14.1 Three-Dimensional Formulas

Terms & Concepts Introduced
1. Face of a solid
2. Lateral area
3. Net
4. Regular right prism
5. Right cylinder
6. Solid figures
7. Surface area

The measurement of area encompasses two dimensions while volume measurement involves three dimensions. We can see these dimensions in area and volume formulas. For example:

- The area of a square: $A = s^2$ (The variable s that is squared reveals two dimensions.)
- The area of a rectangle where l = length, w = width: $A = lw$ (The two variables l and w, because we multiply them together, reveal two dimensions; i.e., the units will be square units.)
- The area of a triangle where a = base, b = height: $A = \frac{1}{2}ab$ (The two variables a and b, because we multiply them together, reveal two dimensions; again, the units will be square units.)
- The area of a circle: $A = \pi r^2$ (The variable r that is squared reveals two dimensions.)
- The volume of a cube: $V = s^3$ (The variable s that is cubed reveals three dimensions.)
- The volume of a sphere: $V = \frac{4}{3}\pi r^3$ (The variable r that is cubed reveals three dimensions.)
- The volume of a rectangular solid, or box, where l = length, w = width, and h = height: $V = lwh$ (The three variables l, w, and h, because they are multiplied together, reveal three dimensions; i.e., the units will be cubed units.)

Length encompasses one dimension, so measurement formulas reveal this too:

- The perimeter of a square: $P = 4s$ (The variable s reveals one dimension.)
- The perimeter of a rectangle where l = length and w = width: $P = 2l + 2w$ (The two variables l and w, because we sum them,[1] still reveal one dimension.)
- The circumference of a circle: $C = 2\pi r$ (The variable r reveals one dimension.)

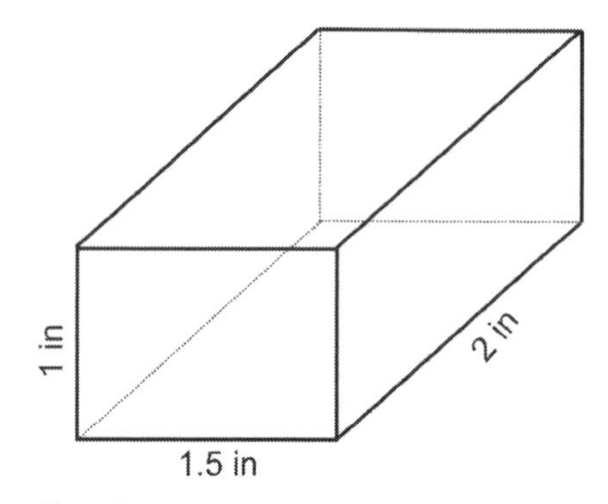

Figure 1.

With three-dimensional or **solid figures**, we can not only calculate volume but surface area. The **surface area** of a solid geometric figure tells you how much material is used to make it. Since area is two-dimensional, to find the surface area of a solid figure all we need to do is find the areas of all the surfaces, i.e., **faces**, and sum the result. Finding the surface area will tell us how much paint is needed to paint the four walls and one ceiling of a room.

To find the surface area of a cube of length s, we must find the areas of its six faces and sum the result. Since the areas of all the faces are the same, the formula for surface area A will be:

$$A = 6s^2$$

[1] As we have noted (Lesson 4.13), adding 3 cm to 7 cm gives us, by factoring cm, cm(3 + 7) = cm(10) = 10 cm. The unit is still one-dimensional. The centimeter unit performs the same function as the variable x in $3x + 7x = x(3 + 7) = x(10) = 10x$.

To find the surface area of a rectangular solid of dimensions l, w, and h, we have to again find the areas of its six faces and sum the result. In Figure 1, we see that three are three pairs of uniquely determined rectangles, or three pairs of congruent rectangles. We find the area of each pair and then sum them to get the total surface area. We get:

$2(1 \text{ in})(1.5 \text{ in}) = 3 \text{ in}^2$
$2(1.5 \text{ in})(2 \text{ in}) = 6 \text{ in}^2$
$2(1 \text{ in})(2 \text{ in}) = 4 \text{ in}^2$

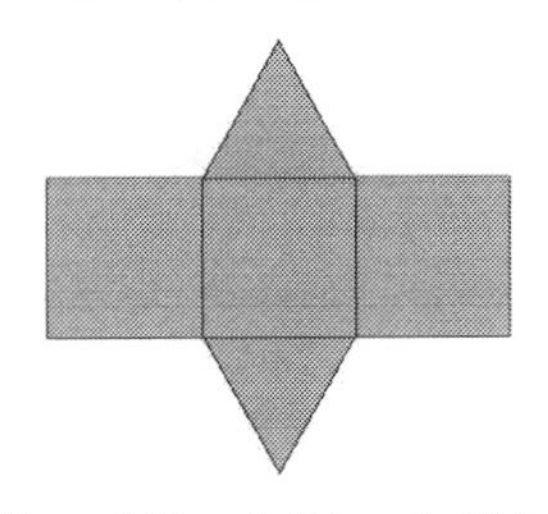

Figure 2. Net of a Triangular Right Prism.

Surface area of box: $3 \text{ in}^2 + 6 \text{ in}^2 + 4 \text{ in}^2 = \text{in}^2(3 + 6 + 4) = \text{in}^2(13) = 13 \text{ in}^2$

Given l, w, and h, the surface area A of any rectangular solid is:

$A = 2lw + 2lh + 2wh$

Figure 4. Coin prism.

In review, the volume of a solid geometric figure is the measure of space it contains, i.e., the figure's capacity. Again, the volume measurement will always be three dimensions; therefore, the units will be cubic units; e.g., in^3, cm^3, etc. Volume answers this question: A solid object contains how many of these cubes?

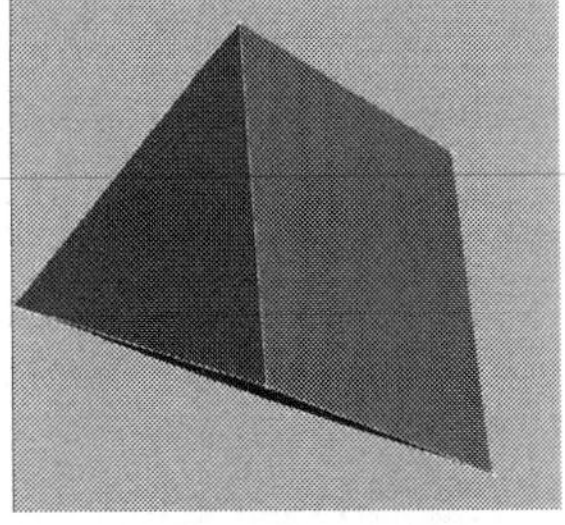

Figure 3. Triangular Right Prism.

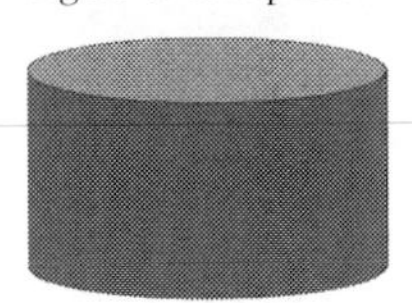

Figure 5. Right cylinder.

PRISMS AND CYLINDERS

A **regular right prism** is a solid that has a pair of regular polygons for its bases. The rest of its faces consist of congruent rectangles formed to make right angles to each base. We name these types of prisms according to the shapes of their bases. These bases can be any regular polygon, triangle, square, pentagon, hexagon, etc.

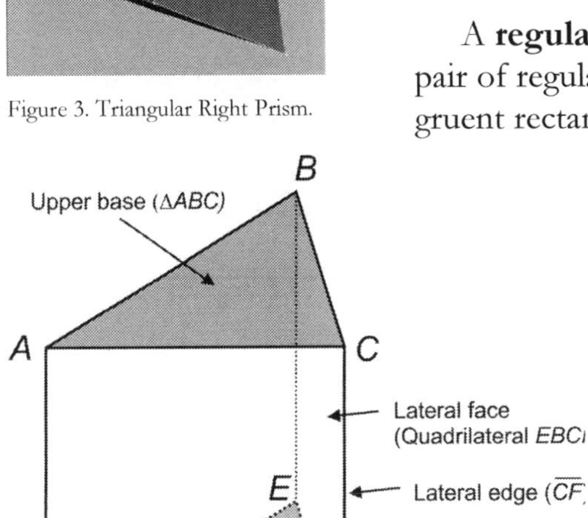

Figure 6. Geography of a prism.

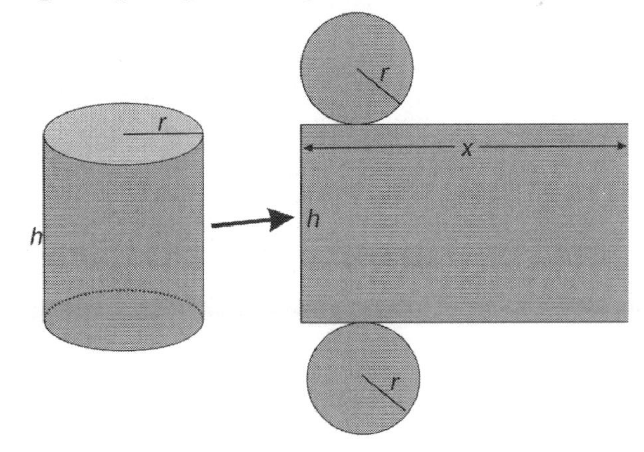

Figure 7. Net of a Right Cylinder.

To find the surface area of a prism, we find the areas of each face. To help us do this, we create a **net** of the structure (Figure 2).[2] For example, in a triangular prism (Figure 3 and Figure 6), we must find

[2] A net is the shape of a three-dimensional figure when laid out flat in two-dimensions.

the area of its two triangular bases, they will be congruent, and the area of the three congruent rectangles that form the **lateral area** of the prism.[3]

Cylinders are like prisms except their bases are circles, not polygons. Cylinders unfold as we take the regular polygons comprising the bases of a prism and increase the number of sides to infinity. At the threshold of infinity, at the limit, the sides become the circumference of a circle. A **right cylinder** is a solid that has two circular bases parallel to each other and connected at right angles by a curved surface (Figure 5). A can of soup is an example of a right cylinder.

To find the surface area of a cylinder, we must take it apart and look at the three pieces that comprise its shape (Figure 7). Immediately, we see that the lateral area of the right cylinder is a rectangle after you flatten it. We need to sum the area of these three parts. The area of the two circles is $2\pi r^2$. For the area of the rectangle, we know the width, h, but what is its length, x? Think carefully. The length x is the circumference of the circle of radius r. Therefore, the lateral area of right cylinder is $2\pi rh$. (Do you see the two dimensions?) Therefore, the formula for the surface area A of a right cylinder is:

$$A = 2\pi r^2 + 2\pi rh \Leftrightarrow A = 2\pi r(r + h)$$

When solving word problems in mathematics, invoke these steps:

1. Read the problem thoroughly to make sure you understand it. Two or more readings may be necessary.
2. Where applicable, draw a picture of the situation to help you see the problem; i.e., translate words to a picture.
3. Name the answer. Determine what the problem is asking you to find and name it like this: Let x = what you need to find.
4. Write down a basic formula that fits the situation (e.g., area formula of a circle, etc.).
5. If there is no formula that fits the problem perfectly, you must build your own using algebraic notation. You may need to combine multiple formulas, or apply more than one formula in multiple steps. If you can do this step, you are on your way to becoming an accomplished algebraist.

VOLUME FORMULAS

What about the volumes of these solid figures? Let's apply some careful reasoning. The volume $V_{\text{rectangular solid}}$ of any rectangular solid is the product of its length, width, and height. We write:

$$V_{\text{rectangular solid}} = lwh$$

We let B = area of the base of this solid, or B = lw. Therefore:

$$V_{\text{rectangular solid}} = Bh$$

The volume V_{cube} of a cube is the cube of the length of its side:

$$V_{\text{cube}} = s^3$$

Again, we can let B = area of the base of this solid, or B = s^2. Since $s = h$, then:

$$V_{\text{cube}} = Bh$$

Likewise, the volume $V_{\text{regular right prism}}$ of a regular right prism is the area of its base times its height, or:

$$V_{\text{regular right prism}} = Bh$$

[3] Remember, *lateral* is Latin meaning "side." It is part of quadrilateral meaning "four sides."

If the base is a triangle where a is the length of the triangle's base and b is the altitude of the triangle, then $B = \frac{1}{2}ab$. By substitution, we get:

$V_{\text{regular right prism}} = \frac{1}{2}abh$

The volume $V_{\text{right cylinder}}$ of a right cylinder is also the area of its base times its height, or:

$V_{\text{right cylinder}} = Bh$

Since $B = \pi r^2$, then, by substitution, we get:

$V_{\text{right cylinder}} = \pi r^2 h$

EXERCISES

Define the following terms:

1. Solid figures
2. Face of a solid
3. Surface Area
4. Regular right prism
5. Net
6. Right cylinder
7. Lateral area

Give one example in the objective world where you experience:

8. A three-dimensional shape that represents a real number that is not rational.
9. A rational number that is not an integer.
10. An integer that is not a positive number.
11. A prime number that is odd.

A right cylinder has a diameter of 12 in and a height of 7 in.

12. Find its approximate total surface area in square feet. Use 22/7 as an approximate of π and round your answer to the nearest tenth.
13. Find its approximate volume in cubic inches. Use 22/7 as an approximate of π.

Figure 8 reveals the specifications of a railroad car designed to carry crude oil.

14. Find its approximate volume in cubic feet, rounded to the nearest tenth. Use 22/7 as an approximate of π. Assume all figures are right cylinders and ignore the slight volume overlap where the three lesser cylinders intersect the one vertical cylinder.

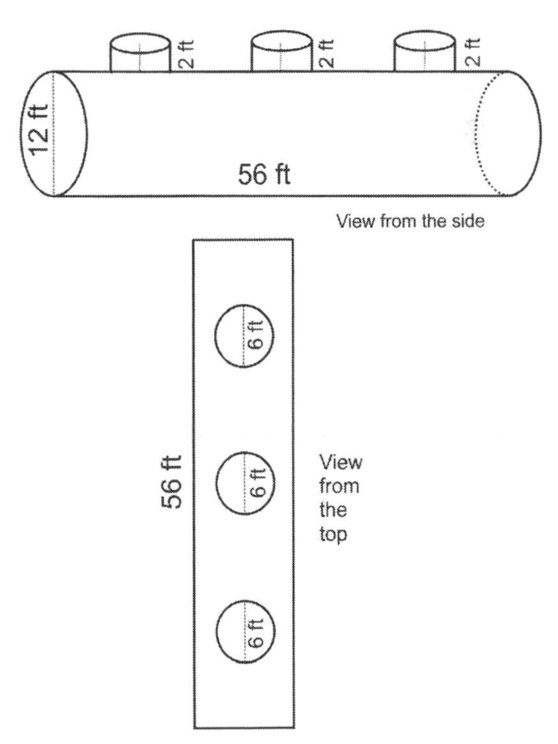

Figure 8.

Figure 9 shows the base of a building 350 feet high where the two right triangles are congruent.

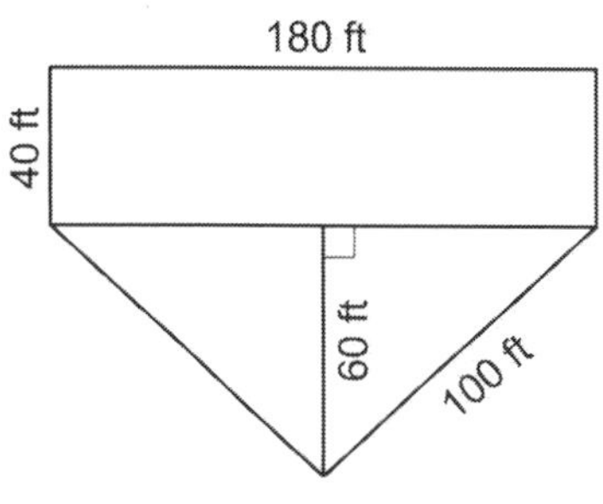

Figure 9.

15. What is the area of the base?
16. What is the volume of the building?

Here are the formulas for the volume V and surface area A of a sphere with r as its radius (Figure 10):

$V = \frac{4}{3}\pi r^3$ and $A = 4\pi r^2$

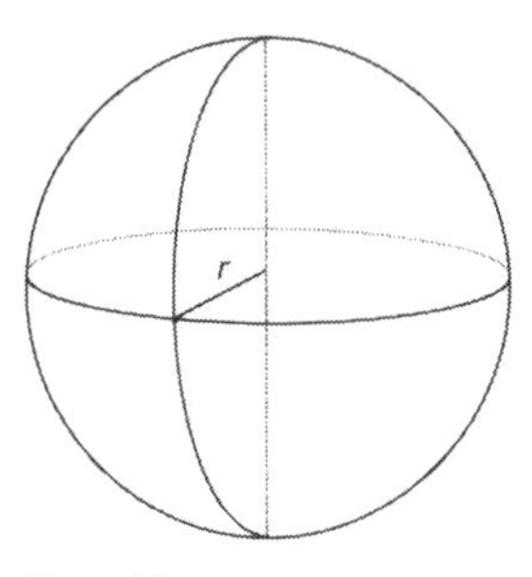

Figure 10.

Recall that the area and circumference formulas, A and C, for a circle with r as its radius are:

$A = \pi r^2$ and $C = 2\pi r$

Note, too, when a circle rotated about its diameter, it generates a sphere. Therefore, there is an inherent and beautiful relationship between the circle of two dimensions and the sphere of three dimensions. It requires the methods of Calculus to prove these sphere formulas, but we will derive their proofs by another means in Lessons 14.6 and 14.7. For now, to help us see a connection between these two formulas, we use a formula from Differential Calculus that helps us calculate the derivative of a function or its rate of instantaneous change. In review:

Given: $y = ax^n$

The derivative of y, $\frac{dy}{dx}$ or y', is:

$$y' = nax^{n-1}$$

Use this formula to answer the following:

17. (a) Find the derivative $\frac{dV}{dr}$ of $V = \frac{4}{3}\pi r^3$ (Remember, π is a number and r is the variable.)
    (b) What do you notice about your result?

18. (a) Find the derivative $\frac{dA}{dr}$ of $A = \pi r^2$ (Again, π is a number and r is the variable.)
    (b) What do you notice about your result?
19. Try to explain what the results in Questions 17 and 18 mean in terms of "rate of instantaneous change." What do you notice about your result?

Answer the following questions:

20. Explain why $V = lwh$ measures three dimensions while $P = 2l + 2w$ measures one dimension.
21. Explain why the formula for the area of a trapezoid measures two dimensions.
22. Solve $A = 6s^2$ for s.
23. Solve $A = 2\pi r(r + h)$ for h.
24. Solve $A = 2lw + 2lh + 2wh$ for w.
25. Solve $A = 4\pi r^2$ for r.
26. Solve $V = \frac{4}{3}\pi r^3$ for r.
27. In Figure 11, an open right cylinder is four inches in height and six inches in circumference. On the inside, one inch from the top is some honey. On the outside, one inch from the bottom is a fly.
    (a) What is the shortest path for the fly to walk to the honey?
    (b) What is the distance of this path? (Hint: Unfold the cylinder into a rectangle.)

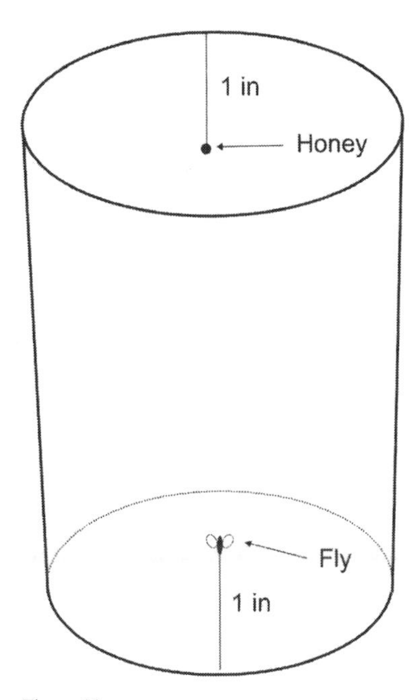

Figure 11.

28. In Figure 12, how many blocks do you see?

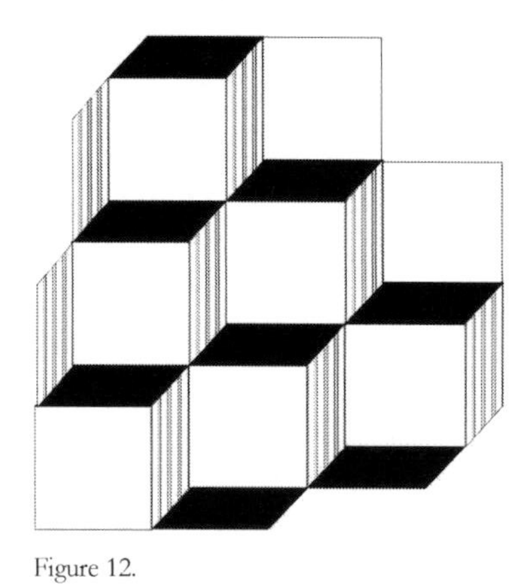

Figure 12.

29. Study Figure 13 and find *r*, the radius of the inscribed circle *O*.

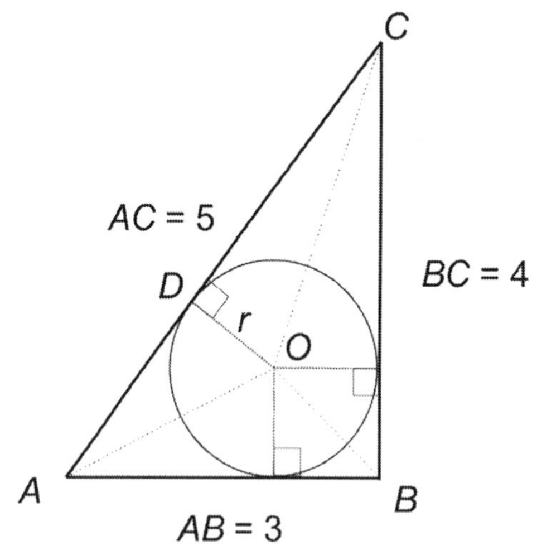

Figure 13.

Do the following construction:

30. Figure 14 is a net for the construction of a non-regular pyramid. Copy it three times on hard copy stock paper. Carefully trim the figure along the solid lines with a scissors. To enable folding, carefully score, but do not cut, the dotted lines with a ruler and a sharp instrument like a fine point pen or an X-Acto knife. If you use the X-Acto knife, be very careful not to injure yourself or ruin the table underneath. Get a flexible plastic cutting mat before you do score anything with an X-Acto knife. Fold one way along each crease thus created to get a clean, sharp edge. You should see the formation of a non-regular square prism as you fold. Tape, or better yet, glue the prism together. Repeat this procedure three times to make three congruent non-regular square pyramids. Then, try to fit the three pieces together to form a cube. What does this exercise demonstrate about the volume of a cube and the volume of a pyramid?

31. If the volume of a right cylinder is $V = \pi r^2 h$, make a conjecture about the volume formula for a right cone with the same height and base radius.

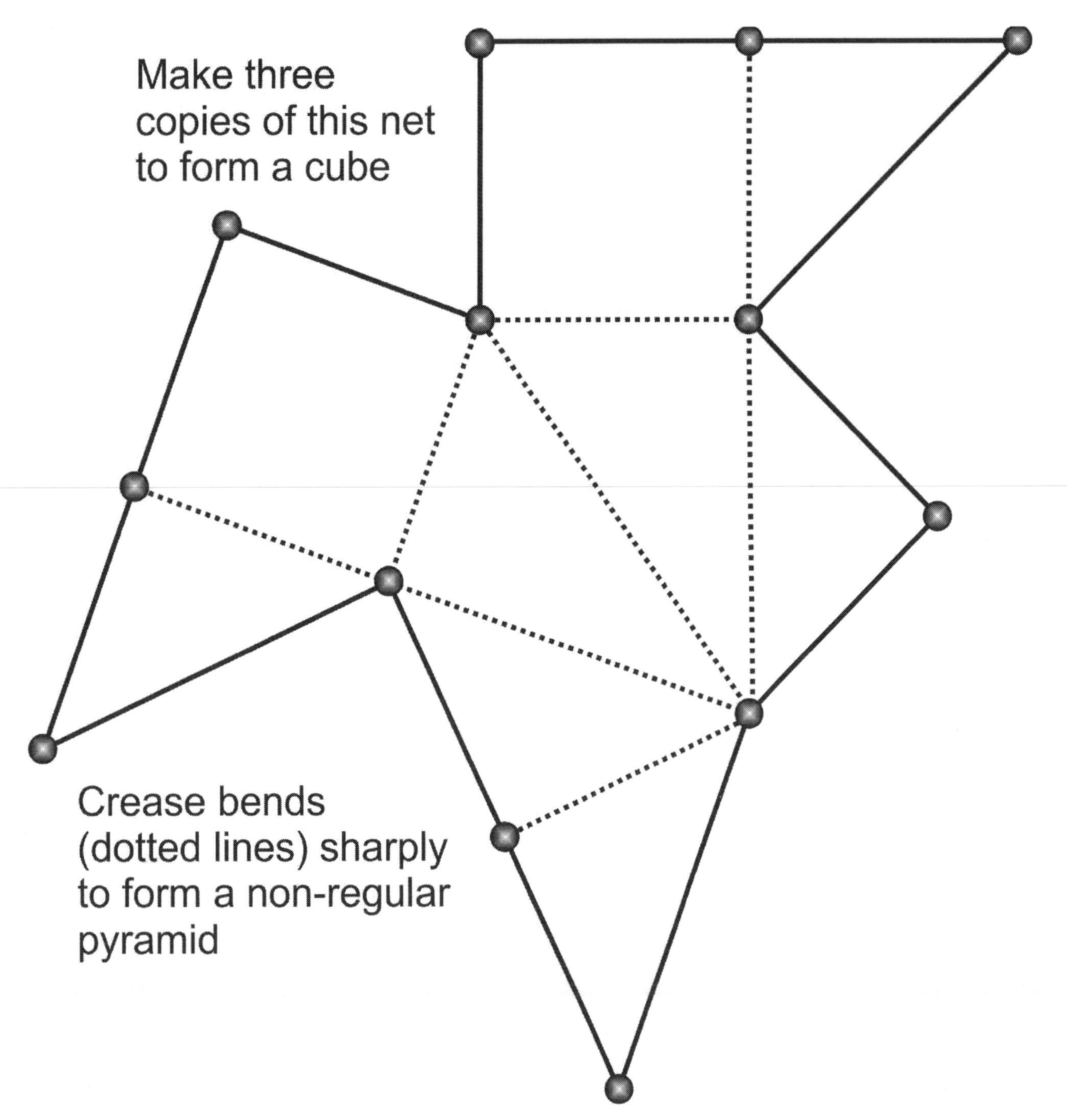
Make three copies of this net to form a cube
Crease bends (dotted lines) sharply to form a non-regular pyramid

Figure 14.

GEOMETRY FORMULAS

Plane or Two-dimensional Geometry		Solid or Three-dimensional Geometry	
Rectangle Area = lw Perimeter = $2l + 2w$	w, l	Rectangular solid Volume = lwh	h, w, l
Square Area = s^2 Perimeter = $4s$	s, s	Cube Volume = s^3	s, s, s
Triangle Area = $\frac{1}{2}bh$ or $\frac{bh}{2}$	h, b	Right cylinder Volume = $\pi r^2 h$ Surface area = $2\pi r(h + r)$	r, h, r
Sum of angle measures of the three internal angles of a triangle $m\angle 1 + m\angle 2 + m\angle 3 = 180°$	1, 2, 3		
Right triangle $c^2 = a^2 + b^2$	a, c, b		
Parallelogram Area = bh	b, h	Right cone Volume = $\frac{1}{3}\pi r^2 h$ Surface area = $\pi r(r + s)$	h, s, r
Trapezoid Area = $\frac{1}{2}h(a + b)$	a, h, b		
Circle Area = πr^2 Circumference = $\pi d = 2\pi r$	r, d	Sphere Volume = $\frac{4}{3}\pi r^3$ Surface area = $4\pi r^2$	r

14.2 Pyramids and Cones

Terms & Concepts Introduced
1. Arc length
2. End-behavior
3. Frustum of a right cone
4. Leading coefficient
5. Oblique solid
6. Regular pyramid
7. Right cone
8. Slant height of a right cone
9. Zeroes of a function

Figure 1. Molecular structure of a diamond. Source: iStockPhoto.

A diamond is the hardest substance known to man and one of the most beautiful, i.e., symmetric, physical substances that the Father, Son, and Spirit have created. It is made up of the chemical element carbon, and its structure is a three-dimensional network where each atom is surrounded by four others. The basic unit of this network is the regular tetrahedron, a three-dimensional figure we will explore in more detail in Lesson 14.4.

A diamond forms a pyramid. We have already investigated pyramids with square bases; i.e., the Great Pyramid of Egypt. The base of the diamond pyramid is an equilateral triangle. A **regular pyramid** is a solid that has a regular polygon for its base and congruent isosceles triangles for its lateral faces.

Figure 2. Great Pyramid of Egypt. Source: iStockPhoto.

Like prisms, we name a pyramid according to the shape of its base. Finding the surface area of a pyramid is finding the areas of all its faces. What about the volume?

Volume of a Square Pyramid

Let's employ some careful reasoning, reasoning that involves infinite processes and atoms, to find out. First, let's consider a square pyramid made up of spherical balls. We will picture these balls as atoms, starting very large, but then getting lesser and lesser.

What is the total number of balls in a pyramid if the base is 2 by 2, 3, by 3, 4 by 4, 5 by 5, and 6 by 6? If necessary, glue some plastic golf balls together to construct Figure 3. We should get these answers:

Figure 3. Square Pyramid. Source: James D. Nickel.

2 by 2: 5 balls
3 by 3: 14 balls
4 by 4: 30 balls
5 by 5: 55 balls
6 by 6: 91 balls

Do you see a pattern? How many balls are we adding with each layer?

9, 16, 25, 36, etc.

These are square numbers, and this makes perfect sense.

Now consider the number of balls forming a cube, 2 by 2, 3, by 3, 4 by 4, 5 by 5, and 6 by 6. Using $V = s^3$, we get:

2 by 2: 8 balls
3 by 3: 27 balls
4 by 4: 64 balls
5 by 5: 125 balls
6 by 6: 216 balls

Now, imagine a base 1,000,000 by 1,000,000. What are the total number of balls that fill the pyramid and square? Choosing a large base like this enables us to imagine very small, i.e., infinitesimal atoms. It is easy to find the volume of a cube with $s = 1{,}000{,}000$. We get:

$V = 1{,}000{,}000^3 = (10^6)(10^6)(10^6) = 10^{18}$

What about the volume of a square pyramid? Here is how it unfolds:

2 by 2: $1^2 + 2^2 = 1 + 4 = 5$ balls
3 by 3: $1^2 + 2^2 + 3^2 = 1 + 4 + 9 = 14$ balls
4 by 4: $1^2 + 2^2 + 3^2 + 4^2 = 1 + 4 + 9 + 16 = 30$ balls
5 by 5: $1^2 + 2^2 + 3^2 + 4^2 + 5^2 = 1 + 4 + 9 + 16 + 25 = 55$ balls
6 by 6: $1^2 + 2^2 + 3^2 + 4^2 + 5^2 + 6^2 = 1 + 4 + 9 + 16 + 25 + 36 = 91$ balls

Isn't this beautiful? Mathematicians have derived a formula for finding the number of balls in a square pyramid of base n:

$$1 + 4 + 9 + 16 + 25 + 36 + \ldots + n^2 = \frac{n(n+1)(2n+1)}{6}$$

or

$$1 + 2^2 + 3^2 + 4^2 + 5^2 + 6^2 + \ldots + n^2 = \frac{n(n+1)(2n+1)}{6}$$

Try the formula for a few values of n for confirmation. We can prove this formula by Mathematical Induction. It is left for you to do in a homework exercise.

Let's use this formula to build Table 1.

Table 1

Base	Number of Balls in Pyramid (p)	Number of Balls in Cube (c)	Ratio of p to c
2 by 2	5	8	$5/8 = 0.625$
3 by 3	14	27	$14/27 \approx 0.518$
4 by 4	30	64	$30/64 \approx 0.469$
5 by 5	55	125	$55/125 = 0.440$
6 by 6	91	216	$91/216 = 0.421$
7 by 7	140	343	$140/343 \approx 0.408$

Table 1

Base	Number of Balls in Pyramid (p)	Number of Balls in Cube (c)	Ratio of p to c
8 by 8	204	512	$204/512 \approx 0.398$
9 by 9	285	729	$285/729 \approx 0.391$
10 by 10	385	1000	$385/1000 = 0.385$
100 by 100	338,350	$1,000,000 = 10^6$	0.338
1000 by 1000	333,833,500	$1,000,000,000 = 10^9$	0.333
1,000,000 by 1,000,000	3.33×10^{17}	10^{18}	0.333

Try to duplicate this table using spreadsheet software. You must enter the relevant formulas into all the rows for columns two, three and four. We see that as n gets very large, the ratio approaches 1/3 as a limit. Using limit notation, we write:

$$\lim_{n\to\infty} \frac{p}{c} = \frac{1}{3}$$

We can graph the ratio $\frac{p}{c}$ by setting $y = \frac{p}{c}$ where $x =$ the size of the square base. We write:

$$y = \frac{\frac{x(x+1)(2x+1)}{6}}{x^3}$$

Since $\frac{a/b}{c} = \frac{a}{b} \div c = \left(\frac{a}{b}\right)\left(\frac{1}{c}\right) = \frac{a}{bc}$, we can rewrite the algebraic expression on the right side of the equation:

$$y = \frac{\frac{x(x+1)(2x+1)}{6}}{x^3} \Leftrightarrow y = \frac{x(x+1)(2x+1)}{6x^3}$$

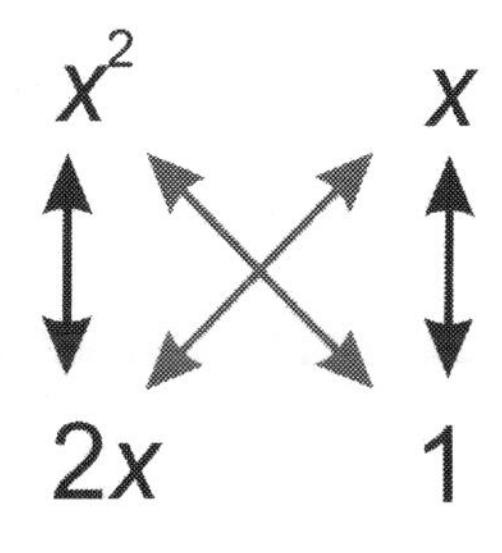

Figure 4.

Since $x(x + 1) = x^2 + x$ and $(x^2 + x)(2x + 1) = 2x^3 + 3x^2 + x$ (Figure 4), then:

$$y = \frac{x(x+1)(2x+1)}{6x^3} \Leftrightarrow y = \frac{2x^3 + 3x^2 + x}{6x^3}$$

We have a function that is a ratio of two functions:

$$y = f(x) = \frac{2x^3 + 3x^2 + x}{6x^3}$$

To see what happens to y as $x \to \infty$, inspect Figure 5.

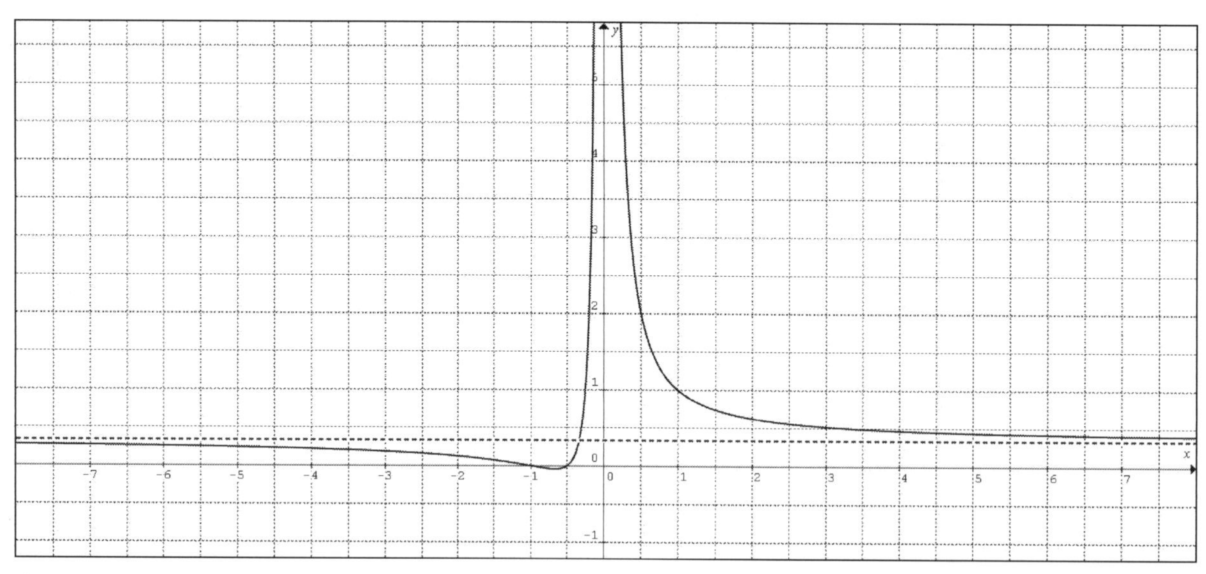

Figure 5.

Note that the graph is continuous in two parts but we are only interested in Quadrant I. As $x \to \infty$, $y \to 1/3$ where $y = 1/3$ is the horizontal asymptote. Using limit notation, we write:

$$\lim_{x \to \infty} y = \frac{1}{3}$$

Let's inspect $y = \frac{2x^3 + 3x^2 + x}{6x^3}$ carefully. Can we find $\frac{1}{3}$ revealed in it? As $x \to \infty$, what term in the numerator dominates the expression? The dominant term is $2x^3$ and 2 is the **leading coefficient.**[1] As x gets very, very large, the other terms, $3x^2$ and x, lose their import so we can drop them. As $x \to \infty$, we need to evaluate this:

$$y = \frac{2x^3}{6x^3}$$

Canceling, we get our horizontal asymptote:

$$y = \frac{\overset{1}{\cancel{2}}\,\overset{1}{\cancel{x^3}}}{\underset{3}{\cancel{6}}\,\underset{1}{\cancel{x^3}}} \Leftrightarrow y = \frac{1}{3}$$

Indeed, when $x \to \infty$, $\frac{1}{3}$ is embedded in $y = \frac{2x^3 + 3x^2 + x}{6x^3}$. As $x \to \infty$, we have a perichoretic dance of infinity! This kind of analysis is the determination of a function's **end-behavior**; i.e., what happens to a function when its argument approaches either $-\infty$ or ∞.

[1] In an algebraic expression, the coefficient of the term with the highest exponent is the leading coefficient.

Is there a vertical asymptote? Note that we can cancel x, assuming $x \neq 0$:

$$y = \frac{\overset{1}{\cancel{x}}(x+1)(2x+1)}{6x^{\overset{2}{\cancel{3}}}} \Leftrightarrow y = \frac{(x+1)(2x+1)}{6x^2}$$

Instead of expanding the numerator, we leave it alone and ask some questions of the fractional expression. First, what value of x will cause problems in the denominator? When $x = 0$, we have division by zero. In the graph, $x = 0$, the y-axis, is the vertical asymptote. It tells us that there are no images for $x = 0$.

Second, what values of x in the numerator satisfy the equation $(x + 1)(2x + 1) = 0$? In other words, when $y = 0$, what values of x make the equation true? We want to find the **zeroes of the function**, where the equation intersects the x-axis. The purpose of Steps 10 and Step 11 was to learn how to find these zeroes. The graph shows us that there are two points where this happens. Can we find these points algebraically?

Let's invoke the Zero Product Rule (Lesson 5.15):

$ab = 0 \Leftrightarrow a = 0$ or $b = 0$

We have $(x + 1)(2x + 1) = 0$ and this equation fits the problem-pattern revealed by the rule. To solve for x, we must do this:

$(x + 1)(2x + 1) = 0 \Leftrightarrow x + 1 = 0$ or $2x + 1 = 0$

Continuing:

$x + 1 = 0$ or $2x + 1 = 0 \Leftrightarrow x = -1$ or $2x = -1 \Leftrightarrow x = -\frac{1}{2}$

Now, look at the graph (Quadrant II and III). The graph intersects the x-axis, when $y = 0$, at two points:

Solution 1. $x = -1$ or the graph intersects the x-axis at $(-1, 0)$

Solution 2. $x = -\frac{1}{2}$ or the graph intersects the x-axis at $(-\frac{1}{2}, 0)$

The equation tells us a lot about the behavior of the graph: (1) the asymptotes, horizontal and vertical, and (2) the zeroes. The asymptotes and the zeroes interpenetrate the equation; they are embedded in it. We just need the algebraic tools to extract these perichoretic gems. We see in this analysis another example of the coinherence between Algebra and Geometry.

Finding zeroes of fractional and other more complex equations is important in physics, and one of the goals of Algebra courses is to teach you how to find these zeroes. The Zero Product Rule is the fundamental tool that helps us extract these zeroes.

We conclude from our analysis that the ratio of the volume of a square pyramid to the volume of a cube is 1:3, or the volume of a square pyramid is one-third the volume of a cube. Using symbols, where $V_{pyramid}$ represents the volume of a pyramid, we write:

$$V_{pyramid} = \frac{1}{3}V_{cube}$$

If B = the area of the base of a square pyramid and h = height of the pyramid, then $V_{pyramid}$, the volume of a pyramid, is:

$$V_{pyramid} = \frac{1}{3}Bh$$

VOLUME OF A RIGHT CONE

A **right cone** is a cone with its vertex directly above the center of its base. In general, a cone is a pyramid with a circular cross section. In Figure 6, we see a square pyramid inscribed in a cube and a right cone inscribed in a right cylinder.

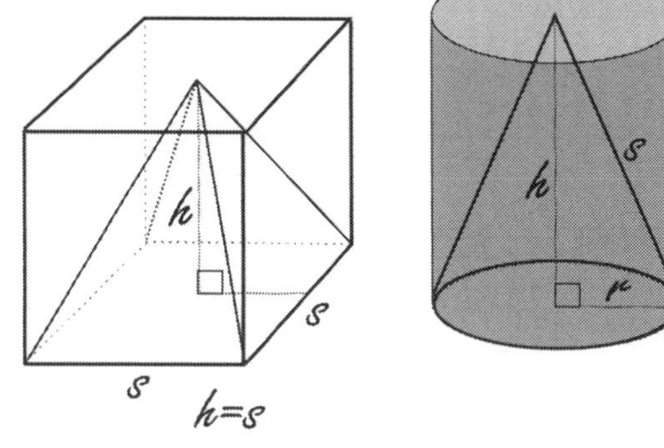

Figure 6.

How do we determine the volume of a right cone? Investigate Figure 7. Into a right cylinder, we inscribe any regular prism, triangular, square, pentagonal, etc. In the figure, we have inscribed a right triangular prism in a right cylinder. Into a right cone, we inscribe any regular pyramid, triangular, square, pentagonal, etc. In the figure, we have inscribed a right square pyramid in a right cone.

We let b represent the area of both the base of the prism and the base of the pyramid and h represent their equal altitudes. Their respective volumes, v, are:

Prisms: $v = bh$

Pyramids: $v = \frac{1}{3}bh$

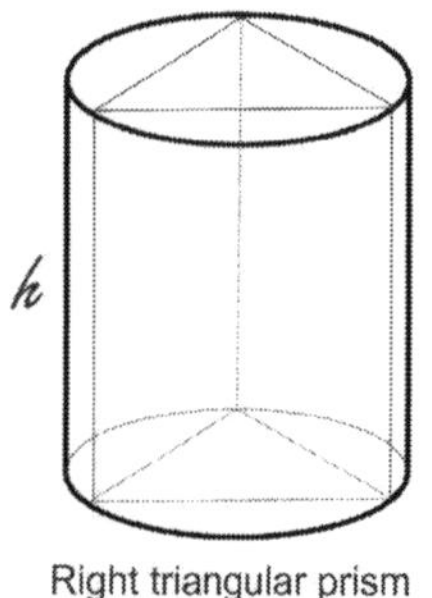

Right triangular prism inscribed in a right cylinder

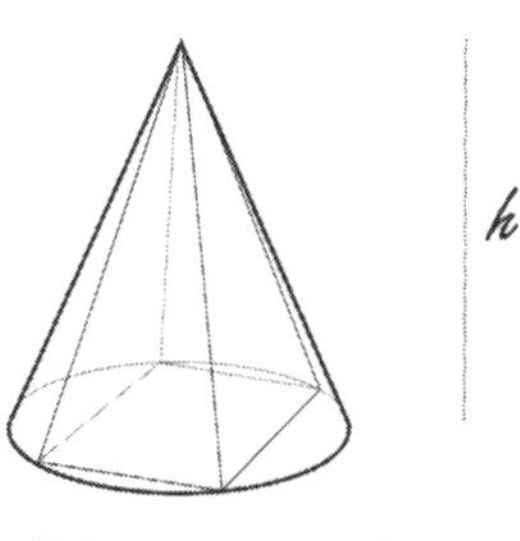

Right square pyramid inscribed in a right cone

Figure 7.

Let's invoke limit thinking. Imagine that the number of lateral faces of the prism or pyramid increases *ad infinitum*. At the limit, b tends to the area B of the base of the right cylinder or right cone with h remaining unchanged. Make sure you visualize this. As a result, v will tend to the limit Bh in the case of the prisms, and $\frac{1}{3}Bh$ in the case of the pyramids. Therefore, the volume V of the right cylinder or right cone is:

Right cylinder: $V = Bh$

Right cone: $V = \frac{1}{3}Bh$

If we let the volume V of a right cone be represented by $V_{right\ cone}$, we write:

$$V_{right\ cone} = \frac{1}{3}Bh \Leftrightarrow V_{right\ cone} = \frac{1}{3}\pi r^2 h \text{ (since } B = \pi r^2\text{)}$$

QED

Using a different type of reasoning, Euclid proved this result in Proposition 10 of Book XII of *The Elements*.

SURFACE AREA OF A RIGHT CONE

The surface area of the right cone, α(right cone), is the area of the base plus its lateral area. The area of the base is πr^2. The lateral area is not a rectangle like the right cylinder. What is its shape? It is a sector of a circle of radius s, the **slant height**.[2] What is this lateral area?

The area of sector ABC, α(sector ABC), is a part of the area of the circle centered at A, α(circle A), where A is the apex[3] of the right cone with radius s. We can write this relationship as a ratio:

$$\frac{\alpha(\text{sector } ABC)}{\alpha(\text{circle } A)}$$

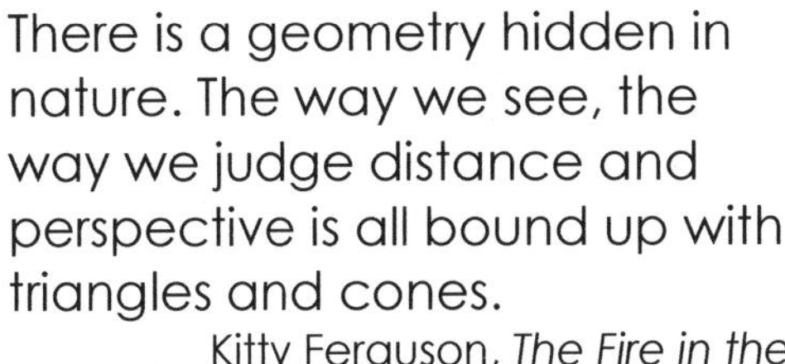

This ratio will be the same as the ratio of the **arc length**[4] of sector ABC, written $m\overset{\frown}{BC}$, to the circumference of Circle A, C(circle A). We can also write this relationship as a ratio:

$$\frac{m\overset{\frown}{BC}}{C(\text{circle } A)}$$

Equating these two ratios, we have this proportion:

$$\frac{\alpha(\text{sector } ABC)}{\alpha(\text{circle } A)} = \frac{m\overset{\frown}{BC}}{C(\text{circle } A)}$$

We want to find the α(sector ABC), the lateral area of the right cone (Figure 8). We know the area and circumference of Circle A:

$$\alpha(\text{circle } A) = \pi s^2$$
$$C(\text{circle } A) = 2\pi s$$

What is $m\overset{\frown}{BC}$? Look carefully at the base and the lateral area. Do you see that $m\overset{\frown}{BC}$ is the same as the circumference of the circle that is the base of the right cone? We write:

$$m\overset{\frown}{BC} = 2\pi r$$

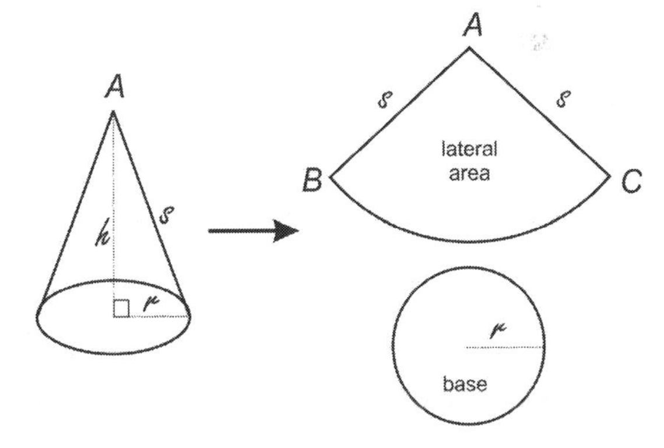

Figure 8. Net of a Right Cone.

We now know three of the four terms of a proportion and, by the Law of Three, we can solve for our unknown, α(sector ABC). We start with our proportion:

[2] The slant height of an object like a pyramid is the distance measured along a lateral face from the base to the apex along the center of the face. It is the altitude of the triangle that comprises the lateral face. A synonym for slant is oblique. The slant height of a right cone is the distance from any point on the circumference of its circular base to the apex of the cone via a straight line along the surface of the cone.

[3] Remember (Lesson 2.6), the apex, meaning "highest point," is the vertex at the tip of an object, a cone or pyramid in this case.

[4] Arc length is distance along the curved line making up the arc.

$$\frac{\alpha(\text{sector } ABC)}{\alpha(\text{circle } A)} = \frac{m\widehat{BC}}{C(\text{circle } A)}$$

By substitution, we get:

$$\frac{\alpha(\text{sector } ABC)}{\pi s^2} = \frac{2\pi r}{2\pi s}$$

Cross-multiplying, we get:

$\alpha(\text{sector } ABC)(2\pi s) = (2\pi r)(\pi s^2)$

Solving for $\alpha(\text{sector } ABC)$, i.e., dividing both sides by $2\pi s$, we get:

$$\alpha(\text{sector } ABC) = \frac{(2\pi r)(\pi s^2)}{2\pi \text{s}} = \frac{2\pi^2 rs^2}{2\pi \text{s}}$$

Cancelling, we get:

$$\alpha(\text{sector } ABC) = \frac{\overset{1}{\cancel{2}}\,\pi^{\overset{1}{\cancel{2}}}\, r s^{\overset{1}{\cancel{2}}}}{\underset{1}{\cancel{2}}\,\underset{1}{\cancel{\pi}}\,\underset{1}{\cancel{s}}} = \pi r^1 s^1 = \pi rs$$

Therefore, the surface area of a right cone, α(right cone), is:

$\alpha(\text{right cone}) = \pi r^2 + \pi rs = \pi r(r + s)$
QED

How about that? The derivation of this formula certainly is a beautiful application of the dance of algebraic operations.

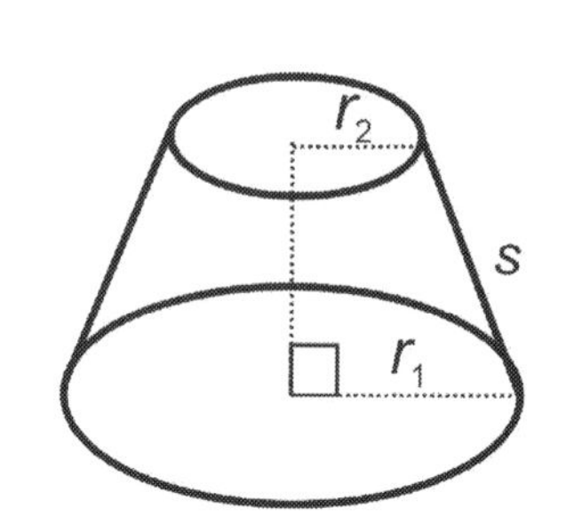

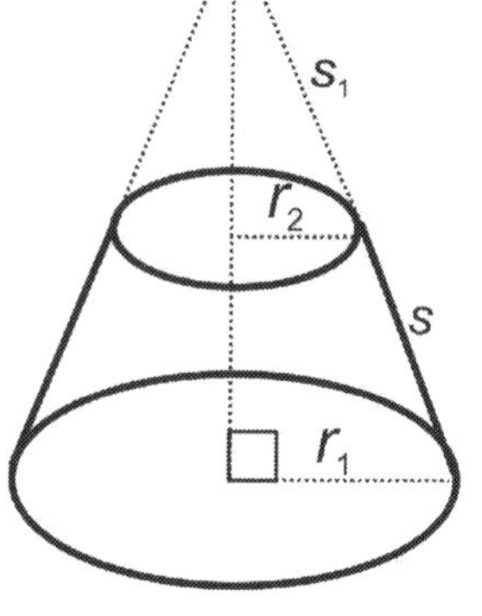

Figure 9. Frustum of a right cone (Surface Area).

FRUSTUM OF A RIGHT CONE

The **frustum**[5] **of a right cone** is the part of a cone enclosed between its base and a cross section parallel to it. The two parallel circles, the base of the cone and its cross section, are the bases of the conical frustum. Traditional lampshades and paper/styrofoam cups are examples of this common three-dimensional shape.

To find the surface area (Figure 9), we first complete the cone of which the frustum is a part. We have two cones, one large and one small. Do you see them? All we need to do is subtract the lateral area of the small cone from the surface area of the large cone to get the surface area of the frustum.

We let α(frustum of a cone) represent the surface area of the frustum of the right cone where $r_1 > r_2$. Therefore:

$\alpha(\text{frustum of a cone}) = \pi r_1(s + s_1) - \pi r_2 s_1$
(Make sure you see this. Remember, we only want to subtract the lateral area of the small cone.)

[5] Frustum is Latin meaning "piece cut off." Frustums of pyramids are also possible.

We need a formula that does not involve s_1 since we only know r_1, r_2, and s of the frustum. Let's simplify things so s_1 is somewhat isolated:

$$\alpha(\text{frustum of a cone}) = \pi r_1(s + s_1) - \pi r_2 s_1 \Leftrightarrow \alpha(\text{frustum of a cone}) = \pi[r_1(s + s_1) - r_2 s_1] \Leftrightarrow$$
$$\alpha(\text{frustum of a cone}) = \pi(r_1 s + r_1 s_1 - r_2 s_1) \Leftrightarrow \alpha(\text{frustum of a cone}) = \pi[\, s_1(r_1 - r_2) + r_1 s]$$

We note two similar triangles (Figure 9) producing this proportion:

$\dfrac{r_1}{r_2} = \dfrac{s + s_1}{s_1}$ (Make sure you see this.)

Solving for s_1, we get:

$$\frac{r_1}{r_2} = \frac{s + s_1}{s_1} \Leftrightarrow r_1 s_1 = r_2(s + s_1) \Leftrightarrow r_1 s_1 = r_2 s + r_2 s_1 \Leftrightarrow r_1 s_1 - r_2 s_1 = r_2 s \Leftrightarrow r_2 s = s_1(r_1 - r_2) \Leftrightarrow s_1 = \frac{r_2 s}{r_1 - r_2}$$

Now, we substitute:

$$\alpha(\text{frustum of a cone}) = \pi[\, s_1(r_1 - r_2) + r_1 s] \text{ and } s_1 = \frac{r_2 s}{r_1 - r_2} \Rightarrow \alpha(\text{frustum of a cone}) =$$

$$\pi\left[\frac{r_2 s}{\cancel{r_1 - r_2}_{\,1}}\left(\cancel{r_1 - r_2}^{\,1}\right) + r_1 s\right] \Leftrightarrow \alpha(\text{frustum of a cone}) = \pi(r_2 s + r_1 s) \Leftrightarrow$$

$\alpha(\text{frustum of a cone}) = \pi s(r_2 + r_1)$
QED
(Note: This area formula looks very much like the area formula for a trapezoid. Do you see why?)

To find the volume of the frustum of a right cone (Figure 10), we subtract the volume of the small cone from the volume of the large cone.

We let V = volume of the frustum of the right cone where $r_1 > r_2$. Therefore:

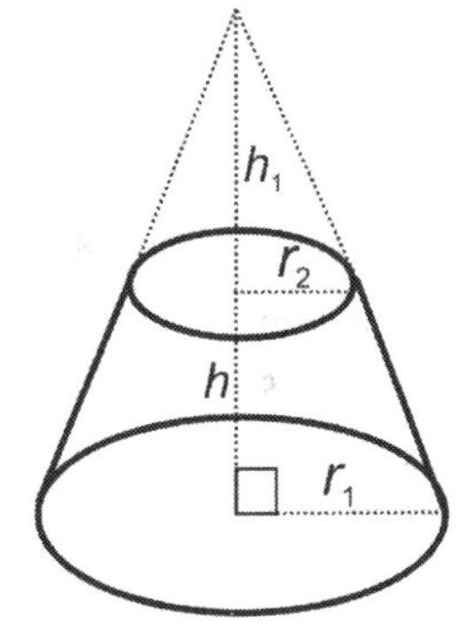

Figure 10. Frustum of a right cone (Volume).

$$V = \frac{1}{3}\pi r_1^2(h + h_1) - \frac{1}{3}\pi r_2^2 h_1$$

Again, we need a formula that does not involve h_1 since we only know r_1, r_2, and h of the frustum. From similar triangles (Figure 10), we can state this proportion:

$$\frac{r_1}{r_2} = \frac{h + h_1}{h_1}$$

Let's solve for h_1 so we can substitute for it:

$$\frac{r_1}{r_2} = \frac{h + h_1}{h_1} \Leftrightarrow r_1h_1 = r_2(h + h_1) \Leftrightarrow r_1h_1 = r_2h + r_2h_1 \Leftrightarrow r_1h_1 - r_2h_1 = r_2h \Leftrightarrow h_1(r_1 - r_1) = r_2h \Leftrightarrow$$

$$h_1 = \frac{r_2 h}{r_1 - r_2}$$

Let's work on the volume formula isolating h_1:

$$V = \frac{1}{3}\pi r_1^2 (h + h_1) - \frac{1}{3}\pi r_2^2 h_1 \Leftrightarrow V = \frac{1}{3}\pi\left[r_1^2 (h + h_1) - r_2^2 h_1\right] \Leftrightarrow$$

$$V = \frac{1}{3}\pi\left[r_1^2 h + r_1^2 h_1 - r_2^2 h_1\right] \Leftrightarrow V = \frac{1}{3}\pi\left[h_1\left(r_1^2 - r_2^2\right) + r_1^2 h\right]$$

Now, we can substitute $\frac{r_2 h}{r_1 - r_2}$ for h_1:

$$V = \frac{1}{3}\pi\left[h_1\left(r_1^2 - r_2^2\right) + r_1^2 h\right] \Leftrightarrow V = \frac{1}{3}\pi\left[\frac{r_2 h}{r_1 - r_2}\left(r_1^2 - r_2^2\right) + r_1^2 h\right] \Leftrightarrow$$

$$V = \frac{1}{3}\pi\left[\frac{r_2 h}{\underset{1}{\cancel{r_1 - r_2}}}\left(r_1 + r_2\right)\left(\overset{1}{\cancel{r_1 - r_2}}\right) + r_1^2 h\right] \Leftrightarrow$$

$$V = \frac{1}{3}\pi\left[r_2 h\left(r_1 + r_2\right) + r_1^2 h\right] \Leftrightarrow V = \frac{1}{3}h\pi\left[r_2\left(r_1 + r_2\right) + r_1^2\right] \Leftrightarrow$$

$$V = \frac{1}{3}h\pi\left(r_2^2 + r_1r_2 + r_1^2\right)$$

QED

OBLIQUE SOLIDS

We are not limited to right prisms, right cylinders, right cones, or right pyramids. **Oblique**[6] **solids** (Figure 11) are also possible, and they require further mathematics if we want to develop formulas for them.

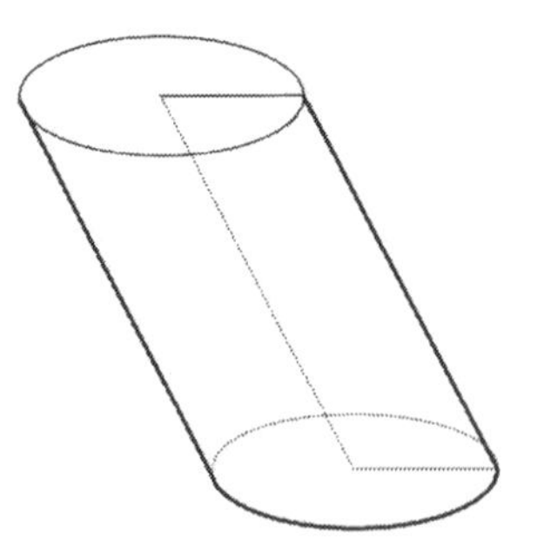

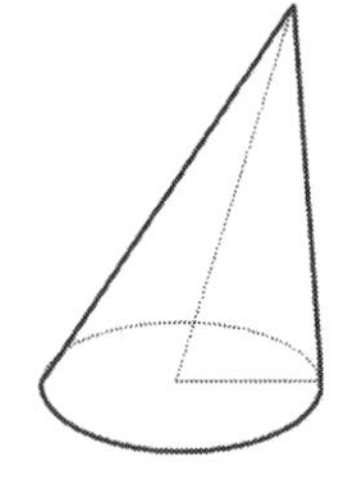

Figure 11. Oblique cylinder and cone.

EXERCISES

Define the following terms:

1. Regular pyramid
2. Leading coefficient
3. End-behavior of a function
4. Zeroes of a function
5. Right cone
6. Slant height of a right cone
7. Arc length

---

[6] An oblique solid, where oblique means "deviating from perpendicular," is one that is distorted so that is seems to lean over at an angle, as opposed to being exactly upright, i.e., perpendicular.

8. Frustum of a right cone
9. Oblique solid

Answer the following questions:

10. Prove that $1^2 + 2^2 + \ldots + n^2 = \frac{1}{6}n(n+1)(2n+1)$ by Mathematical Induction.
11. Solve $A = \pi r^2 + \pi rs$ for s.
12. Solve $V = \frac{1}{3}\pi r^2 h$ for r.
13. Let $A = \alpha$(frustum of a right cone). Solve $A = \pi s(r_2 + r_1)$ for:
    (a) s.
    (b) r_2.
14. Solve $V = \frac{1}{3}h\pi\left(r_2^2 + r_1 r_2 + r_1^2\right)$ for:
    (a) h.
    (b) r_1.
    [Hint: You need to use the quadratic formula for (b). Answering this question will require significant algebraic work.]

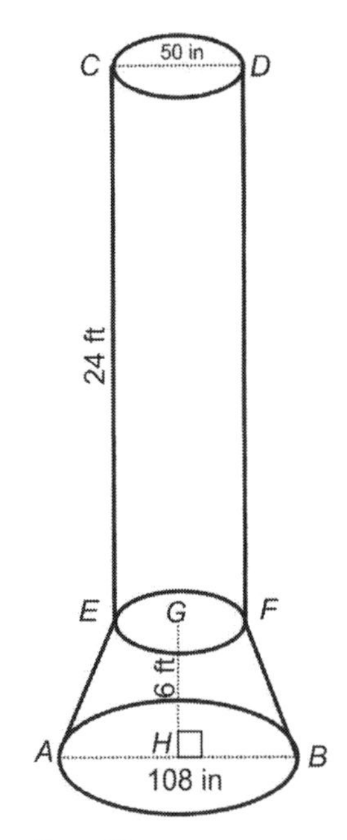

Figure 12.

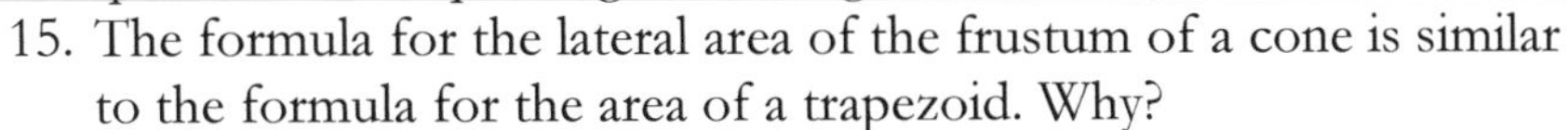

15. The formula for the lateral area of the frustum of a cone is similar to the formula for the area of a trapezoid. Why?

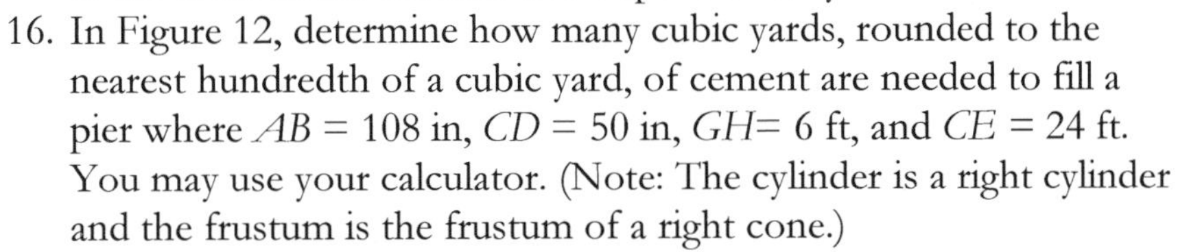

16. In Figure 12, determine how many cubic yards, rounded to the nearest hundredth of a cubic yard, of cement are needed to fill a pier where AB = 108 in, CD = 50 in, GH= 6 ft, and CE = 24 ft. You may use your calculator. (Note: The cylinder is a right cylinder and the frustum is the frustum of a right cone.)

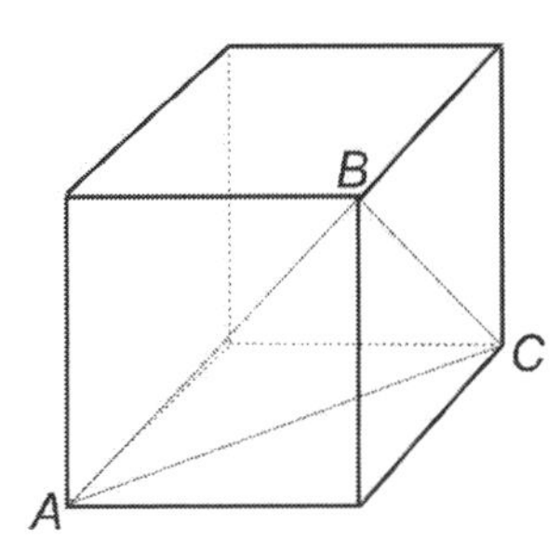

Figure 13.

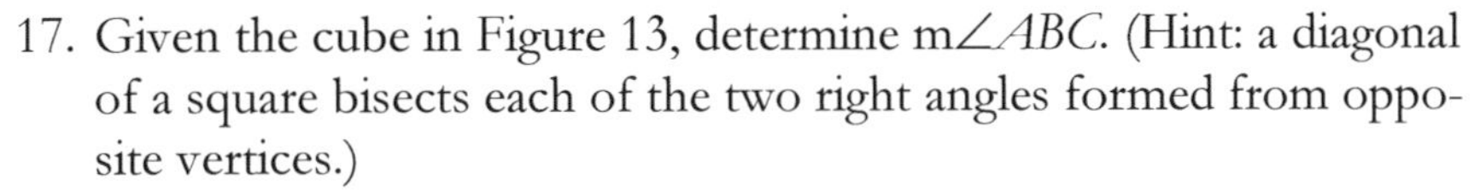

17. Given the cube in Figure 13, determine $m\angle ABC$. (Hint: a diagonal of a square bisects each of the two right angles formed from opposite vertices.)

Using the Pythagorean Theorem as a guide and Figure 14:

18. Make a conjecture concerning the formula for finding the length of a diagonal, d, of a cube in terms of a, b, and c.
19. Prove the conjecture you made in Question 18.

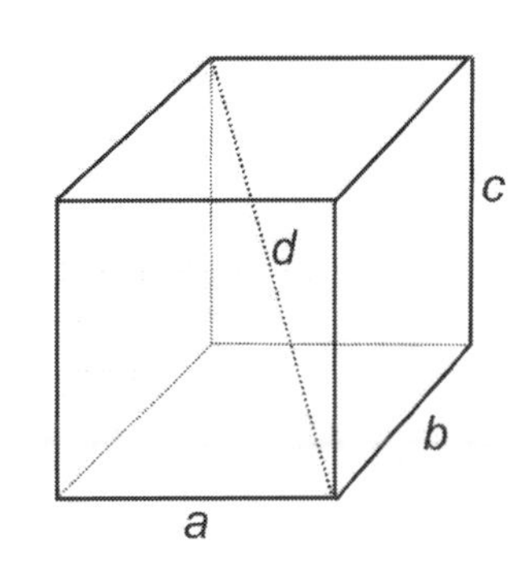

Figure 14.

Justify the following equivalencies/implications:

20. $\frac{r_1}{r_2} = \frac{s + s_1}{s_1} \Leftrightarrow r_1 s_1 = r_2(s + s_1)$
21. $r_1 s_1 = r_2(s + s_1) \Leftrightarrow r_1 s_1 = r_2 s + r_2 s_1$
22. $r_1 s_1 = r_2 s + r_2 s_1 \Leftrightarrow r_1 s_1 - r_2 s_1 = r_2 s$
23. $r_1 s_1 - r_2 s_1 = r_2 s \Leftrightarrow r_2 s = s_1(r_1 - r_2)$
24. $r_2 s = s_1(r_1 - r_2) \Leftrightarrow s_1 = \frac{r_2 s}{r_1 - r_2}$
25. $V = \frac{1}{3}\pi r_1^2(h + h_1) - \frac{1}{3}\pi r_2^2 h_1 \Leftrightarrow V = \frac{1}{3}\pi\left[r_1^2(h + h_1) - r_2^2 h_1\right]$
26. $V = \frac{1}{3}\pi\left[r_1^2(h + h_1) - r_2^2 h_1\right] \Leftrightarrow V = \frac{1}{3}\pi\left[r_1^2 h + r_1^2 h_1 - r_2^2 h_1\right]$

27. $V = \frac{1}{3}\pi\left[r_1^2h + r_1^2h_1 - r_2^2h_1\right] \Leftrightarrow V = \frac{1}{3}\pi\left[h_1\left(r_1^2 - r_2^2\right) + r_1^2h\right] \Leftrightarrow$

28. $V = \frac{1}{3}\pi\left[h_1\left(r_1^2 - r_2^2\right) + r_1^2h\right]$ and $h_1 = \frac{r_2h}{r_1 - r_2} \Rightarrow V = \frac{1}{3}\pi\left[\frac{r_2h}{r_1 - r_2}\left(r_1^2 - r_2^2\right) + r_1^2h\right]$

29. $V = \frac{1}{3}\pi\left[\frac{r_2h}{r_1 - r_2}\left(r_1^2 - r_2^2\right) + r_1^2h\right] \Leftrightarrow V = \frac{1}{3}\pi\left[\frac{r_2h}{r_1 - r_2}\left(r_1 + r_2\right)\left(r_1 - r_2\right) + r_1^2h\right]$

30. $V = \frac{1}{3}\pi\left[\frac{r_2h}{r_1 - r_2}\left(r_1 + r_2\right)\left(r_1 - r_2\right) + r_1^2h\right] \Leftrightarrow V = \frac{1}{3}\pi\left[r_2h\left(r_1 + r_2\right) + r_1^2h\right]$

31. $V = \frac{1}{3}\pi\left[r_2h\left(r_1 + r_2\right) + r_1^2h\right] \Leftrightarrow V = \frac{1}{3}h\pi\left[r_2\left(r_1 + r_2\right) + r_1^2\right]$

32. $V = \frac{1}{3}h\pi\left[r_2\left(r_1 + r_2\right) + r_1^2\right] \Leftrightarrow V = \frac{1}{3}h\pi\left(r_2^2 + r_1r_2 + r_1^2\right)$

Field Project:

33. Without using the benefits of the Pythagorean Theorem (but using the tools of a typical workshop), discover another method of measuring the diagonal of a cube. (Hint: Use Figure 15 as a guide. There is more than one way to do this.)

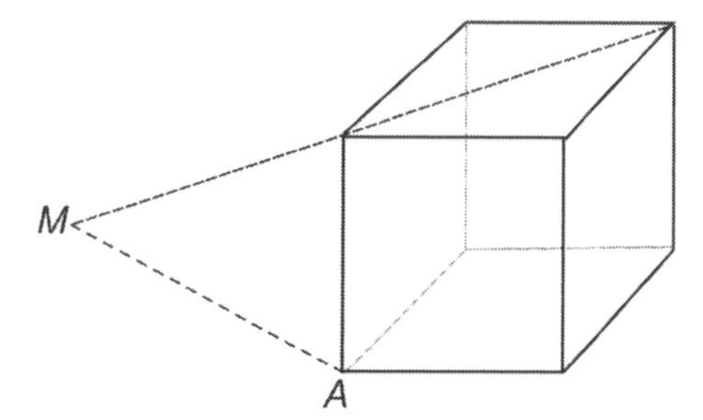

Figure 15.

Find the zeroes, end-behavior, and, if possible, the vertical and horizontal asymptotes of the following functions by algebraic inspection:

34. $y = (2x^2 + x - 7)/(x^2 - 2x - 5)$

35. $y = (x - 4)(x + 2)/(x^2 - 9)$

36. $y = (x^2 + x - 6)/(x - 1)$

37. $y = (x - 3)(x + 6)/(2x + 5)$

38. $y = (3x^3 + 12x^2 - 20x)/(9 - x)$

39. $y = (x - 5)(x + 2)/(3x - 15)$

Graphing question:

40. Graph Questions 34 to 39 and their respective asymptotes to confirm your algebraic analysis.

Answer this question:

41. For a function in the form $y = f(x) = \frac{g(x)}{h(x)}$, explain how to find the zeroes of the function, its end-behavior, and its vertical and horizontal asymptotes, if they exist.

Figure 16. Cones in the Orient. Source: iStockPhoto.

14.3 THE WORLD OF POLYNOMIALS

Terms & Concepts Introduced
1. Extrema
2. Factor Theorem
3. Rational function

Before we explore a beautiful revelation of figures in three dimensions, let's review the equation we graphed in the previous lesson and introduce more mathematical terms.

RATIONAL FUNCTIONS

$$y = \frac{2x^3 + 3x^2 + x}{6x^3}$$

Our graph tells us that a unique image is generated from every argument except when the argument is zero, a value that makes the image of the denominator zero. This fractional expression is a function. We can write:

$$f(x) = \frac{2x^3 + 3x^2 + x}{6x^3}$$

The algebraic expression on the right side is a fraction and a cubic function occupies both the numerator and denominator. We can graph both the numerator and denominator as separate functions $g(x) = 2x^3 + 3x^2 + x$ and $h(x) = 6x^3$ (Figure 1 and Figure 2):

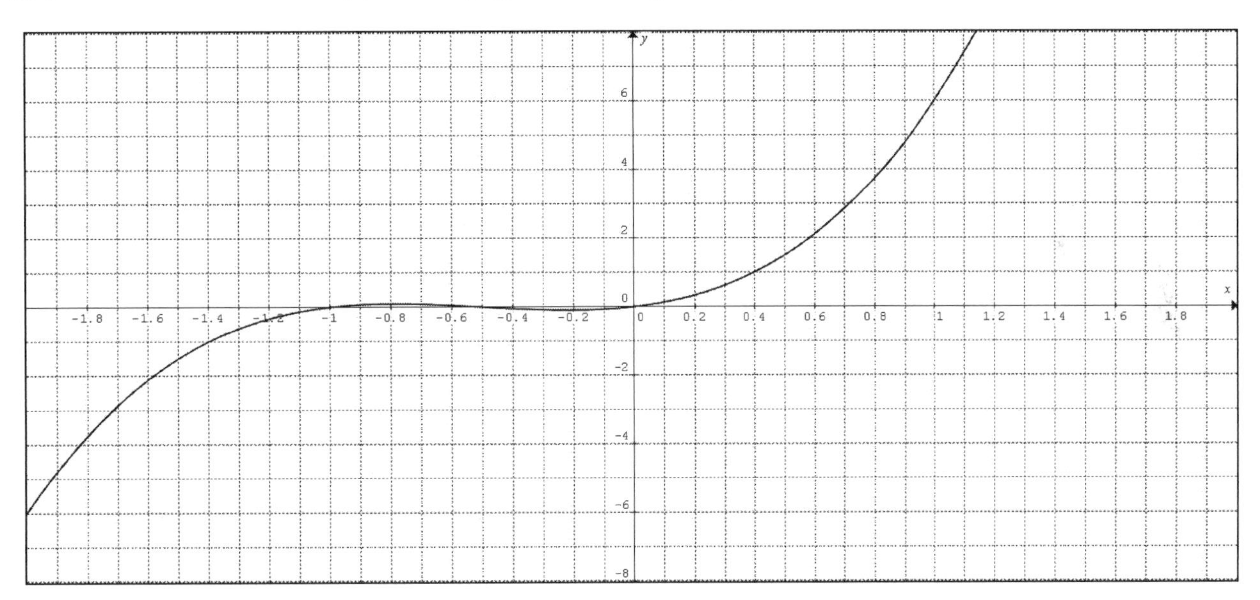

Figure 1. The numerator $g(x)$.

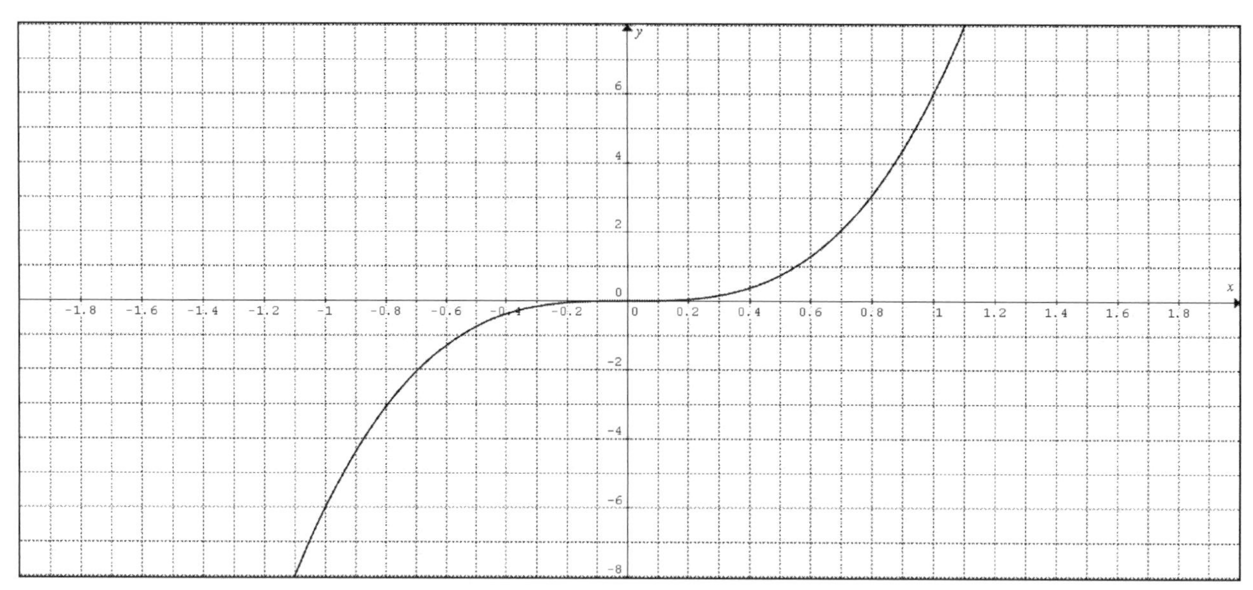

Figure 2. The denominator $h(x)$.

In general, we can write a **rational function** in this form:

$$f(x)=\frac{g(x)}{h(x)} \text{ where } h(x) \neq 0$$

ZEROES AND VERTICAL ASYMPTOTES

As we have noticed in the homework exercises of Lesson 14.2, the zeroes of $f(x)$ are the value(s) of x where $g(x) = 0$. The vertical asymptote is a line in the form $x = a$ where the value of a is the value of x when $h(x) = 0$. But, if the zero of the numerator is the same value, there is no vertical asymptote.

END-BEHAVIOR AND ASYMPTOTES

We determine the end-behavior of a rational function by looking at the leading terms of both the numerator and denominator. Given a rational function $f(x)=\frac{g(x)}{h(x)}$ where $h(x) \neq 0$, the leading term of $g(x)$ is ax^m, and the leading term of $h(x)$ is bx^n, the end-behavior of $f(x)$ is:

$$\frac{ax^m}{bx^n}=\left(\frac{a}{b}\right)x^{m-n}$$

To review with some examples, the end-behavior of:

Example 1. $\frac{6x^2-3x+2}{x+2}$ is $\frac{6x^2}{x}=6x$.

Example 2. $\frac{x^5-3x+8}{3x^2-2}$ is $\frac{x^5}{3x^2}=\frac{1}{3}x^3$.

Example 3. $\frac{9-x^2}{x^3+5}$ is $\frac{-x^2}{x^3}=-\frac{1}{x}$.

Example 4. $\dfrac{(3x-7)(2x^2+3)(3x-2)}{6x^3+2x-3}$ is $\dfrac{18x^3}{6x^3} = 3.$

For large values of the argument of $f(x)$, positive ($x \to \infty$) or negative ($x \to -\infty$), the graph of the rational function resembles the graph of its end-behavior. We summarize the asymptotic dance of the end-behavior of rational functions in Table 1.

Table 1 **Summary of Asymptotic Dance of Rational Functions** $f(x) = \dfrac{g(x)}{h(x)}$	
The ratio of the highest term, or leading term, in both the numerator and denominator is: $\dfrac{ax^m}{bx^n}$	
$m < n$	Horizontal asymptote is the x-axis ($y = 0$).
$m = n$	Horizontal asymptote is $y = k$ ($k \neq 0$) where $k = a/b$.
$m = n + 1$	Slant asymptote of the form of a line $y = kx$ ($k \neq 0$) where $k = a/b$.
$m > n$ where $m - n > 1$	Nonlinear asymptote, quadratic if $m - n = 2$, cubic, if $m - n = 3$, etc.

Both $g(x)$ and $h(x)$ are examples of polynomial functions (Lesson 12.11). In general, a polynomial function, $f(x)$, looks like this:

$f(x) = a_0x^n + a_1x^{n-1} + a_2x^{n-2} + \ldots + a_{n-1}x + a_n$ (Note: $x^1 = x$, $x^0 = 1$, and $a_n = 1a_n$) where:

1. n is a nonnegative integer or x^n is a nonnegative power.
2. n is the degree of the polynomial.
3. $a_0, a_1, a_2, \ldots, a_{n-1}, a_n$ are parameters, the coefficients, respectively, of $x^n, x^{n-1}, x^{n-2}, \ldots, x^1, x^0$ with $a^0 \neq 0$.
4. Each term of the polynomial in the form ax^n is a monomial (Lesson 12.11).
5. a_0 is the leading coefficient.

We have already studied four polynomials (Figure 3):

1. A constant polynomial, or a polynomial of degree zero: $f(x) = ax^0 = a$ where $a \neq 0$, or:

   $f(x) = a_0x^0 = a_0$ where $a_0 \neq 0$
   Example: $y = f(x) = 4$

2. A linear polynomial, or a polynomial of degree one: $f(x) = ax + b$ where $a \neq 0$, or:

   $f(x) = a_0x^1 + a_1x^0 = a_0x + a_1$ where $a_0 \neq 0$
   Example: $y = f(x) = 3x - 2$

3. A quadratic polynomial, or a polynomial of degree two: $f(x) = ax^2 + bx + c$ where $a \neq 0$, or:

   $f(x) = a_0x^2 + a_1x^1 + a_2x^0 = a_0x^2 + a_1x + a_2$ where $a_0 \neq 0$
   Example: $y = f(x) = x^2 - 2$

As we have noted, a quadratic may have two, one, or no distinct real number solutions. They will always have either a maximum or minimum image. The end-behavior of quadratics will always approach positive or negative infinity (+∞ or -∞) in tandem depending on whether their graphs smile or frown.

4. A cubic polynomial, or a polynomial of degree three: $f(x) = ax^3 + bx^2 + cx + d$ where $a \neq 0$, or:

   $f(x) = a_0x^3 + a_1x^2 + a_2x^1 + a_3x^0 = a_0x^3 + a_1x^2 + a_2x + a_3$ where $a_0 \neq 0$
   Example: $y = f(x) = x^3 - 8$

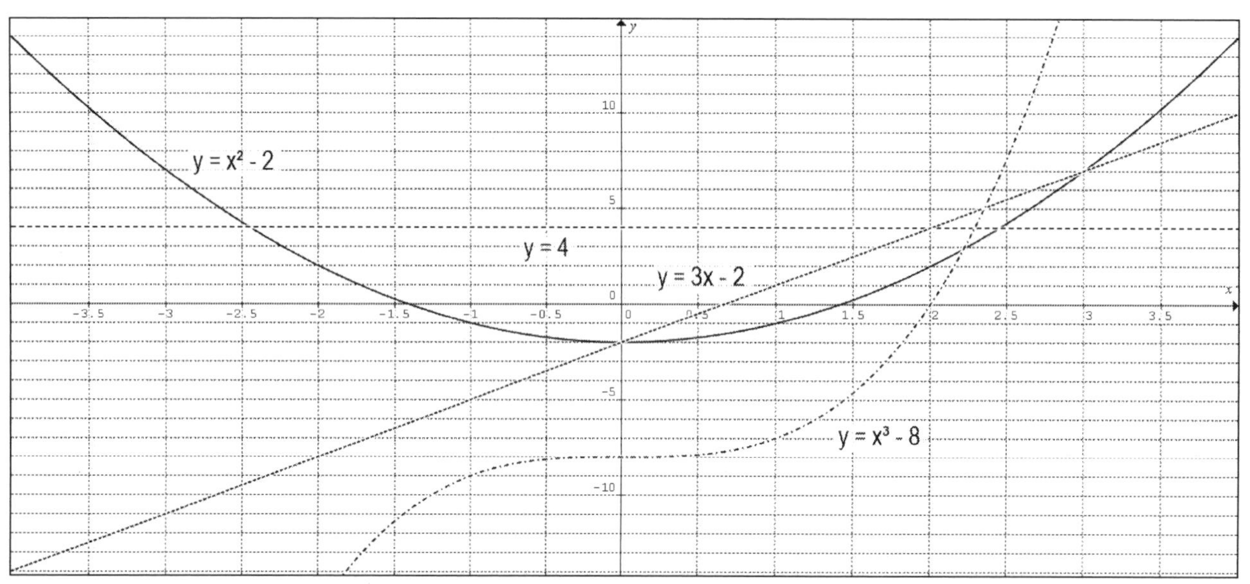

Figure 3. Panoply of polynomials.

Cubic polynomials are more complex than their quadratic neighbor (Figure 4). They may have three, two, or one real number solutions. Graphs of cubics will always intersect the x-axis so they will always have at least one real number solution. The end-behavior of cubics will always approach negative infinity (-∞) on the left side and positive infinity (+∞) on the right side if $a_0 > 0$, or vice-versa if $a_0 < 0$. Regarding maximum or minimum images, they will always be local, i.e., within a given interval, one maximum and the other minimum. It is possible that a cubic will not have a local maximum or minimum.

Mathematician John Derbyshire (1945-) notes the position of polynomials in the arena of mathematics:

"Polynomial has a fair claim to being the single most important concept in algebra, both ancient and modern."[1]

Mathematician John Tabak reflects on the importance of the study of this mathematical object:

"Polynomials play an important role in scientific and engineering computations."[2]

---

[1] John Derbyshire, *Unknown Quantity: A Real and Imaginary History of Algebra* (Washington, DC: Joseph Henry Press, 2006), p. 15.
[2] John Tabak, *Algebra: Sets, Symbols & the Language of Thought* (New York: Facts on File, Inc., 2004), p. 88.

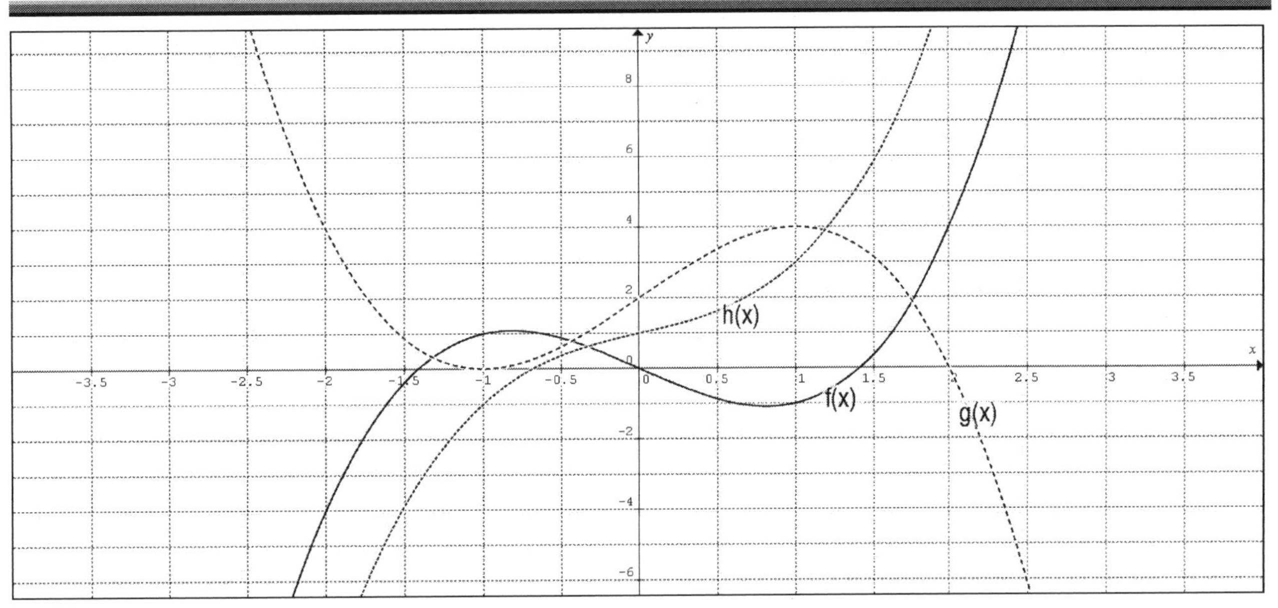

Figure 4. Types of cubic functions: (1) $f(x) = x^3 - 2x$ (Three zeroes, one local maximum and one local minimum.), (2) $g(x) = -x^3 + 3x + 2$ (Two zeroes, one local minimum and one local maximum.), (3) $h(x) = x^3 + x + 1$ (One zero, no local minimum or local minimum.)

Algebra is primarily the study of how to work with polynomials; i.e., finding their solution(s). Calculus is the study, in part, of the behavior of polynomials. Engineers put polynomials to work in the construction of all sorts of three-dimensional objects: buildings, dams, roads, etc. Physicists use polynomials to understand the dynamics of motion.

A POLYNOMIAL REVEALED

Suppose a manufacturing company wants to maximize the volume of a rectangular solid and, due to market study or factory limitations, the company needs to create an open-lid box from a rectangular box of width 27 inches and length 36 inches (Figure 5). How must this box be to generate maximum volume?

To create the box, we must cut out the four corners as shown. We let the dimensions of this cut-out be x inches. To derive the equation for the volume, we use the formula V = lwh. Each of these three dimension are:

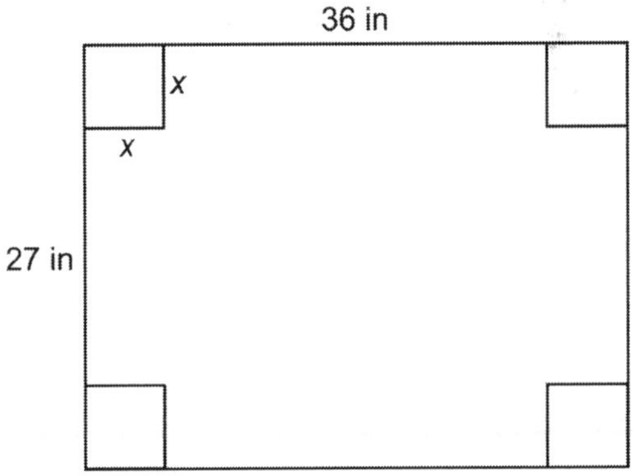

Height: x
Width: $27 - 2x$
Length: $36 - 2x$

36 in
x
x
27 in

Figure 5.

The volume is:

$$V = x(27 - 2x)(36 - 2x) \Leftrightarrow V = (27x - 2x^2)(36 - 2x) \Leftrightarrow V = 4x^3 - 126x^2 + 972x$$

We have a cubic polynomial, a polynomial of degree three, consisting of three terms. (Note: There is no constant term.) In functional notation, we write:

$$y = f(x) = 4x^3 - 126x^2 + 972x$$

How to we find the maximum image of this function? Or, how do we find the x-coordinate that gives the maximum y-coordinate given the constraints of the dimensions of the rectangular box? Let's do invoking the Differential Calculus. First, we calculate the derivative of each term. The derivative of:

$y_1 = 4x^3 \Rightarrow y_1' = 12x^2$
$y_2 = -126x^2 \Rightarrow y_2' = -252x$
$y_3 = 972x \Rightarrow y_3' = 972$

By calculating the derivative of each term, we have found the derivative of $f(x)$, i.e., $f'(x)$ or $\frac{dy}{dx}$, the sum of the derivatives. We let $g(x)$ be that derivative, i.e., $g(x) = f'(x)$. We write:

$g(x) = 12x^2 - 252x + 972$

We now have a quadratic. We set $g(x) = 0$ and find its zeroes.
First, we calculate $D = b^2 - 4ac$:

$D = (-252)^2 - 4(12)(972) = 16{,}484$

Is 16,484 a perfect square? Let's try the prime factorization method:

16,484	1053
2 8424	3 351
2 4212	3 117
2 2106	3 39
2 1053	3 13

We conclude:

$16{,}484 = 2^4 \cdot 3^4 \cdot 13$

Since 13 is a prime number factor that occurs only once, 16,484 is not a square. To find the zeroes, we invoke the Quadratic Formula:

$$x = \frac{252+\sqrt{2^4\cdot 3^4\cdot 13}}{24} \text{ or } x = \frac{252-\sqrt{2^4\cdot 3^4\cdot 13}}{24} \Leftrightarrow x = \frac{252+36\sqrt{13}}{24} \text{ or } x = \frac{252-36\sqrt{13}}{24} \Leftrightarrow$$

$$x = \frac{21+3\sqrt{13}}{2} \text{ or } x = \frac{21-3\sqrt{13}}{2} \Leftrightarrow x \approx 15.91 \text{ or } x \approx 5.09$$

What do these solutions say to us? Let's graph the cubic and find out (Figure 6). We expand the range to account for three changes of direction, starting from left to right.

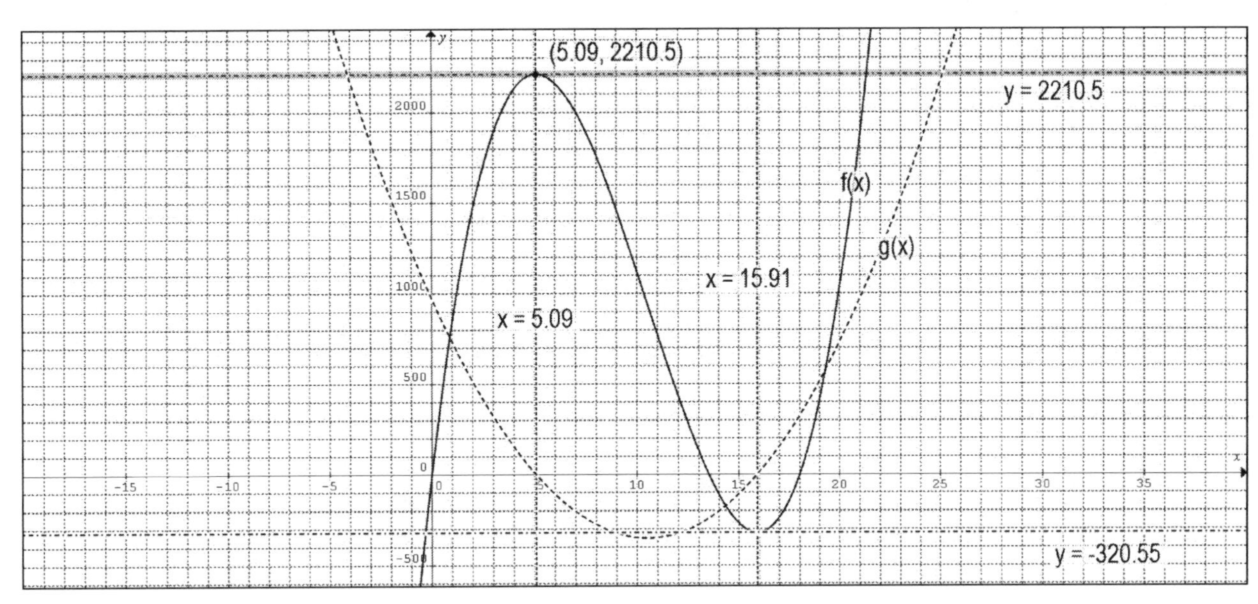

Figure 6.

We immediately see that when $x \approx 5.09$, we have the x-coordinate of the maximum image of the cubic between $x = 0$ and $x \approx 13$. When $x \approx 15.91$, we have the x-coordinate of the minimum image of the cubic between $x = 13.5$ and $x = 18$. The zeroes of the quadratic, the x-coordinates, when acting as the arguments of the cubic, generate the cubic's **extrema,**[3] i.e., its maximum and minimum. This relationship is beautiful perichoresis: the first derivative of a cubic is a quadratic and its zeroes are pointers to the cubic's local maximum or local minimum. The zeroes of the first derivative and embedded in the extrema of the cubic and the extrema of the cubic are embedded in the zeroes of the first derivative.

Note the two horizontal lines, $y = 2210.5$ and $y = -320.55$. They intersect the cubic at its local extrema. They are, therefore, tangent lines. The slope of both lines is zero. This observation confirms that the zeroes of the first derivative tell us where the slope of line tangent to the cubic is zero and this situation happens only at the minimum or maximum image.

When $x < 0$, the images of the cubic continue as ever increasing negative values, i.e., they are racing toward negative infinity ($-\infty$). When $x \geq 18$, the images of the cubic continue as ever increasing positive values, i.e., they are racing toward positive infinity ($+\infty$). The maximum image of the cubic, given the constraints of the dimensions of the rectangular box and the graph itself, must be the y-coordinate when $x \approx 5.09$. That image is approximately 2210.55 cubic inches. Therefore, if we cut the corners 5.09 inches from the ends, the volume of the result box will be the maximum volume.

EXERCISES

Define the following terms:

1. Rational function
2. Extrema
3. Factor Theorem (See Homework exercise below.)

---

[3] In Latin, the meaning of *extrema* (plural) is "utmost." An extremum (singular) is a point where a function is either at its maximum or minimum, either for an interval of a function, a local extremum, or for the entire function, a global extremum.

True or False:

4. Every polynomial function is a rational function.
5. A polynomial is either a monomial or the sum of monomials.
6. $y = {}^1/_x$ is a polynomial.
7. The formula for the sum of a finite geometric series is a rational function in r.

Answer the following questions:

8. Show that $\sqrt{2^4 \cdot 3^4 \cdot 13} = 36\sqrt{13}$.
9. Show that $\dfrac{252+36\sqrt{13}}{24} = \dfrac{21+3\sqrt{13}}{2}$.
10. Show that $(27x - 2x^2)(36 - 2x) = 4x^3 - 126x^2 + 972x$.
11. Find the zeroes of $f(x) = 4x^3 - 126x^2 + 972x$ by factoring the x and then use of the Quadratic Formula for the remaining quadratic.
12. An open box with a square base is to be made from 400 in^2 of lumber.
    (a) What dimensions should be chosen so that the box has maximum volume? Give your answer exactly (simple radical form) and as an approximation rounded to the nearest thousandths. You may use a calculator to do the rounding only. Make sure you check your solutions.
    (b) State the volume exactly and as an approximation rounded to the nearest tenth. You may use a calculator to do the rounding only.
    (c) Graph the volume function to confirm you answers in (a) and (b).
13. A box with a square base and a cover is to be made from 400 in^2 of lumber.
    (a) What dimensions should be chosen so that the box has maximum volume? Give your answer exactly (simple radical form) and as an approximation rounded to the nearest thousandths. You may use a calculator to do the rounding only. Make sure you check your solutions.
    (b) State the volume exactly and as an approximation rounded to the nearest tenth. You may use a calculator to do the rounding only.
    (c) Graph the volume function to confirm you answers in (a) and (b).
14. A manufacturer wishes to construct cylindrical tin cans such that each can is made of a fixed amount of tin and has maximum volume.
    (a) If the fixed amount of tin is 100 in^2, what should the radius r of the base and the height h of the cylinder be? Give your answer exactly (in terms of π) and as an approximation rounded to the nearest thousandths. You may use a calculator to do the rounding only. Make sure you check your solutions.
    (b) State the volume exactly and as an approximation rounded to the nearest tenth. You may use a calculator to do the rounding only.
    (c) Graph the volume function to confirm you answers in (a) and (b).

Given the following rational functions, determine (a) the real number zeroes (Hint: Find zeroes, if any, for cubic functions graphically by finding the point of intersection between the cubic and $y = 0$), (b) the vertical asymptote, and (c) graph the function along, vertical asymptote, and its asymptotic end-behavior:

15. $f(x) = \dfrac{(x-1)(x+4)}{x-2}$
16. $f(x) = \dfrac{2x^3 + 6x - 10}{3 - x}$

17. $f(x) = \dfrac{2x^3 + x - 5}{x^2 - 2x - 3}$

18. $f(x) = \dfrac{(x-5)(x+4)}{3x+4}$

19. $f(x) = \dfrac{(x-3)(x+2)}{x^2 - 4}$

20. $f(x) = \dfrac{4x^5 - 9x}{x^3 - 16x}$

The method of dividing one polynomial by another is like long division in arithmetic (Step 5). Here is the algorithm:

We want to find the quotient of the rational function $f(x) = \dfrac{6x^3 + 4x^2 + 7x - 5}{3x - 1}$. We set up the problem like this:

$$3x - 1 \quad 6x^3 + 4x^2 + 7x - 5$$

Step 1. We ask how many times $3x$ goes into $6x^3$. Our answer is placed directly below the next term in the dividend.

$$\begin{array}{ll} 3x - 1 & 6x^3 + 4x^2 + 7x - 5 \\ & \quad\quad\; 2x^2 \end{array}$$

Step 2 and 3. We multiply our temporary quotient by the divisor, term by term, subtracting the matching term in the dividend from our product:

$2x^2(3x) = 6x^3$ and $6x^3 - 6x^3 = 0$

$2x^2(-1) = -2x^2$ and $4x^2 - (-2x^2) = 4x^2 + 2x^2 = 6x^2$

We write the remainder above the appropriate term in the dividend:

$$\begin{array}{ll} & \quad\quad\; {\scriptstyle 6x^2} \\ 3x - 1 & 6x^3 + 4x^2 + 7x - 5 \\ & \quad\quad\; 2x^2 \end{array}$$

We continue this algorithm until we get either a remainder or a remainder of zero. We can also check our answer by calculating the product of the quotient and the divisor.

The results of the second iteration of the algorithm is:

$$\begin{array}{ll} & \quad\quad\; {\scriptstyle 6x^2} \quad\; {\scriptstyle 9x} \\ 3x - 1 & 6x^3 + 4x^2 + 7x - 5 \\ & \quad\quad\; 2x^2 + 2x \end{array}$$

The results of the third iteration of the algorithm is:

$$\begin{array}{ll} & \quad\quad\; {\scriptstyle 6x^2} \quad\; {\scriptstyle 9x} \quad {\scriptstyle -2} \\ 3x - 1 & 6x^3 + 4x^2 + 7x - 5 \\ & \quad\quad\; 2x^2 + 2x + 3 \end{array}$$

Quotient: $2x^2 + 2x + 3$ R-2 or, better yet, $2x^2 + 2x + 3 + \frac{-2}{3x-1}$

Check:

$$\begin{array}{r} 2x^2+2x+3 \\ 3x-1 \end{array}$$ (Note: Use the three-by-three multiplication paradigm.)

Multiplying, we get:

$$6x^3+4x^2+7x-3$$

Adding -2 to this expression, we get:

$$6x^3+4x^2+7x-5 \checkmark$$

Divide and check your work:

21. $\frac{2x^3-9x^2+11x-3}{2x-3}$

22. $\frac{x^4-1}{x+1}$
(Hint: Write $x^4 - 1$ as $x^4 + 0x^3 + 0x^2 + 0x - 1$)

23. $\frac{8x^3+1}{2x-1}$

24. $\frac{x^4+x^2+1}{x^2-x+1}$

Polynomial division is often use to help us find all the zeroes of a polynomial if we know one zero. For example, if we know that one zero is r, we know that $(x - r)$ will be a factor of that polynomial. This observation is known as the **Factor Theorem.**[4] Why? Consider solving the quadratic $x^2 - 5x + 6 = 0$. It is factorable:

$$x^2 - 5x + 6 = 0 \Leftrightarrow (x - 3)(x - 2) = 0 \Leftrightarrow x = 3 \text{ or } x = 2$$

Since 3 is a zero, then $(x - 3)$ is a factor of $x^2 - 5x + 6$. In a similar way, since 2 is a zero, then $x - 2$ is a factor of $x^2 - 5x + 6$. If we divide $x^2 - 5x + 6$ by $x - 3$, we get the other factor, i.e., $x - 2$:

$$\begin{array}{ll} & \scriptstyle{-2x} \quad \scriptstyle{0} \\ x-3 & x^2-5x+6 \\ & x-2 \end{array}$$

And, if we divide $x^2 - 5x + 6$ by $x - 2$, we get the other factor, i.e., $x - 3$:

$$\begin{array}{ll} & \scriptstyle{-3x} \quad \scriptstyle{0} \\ x-2 & x^2-5x+6 \\ & x-3 \end{array}$$

[4] The Factor Theorem states that a polynomial function that has a factor of $(x - r)$ means that r is a zero of that function. For quadratics where $a = 1$, the Factor Theorem states that if the graph of $x^2 + cx + d$ intersects the x-axis at a and b, then $x^2 + cx + d = (x - a)(x - b)$. In general, if any quadratic intersects the x-axis at a and b, then it factors into $k(x - a)(x - b)$, for some k.

In general, if we divide the polynomial by $(x - r)$, we will reduce its degree by one and if have a cubic to start with, after we divide we will have a quadratic that we can then solve. Using these ideas, (a) find the exact zeroes of the following polynomial functions and (b) graph each to confirm your results: (Note: include complex number solutions as zeroes if the case warrants it.)

25. $y = f(x) = x^3 - 2x^2 - 5x + 6$ if one zero is 1.
26. $y = f(x) = 4x^3 - 7x^2 - 5x + 6$ if one zero is 2.
27. $y = f(x) = 2x^3 - 3x^2 - 27$ if one zero is 3.
28. $y = f(x) = x^3 + 6x^2 + 3x - 20$ if one zero is -4.
29. $y = f(x) = x^4 - 2x^3 - 7x^2 + 8x + 12$ if two of its zeroes are -1 and 3.

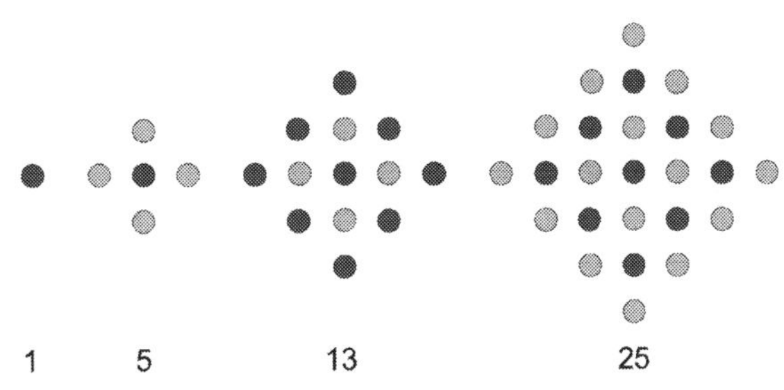

Figure 7. The first four centered square numbers.

For the following questions, use the centered square numbers depicted in Figure 7 as an aid:

30. (a) Generate a two-column table representing the first six centered square numbers.
    (b) Extend this table by using delta analysis to determine the formula for finding the nth centered square number. (Hint: Review the relevant homework problems in Lesson 11.6, 11.11, and 13.13.)
31. Graph your formula on the x-y coordinate plane.

Answer the following questions:

32. Derive a cubic polynomial function that has zeroes of 4, -5, or 2.
33. Investigate several polynomials of even and odd degree with leading coefficients both positive and negative. (a) What is the end-behavior of the left side of the graph of the polynomial in each case? Graph goes up or graph goes down? (b) the right side?
34. Derive the cubic polynomial function that has zeroes of 4, -1, and -2 and $f(1) = 3$; i.e., (1, 3) is a point on the graph. [Hint: Let the dilation factor be c. We write: $y = f(x) = c(a_0x^3 + a_1x^2 + a_2x + a_3)$]
35. Derive the quadratic polynomial function that has a zero of 3 and $f(2) = -3$.
36. Explain the similarity between a polynomial of degree n, i.e.,
    $f(x) = a_0x^n + a_1x^{n-1} + a_2x^{n-2} + \ldots + a_{n-1}x + a_n$, and the n-digit positive integer
    $a_1a_2a_3\ldots a_n = a_110^{n-1} + a_210^{n-2} + a_310^{n-3} + \ldots + a_{n-3}10^3 + a_{n-2}10^2 + a_{n-1}10 + a_n$.

> Mathematical sophistication is independent of technical background. Background refers to how much mathematics you know. Sophistication refers to how deeply you know it.
>
> Jerry P. King, *Mathematics in 10 Lessons: The Grand Tour* (2009), p. 82.

14.4 Three-Dimensional Beauty

Terms & Concepts Introduced
1. Euler Characteristic
2. Hexahedron
3. Icosahedron
4. Octahedron
5. Regular Polyhedra
6. Tetrahedron
7. Topology

The Infinite Set of Regular Polygons

There are technically an infinite number of regular convex[1] plane figures where all angles equal and all sides equal, the regular polygons. Figure 1 shows the first six: equilateral (equal sides) triangle, square, regular pentagon (five angles), regular hexagon (six angles), regular heptagon (seven angles), and regular octagon (eight angles).

All corresponding parts of each of these regular convex figures are equal (i.e., all edges [or sides] and all interior angles in each figure are equal). Note also that only two edges meet at each vertex of each figure.

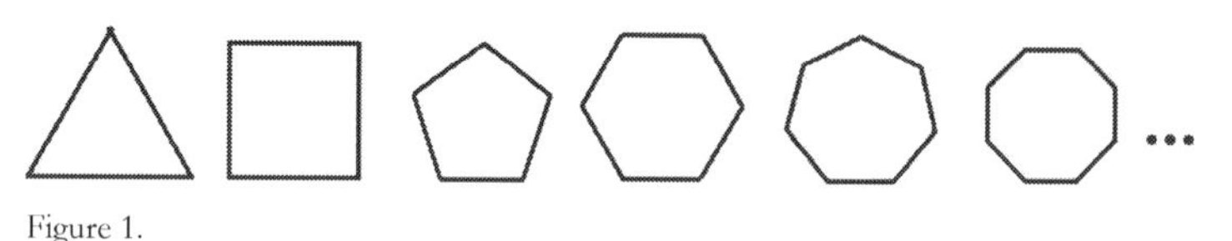

Figure 1.

The Five Regular Polyhedra

Let's now move to the three-dimensional world. Since, in two dimensions, there are an infinite number of regular polygons, can we, using reasoning by analogy, conclude that, in three dimensions, there are an infinite number of **regular polyhedra,**[2] a solid whose faces are all regular polygons? This conclusion about three dimensions seems to be a natural inference from the two-dimensional situation. The way mathematicians think about three-dimensional figures like regular polyhedra is to employ the methods of one of its most interesting branches, **topology.**[3] Using this branch of mathematical study, we can analyze this problem by investigating two unique properties of regular polyhedra: (1) the same number of edges bound each face and (2) the same number of edges meet at every vertex.

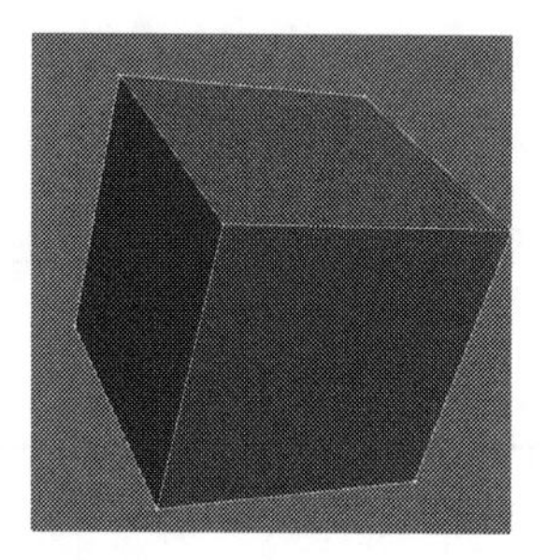

Figure 2:.Cube (Hexahedron).
Source: Great Stella Software.

---

[1] Convex is derived from the Latin *convexus* meaning "rounded." To review, in a convex polygon, the line segment connecting any two points inside the polygon will always stay completely inside the polygon.

[2] *Polyhedra* (plural) is Greek and generally translated as "many faces." *Hedra,* in Greek, literally means "seat or base." Since the faces of polyhedra are flat, you can seat them on a flat surface and they will remain secure and unmovable; i.e., they will not roll like spheres. In Euclid's *Elements,* he appears to be working toward these shapes in his last book, Book XIII, as the goal of his study.

[3] Topology is the study of those properties of geometric forms that remain invariant, i.e., fixed, under certain transformations, as in bending or stretching.

To illustrate, picture the cube or **hexahedron**,[4] a regular polyhedron (Figure 2). The cube has eight vertices, six square faces, and 12 edges where four edges bound each face and three edges meet at each vertex. The German mathematician Johannes Kepler (1571-1630) associated this solid with the Earth because land is a very stable object; in fact, the most stable. In this, Kepler followed the ideas of the Greek philosopher Plato (427-347 BC) who, in the 4th century BC and following his elder Empedocles (495-430 BC), identified four basic elements (*stoicheia*) of the cosmos: Earth, Air, Water, and Fire.[5]

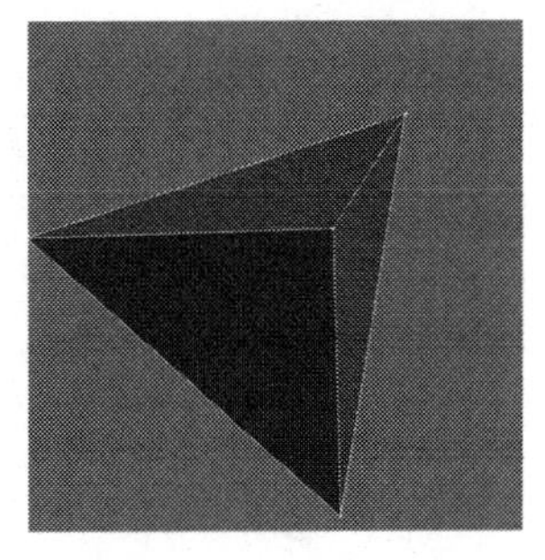

Figure 3. Tetrahedron. Source: Great Stella Software.

Next, consider the **tetrahedron**.[6] A tetrahedron has four vertices, four equilateral triangle faces, and six edges where three edges bound each face and three edges meet at each vertex (Figure 3). Kepler, again following Plato, associated it with the element Fire, the tiniest, lightest, most mobile, and the sharpest of the elements.

Note that the two properties, (1) equal edges bounding each face and (2) equal edges meeting at each vertex, have nothing to do with size or shape. Here is where topological tools show us that only five regular polyhedra can satisfy these two requirements.

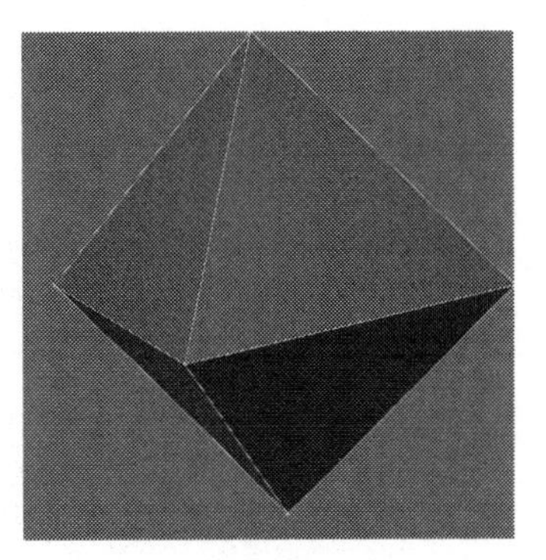

Figure 4. Octahedron. Source: Great Stella Software.

---

[4] A *hexahedron*, Greek for "six faces," is a solid figure where each face is a square and all faces are congruent. The *-hedron* suffix means hexahedron is a singular noun.

[5] This ancient Greek view still marks our language. We speak of a storm as the "raging of the elements." We wear coats to "protect ourselves from the elements." We also speak of people with a "fiery nature" or demons as "aerial spirits."

[6] A *tetrahedron*, Greek for "four faces," is a solid figure where each face is an equilateral triangle and all faces are congruent.

We have noted two of these figures, the hexahedron and the tetrahedron. The other three are the **octahedron,**[7] dodecahedron (Lesson 9.6),[8] and **icosahedron.**[9]

It should be easy to see that an octahedron has, of course, eight faces, 12 edges, and six vertices (Figure 4). Kepler noted that could easily spin this shape, a good reason for it to represent the element Air.

How many edges, faces, and vertices are there in a dodecahedron and an icosahedron? Instead of just counting, it is easy to get lost with these figures, we might want to apply a more systematic approach.

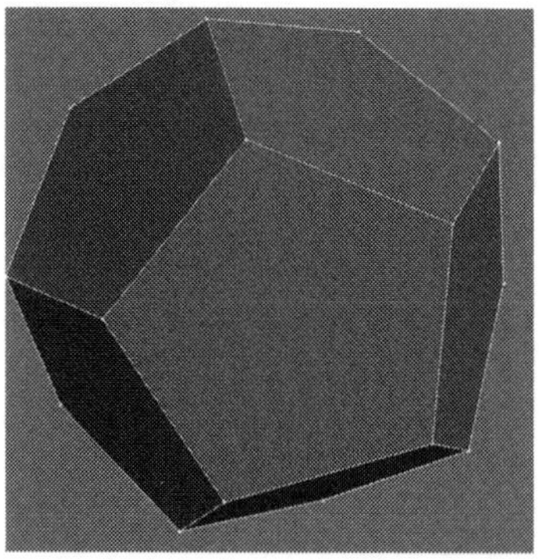

For example, we know that the dodecahedron has 12 faces (Figure 5). Kepler associated it with the universe because of the twelve signs, i.e., constellations, of the Zodiac. How many edges on each face? 5. We could calculate the product of 12 and 5 to get the number of edges, but there would be a problem with this approach. How many faces does each edge share? 2. Therefore, we must divide the product of 12 and 5 by 2:

$$\frac{\overset{6}{\cancel{12}}\cdot 5}{\underset{1}{\cancel{2}}} = 30$$

Figure 5. Dodecahedron. Source: Great Stella Software.

Similarly, the face of each dodecahedron has five vertices. We could again calculate the product of 12 and 5 to get the number of vertices, but we would encounter the same problem as before; i.e., each vertex shares a face. How many faces does each vertex share? 3. To calculate the number of vertices in a dodecahedron, we compute:

$$\frac{\overset{4}{\cancel{12}}\cdot 5}{\underset{1}{\cancel{3}}} = 20$$

For the icosahedron, there are 20 faces with each face having three edges and each edge shares two faces (Figure 6). Kepler, like Plato, associated this solid with the element Water. To calculate the number of edges in an icosahedron, we compute:

$$\frac{\overset{10}{\cancel{20}}\cdot 3}{\underset{1}{\cancel{2}}} = 30$$

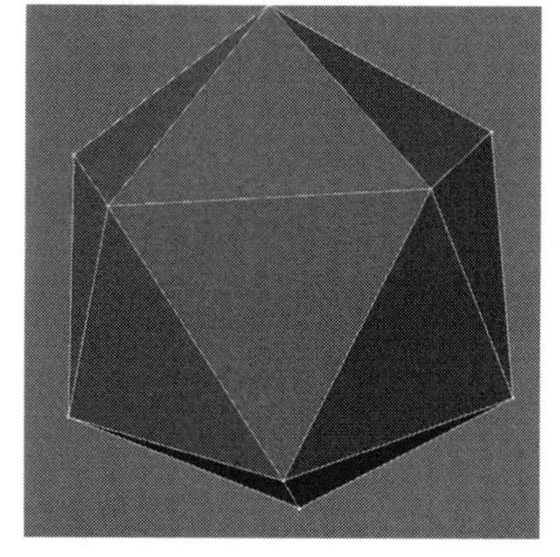

Figure 6. Icosahedron. Source: Great Stella Software.

[7] An *octahedron*, Greek for "eight faces," is a solid figure where each face is an equilateral triangle and all faces are congruent. Kepler, like Plato, associated this shape with the element Air, intermediate in size, weight, and fluidity.

[8] A *dodecahedron*, Greek for "twelve faces," is a solid figure where each face is a regular pentagon and all faces are congruent; *dodeca* means "2 plus 10" or "twelve." Plato associated this shape with the universe. This shape is what Plato's creator, the demiurge, used to arrange the heavens. Demiurge is a Latinized form of the Greek δημιουργός, meaning "artist or craftsman."

[9] An *icosahedron*, Greek for "twenty faces," is a solid figure where each face is an equilateral triangle and all faces are congruent. Kepler, following Plato, associated this nearly spherical shape with the element Water, the most mobile and fluid of the elements.

Each of the 20 faces of an icosahedron has three vertices and each vertex shares five faces. To calculate the number of vertices in an icosahedron, we compute:

$$\frac{\overset{4}{\cancel{20}} \cdot 3}{\underset{1}{\cancel{5}}} = 12$$

Figure 7. The Five Platonic Solids. Source: Great Stella Software.

We tabulate our observations in Table 1. I would highly recommend that you build these solids. There are many links on the Internet with appropriate nets.

Table 1				
Regular Polyhedra	**Shape of Face**	***F* (Number of Faces)**	***V* (Number of Vertices)**	***E* (Number of Edges)**
Tetrahedron	Equilateral Triangle	4	4	6
Hexahedron	Square	6	8	12
Octahedron	Equilateral Triangle	8	6	12
Dodecahedron	Regular Pentagon	12	20	30
Icosahedron	Equilateral Triangle	20	12	30

There is a discernible pattern relating the number of faces, vertices, and edges in each regular polyhedron. Can you figure it out? The Swiss mathematician Leonhard Euler (1707-1783), the founder of topology, did. Here is the formula, named the **Euler Characteristic**:

$F + V = E + 2 \Leftrightarrow V - E + F = 2$

EXERCISES

Define the following terms:

1. Regular Polyhedra
2. Topology
3. Hexahedron
4. Tetrahedron
5. Octahedron
6. Icosahedron
7. Euler Characteristic

> So their combinations with themselves and with each other give rise to endless complexities, which anyone who is to give a likely account of reality must survey.
>
> Plato (427-347 BC), *The Timaeus.*

In general, given a regular polygon with n sides, can we develop a formula for A, the measure of each of the n equal angles? Copy Figure 8, and let's use it to see how we can find it:

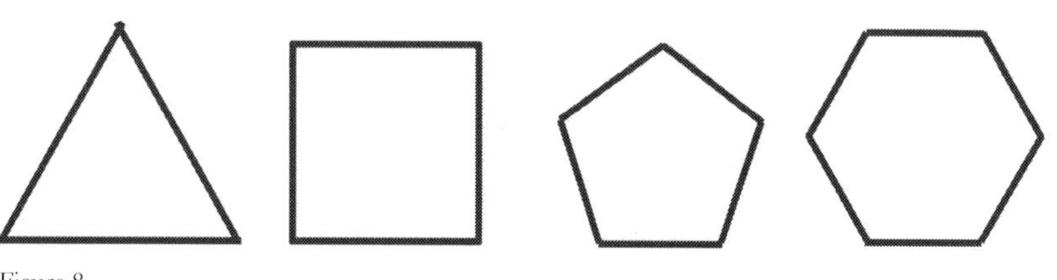

Figure 8.

8. We know that the sum of the angles of a triangle ($n = 3$) is 180°. For an equilateral/equiangular triangle, what is A?
9. For a square ($n = 4$), by definition, all the interior angles of a square are right angles. In the copied square, connect one vertex to its opposite vertex. How many non-overlapping triangles result?
10. Are all of the angles of these triangles a part of the interior angles of the square?
11. What is the sum of the angles in the two triangles?
12. Determine A for a square.
13. For $n = 5$ (a regular pentagon), connect the vertices to make three triangles that do not overlap. What is the sum of the measures of these triangles?
14. Are all the angles of these triangles a part of the interior angles of the square?
15. Determine A for a regular pentagon.
16. For $n = 6$ (a regular hexagon), connect the vertices to make four triangles that do not overlap. What is the sum of the measures of these triangles?
17. Are all the angles of these triangles a part of the interior angles of the square?
18. Determine A for a regular hexagon.
19. From the pattern revealed for regular 3-gons to 6-gons, develop a formula for A. (Hint: Build a three-column table for n, your calculation involving 180° to get A, and A, the result of that calculation.)
20. Determine A for a regular heptagon. Round to the nearest hundredth.
21. Determine A for a regular octagon.

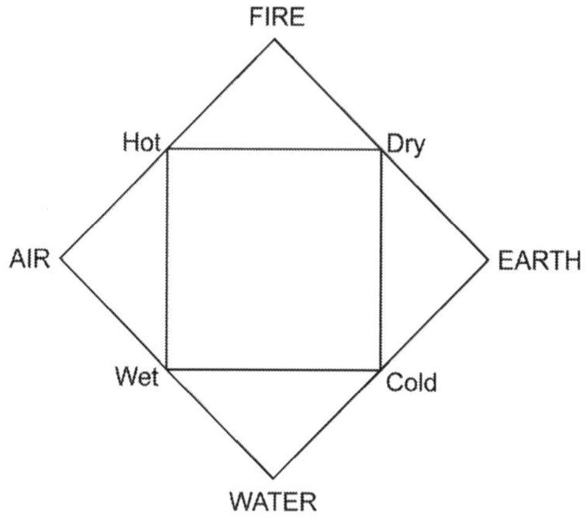

Figure 9. The four elements of the Greek-understood universe, representing opposition and alliance, along with the four qualities of the Greek philosopher Empedocles (495-430 BC), representing the same relationships.

22. Determine A for a regular nonagon.
23. Determine A for a regular dodecagon.
24. What kind of function is the formula you developed in Question 19?
25. Graph the function you derived in Question 19.
26. If they exist, state the end-behavior, the vertical asymptote, and the horizontal asymptote of this function.
27. What does the end-behavior of this function reveal to you?

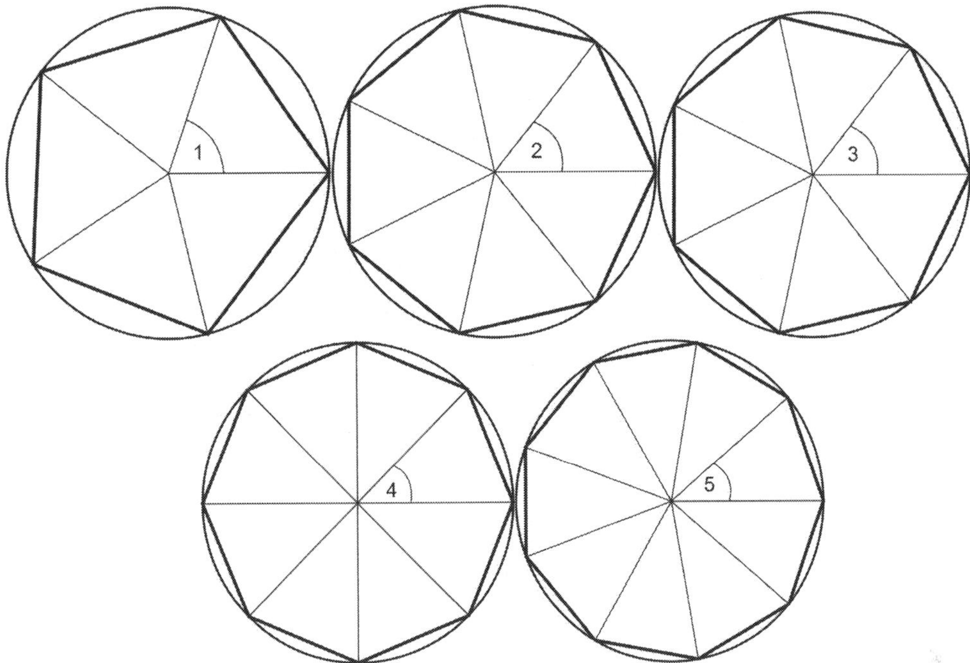

Figure 10.

28. Calculate the same values of A using the measure of angles 1, 2, 3, 4, and 5 in Figure 10. All polygons are regular and do not use a protractor. (Hint: Recall from the homework question in Lesson 5.7 that, for each figure, the isosceles triangles are congruent to each other.)

The Euler Characteristic and a Soccer Ball.

Let's use the Euler Characteristic to determine the necessary number of pentagons and hexagons in the construction of a soccer ball (Figure 11).[10] (Note: Each pentagon is surrounded by five hexagons.) Let P and H represent the number of pentagonal and hexagonal faces respectively.

29. Let F equal the total number of faces. Write an equation involving F, P, and H.

Figure 11.

Next, we develop a formula for the total number of edges and vertices.

30. Since the edges are shared by two faces, write an equation for E in terms of P and H.
31. Since three faces meet at a vertex, write an equation for V in terms of P and H.
32. We know that $V - E + F = 2$ (Euler Characteristic). From your work so far, find P.

[10] Technically, a soccer ball is a semi-regular polyhedron known as a truncated icosahedron. This figure is part of a group of thirteen solids named after Archimedes, i.e., the Archimedean solids.

We assume there are no flat regions where three hexagons meet at a vertex. Therefore, each vertex is connected to exactly two hexagons and one pentagon.

33. Each vertex is associated with a single pentagon. What is the total number of vertices V?
34. Use the vertex formula you derived in Question 31 to solve for H.
35. How many edges are there in the soccer ball? (Hint: Use the edge formula you derived in Question 30.)

The Euler Characteristic and Doodles (Figure 12).

36. Draw at random any shape without lifting your pencil from your paper (make sure that your lines cross several times).
37. Mark a dot at each point where the line you drew intersects and at the starting and ending point.
38. Count the dots you have marked. (In Figure 12, there are eight dots.)
39. Count the curved segments between the dots. (Hint: Follow the path of your original drawing and count between the dots. In Figure 12, there are 13 curved segments.)
40. Count all the regions of the drawing making sure that you count the outer region, too. (In Figure 12, there are seven regions.)
41. Let V = number of dots, E = number of curved segments, and F = number of regions. Calculate $V - E + F$.
42. Compare your answer with the Euler Characteristic, i.e., $V - E + F = 2$. What do you notice?

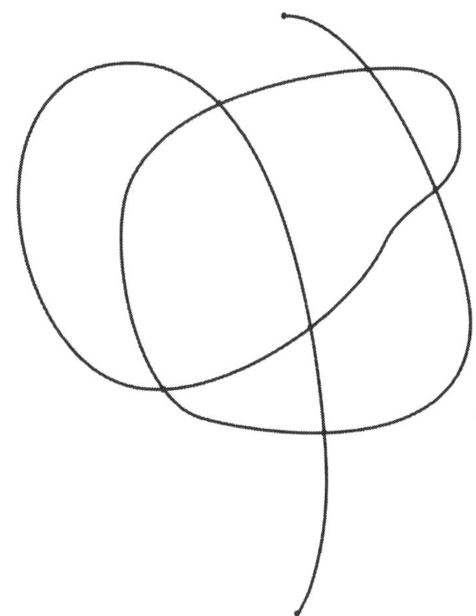

Figure 12.

No matter what figure you draw, this relationship, $V - E + F = 2$, will always be true. Why? Follow along and answer these questions based on Figure 12:

43. At the point you begin your drawing, what is V?
44. What is F?
45. Calculate $V - E + F$.
46. As you draw your first "edge," consider what happens when you encounter the next vertex. Follow along in your drawing. What is E?
47. What is V?
48. What is F?
49. Calculate $V - E + F$.
50. When you add an edge and a vertex, what is the net change?
51. If we connect two edges at one vertex, we create a new face. How many faces have you added?
52. How many edges have you added?
53. How many vertices have you added?
54. What is the net change $V - E + F$?
55. By this reasoning, we can conclude that the Euler Characteristic always holds. What type of mathematical reasoning did we use?

The Seven Bridges of Königsberg.

Topology as a branch of mathematics began with some observations made by the great Swiss mathematician Leonhard Euler (1707-1783). Born in Switzerland and the son of a pastor in the Reformed tradition, Euler possessed remarkable gifts of concentration and analytical ability, demonstrated by the fact that he obtained his Master's Degree in mathematics at age 16. He wrote math textbooks that are still the standard today. In addition to textbook writing, he wrote highly original research papers, at a rate of about eight hundred pages a year, during most of his lifetime.[11] The last seventeen years of his life were spent in blindness due to cataracts, but that did not stop his productivity. Sustained by his faith, he dictated his research and findings. His powers of concentration also enabled him to do this because he was able to perform complex mathematical calculations in his head, calculations that other competent mathematicians had trouble with on paper! It can be said of Euler, "As he thinks, he calculates." His works, *Opera Omnia*, are presently being collected by *The Euler Committee of the Swiss Academy of Sciences.* To date, a total of eighty volumes have been published so far. When finished, it will contain eighty-four volumes.

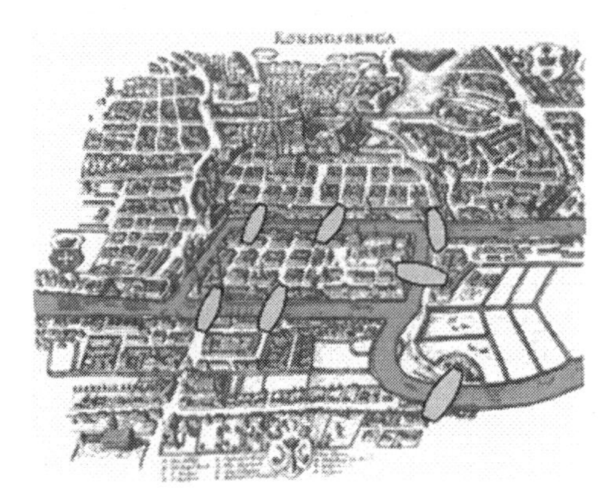

Figure 13. Source: Public Domain

Euler did not spend all of his life isolated in his study. He married and fathered thirteen children. He loved having them around too. They would play around his feet while he did his mathematics. He taught his own children, and grandchildren, making scientific games for them and instructing them in the Scriptures every evening.

Euler spent time as a court mathematician and math professor in Saint Petersburg at the invitation of Catherine I (1684-1727), empress of Russia. While in Russia, Euler encountered and solved a puzzle that made use of the rudiments of topology. Running through the center of the city of Königsberg, now known as Kaliningrad, was the river Pregel, which had two islands. These islands were joined to each other and the shores by means of seven bridges (Figure 13).

What was the puzzle that Euler solved? Could a person, starting at any point, walk across these bridges and get back to the starting point having (a) walked across all the bridges and (b) having walked across each bridge only once?

56. Take some time now to try it out. Did you get it to work? If you did, send me a postcard and I'll give you some prime real estate in the Florida everglades.

Let's see if we can simply this puzzle with some topological stretching. First, we want to remove the walks along the banks of the river. Since the problem would not be altered if the bridges leading to the same island or shore converged at the same points, then the problem can be turned into Figure 14. Note the four points of convergence.

Next, let's remove the river and bridges from the drawing and keep the four points and the line segments connecting them (Figure 15). This is the schematic that Euler used to solve the puzzle.

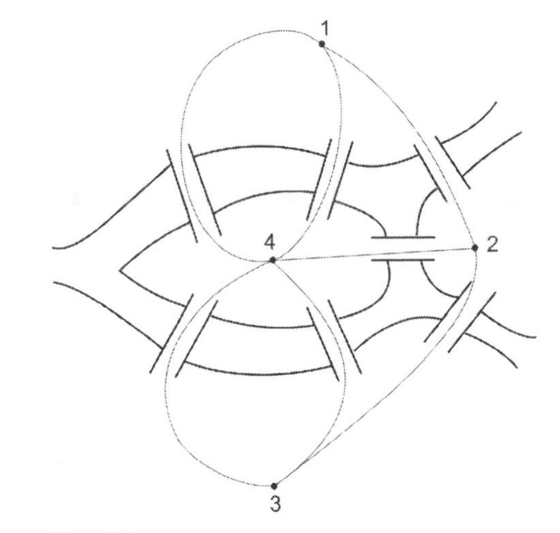

Figure 14.

[11]Morris Kline, *Mathematical Thought from Ancient to Modern Times* (New York: Oxford University Press, 1972), p. 402.

The puzzle can now be restated. First, you can start at any point on the diagram.

57. Can you draw this figure with one stroke of a pencil and without lifting the pencil off the paper in such a way that (a) no part of the figure is drawn twice and (b) you finish drawing the figure at the starting point?

Euler concluded that the puzzle was, and still is, unsolvable. By doing so, he developed a rule that can be used to solve problems like this.

> He showed that you could draw a path that traverses each line once if every point of the drawing is at the junction of an even number of lines.

Consider the points in the drawing:

1. The top point has three lines connecting to it.
2. The middle left point has five lines connecting to it.
3. The middle right point has three lines connecting to it.
4. The bottom point has three lines connecting to it.

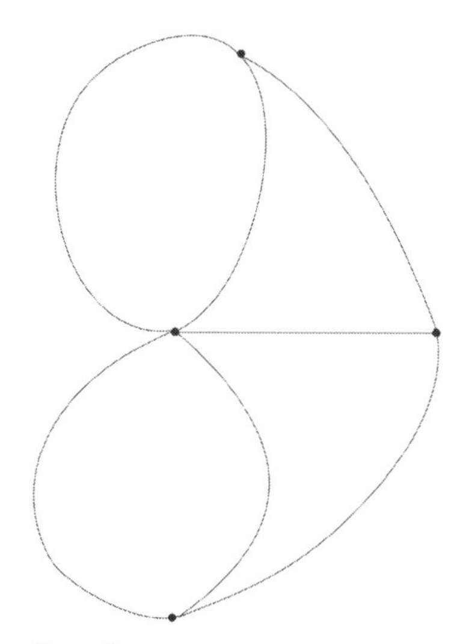
Figure 15.

His reasoning is so simple that it is profound. If one can draw a figure under the conditions given, then one must begin from the starting point and return to it, and every time the pencil comes to a vertex, i.e., another point, it must leave that vertex in order to go to the next one. Therefore, every line coming to a vertex has a companion line, i.e., the one leaving the vertex, and therefore at every vertex there must be an even number of lines meeting.

Note that from the original map of the seven bridges, by stretching we have created a schematic that retains the original geographical properties, but not the original shape, i.e., its angles and lengths. This type of reformulation is the essence of what topology is all about.

58. Let's try this rule out on the diagram of an envelope (Figure 16). There are five points. Can we draw the figure without lifting our pencil from the paper if we end at our the starting point?

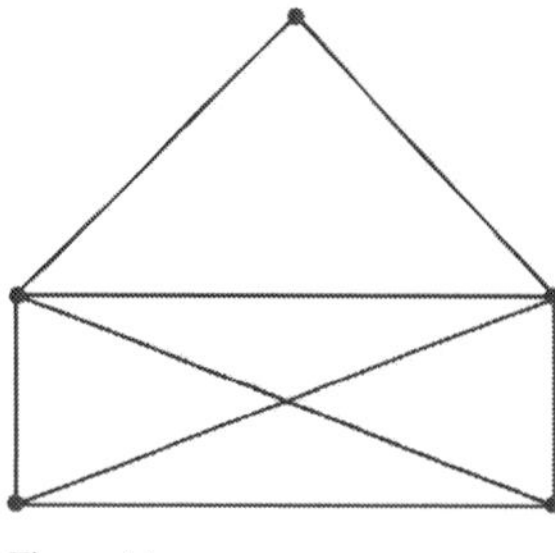
Figure 16.

59. Can we draw the figure without lifting our pencil from the paper if we end at a point different from the starting point?
60. In Figure 9, can we draw the figure without lifting our pencil from the paper if we end at our the starting point?

Note two important observations. First, topology began with the solution to a puzzle. Second, some three centuries later, we find that the principles of topology are essential to some branches of science. Physicists use topology in the description of electric circuits, organic chemists use these principles in molecular models, and engineers use it in the planning of street, highway, and metropolitan transit networks. Topology is useful in every case where one wants to analyze a structure or form irrespective of metric measure.

Field Project:

61. Construct the five regular polyhedra. Again, there are many links on the Internet to retrieve the appropriate nets.

Figure 17. Giant's Causeway, Co. Antrim, Northern Ireland. The area consists of about 40,000 intelocking basalt colums, formed by the contraction of lava as it cooled. The majority of these structures are hexagonal in shape. Source: Wikimedia Commons.

14.5 Geometry and Reality

Terms & Concepts Introduced
1. Apothem
2. Crystallography
3. Cubic system
4. Duality
5. Hexagonal system
6. Homogeneous
7. Inorganic
8. Isometric
9. Monoclinic system
10. Orthorhombic system
11. Rhombohedral system
12. Solid angle
13. Tessellation
14. Tetragonal system
15. Triclinic system

Topology tells us that we cannot reason as we did from an infinite number of regular polygons in two dimensions to an infinite number of regular polyhedra in three dimensions. We noted that in two dimensions, only two edges meet at each vertex of every polygon. In three dimensions, you can have any number of edges meet at each vertex and, furthermore, any number of faces. For example, you could have 50 edges meet at a vertex and six at another. One face could be a square while another face could be a 40-sided polygon. To restrict a solid figure to equal edges bounding each face and equal edges meeting at each vertex confines the number of such figures to five.

Why Only Five Regular Polyhedra?

There are several ways to prove that there are only five Platonic solids.[1] Remember, mathematical proof does not prove anything just by the exercise of rational, independent thought. Our thinking is grounded on the *logos* who is Christ and, therefore, can never be independent. That thinking is independent is often an unspoken assumption made by mathematicians. Mathematical proof is one way in which man uses the gift of logical reasoning, a gift from the Triune God, to justify both visible and invisible patterns of the Trinity's perichoretic creation. That there are five Platonic solids, only five, is one of those given patterns. Review Table 1.

Table 1

Regular Polyhedra	F (Number of Faces)	V (Number of Vertices)	E (Number of Edges)
Tetrahedron	4	4	6
Hexahedron	6	8	12
Octahedron	8	6	12
Dodecahedron	12	20	30
Icosahedron	20	12	30

Our proof will employ Euler's Characteristic:

Equation 1. $V - E + F = 2$

Let s = the number of sides in each of the faces in each figure. It will have F identical faces. Based upon our observations in Lesson 14.4, the value of F can be 4, 6, 8, 12, or 20. Since each edge belongs to two faces, it is therefore connected twice to sF (Table 2), or:

Equation 2. $sF = 2E$

[1] From our work in the previous lesson, we should now know why these solids are named Platonic Solids for it was the ancient Greek philosopher Plato (427-347 BC) who, intrigued by the three-dimensional symmetries revealed in these shapes, hypothesized in his dialogue, the *Timaeus*, that the four elements of Empedocles were made of four of these regular solids.

Table 2			
Shape	***sF***		***2E***
Hexahedron	$4 \cdot 6$	=	$2 \cdot 12$
Tetrahedron	$3 \cdot 4$	=	$2 \cdot 6$
Octahedron	$3 \cdot 8$	=	$2 \cdot 12$
Dodecahedron	$5 \cdot 12$	=	$2 \cdot 30$
Icosahedron	$3 \cdot 20$	=	$2 \cdot 30$

We then solve for F by dividing both sides of Equation 2 by s. We get:

Equation 3. $F = \frac{2E}{s}$

Let r = the number of edges that meet at each vertex V. Table 3 summarizes r for each of the Platonic solids.

Table 3		
Shape	***V***	***r***
Hexahedron	8	3
Tetrahedron	4	3
Octahedron	6	4
Dodecahedron	20	3
Icosahedron	12	5

Since each edge connects two vertices, it is therefore connected twice to rV (Table 4), or:

Equation 4. $rV = 2E$

Table 4			
Shape	***rV***		***2E***
Hexahedron	$3 \cdot 8$	=	$2 \cdot 12$
Tetrahedron	$3 \cdot 4$	=	$2 \cdot 6$
Octahedron	$4 \cdot 6$	=	$2 \cdot 12$
Dodecahedron	$3 \cdot 20$	=	$2 \cdot 30$
Icosahedron	$5 \cdot 12$	=	$2 \cdot 30$

We next solve for V by dividing both sides of Equation 4 by r. We get:

Equation 5. $V = \frac{2E}{r}$

Substituting Equation 3 and Equation 5 into Equation 1, we get:

Equation 6. $\frac{2E}{r} - E + \frac{2E}{s} = 2$

Using algebraic operations, we can translate Equation 6 into Equation 9 as follows:

Equation 7. $\frac{2}{r} - \frac{E}{E} + \frac{2}{s} = \frac{2}{E}$ (Divide both sides of Equation 6 by E.)

Equation 8. $\frac{1}{r}-\frac{1}{2}+\frac{1}{s}=\frac{1}{E}$ (Divide both sides of Equation 7 by 2.)

Equation 9. $\frac{1}{r}+\frac{1}{s}=\frac{1}{E}+\frac{1}{2}$ (Add $\frac{1}{2}$ to both sides of Equation 8.)

Since a polygon must have at least three sides and at least three edges that must meet at each vertex of a polyhedron, $s \geq 3$ and $r \geq 3$.

Study Equation 9. What is it revealing about r and s? If both $s > 3$ and $r > 3$, we arrive at a contradiction. For example, let $s = 4$ and $r = 4$. Then, we have: (Follow the logic carefully.)

$\frac{1}{4}+\frac{1}{4}=\frac{1}{E}+\frac{1}{2} \Leftrightarrow \frac{1}{2}=\frac{1}{E}+\frac{1}{2} \Leftrightarrow 0=\frac{1}{E}$ (This equation is impossible since $E > 0$.)

If $s = 5$ and $r = 4$, then:

$\frac{1}{4}+\frac{1}{5}=\frac{1}{E}+\frac{1}{2} \Leftrightarrow \frac{9}{20}=\frac{1}{E}+\frac{1}{2} \Leftrightarrow -\frac{1}{20}=\frac{1}{E} \Leftrightarrow E = -20$ (This equation is impossible since $E > 0$.)

By this reasoning, we only need to find the possible values of r when $s = 3$ and s when $r = 3$. Setting $s = 3$ in Equation 9, we get:

$\frac{1}{r}+\frac{1}{3}=\frac{1}{E}+\frac{1}{2} \Leftrightarrow \frac{1}{r}=\frac{1}{E}+\frac{1}{6} \Leftrightarrow \frac{1}{E}=\frac{1}{r}-\frac{1}{6}$

This equation, $\frac{1}{E}=\frac{1}{r}-\frac{1}{6}$, is true only if $r = 3$, 4, or 5. If $r = 6$, then $E = 0$, a contradiction. If $r > 6$, the $E < 0$, a contradiction. Note the corresponding values of E in Table 5.

Table 5		
r (edges)	**E**	**Regular Polyhedra**
3	6	Tetrahedron
4	12	Octahedron
5	30	Icosahedron

Note that the values of E in this table account for three regular polyhedra.

Now, let's set $r = 3$ in Equation 9. We get:

$\frac{1}{3}+\frac{1}{s}=\frac{1}{E}+\frac{1}{2} \Leftrightarrow \frac{1}{s}=\frac{1}{E}+\frac{1}{6} \Leftrightarrow \frac{1}{E}=\frac{1}{s}-\frac{1}{6}$

We get the same result in terms of s. We get this result because Equation 9 is symmetric with regards to the variables s and r, i.e., we can exchange these variables. Therefore, we generate a similar table, Table 6.

Table 6		
s (sides)	**E**	**Regular Polyhedra**
3	6	Tetrahedron
4	12	Cube
5	30	Dodecahedron

Note that the values of E account for two of the other regular polyhedra, while the tetrahedron is repeated.

These cases exhaust all the possibilities. Although there are infinitely many regular polygons in a two-dimensional plane, there are only five regular solids in three-dimensional space. QED

DUALITY

Note also, because of this symmetry, these solids are the duals of the ones obtained when $r = 3$ or $s = 3$. **Duality** is a geometrical principle that shows the symmetry between two figures when we interchange their parts. By the duality principle, for every regular polyhedron, there exists another regular polyhedron where we can substitute the number of faces with the number of vertices and vice versa. This polyhedron is known as the dual, or the reciprocal (Table 7). The tetrahedron is the dual of itself, the octahedron is the dual of the cube, the cube is the dual of the octahedron, the icosahedron is the dual of the dodecahedron, and the dodecahedron is the dual of the icosahedron.

Table 7

r or s	*E*	Regular Polyhedra (*r*)	Dual (*s*)
3	6	Tetrahedron	Tetrahedron
4	12	Octahedron	Cube
5	30	Icosahedron	Dodecahedron

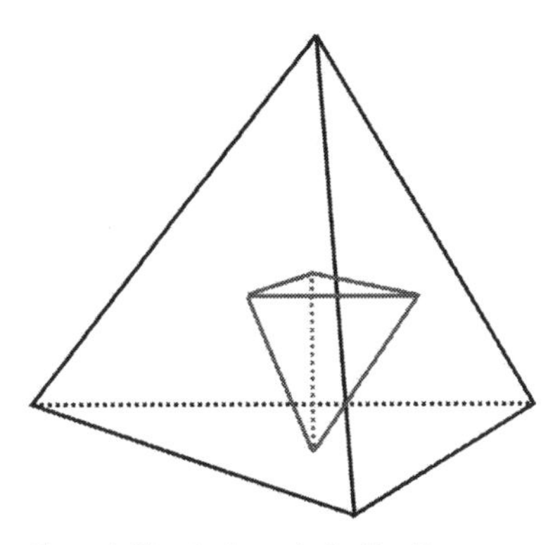

Figure 1. Tetrahedron, dual of itself.

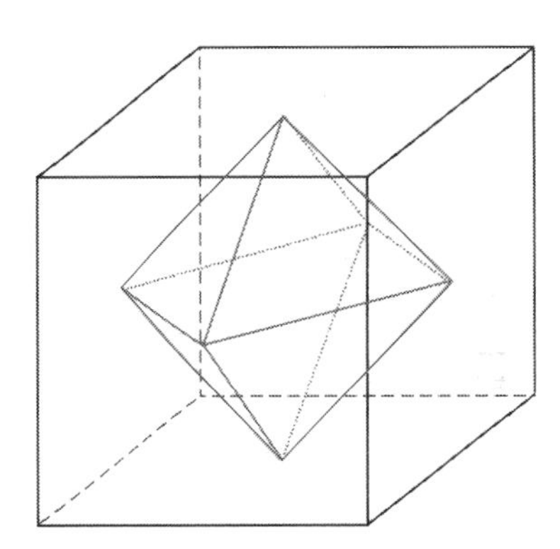

Figure 2. Octahedron, dual of the Cube.

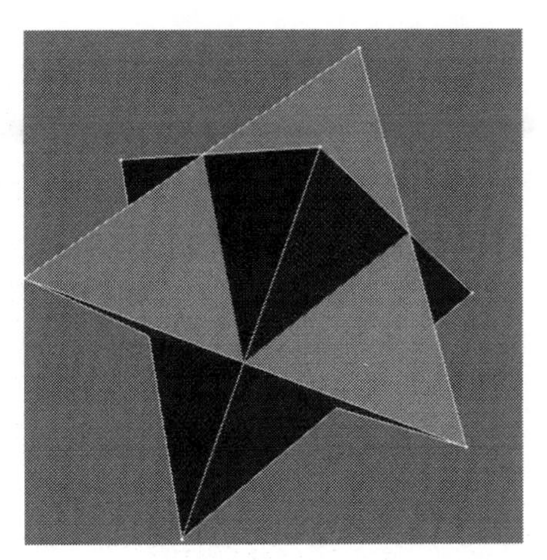

Figure 3. Interpenetrating tetrahedrons. Source: Great Stella Software.

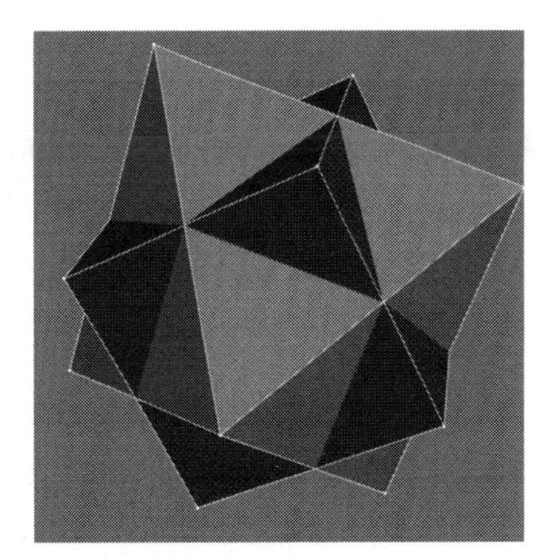

Figure 4. Hexahedron interpenetrated by the octahedron and octahedron interpenetrated by the hexahedron. Source: Great Stella Software.

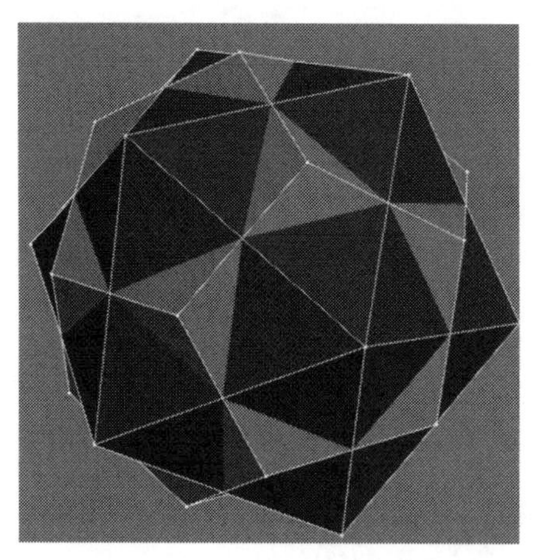

Figure 5. Icosahedron interpenetrated by the dodecahedron and dodecahedron interpenetrated by the icosahedron. Source: Great Stella Software.

CRYSTALLINE GEOMETRY

The basic building block of silicates is a **tetrahedron** of **four oxygen** atoms surrounding **one silicon** atom. These tetrahedra link together in six patterns that dictate the internal structure of each silicate mineral.

Figure 6. Silicon atom. Source: James D. Nickel.

What is even more amazing about the reality that there are only five regular solids in space is that many of the small details of the Triune God's creation reflect this restriction; i.e., it is a creational restraint. Most crystals grow in the beautiful shapes of regular polyhedra. For example, sodium chlorate crystals appear in the shape of cubes and tetrahedra, while chrome alum crystals are in the form of octahedra. Equally fascinating are the appearance of dodecahedra and icosahedra crystals in the skeletal structures of Radiolaria, i.e., microscopic sea animals.

Figure 7. Amethyst Crystal. Source: iStockPhoto.

Pyrite

Figure 8. Source: Harold R. Jacobs.

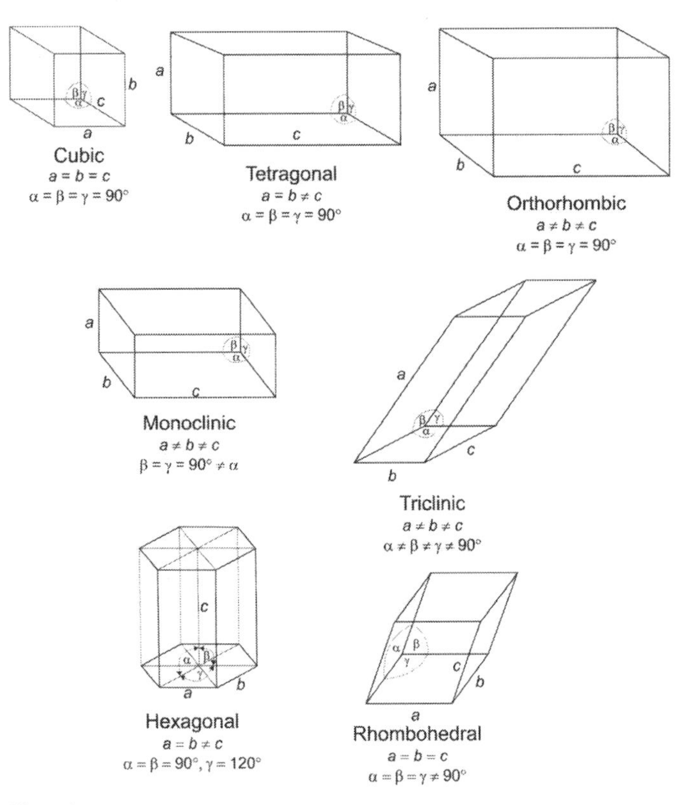

Figure 9.

Minerals, created by the Father, Son, and Spirit as a gift to us, are technically defined as **homogeneous**[2] **inorganic**[3] solid substances having a definite chemical composition and characteristic crystalline structure, color, and hardness. Mineralogists study crystals (**crystallography**), not only for their intrinsic beauty but because these structures provide clues to the arrangement of atoms within a mineral thus offering an important means of identification. Only a few minerals, such as opal and silica glass, lack a crystal structure.

Scientists categorize all crystals in one of seven groups, or systems (Figure 9). Six of the seven systems have six faces. Only one has eight faces. The seven are:

1. A **cubic system** is a cube. It is also named an **isometric** (equal measure) system.
2. A **hexagonal system** is a hexagonal right prism.
3. A **rhombohedral system** is a solid bounded by six rhombic faces where a rhombus is an oblique-angled equilateral parallelogram. Recall that a rhombus is any equilateral parallelogram except a square (Lesson 3.3).
4. A **tetragonal**[4] **system** is a rectangular solid where two of its six opposite faces are squares.
5. An **orthorhombic**[5] **system** is a general rectangular solid; i.e., each of its three pairs of two congruent rectangular faces is unique.

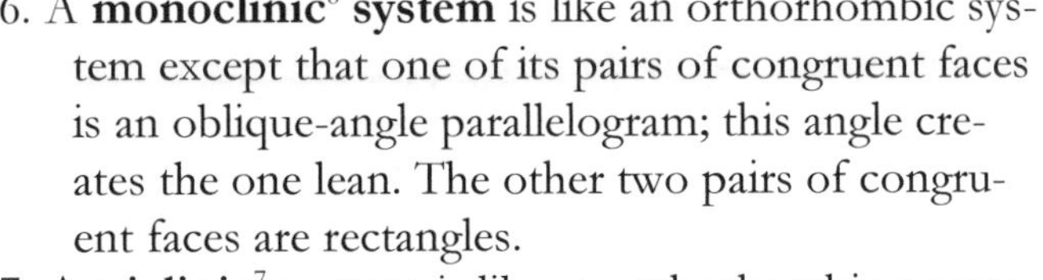

6. A **monoclinic**[6] **system** is like an orthorhombic system except that one of its pairs of congruent faces is an oblique-angle parallelogram; this angle creates the one lean. The other two pairs of congruent faces are rectangles.
7. A **triclinic**[7] **system** is like an orthorhombic system except that all three of its pairs of congruent faces are oblique-angle parallelograms.

Figure 10. Source: United States Postal Service.

[2] *Homogeneous*, from the Greek, means "same kind or same nature."

[3] *Inorganic* means "non-living" as opposed to organic which means "living."

[4] A *tetragon* is a polygon having four angles, or four sides.

[5] *Ortho* means "straight" or "right angled."

[6] *Monoclinic* means "one lean."

[7] *Triclinic* means "three leans."

Scientists further divide these seven systems into thirty-two symmetry[8] classes and 230 space-groups based on internal structure.[9] Treatment of these subdivisions constitutes the study of crystallography.[10]

Note the observations made by mathematician James R. Newman (1907-1966):

> In the development of crystallography the mathematics of group theory and of symmetry has ... played a remarkable part ... mathematicians by an exhaustive logical analysis of certain properties of space and of the possible transformations (motions) within space [i.e., topology – JN], *decreed the permissible variations of internal structure of crystals before observers were able to discover their actual structure* [italics added – JN]. Mathematics, in other words, not only enunciated the applicable physical laws, but provided an invaluable syllabus or research to guide future experimenters. The history of the physical sciences contains many similar instances of mathematical prevision.[11]

> The geometry of crystalline formations imposes their mathematical framework upon our minds. It is only as we allow the mathematical structure of the physical creation to disclose patterns to us that our thinking can sync with this dance and understand it.
>
> Paraphrase of Thomas F. Torrance, *God and Rationality* (1971), p. 182.

Carefully reread these observations. Let's unpack them from a Trinitarian viewpoint. Note that mathematicians had already discovered, by logical analysis, what crystallographers found later, by empirical study. Before these scientists began their explorations, mathematicians had already proved that we can group the symmetry elements of crystals in only thirty-two ways. Here we see that mathematicians, following the dance of logical reason, blazed a trail for crystallographers to follow.

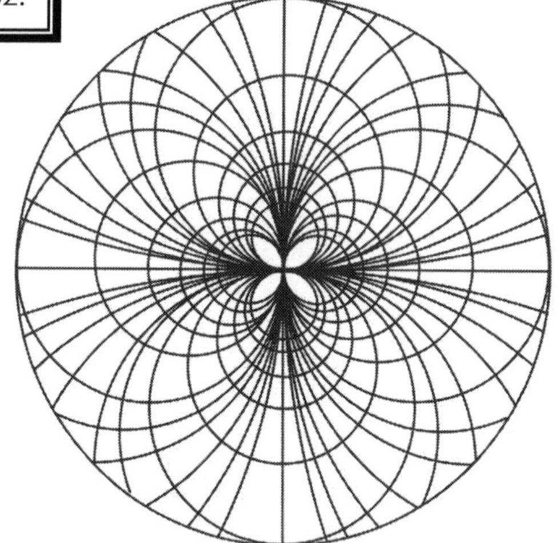

Figure 11. Crystalline Symmetry. In 1912, physicist Max von Laue passed X-rays through a spherical crystal onto a photographic plate. Points appeared that were arranged in perfect symmetry. We join these points to form this design.

In their research of crystals, scientists confirmed the conclusions of the mathematicians. This fact reflects upon the remarkable connectivity between man's mind, his ability to reason, and the physical world. The mind of man, with his mathematical capabilities, and the physical world, with its mathematical properties, cohere because of a common Creator. There is a dance between man's mind within and creation without because of the Triune dance of the Author and Sustainer of both. Therefore, we should not

---

[8] We have already seen symmetry twice in this lesson: (1) algebraic symmetry and (2) topological duality. As we have noted, symmetry, from the Greek, means "like measure." For a figure to reflect symmetry means that we can determine an exact correspondence of form and constituent configuration on opposite sides of a dividing line or plane or about a center or an axis. Note that butterfly wings are symmetric; the axis of symmetry is the body of the butterfly.

[9] See Philippe Le Corbeiller, "Crystals and the Future of Physics," in *Scientific American* (January 1953), 50-55.

[10] See Frederick H. Pough, *A Field Guide to Rocks and Minerals* (Boston: Houghton Mifflin, [1953, 1955] 1960) or Charles A. Sorrell, *Rocks and Minerals* (New York: Golden Press, 1973).

[11] James R. Newman, *The World of Mathematics* (New York: Simon and Schuster, 1956), 2:852-853.

be surprised to find a multitude of instances where mathematical conclusions not only comport with but also direct the physical sciences, just as Newman summarized in the last two sentences of the above quote.

> We create mathematics, its symbols and principles. But, we cannot simply bend these creations any way we choose. We are constrained by the relationship between mathematical objects and the connection between mathematical objects and the mathematical structure of the physical creation.
>
> James D. Nickel

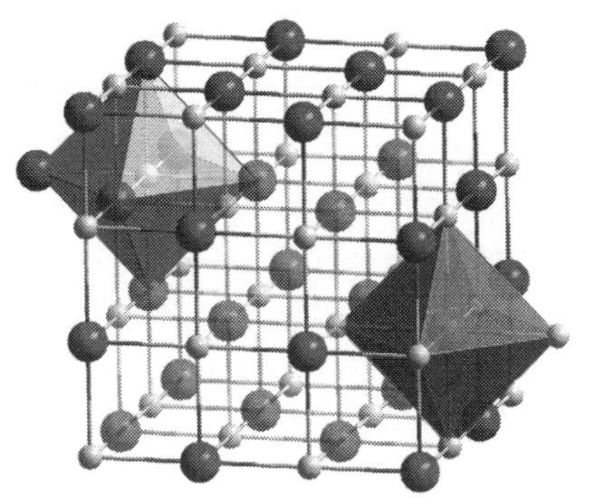

Figure 12. Crystal structure of NaCl (Salt) with coordinated polyhedral. Source: Public Domain.

EXERCISES

Define the following terms:

1. Duality
2. Homogeneous
3. Inorganic
4. Crystallography
5. Cubic system
6. Isometric
7. Hexagonal system
8. Rhombohedral system
9. Tetragonal system
10. Orthorhombic system
11. Monoclinic system
12. Triclinic system
13. Solid angle (See homework exercise below.)
14. Tessellation (See homework exercise below.)
15. Apothem (See homework exercise below.)

> Science is possible only because of the remarkable correlation, the perichoretic interpenetration, that exists between thought patterns intrinsic to our minds and the patterns embodied in the intelligibility of physical reality. This connection between the human mind and the physical universe holds together due to the thoroughgoing faithfulness of the Triune God, the God who, from His loving intelligibility not only freely created all things but holds all things together in the glorious mystery of the inner perichoresis of His onto-relational being.
>
> James D. Nickel

Solve the following equations for the variable indicated:

16. $C = \frac{5}{9}(F - 32)$ for F.
17. $F = \frac{9}{5}C + 32$ for C.

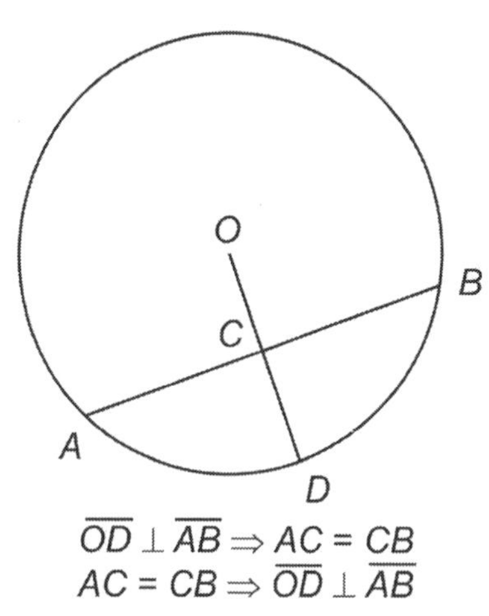

Figure 13.

Prove these two propositions (Figure 13):

18. If a line through the center of a circle is perpendicular to a chord, it also bisects it. Give reasons justifying each step of your proof. (Hint: Review the definition of a chord in Lesson 12.6 and seek to create two right triangles.)
19. If a line through the center of a circle bisects a chord that is not its diameter, it is also perpendicular to it. Give reasons justifying each step of your proof. (Hint: Seek to create two congruent triangles.)

Field Project: As we have noted, a regular polyhedron has equal regular polygon faces and identical vertices. The following geometric demonstration shows how there can only be five regular polyhedra. We must first define an angle in three dimensions; i.e., a **solid angle**. A solid angle is an angle formed by three or more planes intersecting in a common point or vertex.

20. Let's see if we can construct a solid angle from a set of flat, i.e., two-dimensional, equilateral triangles, the first regular polygon. Trace the following sets of equilateral triangles, the group of three, four, and five in Figure 14, on a separate sheet of construction or hard stock paper. Cut out each set, and fold each into a solid angle in the direction of the arrow. To make the folding easier, you might want to score the lines with a straightedge and a sharp instrument

or knife. Be gentle with the scoring and *be careful not to cut yourself* or ruin the table upon which you are cutting. These three folds are all we can do since a set of six equilateral triangles forms a **tessellation,**[12] or a perfect mosaic.

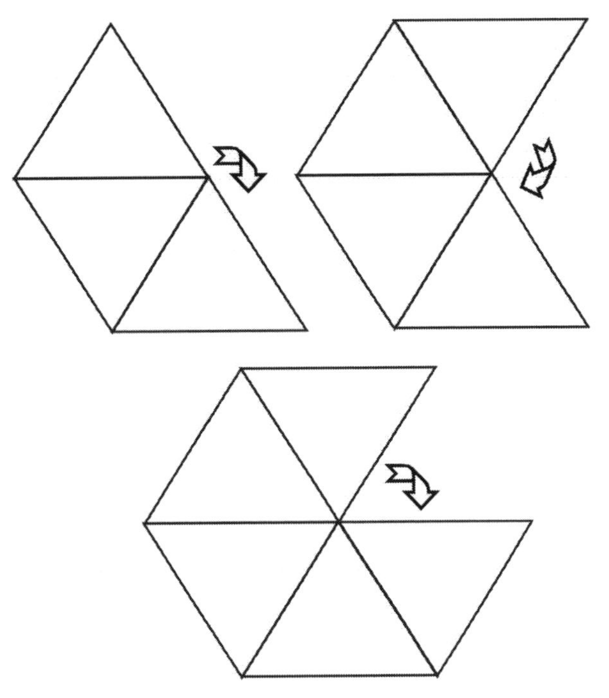

Figure 14.

[12] A tessellation on a plane surface occurs by repeated use of a single shape, or a combination of shapes, without gaps or overlapping. In ancient Greece and Roman, *tesserae* meant tokens. A *tesserae* was a small tablet made of wood or bone.

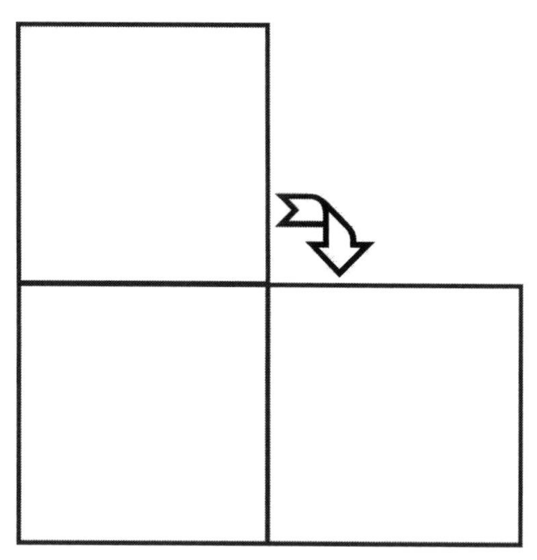

Figure 15.

21. Let's next construct a solid angle from a set of flat squares (Figure 15), the next regular polygon. Trace the set of three squares on construction or hard stock paper, cut, score, and fold it into a solid angle in the direction of the arrow. This singular fold is all we can do since a set of four squares forms a tessellation.

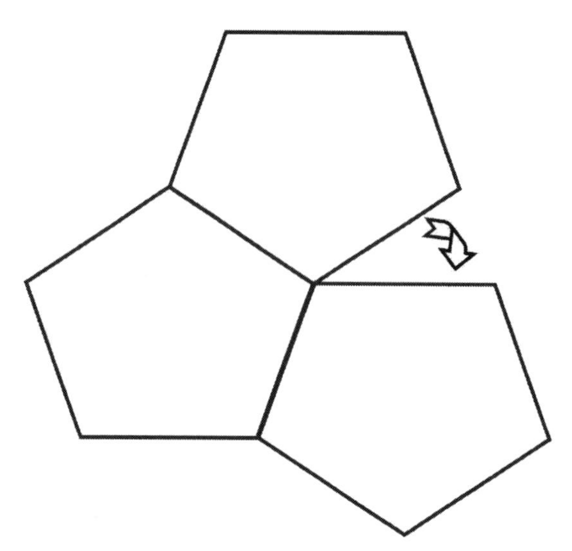

Figure 16.

22. Let's construct a solid angle from a set of a set of three regular pentagons (Figure 16), the next regular polygon. Trace the set of three regular pentagons on construction or hard stock paper, cut, score, and fold it into a solid angle in the direction of the arrow. We cannot go any higher than three since there is no room to lay four flat regular polygons.

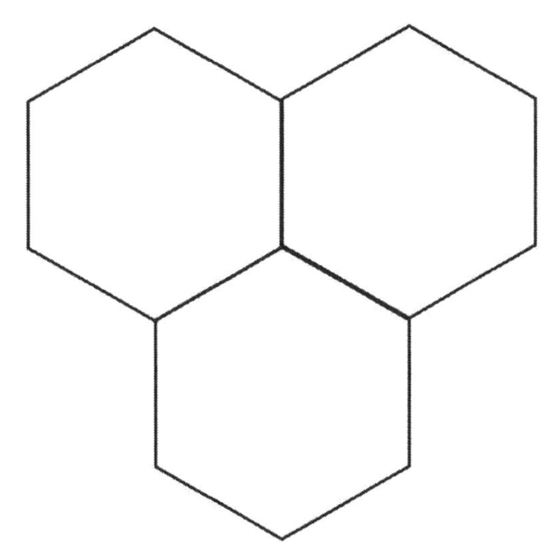

Figure 17.

23. If we start with three regular hexagons (Figure 17):
    (a) What do you notice?
    (b) Can you fold them into a solid angle?
24. What happens with a regular heptagon?
25. What happens with a regular octagon?
26. What is required to fold a regular polygon into a solid angle?
27. From Question 26, we have shown that working with sets of regular two-dimensional polygons, *we can construct only five solid angles*, what Euclid proved in his last proposition of *The Elements*, Book XIII, Proposition 18. He based his proof on Proposition 21 of Book XI of *The Elements*, "Any solid angle is contained by plane angles less than four right angles (i.e., 360°)." From these constructions, we can form the five regular polyhedra. Match each structure with its associated regular polyhedron.

Figure 18. Source: iStockPhoto.

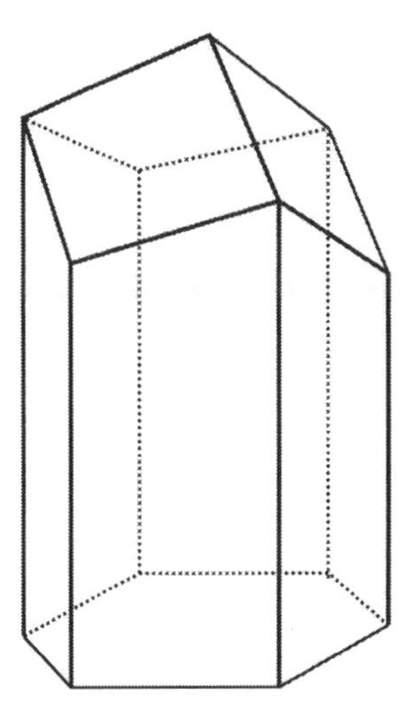

Figure 19. Shape of a honeycomb cell.

Bees and Hexagons.

Honeybees construct their honeycomb in almost perfect hexagons joined to form a continuous three-dimensional mosaic of cells. Let's investigate the gift that the Triune Creator has implanted within the bee to make this best shape, i.e., the shape that generates the maximum area. In this context, also note that bees make honey which, in its chemical composition, has hexagonal symmetry. The ancient Greeks proved, the reasoning that answered Question 26, that only three regular pentagons form a continuous mosaic of cells, i.e., a continuous matrix with common walls and no gaps: the square, the equilateral triangle, and the hexagon. Use Figure 20 to guide you in your answers to the following questions:

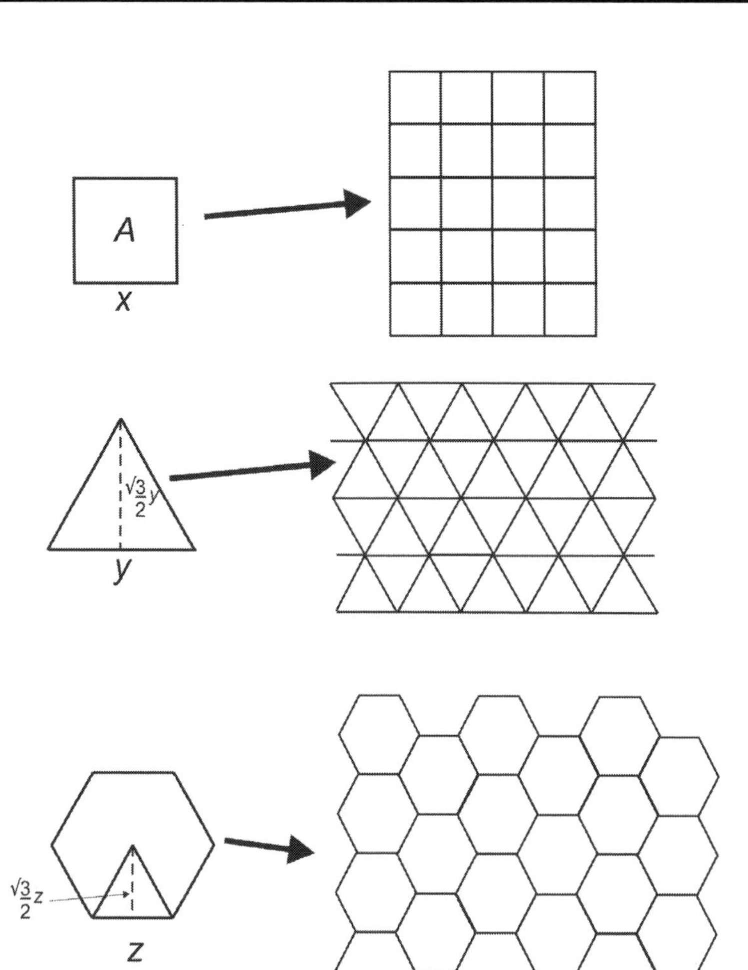

Figure 20. Bee packing.

28. How many squares are needed to form a tessellation?
29. How many equilateral triangles are needed to form a tessellation?
30. How many regular hexagons are needed to form a tessellation?
31. Consider a cell with perimeter p.
    (a) If this perimeter encloses a square, what is x, the length of one side?
    (b) What is the area A in terms of p?
32. Consider an equilateral triangle whose side is length y. Show that the altitude a (the height) of this triangle is $\frac{\sqrt{3}}{2}y$. (Hint: Review Lesson 12.6.)
33. What is the area A of this equilateral triangle?
34. If this triangle has perimeter p, we can substitute $\frac{p}{3}$ for y. Why?
35. Determine the area A of this equilateral triangle in terms of p.

36. The area of a regular hexagon is given by the formula $A = \frac{1}{2}ap$ where a = its **apothem**[13] (the perpendicular line segment from its center to one of its sides) and p = its perimeter. If the length its side is z, then show that its apothem is $\frac{\sqrt{3}}{2}z$. (Hint: Use the same reasoning invoked to answer Question 32.)
37. In terms of z and p determine the area A of the regular hexagon.

> Bees ... by virtue of a certain geometrical forethought ... know that the hexagon is greater than the square and the triangle, and will hold more honey for the same expenditure of material.
>
> Pappus (ca. 300 AD).

38. Determine z in terms of p.
39. Determine the area A of the regular hexagon in terms of p.
40. Which of the three figures, the square, the equilateral triangle, or the hexagon, generate the maximum area? (Do this in two ways: (1) Using your scientific calculator and (2) making use of your knowledge of fraction.)

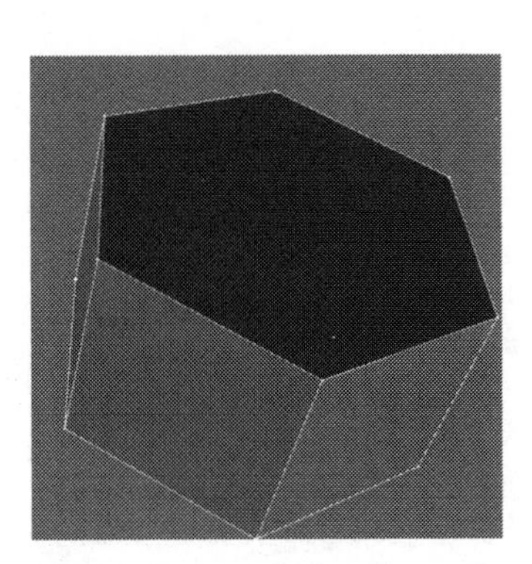

Figure 21. Hexagonal prism. Source: Great Stella Software.

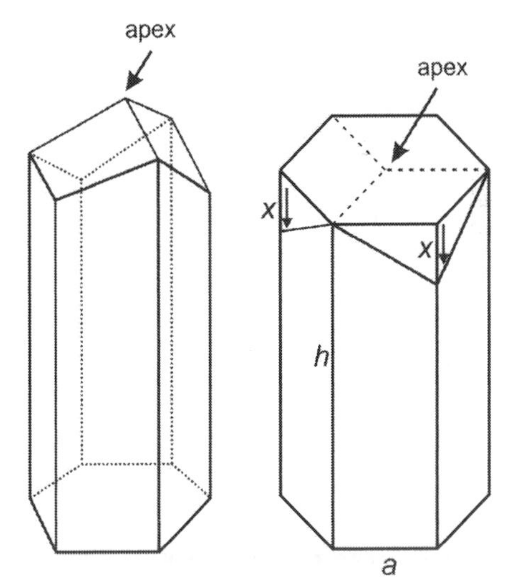

Figure 22. Analysis of the shape of a honeycomb cell.

Calculus and the Construction of the Honeycomb.

The honeybee constructs the honeycomb by tessellating a series of regular hexagonal prisms with one end open and the other end a pointed trihedral apex (Figure 22). The bee fabricates the displacement x so that the waxed surface area is minimal; i.e., the bee also does less work for the same space when compared to the construction of square or triangular tessellations. Using the Differential Calculus, we can prove that the Father, Son and Holy Spirit have designed the bee

[13] Apothem means "theme of the base." In general, an apothem is line segment from the center of a regular polygon at right angles to any of its sides.

to construct a comb using the minimal surface area, i.e., the least amount of wax. If we let A = surface area, mathematicians have, by a geometrical argument,[14] developed this function of A in terms of x:

$$A(x) = 6\left(ab - \frac{ax}{2}\right) + 3a\sqrt{3}\sqrt{x^2 + \frac{a^2}{4}}$$

where a = length of each side of the hexagon, h = height of the hexagonal prism, and x = displacement.

41. If $x = 0$, there is no trihedral base; it is flat. But, A is not minimal. To find the minimal surface area, we take the first derivative of A with respect to x (Hint: we will have to apply the chain rule). Then, set this derivative equal to zero and solve for x. (a) Set $a = 1$ [We will not use any units for this problem.] and find the value of x that will give us the minimal surface area, to five significant figures. (b) What is the surface area, to the nearest tenth? You may use your scientific calculator to determine x and $A(x)$.
42. Graph the behavior of this function.
43. Does h play a part in determining x?
44. Use your scientific calculator to determine what happens to x and the surface area when a = 2.

If the universe is mathematical in some deep sense, then the mysterious undecidabilities demonstrated by Gödel and Turing are part of the fabric of the universe rather than merely products of our minds. They show that even a mathematical universe is more than axioms, more than computation, more than logic – and more than mathematicians can know.

John D. Barrow, "The Mathematical Universe." In *Natural Science* (May 1989), p. 311.

Figure 23. Devil's Postpile, near Mammoth Lakes, California (USA), a set of basalt columns formed by the contraction of lava as it cooled. If the cooling of the lava had not been variational, all the structures would be hexagonal in shape. Source: Wikimedia Commons.

[14] We will not demonstrate this argument.

14.6 Sphere Formulas 1

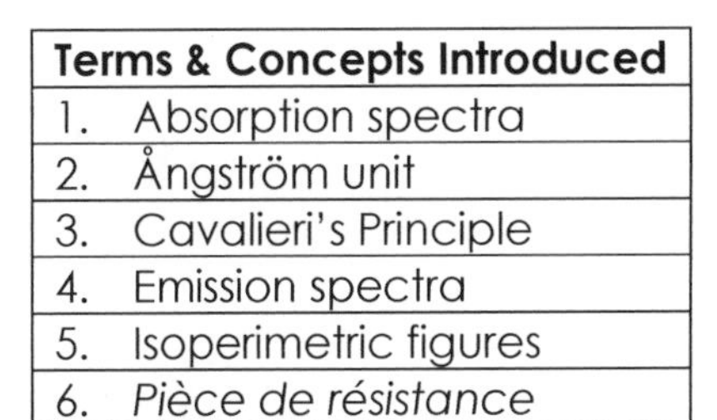

Terms & Concepts Introduced
1. Absorption spectra
2. Ångström unit
3. Cavalieri's Principle
4. Emission spectra
5. Isoperimetric figures
6. *Pièce de résistance*

Before we conclude these studies into the fascinating world of mathematics, let's take two lessons to prove the sphere formulas for volume and surface area in two different ways.

Volume of a Sphere

First, we setup some preliminaries for proving the volume formula (Figure 1). Given the sphere with center at O and radius r, let's slice it with a plane at a distance d from O, i.e., $AO = d$. We have created a cross-section of the sphere, a circle with center at A and radius x. Invoking the Pythagorean Theorem, we get:

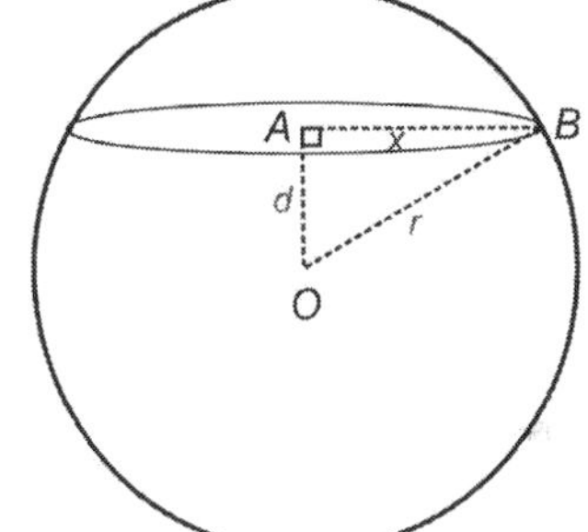

Figure 1.

$$x^2 + d^2 = r^2 \Leftrightarrow x^2 = r^2 - d^2$$

The area of the cross-section or the area of Circle A, α(circle A), is:

$$\alpha(\text{circle } A) = \pi x^2$$

Substituting for x^2, we get:

$$\alpha(\text{circle } A) = \pi(r^2 - d^2) = \pi r^2 - \pi d^2$$

We can interpret this result as the difference between the areas of two circles with respective radii r and d (Figure 2).

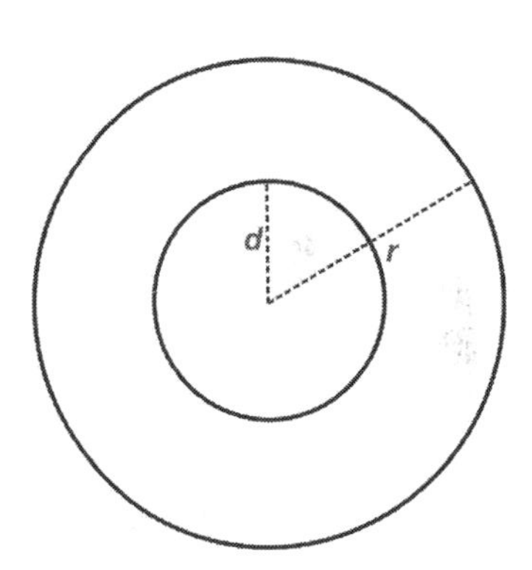

Figure 2.

Next, we invoke a principle first articulated by the Italian mathematician Bonaventura Cavalieri (1598-1647), one of Galileo Galilei's students. The principle is simple. Investigate the two stacks of coins (Figure 3). Despite the different way of stacking, the five coins in both sides represent the same total volume. Why? The individual five cross-section coins are congruent. This perspective of cross-sections is **Cavalieri's Principle**. More accurately, if two geometric solids lie in the same plane and if every plane parallel to this plane that intersects both solids so that the resulting cross-sections have equal areas, then the two solids have equal volumes.

Figure 3. Source: James D. Nickel.

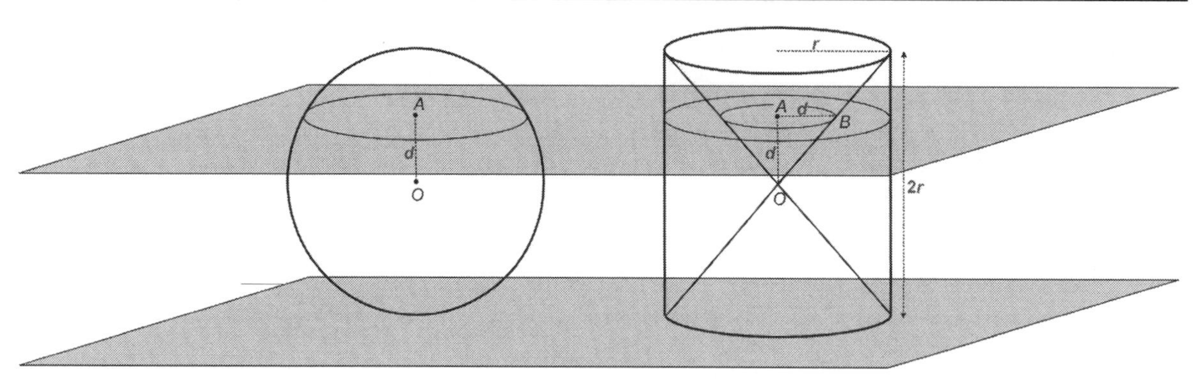

Figure 4.

To apply his principle to find the volume of sphere O, we construct a geometric solid that has the same kind of cross section. In Figure 4, the solid on the right is a right cylinder where with two right cones removed. These two hollowed out right cones meet at the center O of the right cylinder, the same point as sphere O. The cylinder's height is $2r$, and it is the same as the diameter of the sphere. Both solids rest on the bottom plane. The plane slices the two solids at a distance d from both centers. The donut hole, the cross-section in the right cylinder, has this area:

$$\pi r^2 - \pi d^2$$

By our construction, the area of the donut hole is the same as the corresponding cross-section of the sphere. By Cavalieri's Principle, both solids must have the same volume. What is the volume of the cylinder that has the two cones removed? It is the volume V of the sphere.

$$V_{\text{cylinder}} = \pi r^2(2r) = 2\pi r^3$$

$$V_{\text{two cones}} = 2\left[\frac{1}{3}\pi r^2(r)\right] = \frac{2}{3}\pi r^3$$

$$V_{\text{cylinder}} - V_{\text{two cones}} = 2\pi r^3 - \frac{2}{3}\pi r^3 = \pi r^3\left(2 - \frac{2}{3}\right) = \pi r^3\left(\frac{4}{3}\right) = \frac{4}{3}\pi r^3$$

Using Cavalieri's Principle, we have derived the volume of the sphere:

$$V = \frac{4}{3}\pi r^3$$

QED (Indeed, a nifty dance of logic, isn't it?)

SURFACE AREA OF A SPHERE

To find the surface area of a sphere, we will use a method of Integral Calculus that invokes infinite processes.[1]

We imagine that we divide the volume of the sphere of radius r into an infinite number of right hexagonal pyramids. We show one of those pyramids in Figure 5. Every apex meets at the center O and all the bases combined encapsulate, or tessellate, the surface area of the sphere. The altitude of each of these pyramids is the radius of the sphere or r. Therefore, the volume of each of these pyramids $\frac{1}{3}Br$ and the volume of all of them is the volume V of the sphere is:

[1] We will follow the reasoning of Johannes Kepler (1571-1630).

$$V = \frac{1}{3}B_1 r + \frac{1}{3}B_2 r + \frac{1}{3}B_3 r + \ldots$$

Factoring $\frac{1}{3}r$ we get:

$$V = \frac{1}{3}r\left(B_1 + B_2 + B_3 + \ldots\right)$$

The surface area A of the sphere, α(area of sphere), is this:

α(area of sphere) = $B_1 + B_2 + B_3 + \ldots$

By substitution, we get:

$$V = \frac{1}{3}r\left[\alpha\left(\text{sphere}\right)\right]$$

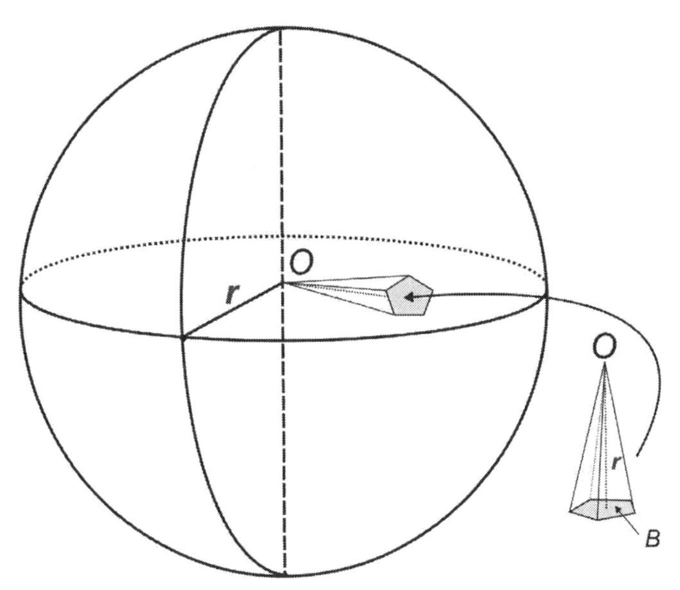

Figure 5.

Solving for α(area of sphere), we get:

$$\alpha\left(\text{area of sphere}\right) = \frac{V}{\frac{1}{3}r}$$

By our previous proof, we know this:

$$V = \frac{4}{3}\pi r^3$$

By substitution, we get:

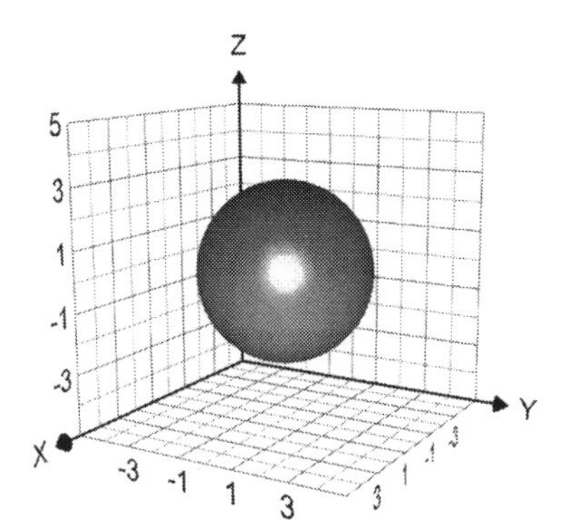

Figure 6. The geometry of three dimensions on the x-y-z axes; the sphere: $x^2 + y^2 + z^2 = 9$.

$$\alpha\left(\text{area of sphere}\right) = \frac{\frac{4}{3}\pi r^{\not{3}\,2}}{\frac{1}{3}\not{r}_{\,1}} = \frac{\frac{4}{3}\pi r^2}{\frac{1}{3}} = \frac{4}{\not{3}_{\,1}} \cdot \frac{\not{3}^{\,1}}{1}\pi r^2 = 4\pi r^2$$

Therefore:

α(area of sphere) = $4\pi r^2$

QED (***pièce de résistance***[2])

[2] *pièce de résistance* is French meaning "a piece of resistance." The phrase is used with reference to a remarkable part of a creative piece of work. The method of Integral Calculus proves this formula exactly. We have only approximated this method with this argument. Our logic is intuitive and makes sense although we could never actually fill the sphere with these right hexagonal pyramids.

EXERCISES

Define the following terms:

1. Cavalieri's Principle
2. *Pièce de résistance*
3. Isoperimetric figures (See homework exercise below.)
4. Emission spectra (See homework exercise below.)
5. Absorption spectra (See homework exercise below.)
6. Ångström unit (See homework exercise below.)

Figures that are **isoperimetric** are figures that have equal perimeters. All the shapes in Figure 7 have perimeters of 72 cm. The areas, however, are all different.

7. Guess which figure has the largest area.
8. Calculate the area for each figure, rounded to the nearest square centimeter when applicable. Use 3.14 as an approximate of π rounded to 3 significant figures. Was your guess correct?

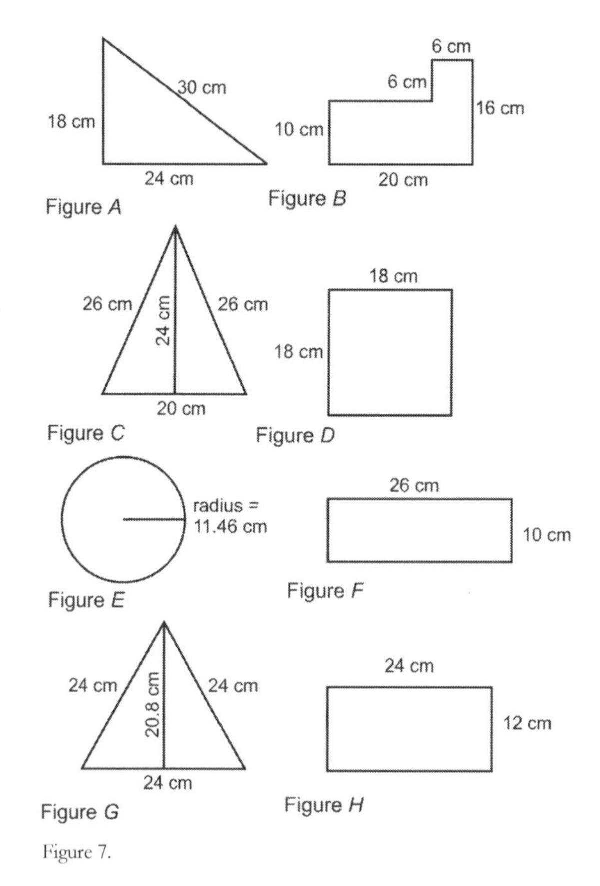

Figure 7.

Answer the following questions:

9. In Heron's formula for the area A of a triangle, show why the units generated by it are square units.
10. Write the formula for the surface area of a sphere in terms of d, its diameter.
11. Write the formula for the volume a sphere in terms of d, its diameter.
12. With a scientific calculator, find the north latitude, rounded to the nearest tenth, when 1° of longitude at that latitude is (a) 50 miles, (b) 35 miles, (c) 15 miles. Use π on your calculator and use 3947 miles for the radius of the Earth. (Hint: See homework in Lesson 12.10.)
13. Find the area of the two triangles in Figure 8. Which has the greater area? Does this surprise you?

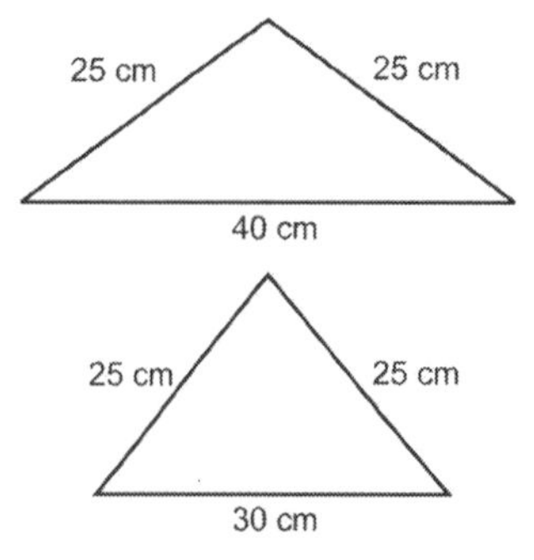

Figure 8.

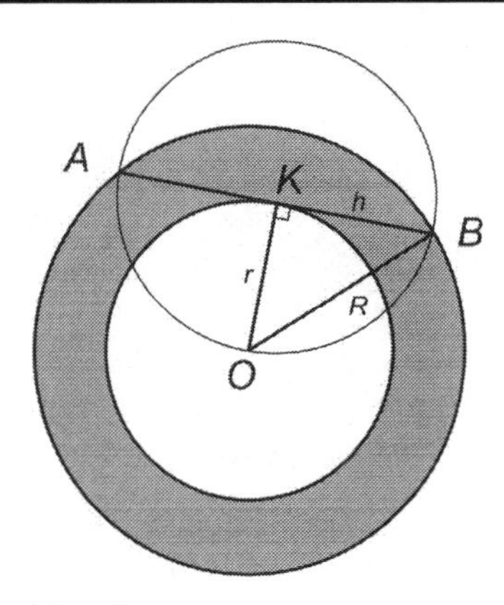

Figure 9.

14. Consider any size circular track made up of any two concentric circles (Figure 9) with O as their common center where r is the radius of the lesser circle, and R is the radius of the greater circle. Show that the area of the track (the shaded area) equals the area of a circle K whose diameter is chord $\overline{AB}$ of the greater circle that is tangent to the lesser circle. (Hint: We know $\overline{AB} \perp \overline{OK}$ and K, the center of circle K, is the midpoint of $\overline{AB}$ by a homework exercise in Lesson 14.5.)

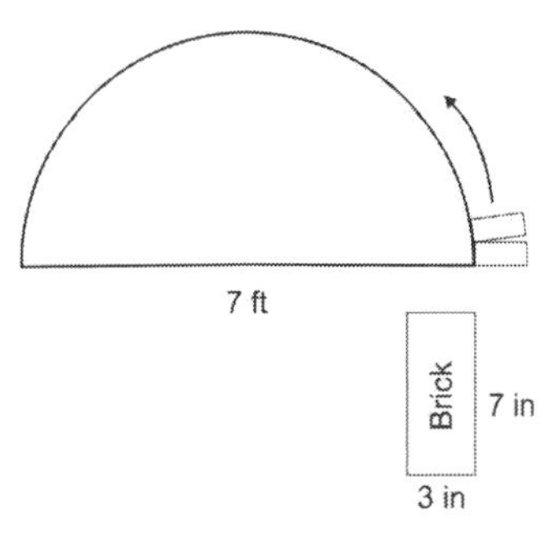

Figure 10.

Use Figure 10 to answer the next two questions:

15. How many bricks are necessary to build a semicircular border as illustrated in Figure 10? Build a formula first because you will use it to answer the next question. Use π given by your scientific calculator.
16. What should the diameter, rounded to the nearest tenth of a foot, of the semicircle be if you have 100 bricks, 3 inches by 7 inches, to build the border? Use π given by your scientific calculator.

Use a scientific calculator to answer the next set of questions about volume and surface area. Where needed, use π given by your calculator and be very careful with your calculator work.

17. (a) Find the length and width, rounded to the nearest thousandth, of a rectangular solid with a square base whose volume is 1000 ft^3 and height h is 20 ft.
    (b) Find its surface area, rounded to the nearest square foot.
18. (a) Find the side s of a cube whose volume is 1000 ft^3.
    (b) Find its surface area.
19. (a) Find the radius r, rounded to the nearest hundredth, of a right circular cylinder whose volume is 1000 ft^3 and height h is 6.83 ft.
    (b) Find its surface area, rounded to the nearest foot.

20. (a) Find the radius r, rounded to the nearest thousandth, of a half-sphere whose volume is 1000 ft^3. (b) Find its surface area rounded to the nearest foot.
21. (a) Find the height h, rounded to the nearest hundredth, of a right circular cylinder whose volume is 1000 ft^3 and radius r is 5.42 ft.
    (b) Find its surface area, rounded to the nearest foot.
22. (a) Find the radius r, rounded to the nearest thousandth, of a sphere whose volume is 1000 ft^3.
    (b) Find its surface area rounded to the nearest foot.
23. Create a four-column table summarizing your results of the previous six questions. Label the four columns Shape, Dimensions (ft), Surface Area (ft^2), and Volume (ft^3).
24. Which of the above figures encloses the same volume with the least surface area?
25. Why are canned goods packed in right cylinders?

Algebra and the Balmer Series.

The following questions will show you how science, the study of the nature of God's creation, and mathematics, as a tool of description, interpenetrate in the context of decimal fractions, ratios, and algebraic operations. We will trace the wonderful way a 19th-century Swiss mathematician/scientist named Johann Jakob Balmer (1825-1898) worked the tools of mathematics.

Figure 11. Johann Jakob Balmer. Source: Public Domain.

In the 19th century, Anders Jonas Ångström (1814-1874), a Swiss Astronomer, was one of the first scientists to use a new instrument called the spectrograph. A spectrograph breaks light into an array or spectrum of component colors; e.g., a prism is a spectrograph. Each color in a spectrum represents light of a particular wavelength; i.e., color can be quantified. Ångström noted that the spectra of the yellowish-white light from the spherical Sun are composed of a continuous band of wavelengths. When Ångström examined the light emitted, the **emission spectra**, by certain hot gasses (e.g., hydrogen – when heated, its color is a strange shade of violet), instead of a smeared-out, continuous spectrum, he found discrete lines at specific wavelengths. Emission spectra is an inverse of **absorption spectra**; i.e., when you look at any light source, like our Sun, through a gas of specific atomic composition like hydrogen, you will see dark lines[3] at the same wavelength positions as you would in the emission spectrum for the same gas. Emission spectra turned out to be the key to analyzing the chemical composition of the stars since they consist of a large amount of heated, of course, hydrogen gas. Scientists later discovered that each spectral line, wavelength, arose from a different state of vibration, a different dance, of the hydrogen atoms in its gas.

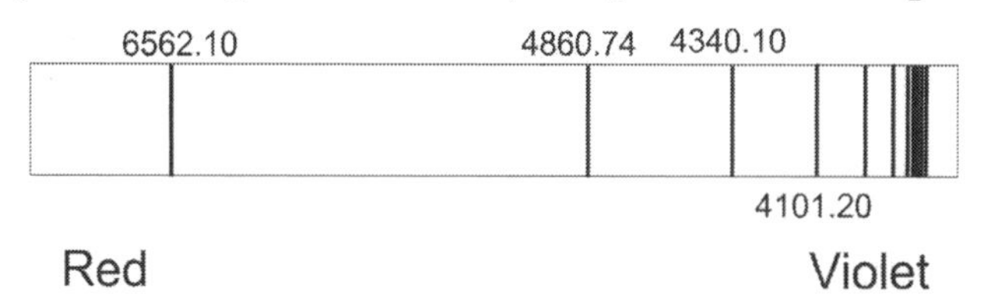

Figure 12. Spectral analysis of hydrogen.

26. In 1884, Balmer, a private tutor at the University of Basel, asked himself, "Is there any mathematical relationship between the wavelengths of the spectral lines of heated hydrogen? Is

[3] These lines are named Fraunhofer lines in honor of the German physicist Joseph von Fraunhofer (1787-1826).

there a pattern? Do these numbers connect in some way?" Ångström's meticulous measurements provided Balmer with four numbers: [4]

6562.10
4860.74
4340.10
4101.20

Table 1	
1 Å =	
10^{-10} m	meters
10^{-8} cm	centimeters
10^{-7} mm	millimeters
10^{-4} μm	micrometers
0.1 nm	nanometers
100 pm	picometers

He let $H_\alpha = 6562.10$, the alpha line in the red region of the hydrogen spectrum, $H_\beta = 4860.74$, the beta line in the violet region of the hydrogen spectrum, $H_\gamma = 4340.10$, the gamma line, and $H_\delta = 4101.20$, the delta line. At lower frequencies, these lines crowded closer and closer together toward the violet end of the hydrogen spectrum. Take note of this, for Balmer's mathematics will soon describe and predict this crowding. Balmer wondered whether these numbers derived from a measurement scale were rational or irrational. To get his answer, he began to experiment with them. He started by calculating the ratios $\frac{H_\alpha}{H_\beta}$, $\frac{H_\alpha}{H_\gamma}$, and $\frac{H_\alpha}{H_\delta}$. With a scientific calculator, determine these ratios rounding your answer to seven decimal places.

27. Balmer observed his three answers. It looked like slight observational/measurement errors had come into play. That is, it could be that, ideally, $\frac{H_\alpha}{H_\beta} = 1.35$, $\frac{H_\alpha}{H_\gamma} = 1.512$, and $\frac{H_\alpha}{H_\delta} = 1.60$. This observation meant that these numbers could very well be rational numbers. Determine the integer ratios that produce these decimal fractions. (Hint: $1.60 = \frac{160}{100}$)

28. Balmer set the third ratio $\frac{H_\alpha}{H_\beta} = \frac{72}{45}$ (not in lowest terms) to ease the mathematics to come. He then asked, "Is there some common factor in these ratios, a fundamental number of hydrogen?" That is, for the first ratio, does $\frac{H_\alpha}{H_\beta} = bk_1$, where b is a constant and k_1 is an integer? For the second ratio, does $\frac{H_\alpha}{H_\gamma} = bk_2$, where b is the same constant and k_2 is an integer? For the third ratio, does $\frac{H_\alpha}{H_\delta} = bk_3$ where b is the same constant and k_3 is an integer? Substitute the ratios with numbers (make sure you use $\frac{72}{45}$ for $\frac{H_\alpha}{H_\beta}$) and perform an algebraic operation to generate an equation in the form $r_1 = r_2bk_n$ where $n = 1, 2, 3$.

29. Balmer, like you, generated a system of three equations in four unknowns, b, k_1, k_2, and k_3. But, he could not find any value of b that would satisfy all three equations. His next step was

[4] These numbers are in **Ångström** (Å) units where 1 Å = 0.0000001 mm. The unit is so named in honor of the Swedish physicist Anders Jonas Ångström. See Table 1 in Lesson 12.8.

a brilliant leap of faith. Maybe the common factor is not an integer, but a ratio of two integers; i.e., maybe each could write H_x in the form $b\left(\frac{n}{d}\right)$ where n and d are integers. For the first ratio, $\frac{H_\alpha}{H_\beta}$, he wrote:

$$\frac{H_\alpha}{H_\beta} = \frac{b\left(\frac{n_1}{d_1}\right)}{b\left(\frac{n_2}{d_2}\right)}$$

Second ratio:

$$\frac{H_\alpha}{H_\gamma} = \frac{b\left(\frac{n_1}{d_1}\right)}{b\left(\frac{n_3}{d_3}\right)}$$

Third ratio:

$$\frac{H_\alpha}{H_\delta} = \frac{b\left(\frac{n_1}{d_1}\right)}{b\left(\frac{n_4}{d_4}\right)}$$

> Everything we know in the created universe, macrocosmically or microcosmically, we learn from light signals, but their mathematical patterns have to be deciphered and coordinated with word in the formulation of scientific theory and the development of knowledge.
> Thomas F. Torrance, *Theological and Natural Science* (2002), p. 15.

(a) Using algebraic operations, simplify the three expressions on the right side of these equations.
(b) What happens to b?

30. Next, Balmer set his ratios as follows:

$$\frac{H_\alpha}{H_\beta} = \frac{27}{20} = \frac{n_1 d_2}{d_1 n_2}$$

$$\frac{H_\alpha}{H_\gamma} = \frac{189}{125} = \frac{n_1 d_3}{d_1 n_3}$$

$$\frac{H_\alpha}{H_\delta} = \frac{72}{45} = \frac{n_1 d_4}{d_1 n_4}$$

In the first ratio, $n_1 d_2 = 27$. Write five other equations derived from these ratios.

31. Balmer now had produced six equations in eight unknowns. Take a good look at them and see if you can determine a strategy to solve them. Think through a strategy before you continue.
32. From the first equation, either $n_1 = 9$ and $d_2 = 3$ or $n_1 = 3$ and $d_2 = 9$. Let's go ahead and let $n_1 = 9$ and $d_2 = 3$. Using the third equation, solve for d_3.
33. Using the fifth equation, solve for d_4.

34. From the second equation, $d_1n_2 = 20$, the fourth equation, $d_1n_3 = 125$, and from the sixth equation, $d_1n_4 = 45$, we know that d_1 must be a common factor of 20, 125, and 45. Solve for d_1.
35. Solve for:
    (a) n_2
    (b) n_3
    (c) n_4.

Balmer now had a solution set for d_1, d_2, d_3, n_1, n_2, and n_3. He now used these values to find b. Solve for b in each of the following cases: (You may use your calculator and round off to the nearest hundredth.)

36. $H_\alpha = 6562.10 = b\left(\frac{n_1}{d_1}\right) = b\left(\frac{9}{5}\right)$

37. $H_\beta = 4860.74 = b\left(\frac{n_2}{d_2}\right) = b\left(\frac{4}{3}\right)$

38. $H_\gamma = 4340.10 = b\left(\frac{n_3}{d_3}\right) = b\left(\frac{25}{21}\right)$

39. $H_\delta = 4101.20 = b\left(\frac{n_4}{d_4}\right) = b\left(\frac{9}{8}\right)$

The solution for b in each case are very close to one number, and this number is the frequency where the spectral lines of hydrogen gas become too close together to distinguish; i.e., they converge to this number as a limit at the violet end of the spectrum. With better precision of initial measurement, $b = 3645.6$, the fundamental number of hydrogen. Stand back and look at what Balmer did. He used some creative thinking, made some guesses, applied some mathematics, and come up with a number that is a physical description of a key component of hydrogen gas. We have shown that the tools of mathematics describe, even predict, a real physical situation.

40. Next, Balmer investigated the ratios $\frac{9}{5}, \frac{4}{3}, \frac{25}{21}$, and $\frac{9}{8}$. Is there a pattern to these ratios? What stands out about these numbers? (Hint: Look at the numerators, there is one pattern, and denominators, there are two patterns, separately.)
41. (a) Write your observations from Question 40 algebraically in two different ways, letting m range from 2 to 6. Build a table of your results.
    (b) Which of the two expressions give the four ratios?
42. From this analysis, Balmer developed a formula for calculating the wavelength (λ) of the lines of the hydrogen spectrum, the Balmer series.[5] The formula is of the form $\lambda = bk$ where k is your answer to Question 41b.
    (a) Write this the formula for λ replacing b and k with the appropriate number/algebraic expression.
    (b) With this formula and a calculator, validate the four starting values for λ when $m = 3, 4, 5$, and 6. (Hint: Your answers will be very close to 6562.10, 4860.74, 4340.10, and 4101.20)
43. (a) Find the end-behavior of λ, or the limit of λ as $m \to \infty$.

[5] Since we are listing the wavelengths, this list is a sequence. In the world of physics, this sequence is known as a series.

(b) What does your answer mean?
(c) What is the horizontal asymptote of λ?
(d) Graph λ to verify the end-behavior and horizontal asymptote.

Some years after Balmer's work, the Swedish physicist Johannes Robert Rydberg (1854-1919) put the formula into a more convenient form.

44. He began by taking the reciprocal of λ; i.e., he let v (wave number) $= \frac{1}{\lambda}$. Derive an algebraic expression for v.
45. Multiply both numerator and denominator of the right side of the equation for v by 4 and simplify the constant, $\frac{4}{3645.6}$, by doing the division with a scientific calculator, rounding to the nearest millionth. (Note: The unit is the Ångström unit, Å).

Figure 13. Johannes Robert Rydberg.
Source: Public Domain.

46. The constant 4/3645.6 is now known as the Rydberg constant R.
    (a) Substitute this number with R and simplify the rational algebraic expression by using the identity $\frac{a-b}{c} = \frac{a}{c} - \frac{b}{c}$ and writing any square number in x^2 form.
    (b) What are the restrictions on m?
47. It is possible to imagine a series similar to the Balmer series where the square number is 1^2, 3^2, and 4^2. (a) Write three different versions of v with these square numbers.
    (b) What are the restrictions on m for each?
48. In general, we can substitute the square numbers with n^2. Write v in terms of R, n, and m.
49. If $n = 1$, we have the Lyman series, named after the American physicist Theodore Lyman (1874-1954) who discovered it in 1906. Would the wavelengths of this series be shorter or longer than the Balmer series? Why?
50. If $n = 3$, we have the Paschen series, named after the German physicist Friedrich Paschen (1865-1947) who discovered it in 1908. Would the wavelengths of this series be shorter or longer than the Balmer series? Why?

If $n = 4$, we have the Brackett series, named after the American physicist Frederick S. Brackett (1896-1988) who discovered it in 1922. The values of n from 1 to 4 represent discrete or integral electron energy jumps in quantum physics, from the first fundamental level to the fourth. What is stunning about these demonstrations is that the abstract algebraic work interpenetrates the physical reality of the atomic world.

According to modern information theory, we can derive no other solution or any other formula from these four numbers. Balmer, the discoverer of this formula, said in 1885, "It appeared to me that hydrogen ... more than any other substance is destined to open new paths to the knowledge of the structure of matter and its properties. In this respect the numerical relations among the wavelengths of the first four hydrogen spectral lines should attract our attention particularly."[6]

> Francis Bitter (1902-1967), past Professor of Geophysics and Director of the National Magnet Laboratory at M.I.T. (Massachusetts Institute of Technology), reflected upon the connection between Balmer's formula and the actual data, "The agreement ... is startling and mysterious, at least until it is explained, and it illustrates beyond equivocation the great simplicity – one might even say beauty – in this hidden world beyond the range of our five senses."
>
> Francis Bitter, *Mathematical Aspects of Physics: An Introduction* (1963), p. 18.

> ... mathematics inheres in matter. You could say that this one example shows that mathematics, as an entity, is at least as real as the so-called real world, perhaps even more real.
>
> A. K. Dewdney, *A Mathematical Mystery Tour: Discovering the Truth and Beauty of the Cosmos* (1999), p. 111.

> It is not fashionable to speak of scientific matters in a philosophical or religious context. But I am continually struck by trains of thought like the one I have sketched out. The world we live in is clearly not a random jumble of objects, forces, and motions. There is a design. There is every indication of a creation, of complex ordering techniques. Are not the patterns which lie beyond what men or beasts or insects have made, the patterns that we can usually see only with our inner eyes, are they not real clues to the nature of creation, and the Creator?"
>
> Francis Bitter, *Mathematical Aspects of Physics: An Introduction* (1963), p. 23.

[6] Cited in Joy Manners, ed. *Quantum Physics: An Introduction* (London: The Institute of Physics, 2000), p. 11.

14.7 Sphere Formulas 2 – The Method of Archimedes

Term Introduced
1. Stereometry

The philosopher Plato (427-347 BC) expressed a general scorn of the material realm. For him, the philosophic spirit is one that transcends the material and gazes upon the perfections of the ideal that is immaterial. Since Greek Geometry was a study of ideal forms, the perfect circle, triangle, square, etc., it was the quintessential road to intellectual perfection.[1] As we have noted, Euclid's (ca. 300 BC) *Elements*, one of the most famous mathematics textbooks of all time, followed this Platonic scheme by building a system of geometry starting with foundational axioms/definitions that lead to a host of geometric theorems via deductive analysis. Commenting on Euclid's work, mathematics historian Herbert Meschkowski (1909-1990) said, "Every effort was made not to rely on the unsupported intuition but to construct geometry as a scientific system with a precise axiomatic foundation."[2] In Euclid's treatise, there is not a single instance of the application of geometry to the physical world or of any heuristic starting point for any of his theorems.

A few generations after the initial publication of *Elements*, the technician Archimedes of Syracuse (ca. 287-212 BC) introduced heuristics into geometric analysis.[3] He still retained much of Plato in his thinking. According to 2nd century Roman historian Plutarch, in *Life of Marcellus* (chapter 14), Archimedes considered "mechanical work and every art concerned with the necessities of life an ignoble and inferior form of labor and therefore exerted his best efforts only in seeking knowledge of those things in which the good and the beautiful were not mixed with the necessary."[4] Forced by the pressing circumstances of his times (war, economics, agriculture, and thievery to name a few), his skill at "ignoble" work was astonishing.[5]

Unlike Euclid, Archimedes used reasoning about physical processes, i.e., mechanics, to help him solve problems in mathematics.[6] He said:

> Certain theorems first became clear to me by means of a mechanical method. Then, however, they had to be proved geometrically since the method provided no real proof. It is obviously easier to find a proof when we have already learned something about the question by means of the method than it is to find one without such advance knowledge.

---

[1] It was the Greeks who perfected the method of abstraction, the method of laying aside unimportant details so that the essence of an issue could be considered. Abstraction is both a gift of God and essential to thinking. Unfortunately, the Greeks embraced a dualism that separated the immaterial from the material. They absolutized abstraction and generally disregarding empirical analysis which is the foundation of operational science. For the ivory towered Platonist, the intellect is the primary and only way to properly perceive the good, the beautiful, and the true. Historically, embracing the view that the Triune God revealed in Jesus is the creator of the human mind, a mind that can think abstractly, and the physical world, a world that reflects principled patterns, formed the womb for the viable birth of operational science, a birth that inert Greek thinking could never generate. See Stanley L. Jaki, *Science and Creation* (Edinburgh: Scottish Academic Press, 1986) and *The Origin of Science and the Science of Its Origin* (Edinburgh: Scottish Academic Press, 1978). For an explication of dualism, see Thomas F. Torrance, "Emerging from the Cultural Split," in *The Ground and Grammar of Theology* (Charlottesville: University Press of Virginia, 1980), pp. 15-43.

[2] Herbert Meschkowski, *Ways of Thought of Great Mathematicians: An Approach to the History of Mathematics* (San Francisco: Holden-Day, 1964), p. 14.

[3] We have already met Archimedes in Lesson 3.8, 5.1, 5.4, and 8.3, and 8.8.

[4] Cited in G. E. R. Lloyd, *Greek Science After Aristotle* (New York: W. W. Horton, 1973), pp. 93-94. Lloyd's source is the Loeb translation of B. Perrin, *Plutarch's Lives*, Vol. 5 (Cambridge: Harvard University Press, 1917). Plutarch lived from ca. 46 to 120.

[5] Archimedes discovered many truths about mechanics and hydrostatics.

[6] For a compilation of the works of Archimedes, see Robert Maynard Hutchins, ed., *Great Books of the Western World* (Chicago: Encyclopædia Britannica, 1952), 11:401-592.

> That is why, for example, we must give Democritus, who was the first to state the theorems that the cone is a third of the cylinder and the pyramid of the prism, but who did not prove them, as much credit as we give to Eudoxus, who was the first to prove them.[7]

In Lesson 14.6, we showed how to find the volume and surface area of a sphere using, respectively, Cavalieri's Principle and volumes of pyramids. We shall now show a more ancient method to derive these formulas by investigating the method of Archimedes, who also made use of the same principle Cavalieri invoked.[8] The two methods, albeit dissimilar in their starting points, interpenetrate since they both make use of the Cavalieri principle to produce the same formulas.

THE LAW OF THE LEVER REVISITED

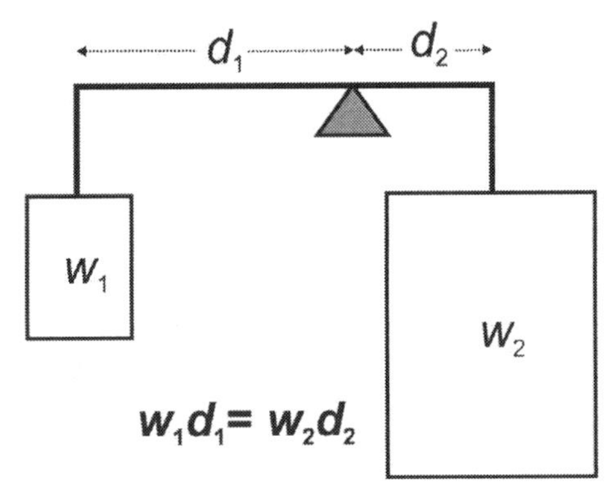

Figure 1.

To one's wonderment, Archimedes' heuristic starting point for deriving the sphere formulas was the principle of the lever (Lesson 8.3). To review, a child plays with a friend on a seesaw with a goal to balance it. Depending on their weights, they could change positions, or move closer to or farther from the fulcrum, so that both would even the saw by stopping its motion when it is parallel to the ground. In the terminology of physics, a seesaw balances when the moments on each side of its fulcrum are equal. Figure 1 illustrates the Archimedean Law of the Lever where w_1 and w_2 represent the respective weights of two objects and d_1 and d_2 represent the distance from the center of gravity of these weights to the fulcrum of the lever. The lever balances when the moments are equal, or:

$$w_1d_1 = w_2d_2$$

The principle of the lever was known to the Greeks long before the birth of Archimedes. It is what Archimedes did with this principle that is unprecedented. Archimedes reasoned from this law to develop important formulas in solid geometry, also known as **stereometry**.[9] Instead of balancing weights about a fulcrum, Archimedes envisioned balancing geometric objects about their center of gravity. He considered the two-dimensional situation in Figure 2, balancing a square with a circle. The radius of the circle is r and its distance from the fulcrum is x. Considering area analogous with weight, Archi-

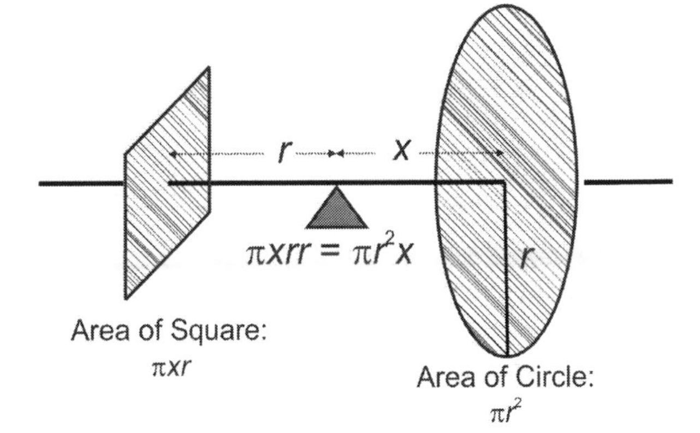

Figure 2.

[7] "The Method of Archimedes" in T. L. Heath, ed. *The Works of Archimedes* (Mineola: Dover Publications, [1912] 2002), p. 13.
[8] What follows is a summary of the method of Archimedes by William M. Priestley, *Calculus: A Liberal Art* (New York: Springer-Verlag, [1974] 1988), pp. 347-350. Bonaventura Cavalieri certainly knew about this Archimedean procedure.
[9] In Greek, *stereometry* literally means the "measure of solids."

medes calculated the moment of the circle to the fulcrum as $\pi r^2 x$. He then let r = distance of the square from the fulcrum. Therefore, by the Law of the Lever, the area of the square, α(Square), multiplied by r is:

$$\alpha(\text{Square})r = \pi r^2 x \Leftrightarrow \alpha(\text{Square}) = \frac{\pi r^2 x}{r} \Leftrightarrow \alpha(\text{Square}) = \pi r x$$

Next (Figure 3), Archimedes considered the situation where the area of the square, $\pi r x$, is substituted by the combined area of the two circles. The center of gravity of the two circles on the left is the same as the center of gravity of the square in Figure 2. We let x = the radius of the bottom circle on the left. Therefore, the area of the bottom circle is πx^2. To maintain equilibrium, the area of the top square must be $\pi r x - \pi x^2$ since:

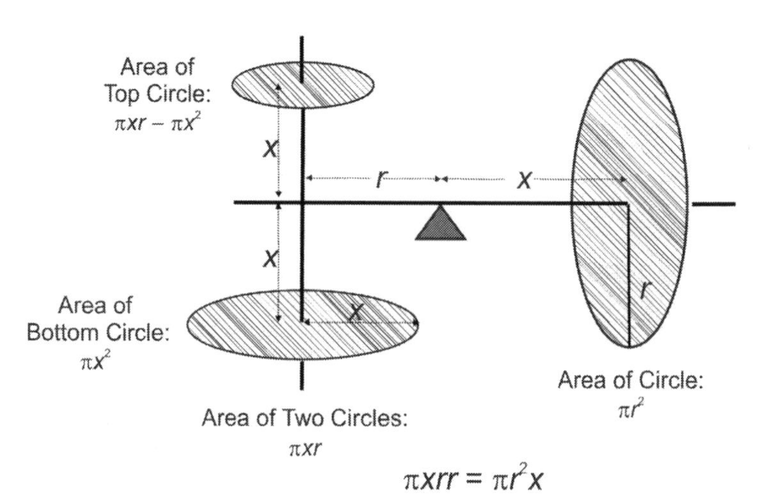

Figure 3.

$$\pi r x - \pi x^2 + \pi x^2 = \pi r x, \text{ the area of the square.}$$

VOLUME OF A SPHERE

Now, Archimedes considered generating a sphere around the top circle, a right cone around the bottom circle, and a cylinder around the circle at the right of the fulcrum to exactly balance each vertical slice through the right cylinder by a corresponding pair of horizontal slices in the sphere and the right cone (Figure 4).[10]

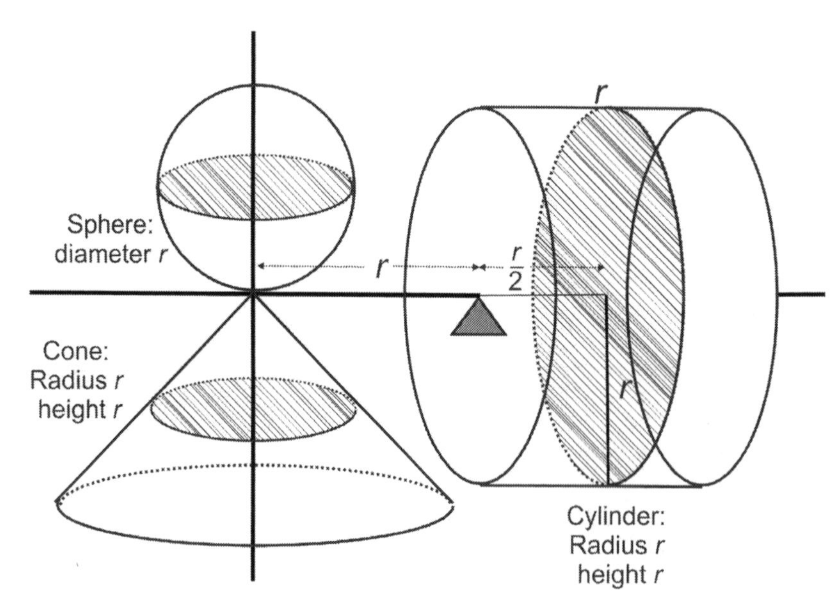

Figure 4.

Archimedes was now able to develop a formula for the volume of the sphere. He knew that the laughing philosopher Democritus (ca. 460-ca. 370 BC), one who was always ready to see the funny side of life, had already shown the relationship between the

[10] This method, repeated by Bonaventura Cavalieri, portends the methods of the Integral Calculus.

volume of a right cone and that of a right cylinder of equal base and height, and similarly for the square pyramid and cube. In other words, he knew that the volume of the right cone is $\frac{1}{3}$ the volume of the right cylinder and the volume of a square pyramid is also $\frac{1}{3}$ the volume of a cube (Lesson 14.2).

Since the configuration in Figure 4 balances, Archimedes applied the Law of the Lever. We let V_{cone} = volume of the right cone, V_{sphere} = volume of the sphere, and $V_{cylinder}$ = volume of the right cylinder.

We get:

$$(V_{cone} + V_{sphere})r + (V_{cylinder})\left(\frac{r}{2}\right)$$

(Note: $\frac{r}{2}$ is the length of the moment arm from the fulcrum to the center of gravity of the right cylinder.)

Dividing this equation by r, we get:

$$V_{cone} + V_{sphere} = \frac{V_{cylinder}}{2}$$

Subtracting V_{cone} from both sides, we get:

$$V_{sphere} = \frac{V_{cylinder}}{2} - V_{cone}$$

Since $V_{cylinder} = \pi r^3$ and $V_{cone} = \frac{1}{3}\pi r^3$, by substitution, we get:

$$V_{sphere} = \frac{\pi r^3}{2} - \frac{\pi r^3}{3} \Leftrightarrow V_{sphere} = \frac{\pi r^3}{6}$$

We now have the volume of a sphere of known diameter r. Since d is the common representation for diameter, we can restate the volume formula in terms of both the diameter d and radius r recognizing that $d = 2r$.

$$V_{sphere} = \frac{\pi d^3}{6} \text{ and } d = 2r \Rightarrow$$

$$V_{sphere} = \frac{\pi (2r)^3}{6} \Leftrightarrow V_{sphere} = \frac{\pi\left(\overset{4}{\cancel{8}} r^3\right)}{\underset{3}{\cancel{6}}} \Leftrightarrow V_{sphere} = \frac{4}{3}\pi r^3$$

QED

SURFACE AREA OF A SPHERE

Archimedes next tackled the surface area of a sphere by noting this similar relationship:

> ... judging from the fact that any circle is equal to a triangle with base equal to the circumference and height equal to the radius of the circle, I apprehended that, in like manner, any sphere is equal to a cone with base equal to the surface of the sphere and height equal to the radius.[11]

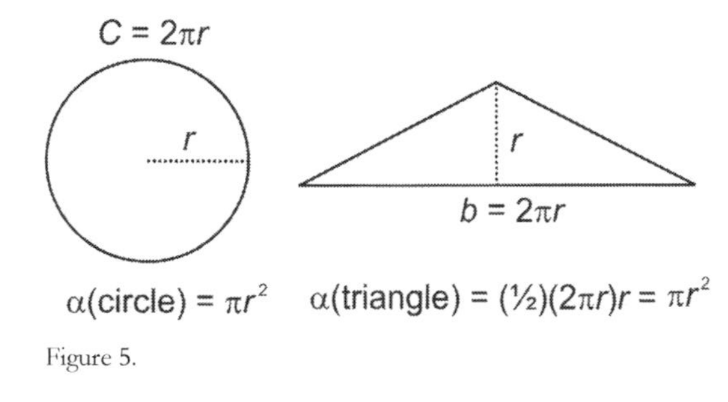

Figure 5.

He first compared the area of a circle with the area of a triangle. Figure 5 reveals the connection he made. As we should see, he used this diagram to prove the area formula for a circle.[12]

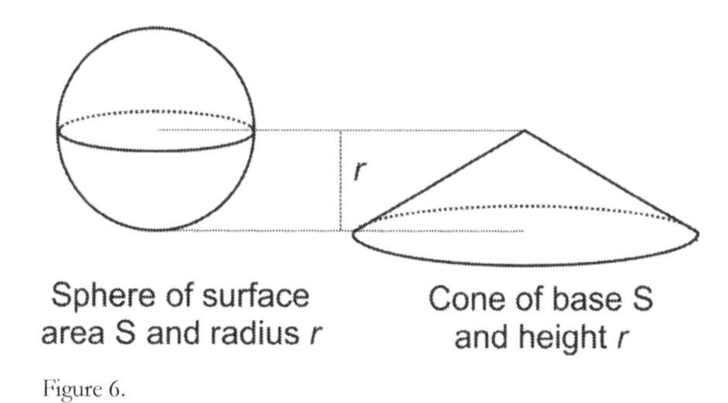

Figure 6.

Figure 6 reveals the same thinking that Archimedes applied to the sphere and right cone, where S is the surface area of the sphere. By his reasoning, we write:

$$\frac{4}{3}\pi r^3 = \frac{1}{3}Sr$$

Solving for S, we get:

$$\frac{4}{3}\pi r^3 = \frac{1}{3}Sr \Leftrightarrow 4\pi r^3 = Sr \Leftrightarrow S = \frac{4\pi r^3}{r} \Leftrightarrow$$

$$S = 4\pi r^2$$

In a sphere, a great circle is defined as the locus of points that is the intersection of the sphere and a plane containing its center (Lesson 3.2). The area of any great circle of radius r is, therefore, πr^2. The formula for the surface area of a sphere shows that this area is exactly four times the area of any great circle.

The beauty revealed by the genius of Archimedes is not only his rigor but his ability to see connections and to reason to mathematical conclusions using a mechanical starting point. By his method, Archimedes showed us a link between physical reality and mathematical thinking. His ignoble, or non-Platonic work, reveals a *balanced* connection between concrete reality and abstract thinking.[13] Since the Triune God is the Creator of both the physical world and the human mind, the successes of the Archimedean method turns on the fulcrum of the Creator of all things.

---

[11] Heath, *The Works of Archimedes*, pp. 20-21.

[12] *Ibid.*, pp. 91-93.

[13] This connection is another example of unity in diversity, indeed, perichoresis.

EXERCISES

1. Define stereometry.

Under ideal circumstances, sound or light waves emitted from a source spread out in a spherical fashion from that source. As the distance from the source increases, the energy of the waves is spread over a greater area and thus the perceived intensity decreases. We measure this intensity by this formula:

$I = \dfrac{P}{4\pi r^2}$ where:

I is the intensity; it tells us how much energy we receive from the source per second and per square meter.

$4\pi r^2$ is the surface area of a sphere.

P is the power of the source. Power is the rate at which energy is expended (Lesson 8.2). The unit of power in electricity is the watt (W), named after James Watt (1736-1819), Scottish inventor and engineer. We measure I in W/m^2. To calculate I properly we need the power of the source P (in W) and the distance r (in meters) to it.

2. Your eardrums will burst when $I = 10{,}100\ \text{W/m}^2$. What power is needed to generate this intensity if we are one meter from the source? Determine your answer using appropriate units in every step, use a scientific calculator and invoke its value of π, and round your answer to the nearest unit.

Answer these questions using Figure 7:

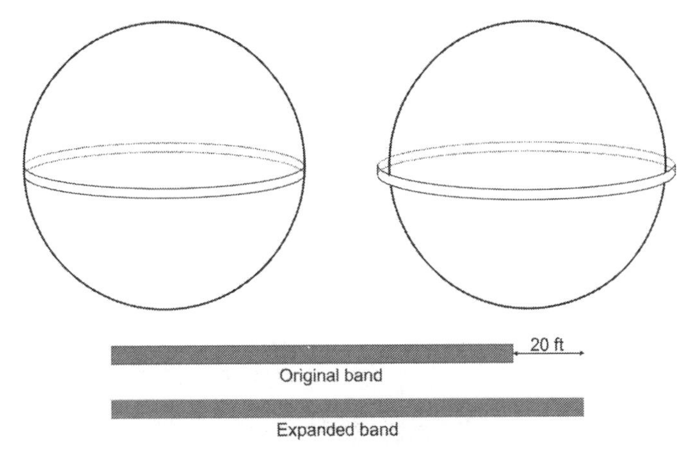

Figure 7.

3. Assume that a band is stretched tightly around the Earth at its equator. If we expand the length of the band by 20 feet, how high, rounded to the nearest hundredth, would the band be above the surface of the Earth? Use a scientific calculator and invoke its value of π.
4. Would your answer to Question 3 be valid for any size sphere? Why or why not?

5. Develop a general formula to find the height h of the band above a sphere by increasing the circumference of the sphere by k feet.

Archimedes and π.

Archimedes used an ingenious method to estimate π using geometric principles introduced in Lesson 13.8, the *Circle* section. In this demonstration, we will follow the method he used to estimate the upper and lower limits of π. First, he drew a circle and set the diameter equal to one unit in length (Figure 8). Next, he constructed a square $PQRS$ with each of its four sides tangent to the circle. In Euclidean geometry, this square is circumscribed around the circle. Then, he constructed a second square $TUVW$ contained in the circle with its vertices tangent to the circle. This square is inscribed within the circle.

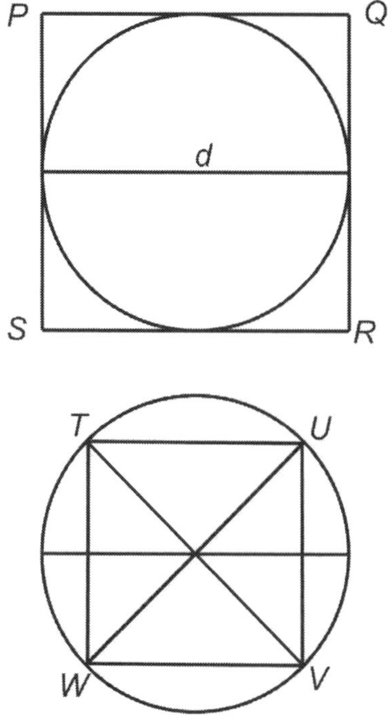

Figure 8. Circumscribed and inscribed squares.

6. It should be intuitively obvious that the perimeter of the inscribed square is less than the length of the circumference of the circle and that the circumference of the circle is less than the length of the perimeter of the circumscribed square. Let a = perimeter of the inscribed square, C = circumference of the circle, and b = perimeter of the circumscribed square. Write an expression using the inequality sign < comparing a, c, and b.
7. Let d = diameter of the circle. Divide every term of the inequality that you wrote in Question 6 by d.
8. Note that $\pi = \frac{C}{d}$. Substitute $\frac{C}{d}$ with π in the inequality you wrote in Question 7.

Following this thinking of Archimedes, we now have bounded π by an upper and lower limit; i.e., $x < \pi < y$.

9. Since $PQRS$ is a square, then its perimeter b is $4(PQ)$. What part of the circle is PQ?
10. From Question 9 determine the upper bound; i.e., y.
11. To calculate the lower bound, i.e., x, we proceed as follows. Note that ΔTWV is a right triangle. By the Pythagorean Theorem, write an equation in terms of TW, WV, and d.

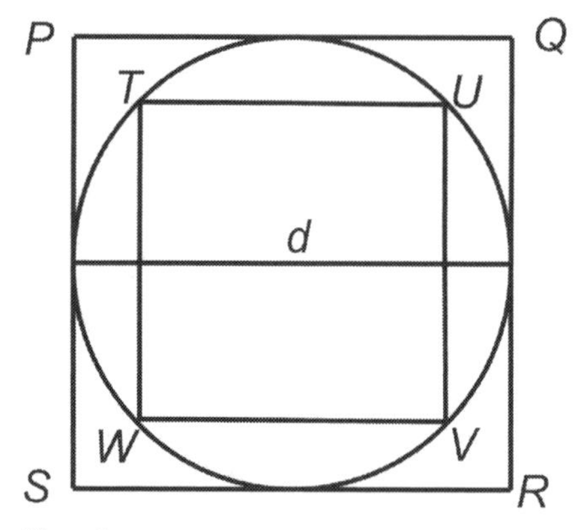

Figure 9.

12. Since $TUVW$ is a square, then $TW = WV$. Substitute WV for TW in the equation you wrote to answer Question 11.
13. Solve the equation you wrote in Question 12 for TW.
14. Since $TUVW$ is a square, then its perimeter is $4(TW)$. By substitution and remembering that $d = 1$, determine the exact lower bound; i.e., x. Write your answer in simple radical form.

15. Write the boundary limits in the form of $x < \pi < y$. Approximate x to the nearest hundredth. Figure 9 pictures these bounds.

Next, Archimedes calculated the limits, lower and upper bounds, of π using regular hexagons. He started by constructing a circle with radius r and a regular hexagon inscribed within it (Figure 10).

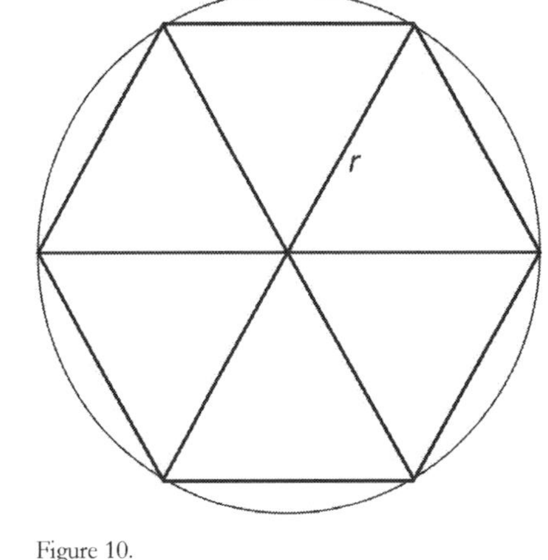

Figure 10.

16. Show that the hexagon is made up of six equilateral triangles. (Hint: If you divide 360° by 6, you get the size of the central angle in each of these triangles. Remember, an isosceles triangle and an equilateral triangle are equivalent.)
17. If the hexagon's perimeter is p, write a formula for:
    (a) p in terms of r, the radius of the circle.
    (b) p in terms of d, the diameter of the circle.
18. Show that $\pi > 3$. (Hint: Note that the circumference C of a circle, given by the formula $C = 2\pi r = \pi d$, is greater than the perimeter of the hexagon.)

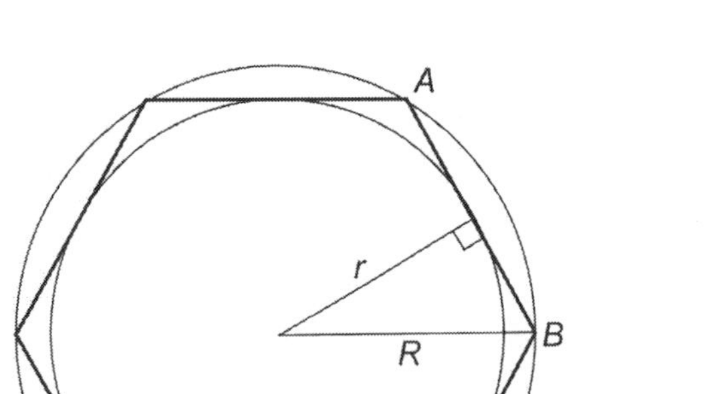

Figure 11.

19. Now, consider a regular hexagon with an inscribed circle of radius r and a circumscribed circle of radius R (Figure 11). Let P = the perimeter of the hexagon. Let C = the circumference of the lesser circle. Show that P > C.

20. Applying the Pythagorean Theorem to the right triangle shown, prove $\frac{R}{r} = \frac{2\sqrt{3}}{3}$.

21. Prove $\frac{P}{2r} = 2\sqrt{3}$. (Hint: Use $P = 6R$ to start your reasoning.)

22. Show $\pi < 2\sqrt{3}$.

23. Round $2\sqrt{3}$ to the nearest hundredth and state the boundary conditions on π.

After calculating the limits of π using a hexagon, he continued this type of logic for a regular 12-gon.

24. Archimedes next considered inscribing a regular polygon with 12 sides in a circle of radius *r* and circumference C (Figure 12). How many isosceles triangles make up this regular polygon?
25. What is the central angle of each of these isosceles triangles?
26. Show that if the legs of such an isosceles triangle have the length *r* (the radius of the circle *O*), then its base has length $r\sqrt{2-\sqrt{3}}$. (Hint: Use Figure 13 to guide you. Find the length of the altitude of an equilateral triangle first whose angles each measure 60°. Then use your trusted friend, the Pythagorean Theorem. This proof will challenge you.)
27. Show that the perimeter *P* of a 12-sided regular polygon inscribed within a circle of radius *r* is given by $P = 12r\sqrt{2-\sqrt{3}}$.
28. Use your result in Question 27 to prove that $\pi > 6\sqrt{2-\sqrt{3}}$. (Hint: Let C = circumference of the circle, then $P < C$. Therefore, $\frac{P}{2r} < \frac{C}{2r}$.)
29. Now, consider circumscribing a 12-sided regular polygon about the same circle of radius *r* and circumference C. If *p* is the perimeter of the inscribed regular polygon and *P* is the perimeter of the circumscribed regular polygon, show that $\frac{P}{p} = \frac{B}{b}$ where *B* and *b* are the respective lengths of bases of the isosceles triangles making up the circumscribed and inscribed polygons. (Hint: $P = 12B$ and $p = 12b$.)
30. Show, by the proportional law of similar triangles, that $\frac{B}{b} = \frac{r}{h}$, where *h* is the height, or the altitude, of the isosceles triangle with base *b*. [Hint: Use Figure 12

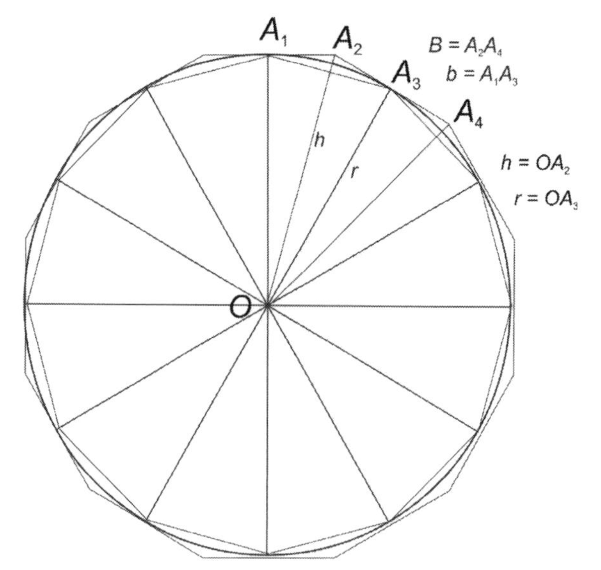

Figure 12.

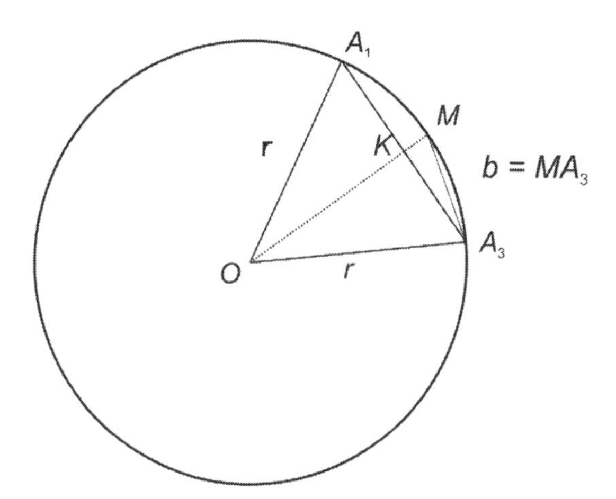

Figure 13. Zooming in.

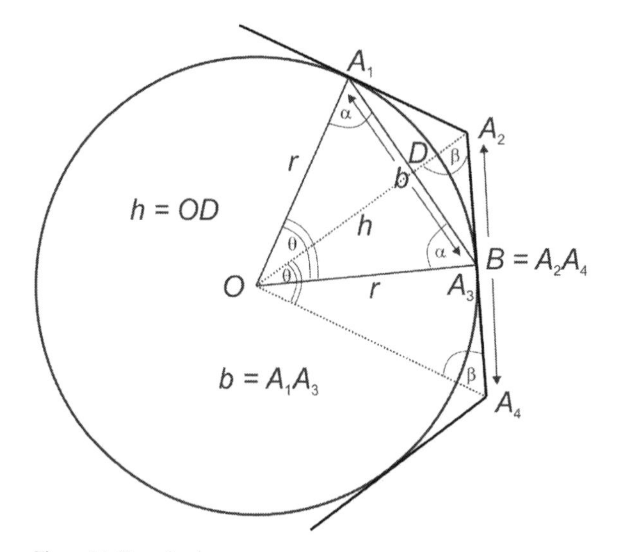

Figure 14. Zooming in.

and Figure 14 as guides for your reasoning. You will need to employ the AA Similarity Theorem (compare ΔOA_1A_3 with ΔOA_2A_4) and the *pons asinorum* theorem as part of your proof. This proof will challenge you.]

31. Show that $h = \left(\frac{r}{2}\right)\sqrt{2+\sqrt{3}}$.

32. Use Question 29, Question 30, and Question 31 to show $\frac{P}{p} = \frac{2}{\sqrt{2+\sqrt{3}}}$.

33. Calculate the ratio $\frac{P}{2r}$ by multiplying $\frac{P}{p}$ by $\frac{p}{2r}$. (Hint: We already know that $\frac{p}{2r} = 6\sqrt{2-\sqrt{3}}$.)

34. From Question 33, show that $\pi < 12(2 - \sqrt{3})$.

35. We now have bounded π as follows: $6\sqrt{2-\sqrt{3}} < \pi < 12(2-\sqrt{3})$. Using your scientific calculator, determine the lower and upper bounds of π to five significant figures.

Just imagine Archimedes, the great ancient human calculator, doing this for a 96-sided regular polygon! His boundary conditions for π, using a regular 96-gon, are approximately stated as a mixed number:

$$3\frac{10}{71} < \pi < 3\frac{10}{70}$$

Rounded, as a decimal:

$3.1408 < \pi < 3.1429$

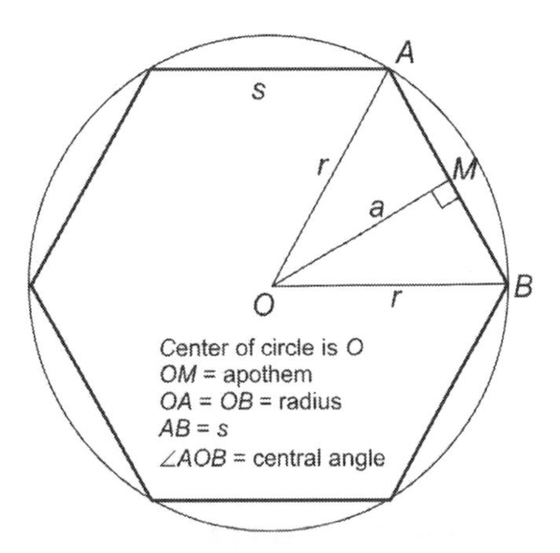

Figure 15.

Calculating the Circumference and Area of a Circle using Limits and Trigonometry.

We are going to take the lead given by Archimedes and use regular polygons to help us derive the formula for the circumference and area of a circle. Inspect the regular hexagon inscribed in a circle (Figure 15). We are going to use it as a guide to develop our general formulas.

36. We let the perimeter p of any regular is the length of its sides, s, by the number of its sides, n. Write an equation for p in terms of s and n.
37. In Figure 15, $\Delta AOM \cong \Delta BOM$. Why?
38. What can we conclude about AM and BM? Why?
39. Write an equation for AM in terms of s.

40. Write an expression for the measure of a central angle of a regular polygon without using the degrees unit.
41. Let $\theta = m\angle AOM$ and write an equation for θ.
42. Write an equation for $\sin\theta$ in terms of s and r.
43. Write a formula for p in terms of n and r.
44. (a) What does this formula tell you about the perimeter of a regular n-gon?
    (b) Is there a connection between this relationship and a similar relationship in a circle? If yes, what is it?
45. Let a = the apothem of a regular n-gon. Write a formula for the area of ΔAOB, or $\alpha(\Delta AOB)$, in terms of s and a.
46. Write a formula for the total area A of all such triangles in a regular n-gon in terms of n, s, and a.
47. Write a formula for the total area A of all such triangles in a regular n-gon in terms of p and a.
48. Write an equation for $\cos\theta$ in terms of a and r.
49. Write a formula for A, the area of a regular n-gon, in terms of n and r.
50. (a) What does this formula tell you about the area of a regular n-gon?
    (b) Is there a connection between this relationship and a similar relationship in a circle? If yes, what is it?
51. Find x in $\lim_{n\to\infty}\left(n\sin\frac{180}{n}\right) = x$. (Hint: Use a graph to help you.)
52. Find y in $\lim_{n\to\infty}\left(\cos\frac{180}{n}\right) = y$. (Hint: Use a graph to help you.)
53. From your answers to Questions 51 and 52, determine, with algebraic explanation:
    (a) The formula for the circumference of a circle.
    (b) The formula for the area of a circle.

    [Make use of the following observations: $\lim_{n\to\infty} ka = k\left(\lim_{n\to\infty} a\right)$, where k is a constant and a is an expression in n, and $\lim_{n\to\infty} ab = \left(\lim_{n\to\infty} a\right)\left(\lim_{n\to\infty} b\right)$, where a and b represent an expression in n.]

Some Deductions from Isaac Newton's Universal Law of Gravitation: Calculating the Mass of the Earth.
As we have noted, Isaac Newton (1642-1727) adopted a conjecture made by many of his contemporaries that the force of attraction, F, between any two bodies of masses m and M, respectively, separated by distance r is given by the formula:

$$F = G\frac{mM}{r^2}$$

In this formula, G is a constant, the constant of gravitation. Its value depends upon the units used for mass, force, and distance.

54. What is the dependent variable (Review Lesson 10.2.) in this formula or law?
55. What are the independent variables (Review Lesson 10.2.) in this law?
56. If $G = 1$, $m = 2$, and $M = 3$, find F.

To apply the Law of Gravitation, Newton adopted another physical principle just as important. Newton knew that the force of gravity near the surface of the Earth gives to objects an acceleration of 32 ft/s^2 (or 9.8 m/s^2) and the force is 32 times (or 9.8 times) the mass of the object.

Newton generalized this relationship and affirmed that whenever any force acts on an object, it gives that object acceleration, i.e., a push. The relationship of force F, the mass of the object m, and acceleration a imparted to the object is given by the formula $F = ma$, Newton's Second Law of Motion. We have already noted that, for an object near the surface of the Earth, F measures its weight, the measure of the force that gravitation exerts on a body of mass m.

57. Newton proceeded to test his conjectures. First, he rewrote

$$F = G\frac{mM}{r^2}$$

as

$$F = mG\frac{M}{r^2}.$$

How can this be justified?

58. Comparing $F = mG\frac{M}{r^2}$ with $F = ma$, Newton, by substitution, wrote an expression for a. What is it?

59. If M is the mass of the Earth and m is the mass of a small body near the surface of the Earth, Newton set r, the distance between the two, to be equal to the radius of the Earth. He conjectured, and later proved, that we can regard the mass of the Earth as though it concentrates at the center of the Earth, its point-mass. To simplify matters, we let $r = 4000$ miles. This value is the same for all objects near the surface of the Earth. Moreover, the mass M of the Earth is constant, and the gravitational constant G is also constant. Therefore, for all objects near the surface of the Earth, what could Newton conclude about the acceleration a?

Before Newton was born, the Italian scientist Galileo Galilei (1564-1642) had come to the same conclusion by a series of empirical experiments. Thus, Newton's law, developed by deduction, had been confirmed via induction. Notice the interplay between deduction and induction. This interplay is the backbone of good science.

60. Solve $F = G\frac{mM}{r^2}$ for G.

61. Actual experiments have been made to measure G using standard English units, i.e., the foot-pound-second unit of force where distance is in feet, mass in pounds, and force in poundals (ft-lb-sec). These calculations established $G = 1.07 \times 10^{-9}$ ft^3/pounds/sec^2. In the centimeter-gram-second (cgs) system of units, $G = 6.67 \times 10^{-8}$ m^3/kg/s^2. Knowing G, we can proceed to calculate the mass of the Earth. Solve your answer to Question 58, $a = G\frac{M}{r^2}$. for M.

62. Using your scientific calculator, convert the radius of the Earth, $r = 4000$ miles, to feet. Write your answer in Scientific Notation using to significant figures.

63. Given: $a = 32$ ft/sec^2, $G = 1.07 \times 10^{-9}$ ft^3/pounds/sec^2, and $r =$ distance in feet. Using a scientific calculator:
(a) find M, the mass of the Earth in pounds, written in Scientific Notation, to two significant figures.
(b) Confirm how the units cancel leaving only pounds.

64. Using the unit conversion factor of 2000 pounds = 1 ton and a scientific calculator, calculate the mass of the Earth in tons to two significant figures in Scientific Notation.

65. Using the unit conversion factor of one pound = 0.45 kg and a scientific calculator, calculate the mass of the Earth in kilograms to two significant figures in Scientific Notation.

Some Deductions from Isaac Newton's Universal Law of Gravitation: Calculating the Density of the Earth.

66. We can assume that the Earth is spherical in shape. We know that the volume V of a sphere is $V = \frac{4}{3}\pi r^3$. Using your scientific calculator and invoking its value for π, compute the volume of the Earth in cubic feet. Write your answer in Scientific Notation in three significant figures.
67. The density of any object is its mass divided by the volume (Lesson 7.5). Using your scientific calculator and your knowledge of the mass of the Earth in pounds, compute the density of the Earth in pounds per cubic foot, rounded to the nearest unit.
68. The density of water is 62.5 pounds/ft^3. Using your scientific calculator, compute how many times greater is the density of the Earth than the density of water, rounded to the nearest tenth.

Some Deductions from Isaac Newton's Universal Law of Gravitation: Calculating the Mass of the Sun.

69. Let S = the mass of the Sun, E = the mass of the Earth, and r = distance from the Earth to the Sun. From Newton's Universal Law of Gravitation:

    $$F = G\frac{SE}{r^2}$$

    According to Newton's second law of motion, the force that the Sun exerts on the Earth gives the Earth an acceleration a such that $F = Ea$. Since these force equations are the same, set them equal.
70. Divide both sides of the equation you wrote in Question 69 by E (i.e., cancel E).
71. Solve the equation you wrote in Question 70 for S, the mass of the Sun.
72. We know the acceleration, a, that the Sun imparts to the Earth to be:

    $$a = \frac{v^2}{r}$$

    (See the homework exercise in Lesson 12.1. See also the Analysis of Acceleration section in Lesson 12.8.)

    Substitute $a = \frac{v^2}{r}$ into the equation you wrote Question 71.
73. You should have an equation for S in terms of v, r, and G. We know $G = 1.07 \times 10^{-9}$ ft^3/pounds/sec^2. To keep things simple, we let r, the distance from the Earth to the Sun, to be 93,000,000 miles. Using your scientific calculator, convert r to feet and express in Scientific Notation to two significant figures.
74. We can calculate the velocity, v, of the Earth by dividing the circumference of the Earth's orbit, assumed to be circular, by the number of seconds in one year. Using your scientific calculator, calculate the number of seconds in one year, assuming 365 days. Express your answer in Scientific Notation to three significant figures.
75. Since the circumference of a circle, C, is given by the formula $C = 2\pi r$, calculate the circumference of the Earth as it orbits the Sun in feet. Express your answer in Scientific Notation to three significant figures. You may use your scientific calculator.
76. Using your scientific calculator, calculate the Earth's velocity v in ft/sec. Express your answer in Scientific Notation to two significant figures.

77. We now know v, r, and G (in consistent units). Using your scientific calculator, find the mass of the Sun in pounds. Express your answer in Scientific Notation to three significant figures.
78. To two significant figures, determine with your scientific calculator how many times more is the mass of the Sun compared to the mass of the Earth?

> By this work with Newton's Universal Law of Gravitation, we can see the incredible power that algebraic operations and deductive reasoning brings to the scientific table.

Figure 16. Courtesy of NASA.

14.8 Recap

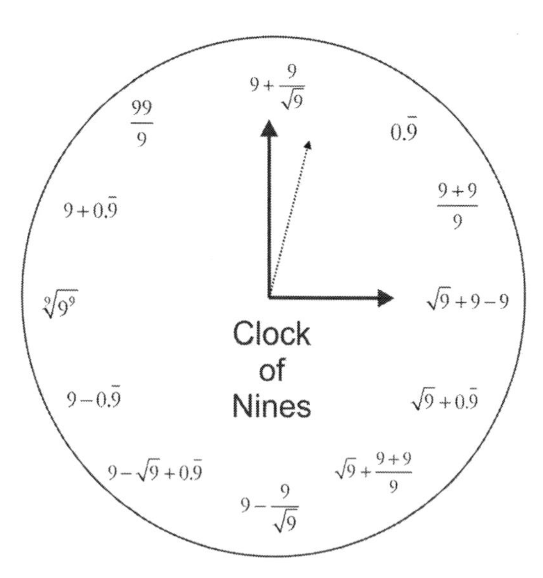

Figure 1.

Review

Congratulations for completing *The Dance of Number* curriculum. Stand back, for a moment, and review the material that you have mastered. Here are the significant highlights:

Terms and Concepts Introduced
1. Complex fraction
2. Continued fraction
3. Continued radicals
4. Diophantine analysis
5. Epistemology
6. Ethics
7. Lucas numbers
8. Philosophy
9. Rhetorical algebra
10. Syncopated algebra

1. Establishing the ground of created rationality in the Uncreated rationality of the Triune God.
2. Understanding of positional notation and its fascinating history.
3. Understanding the beauty of the base 10 decimal system.
4. Adding and Subtracting whole numbers on the Japanese Soroban as the basis for invoking a left-to-right speed paradigm using complements.
5. Multiplying and dividing whole numbers, left-to-right, using the Distributive Law.
6. Rules for adding, subtracting, multiplying, and dividing integers, or any signed numbers.
7. Addition, subtraction, multiplication, and division of fractions and decimals, which are fractions written in another form.
8. Changing from any unit to another unit, knowing the unit multiplier.
9. Many revelations of fractions and decimals as they interpenetrate ratios, proportions, and percentages.
10. An introduction to Probability and Statistics.
11. A fascinating exploration of exponentiation, extraction of roots, logarithms, trigonometry, and complex numbers.

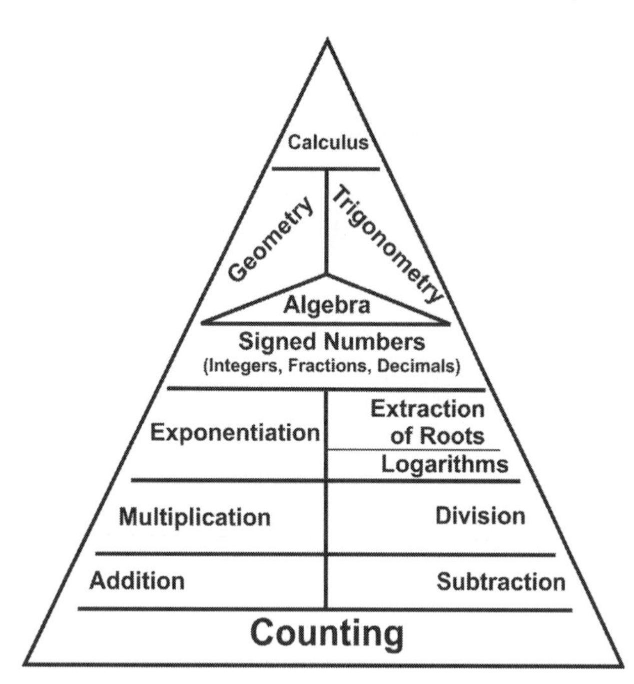

Figure 2.

12. An introduction to the methods, the order and operations, of Algebra, including solving and graphing many types of equations.
13. An introduction to measurement, Geometry, and the rudiments of Calculus reasoning.
14. Many examples and demonstrations of the way mathematicians use logic to prove theorems about number and space, i.e., two-dimensional and three-dimensional geometry.

> ... anyone with a taste for figures and an interest in reading can find a vast enjoyment in the symmetry and harmony of basic mathematics and in the solving of mathematical problems.
>
> Aaron Bakst, *Mathematics: Its Magic and Mystery* (1952), p. v.

As indicated in Figure 2, you are well on your way up the pyramid of mathematics, where Calculus is at the pinnacle.[1] Given your mastery of the concepts taught in *The Dance of Number* curriculum, this journey will be a delight.

PERICHORESIS

As we have learned, perichoresis, *perichoreo* in Greek, is a theological word developed by the church fathers to explicate what it means for the persons of the Trinity to mutually indwell each other in intimate fellowship (John 14:10, 20). A dance metaphor is connected to this word because the Greek word *perichoreuo* means "to dance around."

> ... one's intellectual and aesthetic life cannot be complete unless it includes an appreciation of the power and beauty of mathematics.
>
> Jerry P. King, *The Art of Mathematics* ([1992] 2006), p. 3.

It is this onto-relational God who has created all things, invisible and visible. There is, therefore, a perichoretic structure, a dance, in creation. This dance is the unity behind the diversity of the cosmos, the rational dynamic that is the ground of all that exists. This unity exists because all things cohere in Jesus Christ, the Word of the Father, the Word of creation, God the Son made flesh (John 1:14). It is the Son who reveals to us the perichoretic nature, the dance of the dynamism of His relationship to His Father in the Holy Spirit. One aspect of the perichoretic structure of creation is number, and the study and development of number is Mathematics. Since space interpenetrates number, numerical and spatial patterns bring to light the rational order, the beauty, the perichoretic dance of creation.

Genesis 1 reveals that the Triune God made man, male and female, in His image, *imago Dei* in Latin. Image in this sense means reflection, to a limited and finite extent, of the person and character of the Triune God, the Creator. His dance is therefore in us. We are wired for perichoresis and therefore can see it in creation if we just open our eyes.

---

[1] Calculus is not the apex of the pyramid of mathematics since there is much more to mathematics. Calculus is the door that leads you into a wonderland of advanced mathematics. The goal you should be aiming for in your educational journeys is the mastery of the rich intellectual treasure of Calculus reasoning. The ideas in Lessons 13.17 to 13.19 are a small aperture though which you can peek into this wealth.

> We have come finally to the undeniable and irresistible conclusion that our mathematics and physical reality are inseparable. Mathematics, insofar as it tells us what the physical world contains and insofar as the expression of that knowledge can only be in mathematical language and concepts, is as real as tables and chairs. ... mathematics remains the method par excellence for the investigation, representation, and mastery of nature. In some domains it is all we have; if it is not reality itself, it is the closest to reality we can get.
>
> Morris Kline, *Mathematics and the Search for Knowledge* (1985), pp. 226-227.

We have unearthed many examples of perichoresis in the world of mathematics, the profound interconnectedness between its ideas and objects. We see it in the interplay between the concrete and the abstract. There is a magnificent, wondrous, and, indeed, to some, mysterious dance between abstract mathematics and the rational nature of the physical creation. Both inhere in each other in a perichoretic dance. The integration of being and structure is why algebraic operations applied to mathematical statements can generate new statements that are also dance with the way things work in the universe. This interpenetration, this perichoresis, is why, in the words of Albert Einstein, human thought which is independent of experience, is so admirably appropriate to the objects of reality.

In the next couple of pages, we will review only a portion of the perichoretic dance that is mathematics explicated in the four volumes of *The Dance of Number*. Refer to the index of each volume to get an exhaustive catalogue.

There is a perichoretic interpenetration between the addends and the sum, between the minuend, subtrahend, and difference, between factors and their product, and between the dividend, divisor, and quotient.

We cannot separate the perimeter of a rectangle from its dimensionality; they mutually indwell each other and thus reflect the perichoretic nature of number and the dimensions of geometric objects. Each side of a rectangle mutually indwells, or determines, the perimeter; the perimeter is in each side, and each side is in the perimeter. The same mutual indwelling appears in area and volume.

The Distributive Law of Multiplication over Addition governs any multiplication problem where one factor has two or more digits. This law mutually indwells the algorithm of multiplication and its inverse, division. The Distributive Law is, as we noted, the interpenetrating principle of the dance of the four foundational operations of arithmetic.

Number systems are perichoretic in nature as one system is contained in the other: $\mathbb{N} \subset \mathbb{Z} \subset \mathbb{Q} \subset \mathbb{R} \subset \mathbb{C}$.

In logic, there is a perichoretic dance between logical equivalence and its two implications, the conditional statement and its converse. Or, in general, $a \Leftrightarrow b$ means $a \Rightarrow b$ and $b \Rightarrow a$.

With fractions (Lesson 6.3), geometry interpenetrates the arithmetic of the GCF algorithm. The algorithm is in the area of a rectilinear figure, and the area of a rectilinear figure is in the algorithm.

Percentages, fractions, and decimals are perichoretic dance partners. In the wonderful world of rational numbers, each concept is involved in the other.

With levers (Lesson 8.3), we saw how geometry, number, and the mechanism interrelate. There is an interpenetration linking the machine, physical ideas, Geometry, and Arithmetic.

Pascal's Triangle is replete with perichoretic wonders. We find in the numbers of the triangle powers of two, the combination formula, the Binomial Theorem, perfect squares, and the Fibonacci Sequence.

$$ {}_0C_0 = P_0 $$
$$ {}_1C_0 \cdot {}_1C_1 = P_1 $$
$$ {}_2C_0 \cdot {}_2C_1 \cdot {}_2C_2 = P_2 $$
$$ {}_3C_0 \cdot {}_3C_1 \cdot {}_3C_2 \cdot {}_3C_3 = P_3 $$
$$ {}_4C_0 \cdot {}_4C_1 \cdot {}_4C_2 \cdot {}_4C_3 \cdot {}_4C_4 = P_4 $$
$$ {}_5C_0 \cdot {}_5C_1 \cdot {}_5C_2 \cdot {}_5C_3 \cdot {}_5C_4 \cdot {}_5C_5 = P_5 $$
$$ {}_6C_0 \cdot {}_6C_1 \cdot {}_6C_2 \cdot {}_6C_3 \cdot {}_6C_4 \cdot {}_6C_5 \cdot {}_6C_6 = P_6 $$
$$ {}_7C_0 \cdot {}_7C_1 \cdot {}_7C_2 \cdot {}_7C_3 \cdot {}_7C_4 \cdot {}_7C_5 \cdot {}_7C_6 \cdot {}_7C_7 = P_7 $$
$$ {}_8C_0 \cdot {}_8C_1 \cdot {}_8C_2 \cdot {}_8C_3 \cdot {}_8C_4 \cdot {}_8C_5 \cdot {}_8C_6 \cdot {}_8C_7 \cdot {}_8C_8 = P_8 $$
$$ {}_9C_0 \cdot {}_9C_1 \cdot {}_9C_2 \cdot {}_9C_3 \cdot {}_9C_4 \cdot {}_9C_5 \cdot {}_9C_6 \cdot {}_9C_7 \cdot {}_9C_8 \cdot {}_9C_9 = P_9 $$

$$ \lim_{n\to\infty} \frac{P_{n-1}P_{n+1}}{P_n^2} = e $$

Figure 3. Stunning perichoretic wonder!

In Lesson 9.6, we saw how the permutation formula is involved in our birthday problem.

In our study of the harmonic sequence (Lesson 9.8), when we play a note of 200 Hz, our ears hear part of the 100 Hz sound; i.e., there is an interpenetration telling our senses that there is a relationship between the 100 Hz sound and the sound an octave higher.

The abstract conceptions of the origin, quadrants, axes, and coordinates indwell fundamental relations of the physical creation. The Cartesian coordinate plane reveals the perichoresis between Algebra and Geometry. For example, the simplest linear equation, $y = x$, interpenetrates a function and its inverse in terms of the geometry of reflections. Geometry, therefore, unfolds the beauty between an algebraic function and its inverse in ways that we cannot see in any other way. Algebra and Geometry interpenetrate in symmetric wonder. When solving quadratic equations, we can convert what we have do geometrically to algebraic symbols to demonstrate the perichoretic nature of completing the square.

Together, a rule in algebraic function notation, a table revealing discrete points, and a graph form a perichoretic relationship. The rule is in the table and the graph, the table is in the rule and the graph, and the graph is in the rule and the table.

In more advanced functions, e.g., quadratic, cubic, and rational, the end-behavior, asymptotes, and zeroes of a function are embedded in the algebraic notation.

The ubiquitous Pythagorean Theorem is in every right triangle, and a right triangle is in the Pythagorean Theorem. As a consequence of this theorem, $\sqrt{2}$ is always be embedded, as a perichoretic dance, in the diagonal of any square.

The equiangular spiral is embedded both within the Fibonacci Sequence and the analysis of the equal-tempered chromatic scale in the Polar Coordinate plane.

In Lesson 11.10, we saw that when a number increases by a factor of 10, the pattern for cube roots repeats itself in threes while the same pattern for square roots repeats itself in twos. This pattern exists because of the squaring, two dimensions, and cubing, three dimensions, nature of the processes. There is a beautiful perichoresis in these observations.

In Lesson 11.11, we discovered a unique perichoretic relationship between squares and cubes.

In the Quadratic Formula, the parameters *a*, *b*, and *c* of the problem-pattern of a quadratic are involved its solution. There is a coherence between the parameters and the solution of a quadratic, a revealing a beautiful perichoretic dance.

The dance between logarithms, the principles of trigonometry, and complex numbers is stunning to behold. Euler's Identity, $e^{i\pi} + 1 = 0$, the conclusion of our studies in Step 12, is a perichoretic wonder.

In Lesson 13.13, we discovered that the formula for the area of a trapezoid interpenetrates the Gaussian Formula. What makes mathematics interesting and fun is the discovery of interpenetrating, indeed, perichoretic connections like this.

An arithmetic sequence coinheres with a linear function. A geometric sequence coinheres with an exponential function.

One over three ($\frac{1}{3}$, 1 divided by 3) and the formula $S_n = \frac{t_1}{1-r}$ coinhere. Both forms generate the same answer, but by different methods. The methods interpenetrate in perichoretic fashion.

We understand mathematics, as a whole, from a multiplicity of perspectives, each pervading and reciprocating the other. Mathematics is a formal, structured language system having internal laws, syntax, and relationships. Mathematics is an application of logic and logic permeates mathematics. We cannot prove anything in mathematics without the appeal to laws of logic. Intuition, the feeling for the beauty of symmetry, is the source of many mathematical discoveries. Our experience of mathematics flows from our interaction with the rationality of an external world. Mathematics reflects and reports the dance-pattern of the universe. That the intuitions of mathematics are compatible with empirical reality are, to some, an unsolvable mystery. It is the revelation of the Triune Creator by Christ, the *Logos*, that accounts for and is the ground of the rationality of our minds and the rationality of the world outside of our minds. To correct and improve the Kline quote, it is Christ who is the mediator between man and creation. His mind is the ground of the way we think as our thinking connects with the creation of His making. Mathematics is a tool we create to reflect this connection.

Although mathematics interpenetrates language, logic, intuition, and empirical reality, it is not reducible to any of these fields.[2] Mathematics is a rich, multi-variate discipline, replete with wonder, mystery, and beauty.

> Mathematics mediates between man and nature, between man's inner and outer worlds.
>
> Morris Kline, *Mathematics and the Search for Knowledge* (1985), p. 226.

[2] Mathematics is not a subdivision of language, logic, intuition, or empirical reality. Mathematics, although distinct from these fields, interpenetrates all of them in the wonder of a deeply relational perichoresis.

THE GROUND OF RATIONALITY

We have explored the deep rationality of mathematics, both within its structure and how it reports on and interconnects with the rationality of the universe. In Step 1, we established the Trinitarian grounds for such rationality. Let's review and extend this discussion before we sum up our studies.

The Lord Jesus Christ said (John 14:6),

> "I am the way, the truth and the life. No one comes to the Father except through Me."

> Each individual man should do all he can to impress his own mind with the extent, the order, and the unity of the universe, and should carry these ideas with him as he reads such passages as the 1st Chap. of the Ep. to Colossians.
>
> James Clerk Maxwell (1831-1879), letter to Bishop Ellicott, 22 November 1876. In Lewis Campbell and William Garnett, *The Life and Times of James Clerk Maxwell* (1882), p. 395.

THE WAY

Jesus is the Way to the Father because He is the way of the Father. The Apostle Paul (Ephesians 2:18) states,

> "for through Him [Jesus] we both [Jew and Gentile] have our access in one Spirit to the Father."[3]

No one *pros ton patera*, comes to the Father, but by Jesus. The Greek preposition *pros* means "face to face," in a fellowship that is transparent, a communion of unfeigned completeness and acceptance. *Pros* is the same preposition the Apostle John used in John 1:1 to proclaim that the Word who was in the beginning was "with God (*pros ton theon*)."

The Son Incarnate, the Word (*logos*) who became flesh in Jesus (John 1:14), is the pathway that we walk into the presence of the Father by the Spirit. Every human being has chosen a path in opposition to this "way of holiness" (Isaiah 35), a way that leads to the precipice of perdition. The Triune God does not desire that man perish in this false way (John 3:16-17; II Peter 3:9). The Gospel is the declaration to crooked man, walking on the wrong path, that Jesus is the Way, by the Spirit, to the circle of the face-to-face fellowship He knows with His Father. Jesus is the way to man's true home, his true abiding place (John 14-16). Therefore, God commands crooked man walking on the false path to repent, to change his mind (*metanoia*[4]), to straighten up in the Way that is Jesus.[5] Following Jesus in the Way is to abide in the way He walks, in the way of His fellowship with His Father. The person of His Spirit, poured out on all flesh (Acts 2:16f), is the **ethical**[6] energy bringing us into union with Christ. The giving of the Spirit is

---

[3] The grammar of the Greek indicates that the way is both the truth and life. The Greek word *kai* translated "and" indicates a cumulative force; i.e., Jesus is the way which is the truth which is the life.

[4] In the Greek, *metanoia* means "to change the mind."

[5] We can straighten up in the Way because Jesus, in His vicarious humanity, has straightened man by taking crooked man to death and raising him to new life in His bodily resurrection.

[6] Ethics is a branch of philosophy and it is not only the study of how one lives, it is the study of the ground of living. For the Christian faith, ethics is not just a matter of morality, i.e., good versus bad behavior. Right living is life in the New Creation, a quality of life grounded in union with the vicarious man, Jesus Christ, as He, by the gift of the Holy Spirit, carries us into the

the fruit of the Son's redemptive work, the gift that enables us to walk in His way. Christ is also the way to wisdom (Colossians 2:3). **Philosophy** means "love of wisdom." Since Christ is wisdom and knowledge personified, then a true philosopher is a lover of Christ by the Spirit.

THE TRUTH

The Way of Jesus is the true (*aletheia*) way. All other pathways are false. Man's problem is not just a matter of ethics; it is also **epistemological.**[7] He does not understand the nature of Truth. He has a wrong vision of God. Jesus, as the truth, enlightens every man that comes into the world (John 1:1-4). This enlightenment means that Christ bestows upon all men the ability to know what they know. It is light in the person of Christ that makes any knowledge possible. Jesus said (John 8:31-32):

> "If you abide in My word, you are My disciples indeed. And you will know the truth, and the truth shall make you free."

The truth that is in Jesus the Way brings ethical and epistemological freedom to humanity.

THE LIFE

The way of Jesus is the way of life (*zoe*). *Zoe* is the dynamism of life in its truth; it is not biological life, from a different Greek word *bios*. In Jesus, we know the Father which is *aeonios zoe*, eternal life, the life of the Ages (John 17:3), a quality of life before it is a duration of life. Through Jesus, the true *logos*, all things, including all humanity, were made (Genesis 1:1; John 1:1-3). It is in the *logos* of God that all things consist (Colossians 1:17). It is the word (*rhema*[8]) of His power (*dunamis*[9]) that upholds all things (Hebrews 1:3). A personal *logos* made the world and all humanity, giving *zoe* to all things (John 1:3-4). Not only has the *logos* made the world, He also entered the world, as the glory as of the only-begotten of the Father, taking to Himself the fallen human flesh of every man (Romans 8:3). The *logos* tabernacled in the flesh of man[10] to save man and the cosmos (John 1:14, John 3:16-17, II Corinthians 5:11-6:3).

In philosophy, metaphysics is the study of the nature of reality (Lesson 9.1). Scripture reveals Jesus the Word as the true reality, the ground of all being and existence. Scripture unfolds a transcendent *logos*, an eternal, yet personal Creator and a created order that reflects a pervasive rationality, the way wisdom in the person of Christ, the ultimate rationality, made it (Proverbs 8:12-36). Mathematics reports on the reality of that rationality.

SUMMING-UP OUR STUDIES

All mathematical patterns in the perichoretic structure of creation, numerical or spatial, find their ultimate source of interconnectedness, rationality, order, beauty, and meaning in the second person of the Trinity. The dance of number is grounded in the person of Christ.

As we have explored the beautiful and fascinating world of mathematics, I hope that you have been able to appreciate

> Mathematics enlightens us about our worlds, but by itself it does not and cannot define the realities of those worlds.
>
> Ernest Zebrowski, *A History of the Circle* (1999), p. 50.

---

abundant life that is His knowledge of the Father [Galatians 2:20 (King James Version), Galatians 6:14-15; II Corinthians 5:17; Matthew 11:25-28; John 10:10].

[7] Epistemology (*episteme*, in Greek, means "knowledge") is a branch of philosophy that is the study of the nature of knowledge.

[8] In the Greek, *rhema* means "express statements" or "the utterance of a living voice."

[9] In the Greek, *dunamis* means "power that is inherent," power that is the nature of the person it describes.

[10] "The Word was made flesh and dwelt among (*en*) us" (John 1:14a) can be translated "The Word became flesh and dwelt in us." The Greek preposition ἐν, transliterated *en*, means "in," not "among." Note how John uses this preposition in the rest of the first chapter, i.e., vv. 2, 4, 5, 10, 23, 28, 31, and 33.

and master some of its manifold patterns and laws. This dance is a part of God's pre-established universe. You, like everyone else, are made in the image of God. The universe that exists outside of our existence is replete with patterns, structure, and order, a dance of unimaginable beauty. We study the works of the Triune God in part by mastering mathematics. Creation images its Creator and so do you. That is why, when you explore and learn the patterns of mathematics, you enter into the realm, albeit only a very dim realm, of "thinking God's thoughts after Him."

In 1874, when the Scottish physicist James Clerk Maxwell (1831-1879) designed the famous Cavendish Laboratory in Cambridge University, he ordered this Latin inscription to be placed over the entryway.

Magna opera Domini exquisita in omnes voluntates ejus.
The works of the Lord are great, studied by all who delight in them.
Psalm 111:2

As you advance in your studies, may you also advance in your delight in the works of the Triune God, and as a result, your delight in the personal beauty of the onto-relational Trinity, the Author and Sustainer of those works.

> Thus number may be said to rule the whole world of quantity, and the four rules of arithmetic may be regarded as the complete equipment of the mathematician.
> James Clerk Maxwell (1831-1879), Scottish physicist.

EXERCISES

Define the following terms:

1. Ethics
2. Philosophy
3. Epistemology

(For the following terms, see homework exercises below.)

4. Diophantine analysis
5. Syncopated algebra
6. Rhetorical algebra

> Christ, the Son of God, is the logos or the ultimate logic (John 1:1-3). He is the ultimate justification of all rational thinking. The living and dynamic Christ is the Creator and Sustainer of every thinking person. Loving the Father through Christ by the Spirit does not consist, therefore, of ratiocination only; it means participating with the Trinity in reciprocal and authentic relationship, a communion that necessitates an interaction with the totality of your being (Mark 12:29-31).
> James D. Nickel

7. Complex fraction
8. Continued fraction
9. Lucas numbers
10. Continued radicals

Answer this question:

11. What is the relationship between the Golden Ratio and the Fibonacci Sequence?

> The natural world, on which mathematics reports, overwhelms us with its splendor, beauty, immensities, fragilities, incalculable diversity, endless combinations, minute intricacies, and immeasurable grandeurs. It is through mathematics that we can explore some of this wonder, wonder only beholden by the beauty and capability of rational thinking embodied in the framework of mathematics.
>
> James D. Nickel

> Mathematical formulae really hold good for the inner order of nature. Number or at least something corresponding to it, is embedded, as it were, in nature, and therefore not only is nature amenable to rational inquiry, but the mathematical formulations that arise out of it can only be in a form which expresses at once the nature of the object and the mode of its cognition. This is pushed to its extreme point in the view of Sir James Jeans that number is embedded in nature because it was created by a Pure Mathematician (aka. God). At the opposite extreme is the view that it is we alone who inject number into nature. If the first extreme rests upon a univocal relation between mathematics in nature and mathematics in God the latter does not take seriously that some real coordination is involved between our scientific theories and the rational structures of nature.
>
> Thomas F. Torrance, *Theological Science* (1969), p. 94.

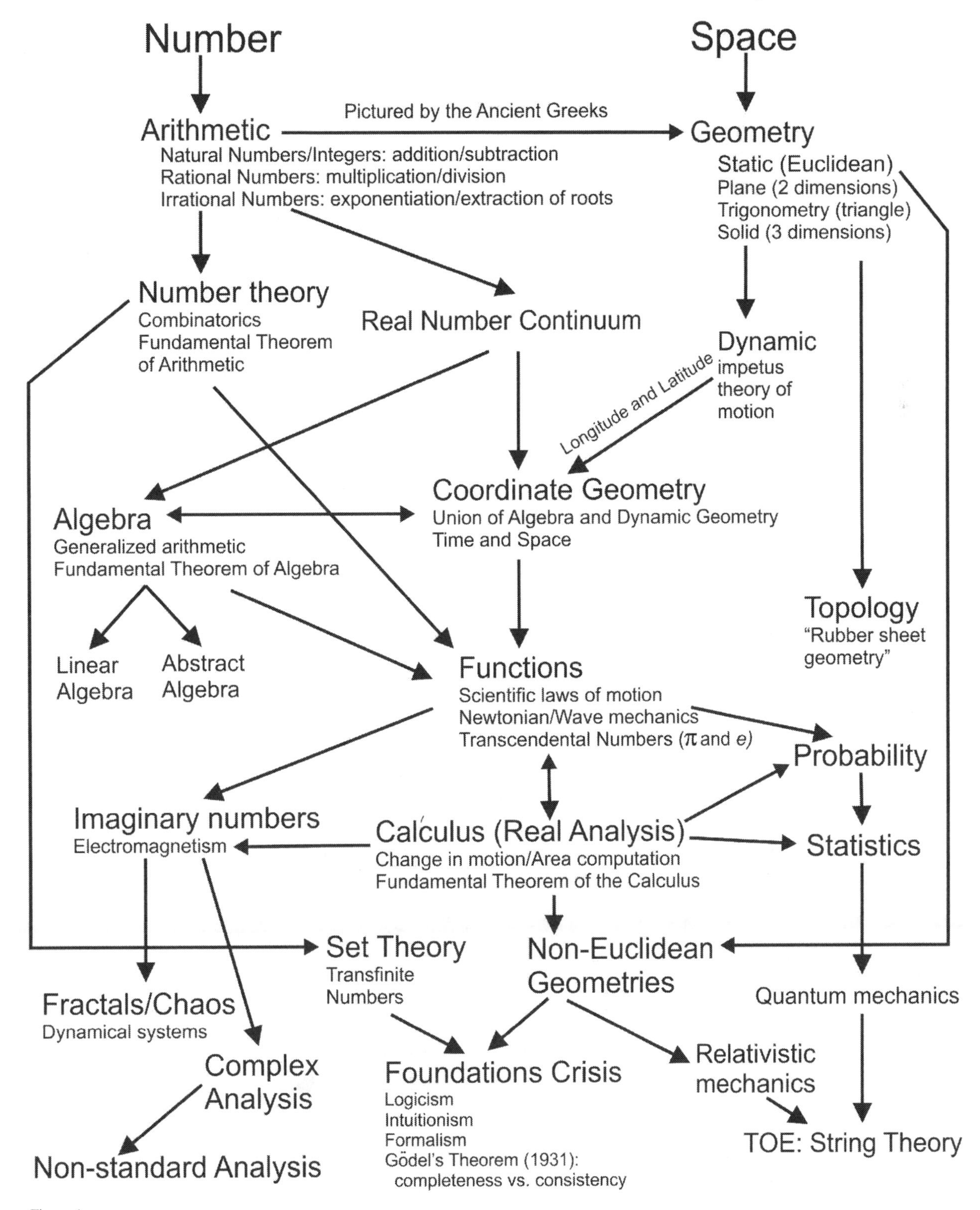

Mathematical Landscape
Number
Space
Arithmetic
Pictured by the Ancient Greeks
Geometry
Natural Numbers/Integers: addition/subtraction
Rational Numbers: multiplication/division
Irrational Numbers: exponentiation/extraction of roots
Static (Euclidean)
Plane (2 dimensions)
Trigonometry (triangle)
Solid (3 dimensions)
Number theory
Combinatorics
Fundamental Theorem of Arithmetic
Real Number Continuum
Dynamic
impetus theory of motion
Longitude and Latitude
Coordinate Geometry
Union of Algebra and Dynamic Geometry
Time and Space
Algebra
Generalized arithmetic
Fundamental Theorem of Algebra
Linear Algebra
Abstract Algebra
Topology
"Rubber sheet geometry"
Functions
Scientific laws of motion
Newtonian/Wave mechanics
Transcendental Numbers (π and e)
Probability
Imaginary numbers
Electromagnetism
Calculus (Real Analysis)
Change in motion/Area computation
Fundamental Theorem of the Calculus
Statistics
Set Theory
Transfinite Numbers
Non-Euclidean Geometries
Quantum mechanics
Fractals/Chaos
Dynamical systems
Complex Analysis
Foundations Crisis
Logicism
Intuitionism
Formalism
Gödel's Theorem (1931): completeness vs. consistency
Relativistic mechanics
TOE: String Theory
Non-standard Analysis

Figure 4.

Answering the next six questions will give you an idea of what research in ancient Greek mathematics was like (Figure 5). Notice the comparisons involving one, two, and three dimensions.

12. What is the ratio of the length of a diagonal of a square to the length of its side?
13. What is the ratio of the circumference of a circle to its diameter?
14. What is the ratio of the area of a circle to the area of a square built upon the circle's radius?
15. What is the ratio of the surface area of a sphere to the area of a circle through its equator?
16. What is the ratio of the volume of a right cylinder to the volume of a sphere inscribed in that cylinder?
17. What is the ratio of the volume of a cube to the volume of a right pyramid inscribed in that cube?
18. What is the relationship between the volume of a right cone with height and radius of r, the volume of a half-sphere of radius r, and the volume of a right cylinder with height and radius of r (Figure 6)? (Hint: Develop a ratio comparing the volumes of the three objects; i.e., $x:y:z$ where x, y, and z are positive integers.)

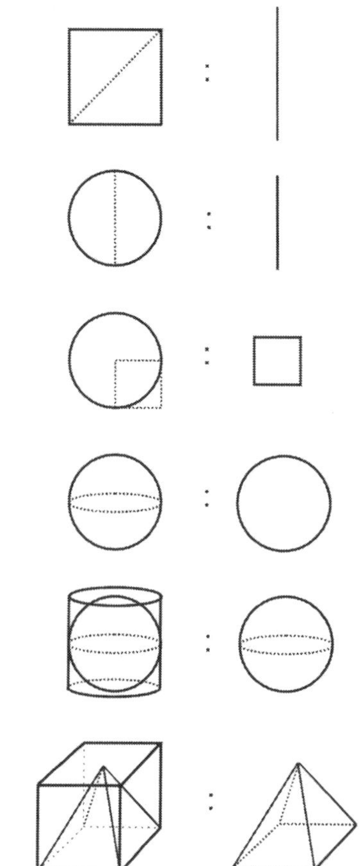
Figure 5. Six famous Greek ratios.

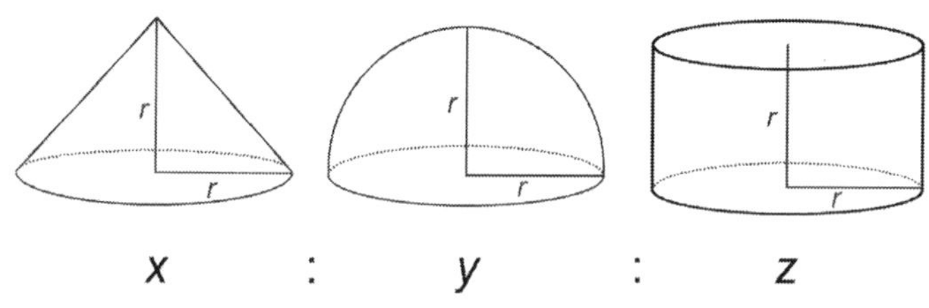

Figure 6. Cone, half-sphere, and cylinder.

In the 9th century AD, the Indian Mahavira presented this problem to his readers: One night, in a month of the spring season, a certain young lady was lovingly happy with her husband in a big mansion, white as the moon, set in a pleasure garden with trees bent down with flowers and fruits, and resonant with the sweet sounds of parrots, cuckoos and bees which were all intoxicated with the honey of the flowers. Then, on a love-quarrel arising between husband and wife, her pearl necklace was broken. The maid-servant collected one-third of the pearls and one-sixth fell on the bed. Then half of what remained and half of what remained after that and again one-half of what remained after that and so on, six times in all, fell scattered everywhere. After that, the string still held 1161 pearls.

19. How many pearls had there been in the necklace? Carefully lay out the facts of the problem, letting x = the number of pearls in the necklace, and solve.

Around 250, Diophantus, a Greek mathematician living in Alexandria, Egypt, and a Christian, made the first step to separate algebra from geometric methods.[11] He used symbols to represent frequently used quantities, operations, and powers of variables. For example, he used the Greek letter *sigma* (ς), the last letter of the Greek word *arithmos*, to represent an unknown quantity. We use the proverbial letter "x" today. We call this type of algebra **syncopated** from the Greek "to cut short." Before Diophantus, all algebraic problems were **rhetorical**; i.e., they were written in sentences without using symbols.

[11] Finding integral solutions to equations is known as **Diophantine analysis**, so named in honor of this famous Greek algebraist.

20. All that is known of the life of the Greek mathematician Diophantus of Alexandria is a curious riddle requiring algebra to solve. The problem, found in an anthology called the *Palatine*, assembled by the grammarian Metrodorus (ca. 500), states, "His boyhood lasted 1/6 of his life, his beard grew after 1/12 more, and after 1/7 more he married. Five years later his son was born, and the son lived to half his father's age. The father died four years after his son. How old was Diophantus when he died?" Let x = his age at death and solve.
21. A common puzzle appeared in the late 19th century when the prices of farm animals were much lower. A farmer spent \$100 to buy 100 animals of three different kids. Each sheep cost \$10, each goat \$3.50, and each chicken \$0.50. Assuming that the farmer bought at least one sheep, one goat, and one chicken, how many of each animal did the farmer buy? (Hint: This problem is an example of Diophantine analysis since your solutions must be positive integers. Let x = number of sheep, y = number of goats. What expression, in terms of x and y, represents the number of chickens?)

Extension on the Method Archimedes used to Calculate the Approximate Value of π.

In the 17th century, the Scottish mathematician James Gregory (1638-1675) observed that we can find the inscribed and circumscribed perimeters of regular polygons calculated by successively doubling the number of sides using harmonic and geometric means, if done in a certain way. In other words, the harmonic and geometric means interpenetrate the calculation of π after the initial geometric work for a regular 6-gon is established. In Lesson 9.9, we learned that the harmonic mean h of two numbers a and b is $h = \dfrac{2ab}{a+b}$. The geometric mean g (Lesson 11.6 homework exercises) of two numbers a and b is $g = \sqrt{ab}$.

Limits are as simple as pi.

22. For the hexagon, a 6-sided regular polygon, the boundary conditions on π are $3 < \pi < 2\sqrt{3}$ (Lesson 14.7 homework). Calculate the harmonic mean of 3 and $2\sqrt{3}$ simplifying your answer as much as possible, leaving it in radical form.[12]
23. Calculate the geometric mean of 3 and your answer to Question 22 simplifying your answer as much as possible, leaving it in radical form.
24. Compare your results in Question 22 and Question 23 with the Archimedean limits of π for a 12-sided regular polygon, a regular 12-gon; i.e., $6\sqrt{2-\sqrt{3}} < \pi < 12(2-\sqrt{3})$. What pattern do you notice?
25. Assuming this pattern continues (it can be proven), calculate the numbers corresponding to 24 sides, a regular 24-gon. Use your scientific calculator and write your answers as a decimal truncated to ten significant figures.
26. With your scientific calculator, determine the upper and lower bounds for π corresponding to 48 sides, a regular 48-gon, truncated to ten significant figures.
27. With your scientific calculator, determine the upper and lower bounds for π corresponding to 96 sides, a regular 96-gon, truncated to ten significant figures.
28. Starting with a regular 6-gon, use spreadsheet software to extend your doubling calculation until your computer's 15-significant figure decimal representation is the same for both lower and upper limits for π. This means that your computer has calculated π as accurately as it can.

---

[12] The denominator will look like $a+\sqrt{b}$. To rationalize the denominator in this form (Lesson 12.6), we multiply both the numerator and denominator by the radical conjugate (cf. complex conjugate in Lesson 12.11) of $a+\sqrt{b}$, i.e., $a-\sqrt{b}$.

A **complex fraction** is a fraction that has one or more fractions in either the numerator or denominator. Answer the following questions these kinds of fractions:

29. Simplify $\dfrac{x^2-4}{\dfrac{1}{2}-\dfrac{1}{x}}$ as a polynomial. Assume $x \neq 2$.

30. Simplify $\dfrac{1+\dfrac{1}{x}}{1-\dfrac{1}{x^2}}$ as a rational fraction. Assume $x \neq 0$, -1, or 1.

31. Simplify $1+\dfrac{1}{x+\dfrac{1}{x}}$ as a rational fraction. Assume $x \neq 0$.

32. Simplify $x+\dfrac{1}{x-\dfrac{1}{x}}$ as a rational fraction fully factored. Assume $x \neq 0$, -1, or 1.

33. Note the pattern and fill in the blanks with fractions reduced to lowest terms:

(a) $1-\dfrac{1}{2^2}=1-\dfrac{1}{4}=$ ____

(b) $\left(1-\dfrac{1}{2^2}\right)\left(1-\dfrac{1}{3^2}\right)=\left(\dfrac{3}{4}\right)\left(\dfrac{8}{9}\right)=$ ____

(c) $\left(1-\dfrac{1}{2^2}\right)\left(1-\dfrac{1}{3^2}\right)\left(1-\dfrac{1}{4^2}\right)=\left(\dfrac{2}{3}\right)\left(\dfrac{15}{16}\right)=$ ____

(d) $\left(1-\dfrac{1}{2^2}\right)\left(1-\dfrac{1}{3^2}\right)\left(1-\dfrac{1}{4^2}\right)\left(1-\dfrac{1}{5^2}\right)=\left(\dfrac{5}{8}\right)\left(\dfrac{24}{25}\right)=$ ____

(e) $\left(1-\dfrac{1}{2^2}\right)\left(1-\dfrac{1}{3^2}\right)\left(1-\dfrac{1}{4^2}\right)\left(1-\dfrac{1}{5^2}\right)\left(1-\dfrac{1}{6^2}\right)=\left(\dfrac{3}{5}\right)\left(\dfrac{35}{36}\right)=$ ____

(f) $\left(1-\dfrac{1}{2^2}\right)\left(1-\dfrac{1}{3^2}\right)\left(1-\dfrac{1}{4^2}\right)\left(1-\dfrac{1}{5^2}\right)\left(1-\dfrac{1}{6^2}\right)\left(1-\dfrac{1}{7^2}\right)=\left(\dfrac{7}{12}\right)\left(\dfrac{48}{49}\right)=$ ____

(g) $\left(1-\dfrac{1}{2^2}\right)\left(1-\dfrac{1}{3^2}\right)\left(1-\dfrac{1}{4^2}\right)\left(1-\dfrac{1}{5^2}\right)\left(1-\dfrac{1}{6^2}\right)\left(1-\dfrac{1}{7^2}\right)\left(1-\dfrac{1}{8^2}\right)=\left(\dfrac{4}{7}\right)\left(\dfrac{63}{64}\right)=$ ____

34. Write a general pattern, an algebraic expression, to find the nth term of this pattern.
35. Build a table for the product of the first through eighth terms and then a general expression for the nth product, or $P(n)$.
36. What is the end-behavior of $P(n)$?

Some Deductions from Isaac Newton's Universal Law of Gravitation: Confirming Kepler's Third Law of Planetary Motion.

37. Johannes Kepler (1571-1630) had empirically proved that the square of the time t it takes for a planet to make one revolution around the Sun is proportional to the cube of the radius r, a value that represents the average distance of the planet from the Sun. In symbols, $t^2 = kr^3$ where k is a constant for all planets. Newton could use his Universal Law of Gravitation to deduce this law, a great triumph of deductive thought. To make matters simple, we shall assume that the orbit of a planet around the Sun is circular. (The true path is elliptical, as proved by Kepler.) Let m be the mass of any

planet, M be the mass of the Sun, and r the average distance between them. By Newton's Universal Law of Gravitation, $F = \frac{GmM}{r^2}$. We also know from Lesson 12.1 that the centripetal acceleration, a, that the Sun imparts on any planet is given by the formula $a = \frac{v^2}{r}$. Newton's second law of motion states that $F = ma$. Substitute $a = \frac{v^2}{r}$ into this formula.

38. The velocity v of any planet is the circumference of its path divided by the time t of its orbit around the Sun. If the circumference C is $C = 2\pi r$, write a formula for the velocity v (distance divided by time).
39. Substitute the formula in Question 38 into the formula you derived in Question 37. Simplify as much as possible.
40. Equate the two expressions for F that you have derived so far.
41. Divide both sides of the equation you wrote in Question 40 by m (i.e., cancel m).
42. Multiply both sides of the equation you wrote in Question 41 by t^2.
43. Solve the equation you wrote in Question 42 for t^2.
44. Note that G and M are constant. Therefore, $\frac{4\pi^2}{GM}$ is constant. Let $k = \frac{4\pi^2}{GM}$ and QED the proof.

Fibonacci Sequence and Continued Fractions.

45. Let's consider the ratio of two consecutive Fibonacci numbers. The ratio of the third Fibonacci number to the second Fibonacci number is 2/1. We can rewrite the numerator as 1 + 1. We get:

$$\frac{2}{1} = \frac{1+1}{1} = 1 + \frac{1}{1}$$

$1 + \frac{1}{1}$ is a **continued fraction.**[13] The next ratio would be 3/2. We can rewrite 3 as 2 + 1. Therefore:

$$\frac{3}{2} = \frac{2+1}{2} = 1 + \frac{1}{2}$$

Since ½ is the reciprocal of 2/1, we can rewrite 3/2 as:

$$1 + \cfrac{1}{1 + \cfrac{1}{1}}$$ (Note: the reciprocal of $1 + \frac{1}{1}$ is $\cfrac{1}{1 + \cfrac{1}{1}}$)

From this reasoning, what can you conclude about the quotient of any two consecutive Fibonacci numbers?

46. If we consider the entire set of Fibonacci numbers, the ratio of two consecutive Fibonacci numbers approaches a limit, defined as φ, the Greek letter *phi*, the Golden Ratio. (See the φ-related homework in Lesson 13.14.) We can write φ as a continued fraction in the form

[13] We find the earliest use of continued fractions in *L'Algebra* (1572), by the Italian mathematician Rafael Bombelli (1526-1572).

$$\varphi = 1+\cfrac{1}{1+\cfrac{1}{1+\cfrac{1}{1+\cfrac{1}{1+\cfrac{1}{1+\dots}}}}}$$

Pause and consider the exquisite beauty of this equation. Now, consider a frame around the section as shown below. Notice the self-similarity.

$$\varphi = 1+\cfrac{1}{\boxed{1+\cfrac{1}{1+\cfrac{1}{1+\cfrac{1}{1+\cfrac{1}{1+\dots}}}}}}$$

What number is the expression in this frame equal?

47. From Question 46, we can derive the following equation: $\varphi = 1+\frac{1}{\varphi}$. Pause and note what you have done. You have taken an infinite process and expressed it in a finite statement, a fact should stun you as you consider its implications. Mathematics is an excellent tool whereby you can corral the infinite. Multiply both sides of this equation by φ.
48. Now, subtract φ from both sides of the equation you wrote in Question 47.
49. (a) Next, subtract 1 from both sides of the equation you wrote in Question 48.
    (b) What kind of equation have you derived?
50. (a) Solve the equation you wrote in Question 49 for the exact values of φ.
    (b) Round your solutions to the nearest thousandths.
    (c) What do you recognize in your answers? (Hint: Refer to the Fibonacci-related homework in Lesson 8.8, Lesson 8.11, and Lesson 10.8. Also, review the homework related to φ in Lesson 13.14.)

You can use the Fibonacci principle to start with any two numbers and generate any sequence of numbers. Mathematicians name these numbers **Lucas numbers**. For example, instead of starting with 1, 1, we will start with 2, 1. We get this sequence: 2, 1, 3, 4, 7, 11, 18, 29, 47, 76, 123, 199, etc. Let's consider the limit to which the ratio of two consecutive numbers in this sequence approaches.

51. Let's proceed with the continued fraction process. Starting with the third and fourth numbers, we get: $\frac{4}{3} = 1+\frac{1}{3}$

    From the fourth and fifth numbers, we get:

> Instead of equating man-made mathematics with the mind of God, it is better to articulate the following argument.
>
> The cosmos is rationally structured and sustained through the Word of the Father, the *Logos* who is Christ, and the Holy Spirit. The rationality of number is grounded in this incredibly wise language fabric. Mathematics, therefore, is one way of ordering, understanding, and reporting on the dance of this interconnected cosmos, a universe generated by the love of the deeply relational Trinity.
>
> James D. Nickel

$$\frac{7}{4} = 1 + \cfrac{1}{1 + \cfrac{1}{3}}$$

From the fifth and sixth numbers, we get:

$$\frac{11}{7} = 1 + \cfrac{1}{1 + \cfrac{1}{1 + \cfrac{1}{3}}}, \text{ etc.}$$

What can you conclude about this continued fraction?

$$1 + \cfrac{1}{1 + \cfrac{1}{1 + \cfrac{1}{1 + \cfrac{1}{1 + \cfrac{1}{1 + \frac{1}{3} \cdots}}}}}$$

52. Your answer should reveal a new twist the Fibonacci algorithm, $F_{n-1} + F_n = F_{n+1}$, as it relates to the unity in diversity principle, i.e., perichoresis. What is it?

Continued radicals, as known as nested radicals, are of the form $\sqrt{a + \sqrt{b + \sqrt{c + \sqrt{d + \sqrt{\ldots}}}}}$. As with continued fractions, we must ask the question, does $\sqrt{a + \sqrt{b + \sqrt{c + \sqrt{d + \sqrt{\ldots}}}}}$ equal something? Or, as a mathematician would ask, does it converge to a limit? Let us take the simplest case: $\sqrt{n + \sqrt{n + \sqrt{n + \sqrt{n + \sqrt{\ldots}}}}}$. And let us assume that $L = \sqrt{n + \sqrt{n + \sqrt{n + \sqrt{n + \sqrt{\ldots}}}}}$. The following exercises help us to determine L:

53. Add n to both sides of the equation $L = \sqrt{n + \sqrt{n + \sqrt{n + \sqrt{n + \sqrt{\ldots}}}}}$.
54. Extract the positive square root of both sides. (Be ready for a surprise!)
55. What does the right side of the equation in Question 54 equal?
56. Simplify the equation in Question 54.
57. Square both sides of the equation you derived in Question 56.
58. Solve the equation you derived in Question 57 for n.
59. Therefore, if we want a continued radical whose limit is L we just plug any L into the equation in Question 58 and solve for n and we can generate its continued radical. Suppose we want the continued radical to be equal to 2. If $L = 2$, solve for n.
60. From you answer in Question 59, generate the continued radical.
61. If $L = 7$, generate the continued radical.
62. With a scientific calculator and to six significant figures, compute the first four partial radicals in Question 61 to confirm your answer.
63. By this work with continued radicals, prove $\varphi = \sqrt{1 + \sqrt{1 + \sqrt{1 + \sqrt{1 + \sqrt{\ldots}}}}}$.

64. Express the Golden Ratio φ as a continued fraction and continued radical and show that the continued fraction and continued radical are equal.
65. Prove φ is irrational. (Hint: Use what you know of the φ and approach the proof indirectly, i.e., *reduction ad absurdum*.

$$1+\cfrac{1}{1+\cfrac{1}{1+\cfrac{1}{1+\cfrac{1}{1+\cfrac{1}{1+\dots}}}}}=\frac{\sqrt{5}+1}{2}=\sqrt{1+\sqrt{1+\sqrt{1+\sqrt{1+\sqrt{\dots}}}}}$$

Perichoresis!

$$e=2+\cfrac{2}{2+\cfrac{3}{3+\cfrac{4}{4+\cfrac{5}{5+\cfrac{6}{6+\cfrac{7}{7+\cfrac{8}{8+\ddots}}}}}}}$$

Discovered by Leonhard Euler.

$$\frac{2}{\pi}=\sqrt{\frac{1}{2}}\left(\sqrt{\frac{1}{2}+\frac{1}{2}\sqrt{\frac{1}{2}}}\right)\left(\sqrt{\frac{1}{2}+\frac{1}{2}\sqrt{\frac{1}{2}+\frac{1}{2}\sqrt{\frac{1}{2}}}}\right)\cdots$$

Discovered by François Viète in 1593.

$$\frac{e^{\pi-1}}{e^{\pi+1}}=\cfrac{\pi}{2+\cfrac{\pi^2}{6+\cfrac{\pi^2}{10+\cfrac{\pi^2}{14+\cfrac{\pi^2}{18+\ddots}}}}}$$

Discovered by Srinivasa Ramanujan (1887-1920).

O Lord, our Lord, how excellent is Thy name in all the earth, who has set Thy glory above the heavens, and out of the mouths of babes and sucklings hast perfected praise. When we consider Thy heavens and the work of Thy fingers, the moon and the stars which Thou hast ordained, teach us to know that Thou art mindful of us, and visited us, making us rulers over the works of Thy hands, showing us the wisdom of Thy laws, and crowning us with honor and glory in our earthly life; and looking higher than the heavens, may we see Jesus, made a little lower than the angels for the suffering of death, crowned with glory and honor, that He, by the grace of God, should taste death for every man. O Lord, fulfill Thy promise, and put all things in subjection under His feet. Let sin be rooted out from the earth, and let the wicked be no more. Bless thou the Lord, I my soul, praise the Lord.

James Clerk Maxwell (1831-1879), a prayer found in his papers. In Lewis Campbell and William Garnett, *The Life and Times of James Clerk Maxwell* (1882), p. 323.

The ground of knowledge is Christocentric. Jesus the Word is the uncreated Light, who, as the radiating voice of the Father, is the source of created light and it is by that created light we can recognize number in form and form in number. We, created in God's image, can only recognize number and form because of its intelligibility, an intelligibility grounded in the Logos, the wisdom of God. Both our minds and the universe outside of our minds coinhere because Christ the Logos, motivated by the effulgent light of the love He has shared from eternity with His Father by the Spirit, created both from nothing. Jesus Christ is the light of the cosmos, the light that enlightens all men (John 1:1-3; 8:12).

James D. Nickel

The spirit of genuine mathematics, i.e., its methods, concepts, and structure – in contrast to mindless calculations – constitutes one of the finest expressions of the human spirit. The great areas of mathematics – Algebra, Number Theory, Combinatorics, Real and Complex Analysis, Topology, Geometry, Trigonometry, etc. – have arisen from man's experience of the world that the Triune God has created and currently sustains. These branches of mathematics, constructively developed by man made in the image of God, enable man to systematize the given order and coherence, the unity and diversity, of creation mediated to us by the Creator and Upholder of all things, the logos and wisdom of the Triune God revealed in the person of His Incarnate Son, the Lord Jesus Christ. This systematization not only gives man a tool whereby he can take effective dominion over the creation under God in Christ, but also gives man the experience and enjoyment of a rich intellectual beauty that borders the sublime in its infinitely complex, yet structured mosaic.

James D. Nickel

TERMS/CONCEPTS/ABBREVIATIONS

	Lesson
Absolute value/modulus of a complex number	12.12
Absorption spectra	14.6
Algebraic function	12.7
Almagest	12.6
Amplitude	12.8
Ångström unit	14.6
Antecedent	13.2
Antithetical thinking	13.2
Apothem	14.5
Arc length	14.2
arccos	12.9
arcsin	12.9
arctan	12.9
Argument (logic)	13.2
Argument/amplitude of a complex number	12.12
Arithmetic sequence	13.13
Arithmetic series	13.13
Asserting the consequent	13.2
ASTC	12.7
Astrolabe	12.10
Asymmetric cryptosystem	13.12
Axiomatic-Deductive System	13.2
Batter	12.10
Bearing	12.13
Biconditional statements	13.2
Boundary	13.2
Calculus	13.17
Cavalieri's Principle	14.6
Central angle	12.6
Centripetal acceleration	12.1
Chain rule for differentiation	13.19
Characteristic of a log	12.5
Characteristic triangle	13.18
Chord	12.6
Chromatic scale	13.14
Circular functions	12.6
Circumscribe	13.8
Coherence statement	13.2
Common logarithms	12.4

	Lesson
Completeness	13.6
Complex analysis	12.11
Complex conjugate	12.11
Complex fraction	14.8
Complex number plane	12.11
Complex numbers	12.11
Conclusion	13.2
Conclusion of an argument	13.3
Conditional statement	13.2
Consequent	13.2
Consistency	13.6
Continued fraction	14.8
Continued radicals	14.8
Contrapositive	13.2
Convergent series	13.15
Corollary	12.6
Cosecant	12.6
Cosine	12.6
Cosmology	13.8
Cotangent	12.6
Coterminal angles	12.7
Crest	12.8
Cryptanalysis	13.12
Cryptography	13.12
Crystallography	14.5
Cubic system	14.5
Decryption	13.12
Decryption function	13.12
Deductive thinking	13.1
Degree of a polynomial	12.11
Denying the antecedent	13.2
Difference quotient	13.18
Difference rule for differentiation of a polynomial	13.19
Diophantine analysis	14.8
Direct proof	13.3
Directed angle	12.6
Displacement	12.8
Divergent series	13.15
Division Law of Logs	12.2
Duality	14.5
Emission spectra	14.6

	Lesson
Quantum logic	13.10
Radian measure	12.6
Radius vector	12.8
Radix method of computing logarithms	12.3
Random sample	13.12
Ratiocination	13.2
Rational function	14.3
Rationalizing the denominator	12.6
Recognition statement	13.2
Reductio ad absurdum	13.9
Reference angle	12.9
Regular right prism	14.1
Regular polyhedra	14.4
Regular pyramid	14.2
Rhetorical algebra	14.8
Rhombohedral system	14.5
Right cone	14.2
Right cylinder	14.1
Rigorous argument	13.2
SAS Triangle Area Formula	12.12
Secant	12.6
Second derivative	13.19
Secret decryption key	13.12
Seked	12.10
Semi-perimeter of a triangle	13.3
Series	13.13
Sextant	12.10
Sigma notation	12.4
Sine	12.6
Slant height of a right cone	14.2
Slide rule	12.2
Solid angle	14.5
Solid figures	14.1
Standard deviation	12.4
Standard form of the exponential decay function	13.14
Standard form of the exponential growth function	13.14
Stereometry	14.7
Stoicheia	13.2
Sum rule for differentiation of a polynomial	13.19
Surface area	14.1
Syllogism	13.3

	Lesson
Symmetric cryptosystem	13.12
Syncopated algebra	14.8
Tangent	12.6
Terminal side of an angle	12.6
Terminating decimal	12.6
Tessellation	14.5
Tetragonal system	14.5
Tetrahedron	14.4
The convergence of an infinite series to a limiting value	13.15
Three Laws of Motion	13.10
Topology	14.4
Transcendental function	12.7
Trapdoor one-way function	13.12
Triangulation	12.10
Triclinic system	14.5
Trigonometric functions	12.6
Trough	12.8
Turning point	13.19
Uncertainty principle	13.10
Unit circle	12.6
Wave height	12.8
Wavelength	12.8
Zeroes of a function	14.2

Prefixes	
a-	on, in, at
ab-, abs-	away, from
ali-	one of two
ana-	up
ante-	before
anti-	against
apo-	away, from
bi-	two
centi-, centri-	one hundred
circum-	around
co-, coe-, col-, com-, con-, cor-	with, together, complete
contra-	opposite
counter-	against
de-	reverse, down, completely
dec-, deca-	ten
di-	apart
dia-	through
dis-	reverse, negation, apart
dodeca-	twelve
e-, ec-, ek-, ex-	from, out of
em-, en-	in, into
hemi-	half
hept-	seven
hex-	six
hiero-	sacred
histo-	web, tissue
hyper-	over, above, greater than
hypo-	under, blow, less than
icosa-	twenty
in-, ir-	in, into, not
infra-	below
inter-	between
intra-	within
iso-	equal
kilo-	one thousand
macro-	large
magni-	great
meg-	great
mes-	middle

Prefixes	
meta-	with, after, development
micro-	small
milli-	one thousand
mono-	single
multi-	many
non-	not
non-	nine (Latin)
oct-	eight
off-	from
omni-	all
ortho-	straight, right
over-	above
pan-	all
par-	beside
para-	ward off
pent-	five
per-	through
peri-	around
poly-	many
post-	after
pre-	before
pro-	in front of, forward
re-	back, again
retro-	backward
semi-	half
sex-	sixth
stereo-	solid
sub-	under, after
super-	over, above
sym-	with
sys-	with
tetra-	four
trans-	over, across
tri-	three
un-	not
vice-	in place of

Roots	
acu	sharp
add	put

Roots	
alti	high
ampli	large
angle	corner
annus	year
apert	open
apex	tip
apotheca	storehouse
arc	curve, bow
argu	make clear
area	vacant piece of level ground
arithmos	number
assoc	share
aster	star
auto	self
avoirdupois	have weight
axiom	worthy
bar	heavy
base	pedestal
bene	well
calculi	pebble
calor	heat
cancel	delete
capac	that can contain
cardinal	hinge, pivot
carn	flesh
cave	hollow
cader	fall
ceder	go
celer	swift
celest	heavens
centr	center
cept	take
cern	separate
chord	string
choresis	contain space or room
chromo	color
chron	time
cipher	zero
cis	cut
clud	shut
cogn	learn

Roots	
combin	join two by two
commu	exchange
comp	put
comple	fill up
coni	cone
convex	arch, vault
copte	strike, cut off
corona	crown
cosm	universe
crete	grow
cruent	fall, rush
crypt	hidden
crystal	ice
cubit	elbow, forearm
cur	meet, run toward
cycl	circle
cylind	roll
cym	wave
denom	name
dense	press close
deus	God
dic(x)	make known, say
digit	finger, toe
digm	show
distribute	divide up
divide	force apart
domain	belonging to a lord
duce	lead
dupl	two
dynam	power
ellipsis	leave out, less than
efficient	accomplishing
emiss	sent out
episte	knowledge
equ	make equal
esse	to be
exponent	putting out
factor	done
fer	carry, bring
finite	finished
flex	bend

Roots	
focus	fireplace, hearth
force	strong
fract	break
frequent	crowded
fulc	prop up
funct	perform
funda	found
gen	origin
genos	race, kind
ge, geo	earth
glory	essential nature at its fullest
gno	know
grad	step
graph	drawing
gravi	heavy
gyr	rotate
harmo	joining, concord
hedra	face
heli	sun
here	stick
hodo	way
homo	same
horo	time
ident	same
infra	below
iso	equal
jabr	reunite, restore
ject	throw
join	join
junct	join
kin	movement
lat	side, broad
later	side
lever	lift
libra	balance
limit	boundary, threshold, frontier
locus	place
logos	word, reason, study of
long	long
macro	large
magni	large

Roots	
mantissa	makeweight
mathe	teach, disciple
max	great
med	middle
meg	large
meniscus	crescent (moon)
mer	part
mes	middle
meter	measure
micro	small
mid	less
min	least
minuend	diminish
mis (mit)	put or send
mol	mass
mono	single
morph	form
momentum	move
myria	many
nomos	part, portion, name
nota	mark
nov	new
obtuse	blunt
ocular	eye
od	way, course
olig	few
omni	all
onto	being
opposite	set against
ordo, ordinal	order
origin	rise
oscill	swing
pas	step or pace
pattern	model
ped	foot
pend	hang
per	for each
permut	change completely
pet	seek
petend	something
phil	loving

Roots	
phon	sound
phot	light
physic	natural
plane	flat surface
pico	one millionth
pod	foot
polar	axis
portion	share
posit	put, assert
postu	asked
pound	put
prim	first
prism	saw
product	something made
proba	test, demonstrate
pros	towards
proper	one's own, special
prot	first
ptotos	apt to fall
psych	mind
quad	square, four
quot	how many
quant	how much
rad	ray
radic	root
rang	rank, put in order, movement over an area
ratio(nal)	reason
ray	spoke
rect	straight
regular	rule
riv	brook, stream
rot	turn
royal	regal
scal	ladder
scend	climb
sciss	cut
scolios	bent
scope	watch
scribe	write
sect	cutting
seri	join, connect

Roots	
sequence	following
skelos (celes)	leg
simi	like
sinu	curve
sist	stand (still), take a stand
sexagesimal	sixtieth
sol	sun
solid	entire
solut	loosen
sorb	suck in
spect	look
sphere	ball
spir	breath
spond	pledge
stare	stand
stasis	stand, state
stell	star
stitute	place
sup	fill up
surd	deaf, speechless, not explainable
sym	together
syn	with
tauto	same
tanger	touch
tele	far off
tend	stretch
term	end, boundary, limit, terminate
terr	earth
tesse	four
theore	see
therm	heat
thesis	placing
tinu	hold
tom	cut
ton	tone
top	place
torq	twist
tract	draw
trapeza	table
trop	turning
truncat	maimed

Roots	
ultra	beyond
umbra	shade
undul	wave
urg	work
vacu	void
vari	various
vector	carry, convey
verg	incline
vers	turn
via	way
volv	turn, roll
zenith	path overhead

Suffixes	
-a	[plural; neuter]
-ae	[plural]
-ane	denoting
-arium	used for
-ary	used for
-asis	unhealthy
-ate	like, possessing
-bola	throw
-cele	swell
-ceptor	receiver
-cide	killer of
-cle	small
-clude	shut, close
-duce	lead
-dyma	putting on or off
-dysis	putting on or off
-ella	small
-ence	state of
-ennial	yearly
-escent	growing
-esia	act, state of
-fic	make
-fid	split
-form	form of, shape of
-fy	make
-geny	origin

Suffixes	
-gerous	bearing
-gon	angle
-gram	write
-i	[plural]
-ia	pertaining to
-ic	having
-id	having
-idium	small
-ina	sub-class
-ine	pertaining to
-ite	belonging to
-itis	inflammation
-ject	throw
-lapse	slip
-lipse	leave
-lite	minerals
-lysis	loosening
-lyte	loosening
-ma	act of
-me	act of
-mycin	fungi
-nome	ordered study
-ode	of nature of
-oid	form of
-ole	small
-ose	full of
-ous	pertaining to
-penia	lack of
-physis	growth
-plexy	paralysis
-ploid	division of
-poeia	making
-ponic	toil
-pus	foot
-rhage	breaking
-rhexis	breaking
-s	[plural]
-sis	act, state of
-sol	spread out
-stasis	stand, state
-stat	standing

Suffixes	
-strate	spread out
-thetic	setting down
-tion	act or process of something
-tude	state, condition, or quality
-ula	small
-ule	small
-um	[plural]
-us	[singular; masculine]
-y	act, state of

Mathematical Symbols

Symbol	Lesson	Symbol	Lesson	Symbol	Lesson
Σ	12.4	NOT	13.9	$f'(x)$	13.17
$\cong$	12.6	XNOR	13.9	$\dot{y}$	13.17
$\mathbb{C}$	12.11	⊏	13.10	y'	13.17
$\rightarrow\leftarrow$	13.9	$\equiv$	13.12	$\forall$	13.18
NAND	13.9	φ	13.14	$\exists$	13.18
NOR	13.9	$\frac{dy}{dx}$	13.17	$\frac{d^2y}{dx^2}$	13.19

Greek Alphabet

Greek Letter (Capital, Lower Case)	Greek Name	English Equivalent	Greek Letter (Capital, Lower Case)	Greek Name	English Equivalent
Α, α	Alpha	a	Ν, ν	Nu	n
Β, β	Beta	b	Ξ, ξ	Xi	x
Γ, γ	Gamma	g	Ο, ο	Omicron	ŏ
Δ, δ	Delta	d	Π, π	Pi	p
Ε, ε	Epsilon	ĕ	Ρ, ρ	Rho	r
Ζ, ζ	Zeta	z	Σ, σ or ς	Sigma	s
Η, η	Eta	ē	Τ, τ	Tau	t
Θ, θ	Theta	th	Υ, υ	Upsilon	u
Ι, ι	Iota	i	Φ, ϕ or φ	Phi	ph
Κ, κ	Kappa	k	Χ, χ	Chi	ch
Λ, λ	Lambda	l	Ψ, ψ	Psi	ps
Μ, μ	Mu	m	Ω, ω	Omega	ō

Geometric Constructions

	Lesson
Quadrature of a rectangle	13.3
Quadrature of a triangle	13.4
Quadrature of a polygon	13.6
Construct a lune	13.7
Quadrature of a lune	13.7
Construct a line segment congruent to a given line segment (Euclidean)	13.7
Construct a line parallel to a given line through a given point	13.10

BIBLIOGRAPHY

______. *Donald in Mathmagic Land.* Burbank: The Walt Disney Company, 1959.
______. *Historical Topics for the Mathematics Classroom.* 31st NCTM yearbook. Reston: National Council of Teachers of Mathematics, [1969] 1989.
Abbott, Edwin A. *The Annotated Flatland: A Romance of Many Dimensions.* New York: Basic Books, 2002.
Adam, John A. *A Mathematical Nature Walk.* Princeton: Princeton University Press, 2009.
Adleman, Leonard M., Ron L. Rivet, and Adi Shamir. "A Method for Obtaining Digital Signatures and Public-key cryptography." *Communications of the ACM* (1978), 21:120-126.
Adrian, Y. E. O. *The Pleasures of Pi, e and Other Interesting Numbers.* Singapore: World Scientific, 2006.
______. *Trig or Treat.* Singapore: World Scientific, 2007.
Aharoni, Ron. *Arithmetic for Parents: A Book for Grownups about Children's Mathematics.* El Cerrito: Sumizdat, 2007.
______. *Mathematics, Poetry and Beauty.* Singapore: World Scientific, 2015.
Artmann, Benno. *Euclid: The Creation of Mathematics.* New York: Springer-Verlag, 1999.
Ashton, Anthony. *Harmonograph: A Visual Guide to the Mathematics of Music.* New York: Walker & Company, 2003.
Asimov, Isaac. *Asimov on Numbers.* Bell Publishing, 1982.
______. *Asimov's New Guide to Science.* New York: Basic Books, [1960, 1965, 1972] 1984.
______. *Understanding Physics.* Dorset Press, [1966] 1988.
Athanasius. *On the Incarnation.* Crestwood: St. Vladimir's Seminary Press, 1996.
Ball, Keith. *Strange Curves, Counting Rabbits, and other Mathematical Explorations.* Princeton: Princeton University Press, 2003.
Banner, Adrian. *The Calculus Lifesaver.* Princeton: Princeton University Press, 2007.
Barnett, I. A. *Some Ideas About Number Theory.* Washington, DC: National Council of Teachers of Mathematics, 1961.
Barr, Stephen M. *Modern Physics and Ancient Faith.* Notre Dame: University of Notre Dame Press, 2003.
Barrow, John D. *Pi in the Sky: Counting, Thinking, and Being.* Oxford: Clarendon Press, 1992.
Baumgardt, Carola. *Johannes Kepler: Life and Letters.* New York: Philosophical Library, 1951.
Beckenbach, Edwin and Richard Bellman. *An Introduction to Inequalities.* New York: Random House, 1961.
Beckmann, Petr. *A History of π (pi).* New York: St. Martin's Press, 1971.
Bell, Eric Temple. *Mathematics: Queen and Servant of Science.* New York: McGraw-Hill, 1951.
______. *Men of Mathematics.* New York: Simon and Schuster, [1937, 1965] 1986.
______. *The Development of Mathematics.* Mineola: Dover Publications, [1940, 1945] 1992.
______. *The Magic of Numbers.* Mineola: Dover Publications, [1946] 1991.
Benacerraf, Paul and Hilary Putnam, ed. *Philosophy of Mathematics: Selected Readings.* Englewood Cliffs: Prentice-Hall, 1964.
Benjamin, Arthur and Michael Shermer. *Secrets of Mental Math.* New York: Three Rivers Press, 2006.
Bennett, Deborah J. *Logic Made Easy.* New York: W. W. Norton, 2004.
Benson, Donald C. *A Smoother Pebble: Mathematical Explorations.* New York: Oxford University Press, 2013.
______. *The Moment of Proof: Mathematical Epiphanies.* Oxford: Oxford University Press, 1999.
Bentley, W. A. and W. J. Humphreys. *Snow Crystals.* New York: Dover Publications, [1931] 1962.
Bergamini, David. *Mathematics.* Alexandria: Time-Life Books, 1980.
Berkson, William. *Fields of Force: The Development of a World View from Faraday to Einstein.* New York: Halsted Press, 1974.
Berlinski, David. *A Tour of the Calculus.* New York: Vintage Books, 1995.
______. *Infinite Ascent: A Short History of Mathematics.* New York: The Modern Library, 2005.

______. *Newton's Gift: How Sir Isaac Newton Unlocked the System of the World.* New York: Touchstone, [2000] 2002.
______. *One, Two, Three: Absolutely Elementary Mathematics.* New York: Vintage Books, 2011.
______. *The Advent of the Algorithm: The 300-Year Journey from an Idea to the Computer.* New York: Harcourt, Inc., 2000.
Bernal, J. D. *A History of Classical Physics: From Antiquity to the Quantum.* New York: Barnes & Noble Books, [1972] 1997.
Bers, Lipman with Frank Karal. *Calculus, Second Edition.* New York: Holt, Rinehart and Winston, [1969] 1976.
Bitter, Francis. *Mathematical Aspects of Physics: An Introduction.* Garden City: Anchor Books, 1963.
Bittinger, Marvin L. *Basic Mathematics, Ninth Edition.* New York: Addison Wesley, 2003.
Blocker, Linda and Julia Hill. *Culinary Math.* New York: John Wiley & Sons, 2002.
Bloesch, Donald G. *A Theology of Word & Spirit: Authority & Method in Theology.* Downers Grove: InterVarsity Press, 1992.
______. *God the Almighty: Power, Wisdom, Holiness, Love.* Downers Grove: InterVarsity Press, 1995.
______. *Jesus Christ: Savior & Lord.* Downers Grove: InterVarsity Press, 1997.
______. *Holy Scripture: Revelation, Inspiration & Interpretation.* Downers Grove: InterVarsity Press, 1994.
______. *The Holy Spirit: Works & Gifts.* Downers Grove: InterVarsity Press, 2000.
Boyer, Carl. *A History of Mathematics.* rev. Uta C. Merzbach. New York: John Wiley & Sons, [1968] 1991.
______. *History of Analytic Geometry.* Mineola: Dover Publications, [1956] 2004.
______. *The History of the Calculus and its Historical Development.* New York: Dover Publications, [1949] 1959.
______. *The Rainbow: From Myth to Mathematics.* New York: Thomas Yoseloff, 1959.
Brookhard, Clint. *Go Figure! Using Math to Answer Everyday Imponderables.* Chicago: Contemporary Books, 1998.
Brown, Richard, ed. *30-Second Math.* New York: Metro Books, 2012.
Brown, Sam. *All About Telescopes.* Barrington, New Jersey: Edmund Scientific, 1975.
Bruce, Colin. *Conned Again, Watson: Cautionary Tales of Logic, Math, and Probability.* Cambridge: Perseus Publishing, 2001.
______. *The Einstein Paradox: And Other Science Mysteries Solved by Sherlock Holmes.* Reading: Perseus Publishing, 1997.
Budiansky, Stephen. *Battle of Wits.* New York: The Free Press, 2000.
Burger, Edward B. and Michael Starbird. *The Heart of Mathematics: An Invitation to Effective Thinking.* Emeryville: Key Curriculum Press, 2000.
Burke, James. *Connections.* Boston: Little, Brown and Company, 1978.
Byerly, T. Ryan. *Introducing Logic and Critical Thinking: The Skills of Reasoning and the Virtues of Inquiry.* Grand Rapids: Baker Academic, 2017.
Byl, John. *The Divine Challenge: On Matter, Mind, Math, and Meaning.* Carlisle: The Banner of Truth Trust, 2004.
Cajori, Florian. *A History of Mathematical Notations.* Mineola: Dover Publications, [1928, 1929] 1993.
Calinger, Ronald. *A Contextual History of Mathematics.* Upper Saddle River: Prentice Hall, 1999.
Camm, F. J. *A Refresher Course in Mathematics.* Mineola: Dover Publications, [1943, 1953] 2003.
Campbell, Lewis and William Garnett. *The Life and Times of James Clerk Maxwell.* London: Macmillan and Company, 1882.
Cardwell, Donald. *Wheels, Clocks, and Rockets: A History of Technology.* New York: W. W. Norton, 1995.
Caspar, Max. *Kepler.* C. Doris Hellman, trans. Mineola: Dover Publications, [1959] 1993.
Casti, John L. and Werner DePauli. *Gödel: A Life of Logic.* Cambridge: Perseus Publishing, 2000.
Chapman, Colin R. *Weights, Money and Other Measures Used by Our Ancestors.* Baltimore: Lochin Publishing, [1995, 1996] 1997.

Chenier, Norman J. *Practical Math Application Guide.* Gladstone: Chenier Educational Enterprises, 2005.

______. *Practical Math Dictionary.* Gladstone: Chenier Educational Enterprises, 1997.

Clawson, Calvin C. *Conquering Math Phobia: A Painless Primer.* New York: John Wiley & Sons, 1991.

______. *Mathematical Mysteries: The Beauty and Magic of Numbers.* Cambridge: Perseus Publishing, 1996.

______. *Mathematical Sorcery: Revealing the Secrets of Numbers.* Cambridge: Perseus Publishing, 1999.

______. *The Mathematical Traveler: Exploring the Grand History of Numbers.* Cambridge: Perseus Publishing, 1994.

Clegg, Brian. *Are Numbers Real? The Uncanny Relationship of Mathematics and the Physical World.* New York: St. Martin's Press, 2016.

______. *Inflight Science: A Guide to the World from Your Airplane Window.* London: Icon Books, 2011.

Cohen, Don. *Calculus By and For Young People.* Champaign: Don Cohen, 1991.

Colerus, Egmont. *Mathematics for Everyman: From Simple Numbers to the Calculus.* trans. B. C. and H. F. Brookes. Mineola: Dover Publications, [1937, 1958] 2002.

Collingwood, R. G. *An Essay on Metaphysics.* London: Oxford University Press, 1940.

Collins, A. Frederick. *Rapid Math Without a Calculator.* New York: Carol Publishing Group, [1956, 1987] 1989.

Conway, John H. and Richard K. Guy. *The Book of Numbers.* New York: Copernicus/Springer-Verlag, 1996.

Cook, Nigel P. *Introductory Mathematics.* Englewood Cliffs: Prentice Hall Career & Technology, 1995.

Cook, Theodore A. *The Curves of Life.* New York: Dover Publications, [1914] 1979.

Cooke, Nelson M. *Mathematics for Electricians and Radiomen.* New York and London: McGraw-Hill Book Company, 1942.

Cooke, Roger. *Classical Algebra: Its Nature, Origins, and Uses.* Hoboken: John Wiley & Sons, 2008.

Copi, Irving M. *Introduction to Logic, Tenth Edition.* Englewood Cliffs: Prentice-Hall, 1998.

Courant, Richard and Herbert Robbins. *What is Mathematics? An Elementary Approach to Ideas and Methods.* rev. Ian Stewart. New York: Oxford University Press, [1941, 1969, 1978] 1996.

Court, Nathan A. *Mathematics in Fun and in Earnest.* Mineola: Dover Publications, [1935, 1945, 1948, 1953, 1954, 1955, 1956, 1958] 2006.

Crease, Robert P. *The Great Equations: Breakthroughs in Science from Pythagoras to Heisenberg.* New York: W. W. Norton and Company, 2008.

Crombie, Alistair C. *The History of Science from Augustine to Galileo.* Mineola: Dover Publications, [1959, 1970, 1979] 1995.

Crosby, Alfred W. *The Measure of Reality: Quantification and Western Society, 1250-1600.* Cambridge: Cambridge University Press, 1997.

Crump, Thomas. *A Brief History of Science as Seen Through the Development of Scientific Instruments.* London: Constable & Robinson, [2001] 2002.

Curren, Anna M. and Laurie D. Munday. *Math for Meds: Dosages and Solutions, Seventh Edition.* San Diego: W. I. Publications, 1995.

Dalton, LeRoy C. *Algebra in the Real Word: 38 Enrichment Lessons for Algebra 2.* Palo Alto: Dale Seymour Publications, 1983.

Dantzig, Tobias. *Number: The Language of Science.* New York: Doubleday Anchor, [1930, 1933, 1939] 1954.

Dauben, Joseph W. *Georg Cantor: His Mathematics and Philosophy of the Infinite.* Cambridge: Harvard University Press, 1979.

Davies, P. C. W. *Space and Time in the Modern Universe.* Cambridge: Cambridge University Press, 1977.

______. *The Forces of Nature.* Cambridge: Cambridge University Press, 1979.

Davis, Donald M. *The Nature and Power of Mathematics.* Princeton: Princeton University Press, 1993.

Davis, Morton D. *The Math of Money.* New York: Copernicus Books, 2001.

Davis, Philip J. *The Lore of Large Numbers.* New York: Random House, 1961.

Davis, Philip J. and Reuben Hersh. *The Mathematical Experience.* Boston: Houghton Mifflin Company, 1981.

______. *Descartes' Dream: The World According to Mathematics.* Boston: Houghton Mifflin Company, 1986.
De Haan, Lex and Toon Koppelaars. *Applied Mathematics for Database Professionals.* Berkeley: Apress, 2007.
Del Re, Giuseppe. *The Cosmic Dance: Science Discovers the Mysterious Harmony of the Universe.* Philadelphia: Templeton Foundation Press, 2000.
Den Hartog, J. P. *Mechanics.* New York: Dover Publications, [1948] 1961.
Derbyshire, John. *Unknown Quantity: A Real and Imaginary History of Algebra.* Washington, DC: Joseph Henry Press, 2006.
Devlin, Keith. *Life by the Numbers.* New York: John Wiley & Sons, 1998.
Dewdney, A. K. *200% of Nothing: An Eye-opening Tour through the Twists and Turns of Math Abuse and Innumeracy.* New York: John Wiley & Sons, 1993.
______. *A Mathematical Mystery Tour: Discovering the Truth and Beauty of the Cosmos.* New York: John Wiley & Sons, 1999.
DeWitt, Richard. *Worldviews: An Introduction to the History and Philosophy of Science.* Chichester: Wiley-Blackwell, [2003] 2010.
Dolnick, Edward. *The Clockwork Universe: Isaac Newton, the Royal Society & the Birth of the Modern World.* New York: HarperCollins Publishers, 2011.
Dörrie, Heinrich. *100 Great Problems of Elementary Mathematics: Their History and Solution.* David Antin, trans. Mineola: Dover Publications, [1959] 1965.
Downing, Douglas. *Dictionary of Mathematical Terms.* Hauppauge: Barron's Educational Series, [1987] 1995.
Downs, J. W. *Practical Conic Sections.* Mineola: Dover Publications, [1993] 2003.
Doxiadis, Apostolos and Christos H. Papadimitriou. *Logicomix: An Epic Search for Truth.* New York: Bloomsbury, 2009.
Driver, R. H. *Why Math?* New York: Springer-Verlag, 1984.
Du Sautoy, Marcus. *Symmetry: A Journey into the Patterns of Nature.* New York: HarperCollins, 2008.
______. *The Music of the Primes: Searching to Solve the Greatest Mystery in Mathematics.* New York: HarperCollins, 2003.
Duncan, David Ewing. *Calendar: Humanity's Epic Struggle to Determine a True and Accurate Year.* New York: Avon Books, 1998.
Dunham, William. *Euler: The Master of Us All.* The Mathematical Association of America, 1999.
______. *Journey Through Genius: The Great Theorems of Mathematics.* New York: Penguin Books, [1990] 1991.
______. *The Calculus Gallery: Masterpieces from Newton to Lebesgue.* Princeton: Princeton University Press, 2005.
______. *The Mathematical Universe: An Alphabetical Journey Through the Great Proofs, Problems, and Personalities.* New York: John Wiley & Sons, 1994.
Edwards, Charles H., Jr. *The Historical Development of the Calculus.* New York: Springer-Verlag, 1979.
Einstein, Albert. *Ideas and Opinions.* New York/Avenel: Wings Books, 1954.
______. *Out of My Later Years.* New York: Carol Publishing Group, [1956, 1984] 1991.
______. *The World As I See It.* Alan Harris, trans. Secaucus: Citadel Press, 1979.
Einstein, Albert and Leopold Infeld. *The Evolution of Physics: From Early Concepts to Relativity and Quanta.* Walter Isaacson, foreward. New York: Touchstone, [1938, 1966] 2007.
Ellenberg, Joran. *How Not to Be Wrong: The Power of Mathematical Thinking.* New York: Penguin Books, 2014.
Engel, Morris S. *With Good Reason, Sixth Edition.* New York: Bedford Books/St. Martin's Press, 2000.
Epstein, Lewis Carroll. *Thinking Physics.* San Francisco: Insight Press, [1979, 1981, 1983, 1985, 1986, 1987, 1988, 1989, 1990, 1991, 1992, 1993, 1994, 1995, 1997, 1999, 2002] 2005.
Esty, Warren W. "Language Concepts of Mathematics." *Focus on Learning Problems in Mathematics* (14:4), Fall 1992.
______. "Learning PreCalculus Concepts Using Graphing Calculators and Emphasizing Symbolic Language." *Proceedings of the Thirteenth Annual Conference on Technology in Collegiate Mathematics.* Gail Goodell, ed. New York: Addison Wesley Longman, 2001.

______. *PreCalculus, Fifth Edition.* New York: Pearson, [2007] 2010.
______. "Teaching About Inverse Functions." *The AMATYC Review* (26:2), Spring 2005.
______. *The Language of Mathematics, Nineteenth Edition.* Bozeman: Montana State University, 2011.
______. "Understanding Mathematics Using Graphics Calculators" *Proceedings of the Ninth Annual Conference on Technology in Collegiate Mathematics.* Gail Goodell, ed. New York: Addison Wesley Longman, 1998.
______. "What Do We Need to Teach About Algebra Now That 'Calculators Can Do it All'?" *Proceedings of the Tenth Annual Conference on Technology in Collegiate Mathematics.* Gail Goodell, ed. New York: Addison Wesley Longman, 2001.
Esty, Warren W. and Anne R. Teppo. "A General-Education Course Emphasizing Mathematical Language and Reasoning." *Focus on Learning Problems in Mathematics* (16:1), Winter 1994.
______. "Algebraic Thinking, Language and Word Problems." *Communication in Mathematics, K-12 and Beyond.* Reston: National Council of Teachers of Mathematics, 1996.
______. "Grade Assignment Based on Progressive Improvement." *The Mathematics Teacher* (85:8), November 1992.
Esty, Warren W. and Norah C. Esty. *Proof: Introduction to Higher Mathematics, Fifth Edition.* Bozeman, 2010.
Euler, Leonhard. *Introduction to the Analysis of the Infinite, Book II.* John D. Blanton, trans.. New York: Springer-Verlag, [1748] 1990.
Eves, Howard. *An Introduction to the History of Mathematics.* New York: Holt, Rinehart and Winston, [1953, 1964, 1969] 1976.
______. *Foundations and Fundamental Concepts of Mathematics.* Mineola: Dover Publications, [1958, 1965] 1990.
______. *In Mathematical Circles: Quadrants I and II.* Boston: Prindle, Weber & Schmidt, 1969.
______. *In Mathematical Circles: Quadrants III and IV.* Boston: Prindle, Weber & Schmidt, 1969.
Ferguson, Kitty. *Measuring the Universe: Our Historic Quest to Chart the Horizons of Space and Time.* New York: Walker and Company, 1999.
______. *Pythagoras: His Lives and the Legacy of a Rational Universe.* London: Icon Books, 2008.
______. *The Fire in the Equations: Science, Religion & the Search for God.* Grand Rapids: William B. Eerdmans Publishing Company, 1994.
Feynman, Richard P. *Six Easy Pieces: Essentials of Physics Explained by Its Most Brilliant Teacher.* Reading: Addison-Wesley Publishing Company, [1963, 1989] 1995.
______. *Six Not-So-Easy Pieces: Einstein's Relativity, Symmetry, and Space-Time.* New York: Basic Books, [1963, 1989, 1997] 2011.
______. *The Character of Physical Law.* Cambridge: The MIT Press, [1965] 1967.
______. *The Feynman Lectures on Physics: Commemorative Issue.* 3 vol. Reading: Addison-Wesley Publishing Company, [1963] 1989.
______. *The Meaning of It All: Thoughts of a Citizen-Scientist.* New York: Basic Books, 1998.
______. *The Pleasure of Finding Things Out.* New York: Basic Books, 1999.
______. *QED: The Strange Theory of Light and Matter.* Princeton: Princeton University Press, [1985, 1988, 2006] 2014.
Feynman, Richard P., Michael A. Gottlieb, and Ralph Leighton. *Tips on Physics: A Problem-Solving Supplement to The Feynman Lectures on Physics.* San Francisco: Pearson/Addison-Wesley Publishing Company, 2006.
Field, Andrew. *The Great Math Experience: Engaging Problems for Middle School Mathematics.* Victoria: Trafford Publishing, 2004.
Fish, Daniel W. *Robinson's Shorter Course: The Complete Arithmetic.* New York and Chicago: Ivision, Blakeman, Taylor & Company, 1874.
Fisher, Richard W. *Mastering Essential Math Skills.* Los Gatos: Math Essentials, 1998.
Flannery, David. *The Square Root of 2: A Dialogue Concerning a Number and a Sequence.* New York: Copernicus Books, 2006.
Flansburg, Scott. *Math Magic.* New York: HarperCollins, [1993] 1994.

Fleisch, Daniel. *A Student's Guide to Maxwell's Equations.* Cambridge: Cambridge University Press, 2008.
Flynn, Mike. *Infinity in Your Pocket.* New York: Barnes & Noble, 2005.
Forbes, Nancy and Basil Mahon. *Faraday, Maxwell, and the Electromagnetic Field.* Amherst: Prometheus Books, 2014.
Fourier, Joseph. *The Analytical Theory of Heat.* Alexander Freeman, trans. Cambridge: Cambridge University Press, 1878.
Franzén, Torkel. *Gödel's Theorem: An Incomplete Guide to Its Use and Abuse.* Wellesley: A K Peters, 2005.
Friedberg, Richard. *An Adventurer's Guide to Number Theory.* Mineola: Dover Publications, [1968] 1994.
Galilei, Galileo. *Dialogue Concerning Two Chief World Systems.* New York: The Modern Library, [1953, 1962, 1967, 1981] 2001.
______. *Dialogues Concerning Two New Sciences.* New York: Dover Publications, [1914] 1954.
______. *Discoveries and Opinions of Galileo.* Stillman Drake, trans. New York: Doubleday, 1957.
______. *Operations of the Geometric and Military Compass.* Washington, DC: The Dibner Library of the History of Science and Technology and the Smithsonian Institution Press, [1606] 1978.
Gardner, Martin. *Aha! Gotcha: Paradoxes to Puzzle and Delight.* San Francisco: W. H. Freeman, [1975] 1982.
______. *Aha! Insight.* San Francisco: W. H. Freeman, 1978.
Gazalé, Midhat. *Number: From Ahmes to Cantor.* Princeton: Princeton University Press, 2000.
Gelfand, Israel M. and Alexander Shen. *Algebra.* Boston: Birkhäuser, 1993.
Gelfand, Israel M., E. G. Glagoleva, and A. A. Kirillov. *The Method of Coordinates.* Boston: Birkhäuser, 1990.
Gelfand, Israel M., E. G. Glagoleva, and E. E. Shnol. *Functions and Graphs.* Mineola: Dover Publications, [1969] 2002.
Gelfand, Israel M. and Mark Saul. *Trigonometry.* Boston: Birkhäuser, 2001.
Gelfand, Sergei I., M. L. Gerver, A. A. Kirillov, N. N. Konstantinov, and A. G. Kushnirenko. *Sequences, Combinations, Limits.* Mineola: Dover Publications, [1969] 2002.
Ghyka, Matila. *The Geometry of Art and Life.* New York: Dover Publications, [1946] 1977.
Gibilisco, Stan and Norman Crowhurst. *Mastering Technical Mathematics.* New York: McGraw-Hill, [1961] 1999.
Gies, Frances & Joseph. *Cathedral, Forge, and Waterwheel: Technology and Invention in the Middle Ages.* New York: HarperCollins, 1994.
______. *Leonardo of Pisa and the New Mathematics of the Middle Ages.* New York: Thomas Y. Crowell, 1969.
Gillings, Richard. *Mathematics in the Time of the Pharaohs.* New York: Dover Publications, [1972] 1982.
Glover, Thomas J. *Pocket Ref.* Littleton, Colorado: Sequoia Publishing, 2000.
Glynne-Jones, Tim. *The Book of Numbers.* Arcturus, nd.
Gödel, Kurt. *On Formerly Undecidable Propositions of Principia Mathematics and Related Systems.* Mineola: Dover Publications, [1931, 1962] 1992.
Goodstein, David L. and Judith R. Goodstein. *Feynman's Lost Lecture: The Motion of Planets Around the Sun.* New York: W. W. Norton & Company, 1996.
Gould, Rupert T. *The Marine Chronometer: Its History and Development.* London: J. D. Potter, 1923.
Gowers, Timothy. *Mathematics: A Very Short Introduction.* Oxford: Oxford University Press, 2002.
Gowers, Timothy, ed. *The Princeton Companion to Mathematics.* Princeton and Oxford: Princeton University Press, 2008.
Grattan-Guiness, Ivor. *The Rainbow of Mathematics: A History of the Mathematical Sciences.* New York: W. W. Norton, [1997] 2000.
Gray, Peter M. D. *Logic, Algebra and Databases.* Chichester: Ellis Horwood Limited, 1984.
Gregory of Nyssa. *Treatise on the Inscriptions of the Psalms.* Ronald E. Heine, trans. Oxford: Clarendon Press, 1995.
Grillo, Paul Jacques. *Form, Function and Design.* New York: Dover Publications, [1960] 1975.
Griffin, Frank Loxley. *An Introduction to Mathematical Analysis.* Boston: Houghton Mifflin, 1936.

Guedj, Denis. *Numbers: The Universal Language*. New York: Harry N. Abrams, 1997.
Guillen, Michael. *Bridges to Infinity: The Human Side of Mathematics*. London: Rider & Company, 1984.
______. *Five Equations That Changed the World: The Power and Beauty of Mathematics*. New York: Hyperion, 1995.
Gullberg, Jan. *Mathematics: From the Birth of Numbers*. New York: W. W. Norton, 1997.
Gunton, Colin E. *The One, The Three and The Many: God, Creation and the Culture of Modernity*. Cambridge: Cambridge University Press, 1993.
Gutenmacher, Victor and N. B. Vasilyev. *Lines and Curves: A Practical Geometry Handbook*. Boston: Birkhäuser, [1980] 2004.
Hahn, Alexander J. *Calculus in Context: Background, Basics, and Applications*. Baltimore: Johns Hopkins University Press, 2017.
Hamming, Richard W. *Methods of Mathematics Applied to Calculus, Probability, and Statistics*. Mineola: Dover Publications, [1985] 2004.
______. *Numerical Methods for Scientists and Engineers*. New York: Dover Publications, [1962, 1973] 1986.
______. "The Unreasonable Effectiveness of Mathematics." *American Mathematical Monthly*, 87 (1980), 81-90.
Handley, Bill. *Speed Mathematics: Secrets of Lightning Mental Calculation*. Hoboken: John Wiley & Sons, [2000, 2003] 2004.
Hansen, Bert. *Nicole Oresme and the Marvels of Nature*. Toronto: Pontifical Institute of Mediaeval Studies, 1985.
Hardy, Godfrey H. *A Course in Pure Mathematics, Tenth Edition*. Cambridge: The Syndics of the Cambridge University Press, [1908] 1952.
______. *A Mathematician's Apology*. Cambridge: Cambridge University Press, 1967.
Hart, David Bentley. *The Beauty of the Infinite*. Grand Rapids: William B. Eerdmans Publishing Company, 2003.
Hartkopf, Roy. *Math Without Tears*. Boston: G. K. Hall & Co., [1965] 1985.
Havel, Julian. *The Irrationals: A Story of the Numbers You Can't Count On*. Princeton: Princeton University Press, 2012.
Hawking, Stephen, ed. *God Created the Integers: The Mathematical Breakthroughs that Changed History*. Philadelphia: Running Press, 2005.
Heath, Robin. *Sun, Moon, & Earth*. New York: Walker & Company, 1999.
Heath, Royal Vale. *Mathemagic*. New York: Dover Publications, [1933] 1953.
Heath, Thomas L. *A History of Greek Mathematics*. 2 vol. New York: Dover Publications, [1921] 1981.
Heath, Thomas L., ed. *Euclid: The Thirteen Books of The Elements*. 3 vol. New York: Dover Publications, [1925] 1956.
______. *The Works of Archimedes*. Mineola: Dover Publications, [1897, 1912] 2002.
Heaton, Luke. *A Brief History of Mathematical Thought: Key Concepts and Where They Came From*. London: Constable & Robinson, 2015.
Heilbron, J. L. *Geometry Civilized: History, Culture, and Technique*. Oxford: Clarendon Press, [1998] 2000.
______. *The Sun in the Church: Cathedrals as Solar Observatories*. Cambridge and London: Harvard University Press, 1999.
Heisenberg, Werner. *The Physical Principles of the Quantum Theory*. C. Eckart and F. C. Hoyt, trans.. Chicago: University of Chicago Press, 1930.
Herz-Fischler, Roger. *A Mathematical History of the Golden Number*. Mineola: Dover Publications, [1987] 1998.
Hewitt, Paul G. *Conceptual Physics*. Menlo Park: Addison-Wesley Publishing Company, 1987.
Hilbert, David. *Foundations of Geometry* (*Grundlagen der Geometrie*). Leo Unger, trans. La Salle: Open Court, 1971.
Hilbert, David and S. Cohn-Vossen. *Geometry and the Imagination*. P. Nemenyi, trans. New York: Chelsea Publishing Company, 1952.
Hoffmann, Banesh. *Relativity and its Roots*. Mineola: Dover Publications, [1983] 1999.

Hogben, Lancelot. *Mathematics for the Millions*. New York: W. W. Norton, [1937, 1983] 1993.
______. *The Wonderful World of Mathematics*. New York: Doubleday, 1968.
Hoggatt, Verner E. *Fibonacci and Lucas Numbers*. Boston: Houghton Mifflin Company, 1969.
Hooykaas, Reijer. *Religion and the Rise of Modern Science*. Grand Rapids: Eerdmans, 1972.
Horsburgh, E. M., ed. *Handbook of the Napier Tercentenary Celebration, or Modern Instruments and Methods of Calculation*. Los Angeles: Tomash Publishers, [1914] 1982.
Howard, W. J. *Doing Simple Math in Your Head*. Chicago: Chicago Review Press, 1992.
Huff, Darrell. *How to Lie with Statistics*. New York: W. W. Norton, [1954, 1982] 1993.
Hughes, Tom. *Chemistry Connections: Ideas to Interpret Your Changing World*. Dubuque: Kendall/Hunt Publishing Company, [1975] 1983.
Hummel, Charles E. *The Galileo Connection: Resolving Conflicts between Science & the Bible*. Downers Grove: InterVarsity Press, 1986.
Huntley, H. E. *The Divine Proportion: A Study in Mathematical Beauty*. New York: Dover Publications, 1970.
Ifrah, Georges. *The Universal History of Computing*. New York: John Wiley & Sons, 2001.
______. *The Universal History of Numbers*. New York: John Wiley & Sons, 2000.
Ivins, William M. Jr. *Art and Geometry: A Study in Space Intuitions*. New York: Dover Publications, 1964.
Jacobs, Harold R. *Elementary Algebra*. San Francisco: W. H. Freeman, 1979.
______. *Geometry*. San Francisco: W. H. Freeman, 1974.
______. *Mathematics: A Human Endeavor*. San Francisco: W. H. Freeman, [1970, 1982] 1994.
Jaki, Stanley L. *A Late Awakening and Other Essays*. Port Huron: Real View Books, 2006.
______. *Chance or Reality and Other Essays*. Lanham: University Press of America, 1986.
______. *God and the Cosmologists*. Fraser: Real View Books, [1989] 1998.
______. *Numbers Decide and Other Essays*. Pinckney: Real View Books, 2003.
______. *Patterns or Principles and Other Essays*. Wilmington: Intercollegiate Studies Institute, 1995.
______. *Science and Creation*. Edinburgh: Scottish Academic Press, 1986.
______. *The Absolute Beneath the Relative and Other Essays*. Lanham: University Press of America, 1988.
______. *The Drama of Quantities*. Port Huron: Real View Books, 2005.
______. *The Limits of a Limitless Science and Other Essays*. Wilmington: Intercollegiate Studies Institute, 2000.
______. *The Only Chaos and Other Essays*. Lanham: University Press of America, 1990.
______. *The Relevance of Physics*. Edinburgh: Scottish Academic Press, [1966, 1970] 1993.
______. *The Road of Science and the Ways to God*. Edinburgh: Scottish Academic Press, 1978.
______. *The Savior of Science*. Grand Rapids: William B. Eerdmans Publishing Company, 2000.
Jammer, Max. *Concepts of Force: A Study in the Foundations of Dynamics*. Mineola: Dover Publications, [1957] 1999.
______. *Concepts of Mass in Classical and Modern Physics*. Mineola: Dover Publications, [1961, 1989] 1997.
______. *Concepts of Space: The History of Theories of Space in Physics*. Mineola: Dover Publications, [1954, 1969] 1993.
______. *Einstein and Religion*. Princeton: Princeton University Press, 1999.
Jeffrey, Alan. *Mathematics for Engineers and Scientists*. Boca Raton: Chapman & Hall/CRC Press, 2005.
Jespersen, James and Jane Fitz-Randolph. *From Sundials to Atomic Clocks: Understanding Time and Frequency*. New York: Dover Publications, [1977] 1982.
Johnson, Darrell W. *Experiencing the Trinity*. Vancouver: Regent College Publishing, 2002.
Johnson, Trevor and Hugh Neill. *Teach Yourself Mathematics*. Chicago: McGraw-Hill, [2001] 2003.
Joseph, Christopher, Gen. Ed. *A Measure of Everything: An Illustrated Guide to the Science of Measurement*. Buffalo: Firefly Books, 2005.
Julius, Edward H. *Rapid Math in 10 Days*. New York: Perigee, 1994.
Kac, Mark and Stanislaw M. Ulam. *Mathematics and Logic*. Mineola: Dover Publications, [1968] 1992.

Kaiser, Christopher B. *Creation and the History of Science.* Grand Rapids: William B. Eerdmans Publishing Company, 1991.

______. *The Doctrine of God.* Westchester: Crossway Books, 1982.

Kaplan, Andrew. *Math on Call: A Mathematics Handbook.* Wilmington: Great Source Education Group, 2004.

Kaplan, Robert. *The Nothing That Is: A Natural History of Zero.* New York: Oxford University Press, 1999.

Kaplan, Robert & Ellen Kaplan, *Hidden Harmonies: The Lives and Times of the Pythagorean Theorem.* New York: Bloomsbury Press, 2011.

Kappraff, Jay. *Connections: The Geometric Bridge Between Art and Science.* New York: McGraw-Hill, 1991.

Kasner, Edward and James R. Newman. *Mathematics and the Imagination.* Mineola: Dover Publications, [1940] 2001.

Kay, David C. *College Geometry.* New York: Holt, Rinehart and Winston, 1969.

Kelly, Gerard W. *Short-Cut Math.* Mineola: Dover Publications, [1969] 1984.

Kepler, Johannes. *Epitome of Copernican Astronomy & Harmonies of the World.* Amherst: Prometheus Books, 1995.

______. *Mysterium Cosmographicum – The Secret of the Universe.* A. M. Duncan, trans. New York: Abaris Books, 1981.

______. *New Astronomy.* William H. Donahue, trans. Cambridge: Cambridge University Press, 1992.

______. *The Six-Cornered Snowflake.* Colin Hardie, trans.. Oxford: Clarendon Press, 1966.

Kibble, Tom W. B. and Frank H. Berkshire. *Classical Mechanics, Fifth Edition.* London: Imperial College Press, 2004.

King, Jerry P. *Mathematics in 10 Lessons: The Grand Tour.* Amherst: Prometheus Books, 2009.

______. *The Art of Mathematics.* Mineola: Dover Publications, [1992] 2006.

Klaf, A. A. *Arithmetic Refresher.* Mineola: Dover Publications, 1964.

Klein, Herbert Arthur. *The Science of Measurement: A Historical Survey.* Mineola: Dover Publications, [1974] 1988.

Klein, Jacob. *Greek Mathematical Thought and the Origin of Algebra.* Mineola: Dover Publications, [1968] 1992.

Kline, Morris. *Calculus: An Intuitive and Physical Approach.* New York: John Wiley & Sons, [1967] 1977.

______. *Mathematical Thought from Ancient to Modern Times.* New York: Oxford University Press, 1972.

______. *Mathematics and the Physical World.* New York: Dover Publications, [1959] 1981.

______. *Mathematics and the Search for Knowledge.* New York: Oxford University Press, 1985.

______. *Mathematics for the Nonmathematician.* Mineola: Dover Publications, [1967] 1985.

______. *Mathematics in Western Culture.* Reading: Addison-Wesley Publishing Company, 1962.

______. *Mathematics: The Loss of Certainty.* New York: Oxford University Press, 1980.

______. *Why Johnny Can't Add: The Failure of the New Math.* New York: Vintage Books, [1973] 1974.

______. *Why The Professor Can't Teach: Mathematics and the Dilemma of University Education.* New York: St. Martin's Press, 1977.

Kline, Morris, ed. *Mathematics: An Introduction to Its Spirit and Use.* San Francisco: W. H. Freeman and Company, [1948, 1949, 1950, 1951, 1952, 1953, 1954, 1955, 1958, 1959, 1961, 1963, 1964, 1966, 1967, 1968, 1969, 1970, 1971, 1976, 1978] 1979.

Knudsen, Jens M. and Poul G. Hjorth. *Elements of Newtonian Mechanics.* Berlin: Springer-Verlag, 1995.

Kogelman, Stanley and Barbara R. Heller. *The Only Math Book You'll Ever Need.* New York: Dell Publishing, 1986.

Kressin, Keith. *Understanding Mathematics: From Counting to Calculus.* Ramona: K Squared Publishing, 1997.

Kruger, C. Baxter. *The Great Dance: The Christian Vision Revisited.* Vancouver: Regent College Publishing, 2000.

Labarre, Anthony E., Jr. *Intermediate Mathematical Analysis.* New York: Holt, Rinehart and Winston, 1968.

LaCugna, Catherine Mowry. *God for Us: The Trinity & Christian Life.* New York: Harper Collins, 1991.

Lagrange, Joseph Louis. *Lectures on Elementary Mathematics.* Mineola: Dover Publications, [1898] 2008.

Land, Frank. *The Language of Mathematics.* London: John Murray, 1960.
Lang, Serge. *Basic Mathematics.* New York: Springer-Verlag, 1971.
______. *The Beauty of Doing Mathematics: Three Public Dialogues.* New York: Springer-Verlag, 1985.
Lang, Serge and Gene Murrow. *Geometry, Second Edition.* New York: Springer-Verlag, [1983] 1988.
Langdon, Nigel and Charles Snape. *A Way with Maths.* Cambridge: Cambridge University Press, 1984.
Lawler, Robert. *Sacred Geometry: Philosophy and Practice.* London: Thames and Hudson, 1982.
Leithart, Peter J. *Traces of the Trinity: Signs of God in Creation and Human Experience.* Grand Rapids: Brazos Press, 2015.
Lennox, John C. *Determined to Believe? The Sovereignty of God, Freedom, Faith, and Human Responsibility.* Oxford: Monarch Books, 2017.
Levi, Mark. *The Mathematical Mechanic: Using Physical Reasoning to Solve Problems.* Princeton: Princeton University Press, 2009.
Liebeck, Martin. *A Concise Course in Pure Mathematics, Fourth Edition.* Boca Raton: CRC Press, 2016.
Livio, Mario. *The Golden Ratio: The Story of Phi, the World's Most Astonishing Number.* New York: Broadway Books, 2002.
Loder, James E. and W. Jim Neidhardt. *The Knight's Move: The Relational Logic of the Spirit in Theology and Science.* Colorado Springs: Helmers & Howard, 1992.
Lucas, Jerry. *Becoming a Mental Math Wizard.* White Hall: Shoe Tree Press, 1991.
Lundy, Miranda. *Sacred Geometry.* New York: Walker & Company, 1998.
______. *Sacred Number: The Secret Qualities of Quantities.* New York: Walker & Company, 2005.
Maatman, Russell. *The Unity in Creation.* Sioux Center: Dordt College Press, 1978.
MacCormick, John. *9 Algorithms that Changed the Future: The Ingenious Ideas that Drive Today's Computers.* Princeton: Princeton University Press, 2012.
Mandelbrot, Benoit. *The Fractal Geometry of Nature.* New York: W. H. Freeman, 1983.
Maor, Eli. *e: The Story of a Number.* Princeton: Princeton University Press, 1994.
______. *The Pythagorean Theorem: A 4,000 Year History.* Princeton: Princeton University Press, 2007.
______. *To Infinity and Beyond: A Cultural History of the Infinite.* Princeton: Princeton University Press, [1987] 1991.
______. *Trigonometric Delights.* Princeton: Princeton University Press, 1998.
Martineau, Jason. *The Elements of Music: Melody, Rhythm, & Harmony.* New York: Walker & Company, 2008.
Maxwell, James Clerk. *The Dynamical Theory of the Electromagnetic Field.* Thomas F. Torrance, ed. Eugene: Wipf and Stock Publishers, 1983.
Mazer, Arthur. *The Ellipse: A Historical and Mathematical Journey.* Hoboken: John Wiley & Sons, 2010.
Mazur, Barry. *Imagining Numbers (particularly the square root of minus fifteen).* New York: Farrar, Straus, and Giroux, 2003.
McKay, H. *The World of Numbers.* New York: The Macmillan Company, 1946.
Menninger, Karl. *Number Words and Number Symbols: A Cultural History of Numbers.* Mineola: Dover Publications, [1969] 1992.
Meschkowski, Herbert. *Evolution of Mathematical Thought.* San Francisco: Holden-Day, 1965.
______. *Ways of Thought of Great Mathematicians: An Approach to the History of Mathematics.* San Francisco: Holden-Day, 1964.
Miller, Denning. *Popular Mathematics: The Understanding and Enjoyment of Mathematics.* New York: Coward-McCann, Inc., 1942.
Millikan, Robert A. and Henry G. Gale. *A First Course in Physics.* Boston: Ginn & Company, 1906.
Minnaert, M. *The Nature of Light & Color in the Open Air.* H. M. Kremer-Priest, trans. New York: Dover Publications, 1954.

Moritz, Robert Edouard. *Memorabilia Mathematica: The Philomath's Quotation Book*. Washington, DC: The Mathematical Association of America, [1914] 1942.
Morris, Tim and Don Pletcher. *Science & Grace: God's Reign in the Natural Sciences*. Wheaton: Crossway Books, 2006.
Muir, Jane. *Of Men and Numbers: The Story of Great Mathematicians*. Mineola: Dover Publications, [1961] 1996.
Muschla, Judith A. and Gary Robert Muschla. *Math Starters!* San Francisco: Jossey-Bass, 1999.
______. *The Math Teacher's Book of Lists, Second Edition*. San Francisco: Jossey-Bass, 2005.
Nagel, Ernest and James R. Newman. *Gödel's Proof*. London: Routledge and Kegal Paul, 1958.
Nahin, Paul J. *An Imaginary Tale: The Story of* $\sqrt{-1}$. Princeton: Princeton University Press, 1998.
______. *When Least is Best*. Princeton: Princeton University Press, 2004.
Narlikar, Jayant V. *The Lighter Side of Gravity*. New York: W. H. Freeman, 1982.
Neagoy, Monica. *Planting the Seeds of Algebra*. Thousand Oaks: Corwin Press, 2015.
Neugebauer, Otto. *The Exact Sciences in Antiquity*. New York: Dover Publications, [1957] 1969.
Newbigin, Lesslie. *Foolishness to the Greeks: The Gospel and Western Culture*. Grand Rapids: William B. Eerdmans Publishing Company, 1986.
Newman, James R. *The World of Mathematics*. 4 vol. New York: Simon and Schuster, 1956.
Newman, Rochelle and Donna M. Fowler. *Space, Structure and Form: Interweaving Art, Math and Nature in Three Dimensions*. Bradford/Madison: Pythagorean Press/Brown & Benchmark Publishers, 1996.
Newman, Rochelle and Martha Boles. *The Surface Plane, The Golden Relationship: Art, Math & Nature*. Bradford: Pythagorean Press, 1992.
______. *Universal Patterns, The Golden Relationship: Art, Math & Nature*. Bradford: Pythagorean Press, [1983, 1987, 1990] 1992.
Newton, Isaac. *Opticks*. New York: Dover Publications, [1704, 1931, 1952], 1979.
______. *The Principia*. Andrew Motte, trans. Amherst: Prometheus Books, [1687, 1713, 1726, 1848] 1995.
Nicastro, Nicholas. *Circumference: Eratosthenes and the Ancient Quest to Measure the Globe*. New York: St. Martin's Press, 2008.
Nickel, James. *Mathematics: Is God Silent?* Vallecito: Ross House Books, [1990] 2001.
______. *The Incarnation of the Word and the Transformation of the Landscape of Mathematics*. Wenatchee: Sound Mind Press (Kindle Version), 2012.
______. *The Incarnation of the Word and the Transformation of the Landscape of Mathematics*. Wenatchee: Sound Mind Press/Mt. Hermon: Center for Cultural Leadership, 2012.
Niven, Ivan. *Numbers: Rational and Irrational*. New York: Random House, 1961.
Nussenzveig, H. Moyses. "The Theory of the Rainbow." *Scientific American*, 236 (1977), 116-127.
O'Collins, Gerald. *The Tripersonal God: Understanding and Interpreting the Trinity*. New York: Paulist Press, 1999.
Ogilvy, C. Stanley. *Excursions in Mathematics*. Mineola: Dover Publications, [1956] 1994.
Olsen, Scott. *The Golden Section: Nature's Greatest Secret*. New York: Walker & Company, 2006.
Ore, Oystein. *Number Theory and Its History*. New York: Dover Publications, [1948] 1976.
Osserman, Robert. *Poetry of the Universe*. New York: Anchor Books, 1995.
Pappas, Theoni. *Mathematical Footprints*. San Carlos: World Wide Publishing/Tetra, 1999.
______. *More Joy of Mathematics*. San Carlos: World Wide Publishing/Tetra, 1991.
______. *The Joy of Mathematics*. San Carlos: World Wide Publishing/Tetra, 1989.
______. *The Magic of Mathematics: Discovering the Spell of Mathematics*. San Carlos: World Wide Publishing/Tetra, 1994.
______. *The Music of Reason: Experience the Beauty of Mathematics through Quotations*. San Carlos: World Wide Publishing/Tetra, 1995.
Pascal, Blaise. *Pensées*. New York: E. P. Dutton & Co., Inc., 1958.
Pearcey, Nancy R. and Charles B. Thaxton. *The Soul of Science: Christian Faith and Natural Philosophy*. Wheaton: Crossways Books, 1994.

Pedoe, Dan. *Geometry and the Visual Arts*. New York: Dover Publications, [1976] 1983.
______. *The Gentle Art of Mathematics*. New York: Dover Publications, [1959] 1973.
Perry, O. & J. Perry. *Mastering Mathematics*. London: The Macmillan Press, 1982.
Péter, Rózsa. *Playing with Infinity: Mathematical Explorations and Excursions*. New York: Dover Publications, [1961] 1976.
Pickar, Arnold D. *Preparing for General Physics, Calculus Version*. Reading: Addison-Wesley Publishing Company, 1993.
Pickover, Clifford A. *The Loom of God: Tapestries of Mathematics and Mysticism*. New York: Sterling Publishing, 2009.
Plantinga, Alvin and Nicholas Wolterstroff, ed. *Faith and Rationality: Reason and Belief in God*. Notre Dame: University of Notre Dame Press, 1983.
Poincaré, Henri. *The Foundations of Science*. Lancaster: The Science Press, [1913] 1946.
Polanyi, Michael. *Personal Knowledge: Towards a Post-Critical Philosophy*. Chicago: University of Chicago Press, [1958] 1962.
Polster, Burkard. *Q. E. D., Beauty in Mathematical Proof*. New York: Walker & Company, 2004.
Pólya, George. *How to Solve It: A New Aspect of Mathematical Method*. Princeton: Princeton University Press, [1945, 1957, 1973, 1985] 1988.
Posamentier, Alfred S. *Math Charmers*. Amherst: Prometheus Books, 2003.
______. *Math Wonders*. Alexandria: Association for Supervision and Curriculum Development, 2003.
______. *Pre-Algebra Come Alive*. Thousand Oaks: Corwin Press, 2000.
Posamentier, Alfred S. and Herbert A. Hauptman. *101 Great Ideas for Introducing Key Concepts in Mathematics: A Resource for Secondary School Teachers*. Thousand Oaks: Corwin Press, 2001.
Posamentier, Alfred S. and Ingmar Lehmann. *π: A Biography of the World's Most Mysterious Number*. Amherst: Prometheus Books, 2004.
______. *The (Fabulous) Fibonacci Numbers*. Amherst: Prometheus Books, 2007.
Poythress, Vern S. "A Biblical View of Mathematics." *Foundations of Christian Scholarship*. Gary North, ed. Vallecito: Ross House Books, 1976.
______. "Creation and Mathematics." *The Journal of Christian Reconstruction: Symposium on Creation* (1:1). Gary North, ed. Vallecito: Chalcedon, 1974.
______. "Mathematics as Rhyme." In *A Third Conference on Mathematics from a Christian Perspective*. Robert L. Brabenec, ed. Wheaton: Wheaton College, 1981.
______. *Redeeming Mathematics*. Wheaton: Crossway, 2015.
______. *Redeeming Science*. Wheaton: Crossway Books, 2006.
______. "Science as Allegory." In *A Third Conference on Mathematics from a Christian Perspective*. Robert L. Brabenec, ed. Wheaton: Wheaton College, 1981.
Prestige, G. L. *God in Patristic Thought*. London: SPCK, 1952.
Priest, Graham. *Logic: A Very Short Introduction*. Oxford: Oxford University Press, 2000.
Priestley, William M. *Calculus: A Liberal Art*. New York: Springer-Verlag, [1974] 1998.
______. *Calculus: An Historical Approach*. New York: Springer-Verlag, 1979.
______. "Mathematics and Poetry: How Wide the Gap?" *The Mathematical Intelligencer* (12:1). New York: Springer-Verlag, 1990.
Pritsker, Boris. *Geometrical Kaleidoscope*. Mineola: Dover Publications, 2017.
Rademacher, Hans and Otto Toeplitz. *The Enjoyment of Mathematics*. Mineola: Dover Publications, [1966] 1990.
Randall, John. *The Making of the Modern Mind*. New York: Columbia University Press, [1926] 1940.
Ravielli, Anthony. *An Adventure in Geometry*. New York: Viking Press, 1957.
Reeves, Michael. *The Good God: Enjoying Father, Son and Spirit*. London: Paternoster, 2012.
Reid, Constance. *From Zero to Infinity*. Wellesley: A K Peters, Ltd., [1955, 1960, 1964, 1992] 2006.

Reimer, Luetta and Wilbert. *Historical Connections in Mathematics: Resources for Using History of Mathematics in the Classroom.* 3 vol. Fresno: AIMS Education Foundation, 1992, 1993, 1995.

______. *Mathematicians are People, Too.* 2 vol. Palo Alto: Dale Seymour Publications, 1990, 1995.

Resnikoff, H. L. and R. O. Wells, Jr. *Mathematics in Civilization.* New York: Dover Publications, [1973] 1984.

Ressler, Stephen. *Do-It-Yourself Engineering.* Chantilly: The Teaching Company, 2017.

Rezende, Lisa. *Chronology of Science.* New York: Checkmark Books, 2006.

Rising, Gerald R. *Inside Your Calculator: From Simple Programs to Significant Insights.* Hoboken: John Wily & Sons, 2007.

Rohrlich, Fritz. *From Paradox to Reality: Our Basic Concepts of the Physical World.* Cambridge: Cambridge University Press, [1987] 1990.

Rooney, Anne. *The Story of Chemistry: From the Periodic Table to Nanotechnology.* London: Arcturus, 2017.

Ross, Debra Anne. *Master Math: Basic Math and Pre-Algebra.* Franklin Lakes: Career Press, 1996.

Rothman, Tony. *Instant Physics: From Aristotle to Einstein, and Beyond.* New York: Byron Visual Publications, 1995.

Rucker, Rudy. *The Fourth Dimension.* Boston: Houghton Mifflin Company, 1984.

Rudman, Peter S. *The Babylonian Theorem: The Mathematical Journey to Pythagoras and Euclid.* Amherst: Prometheus Books, 2010.

Ruffini, Remo. "The Princeton Galaxy." Interviews by Florence Heltizer. *Intellectual Digest*, 3 (1973), 27.

Russell, Colin. A. *Cross-Currents: Interactions Between Science & Faith.* Grand Rapids: William B. Eerdmans Publishing Company, 1985.

Russell, Colin. A., ed. *Science and Religious Belief: A Selection of Recent Historical Studies.* London: The Open University Press, 1973.

Salmon, George. *A Treatise on Conic Sections, Sixth Edition.* Watchmaker Publishing, 2009.

Sawyer, Walter W. *Mathematician's Delight.* Harmondsworth: Penguin Books, 1943.

_____. *Prelude to Mathematics.* Harmondsworth: Penguin Books, 1955.

_____. *The Search for Pattern.* Harmondsworth: Penguin Books, 1970.

_____. *Vision in Elementary Mathematics.* Harmondsworth: Penguin Books, 1964.

Schiffer, M. M. and Leon Bowden. *The Role of Mathematics in Science.* Washington, DC: The Mathematical Association of America, 1984.

Schumer, Peter D. *Mathematical Journeys.* Hoboken: John Wiley & Sons, 2004.

Seife, Charles. *Zero: The Biography of a Dangerous Idea.* New York: Penguin, 2000.

Shafarevich, Igor R. *Discourses on Algebra.* New York: Springer-Verlag, [2000] 2003.

Sierpinski, Waclaw. *Pythagorean Triangles.* Mineola: Dover Publications, [1962] 2003.

Simmons, George F. *Precalculus Mathematics in a Nutshell.* New York: Barnes & Noble, [1987] 1997.

Singh, Jagjit. *Great Ideas of Modern Mathematics: Their Nature and Use.* New York: Dover Publications, 1959.

Skinner, Stephen. *Sacred Geometry: Deciphering the Code.* New York: Sterling Publishing, 2006.

Smeltzer, Donald. *Man and Number.* Emerson Books, 1958.

Smith, David Eugene. *A Source Book in Mathematics.* New York: Dover Publications, [1929] 1959.

_____. *History of Mathematics: General Survey of the History of Elementary Mathematics, Volume 1.* New York: Dover Publications, [1923, 1951] 1958.

_____. *History of Mathematics: Special Topics of Elementary Mathematics, Volume 2.* New York: Dover Publications, [1925, 1953] 1958.

_____. *Number Stories of Long Ago.* Merchant Books, 2008.

Smith, Karl J. *The Nature of Mathematics, Fifth Edition.* Monterey: Brooks/Cole Publishing Company, [1973, 1976, 1980, 1984] 1987.

Smith, Robert D. *Technical Mathematics.* Albany: Delmar Publishers, [1982, 1983, 1985] 1996.

Smith, Sanderson. *Agnesi to Zeno: Over 100 Vignettes from the History of Math.* Berkeley: Key Curriculum Press, 1996.

Snoke, David W. *Natural Philosophy: A Survey of Physics and Western Thought.* Colorado Springs: Access Research Network, 2003.
Sobel, Dava. *Longitude.* New York: Walker and Company, 1995.
Solomonovich, Mark. *Euclidean Geometry: A First Course.* [2003, 2004] 2005.
Sondheimer, Ernst and Alan Rogerson. *Numbers and Infinity: A Historical Account of Mathematical Concepts.* Mineola: Dover Publications, [1981] 2006.
Sorabji, Richard, ed. *Philoponus and the Rejection of Aristotelian Science.* London: Duckworth, 1987.
Spitzer, Leo. *Classical and Christian Ideas of World Harmony.* Anna Granville Hatcher, ed. Baltimore: Johns Hopkins University Press, 1963.
Spivak, Michael. *Calculus.* Houston: Publish or Perish, [1967, 1980, 1994] 2008.
Sri, Jagadguru Swami and Bharati Krsna Tirthaji Maharaja. *Vedic Mathematics.* Delhi: Motilal Banarsidass, 1992.
Steen, Lynn A., ed. *Mathematics Today: Twelve Informal Essays.* New York: Vintage Books, [1978] 1980.
Steensma, Geraldine J. and Harro W. Van Brummelen, ed. *Shaping School Curriculum: A Biblical View.* Terre Haute: 1977.
Stein, Sherman K. *Mathematics: The Man-Made Universe.* San Francisco: W. H. Freeman and Company, [1963, 1969] 1976.
_____. *Strength in Numbers: Discovering the Joy and Power of Mathematics in Everyday Life.* New York: John Wily & Sons, 1996.
Stein, Sherman K. and Calvin D. Crabill. *Algebra II/Trigonometry.* San Francisco: W. H. Freeman, [1970] 1976.
Steiner, Mark. *The Applicability of Mathematics as a Philosophical Problem.* Cambridge: Harvard University Press, 1998.
Steinhaus, Hugo. *Mathematical Snapshots.* Oxford: Oxford University Press, [1950, 1960, 1968, 1969] 1983.
Stewart, Ian. *Concepts of Modern Mathematics.* Mineola: Dover Publications, [1975, 1981] 1995.
______. *From Here to Infinity: A Guide to Today's Mathematics.* Oxford: Oxford University Press, [1987, 1992] 1996.
______. *Nature's Numbers: The Unreal Reality of Mathematics.* New York: BasicBooks, 1995. Stickler, Henry. *How to Calculate Quickly.* New York: Dover Publications, [1945] 1955.
Stigler, Stephen M. *Statistics on the Table: The History of Statistical Concepts and Methods.* Cambridge, MA: Harvard University Press, 1999.
Stillwell, John. *Elements of Algebra: Geometry, Numbers, Equations.* New York: Springer-Verlag, 1994.
______. *Elements of Number Theory.* New York: Springer-Verlag, 2003.
______. *Mathematics and Its History.* New York: Springer-Verlag, [1989] 2002.
______. *Numbers and Geometry.* New York: Springer-Verlag, 1998.
______. *Roads to Infinity: The Mathematics of Truth and Proof.* Natick: A K Peters, Ltd., 2006.
______. *The Four Pillars of Geometry.* New York: Springer Science + Business Media, LLC., 2005.
______. *Yearning for the Impossible: The Surprising Truths of Mathematics.* Wellesley: A K Peters, Ltd., 2010.
Stoddard, Edward. *Speed Mathematics Simplified.* Mineola: Dover Publications, [1962, 1965] 1994.
Strachan, Liz. *A Slice of Pi: All the Math You Forgot to Remember From School.* New York: Fall River Press, 2010.
Strogatz, Steven. *The Joy of x: A Guided Tour of Math, from One to Infinity.* New York: Mariner Books, [2012] 2013.
Strohmeier, John and Peter Westbrook. *Divine Harmony: The Life and Teachings of Pythagoras.* Berkeley: Berkeley Hills Books, 1999.
Stroud, K. A. *Engineering Mathematics, Sixth Edition.* New York: Industrial Press, 2007.
Struik, Dirk J. *A Concise History of Mathematics.* New York: Dover Publications, 1948.
______. *A Source Book in Mathematics 1200-1800.* Princeton: Princeton University Press, 1969.
Suppes, Patrick. *Introduction to Logic.* Mineola: Dover Publications, [1957] 1999.
Sutton, Andrew. *Ruler & Compass.* New York: Walker & Company, 2009.

Sutton, David. *Platonic & Archimedean Solids*. New York: Walker & Company, 2002.
Sutton, Oliver G. *Mathematics in Action*. Mineola: Dover Publications, [1954, 1957] 1984.
Tabak, John. *Algebra: Sets, Symbols & the Language of Thought*. New York: Facts on File, Inc., 2004.
______. *Geometry: The Language of Space and Form*. New York: Facts on File, 2004.
______. *Mathematics and the Laws of Nature: Developing the Language of Science*. New York: Facts on File, 2004.
______. *Numbers: Computers, Philosophers & the Search for Meaning*. New York: Facts on File, 2004.
______. *Probability & Statistics: The Science of Uncertainty*. New York: Facts on File, 2004.
Taylor, Lloyd W. *Physics: The Pioneer Science*. 2 vols. New York: Dover Publications, [1941] 1959.
Texas Instruments Learning Center. *The Great International Math on Keys Book*. Texas Instruments Inc., 1976.
Tiner, John Hudson. *Exploring the World of Mathematics*. Green Forest: Master Books, 2004.
Thompson, D'Arcy Wentworth. *On Growth and Form*. Mineola: Dover Publications, [1942] 1992.
Thompson, James Edgar. *Algebra for the Practical Worker*. New York: Van Nostrand Reinhold, [1931, 1946, 1962] 1982.
______. *Arithmetic for the Practical Worker*. New York: Van Nostrand Reinhold, [1931, 1946, 1962] 1982.
______. *Calculus for the Practical Worker*. New York: Van Nostrand Reinhold, [1931, 1946, 1962] 1982.
______. *Geometry for the Practical Worker*. New York: Van Nostrand Reinhold, [1934, 1946, 1962] 1982.
______. *Trigonometry for the Practical Worker*. New York: Van Nostrand Reinhold, [1931, 1946, 1962] 1982.
Thompson, Silvanus P. *Calculus Made Easy*. New York: St. Martin's Press, [1910, 1914] 1946.
Torrance, Thomas F. *Atonement: The Person and Work of Christ*. Robert T. Walker, ed. Downers Grove: InterVarsity Press, 2009.
______. *Christian Theology and Scientific Culture*. New York: Oxford University Press, 1981.
______. *Divine and Contingent Order*. Eugene: Wipf & Stock Publishers, [1998] 2004.
______. *God and Rationality*. New York: Oxford University Press, 1971.
______. *Incarnation: The Person and Life of Christ*. Robert T. Walker, ed. Downers Grove: InterVarsity Press, 2008.
______. *Reality and Scientific Theology*. Edinburgh: Scottish Academic Press, 1985.
______. *Space, Time & Incarnation*. New York: Oxford University Press, 1969.
______. *The Christian Doctrine of God: One Being, Three Persons*. London: Bloomsbury T & T Clark, [1996, 2001] 2016.
______. *The Christian Frame of Mind: Reason, Order, and Openness in Theology and Natural Science*. Colorado Springs: Helmers & Howard, 1989.
______. *The Ground and Grammar of Theology*. Charlottesville: University Press of Virginia, 1980.
______. *The Trinitarian Faith*. London: Bloomsbury T & T Clark, [1991, 1997] 2016.
______. *Theological and Natural Science*. Eugene: Wipf & Stock Publishers, 2002.
______. *Theological Science*. New York: Oxford University Press, [1969] 1978.
______. *Theology in Reconciliation*. Grand Rapids: William B. Eerdmans Publishing Company, 1976.
______. *Theology in Reconstruction*. Grand Rapids: William B. Eerdmans Publishing Company, 1965.
______. *Transformation & Convergence in the Frame of Knowledge: Explorations in the Interrelations of Scientific and Theological Enterprise*. Grand Rapids: William B. Eerdmans Publishing Company, 1984.
Torrance, Thomas F., ed. *Belief in Science and in Christian Life: The Relevance of Michael Polanyi's Thought for Christian Faith and Life*. Eugene: Wipf & Stock Publishers, [1980] 1998.
Transnational College of LEX. *Who is Fourier: A Mathematical Adventure*. Alan Gleason, trans. Boston: Language Research Foundation, 1995.
Turnbull, Herbert Westren. *The Great Mathematicians*. New York: Barnes & Noble, [1929] 1993.
Tyler, Marya Washington. *Real Life Math Mysteries*. Waco: Prufrock Press, 1995.
Van Brummelen, Glen. *The Mathematics of the Heavens and the Earth: The Early History of Trigonometry*. Princeton: Princeton University Press, 2009.

Van Brummelen, Harro W., coordinator. *Mathematics in the Christian School: Preliminary Report.* Toronto: Institute for Christian Studies, 1971.

Van Cleave, Janice. *Math for Every Kid.* New York: John Wiley & Sons, 1991.

Van der Kooi, Cornelis and Gijsbert van den Brink. *Christian Dogmatics: An Introduction.* Reinder Bruinsma and James D. Bratt, trans. Grand Rapids: William B. Eerdmans Publishing Company, [2012] 2017.

Van der Waerden, B. L. *Science Awakening I.* Arnold Dresden, trans. Dordrecht: Noordhoff International Publishing and Princeton Junction: Scholar's Bookshelf, [1975] 1988.

Van Til, Cornelius. *The Defense of the Faith.* Phillipsburg: Presbyterian and Reformed Publishing Company, [1955, 1963] 1967.

Von Baeyer, Hans Christian. *Rainbows, Snowflakes and Quarks.* New York: McGraw-Hill, 1984.

Vergara, William C. *Mathematics in Everyday Things.* New York: Harper & Brothers, 1959.

______. *Science: The Never-Ending Quest.* New York: Harper & Row, 1965.

Waismann, Friedrich. *Introduction to Mathematical Thinking: The Formation of Concepts in Modern Mathematics.* Mineola: Dover Publications, [1951, 1959, 1966] 2003.

Watkins, Matthew. *Useful Mathematical & Physical Formulae.* New York: Walker & Company, 2000.

Webster, Noah. *American Dictionary of the English Language.* San Francisco: Foundation for American Christian Education, [1828, 1967, 1980, 1983] 1985.

Wentworth, G. A. *New Plane and Solid Geometry: A Text-Book of Geometry.* Boston: Ginn & Company, 1898.

Weyl, Hermann. "A Half-Century of Mathematics." *American Mathematical Monthly*, 58 (1951), 523-553.

______. *Philosophy of Mathematics and Natural Science.* Princeton: Princeton University Press, 1948.

______. *Space, Time and Matter.* Henry L. Brose, trans. London: Methuen, 1922.

______. *Symmetry.* Princeton: Princeton University Press, 1952.

______. *The Theory of Groups and Quantum Mechanics.* H. P. Robertson, trans. London: Methuen, 1931.

Whitehead, Alfred North. *Adventures of Ideas.* New York: The Free Press, 1967.

______. *An Introduction to Mathematics.* New York: Henry Holt and Company, 1939.

______. *Essays in Science and Philosophy.* London: Rider and Company, 1948.

______. *Science and the Modern World.* London: Free Association Books, [1926] 1985.

______. *The Aims of Education and Other Essays.* London: Williams and Norgate, 1929.

______. *The Function of Reason.* Princeton: Princeton University Press, 1929.

Wigner, Eugene. *Symmetries and Reflections: Scientific Essays.* Cambridge and London: The MIT Press, 1970.

Wilczek, Frank. *A Beautiful Question: Finding Nature's Deep Design.* New York: Penguin Press, 2015.

Wilder, Raymond. *Mathematics as a Cultural System.* Oxford: Pergamon Press, 1981

Willingham, Daniel T. *Why Don't Students Like School?* San Francisco: Jossey-Bass, 2009.

Wilson, Alistair Macintosh. *The Infinite in the Finite.* New York: Oxford University Press, 1995.

Wolfson, Richard and Jay M. Pasachoff. *Physics for Scientists and Engineers.* Reading: Addison-Wesley Publishing Company, 1999.

Wood, Elizabeth A. *Science from Your Airplane Window.* New York: Dover Publications, [1968] 1975.

Zaccaro, Edward. *Challenge Math.* Bellevue: Hickory Grove Press, 2005.

Zebrowski, Ernest, Jr. *A History of the Circle: Mathematical Reasoning and the Physical Universe.* New Brunswick: Rutgers University Press, 1999.

Zeitz, Paul. *The Art and Craft of Problem Solving.* Hoboken: John Wiley & Sons, 2007.

Zimmerman, Larry L. *Truth and the Transcendent: The Origin, Nature, and Purpose of Mathematics.* Florence: Answers in Genesis, 2000.

Zippin, Leo. *Uses of Infinity.* Mineola: Dover Publications, [1962] 2000.

General Index

Numbers in **bold** indicate where the index entry is defined.
Numbers in *italics* indicate the index entry is in a footnote.

#

6

A

B

C

D

E

F

G

L

M

N

O

P

Q

R

S

T

SCRIPTURE INDEX

Made in the USA
Columbia, SC
14 December 2018